Trigonometry
Version 3.0

Edward B. Burger

FlatWorld

Trigonometry Version 3.0

Edward B. Burger

Published by:

FlatWorld
175 Portland Street
Boston, MA 02114

About the Author

Edward B. Burger

Dr. Edward Burger is President of Southwestern University as well as a professor of mathematics and an educational leader on thinking, innovation, and creativity. Previously, he was the Francis Christopher Oakley Third Century Professor of Mathematics at Williams College. He has delivered over 700 addresses worldwide at venues including Berkeley, Harvard, Princeton, and Johns Hopkins as well as at the Smithsonian Institution, Microsoft Corporation, the World Bank, the International Monetary Fund, the U.S. Department of the Interior, the New York Public Library, and the National Academy of Sciences. He is the author of over 70 research articles, books, and video series (starring in over 4,000 online videos), including the book *The 5 Elements of Effective Thinking*, published by Princeton University Press and translated into over a dozen languages worldwide. His book, *Making Up Your Mind: Thinking Effectively Through Creative Puzzle-Solving*, also published by Princeton University Press, was on several of Amazon's Hot New Releases lists.

In 2006, *Reader's Digest* listed Burger in their annual "America's 100 Best" list as *America's Best Math Teacher*. In 2010, he was named the winner of the Robert Foster Cherry Award for Great Teaching—the largest prize in higher education teaching across all disciplines in the English-speaking world. Also in 2010, he starred in a mathematics segment for NBC-TV on the *Today Show*; that appearance earned him a 2010 Telly Award. The *Huffington Post* named him one of their 2010 Game Changers: "HuffPost's Game Changers salutes 100 innovators, visionaries, mavericks, and leaders who are reshaping their fields and changing the world." In 2012, Microsoft Worldwide Education selected him as one of their "Global Heroes in Education." In 2013, Burger was inducted as an inaugural Fellow of the American Mathematical Society. In 2014, Burger was elected to the Philosophical Society of Texas. He is now in his fourth season of his weekly program on thinking and higher education produced by NPR's Austin affiliate KUT. The series, *Higher ED*, is available at kut.org/topic/higher-ed/ and on iTunes.

Preface

About FlatWorld's Trigonometry

Modern calculus has its roots in 17th century Europe, and is credited with revolutionizing the way we understand concepts such as motion, force, and time, along with many other facets of nature. Calculus provides a means of explaining how the world works. In any situation where change occurs, there is likely to be an application of calculus.

FlatWorld's *Trigonometry* offers the subjects, skills, and insights needed to understand calculus. It is the gateway to dynamic and advanced mathematics and will provide you with the tools you'll need for success in trigonometry and beyond.

This textbook is designed to provide you with a variety of engaging approaches to trigonometry concepts. Video lectures by the award-winning professor Edward B. Burger provide compelling and interactive instruction for the core concepts of trigonometry. You can follow each video lecture by reading the textbook, either in print or online, and extend your understanding by getting relevant practice using the section and chapter review exercises.

Your Path to Success

Keep It Simple
Don't try to tackle a complex problem all in one step. Instead, first identify what you know and what you don't know. Establishing what you do know gives you a solid foundation on which to build your skills and knowledge. Identifying what you do no know will help you to focus more clearly on what you still need to learn.

Make Mistakes
Making mistakes is a great way to learn. Don't be afraid to take a wrong turn, or to explore the uncharted territory. Reaching a wrong answer or winding up at a dead end is actually useful information. Learn to see that every "mistake" is actually a means of getting to what is truly important—the "ah-ha" moment that happens to you when you learn something new.

Ask Questions
Take a few minutes as you begin learning each new concept to ask yourself one or more questions about what it is you need to learn. This will help you focus your thinking as you engage in the material.

... and, be sure to make use of all of the textbook features and online resources available to you.

Acknowledgments

Thank you to the following reviewers, contributors, and colleagues, whose commitment to excellence made this book possible.

Cristina Caputo, *University of Texas*

Julie Hess, *Grand Rapids Community College*

Patrick Jones, *Patrick JMT.com*

Eric Mann, *The Khabele School*

Allison M. Pacelli, *Williams College*

Douglas Quinney, *Keele Unviersity*

Danielle Rivard, *Post University*

Mike Smith, *Ohio Valley University*

1 FUNCTIONS AND THEIR GRAPHS 115

2 TRIGONOMETRIC FUNCTIONS

225

3 ANALYTIC TRIGONOMETRY 331

3.2 SOLVING TRIGONOMETRIC EQUATIONS 345

3.2.1 Solving Equations with a Single Trigonometric Function 345

3.2.2 Solving Equations with a Single Trigonometric Function: Another Example 346

3.2.3 Solving Trigonometric Equations Using Inverse Functions 348

3.2.4 Solving Trigonometric Equations by Factoring 349

3.2.5 Solving Trigonometric Equations Involving a Multiple of an Angle 351

3.2.6 Solving Trigonometric Equations Involving a Multiple of an Angle: Another Example .. 352

3.2.7 Solving Trigonometric Equations of Quadratic Type 353

3.2.8 Solving Trigonometric Equations of Quadratic Type:Another Example 354

3.2.9 Solving Trigonometric Equations Using Fundamental Identities 355

3.2.10 Applications Involving Trigonometric Equations 356

3.3 THE SUM AND DIFFERENCE FORMULAS 360

3.3.1 Introduction to the Sum and Difference Formulas 360

3.3.2 Using the Sum and Difference Formulas to Find Exact Values 360

3.3.3 Using the Sum and Difference Formulas to Find Exact Values: Another Example 362

3.3.4 Using the Sum and Difference Formulas to Verify a Cofunction Identity 362

3.3.5 Using the Sum and Difference Formulas to Verify an Identity 364

3.3.6 Using the Sum and Difference Formulas to Solve an Equation 364

3.4 DOUBLE-ANGLE, HALF-ANGLE, AND PRODUCT-SUM FORMULAS 368

3.4.1 Double-Angle Formulas 368

3.4.2 Using Double-Angle Formulas 369

3.4.3 Using Double-Angle Formulas to Solve Equations 371

3.4.4 Using a Power-Reducing Formula 371

3.4.5 Using Half-Angle Formulas to Find Exact Values 372

3.4.6 Using Product-Sum Formulas 375

4 APPLICATIONS OF TRIGONOMETRY   381

4.1 THE LAW OF SINES 382

4.1.1 Using the Law of Sines Given Two Angles and One Side 382

4.1.2 Using the Law of Sines Given One Angle and Two Sides 384

4.1.3 Using the Law of Sines: The Ambiguous Case 385

4.1.4 Finding the Area of an Oblique Triangle 387

4.1.5 The Law of Sines: An Application 388

4.2 THE LAW OF COSINES 393

4.2.1 The Law of Cosines 393

TRIGONOMETRY

PREREQUISITES:
BASIC ALGEBRA REVIEW

P.1   REAL NUMBERS

OBJECTIVES

- Compare, order, and classify real numbers.
- Use properties of real numbers to simplify expressions.
- Evaluate algebraic expressions.
- Write sets of numbers using different notations: interval notation, set-builder notation, and roster notation.
- Evaluate absolute value expressions.

PREREQUISITE VOCABULARY TERMS

algebraic expression
coefficient
inequality
numeric expression
variable

P.1.1   Ordering and Classifying Real Numbers

Anything that can be quantified or measured, such as temperature, distance, speed, or volume, can be described by a **real number.** The set of all real numbers is divided into several overlapping subsets. One subset of the real numbers, called the **natural numbers**, is made up of the counting numbers starting with 1, 2, 3, . . . (and continuing to infinity). The subset of the real numbers that includes the natural numbers and 0 is called the **whole numbers**. The set of numbers called the **integers** is the subset of the real numbers that includes all positive whole numbers, negative whole numbers, and 0.

These subsets of the real numbers are displayed in the Venn diagram in Figure P.1a.

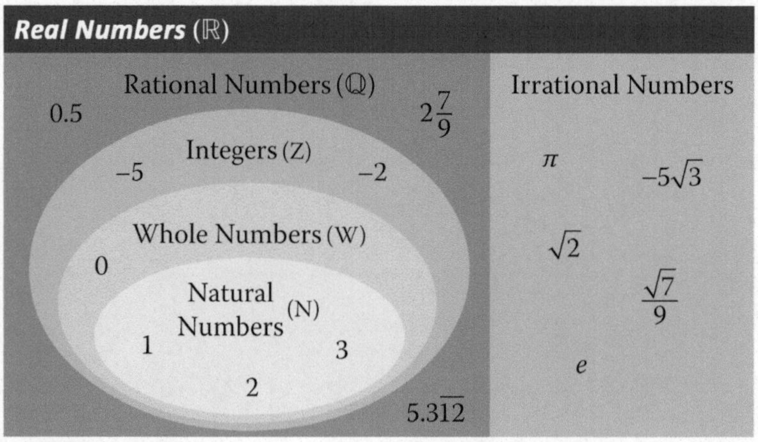

Natural Numbers
1, 2, 3, 4, 5, . . .

Whole Numbers
0, 1, 2, 3, 4, . . .

Integers
. . . , −2, −1, 0, 1, 2, . . .

IMPORTANT

Every natural number is also a whole number, an integer, and a rational number. Every real number can be classified as either a rational or an irrational number.

Figure P.1a

TIP

Irrational numbers and repeating decimals can be written as decimal approximations. Use the ≈ symbol to indicate a decimal approximation.
π ≈ 3.14

Two nonoverlapping subsets of the real numbers are the **rational numbers** and the **irrational numbers**. A rational number is a ratio of integers a to b where $b \neq 0$. So, $\frac{2}{3}$, $-\frac{10}{7}$, and 5 (since 5 can be written as $\frac{5}{1}$) are all examples of rational numbers. Notice that all integers, whole numbers, and natural numbers are rational numbers. All rational numbers can be expressed as either a **terminating decimal** ($\frac{3}{4} = 0.75$) or as a **repeating decimal** ($\frac{16}{3} = 5.3\overline{3}$).

Some decimal numbers do not terminate or repeat. Any real number that is equivalent to a nonterminating, nonrepeating decimal is an **irrational number**. For example, the decimal equivalent to the irrational number $\sqrt{2}$ is 1.41421356237309504880168887242097 . . . , where the decimal-place digits continue infinitely without repeating. The most familiar irrational number is π. Every real number (rational and irrational) can be expressed as a decimal that is either terminating, repeating, or nonterminating and nonrepeating.

Ordering Real Numbers

Real numbers can be represented (plotted) and ordered on a number line, where any number is greater than all real numbers to its left and less than all real numbers to its right (i.e., left to right is least to greatest). For example, 2, –4, and $\frac{3}{4}$ are plotted on the number line in Figure P.1b.

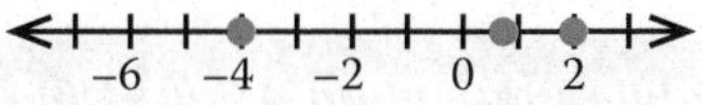

Figure P.1b

The fraction $\frac{3}{4}$ is plotted between 0 and 1.

Clearly, $-4 < \frac{3}{4} < 2$, and this fact is confirmed by the order of the points on the number line, since the numbers are plotted in that order from left to right.

When ordering real numbers, it is often helpful to write fractions, mixed numbers, or irrational numbers as equivalent or approximate decimals, as demonstrated in **Example 1**.

IMPORTANT

For any real numbers a and b, if a < b, then a is to the left of b on a number line. If a = b, then the location of a must be the same as the location of b on a number line.

TIP

Write real numbers as decimals to plot them on a number line and to compare them. Use a calculator to find the decimal approximation of an irrational number.

| EXAMPLE 1 | **Classifying and Ordering a List of Real Numbers** |

Consider the numbers -0.061, $\sqrt{3}$, 1.07, $\frac{4}{3}$, $\sqrt{9}$, and -1. Order the numbers from least to greatest, then classify each number by the subsets of the real numbers to which it belongs.

SOLUTION

Write each nondecimal, noninteger number as a decimal equivalent or approximation.

$\sqrt{3} = 1.732\ldots \approx 1.73$ *Use a calculator and round to the nearest hundredth.*

$\frac{4}{3} = 1.3\overline{3} \approx 1.33$ *Divide 4 by 3 and round to the nearest hundredth.*

$\sqrt{9} = 3$ *9 is a perfect square.*

Use the decimal approximations to order the numbers.

$$-1 < -0.061 < 1.07 < 1.33 < 1.73 < 3$$

Therefore, $-1 < -0.061 < 1.07 < \frac{4}{3} < \sqrt{3} < \sqrt{9}$.

The numbers can be plotted on a number line.

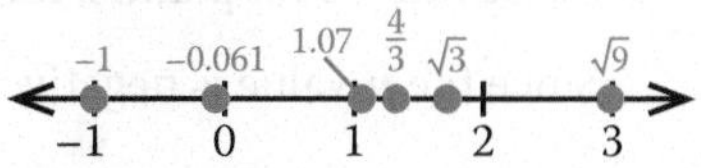

So, from least to greatest, the numbers are: -1, -0.061, 1.07, $\frac{4}{3}$, $\sqrt{3}$, and $\sqrt{9}$.

Use the chart to classify each number.

	Real	Rational	Integer	Whole	Natural	Irrational
–0.061	✓	✓				
$\sqrt{3}$	✓					✓
1.07	✓	✓				
$\frac{4}{3}$	✓	✓				
$\sqrt{9}$	✓	✓	✓	✓	✓	
–1	✓	✓	✓			

P.1.2   Evaluating an Algebraic Expression

An **algebraic expression** is a mathematical expression that includes at least one variable. An algebraic expression also typically includes at least one operation, such as multiplication or subtraction.

Examples of Algebraic Expressions	
x	an unknown value represented by the letter x
$2p + 1$	the product of 2 and p increased by 1
$\dfrac{m^2 - 1}{n}$	m squared decreased by 1, divided by n
$a(b + c)$	the product of a and the sum of b and c

IMPORTANT

A variable is an unknown value that is typically represented by a letter, such as x or n.

To **evaluate** an algebraic expression, substitute a given value for the variable and then simplify the expression by following the order of operations.

IMPORTANT

Order of Operations
1. Complete operations within grouping symbols (e.g., parentheses).
2. Simplify powers (i.e., exponents).
3. Multiply and divide from left to right.
4. Add and subtract from left to right.

EXAMPLE 2   Evaluating an Algebraic Expression

Evaluate each expression using the given value of each variable.

A. $\dfrac{2(k-1)}{10 - k + 2}$ for $k = 4$

B. $pq - 3p^2 + 5(q - p)$ for $p = -3$ and $q = 2$

SOLUTION

A. Substitute 4 for k in the expression. Then simplify the numeric expression by following the order of operations.

$$\frac{2(k-1)}{10-k+2} = \frac{2(4-1)}{10-4+2} = \frac{2(3)}{10-4+2} = \frac{6}{8} = \frac{3}{4}$$

B. Substitute -3 for p and 2 for q, then simplify.

Since the p-value is negative, use parentheses to prevent calculation errors.

$$\begin{aligned} pq - 3p^2 + 5(q - p) &= (-3)(2) - 3(-3)^2 + 5(2 - (-3)) &&\textit{Substitute } p = -3 \textit{ and } q = 2. \\ &= (-3)(2) - 3(-3)^2 + 5(5) &&\textit{Subtract within parentheses.} \\ &= (-3)(2) - 3(9) + 5(5) &&\textit{Simplify the power.} \\ &= -6 - 27 + 25 &&\textit{Multiply.} \\ &= -8 &&\textit{Add and subtract.} \end{aligned}$$

P.1.3   Using Properties of Real Numbers

Additive and Multiplicative Identities and Inverses

When an **identity** is combined (using some operation) with a quantity, the quantity does not change. The **additive identity** is 0 because adding 0 to any real number does not change the value of that number. Similarly, the **multiplicative identity** is 1 because multiplying any real number by 1 does not change the value of that number.

When an **inverse** is combined (using some operation) with some quantity, the result is the operation's identity. The **additive inverse** of any real number is its **opposite** (i.e., the differently signed number that is the same distance from 0 on a number line) because for any real number a, $a + (-a) = 0$ (the additive identity). For example, the additive inverse of 9 is -9 because $9 + (-9) = 0$. Every real number has an additive inverse.

The **multiplicative inverse** of a nonzero real number a is equal to $\frac{1}{a}$, since $a \cdot \frac{1}{a} = 1$, and 1 is the multiplicative identity. The multiplicative inverse of a real number is also known as the number's **reciprocal**. Every real number except 0 has a multiplicative inverse.

Identities and Inverses of Real Numbers

	Additive		Multiplicative	
Identity	0	*If a is any real number, then $a + 0 = a$.*	1	*If a is any real number, then $a \cdot 1 = a$.*
Inverse of a	$-a$	*If a is any real number, then $a + (-a) = 0$.*	$\frac{1}{a}$ (when $a \neq 0$)	*If a is any real number, except 0, then $a \cdot \frac{1}{a} = 1$*

EXAMPLE 3   Finding Inverses of Real Numbers

State the additive and multiplicative inverses of -20, $\frac{9}{10}$, 0.75, and $-\frac{1}{n}$. Assume that $n \neq 0$.

SOLUTION

The additive inverse of a number is its opposite.
The multiplicative inverse of a number is its reciprocal.

	Additive Inverse		Multiplicative Inverse	
-20	20	*$-20 + 20 = 0$*	$-\frac{1}{20}$	*$-20 \cdot -\frac{1}{20} = 1$*
$\frac{9}{10}$	$-\frac{9}{10}$	*$\frac{9}{10} + \left(-\frac{9}{10}\right) = 0$*	$\frac{10}{9}$	*$\frac{9}{10} \cdot \frac{10}{9} = 1$*
0.75	-0.75	*$0.75 + -0.75 = 0$*	$\frac{4}{3}$	*$0.75 = \frac{3}{4}$ and $\frac{3}{4} \cdot \frac{4}{3} = 1$*
$-\frac{1}{n}$	$\frac{1}{n}$	*$-\frac{1}{n} + \frac{1}{n} = 0$*	$-n$	*$-\frac{1}{n} \cdot (-n) = 1$*

The Commutative, Associative, and Distributive Properties

There are several properties which allow an expression to be manipulated and simplified without changing its value. Sums and products of real numbers can be rearranged or regrouped (without changing the value of the expression) by the **Commutative** and **Associative Properties**.

Properties of Real Numbers: Commutative and Associative		
	Addition	Multiplication
Commutative Property	$a + b = b + a$	$ab = ba$
Associative Property	$(a + b) + c = a + (b + c)$	$(a \cdot b) \cdot c = a \cdot (b \cdot c)$

a, b, and c represent any ▶ real number.

These properties are demonstrated in the following equations.

$$5 + 4 = 4 + 5 \qquad \textit{Commutative Property of Addition}$$
$$3 \cdot 4 = 4 \cdot 3 \qquad \textit{Commutative Property of Multiplication}$$
$$(1 + 2) + 8 = 1 + (2 + 8) \qquad \textit{Associative Property of Addition}$$
$$(6 \cdot 2) \cdot 3 = 6 \cdot (2 \cdot 3) \qquad \textit{Associative Property of Multiplication}$$

By the **Distributive Property**, a real number can be multiplied by each **number** in a sum or difference of real numbers without changing the value of the expression.

Properties of Real Numbers: Distributive
$a(b + c) = ab + ac \qquad a(b - c) = ab - ac$

a, b, c, and d represent ▶ any real number.

For example, consider the expression $3(2 + 5)$. Applying the order of operations to simplify the expression yields $3(2 + 5) = 3(7) = 21$. By the Distributive Property, multiplying 3 by each number in the sum first yields the same result: $3(2 + 5) = 3 \cdot 2 + 3 \cdot 5 = 6 + 15 = 21$.

EXAMPLE 4   Identifying Properties of Real Numbers

Identify the properties demonstrated in each equation.

A. $\frac{2}{3} + \left(\frac{1}{8} + \frac{1}{3}\right) = \left(\frac{2}{3} + \frac{1}{3}\right) + \frac{1}{8}$ **B.** $2(x + y) = 2y + 2x$

IMPORTANT

The Commutative, Associative, and Distributive Properties can be applied to expressions that are algebraic as well as numeric.

SOLUTION

A. The numbers are reordered, as well as regrouped.

$$\frac{2}{3} + \left(\frac{1}{8} + \frac{1}{3}\right) = \frac{2}{3} + \left(\frac{1}{3} + \frac{1}{8}\right) \qquad \textit{Reorder the fractions within parentheses by the Commutative Property of Addition.}$$

$$= \left(\frac{2}{3} + \frac{1}{3}\right) + \frac{1}{8} \qquad \textit{Regroup the fractions by the Associative Property of Addition.}$$

The Commutative and Associative Properties of Addition are demonstrated in the equation.

IMPORTANT

Assume that variables in algebraic expressions represent real numbers unless otherwise stated.

B. By the Distributive Property, 2 can be multiplied by each term in the sum $x + y$.

$$2(x + y) = 2x + 2y \qquad \textit{Multiply 2 by each term in the sum by the Distributive Property.}$$
$$= 2y + 2x \qquad \textit{Reorder the terms by the Commutative Property of Addition.}$$

Alternatively, the Commutative Property of Addition can be applied first.

$$2(x + y) = 2(y + x) \qquad \textit{Reorder the terms by the Commutative Property of Addition.}$$
$$= 2y + 2x \qquad \textit{Multiply 2 by each term in the sum by the Distributive Property.}$$

The Distributive Property and the Commutative Property of Addition are demonstrated in the equation.

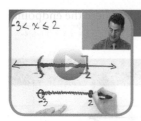

P.1.4   Inequalities and Interval Notation

An inequality expresses an ordered relationship between two quantities, such as between two numbers, two variables, or between a variable and a number, as in $x < 6$, $n \geq 0$, or $1 < z \leq 5$. The **solution set** for each of these inequalities (i.e., the set of all real numbers that are solutions to the inequality) is a subset of the real numbers called an **interval**.

DEFINITION

An **interval** is the set of all real numbers between two real numbers a and b, where a and b are called the interval's endpoints.

An interval has two endpoints, but those endpoints are not necessarily included in the interval. For example, the solution set of the inequality $-1 < x \leq 3$ includes all real x-values that are greater than 1 and less than or equal to 3. Therefore, the solution set is the interval with endpoints -1 and 3, where 3 is included in the interval (because x is less than *or equal to* 3), but -1 is not included in the interval (because x is greater than *but not equal to* -1).

Consider the inequality $x \geq 2$. The solution set includes all real x-values greater than or equal to 2, which is the interval with an endpoint at 2 that extends infinitely from 2 in a positive direction. When an interval extends infinitely in a positive direction, the endpoint is said to be positive infinity (∞). When an interval extends infinitely in a negative direction, the endpoint is said to be negative infinity ($-\infty$). Note that ∞ and $-\infty$ are never included in the interval.

A **closed interval** includes both endpoints and an **open interval** includes neither endpoint. (An interval that includes exactly one endpoint is neither open nor closed.) Examples of the different types of intervals are given in the following table.

	Interval Endpoints and Inequalities			
Inequality	**Solution Set Description**	**Endpoints of Interval**	**Type of Interval**	
$x < 6$	all real numbers less than 6	$-\infty$ and 6	open	*The interval includes neither endpoint.*
$n \geq 0$	all real numbers greater than or equal to 0	0 and ∞	neither open nor closed	*The interval includes only one endpoint.*
$1 \leq z \leq 5$	all real numbers greater than or equal to 1 and less than or equal to 5	1 and 5	closed	*The interval includes both endpoints.*

Graphs of Intervals and Interval Notation

An interval can be expressed as a graph or by using **interval notation**. To express an interval using interval notation, write the endpoints separated by a comma and enclose the endpoints with parentheses, brackets, or one of each. A parenthesis indicates that the endpoint is not included in the interval, and a bracket indicates that the endpoint is included in the interval. A parenthesis is always used with $-\infty$ and ∞, because $-\infty$ and ∞ are never included in the interval.

Alternative Method
On a number line, a bracket can be used instead of a closed point, and a parenthesis can be used instead of an open point.

To graph an interval, plot the interval's numeric endpoint(s) as points on a number line. Use an open point (empty circle) when plotting an endpoint that is not included in the interval, and a closed point (filled circle) when plotting an endpoint that is included in the interval. Shade the region between the endpoints. Shade the number line to the right end to indicate that the interval extends infinitely in the positive direction (∞), or to the left end to indicate that the interval extends infinitely in the negative direction ($-\infty$).

Natural Numbers ▶
{1, 2, 3, 4, 5, . . . }

Whole Numbers
{0, 1, 2, 3, 4, . . . }

Integers
{ . . . , −2, −1, 0, 1, 2, . . . }

Since the sets of natural numbers, whole numbers, and integers are sets of distinct values, roster notation can be used to represent these sets. The following table shows examples of sets in roster notation.

Examples of Sets in Roster Notation	
{1, 2, 3, 4}	*The set includes only 1, 2, 3, and 4.*
{2, 3, 4, . . . }	*The set includes all whole numbers greater than or equal to 2.*
{3, 6, 9, . . . }	*The set includes all positive multiples of 3.*
{−3, −2, −1, . . . , 5}	*The set includes all integers between −3 and 5.*

EXAMPLE 9   **Representing a Set of Numbers Using Roster Notation**

Write the set using roster notation: "all positive integers evenly divisible by 5."

SOLUTION

The set of all positive integers that are evenly divisible by 5 begins with 5 and continues infinitely in a positive direction, including all multiples of 5. List at least the first three elements of the set, and then add an ellipsis to indicate that the set continues infinitely.

$$\{5, 10, 15, 20, \ldots \}$$

WHAT'S THE BIG IDEA?

Roster notation cannot be used to express the solution set for $x > 0$. Explain.

P.1.7   Evaluating Absolute Value Expressions

The distance between a real number, a, and 0 on a number line is called the **absolute value** of a, denoted $|a|$. Since distance is always nonnegative, the absolute value of a number is always nonnegative, and so $|a| \geq 0$.

The following properties can be applied to the absolute value for any real number.

Properties of Absolute Value	
$|a| \geq 0$	*The absolute value of a number is always positive or 0 (i.e., nonnegative).*
$|a| = |-a|$	*A number and its opposite have the same absolute value.*
$|ab| = |a| \cdot |b|$	*The absolute value of a product is equal to the product of the absolute values of the factors.*
$\left|\dfrac{a}{b}\right| = \dfrac{|a|}{|b|}$ (when $b \neq 0$)	*The absolute value of a quotient is equal to the quotient of the absolute values of the numerator and denominator.*

Use these properties and follow the order of operations to simplify a numeric expression containing absolute value. Absolute value behaves like parentheses (grouping symbols) in the order of operations, so simplify any operations within absolute value symbols and then take the absolute value of the number. Additionally, when a number is written immediately before (or after) an absolute value, the operation is understood to be multiplication. For example, $a|b|$ means "the product of a and the absolute value of b."

| **EXAMPLE 10** | Simplifying a Numeric Absolute Value Expression |

Simplify. $10 + 5|7 - 12| - |3^2|$

SOLUTION

Follow the order of operations.

$$10 + 5|7 - 12| - |3^2| = 10 + 5|-5| - |9| \quad \textit{Simplify expressions within the absolute value.}$$
$$= 10 + 5(5) - 9 \quad \textit{Take the absolute value of -5 and 9.}$$
$$= 10 + 25 - 9 \quad \textit{Multiply.}$$
$$= 35 - 9 \quad \textit{Add.}$$
$$= 26 \quad \textit{Subtract.}$$

Simplifying the Absolute Value of an Algebraic Expression

Consider the relationship between the absolute value of a number and the number itself. For any real number a that is

- greater than or equal to 0, the absolute value of a is equal to a.
- less than 0, the absolute value of a is equal to the opposite of a, or $-a$.

These facts are represented symbolically in the following table.

Absolute Value	
For all real numbers a, $|a| = a$ when $a \geq 0$.	For all real numbers a, $|a| = -a$ when $a < 0$.
The absolute value of a is equal to a when a is greater than or equal to 0 (nonnegative).	*The absolute value of a is equal to the opposite of a (i.e., -a) when a is negative.*

CAUTION

The statement "$|a| = -a$ when $a < 0$" does not mean that the absolute value of a number is equal to a negative number. Instead, the statement means that when a number is negative, the absolute value of that number is equal to the opposite of that number.

These two facts can be used to write an algebraic absolute value expression (an expression that contains the absolute value of at least one variable or number) as an equivalent expression that does not include absolute value. Specifically, when $a < 0$, any instance of $|a|$ in an expression can be replaced by $-a$, and when $a \geq 0$, any instance of $|a|$ in an expression can be replaced by a.

| **EXAMPLE 11** | Simplifying an Algebraic Absolute Value Expression |

Simplify $8n - |n|$ when $n \geq 0$, and when $n < 0$.

SOLUTION

If $n \geq 0$, then $|n| = n$. So, substitute n for $|n|$ and simplify.

$$8n - |n| = 8n - n = 7n, \text{ when } n \geq 0.$$

If $n < 0$, then $|n| = -n$. So, substitute $-n$ for $|n|$ and simplify.

$$8n - |n| = 8n - (-n) = 8n + n = 9n, \text{ when } n < 0.$$

Therefore, when $n \geq 0$, $8n - |n| = 7n$, and when $n < 0$, $8n - |n| = 9n$.

In Exercises 35–42, write an inequality for each solution set.

35. $(-\infty, 4]$

36. $\left(-\dfrac{2}{3}, \infty\right)$

37. $[-1.5, \infty)$

38. $(-\infty, -7)$

39. $[5, 10]$

40. $(-0.7, 0]$

41. $[-3.8, 12)$

42. $(2, 5)$

In Exercises 43–48, write the solution set displayed on each number line using the indicated notation(s).

43.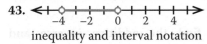
inequality and interval notation

44.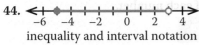
inequality and interval notation

45. ![number line from -8 to 2]
interval notation

46. ![number line from -8 to 2]
interval notation

47. ![number line from -3 to 6]
inequality, interval notation, and set-builder notation

48. ![number line from 0 to 16]
set-builder notation

In Exercises 49–52, write each set using roster notation.

49. all positive integers

50. all positive multiples of 3

51. all even natural numbers

52. all positive powers of 0.1

In Exercises 53–56, simplify.

53. $|1 - 7| - |7 - 1|$

54. $2|-3 + 4| - |-8|$

55. $-4|6 - 9| + 3|-5|$

56. $|-12| - 3|14 - 18|$

In Exercises 57–60, simplify each expression for when $x \geq 0$ and when $x < 0$.

57. $-|x|$

58. $|x| + 2x$

59. $-4x + |x|$

60. $-7|x| - 3x$

In Exercises 61–64, find the distance between m and n.

61. $m = 12$ and $n = -3$

62. $m = -7$ and $n = 4$

63. $m = -3/4$ and $n = 5$

64. $m = -15$ and $n = -3/5$

Extensions

In Exercises 65–70, give three numbers that fit each description, if possible. If there are fewer than three possible numbers, list all possibilities.

65. a rational number that is not an integer

66. a natural number that is not an integer

67. an integer that is not a natural number

68. an integer that is also a whole number and a natural number

69. a whole number that is not a natural number

70. a real number that is not a rational or irrational number

71. A student was asked to evaluate the expression
$$\dfrac{15 - 2(n + 3) + p}{p + m - n} + np \text{ for } n = -3, m = 1, \text{ and } p = 5. \text{ They}$$
completed the first step in the process (the substitution) as shown below. Correct any errors.
$$\dfrac{15 - 2(-3 + 3) + 5}{5 + 1 - 3} + (-3)(5)$$

In Exercises 72–77, use the following information.

If A and B are sets, then the notation $A \cup B$ (the union of A and B) denotes the set of all elements from A combined with all elements from B. The notation $A \cap B$ (the intersection of A and B) denotes the set of the elements that A and B have in common. When A and B have no elements in common, then their intersection is the empty set, denoted $A \cap B = \emptyset$. Using interval notation, write $A \cup B$ and $A \cap B$ for each pair of intervals.

72. $A = (0, 2], B = [1, 9)$

73. $A = [-5, 0], B = [-1, \infty)$

74. $A = (-\infty, 2], B = [1, 9)$

75. $A = (-\infty, -4), B = (-3, \infty)$

76. $A = (-\infty, 0), B = (-5, 1)$

77. $A = (-\infty, 10], B = [10, \infty)$

In Exercises 78–81, use the properties of absolute value to determine whether each statement is true or false for all real values of x and y.

78. $|xy| = |(-x)(-y)|$

79. $|xy| \geq 0$

80. $|x + y| = |x| + |y|$

81. $|x| - |x| = 0$

82. Suppose line segment $\overline{AB}$ has endpoints at $A(-5, 0)$ and $B(7, 0)$, and line segment $\overline{CD}$ has endpoints at $C(3, 10)$ and $D(3, -4)$. Is the length of line segment $\overline{AB}$ equal to the length of line segment $\overline{CD}$? Explain.

83. Suppose parallelogram $ABCD$ has vertices at $A(-6, 7)$, $B(5, 7)$, $C(5, -4)$, and $D(-6, -4)$. Is parallelogram $ABCD$ a rhombus? Explain.

Two additional properties are consequences of the Quotient of Powers Property. First, consider the case of a quotient of powers with like bases where the exponent in the numerator is *less than* the exponent in the denominator, such as $\dfrac{3^2}{3^6}$. Expanding, removing common factors, and writing in exponential notation gives the result $\dfrac{1}{3^4}$. However, notice that applying the Quotient of Powers Property yields $\dfrac{3^2}{3^6} = 3^{2-6} = 3^{-4}$. Therefore, $3^{-4} = \dfrac{1}{3^4}$, which is an example of the **Negative Exponent Property**.

Negative Exponent Property
If a is a nonzero real number and m is an integer, then $a^{-m} = \dfrac{1}{a^m}$.

Now consider a quotient of powers with like bases where the exponents in the numerator and denominator are *equal*, such as $\dfrac{3^6}{3^6}$. Expanding, removing common factors, and writing in exponential notation gives the result 1 (since the numerator and denominator are equal). However, notice that applying the Quotient of Powers Property yields $\dfrac{3^6}{3^6} = 3^{6-6} = 3^0$. Therefore, $3^0 = 1$, which is an example of the **Zero Exponent Property**.

Zero Exponent Property
If a is a nonzero real number, then $a^0 = 1$.

The last property of powers introduced in this section is the **Power of a Quotient Property**, which states that the power of a quotient can be written as a quotient of powers.

Power of a Quotient Property
If a and b are nonzero real numbers and n is an integer, then $\left(\dfrac{a}{b}\right)^n = \dfrac{a^n}{b^n}$.

The properties of powers are summarized in the following table. Note that all apply to exponential expressions where the base is a nonzero real number or an algebraic expression. Assume that an algebraic expression used as the base of a power represents a nonzero real number.

IMPORTANT

In each of these properties, a and b are nonzero real numbers, and m and n are integers.

Properties of Powers	
Product of Powers	$a^m a^n = a^{m+n}$
Power of a Power	$(a^m)^n = a^{m \cdot n}$
Power of a Product	$(ab)^n = a^n b^n$
Quotient of Powers	$\dfrac{a^m}{a^n} = a^{m-n}$
Power of a Quotient	$\left(\dfrac{a}{b}\right)^n = \dfrac{a^n}{b^n}$
Negative Exponent	$a^{-m} = \dfrac{1}{a^m}$
Zero Exponent	$a^0 = 1$

| EXAMPLE 6 | **Using Properties of Powers to Simplify Expressions** |

Simplify. Write each expression using only positive exponents.

A. $\dfrac{b^9}{b^3}$

B. $\dfrac{x^2}{x^{10}}$

SOLUTION

Each expression is a quotient of powers with like bases, so use the Quotient of Powers Property.

Quotient of Powers ▶
Property
$$\dfrac{a^m}{a^n} = a^{m-n}$$

A. $\dfrac{b^9}{b^3} = b^{9-3} = b^6$

B. $\dfrac{x^2}{x^{10}} = x^{2-10} = x^{-8} = \dfrac{1}{x^8}$ *Use the Negative Exponent Property to write x^{-8} with a positive exponent.*

| EXAMPLE 7 | **Using Properties of Powers to Simplify Expressions** |

Simplify. Write each expression using only positive exponents.

A. 4^{-4}

B. $(-2)^{-5}$

C. $\left(\dfrac{1}{2}\right)^{-3}$

D. $\left(-\dfrac{7}{9}\right)^{-2}$

SOLUTION

Negative Exponent ▶
Property
$$a^{-m} = \dfrac{1}{a^m}$$

Each power has a negative exponent, so use the Negative Exponent Property to simplify.

A. $4^{-4} = \dfrac{1}{4^4} = \dfrac{1}{256}$

B. $(-2)^{-5} = \dfrac{1}{(-2)^5} = -\dfrac{1}{32}$

TIP

Applying the Negative Exponent Property does not change the sign of the base.

C. $\left(\dfrac{1}{2}\right)^{-3} = \dfrac{1}{\left(\dfrac{1}{2}\right)^3}$ *Negative Exponent Property*

$= \dfrac{1}{\dfrac{1^3}{2^3}}$ *Power of a Quotient Property*

$= \dfrac{1}{\dfrac{1}{8}}$ *Simplify.*

$= 8$ $1 \div \dfrac{1}{8} = 8$

D. $\left(-\dfrac{7}{9}\right)^{-2} = \dfrac{1}{\left(-\dfrac{7}{9}\right)^2}$ *Negative Exponent Property*

$= \dfrac{1}{\dfrac{(-7)^2}{9^2}}$ *Power of a Quotient Property*

$= \dfrac{1}{\dfrac{49}{81}}$ *Simplify.*

$= \dfrac{81}{49}$ $1 \div \dfrac{49}{81} = \dfrac{81}{49}$

ALTERNATIVE METHOD

Using the Power of a Power Property, write each expression a^{-m} as $\left(a^{-1}\right)^m$, then simplify.

A. $4^{-4} = (4^{-1})^4$ *Power of a Power Property*

$= \left(\dfrac{1}{4}\right)^4$ *Negative Exponent Property*

$= \dfrac{1^4}{4^4}$ *Power of a Quotient Property*

$= \dfrac{1}{256}$ *Simplify.*

B. $(-2)^{-5} = \left((-2)^{-1}\right)^5$ *Power of a Power Property*

$= \left(-\dfrac{1}{2}\right)^5$ *Negative Exponent Property*

$= \dfrac{(-1)^5}{2^5}$ *Power of a Quotient Property*

$= -\dfrac{1}{32}$ *Simplify.*

TIP

The reciprocal of x is $\dfrac{1}{x}$.

The reciprocal of $\dfrac{x}{y}$ is $\dfrac{y}{x}$.

Extensions

In Exercises 61–63, simplify each expression and state the properties of powers that are applied.

61. $\dfrac{(3d^6)^2}{18d(d^5)}$

62. $\dfrac{10w^{-3}}{(2w)^3}$

63. $(-8m)^{-2}(-n)^0\left(\dfrac{-3n^2}{4}\right)^{-3}(m^2)$

In Exercises 64–69, write two expressions that use the given properties and are equal to the given number or expression.

64. Zero Exponent; 1

65. Zero Exponent; 3

66. Quotient of Powers; x^2

67. Quotient of Powers; $\dfrac{2}{x^2}$

68. Product of Powers; $x^{10}y^9z$

69. Power of a Product and Power of a Power; $16x^{12}y^8z^4$

In Exercises 70–72, find and correct the error, if any.

70. $\dfrac{(s^3)(s^6)}{s^{-2}} = s^{3+6-2} = s^7$

71. $(2c^{-5})^{-3} = 2^{-3}c^{-5(-3)} = -8c^{15}$

72. $\left(\dfrac{h^2}{5}\right)^{-3} = \left(\dfrac{5}{h^2}\right)^3 = \dfrac{5^3}{(h^2)^3} = \dfrac{125}{h^6}$

P.3 RATIONAL EXPONENTS AND RADICALS

OBJECTIVES

- Use properties of radicals to evaluate and simplify expressions.
- Use properties of rational exponents to evaluate and simplify expressions.
- Rationalize denominators.

PREREQUISITE VOCABULARY TERMS

irrational number

power

rational number

P.3.1 Finding Real Roots

Addition and subtraction are **inverse operations** because one operation *undoes* the other. For example, for any numbers m and n, $m + n - n = m$. In other words, the value of a number does not change when some number is added to and subtracted from that number. Another example of inverse operations is multiplication and division. Powers also have an inverse operation. The inverse of a number to the nth power is the **nth root** of the number.

> ### DEFINITION
>
> If a and b are real numbers and n is an integer greater than or equal to 2 such that $a = b^n$, then b is an **nth root** of a.

IMPORTANT

Some numbers have nth roots that are not real numbers, but for now, our discussion is limited to real nth roots.

So, an nth root of a real number a is a number such that its nth power is a. Some numbers have more than one nth root. For example, 2 is a sixth root of 64 because $2^6 = 64$. Additionally, -2 is a sixth root of 64 because $(-2)^6 = 64$.

When $n = 2$, the second root is called the **square root**. A third root is referred to as a **cube root**. After $n = 3$, roots are named by the number of the root (e.g., the fourth root and fifth root).

TIP

$n = 2$: square root
$n = 3$: cube root
$n = 4$: fourth root
. . .

EXAMPLE 1   Identifying the Real Roots of a Number

Identify each statement as true or false.

A. 10 and -10 are real square roots of 100.

B. -9 has one real square root: -3.

C. 125 has two real cube roots: 5 and -5.

D. -11 is a real cube root of -1331.

E. 2 and -2 are real fourth roots of 16.

F. -16 has no real fourth roots.

SOLUTION

A. True. Since $10^2 = 100$ and $(-10)^2 = 100$, 10 and -10 are real square roots of 100.

IMPORTANT

There is no real number whose square is -9, so -9 has no real square roots.

B. False. Since $(-3)^2 = 9$, not -9, -3 is not a square root of -9.

C. False. Since $(-5)^3 = -125$, not 125, -5 is not a real cube root of 125. However, since $5^3 = 125$, 5 is a real cube root of 125.

D. True. Since $(-11)^3 = -1331$, -11 is a real cube root of -1331.

E. True. Since $2^4 = 16$ and $(-2)^4 = 16$, 2 and -2 are real fourth roots of 16.

IMPORTANT

Negative real numbers have no real even roots because a real number to an even power is always positive.

F. True. There is no real number whose fourth power is -16, so -16 has no real fourth roots.

EXAMPLE 3	**Simplifying Radical Expressions**

Simplify.

A. $3\sqrt{20} \cdot \sqrt{3}$

B. $8\sqrt{\dfrac{25}{16}}$

SOLUTION

A. The Product Property of radicals can be applied to write the expression using a single radical symbol because the radicals have the same index and they are being multiplied.

$$3\sqrt{20} \cdot \sqrt{3} = 3\sqrt{20 \cdot 3} = 3\sqrt{60}$$

The radical is not in simplest form because the radicand, 60, contains a perfect-square factor. Simplify the radical.

$3\sqrt{60} = 3\sqrt{4 \cdot 15}$	*Since 4 is a perfect-square factor of 60, write 60 as $4 \cdot 15$.*
$= 3\sqrt{4}\sqrt{15}$	*Product Property of Radicals*
$= 3 \cdot 2\sqrt{15}$	*Simplify the radical of the perfect square: $\sqrt{4} = 2$.*
$= 6\sqrt{15}$	*Multiply.*

ALTERNATIVE METHOD

Simplify $\sqrt{20}$ first, then use the Product Property to write the expression using a single radical symbol.

$3\sqrt{20} \cdot \sqrt{3} = 3\sqrt{4 \cdot 5} \cdot \sqrt{3}$	*Since 4 is a perfect-square factor of 20, write 20 as $4 \cdot 5$.*
$= 3\sqrt{4} \cdot \sqrt{5} \cdot \sqrt{3}$	*Product Property of Radicals*
$= 3 \cdot 2\sqrt{5} \cdot \sqrt{3}$	*Simplify the radical of the perfect square: $\sqrt{4} = 2$.*
$= 3 \cdot 2\sqrt{5 \cdot 3}$	*Product Property of Radicals*
$= 6\sqrt{15}$	*Multiply.*

B. Notice that the radical contains a fraction, and the numerator and denominator are both perfect squares. So, use the Quotient Property of radicals to simplify the expression.

$8\sqrt{\dfrac{25}{16}} = 8\left(\dfrac{\sqrt{25}}{\sqrt{16}}\right)$	*Quotient Property of Radicals*
$= 8\left(\dfrac{5}{4}\right)$	*Simplify the radicals.*
$= 10$	*Multiply.*

P.3.3 Adding and Subtracting Radical Expressions

Just as terms in an algebraic expression can be combined (added or subtracted) when they are like terms, radical terms can be combined when the terms contain **like radicals**. Like radicals are radicals that have the same index and the same radicand. As with like terms with a variable, combine like radical terms by adding or subtracting the coefficients, while keeping the radical part of the terms the same. When simplifying an expression with radical terms, simplify each radical first, then look for like radical terms to combine.

EXAMPLE 4   Combining Radical Terms

Simplify each expression.

A. $10\sqrt{3} + 2\sqrt{3}$ **B.** $8\sqrt[3]{7} - \sqrt[3]{7}$ **C.** $-4\sqrt{18} + 5\sqrt{2}$ **D.** $\sqrt{500} - 16\sqrt{20} + \sqrt{2}$

SOLUTION

A. $10\sqrt{3} + 2\sqrt{3} = 12\sqrt{3}$ *The terms are like radical terms, so add the coefficients.*

B. $8\sqrt[3]{7} - \sqrt[3]{7} = 7\sqrt[3]{7}$ *Subtract the coefficients. The coefficient of $\sqrt[3]{7}$ is 1.*

In **C** and **D**, the terms are not like radical terms, but the radicals are not in simplest form. Simplify the radicals and then combine the terms if the radicands are the same.

C. $-4\sqrt{18} + 5\sqrt{2} = -4\sqrt{9 \cdot 2} + 5\sqrt{2}$ *Write 18 as $9 \cdot 2$.*

$= -4 \cdot 3\sqrt{2} + 5\sqrt{2}$ *Simplify the radical.*

$= -12\sqrt{2} + 5\sqrt{2}$ *Multiply.*

$= -7\sqrt{2}$ *Subtract the coefficients.*

D. $\sqrt{500} - 16\sqrt{20} + \sqrt{2} = \sqrt{100 \cdot 5} - 16\sqrt{4 \cdot 5} + \sqrt{2}$ *Write 500 as $100 \cdot 5$ and 20 as $4 \cdot 5$.*

$= 10\sqrt{5} - 16 \cdot 2\sqrt{5} + \sqrt{2}$ *Simplify the radicals.*

$= 10\sqrt{5} - 32\sqrt{5} + \sqrt{2}$ *Multiply.*

$= -22\sqrt{5} + \sqrt{2}$ *Subtract the coefficients.*

IMPORTANT

$\sqrt{5}$ and $\sqrt{2}$ are not like radicals because their radicands are not the same.

P.3.4   Rationalizing a Denominator

Typically, a **fractional expression** (a quotient of algebraic expressions) that contains a radical in the denominator will be written as an equivalent expression in which the denominator is a rational number (so it does not contain a radical), which is called **rationalizing the denominator**. To rationalize a denominator, multiply the fractional expression by a number (or expression) equivalent to 1 that will remove the denominator's radical. The following table generalizes the process for several types of denominators. (Assume that all expressions exist.)

Rationalizing Denominators		
Irrational Denominator	**Rationalizing the Denominator**	**Rational Denominator**
$\dfrac{c}{b\sqrt{n}}$	$\dfrac{c}{b\sqrt{n}} \cdot \dfrac{\sqrt{n}}{\sqrt{n}}$	$\dfrac{c\sqrt{n}}{bn}$
$\dfrac{c}{a+b\sqrt{n}}$	$\dfrac{c}{a+b\sqrt{n}} \cdot \dfrac{a-b\sqrt{n}}{a-b\sqrt{n}}$	$\dfrac{c\left(a-b\sqrt{n}\right)}{a^2 - b^2 n}$
$\dfrac{c}{a-b\sqrt{n}}$	$\dfrac{c}{a-b\sqrt{n}} \cdot \dfrac{a+b\sqrt{n}}{a+b\sqrt{n}}$	$\dfrac{c\left(a+b\sqrt{n}\right)}{a^2 - b^2 n}$
$\dfrac{c}{b\sqrt[3]{n}}$	$\dfrac{c}{b\sqrt[3]{n}} \cdot \dfrac{\sqrt[3]{n^2}}{\sqrt[3]{n^2}}$	$\dfrac{c\sqrt[3]{n^2}}{bn}$

| EXAMPLE 6 | Simplifying a Power with a Rational Exponent |

Simplify each expression.

A. $16^{\frac{1}{2}}$ **B.** $4^{\frac{3}{2}}$ **C.** $27^{\frac{2}{3}}$

SOLUTION

Write each power as a radical where the denominator of the rational exponent is the radical's index and the numerator is either the power of the radicand or the power of the radical. Then simplify.

A. $16^{\frac{1}{2}} = \sqrt{16} = 4$

B. $4^{\frac{3}{2}} = \left(\sqrt{4}\right)^3 = 2^3 = 8$ *Alternatively, the power could be written as $\sqrt{4^3} = \sqrt{64} = 8$.*

C. $27^{\frac{2}{3}} = \left(\sqrt[3]{27}\right)^2 = 3^2 = 9$ *Alternatively, the power could be written as $\sqrt[3]{27^2} = \sqrt[3]{729} = 9$.*

WHAT'S THE BIG IDEA?

Use properties of powers and properties of real numbers to show that $a^{\frac{m}{n}} = \left(\sqrt[n]{a}\right)^m$ and that $a^{\frac{m}{n}} = \sqrt[n]{a^m}$.

Properties of exponents, such as the Product of Powers Property, $a^m \cdot a^n = a^{m+n}$, can be used to simplify radical expressions and expressions with rational exponents. Recall that the Product of Powers Property is applied only to powers with like bases.

| EXAMPLE 7 | Simplifying a Product of Radicals |

Write each product as a single radical, if possible.

A. $\sqrt{3}\left(\sqrt[5]{3}\right)$ **B.** $\sqrt[4]{7^3}\left(\sqrt{7}\right)$

SOLUTION

Write each radical as a power with a rational exponent.

A. $\sqrt{3}\left(\sqrt[5]{3}\right)$

$= 3^{\frac{1}{2}}\left(3^{\frac{1}{5}}\right)$ *Write each radical using a rational exponent.*

$= 3^{\frac{1}{2}+\frac{1}{5}}$ *Product of Powers*

$= 3^{\frac{7}{10}}$ *Simplify the exponent.*

$= \left(\sqrt[10]{3}\right)^7$ *Convert to radical form.*

The radical can be written equivalently as $\sqrt[10]{3^7}$.

B. $\sqrt[4]{7^3}\left(\sqrt{7}\right)$

$= 7^{\frac{3}{4}}\left(7^{\frac{1}{2}}\right)$ *Write each radical using a rational exponent.*

$= 7^{\frac{3}{4}+\frac{1}{2}}$ *Product of Powers*

$= 7^{\frac{5}{4}}$ *Simplify the exponent.*

$= 7^1 7^{\frac{1}{4}}$ *Properties of Exponents*

$= 7\sqrt[4]{7}$ *Convert to radical form.*

Negative Rational Exponents

When a rational exponent is negative, apply the Negative Exponent Property, $a^{-m} = \dfrac{1}{a^m}$, to write the power with a positive exponent.

EXAMPLE 8	Simplifying an Expression with a Negative Rational Exponent

Simplify each expression.

A. $25^{-\frac{1}{2}}$

B. $27^{-\frac{4}{3}}$

SOLUTION

Use the Negative Exponent Property to write each negative rational exponent as a positive rational exponent. Then convert the rational exponent to a radical and simplify.

A. $25^{-\frac{1}{2}} = \dfrac{1}{25^{\frac{1}{2}}} = \dfrac{1}{\sqrt{25}} = \dfrac{1}{5}$

B. $27^{-\frac{4}{3}} = \dfrac{1}{27^{\frac{4}{3}}} = \dfrac{1}{\left(\sqrt[3]{27}\right)^4} = \dfrac{1}{3^4} = \dfrac{1}{81}$

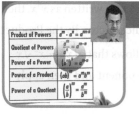

Product of Powers	$a^m \cdot a^n = a^{m+n}$
Quotient of Powers	$\dfrac{a^m}{a^n} = a^{m-n}$
Power of a Power	$(a^m)^n = a^{mn}$
Power of a Product	$(ab)^m = a^m b^m$
Power of a Quotient	$\left(\dfrac{a}{b}\right)^m = \dfrac{a^m}{b^m}$

P.3.6   Simplifying Expressions with Rational Exponents

All of the properties of exponents can be applied to rational exponents as they have been applied previously to integer exponents. When simplifying a product or quotient of powers with rational exponents, it is often best to multiply or divide the powers first (by applying a property of powers). Then convert the simplified power to radical notation.

EXAMPLE 9	Simplifying an Expression with Rational Exponents

Simplify each expression.

A. $9^{\frac{1}{6}} \cdot 9^{\frac{1}{3}}$

B. $\dfrac{16^{-\frac{5}{4}}}{16^{-\frac{1}{2}}}$

C. $\dfrac{243^{\frac{1}{5}}}{243^{\frac{7}{10}} \cdot 243^{\frac{1}{10}}}$

SOLUTION

Use the properties of exponents to write each expression as a single power, then simplify.

A. $9^{\frac{1}{6}} \cdot 9^{\frac{1}{3}} = 9^{\frac{1}{6}+\frac{1}{3}} = 9^{\frac{1}{2}} = \sqrt{9} = 3$

B. $\dfrac{16^{-\frac{5}{4}}}{16^{-\frac{1}{2}}} = 16^{-\frac{5}{4}-\left(-\frac{1}{2}\right)} = 16^{-\frac{3}{4}} = \dfrac{1}{16^{\frac{3}{4}}} = \dfrac{1}{\left(\sqrt[4]{16}\right)^3} = \dfrac{1}{2^3} = \dfrac{1}{8}$

C. $\dfrac{243^{\frac{1}{5}}}{243^{\frac{7}{10}} \cdot 243^{\frac{1}{10}}} = 243^{\frac{1}{5}-\left(\frac{7}{10}+\frac{1}{10}\right)} = 243^{-\frac{3}{5}} = \dfrac{1}{243^{\frac{3}{5}}} = \dfrac{1}{\left(\sqrt[5]{243}\right)^3} = \dfrac{1}{3^3} = \dfrac{1}{27}$

EXAMPLE 11 **Using Rational Exponents to Simplify a Product or Quotient of Radicals**

Simplify. Assume all variables represent positive numbers. $\dfrac{\sqrt{3b^2c}\sqrt{6ac^3}}{\sqrt{2a^5b^8c^{-1}}}$

SOLUTION

Each radical is a square root. So, by the Product and Quotient Properties of radicals, the expression can be written as a single radical. Then multiply to simplify the numerator.

$$\frac{\sqrt{3b^2c}\sqrt{6ac^3}}{\sqrt{2a^5b^8c^{-1}}} = \sqrt{\frac{3b^2c(6ac^3)}{2a^5b^8c^{-1}}} = \sqrt{\frac{18ab^2c^4}{2a^5b^8c^{-1}}}$$

Divide the coefficients and subtract the exponents with like bases to simplify the radicand.

$$\sqrt{\frac{18ab^2c^4}{2a^5b^8c^{-1}}} = \sqrt{9a^{1-5}b^{2-8}c^{4-(-1)}} = \sqrt{9a^{-4}b^{-6}c^5}$$

Find the square root of 9. Write the radical as a rational exponent, then apply the Power of a Product and the Power of a Power Properties.

$$\sqrt{9a^{-4}b^{-6}c^5} = 3(a^{-4}b^{-6}c^5)^{\frac{1}{2}} = 3(a^{-2}b^{-3}c^{\frac{5}{2}})$$

Write the improper fraction as the sum of the whole and fraction parts, then apply the Product of Powers Property.

$$3(a^{-2}b^{-3}c^{\frac{5}{2}}) = 3(a^{-2}b^{-3}c^{2+\frac{1}{2}}) = 3(a^{-2}b^{-3}c^2c^{\frac{1}{2}})$$

Write the negative exponents as positive exponents, and write the power with the rational exponent in radical notation.

$$3(a^{-2}b^{-3}c^2c^{\frac{1}{2}}) = \frac{3c^2}{a^2b^3}\sqrt{c}$$

SECTION P.3 EXERCISES

Warm Up

1. Evaluate. 2^6

2. Simplify. $5x - 7 - y + x + 3y + 1$

3. Simplify. $k^3(k^4)^2$

Just the Facts

Fill in the blanks.

4. If p is the nth root of q, then ____ = q.

5. Given $\sqrt[n]{a}$, the case where $n = 2$ is called the ____ root of a number, and the case where $n =$ ____ is called the cube root of a number.

6. ____ roots of negative numbers do not exist.

7. ____ has one real cube root: -8.

8. 1, 4, 9, 16, and 25 are the first five ____.

9. Radical terms can be combined if the terms contain ____, which have the same ____ and ____.

10. If the denominator of an expression is ____, then multiplying the expression by the denominator's ____, $p + q\sqrt{n}$, will rationalize the denominator.

Essential Skills

In Exercises 1–8, determine whether each statement is true or false.

1. The square roots of 225 are 15 and -15.

2. The fourth roots of 6561 are 9 and -9.

3. 14 is a cube root of 2744.

4. The fifth roots of 100,000 are 10 and -10.

5. -8 is a square root of -64.

6. $-10,000$ has no real fourth roots.

7. -3 is a cube root of -27.

8. The real fifth roots of -3125 are 5 and -5.

In Exercises 9–74, simplify. Do not use a calculator. Rationalize the denominator as necessary. Assume that all variables represent positive numbers.

9. $\sqrt{175}$

10. $-5\sqrt{800}$

11. $\sqrt[3]{\dfrac{128}{8}}$

12. $12\sqrt{\dfrac{75}{16}}$

13. $-6\sqrt{32}$

14. $7\sqrt{40} \cdot 3\sqrt{75}$

15. $4\sqrt[3]{\dfrac{24}{27}}$

16. $15\sqrt{\dfrac{18}{125}}$

17. $3\sqrt[3]{6} + \sqrt[3]{6} + \sqrt[3]{48}$

18. $\sqrt{45} - 7\sqrt{5}$

19. $4\sqrt{8} - \sqrt{200} + 6\sqrt{12}$

20. $-\sqrt[3]{54} + 4\sqrt[3]{24} - \sqrt[3]{21}$

21. $3\sqrt{27} - 5\sqrt{12} + \sqrt{48}$

22. $-8\sqrt{32} + \sqrt{72} + 9\sqrt{18}$

23. $\dfrac{2\sqrt{3}}{\sqrt{6}}$

24. $-\dfrac{2}{\sqrt{13}}$

25. $-\dfrac{5}{\sqrt{75}}$

26. $\dfrac{3\sqrt{6}}{\sqrt{10}}$

27. $\dfrac{4\sqrt{2}}{\sqrt{7}}$

28. $-\dfrac{6}{\sqrt{48}}$

29. $\sqrt[3]{\dfrac{3}{5}}$

30. $-\dfrac{1}{\sqrt[3]{-10}}$

31. $-\dfrac{5}{\sqrt[3]{-3}}$

32. $\dfrac{4}{\sqrt[3]{6}}$

33. $\dfrac{4}{\sqrt{7} + 3}$

34. $\dfrac{1}{\sqrt{5} - 12}$

35. $\dfrac{2}{5 - \sqrt{3}}$

36. $\dfrac{3}{2 + \sqrt{6}}$

37. $\dfrac{6}{8 + \sqrt{10}}$

38. $\dfrac{7}{4 - \sqrt{11}}$

39. $25^{\frac{3}{2}}$

40. $8^{\frac{7}{3}}$

41. $27^{\frac{4}{3}}$

42. $4^{\frac{3}{2}}$

43. $16^{\frac{5}{4}}$

44. $32^{\frac{2}{5}}$

45. $x^{\frac{2}{7}} x^{\frac{3}{14}}$

46. $\sqrt[4]{5}\left(\sqrt{5}\right)^3$

47. $\sqrt[3]{2}\left(\sqrt{2^3}\right)$

48. $m^{\frac{3}{4}} m^{\frac{5}{8}}$

49. $y^{\frac{2}{3}} y^{\frac{5}{6}}$

50. $\sqrt[6]{7}\left(\sqrt{7}\right)^2$

51. $64^{-\frac{4}{3}}$

52. $81^{-\frac{3}{4}}$

53. $49^{-\frac{3}{2}}$

54. $32^{-\frac{2}{5}}$

55. $16^{-\frac{3}{4}}$

56. $78,125^{-\frac{3}{7}}$

57. $\dfrac{27^{\frac{2}{3}}}{27^{\frac{1}{6}}}$

58. $\dfrac{25^{\frac{1}{8}} \cdot 25^{\frac{1}{8}}}{25^{\frac{3}{4}}}$

59. $\dfrac{32^{\frac{4}{5}}}{32^{\frac{1}{2}} \cdot 32^{\frac{1}{10}}}$

60. $\dfrac{36^{-\frac{3}{4}}}{36^{-\frac{1}{4}}}$

61. $\dfrac{27^{-\frac{2}{3}}}{27^{-\frac{4}{3}}}$

62. $\dfrac{49^{\frac{1}{6}} \cdot 49^{\frac{5}{6}}}{49^{\frac{18}{12}}}$

63. $\sqrt{9u^7 v^2 z}$

64. $\sqrt{28 p^8 q r^3}$

65. $\sqrt{72 g^4 h^6 j^3}$

66. $\sqrt[3]{27 a^9 bc^{24}}$

67. $\sqrt[3]{16 mn^{12} p^{16}}$

68. $\sqrt{275 s^4 t p^9}$

A polynomial with degree greater than 5 does not have a specific name, and the names for polynomials with degrees 4 and 5 are rarely used. The names for polynomials with degrees 1, 2, and 3 (linear, quadratic, and cubic, respectively) will be seen often in this course.

A polynomial can have any number of terms, but polynomials with one, two, and three terms have specific names. From the definition, a polynomial with only one term is a monomial. A polynomial with two terms is called a **binomial**, and a polynomial with three terms is called a **trinomial**.

> **IMPORTANT**
>
> *monomial: one term*
> *binomial: two terms*
> *trinomial: three terms*

A polynomial is often classified and named by its degree *and* its number of terms. For example, $b^3 - b$ is a cubic binomial, $7z^2 + 3z - 2$ is a quadratic trinomial, and $2a + 2$ is a linear binomial.

> **IMPORTANT**
>
> *A simplified polynomial should always be written in standard form, unless otherwise stated.*

Polynomials are typically written in **standard form**, where the terms are written in descending order by degree. For example, the quadratic binomial $h^2 - 5$ is in standard form because the first term's degree is greater than the second term's degree. The trinomial $a^2 - a^4 + 2$ is not in standard form because the degree of the first term is less than the degree of the second term. The trinomial can be written in standard form by rearranging the terms so that they are in descending order by degree: $-a^4 + a^2 + 2$. The coefficient of the term with the greatest degree in a polynomial is called the **leading coefficient**. When a polynomial is written in standard form, the leading coefficient is written first.

EXAMPLE 1   Writing a Polynomial in Standard Form and Classifying the Polynomial

Write each polynomial in standard form. Then identify its degree and leading coefficient, and classify it according to its degree and number of terms.

A. $w + 3 - w^2$

B. $1 + 7n^2 - 5n^3$

SOLUTION

A. The polynomial has 3 terms.
- standard form: $-w^2 + w + 3$
- degree: 2
- leading coefficient: −1
- classification: quadratic trinomial

B. The polynomial has 3 terms.
- standard form: $-5n^3 + 7n^2 + 1$
- degree: 3
- leading coefficient: −5
- classification: cubic trinomial

WHAT'S THE BIG IDEA?

What information can be deduced about each of the following polynomials? (Assume that each polynomial contains only one variable.)
- a quartic binomial
- a quadratic monomial
- a quintic polynomial

P.4.2   Adding, Subtracting, and Multiplying Polynomials

The Associative, Commutative, and Distributive Properties are applied when adding, subtracting, and multiplying polynomials. Each process includes applying appropriate operations or properties to remove any parentheses and then combining any like terms, as was done previously when simplifying an expression.

Subtracting Polynomials

When one polynomial is subtracted from another, the subtracted polynomial must be enclosed within parentheses.

$$(a + b) - (c + d - e)$$ *Trinomial $c + d - e$ is subtracted from binomial $a + b$.*

Subtraction of a polynomial can be rewritten (or just thought of) as addition of the negative of the polynomial.

$$(a + b) - (c + d - e) = (a + b) + (-1)(c + d - e)$$

Distributive Property ▶
$$a(b + c) = ab + ac$$
$$a(b - c) = ab - ac$$

To simplify this type of expression, distribute the -1 to *each term* within the parentheses. Multiplying each term by -1 changes the sign of the term (i.e., changes addition to subtraction and subtraction to addition).

$$(a + b) + (-1)(c + d - e) = (a + b) - c - d + e$$

Grouping symbols that are preceded by plus signs, or nothing at all, are unnecessary because they can be removed without changing any of the enclosed terms.

$$(a + b) - c - d + e = a + b - c - d + e$$

Therefore, $(a + b) - (c + d - e) = a + b - c - d + e$. The expression $a + b - c - d + e$ contains no like terms or parentheses, so the expression is simplified.

EXAMPLE 2   **Adding and Subtracting Polynomials**

Simplify.

A. $x^3 + (x^2 + 3x - 4) + 3(2x^3 - x + 1)$ **B.** $[(2x + 3x^2) - x^2] - [x^3 - 3(5x^3 - x) + 4x^2]$

SOLUTION

A. Use the Distributive Property, then combine the like terms.

$$x^3 + (x^2 + 3x - 4) + 3(2x^3 - x + 1)$$

$= x^3 + x^2 + 3x - 4 + 3(2x^3 - x + 1)$	*Remove the parentheses.*
$= x^3 + x^2 + 3x - 4 + 6x^3 - 3x + 3$	*Distribute the 3.*
$= x^3 + 6x^3 + x^2 + 3x - 3x - 4 + 3$	*Group the like terms.*
$= 7x^3 + x^2 - 1$	*Combine the like terms.*

> **TIP**
>
> The parentheses around the polynomial $x^2 + 3x - 4$ can be removed without changing any of the enclosed terms because only a plus sign immediately precedes the opening parenthesis.

B. Start by simplifying within the brackets. Next, use the Distributive Property to remove the parentheses, and then combine the like terms. Remember, the grouping symbols that are preceded by a plus sign, or nothing at all, can be removed without changing any of the enclosed terms.

$$[(2x + 3x^2) - x^2] - [x^3 - 3(5x^3 - x) + 4x^2]$$

$= 2x + 3x^2 - x^2 - [x^3 - 3(5x^3 - x) + 4x^2]$	*Remove the unnecessary grouping symbols.*
$= 2x + 3x^2 - x^2 - [x^3 - 15x^3 + 3x + 4x^2]$	*Distribute the -3.*
$= 2x + 3x^2 - x^2 - x^3 + 15x^3 - 3x - 4x^2$	*Distribute the -1.*
$= 2x - 3x + 3x^2 - x^2 - 4x^2 - x^3 + 15x^3$	*Group the like terms.*
$= -x - 2x^2 + 14x^3$	*Combine the like terms.*
$= 14x^3 - 2x^2 - x$	*Write the polynomial in standard form.*

> **TIP**
>
> Multiplying a polynomial by -1 changes the sign of each term.
>
> $-[x^3 - 15x^3 + 3x + 4x^2]$
> $= (-1)[x^3 - 15x^3 + 3x + 4x^2]$
> $= -x^3 + 15x^3 - 3x - 4x^2$

P.4.4   Special Products of Binomials: Squares and Cubes

The following table summarizes the formulas that can be used to find products of binomials when the binomials contain the same terms (with the same or opposite signs), such as squares and cubes of binomials. These formulas can be helpful, but they are not necessary. You can multiply by using the Distributive Property or FOIL instead of using a formula.

Formulas for Special Products of Binomials

Sum and Difference of Same Terms	$(A + B)(A - B) = A^2 - B^2$
Square of a Sum	$(A + B)^2 = A^2 + 2AB + B^2$
Square of a Difference	$(A - B)^2 = A^2 - 2AB + B^2$
Cube of a Sum	$(A + B)^3 = A^3 + 3A^2B + 3AB^2 + B^3$
Cube of a Difference	$(A - B)^3 = A^3 - 3A^2B + 3AB^2 - B^3$

TIP

*The product of two binomials is a binomial only when the two binomials have the same terms with opposite signs, as in $(a + b)(a - b)$. This case is called a **Sum and Difference of Same Terms**.*

In these formulas, A and B can be real numbers, powers of variables, or any kind of polynomial. Note that A and B do *not* represent the coefficients of the variables.

EXAMPLE 5   Squares and Cubes of Binomials

Simplify.

A. $(x + 5)^2$ **B.** $(3p^3 - 4r)^2$ **C.** $(3 + 5z^2)^3$ **D.** $(4a^5 - \sqrt{2}b)^3$

SOLUTION

A. Since the squared expression is a binomial sum, simplify by using the Square of a Sum Formula, $(A + B)^2 = A^2 + 2AB + B^2$, where $A = x$ and $B = 5$.

$$(x + 5)^2 = x^2 + 2(x)(5) + 5^2 \qquad \textit{Substitute.}$$
$$= x^2 + 10x + 25 \qquad \textit{Simplify.}$$

Check by FOILing

$(x + 5)^2$

$= (x + 5)(x + 5)$

$= x^2 + 5x + 5x + 25$

$= x^2 + 10x + 25$ ✔

B. Since the squared expression is a binomial difference, simplify by using the Square of a Difference Formula, $(A - B)^2 = A^2 - 2AB + B^2$, where $A = 3p^3$ and $B = 4r$.

$$(3p^3 - 4r)^2 = (3p^3)^2 - 2(3p^3)(4r) + (4r)^2 \qquad \textit{Substitute.}$$
$$= (3)^2(p^3)^2 - 2(3p^3)(4r) + (4)^2(r)^2 \qquad \textit{Power of a Product Property}$$
$$= 9(p^6) - 2(3p^3)(4r) + 16(r^2) \qquad \textit{Power of a Power Property}$$
$$= 9p^6 - 24p^3r + 16r^2 \qquad \textit{Multiply.}$$

TIP

When A or B represents a product or sum, be sure to enclose the expression for A or B within parentheses. Otherwise, the powers of products may be evaluated incorrectly.

C. Since the cubed expression is a binomial sum, simplify by using the Cube of a Sum Formula, $(A + B)^3 = A^3 + 3A^2B + 3AB^2 + B^3$, where $A = 3$ and $B = 5z^2$.

$(3 + 5z^2)^3$

$$= (3)^3 + 3(3)^2(5z^2) + 3(3)(5z^2)^2 + (5z^2)^3 \qquad \textit{Substitute.}$$
$$= (3)^3 + 3(3)^2(5z^2) + 3(3)(5)^2(z^2)^2 + (5)^3(z^2)^3 \qquad \textit{Power of a Product Property}$$
$$= (3)^3 + 3(3)^2(5z^2) + 3(3)(5)^2(z^4) + (5)^3(z^6) \qquad \textit{Power of a Power Property}$$
$$= 27 + 3(9)(5z^2) + 3(3)(25)(z^4) + (125)(z^6) \qquad \textit{Evaluate the powers.}$$
$$= 27 + 135z^2 + 225z^4 + 125z^6 \qquad \textit{Multiply.}$$
$$= 125z^6 + 225z^4 + 135z^2 + 27 \qquad \textit{Write the polynomial in standard form.}$$

Power of a Product Property

$(ab)^n = a^n b^n$

D. Since the cubed expression is a binomial difference, simplify by using the Cube of a Difference Formula, $(A - B)^3 = A^3 - 3A^2B + 3AB^2 - B^3$, where $A = 4a^5$ and $B = \sqrt{2}b$.

Power of a Power Property

$(a^m)^n = a^{mn}$ ▶

$$(4a^5 - \sqrt{2}b)^3$$

$$= (4a^5)^3 - 3(4a^5)^2(\sqrt{2}b) + 3(4a^5)(\sqrt{2}b)^2 - (\sqrt{2}b)^3 \qquad \textit{Substitute.}$$

$$= (4)^3(a^5)^3 - 3(4)^2(a^5)^2(\sqrt{2}b) + 3(4a^5)(\sqrt{2})^2(b)^2 - (\sqrt{2})^3(b)^3 \qquad \textit{Power of a Product Property}$$

$$= (4)^3(a^{15}) - 3(4)^2(a^{10})(\sqrt{2}b) + 3(4a^5)(\sqrt{2})^2(b^2) - (\sqrt{2})^3(b^3) \qquad \textit{Power of a Power Property}$$

$$= 64(a^{15}) - 3(16)(a^{10})(\sqrt{2}b) + 3(4a^5)(2)(b^2) - (2\sqrt{2})(b^3) \qquad \textit{Evaluate the powers.}$$

$$= 64a^{15} - 48\sqrt{2}a^{10}b + 24a^5b^2 - 2\sqrt{2}b^3 \qquad \textit{Multiply.}$$

REMEMBER

$\left(\sqrt{2}\right)^3 = \sqrt{2} \cdot \sqrt{2} \cdot \sqrt{2}$
$= \sqrt{4} \cdot \sqrt{2}$
$= 2\sqrt{2}$

SECTION P.4 EXERCISES

Warm Up

Simplify.

1. $5(3x^2 - 7x + 2)$

2. $2(4y + 1) + 10y$

3. $-6p^5qr^2(3p^4r)^2$

Just the Facts

Fill in the blanks.

4. An algebraic expression of the form ax^n is called a ____.

5. Any ____ in a monomial cannot be negative or a fraction.

6. A polynomial is a sum or ____ of ____.

7. A cubic binomial has ____ terms and degree ____.

8. A simplified ____ polynomial in one variable can have at most three terms.

9. The coefficient of the term with the greatest ____ is called the ____.

10. FOIL is a process used for ____ two ____.

Essential Skills

In Exercises 1–6, write each polynomial in standard form. Then identify the leading coefficient and classify it according to its degree and number of terms.

1. $12 + k^2 - 5k$

2. $3x^2 - 8x - 5x^3 + 6$

3. $16m - 6m^3 + 3m^2 - 5m^5$

4. $-4x^3 - 2x^5 - 3$

5. $4b^3 - b + 2b^2 + b^4$

6. $2a - 4a^2 + 2a^3 + 2$

In Exercises 7–32, simplify each expression.

7. $(x^2 - 2x^3 + 16) - (4x^3 + x^2 - x + 10)$

8. $[2a^4 + (5a + 6) - a^2] - [7a - (6a^3 - 2a^2 + 5a) - 4(a + 6)]$

9. $(y^3 + 3y^2 + 5 - 6y) - 4(y + 1) + 3(y^3 - 2y^2 + y)$

10. $(4b^5 + 7b^2 + 2 - b) - (3b^3 - 5b^2 + 6b) - 3(2b + 1)$

11. $[(5m + 6) - 3m^2 + m] - [8m - 2(m^3 + 4m^2 - 5m) - 5m^3]$

12. $5x^4 + 3(5x + 6) - x^2 - [4(x + 9) - (x^3 - 4x^2 + 3x)]$

13. $(5x - 8)(6 - x)$

14. $(4x^2 - 5)(3x^2 + 7)$

15. $(3a^2 + 4)(2a - 5)$

16. $(4h^3 - 1)(5h^3 - 4)$

17. $(2 - 7m^2)(m^2 + 3)$

18. $(b^2 - 6)(2 - 7b^2)$

19. $(x - 1)(3x^3 - 5x^2 + 6x - 1)$

20. $(x + 3)(x^2 + 2x + 4 + x)$

21. $(x^2 + 2x + 5)(2x^2 - 3x + 1)$

22. $(2x^2 + 3xy - 5y^2)^2$

23. $(6y^3 - 2yz - 2z^2)^2$

24. $(2b + 3)(b^3 + 4b^2 - 3b - 7)$

25. $(3x + 7)^2$

26. $(4x - 3y)^2$

27. $(5a^2 + 2bc)^3$

28. $\left(\sqrt{5}p - 2r^4\right)^3$

29. $(2x - 5)(2x + 5)$

30. $(4 + 3m^2)^3$

31. $\left(\sqrt{2}y - 7z^3\right)^3$

32. $(3a^3 - 2b)^2$

Extensions

In Exercises 33–37, simplify each expression.

33. $(9n^2 + n)(9n^2 - n)$

34. $\left(\dfrac{2}{3}x^4 + 6\right)\left(\dfrac{2}{3}x^4 - 6\right)$

35. $((1 + 3b^2) + 5b)((1 + 3b^2) - 5b)$

36. $((9 + 5a) - a^3)^2$

37. $((4r^2 + 2) - r)^3$

38. Write six pairs of binomials that meet these criteria:
    - the product is a quadratic trinomial in terms of x,
    - the product is a sum of terms,
    - the leading coefficient of the product is 8, and
    - the constant term of the product is 12.

39. Write six pairs of binomials that meet these criteria:
    - the product is a quadratic trinomial in terms of x,
    - the product is a sum and difference of terms,
    - the leading coefficient of the product is 6, and
    - the constant term of the product is 10 or −10.

40. Write a pair of binomials whose product is a quadratic binomial in terms of x, where the leading coefficient is 1 and the constant term is −25.

41. Write a pair of binomials whose product is a quadratic binomial in terms of x, where the leading coefficient is 9 and the constant term is -100.

42. Write a pair of binomials whose product is a quartic binomial in terms of x, where the leading coefficient is 4 and the constant term is -64.

43. Write six pairs of binomials that meet these criteria:
    • the product is a cubic polynomial in terms of x,
    • the product is a sum of 4 terms,
    • the leading coefficient of the product is 20, and
    • the constant term of the product is 1.

44. Suppose the lengths of the sides of a rectangle are represented by the expressions $4x^2 + 2$ and $5x + 7$. Write expressions for the perimeter and area of the rectangle.

45. A square pool is surrounded by a rectangular patio. The lengths of the sides of the patio are represented by the expressions $3x + 1$ and $x + 10$. The length of a side of the pool is represented by $x + 2$. Write an expression for the area of the patio.

46. The length of a side of a cube can be represented by the expression $3x + 8$. Write an expression for the surface area of the cube and an expression for the volume of the cube.

P.5 FACTORING

OBJECTIVES

- Factor the GCF (greatest common factor) from polynomials.
- Factor 4-term polynomials using grouping.
- Factor trinomials using trial and error.
- Factor trinomials using the product-and-sum method.
- Use special factoring formulas.

PREREQUISITE VOCABULARY TERMS

binomial

monomial

polynomial

trinomial

P.5.1 Factoring Using the Greatest Common Factor

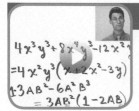

Introduction to Factoring

Factors of a number n are the numbers that divide evenly into n. For example, the factors of 12 are 1, 2, 3, 4, 6, and 12. There are several ways to write 12 as a product of two factors.

$$12 = 1 \cdot 12$$
$$12 = 2 \cdot 6$$
$$12 = 3 \cdot 4$$

The factors in each pair can be reversed, since multiplication is commutative.

Just as a number can be written as a product of its numeric factors, a polynomial can be written as a product of its **polynomial factors**. For example, consider the monomial $12x^2$. There are several ways to write $12x^2$ as a product of two monomial factors.

$$12x^2 = 1 \cdot 12x^2 \qquad 12x^2 = 4 \cdot 3x^2 \qquad 12x^2 = x \cdot 12x \qquad$$ *Again, the factors in each*
$$12x^2 = 2 \cdot 6x^2 \qquad 12x^2 = 6 \cdot 2x^2 \qquad 12x^2 = 2x \cdot 6x \qquad$$ *pair can be reversed, since*
$$12x^2 = 3 \cdot 4x^2 \qquad 12x^2 = 12 \cdot x^2 \qquad 12x^2 = 3x \cdot 4x \qquad$$ *multiplication is commutative.*

A polynomial with more than one term may also be written as a product of its factors by applying the Distributive Property. For example, consider the polynomial $10x + 15$. This can be written as $5(2x) + 5(3)$, because $5(2x) = 10x$ and $5(3) = 15$. Recall that the Distributive Property states that $ab + ac = a(b + c)$. So, by the Distributive Property, $5(2x) + 5(3) = 5(2x + 3)$. Therefore, $10x + 15 = 5(2x + 3)$, and so 5 and $2x + 3$ are factors of the polynomial $10x + 15$.

TIP

When a polynomial is factored, the value of the polynomial does not change, only the appearance.

This process of writing a polynomial as a product of factors, called **factoring a polynomial**, can be thought of as *undoing* multiplication. Some polynomials are **irreducible**, meaning that they cannot be factored because they have no factors other than 1 and the polynomial itself.

IMPORTANT

For some polynomials, the GCF of the terms is 1.

Factoring Out the GCF

Several methods for factoring polynomials will be discussed in this section, beginning with factoring the greatest common factor (GCF) of a polynomial's terms from each term.

For example, consider the binomial $12x^3yz^2 + 8x^2y^4$. The GCF of its terms is the product of

- 4 (the GCF of the coefficients 12 and 8),
- x^2 (the power with the greatest exponent common to x^3 and x^2), and
- y (the power with the greatest exponent common to y and y^4).

So, $4x^2y$ is the GCF of the terms in the binomial $12x^3yz^2 + 8x^2y^4$. Note that the variable z is not included in the GCF because z is not common to both terms in the binomial.

To complete the factorization of $12x^3yz^2 + 8x^2y^4$, factor the GCF from each term in the original polynomial, then use the Distributive Property to write the product of the factors.

$$12x^3yz^2 + 8x^2y^4 = (4x^2y)(3xz^2) + (4x^2y)(2y^3) \quad \textit{Write each term as a product using the GCF.}$$
$$= (4x^2y)(3xz^2 + 2y^3) \quad \textit{Distributive Property}$$

A factorization can always be checked by multiplying to confirm that the product is equal to the original polynomial. By the Distributive Property, $(4x^2y)(3xz^2 + 2y^3) = 12x^3yz^2 + 8x^2y^4$, so the factorization is correct.

EXAMPLE 1   Factoring a Monomial from a Polynomial

Identify the GCF and then factor each polynomial.

A. $15x^4 + 35x^7$ **B.** $8p^5q^4 + 12p^3q^3 - 4pq^2$ **C.** $4a^3 + 9b^2 + 6$

SOLUTION

A. Identify the GCF of the binomial's terms.

- The GCF of the coefficients is 5.
- The GCF of x^4 and x^7 is x^4.   *The greatest exponent common to x^4 and x^7 is 4.*

So, the GCF of the binomial's terms is $5x^4$.

Factor $5x^4$ from each term in the binomial.

$$15x^4 + 35x^7 = 5x^4(3 + 7x^3)$$

CHECK

Check the factorization by multiplying.

$$5x^4(3 + 7x^3) = 5x^4(3) + 5x^4(7x^3) = 15x^4 + 35x^7 \checkmark$$

Product of Powers ▶
$$a^m \cdot a^n = a^{m+n}$$

B. Identify the GCF of the trinomial's terms.

- The GCF of the coefficients is 4.
- The GCF of p^5, p^3, and p is p.   *The greatest exponent common to p^5, p^3, and p is 1.*
- The GCF of q^4, q^3, and q^2 is q^2.   *The greatest exponent common to q^4, q^3, and q^2 is 2.*

So, the GCF of the trinomial's terms is $4pq^2$.

Factor $4pq^2$ from each term in the trinomial.

$$8p^5q^4 + 12p^3q^3 - 4pq^2 = 4pq^2(2p^4q^2 + 3p^2q - 1)$$

CHECK

The factorization can be checked by multiplying.

$$4pq^2(2p^4q^2 + 3p^2q - 1) = 4pq^2(2p^4q^2) + 4pq^2(3p^2q) - 4pq^2(1)$$
$$= 8p^5q^4 + 12p^3q^3 - 4pq^2 \checkmark$$

C. The GCF of the coefficients is 1, and the terms have no common variable. So, the GCF of the trinomial's terms is 1. The polynomial is irreducible.

TIP

$4pq^2(2p^4q^2 + 3p^2q - 1)$ is equivalent to $(2p^4q^2 + 3p^2q - 1)4pq^2$, since multiplication is commutative.

IMPORTANT

If the GCF of a polynomial's terms is 1, the polynomial is not necessarily irreducible.

The GCF of a polynomial's terms is not always a monomial. If each term in a polynomial contains a common binomial factor (or common polynomial with any number of terms), then that common factor must be included in the GCF of its terms, as demonstrated in **Example 2**.

It follows that a reducible (i.e., factorable) trinomial can be written as the product of two binomials that have two pairs of like terms between them. The product of the binomials' first terms will be the first term of the trinomial, and the product of the binomials' last terms will be the last term of the trinomial.

These facts can be used to find a list of pairs of possible binomial factors for a trinomial. Each pair of binomial factors must be multiplied to determine if the factorization is correct.

Steps for Factoring a Trinomial ($ax^2 + bx + c$) Using Trial and Error

❶ Find two like-term factors of the trinomial's first term.

❷ Find two like-term factors of the trinomial's last term.

❸ Write these factors as the first and last terms in two binomials and use the FOIL method with the binomials to determine if the factors are correct.

When writing the binomials in step ❸, you must decide whether to include addition or subtraction between the terms in each binomial. Assuming the sign of the trinomial's first term is positive, if the trinomial's last term is *positive*, then the binomials will both use the *same operation*, and if the trinomial's last term is *negative*, then the binomials will use *different operations*.

More specifically, if the trinomial's

• last and middle term are both positive, then both binomials will be sums.

• last term is positive and the middle term is negative, then both binomials will be differences.

• last term is negative, then one binomial will be a sum and the other will be a difference.

The trinomials in **Example 4** will be of the form $ax^2 + bx + c$, where $a = 1$. In the case where $a = 1$, the binomial's first terms will always be the same (e.g., x and x).

EXAMPLE 4   **Factoring a Trinomial ($a = 1$) by Trial and Error**

Factor.

A. $x^2 + 9x + 8$ **B.** $n^2 + 4n - 12$

SOLUTION

A. The trinomial's last term and middle term are both positive, so the binomial factors will be sums.

❶ Like-term factors of x^2 are x and x.

❷ Like-term factors of 8 are 2 and 4 *or* 1 and 8.

❸ The first term in each binomial factor will be x. The last terms in the binomial factors will be either 2 and 4 *or* 1 and 8. Write the possible binomial pairs and then use the FOIL method to determine the correct factorization.

Possible Factorizations	Product	
$(x + 2)(x + 4)$	$x^2 + 6x + 8$	☒
$(x + 1)(x + 8)$	$x^2 + 9x + 8$	✓

Therefore, $x^2 + 9x + 8 = (x + 1)(x + 8)$.

B. The trinomial's last term is negative. So, one binomial factor will be a sum, and the other will be a difference.

❶ Like-term factors of n^2 are n and n.

❷ Like-term factors of 12 are 3 and 4, 2 and 6, or 1 and 12.

❸ The first term in each binomial factor will be n. The last terms in the binomial factors will be either 3 and 4, 2 and 6, *or* 1 and 12. Write the possible binomial pairs, then use the FOIL method to determine the correct factorization.

Possible Factorizations	Product	
$(n + 3)(n - 4)$	$n^2 - n - 12$	☒
$(n - 3)(n + 4)$	$n^2 + n - 12$	☒
$(n + 2)(n - 6)$	$n^2 - 4n - 12$	☒
$(n - 2)(n + 6)$	$n^2 + 4n - 12$	✓

Therefore, $n^2 + 4n - 12 = (n - 2)(n + 6)$.

> **IMPORTANT**
>
> *When the operations in the binomial factors are different, there are two options for each pair of factors, for example, $(n + 3)(n - 4)$ and $(n - 3)(n + 4)$.*

> **TIP**
>
> *There is no need to write the binomial factors using 1 and 12 since the correct factorization has already been found.*

In the next example, trinomials of the form $ax^2 + bx + c$ where a is *not* 1 will be factored (e.g., $5x^2 + 8x - 3$). Having an a-value not equal to 1 complicates the factoring process because the binomials' first terms will not always be the same. This creates many additional possibilities for the two binomial factors.

EXAMPLE 5   Factoring a Trinomial ($a \neq 1$) by Trial and Error

Factor.

A. $5x^2 - 8x + 3$ **B.** $8p^2 + 31p - 4$

SOLUTION

A. The trinomial's last term is positive, and its middle term is negative. So, the binomial factors will both be differences.

❶ Like-term factors of $5x^2$ are $5x$ and x.

❷ Like-term factors of 3 are 1 and 3.

❸ The first terms in the binomial factors will be $5x$ and x. The last terms will be 1 and 3. Write the possible binomial pairs, then use the FOIL method to determine the correct factorization.

Possible Factorizations	Product	
$(5x - 1)(x - 3)$	$5x^2 - 16x + 3$	☒
$(5x - 3)(x - 1)$	$5x^2 - 8x + 3$	✓

> **TIP**
>
> *Once the correct factors are found, there is no need to continue multiplying possible factorizations.*

Therefore, $5x^2 - 8x + 3 = (5x - 3)(x - 1)$.

P.5.6   Factoring the Difference of Two Squares

Recall that the product of a *sum and difference of same terms* is a special case in which the product of two binomials is also a binomial.

$$(x + 3)(x - 3) = x^2 - 3x + 3x - 9 = x^2 - 9$$

$$(5w + 2y)(5w - 2y) = 25w^2 - 10wy + 10wy - 4y^2 = 25w^2 - 4y^2$$

This pattern can be generalized using the product of $(A + B)$ and $(A - B)$.

$$(A + B)(A - B) = A^2 - B^2$$

It follows that a binomial of the form $A^2 - B^2$, called a **difference of two squares**, can be factored into two binomials that are the sum and difference of same terms.

Factoring Difference-of-Two-Squares Binomials
$A^2 - B^2 = (A + B)(A - B)$

EXAMPLE 9   **Factoring a Difference of Two Squares**

Factor.

A. $1 - 64m^2$

B. $25a^6 - b^4$

SOLUTION

Notice that each binomial is a difference of perfect squares, and that each binomial can be written as a difference of two squares: $A^2 - B^2$.

	$1 - 64m^2$	$25a^6 - b^4$
Perfect-Square Terms	$1 = (1)^2$ and $64m^2 = (8m)^2$	$25a^6 = (5a^3)^2$ and $b^4 = (b^2)^2$
Difference of Two Squares	$(1)^2 - (8m)^2$ $A^2 - B^2$	$(5a^3)^2 - (b^2)^2$ $A^2 - B^2$
A- and B-values	$A = 1$ and $B = 8m$	$A = 5a^3$ and $B = b^2$

CHECK

Multiply to check each factorization.

A. (1 + 8m)(1 − 8m)

= 1 − 8m + 8m − 64m²

= 1 − 64m²

B. (5a³ + b²)(5a³ − b²)

= 25a⁶ − 5a³b² + 5a³b² − b⁴

= 25a⁶ − b⁴

So, the factorizations are correct. ✔

A. Substitute $A = 1$ and $B = 8m$ into $(A + B)(A - B)$ to find the factorization.

$$1 - 64m^2 = (1 + 8m)(1 - 8m)$$

B. Substitute $A = 5a^3$ and $B = b^2$ into $(A + B)(A - B)$ to find the factorization.

$$25a^6 - b^4 = (5a^3 + b^2)(5a^3 - b^2)$$

WHAT'S THE BIG IDEA?

Explain how to identify and factor a perfect-square trinomial and a difference of squares.

P.5.7   Factoring Sums and Differences of Cubes

In the previous topic, it was shown that a difference of squares can be factored into two binomials that are the sum and difference of the same terms. Note that a *sum* of squares cannot be factored into two binomials.

Sums *and* differences of cubes can be factored, but not into two binomials. A **sum of cubes** is a binomial that can be written in the form $A^3 + B^3$. Similarly, a **difference of cubes** is a binomial that can be written in the form $A^3 - B^3$. The following formulas can be used to factor a sum or difference of cubes.

Factoring Sums and Differences of Two Cubes
$A^3 + B^3 = (A + B)(A^2 - AB + B^2)$
$A^3 - B^3 = (A - B)(A^2 + AB + B^2)$

EXAMPLE 10   Factoring a Sum or Difference of Cubes

Factor.

A. $1 + 8c^3$ **B.** $64w^6 - 125y^3z^{12}$ **C.** $d^3 - (1 + g)^6$

SOLUTION

A. The binomial is a sum of perfect cubes. Since $1 = (1)^3$ and $8c^3 = (2c)^3$, it follows that $A = 1$ and $B = 2c$. Substitute $A = 1$ and $B = 2c$ into $(A + B)(A^2 - AB + B^2)$, and simplify to find the factorization.

$$1 + 8c^3 = (1 + 2c)((1)^2 - (1)(2c) + (2c)^2) = (1 + 2c)(1 - 2c + 4c^2)$$

TIP

Note that the trinomial factor $1 - 2c + 4c^2$ is irreducible, so it cannot be factored further.

B. The binomial is a difference of perfect cubes. Since $64w^6 = (4w^2)^3$ and $125y^3z^{12} = (5yz^4)^3$, it follows that $A = 4w^2$ and $B = 5yz^4$. Substitute $A = 4w^2$ and $B = 5yz^4$ into $(A - B)(A^2 + AB + B^2)$, and simplify to find the factorization.

$$64w^6 - 125y^3z^{12} = (4w^2 - 5yz^4)((4w^2)^2 + (4w^2)(5yz^4) + (5yz^4)^2)$$
$$= (4w^2 - 5yz^4)(16w^4 + 20w^2yz^4 + 25y^2z^8)$$

C. The binomial is a difference of perfect cubes. Since $d^3 = (d)^3$ and $(1 + g)^6 = ((1 + g)^2)^3$, it follows that $A = d$ and $B = (1 + g)^2$. Substitute $A = d$ and $B = (1 + g)^2$ into $(A - B)(A^2 + AB + B^2)$, and simplify to find the factorization.

$$d^3 - (1 + g)^6 = (d - (1 + g)^2)((d)^2 + (d)((1 + g)^2) + ((1 + g)^2)^2)$$
$$= (d - (1 + g)^2)(d^2 + d(1 + g)^2 + (1 + g)^4)$$

WHAT'S THE BIG IDEA?

Explain how to identify and factor a sum of cubes and a difference of cubes.

SECTION P.5 EXERCISES

Warm Up

Simplify.

1. $2m^2(8m^2 + m - 4)$

2. $(b + 2)(b + 9)$

3. $(2p + 5)(2p - 5)$

Just the Facts

Fill in the blanks.

4. A factored polynomial is written as the ____ of two or more polynomial factors.

5. $xy^2 + 2x^2y = ($____$)(y + 2x)$

6. $18mn^7 + 24m^2np = ($____$)(3n^6 + 4mp)$

7. $20y^3 + 15y^2 - 30y = ($____$)(4y^2 + 3y - 6)$

8. The factorization of a polynomial can be checked by ____ the polynomial factors.

9. If one factor of a difference of two squares is ____, then the other factor is $(x + y)$.

10. The ____ of two cubes factors into a binomial difference and a trinomial sum.

Essential Skills

In Exercises 1–62, factor each polynomial completely.

1. $2x^3y^8 + 6x^4y^2 + 10x^5y^{10}$

2. $16a^3b^2 + 4a^2b^2 - 12ab^3 - 4ab^2$

3. $3x^2(2x + 5y) + 7y^2(2x + 5y)$

4. $6x^3(2 - y) - 8x^2(2 - y) + 4x(y - 2)$

5. $21b^3(c + 4) + 42b^2(c + 4) - 14b(c + 4)$

6. $15x^3(y + 3) - 40x^2(-3 - y) - 10x(y + 3)$

7. $8a^3(b + 5) - 2a^2(-5 - b) - 22a(b + 5)$

8. $8m^6n^4 - 14m^3n^2 + 2mn^3 - 7mn^2$

9. $10x^2 + 2xy + 15xy + 3y^2$

10. $2y^3 + 3y^2 - 4y - 6$

11. $4a^2 + 8ab + 48b + 24a$

12. $7y^3 + 3y^2 - 56y - 24$

13. $5x^2 - 15xy + 45y - 15x$

14. $6m^2 + 8mn - 12n - 9m$

15. $k^2 + 14k + 24$

16. $z^2 - 9z + 20$

17. $b^2 + 13b - 30$

18. $m^2 - 18m - 40$

19. $a^2 - 5a - 6$

20. $x^2 + x - 20$

21. $3h^2 + 19h + 6$

22. $2x^2 + 11x - 6$

23. $6x^2 - 11x + 3$

24. $7x^2 - 43x - 42$

25. $3b^2 + 7b - 6$

26. $6y^2 - 31y - 30$

27. $14x^2 + 15xy + 4y^2$

28. $3y^4 - 8y^2z + 5z^2$

29. $3p^4 + 4p^2q - 4q^2$

30. $4s^4 - 13s^2t + 12t^2$

31. $5w^6 + 12w^3x - 9x^2$

32. $4t^4 + 5t^2x - 6x^2$

33. $8c^2 - 52c + 60$

34. $40x^2 - 70x + 15$

35. $60m^2 + 51m - 30$

36. $36y^2 + 21y - 30$

37. $80x^2 - 132x + 40$

38. $80s^2 + 68s - 40$

39. $n^2 + 20n + 100$

40. $25x^2 + 30x + 9$

41. $1 - 10z^2 + 25z^4$

42. $16x^2 - 72xy + 81y^2$

43. $49x^2 - 70xy + 25y^2$

44. $4s^2 + 12st + 9t^2$

45. $9x^2 - 49$

46. $121m^2 - n^6$

47. $4p^{10} + 9w^2$

48. $16q^8 - 25r^2$

49. $144x^4 - 100y^2$

50. $9p^4 - 16w^2$

51. $27p^3 + 8$

52. $216x^3 + 1$

53. $u^6 - 8$

54. $64 - 27t^3$

55. $343 - 64y^3$

56. $27w^3 + 1$

57. $q^9 + r^6$

58. $s^6 t^3 - 125u^{12}$

59. $(x + 2y)^6 - 8$

60. $(2r - 3s)^3 + t^9$

61. $(m + n)^9 - 27$

62. $343t^3 z^6 - 64s^3$

Extensions

In Exercises 63–72, factor.

63. $\pi r^2 h + \dfrac{4}{3}\pi r^3 h^2 + \dfrac{1}{3}\pi r^2 h^3$

64. $8m^4 - 20m^2 n - 12n^2$

65. $-84np^2 - 21npz + 28npz^2 + 7nz^3$

66. $30x^2 + 87xy + 30y^2\, 20y^{2n} + 16y^n + 3$

67. $20y^{2n} + 16y^n + 3$

68. $y^5 - 2y^4 - 35y^3$

69. $x^2 + 2ax + a^2 - y^2 + 2by - b^2$

70. $7x^2 + 10\sqrt{7}x + 25$

71. $(8(x - 5y))^3 + 27z^3$

72. $64x^9 - 8y^9$

73. A student factored $2m^4 - am^4 + 6 - 3a$ by grouping and obtained $(m^4 + 3)(2 - a)$. Another student factored the same polynomial and gave an answer of $(a - 2)(3 - m^4)$. Which answer is correct?

74. The area of a rectangle is represented by $9k^2 - 24k + 16$. Find expressions for the dimensions of the rectangle in terms of k.

75. Suppose $cx^2 - 81$ is a difference of two squares and c is a natural number. What must be true about c?

76. Factor $4x^2 y^2 - 7z^2$ into a product of two binomials that are a sum and a difference of same terms.

P.6 RATIONAL EXPRESSIONS

OBJECTIVES

- Simplify and find the domain of rational expressions.
- Multiply, divide, add, and subtract rational expressions.
- Simplify complex fractions.

PREREQUISITE VOCABULARY TERMS

factor (of a polynomial)

fractional expression

polynomial

P.6.1   Rational Expressions and Domain

Consider any polynomial, such as $3x^2 + 5x - 1$. Substituting any real number for x results in a real number. Therefore, all real numbers are *allowable values* for x in $3x^2 + 5x - 1$. The set of allowable values for the variable in an expression is called the expression's **domain**. So, the domain of $3x^2 + 5x - 1$, or of any polynomial, is all real numbers, $(-\infty, \infty)$.

When any value of the variable in an expression results in an undefined value, then this expression's domain is not all real numbers. One type of expression where the domain may not be all real numbers is a **rational expression**.

DEFINITION

> A fractional expression where the numerator and denominator are polynomials (and the denominator is not 0) is called a **rational expression**.

REMEMBER

The numerator and denominator of a fractional expression can be any algebraic expression.

For example, consider the rational expression $\frac{2}{x}$. Since fractions are undefined when the denominator is 0, the domain of $\frac{2}{x}$ is the set of all real numbers except $x = 0$. The domain of $\frac{2}{x}$ can be expressed using interval notation as $(-\infty, 0) \cup (0, \infty)$, or using set-builder notation as $\{x \mid x \neq 0\}$.

Generally, to find the domain of a rational expression, find all values of the variable that result in a 0 denominator, and then exclude those values from the domain. Find the values that result in a 0 denominator by setting the expression in the denominator equal to 0 and solving.

EXAMPLE 1   Finding the Domain of a Rational Expression

Write the domain of each expression using set-builder notation or interval notation.

A. $\dfrac{x + 10}{4 - x}$

B. $\dfrac{3}{x^2 + 3x + 2}$

SOLUTION

Find the values of x that result in a 0 denominator, then exclude those values from the domain.

A. $4 - x = 0 \implies x = 4$ Domain: $\{x \mid x \neq 4\}$ *The domain is all real numbers except 4.*

B. $x^2 + 3x + 2 = 0 \implies (x + 2)(x + 1) = 0 \implies x = -2 \text{ or } -1$

         Domain: $\{x \mid x \neq -2 \text{ and } x \neq -1\}$ *The domain is all real numbers except -2 and -1.*

P.6.2 Simplifying Rational Expressions

Recall that numeric fractions are simplified by removing (canceling) any factors common to the numerator and denominator (other than 1). For example, the fraction $\frac{10}{15}$ can be simplified to $\frac{2}{3}$ by removing the common factor 5 from the numerator and denominator.

$$\frac{10}{15} = \frac{2\,(5)}{3\,(5)} = \frac{2}{3}$$ *A fraction is in simplest form when the numerator and denominator have no common factors other than 1.*

The same process is used for simplifying rational expressions.

Simplifying Rational Expressions

To simplify a rational expression, remove the factors common to the numerator and denominator. If A, B, and C are polynomials such that $B \neq 0$ and $C \neq 0$, then $\frac{AC}{BC} = \frac{A}{B}$.

A rational expression is in **simplest form** when the numerator and denominator have no common factors other than 1.

> **IMPORTANT**
>
> *Always use the original expression to determine the values excluded from the domain.*

Unless otherwise directed, the domain of a rational expression needs to be stated along with the simplified form.

Steps for Simplifying a Rational Expression

❶ Factor the polynomials in the numerator and denominator completely.

❷ Remove all factors common to the numerator and denominator.

❸ Write the remaining factors and multiply.

❹ State the domain of the original expression (unless otherwise directed).

EXAMPLE 2   Simplifying a Rational Expression

Simplify. State the values excluded from the domain, if any.

A. $\dfrac{(2x+3)(x+4)}{2x+8}$ **B.** $\dfrac{24x^2 - 6}{48x^2 + 8x - 16}$

SOLUTION

Factor each polynomial (as needed), then remove the common factors. Exclude from the domain the x-values that result in a 0 denominator in the original expression.

> **IMPORTANT**
>
> *The value excluded from the domain is −4 because $2x + 8$ is 0 when $x = -4$.*

A. $\dfrac{(2x+3)(x+4)}{2x+8} = \dfrac{(2x+3)\,\cancel{(x+4)}}{2\,\cancel{(x+4)}} = \dfrac{2x+3}{2}, x \neq -4$ *The expression is in simplest form because 2 (the denominator) is not a factor of $2x + 3$ (the numerator).*

B. $\dfrac{24x^2 - 6}{48x^2 + 8x - 16} = \dfrac{6(4x^2 - 1)}{8(6x^2 + x - 2)}$ *Factor out the GCF in the numerator and denominator.*

$= \dfrac{6(2x+1)\,\cancel{(2x-1)}}{8\,\cancel{(2x-1)}(3x+2)}$ *Factor the difference of two squares (numerator) and the trinomial (denominator).*

$= \dfrac{3(2x+1)}{4(3x+2)}$ *Remove the common factors.*

$= \dfrac{6x+3}{12x+8}, x \neq \dfrac{1}{2}$ and $x \neq -\dfrac{2}{3}$ *Distribute and write the excluded values.*

B. $\dfrac{6x^2 + 3x}{x+1} \div \dfrac{2x^2 - 3x - 2}{x+4} = \dfrac{6x^2 + 3x}{x+1} \cdot \dfrac{x+4}{2x^2 - 3x - 2}$ — *Multiply by the reciprocal of the divisor.*

$$= \dfrac{(6x^2 + 3x)(x+4)}{(x+1)(2x^2 - 3x - 2)}$$ — *Multiply numerators and denominators.*

$$= \dfrac{(3x)\,\cancel{(2x+1)}\,(x+4)}{(x+1)\,\cancel{(2x+1)}\,(x-2)}$$ — *Factor and remove common factors.*

$$= \dfrac{(3x)(x+4)}{(x+1)(x-2)}$$ — *Write the remaining factors.*

$$= \dfrac{3x^2 + 12x}{x^2 - x - 2}$$ — *Multiply.*

P.6.5 Adding and Subtracting Rational Expressions

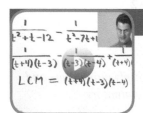

As with numeric fractions, rational expressions can be added or subtracted when the expressions have a common denominator. For rational expressions with unlike denominators, the common denominator is a common multiple of the denominators.

Adding and Subtracting Rational Expressions

Like Denominators

If A, B, and C are polynomials such that $B \neq 0$, then

$$\frac{A}{B} + \frac{C}{B} = \frac{A+C}{B} \quad \text{and} \quad \frac{A}{B} - \frac{C}{B} = \frac{A-C}{B}.$$

Unlike Denominators

If A, B, C, and D are polynomials such that B and $D \neq 0$, then

$$\frac{A}{B} + \frac{C}{D} = \frac{AD + BC}{BD} \quad \text{and} \quad \frac{A}{B} - \frac{C}{D} = \frac{AD - BC}{BD}.$$

TIP

In $\dfrac{A-C}{B}$, if C is a polynomial with more than one term, be sure to distribute the negative to each term in C.

Addition (and subtraction) of rational expressions is easiest when the LCM (least common multiple) of the denominators is used for the common denominator. The LCM of the denominators is the product of the greatest power of the denominators' factors. For example, if the denominators of three rational expressions are xy, x^2, and xz, then the LCM of the denominators is x^2yz.

EXAMPLE 5   Adding and Subtracting Rational Expressions

Simplify. Assume that all variables result in nonzero denominators.

A. $\dfrac{7x}{y^4 z^3} + \dfrac{3}{y^5 z}$

B. $\dfrac{7ab}{a^2 - b^2} - \dfrac{a-b}{a+b}$

SOLUTION

A. The factors in the denominators are powers of y and z. The greatest power of y is y^5, and the greatest power of z is z^3, so the LCM of the denominators is $y^5 z^3$. Since $y^4 z^3(y) = y^5 z^3$, multiply the first term by $\dfrac{y}{y}$. Since $y^5 z(z^2) = y^5 z^3$, multiply the second term by $\dfrac{z^2}{z^2}$.

$$\frac{7x}{y^4 z^3} + \frac{3}{y^5 z} = \frac{7x}{y^4 z^3} \cdot \frac{y}{y} + \frac{3}{y^5 z} \cdot \frac{z^2}{z^2}$$ — *Write the terms with a common denominator.*

$$= \frac{7xy}{y^5 z^3} + \frac{3z^2}{y^5 z^3}$$ — *Multiply.*

$$= \frac{7xy + 3z^2}{y^5 z^3}$$ — *Add the numerators.*

B. Factor the first term's denominator, and then identify the LCM of the denominators.

$$\frac{7ab}{a^2 - b^2} - \frac{a-b}{a+b} = \frac{7ab}{(a+b)(a-b)} - \frac{a-b}{a+b}$$

The factors in the denominators are $(a + b)$ and $(a - b)$, where each is to the power of 1. So, the LCM of the denominators is $(a + b)(a - b)$. The first term's denominator is already $(a + b)(a - b)$. Multiply the second term by $\frac{a-b}{a-b}$, so that its denominator will be $(a + b)(a - b)$.

TIP

The denominator of the first expression is equal to the LCM.

$$\frac{7ab}{(a+b)(a-b)} - \frac{a-b}{a+b} = \frac{7ab}{(a+b)(a-b)} - \frac{(a-b)(a-b)}{(a+b)(a-b)}$$ *Write the terms with a common denominator.*

$$= \frac{7ab - (a-b)(a-b)}{(a+b)(a-b)}$$ *Subtract the numerators.*

$$= \frac{7ab - (a^2 - 2ab + b^2)}{(a+b)(a-b)}$$ *FOIL in the numerator.*

$$= \frac{7ab - a^2 + 2ab - b^2}{(a+b)(a-b)}$$ *Distribute.*

$$= \frac{-a^2 + 9ab - b^2}{a^2 - b^2}$$ *Simplify.*

P.6.6   Rewriting Complex Fractions

A rational expression that contains a rational expression in the numerator or denominator is called a **complex fraction** (i.e., a complex rational expression). Two methods for simplifying complex fractions will be discussed in this topic.

IMPORTANT

A sum or difference of fractions should be combined using a common denominator before writing as division.

Simplifying Complex Fractions

Method 1: Multiply by the Reciprocal
Write the fraction as division, then multiply the dividend (the numerator) by the reciprocal of the divisor (the denominator).

Method 2: Use the LCM
Find the LCM of the denominators, then multiply the expression by the $\frac{\text{LCM}}{\text{LCM}}$.

The methods are demonstrated here using two example complex fractions.

$$\frac{\frac{2}{3}}{\frac{6}{7}}$$ *Equivalent to* $\frac{2}{3} \div \frac{6}{7}$ $$\frac{\frac{3}{x}}{\frac{x+1}{x^2}}$$ *Equivalent to* $\frac{3}{x} \div \frac{x+1}{x^2}$

Method 1: Multiply by the Reciprocal		**Method 2: Use the LCM**	
$\dfrac{\frac{2}{3}}{\frac{6}{7}}$	$\dfrac{\frac{2}{3}}{\frac{6}{7}} = \dfrac{2}{3} \div \dfrac{6}{7} = \dfrac{2}{3} \cdot \dfrac{7}{6} = \dfrac{7}{9}$	$\dfrac{\frac{2}{3}}{\frac{6}{7}} \cdot \dfrac{21}{21} = \dfrac{\frac{2}{3} \cdot 21}{\frac{6}{7} \cdot 21} = \dfrac{14}{18} = \dfrac{7}{9}$	*LCM(3 and 7)* $= 21$
$\dfrac{\frac{3}{x}}{\frac{x+1}{x^2}}$	$\dfrac{\frac{3}{x}}{\frac{x+1}{x^2}} = \dfrac{3}{x} \div \dfrac{x+1}{x^2} = \dfrac{3}{x} \cdot \dfrac{x^2}{x+1} = \dfrac{3x}{x+1}$	$\dfrac{\frac{3}{x}}{\frac{x+1}{x^2}} \cdot \dfrac{x^2}{x^2} = \dfrac{\frac{3}{x} \cdot x^2}{\frac{x+1}{x^2} \cdot x^2} = \dfrac{3x}{x+1}$	*LCM(x and x^2)* $= x^2$

40. $\dfrac{x}{x^2 + x - 2} + \dfrac{2}{x^2 - 5x + 4}$

41. $\dfrac{x}{x^2 + 2x + 1} - \dfrac{3}{x + 1}$

42. $\dfrac{14}{z^2 + 14z - 147} - \dfrac{7}{z^2 - 49}$

43. $\dfrac{x + 1}{3x} + \dfrac{5}{x} - \dfrac{2x}{3x^2 - 3x}$

44. $\dfrac{2x}{x + 1} - \dfrac{x - 4}{x} + \dfrac{2}{x + 1}$

45. $\dfrac{2}{a^3} - \dfrac{1}{a} + \dfrac{4}{a^2}$

46. $\dfrac{3}{x^2 - x} + \dfrac{4}{x} - \dfrac{5}{x - 1}$

47. $\dfrac{2m + 1}{4m^2 + 6m} - \dfrac{3}{2m} + \dfrac{7m}{2m + 3}$

48. $\dfrac{5y}{y + 1} - \dfrac{y - 7}{y} + \dfrac{5}{y + 1}$

49. $\dfrac{\dfrac{3}{x} + 1}{1 + \dfrac{x}{3}}$

50. $\dfrac{\dfrac{4}{2x} - \dfrac{3}{3x}}{\dfrac{2}{x} - \dfrac{3}{2x}}$

51. $\dfrac{\dfrac{5}{x} - \dfrac{1}{3x}}{\dfrac{1}{3x} - \dfrac{3}{2x}}$

52. $\dfrac{1 + \dfrac{9}{x}}{1 + \dfrac{x}{9}}$

53. $\dfrac{\dfrac{2}{x} - \dfrac{1}{2x}}{\dfrac{4}{3x} - \dfrac{1}{4x}}$

54. $\dfrac{\dfrac{6}{2x} - \dfrac{3}{5x}}{\dfrac{2}{x} - \dfrac{2}{2x}}$

55. $\dfrac{n + \dfrac{2}{n}}{n^2 - \dfrac{4}{n^2}}$

56. $\dfrac{\dfrac{5}{x + 5}}{-\dfrac{1}{x} + 2}$

57. $\dfrac{\dfrac{2}{x^2 + 3x}}{-\dfrac{2}{x} + \dfrac{4}{x + 3}}$

58. $\dfrac{\dfrac{5}{2x^2 - 6x}}{\dfrac{2}{x} - \dfrac{1}{x - 3}}$

59. $\dfrac{\dfrac{3}{x - 2}}{\dfrac{2}{x^2 - 2x} - \dfrac{1}{x}}$

60. $\dfrac{\dfrac{7}{7 + y}}{-\dfrac{1}{y} + 4}$

Extensions

In Exercises 61–63, simplify and state the domain of each expression using set-builder notation or interval notation.

61. $\dfrac{3x^3 - 2x^2 - 3x + 2}{15x^2 - 5x - 20}$

62. $\dfrac{3x^3 + 6x^2}{x^2 - x - 12} \cdot \dfrac{x^2 + 5x + 6}{x^2} \div \dfrac{x^2 - x}{x^2 - 2x - 8}$

63. $\dfrac{5}{3 - 2y} + \dfrac{3}{2y - 3} - \dfrac{y - 3}{2y^2 - y - 3}$

In Exercises 64–69, simplify. Assume that all variables result in nonzero denominators.

64. $\left(\dfrac{\dfrac{y + 1}{y - 1} + 1}{\dfrac{y + 1}{y - 1} - 1} \right)^5$

65. $1 + \dfrac{1}{1 + \dfrac{1}{1 + \dfrac{1}{1 + \dfrac{1}{x}}}}$

66. $\dfrac{\dfrac{1}{(x + h)^2 + 9} - \dfrac{1}{x^2 + 9}}{h}$

67. $\dfrac{\sqrt{y + b}}{\sqrt{y - b}} - \dfrac{\sqrt{y - b}}{\sqrt{y + b}}$

68. $\dfrac{\left(b + \dfrac{1}{a} \right)^b \left(b - \dfrac{1}{a} \right)^a}{\left(a + \dfrac{1}{b} \right)^b \left(a - \dfrac{1}{b} \right)^a}$

69. $\dfrac{\dfrac{1}{m^2 - 5m - 14} + \dfrac{1}{m + 1}}{\dfrac{1}{m + 2} - \dfrac{1}{m^2 - 6m - 7}}$

70. True or False? The domain of a rational expression can never be the set of all real numbers.

In Exercises 71–72, write expressions for the perimeter and area of each rectangle with the given length and width.

71. $\dfrac{w + 4}{3}$ and $\dfrac{w - 2}{5}$

72. $\dfrac{3}{l + 4}$ and $\dfrac{2}{l - 5}$

P.7 SOLVING LINEAR AND QUADRATIC EQUATIONS

OBJECTIVES

- Solve linear equations.
- Solve rational equations.
- Solve quadratic equations by factoring and completing the square.
- Write the square root of a negative number as a complex number.
- Use the Quadratic Formula to solve quadratic equations.
- Model geometric situations with quadratic equations.

PREREQUISITE VOCABULARY TERMS

Distributive Property

FOIL

linear expression

perfect-square trinomial

quadratic expression

rational expression

P.7.1 Solving a Linear Equation

A **linear equation** in one variable is an equation that can be written in the form $ax + b = 0$, where x is a variable and a and b are real numbers. To solve a linear equation, apply operations to both sides of the equation, with the goal of isolating the variable on one side of the equation. Note that a linear equation may have one solution, no solutions, or all real numbers as solutions.

To solve a linear equation with the variable on both sides (i.e., $ax + b = cx + d$, where a, b, c, and d are numbers), isolate the x-terms on one side and the constant terms on the other, then divide both sides by the coefficient of x. If either side of the equation contains like terms or parentheses, then simplify each side before applying these solving steps.

EXAMPLE 1   Simplifying and Solving a Linear Equation

Solve. $1 + 3(y + 8) = 7(3 - y) + 14$

SOLUTION

Begin by simplifying each side of the equation. Apply inverse operations to move the variable terms to the left side and the constant terms to the right side only after each side is fully simplified.

$1 + 3(y + 8) = 7(3 - y) + 14$	
$1 + 3y + 24 = 21 - 7y + 14$	*Distribute.*
$3y + 25 = 35 - 7y$	*Combine the like terms on each side.*
$10y + 25 = 35$	*Add 7y to each side.*
$10y = 10$	*Subtract 25 from each side.*
$y = 1$	*Divide each side by 10.*

REMEMBER

Distributive Property
$a(b + c) = ab + ac$
$a(b - c) = ab - ac$

CHECK

Check the solution by substituting $y = 1$ in the original equation.

$1 + 3(1 + 8) \stackrel{?}{=} 7(3 - 1) + 14$	*Substitute y = 1.*
$1 + 3(9) \stackrel{?}{=} 7(2) + 14$	*Simplify within parentheses.*
$1 + 27 \stackrel{?}{=} 14 + 14$	*Multiply.*
$28 = 28$ ✔	*Add.*

Solving Linear Equations with Rational Terms

Equations containing rational terms (i.e., terms that are rational expressions) can be simplified by multiplying the equation by the LCM of the denominators. Alternatively, the **Cross-Products Property** can be used when the equation is a proportion.

Cross-Products Property

If A, B, C, and D are algebraic expressions such that B and $D \neq 0$ and $\dfrac{A}{B} = \dfrac{C}{D}$, then $AD = BC$.

EXAMPLE 2   Solving a Linear Equation with Rational Terms

Solve each equation.

A. $\dfrac{3x - 1}{4} = \dfrac{10 - x}{5}$ **B.** $\dfrac{4(x - 1)}{5} = 1 + \dfrac{x}{2}$

SOLUTION

A. Use the Cross-Products Property (since the equation has one term on each side).

$$\frac{3x - 1}{4} = \frac{10 - x}{5}$$

$5(3x - 1) = 4(10 - x)$ *Cross multiply.*

$15x - 5 = 40 - 4x$ *Distribute.*

$19x = 45$ *Add 4x and 5 to each side.*

$x = \dfrac{45}{19}$ *Divide each side by 19.*

B. Multiply the equation by the LCM of the denominators, 10.

$$10\left(\frac{4(x - 1)}{5}\right) = \left(1 + \frac{x}{2}\right)10$$ *Multiply the equation by 10.*

$\dfrac{40(x - 1)}{5} = 10 + \dfrac{10x}{2}$ *Multiply on the left side and distribute on the right side.*

$8(x - 1) = 10 + 5x$ *Simplify the fractions.*

$8x - 8 = 10 + 5x$ *Distribute.*

$3x - 8 = 10$ *Subtract 5x from each side.*

$3x = 18$ *Add 8 to each side.*

$x = 6$ *Divide each side by 3.*

P.7.2   Solving a Linear Equation with Rationals

An equation where the domain is not all real numbers may have an **extraneous solution**, which is a solution not in the equation's domain. When solving an equation where the domain is not all real numbers, be sure to confirm that any solutions are in the equation's domain (and therefore not extraneous).

For example, recall that the domain of a rational expression includes all real numbers except those that result in a 0 denominator. Likewise, the domain of an equation with rational terms must also exclude values that result in a 0 denominator. Therefore, when solving an equation with rational terms, be sure to verify that any solutions are not extraneous.

Some equations with rational terms that contain a variable in the denominator will simplify to linear form after cross multiplying, or after multiplying the equation by the LCM (least common multiple) of the denominators. These equations can be solved using the same process as used for linear equations with a numeric denominator (as in **Example 2**), with one additional step: check for extraneous solutions, as demonstrated in **Example 3**.

> **REMEMBER**
>
> *Set the denominator equal to 0 and solve to identify values excluded from the domain of a rational expression.*

EXAMPLE 3 Solving a Linear Equation with Rational Terms

Solve each equation.

A. $\dfrac{4}{3x-1} = \dfrac{2}{x-5}$

B. $\dfrac{7y}{y+9} - 2 = \dfrac{2}{y+9}$

SOLUTION

> **REMEMBER**
>
> *Values of the variable that make a denominator 0 must be excluded from the domain of the equation.*

A. Use the Cross-Products Property (since the equation is a proportion).

$$\frac{4}{3x-1} = \frac{2}{x-5}$$

$$4(x-5) = 2(3x-1) \qquad \text{\textit{Cross multiply.}}$$

$$4x-20 = 6x-2 \qquad \text{\textit{Distribute.}}$$

$$-2x = 18 \qquad \text{\textit{Subtract 6x from each side and add 20 to each side.}}$$

$$x = -9 \qquad \text{\textit{Divide each side by -2.}}$$

> **IMPORTANT**
>
> *Alternatively, extraneous solutions can be identified by substituting the solution into the original equation. If the result is a false statement, then the solution is extraneous.*

The values excluded from the equation's domain are $x = \dfrac{1}{3}$ and $x = 5$ because the equation is undefined when x is either of these values. Since -9 is in the equation's domain, $x = -9$ is not an extraneous solution.

B. Multiply the equation by the denominator, $(y+9)$.

$$(y+9)\left(\frac{7y}{y+9} - 2\right) = \left(\frac{2}{y+9}\right)(y+9) \qquad \text{\textit{Multiply the equation by (y + 9).}}$$

$$7y - 2(y+9) = 2 \qquad \text{\textit{Distribute.}}$$

$$7y - 2y - 18 = 2 \qquad \text{\textit{Distribute.}}$$

$$5y - 18 = 2 \qquad \text{\textit{Combine the like terms.}}$$

$$5y = 20 \qquad \text{\textit{Add 18 to each side.}}$$

$$y = 4 \qquad \text{\textit{Divide each side by 5.}}$$

The equation's domain is all real numbers except $y = -9$. Since 4 is in the equation's domain, $y = 4$ is not an extraneous solution.

EXAMPLE 5   Simplifying Square Root Expressions with Negative Radicands

Simplify. Write imaginary expressions in terms of i.

A. $\sqrt{-300}$ **B.** $\sqrt{-20} + \sqrt{-500} - \sqrt{45}$

SOLUTION

A. $\sqrt{-300} = \sqrt{100(-1)(3)} = \sqrt{100} \cdot \sqrt{-1} \cdot \sqrt{3} = 10i\sqrt{3}$

B. $\sqrt{-20} + \sqrt{-500} - \sqrt{45}$

$= \sqrt{(4)(-1)(5)} + \sqrt{(100)(-1)(5)} - \sqrt{(9)(5)}$ *Factor each radicand.*

$= 2i\sqrt{5} + 10i\sqrt{5} - 3\sqrt{5}$ *Simplify each radical.*

$= 12i\sqrt{5} - 3\sqrt{5}$ *Combine the like terms.*

$= -3\sqrt{5} + 12i\sqrt{5}$ *Write the expression in the standard form of a complex number.*

P.7.5   Solving Quadratics by Completing the Square

Now that complex numbers have been defined, quadratic equations with complex solutions can be solved. The methods for solving quadratic equations discussed in the next three topics can be used to solve quadratic equations with real or complex solutions.

Any quadratic equation that can be written with a perfect-square quadratic trinomial on one side and a constant value on the other side can be solved by taking square roots. For example, $x^2 + 12x + 36 = 12$ can be solved by factoring the perfect-square quadratic trinomial $x^2 + 12x + 36$ and then taking ± the square root of both sides.

$$x^2 + 12x + 36 = 12$$

$$(x + 6)^2 = 12$$ *Factor.*

$$x + 6 = \pm\sqrt{12}$$ *Take ± the square root of each side.*

$$x + 6 = \pm 2\sqrt{3}$$ *Simplify the radical.*

$$x = -6 \pm 2\sqrt{3}$$ *Subtract 6 from each side.*

> **TIP**
>
> Perfect-Square Trinomial
> $a^2 + 2ab + b^2 = (a + b)^2$

If the quadratic equation is not written with one side as a perfect-square quadratic trinomial and the other side as a constant value, this method of taking square roots can still be applied to solve the equation, but only after some algebraic manipulation.

Consider the equation $x^2 + 4x + 3 = 8$. Notice that $x^2 + 4x + 3$ is not a perfect-square quadratic trinomial. However, adding 1 to both sides will result in a perfect-square quadratic trinomial on the left side. Then the equation can be solved by taking square roots.

$$x^2 + 4x + 3 = 8$$

$$x^2 + 4x + 4 = 9$$ *Add 1 to each side (making the left side a perfect-square).*

$$(x + 2)^2 = 9$$ *Factor.*

$$x + 2 = \pm 3$$ *Take ± the square root of each side.*

$$x = 1 \quad \text{or} \quad x = -5$$ *Subtract 2 from each side.*

The process of manipulating an expression into the form of a perfect-square trinomial is called **completing the square**. The complicated part of the process can be identifying the value that needs to be added to make the perfect-square trinomial. Examining perfect-square trinomials will give some insight into this process. The following table shows three examples of perfect-square trinomials (where the coefficient of x^2 is 1). Consider the relationship between the coefficient of x and the constant term in each.

Perfect-Square Trinomial	Coefficient of x and the Constant Term	Relationship
$x^2 + 12x + 36$	12 and 36	$\left(\dfrac{12}{2}\right)^2 = 6^2 = 36$
$x^2 + 6x + 9$	6 and 9	$\left(\dfrac{6}{2}\right)^2 = 3^2 = 9$
$x^2 + 8x + 16$	8 and 16	$\left(\dfrac{8}{2}\right)^2 = 4^2 = 16$

The constant term in each perfect-square quadratic trinomial is equal to the square of half the linear term's coefficient (i.e., the coefficient of x). Because this is always true when the coefficient of x^2 is 1 in a perfect-square trinomial, we can use this fact to write a quadratic equation of the form $x^2 + bx = c$ with a perfect-square quadratic trinomial on one side.

IMPORTANT

The purpose of completing the square is to write the equation in a form that can be solved by taking square roots.

Completing the Square

To write $x^2 + bx = c$ as an equation with a perfect-square quadratic trinomial on one side, add $\left(\dfrac{b}{2}\right)^2$ to both sides of the equation.

$$x^2 + bx = c$$

$$x^2 + bx + \left(\frac{b}{2}\right)^2 = c + \left(\frac{b}{2}\right)^2$$

$$\left(x + \frac{b}{2}\right)^2 = c + \left(\frac{b}{2}\right)^2$$

For example, the equation $x^2 + 10x = 7$ can be written with a perfect-square trinomial on the left side by adding 25 to both sides (because $(10/2)^2 = 25$).

$$x^2 + 10x = 7$$
$$x^2 + 10x + 25 = 7 + 25 \quad \textit{Complete the square by adding 25 to both sides.}$$
$$(x + 5)^2 = 32 \quad \textit{Factor and simplify.}$$

This equation could now be solved by taking ± the square root of both sides, simplifying the radical, and then subtracting 5 from both sides.

EXAMPLE 8   **Using the Quadratic Formula to Solve a Quadratic Equation**

Solve. $2m^2 + 3 = m$

SOLUTION

❶ Subtract m from both sides to write the equation in the general form.

$$2m^2 + 3 = m \implies 2m^2 - m + 3 = 0$$

❷ From the general form equation, $a = 2$, $b = -1$, and $c = 3$.

❸ Substitute $a = 2$, $b = -1$, and $c = 3$ into the Quadratic Formula and simplify.

$$m = \frac{-(-1) \pm \sqrt{(-1)^2 - 4(2)(3)}}{2(2)} \qquad \textit{Substitute.}$$

$$= \frac{1 \pm \sqrt{1 - 24}}{4} \qquad \textit{Evaluate the power and multiply within the radicand. Multiply in the denominator.}$$

$$= \frac{1 \pm \sqrt{-23}}{4} \qquad \textit{Subtract in the radicand.}$$

$$= \frac{1 \pm i\sqrt{23}}{4} \qquad \textit{Simplify the radical.}$$

Therefore, the solutions are $m = \dfrac{1 + i\sqrt{23}}{4}$ and $m = \dfrac{1 - i\sqrt{23}}{4}$.

P.7.8   Modeling with Quadratic Geometric Equations

There are many real-life questions that can be answered by writing and solving equations. This process of writing an equation to fit a specific situation is called **modeling**. An unknown quantity is represented by a variable (or algebraic expression) in the model.

Steps for Modeling with an Equation

❶ Identify the unknown value(s).

❷ Translate the given information into algebraic parts.

❸ Set up the model (i.e., write the equation), and solve. State the answer.

❹ Confirm the answer.

Modeling geometric situations with equations usually involves substituting given values into some known formula and then solving for the unknown variable. Many common geometric formulas are quadratic equations, such as the formula for the area of a circle, $A = \pi r^2$. See *Appendix A: Common Formulas and Properties* for additional common formulas.

Using a Relationship between Two Unknown Values

A situation involving two unknown values can be modeled using an equation in two variables. However, if there is a relationship between the two unknown values, then one unknown value can be expressed in terms of the other unknown value. In this case, the situation involving two unknown values can be modeled using an equation in one variable (which can then be solved).

For example, suppose there is a rectangle where the length is 10 feet greater than the width. There are two unknown values, the length of the rectangle and the width of the rectangle, but we can express both unknowns in terms of the same variable because a relationship between the two unknown values is given: the length is 10 feet greater than the width.

If we let the width be w, then the length must be $w + 10$. Thus, the unknown length is expressed in terms of the unknown width. Alternatively, if the length is identified as l, then the width must be $l - 10$.

Note that an additional piece of information regarding the rectangle must be given (such as the perimeter or area of the rectangle) in order to model the situation with an equation in one variable, as demonstrated in **Example 9**.

| EXAMPLE 9 | Modeling a Quadratic Equation for a Geometric Situation |

The rectangular picture inside a frame of the same shape is 3 inches longer than it is wide. The frame extends 2 inches on each side of the picture. The area of the picture and the frame is 108 square inches. Find the dimensions of the frame.

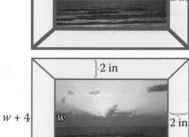

SOLUTION

❶ Since the picture is 3 inches longer than it is wide, let w represent the width of the picture. Then $w + 3$ represents the length of the picture.

❷ The area of the picture and the frame is 108 square inches. Since the frame extends 2 inches on each side of the picture, the length and width of the frame are each 4 inches longer than the length and width of the picture.

Total area	108
Frame width	$w + 4$
Frame length	$(w + 3) + 4 = w + 7$

❸ The formula for the area of a rectangle is $A = lw$.

Total area = frame length · frame width

$$108 = (w + 7)(w + 4)$$

Solve the equation for w.

$$108 = (w + 7)(w + 4)$$
$$108 = w^2 + 11w + 28 \qquad\qquad\qquad FOIL$$
$$0 = w^2 + 11w - 80 \qquad\qquad\qquad Subtract\ 108\ from\ each\ side.$$
$$0 = (w + 16)(w - 5) \qquad\qquad\qquad Factor.$$
$$w + 16 = 0 \quad\text{or}\quad w - 5 = 0 \qquad\qquad Set\ each\ factor\ equal\ to\ 0.$$
$$w = -16 \qquad\quad w = 5 \qquad\qquad Solve\ each\ equation.$$

TIP

This quadratic equation could be solved by factoring, completing the square, or using the Quadratic Formula.

The width of a rectangle cannot be negative, so the only solution is $w = 5$.

The length and width of the frame are represented by $w + 7$ and $w + 4$, so the length of the frame is $5 + 7 = 12$ inches, and the width of the frame is $5 + 4 = 9$ inches. Therefore, the frame's dimensions are 12 inches by 9 inches.

CHECK

❹ Confirm that the area of a 12 inch by 9 inch rectangle is 108 square inches.

$$A = 12(9) = 108 \text{ in}^2 \ \checkmark$$

41. $2k^2 + 3k - 35 = 0$

42. $9x^2 - 14x = 8$

In Exercises 43–48, simplify each expression. Write imaginary expressions in terms of i.

43. $\sqrt{27} + \sqrt{-48}$

44. $-\sqrt{12} - \sqrt{-72}$

45. $-\sqrt{112} - \sqrt{-45}$

46. $-\sqrt{176} - \sqrt{-28}$

47. $\sqrt{-99} - \sqrt{32} + \sqrt{50}$

48. $\sqrt{63} + \sqrt{-44} - \sqrt{125}$

In Exercises 49–60, solve each equation by completing the square.

49. $p^2 + 6p = 18$

50. $x^2 - 8 = -8x$

51. $a^2 - 29 = -8a$

52. $r^2 + 10r - 1 = 22$

53. $y^2 + 182 = -6y - 2$

54. $t^2 + 224 = -14t$

55. $4v^2 + 48v = 32$

56. $-3x^2 - 6x = -1$

57. $-7b^2 - 84b = 216$

58. $5r^2 + 70r = -261$

59. $4d^2 + 45 = -24d$

60. $-5z^2 - 229 = 70z$

In Exercises 61–66, solve each equation by using the Quadratic Formula.

61. $11x^2 + 12x + 1 = 0$

62. $3w^2 + 2w = -1$

63. $9m^2 + 9m - 2 = 0$

64. $3r^2 + 2r - 3 = 0$

65. $4d^2 - 3d = -2$

66. $2x^2 + 3x = 1$

67. A rectangle has an area of 84 square inches, and the length is 8 inches longer than the width. What are the dimensions of the rectangle?

68. At a tennis club, a 15,000-square-foot rectangular area is partitioned into three rectangular courts of equal size. A total of 800 feet of fencing is used to enclose the three courts, including the interior sides. What are the possible dimensions, in feet, of the entire rectangular area?

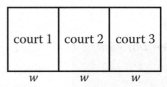

69. A rectangular field is enclosed on three sides by a fence, while the fourth side is a stream. The fence opposite the stream is 9 meters longer than the other sides. If the area of the field is 112 square meters, find its dimensions.

70. At a tennis club, a 16,500-square-foot rectangular area is partitioned into three rectangular courts of equal size. A total of 820 feet of fencing is used to enclose the three courts, including the interior sides. What are the possible dimensions, in feet, of the entire rectangular area?

Extensions

In Exercises 71–76, use the following information.

The perimeter P of a square can be found using the equation $P = 4s$, where s represents the length of a side of the square.

71. Find P when $s = 4$ and when $s = 8$ units.

72. Find s when $P = 6$ and when $P = 35$ units.

73. Find s when $P = 10$ and when $P = 20$ units.

74. Find P when $s = 1/2$ and when $s = 6.2$ units.

75. When the length of a side of a square doubles, does the square's perimeter always double?

76. When the perimeter of a square triples, does the square's side length always triple?

In Exercises 77–82, use the following information.

The equation $P - dP = S$ relates the original price P of an item to the sale price S, where d is the percent of the discount.

77. Find the sale prices of items with original prices $459, $720, and $58 when the discount is 10%.

78. Find the sale prices of items with original prices $18, $150, and $625 when the discount is 18%.

79. Find the percent discount when the original price of an item is $180 and its sale price is $135.

80. Find the percent discount when the original price of an item is $25 and its sale price is $18.

81. Find the original price of an item when the sale price is $93 and the discount is 15%.

82. Find the original price of an item when the sale price is $152 and the discount is 25%.

83. 172 meters of wire is cut into three pieces, where the second piece is 4 meters longer than the first piece, and the third piece is 4/5 as long as the first piece. Use the equation $f + (f + 4) + 0.8f = 172$, where f represents the length of the first piece, to find the length of each piece.

In Exercises 84–86, solve each equation.

84. $\dfrac{2}{3}\left(\dfrac{7}{8} - 4x\right) - \dfrac{5}{8} = \dfrac{3}{8}$

85. $0.008 + 9.62x - 42.8 = 0.944x + 0.0083 - x$

Round the answer to the nearest tenth, if necessary.

86. $\dfrac{4 - 3x}{7} = \dfrac{2 + 5x}{49} - \dfrac{x}{14}$

87. Two cars leave an intersection at the same time. One drives east, while the other travels south at 20 miles per hour faster than the first. After 3 hours, the cars are 300 miles apart. How fast is the southbound car driving?

88. Two buses make a 1680-mile trip. One bus makes the trip in 4 hours fewer than the other, traveling 10 miles per hour faster than the other. How long did it take the slower bus to complete the trip?

89. To solve the equation $4x^2 + 48x = 32x$, a student divides each side by $4x$ and solves the equation $x + 12 = 8$. The resulting solution, $x = -4$, satisfies the original equation. Is there an error? Explain.

90. Solve $ax^2 + bx = 0$ for x, given that a and b are not 0.

91. Write a quadratic equation that has $2 + \sqrt{3}$ and $2 - \sqrt{3}$ as solutions.

92. Two consecutive odd integers have squares that differ by 80. Find the integers.

P.8 OTHER TYPES OF EQUATIONS

OBJECTIVES

- Solve basic polynomial equations by factoring.
- Solve radical equations with one or two radical expressions.
- Solve equations with rational exponents.
- Solve rational equations.
- Use quadratic solving techniques to solve equations of quadratic type.
- Solve absolute value equations with one or two absolute value expressions.

PREREQUISITE VOCABULARY TERMS

absolute value

domain

polynomial

quadratic equation

rational expression

Zero-Product Property

P.8.1   Solving a Polynomial Equation by Factoring

Recall that a polynomial is an expression in terms of x that can be written in the form $a_n x^n + a_{n-1} x^{n-1} + \cdots + a_1 x + a_0$, where the coefficients are real numbers, and n is nonnegative. A **polynomial equation** is an equation that can be expressed as a polynomial equal to 0.

DEFINITION

A **polynomial equation** can be written in the general form
$$a_n x^n + a_{n-1} x^{n-1} + \cdots + a_2 x^2 + a_1 x + a_0 = 0,$$
where $a_0, a_1, a_2, \ldots, a_n$ are real numbers, and n is a nonnegative integer.

TIP

A polynomial equation with degree 2 is a quadratic equation, and a polynomial equation with degree 1 is a linear equation.

A quadratic equation is a polynomial equation where $n = 2$ (i.e., the degree is 2). One method for solving a quadratic equation discussed in the previous section was solving by factoring. Recall that by the Zero-Product Property, if a product of algebraic expressions is equal to 0, then at least one of those expressions must be equal to 0. This property can also be applied to cases where there are three or more algebraic expressions in the product. It follows that if a polynomial equation can be written as a product of factors, then the factoring method can also be used to solve a polynomial equation.

Steps for Solving a Polynomial Equation by Factoring

❶ Write the polynomial equation in general form.

❷ Factor the polynomial.

❸ Set each factor equal to 0, and solve each equation.

Note that the quadratic equations solved previously by factoring were always factored into a product of linear expressions. A polynomial equation can be factored into a product of linear expressions, a product of linear and quadratic expressions, or even a product of factors that are higher-degree expressions. The factoring method can be used to solve a polynomial equation as long as the polynomial's factors form equations (when set equal to 0) that can be solved.

EXAMPLE 1	Solving a Polynomial Equation by Factoring

Solve each equation.

A. $5x^5 = 5x^3$

B. $x^3 + 8x^2 = 13x^2 - 5x + 25$

SOLUTION

Write each equation in general form, and then factor.

A.
$$5x^5 = 5x^3$$

$$5x^5 - 5x^3 = 0 \qquad \text{\textit{Write the equation in general form.}}$$

$$5x^3(x^2 - 1) = 0 \qquad \text{\textit{Factor the GCF from each term.}}$$

$$5x^3(x + 1)(x - 1) = 0 \qquad \text{\textit{Factor the difference of squares.}}$$

$$5x^3 = 0 \quad \text{or} \quad x + 1 = 0 \quad \text{or} \quad x - 1 = 0 \qquad \text{\textit{Set each factor equal to 0.}}$$

$$x = 0 \qquad\qquad x = -1 \qquad\qquad x = 1 \qquad \text{\textit{Solve each equation.}}$$

<aside>
CAUTION

Do not divide both sides of the equation by x^3. If you do so, you will not find the solution $x = 0$. Do not divide an equation by an expression containing a variable unless you know the expression cannot equal 0.
</aside>

CHECK

Each solution can be checked by substituting back into the original equation.

$$x = 0: \ 5(0)^5 \overset{?}{=} 5(0)^3 \qquad x = -1: \ 5(-1)^5 \overset{?}{=} 5(-1)^3 \qquad x = 1: \ 5(1)^5 \overset{?}{=} 5(1)^3$$

$$0 = 0 \checkmark \qquad\qquad\qquad -5 = -5 \checkmark \qquad\qquad\qquad 5 = 5 \checkmark$$

Therefore, the solutions are $x = 0$, $x = -1$, and $x = 1$.

B.
$$x^3 + 8x^2 = 13x^2 - 5x + 25$$

$$x^3 - 5x^2 + 5x - 25 = 0 \qquad \text{\textit{Write the equation in general form.}}$$

$$x^2(x - 5) + 5(x - 5) = 0 \qquad \text{\textit{Factor by grouping.}}$$

$$(x - 5)(x^2 + 5) = 0 \qquad \text{\textit{Factor the binomial (x − 5) from each term.}}$$

$$x - 5 = 0 \quad \text{or} \quad x^2 + 5 = 0 \qquad \text{\textit{Set each factor equal to 0.}}$$

$$x = 5 \qquad\qquad x = \pm i\sqrt{5} \qquad \text{\textit{Solve each equation.}}$$

Therefore, the solutions are $x = -i\sqrt{5}$, $x = i\sqrt{5}$, and $x = 5$.

<aside>
TIP

To solve $x^2 + 5 = 0$, subtract 5 from each side then take ± the square root of each side.

$$x^2 + 5 = 0$$

$$x = \pm i\sqrt{5}$$
</aside>

P.8.2   Solving an Equation Containing a Radical

An equation that contains a radical where the radicand includes a variable is called a **radical equation**. Some radical equations can be solved by isolating the radical expression and then applying a power to each side of the equation to eliminate the radical. The power is equal to the index of the radical. For example, squaring both sides of an equation containing a square root expression will cancel out a square root (assuming the square root expression is isolated on one side). To solve an equation containing a cube root expression, isolate the cube root expression and then raise each side to the third power. After the radical is eliminated, solve the resulting equation using any of the techniques covered previously.

Extraneous solutions can occur when both sides of an equation are raised to some power, so be sure to check each solution in the original equation to confirm that it is not extraneous.

Steps for Solving a Radical Equation with One Radical Expression

❶ Isolate the radical expression on one side of the equation.

❷ Apply a power equal to the radical's index to each side of the equation.

❸ Solve the resulting equation.

❹ Check for extraneous solutions.

EXAMPLE 2   **Solving a Radical Equation**

Solve each equation.

A. $\sqrt{z+10}+2=z$ **B.** $1=\sqrt{x-5}+2$

SOLUTION

A. Isolate the radical expression. Then square both sides, since the radical is a square root (i.e., index = 2), and simplify.

$$\sqrt{z+10}+2=z$$

$$\sqrt{z+10}=z-2 \qquad \textit{Subtract 2 from each side.}$$

$$z+10=(z-2)^2 \qquad \textit{Square both sides.}$$

$$z+10=z^2-4z+4 \qquad \textit{FOIL}$$

The resulting equation is quadratic, so manipulate the equation so that it is in general form, then use one of the quadratic solving techniques.

$$0=z^2-5z-6 \qquad \textit{Write the equation in general form.}$$

$$0=(z-6)(z+1) \qquad \textit{Factor.}$$

$$z=6 \ \text{ or } \ z=-1 \qquad \textit{Set each factor equal to 0 and solve each equation.}$$

> **IMPORTANT**
>
> *Always check for extraneous solutions when the solving steps involve squaring both sides of an equation or taking both sides to any power.*

Check for extraneous solutions.

$$\sqrt{6+10}+2 \overset{?}{=} 6 \qquad\qquad \sqrt{-1+10}+2 \overset{?}{=} -1$$

$$\sqrt{16}+2 \overset{?}{=} 6 \qquad\qquad \sqrt{9}+2 \overset{?}{=} -1$$

$$6=6 \ \checkmark \qquad\qquad\qquad 5 \neq -1$$

Substituting $z=-1$ results in a false statement, so this solution is extraneous.

Therefore, the only solution is $z=6$.

B. Isolating the radical expression gives $-1=\sqrt{x-5}$. There is no number such that its square root is equal to a negative number. Therefore, there is no solution.

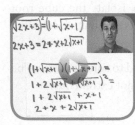

P.8.3 Solving an Equation with Two Radicals

When a radical equation contains two radical expressions A and B such that the index of A is equal to the index of B, and the equation contains no additional terms, then the equation can be solved by simply taking both sides to a power equal to the radical's index (assuming the equation has a solution). Doing so will eliminate the radical from both sides of the equation, leaving an equation where the radicand of A is equal to the radicand of B. Examples of such equations where the index is 2, 3, and 4 follow.

Index = 2 (square root)	Index = 3 (cube root)	Index = 4
Square each side.	Cube each side.	Take each side to the 4th power.
$\sqrt{2x+1} = \sqrt{x+4}$	$\sqrt[3]{x} = \sqrt[3]{2x-5}$	$\sqrt[4]{3x-1} = \sqrt[4]{2x}$
$\left(\sqrt{2x+1}\right)^2 = \left(\sqrt{x+4}\right)^2$	$\left(\sqrt[3]{x}\right)^3 = \left(\sqrt[3]{2x-5}\right)^3$	$\left(\sqrt[4]{3x-1}\right)^4 = \left(\sqrt[4]{2x}\right)^4$
$2x+1 = x+4$	$x = 2x-5$	$3x-1 = 2x$

Additionally, this technique may be applied when one or both of the radical expressions has a coefficient. In the case of a coefficient, be sure to apply the power to the coefficient as well as to the radical expression (by the Power of a Product Property).

In the case where a radical equation contains two square root expressions A and B, and at least one additional term, each side of the equation must be squared twice to find solutions.

Index = 2
Square each side. Be sure to square the coefficients.
$3\sqrt{2x+1} = 5\sqrt{x+4}$
$\left(3\sqrt{2x+1}\right)^2 = \left(5\sqrt{x+4}\right)^2$
$3^2\left(\sqrt{2x+1}\right)^2 = 5^2\left(\sqrt{x+4}\right)^2$
$9(2x+1) = 25(x+4)$

Steps for Solving a Square Root Equation with Two Radical Expressions and Additional Terms

❶ Isolate one of the radical expressions on one side of the equation.

❷ Square both sides of the equation and simplify.

❸ Isolate the remaining radical expression on one side of the equation.

❹ Square both sides of the equation and simplify.

❺ Solve the resulting equation.

❻ Check for extraneous solutions.

EXAMPLE 3   **Solving a Radical Equation**

Solve. $\sqrt{3x+10} + 2 = \sqrt{2x+5} + 3$

SOLUTION

Isolate one of the radical expressions by subtracting either 2 or 3 from both sides. Then square both sides and simplify.

$$\sqrt{3x+10} + 2 = \sqrt{2x+5} + 3$$

$$\sqrt{3x+10} = \sqrt{2x+5} + 1 \qquad \textit{Subtract 2 from each side.}$$

$$\left(\sqrt{3x+10}\right)^2 = \left(\sqrt{2x+5} + 1\right)^2 \qquad \textit{Square both sides.}$$

$$3x+10 = \left(\sqrt{2x+5} + 1\right)\left(\sqrt{2x+5} + 1\right) \qquad \textit{Simplify and expand the power.}$$

$$3x+10 = \left(\sqrt{2x+5}\right)^2 + 2\sqrt{2x+5} + 1 \qquad \textit{FOIL}$$

$$3x+10 = 2x+5 + 2\sqrt{2x+5} + 1 \qquad \textit{Simplify the power.}$$

$$3x+10 = 2x+6 + 2\sqrt{2x+5} \qquad \textit{Combine the like terms.}$$

P.8.5   Solving Rational Equations

Two techniques for solving rational equations were discussed previously. One method is to use the Cross-Product Property. This method can be used when the equation is an equality between two rational expressions (i.e., the equation is a proportion). The second method is to multiply the equation by a common denominator. This method will work for any type of rational equation. If the terms in the equation contain multiple denominators, then multiply the equation by the LCD (least common denominator), which is the LCM of the denominators.

EXAMPLE 5   Solving a Rational Equation

Solve. $\dfrac{1}{w-2} + \dfrac{2}{w+3} = \dfrac{8}{w^2+w-6}$

SOLUTION

The equation contains unlike denominators, so multiply the equation by the LCD (the LCM of $w-2$, $w+3$, and w^2+w-6). The factorization of w^2+w-6 is $(w-2)(w+3)$. Since the other denominators are $w-2$ and $w+3$, the LCD is $(w-2)(w+3)$.

$$\frac{1}{w-2}+\frac{2}{w+3}=\frac{8}{w^2+w-6}$$

$$\frac{1}{w-2}+\frac{2}{w+3}=\frac{8}{(w-2)(w+3)} \qquad \textit{Factor.}$$

$$(w-2)(w+3)\left(\frac{1}{w-2}+\frac{2}{w+3}\right)=\left(\frac{8}{(w-2)(w+3)}\right)(w-2)(w+3) \qquad \textit{Multiply both sides by the LCD.}$$

$$\frac{(w-2)(w+3)}{w-2}+\frac{2(w-2)(w+3)}{w+3}=\frac{8(w-2)(w+3)}{(w-2)(w+3)} \qquad \textit{Distribute and remove common factors.}$$

$$(w+3)+2(w-2)=8 \qquad \textit{Write the remaining factors.}$$

$$w+3+2w-4=8 \qquad \textit{Distribute.}$$

$$3w-1=8 \qquad \textit{Simplify.}$$

$$w=3 \qquad \textit{Solve for } w.$$

Check for extraneous solutions. Substituting $w = 3$ into the original equation results in a true statement, so the solution is $w = 3$.

P.8.6   Solving Equations of Quadratic Type

Expressions that are not quadratic can sometimes be written in quadratic form by substituting a variable for an expression that is a factor in one or two of the terms. For example, consider the expression $x^6 - 5x^3 + 6$. This expression is not quadratic. However, notice that if the power in the middle term, x^3, is squared, the result is the power in the first term, x^6: $(x^3)^2 = x^6$. So, the expression can be written as $(x^3)^2 - 5(x^3) + 6$. If we let $G = x^3$, then the expression can be written as $G^2 - 5G + 6$, which is a quadratic expression. Using this substitution method, a nonquadratic expression can be written in quadratic form.

This method can also be used to write a nonquadratic equation in quadratic form. Once the equation is in quadratic form, any of the quadratic solving techniques may be applied. After the quadratic form of the equation is solved, the last step is to substitute those solutions into the original G-substitution equation. For example, solving $G^2 - 5G + 6 = 0$ by factoring gives $G = 3$ or $G = 2$.

However, $G = 3$ or $G = 2$ are not the solutions of $x^6 - 5x^3 + 6 = 0$. To find the solutions of $x^6 - 5x^3 + 6 = 0$, substitute $G = 3$ and $G = 2$ back into the original G-substitution equation, which is $G = x^3$: $3 = x^3$ or $2 = x^3$. Take the cube root of both sides to solve for x: $x = \sqrt[3]{3}$ or $x = \sqrt[3]{2}$.

EXAMPLE 6   Solving an Equation by Writing as a Quadratic

Solve each equation.

A. $q^4 + 900 = 61q^2$

B. $(2y-1)^{\frac{2}{5}} + 1 = 2(2y-1)^{\frac{1}{5}}$

SOLUTION

A. In general form, the equation is $q^4 - 61q^2 + 900 = 0$. Notice that the equation can be written in the form of a quadratic where q^2 is the variable: $(q^2)^2 - 61(q^2) + 900 = 0$. So, substitute using $G = q^2$ to write the equation in quadratic form.

$$(q^2)^2 - 61(q^2) + 900 = 0$$

$$G^2 - 61G + 900 = 0 \quad \textit{Let } q^2 = G.$$

$$(G - 36)(G - 25) = 0 \quad \textit{Factor.}$$

$$G = 36 \quad \text{or} \quad G = 25 \quad \textit{Set each factor equal to 0 and solve each equation.}$$

$$q^2 = 36 \qquad q^2 = 25 \quad \textit{Substitute } q^2 \textit{ for } G.$$

$$q = \pm 6 \qquad q = \pm 5 \quad \textit{Take } \pm \textit{ the square root of each side.}$$

> **NOTICE THAT**
>
> *G is substituted for a monomial with a whole number exponent: q^2.*

Substitute to check for extraneous solutions.

$(-6)^4 + 900 \overset{?}{=} 61(-6)^2 \quad (-5)^4 + 900 \overset{?}{=} 61(-5)^2 \quad (5)^4 + 900 \overset{?}{=} 61(5)^2 \quad (6)^4 + 900 \overset{?}{=} 61(6)^2$

$1296 + 900 \overset{?}{=} 61(36) \quad 625 + 900 \overset{?}{=} 61(25) \quad 625 + 900 \overset{?}{=} 61(25) \quad 1296 + 900 \overset{?}{=} 61(36)$

$2196 = 2196 \checkmark \qquad\quad 1525 = 1525 \checkmark \qquad\quad 1525 = 1525 \checkmark \qquad\quad 2196 = 2196 \checkmark$

Therefore, the solutions are $q = -6$, $q = -5$, $q = 5$, and $q = 6$.

> **IMPORTANT**
>
> *Raising both sides to the 5th power complicates the equation. So, solving by raising both sides to the 5th power is not a useful option.*

B. In general form, the equation is $(2y-1)^{\frac{2}{5}} - 2(2y-1)^{\frac{1}{5}} + 1 = 0$. Notice that the binomial $(2y - 1)$ is used in each term with a power. Additionally, notice that the equation can be written in quadratic form where $(2y-1)^{\frac{1}{5}}$ is the variable: $((2y-1)^{\frac{1}{5}})^2 - 2(2y-1)^{\frac{1}{5}} + 1 = 0$.

So, substitute using $G = (2y-1)^{\frac{1}{5}}$ to write the equation in quadratic form.

$$((2y-1)^{\frac{1}{5}})^2 - 2(2y-1)^{\frac{1}{5}} + 1 = 0$$

$$G^2 - 2G + 1 = 0 \quad \textit{Let } (2y-1)^{\frac{1}{5}} = G.$$

$$(G-1)(G-1) = 0 \quad \textit{Factor.}$$

> **NOTICE THAT**
>
> *G is substituted for a binomial with a rational exponent: $(2y-1)^{\frac{1}{5}}$.*

Solving $G - 1 = 0$ yields $G = 1$. Substitute $(2y-1)^{\frac{1}{5}}$ for G and solve.

$$(2y-1)^{\frac{1}{5}} = 1$$

$$((2y-1)^{\frac{1}{5}})^5 = 1^5 \quad \textit{Raise each side to the 5th power.}$$

$$2y - 1 = 1 \quad \textit{Simplify.}$$

$$y = 1 \quad \textit{Solve for y.}$$

Check for extraneous solutions. Substituting $y = 1$ into the original equation results in a true statement, so the solution is $y = 1$.

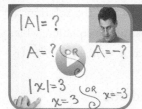

P.8.7   Solving Absolute Value Equations

Recall that the absolute value of a number is the distance between that number and 0 on a number line. Since absolute value is a distance, the absolute value of a number is always positive. Consider the equation $|A| = B$, where A and B are some numbers. If $|A| = B$, then A must be equal to either B or $-B$. The following property follows from this statement.

Absolute Value Equations

If A and B are some numbers or algebraic expressions such that $|A| = B$, then $A = \pm B$. So, the equation $|A| = B$ can be written as the two equivalent equations $A = B$ and $A = -B$.

This property is used to solve equations in which a variable is contained within one or more absolute value expressions, called **absolute value equations**. The domain of an absolute value equation may not be all real numbers. Therefore, solving an absolute value equation may produce extraneous solutions.

Steps for Solving an Absolute Value Equation

❶ Isolate an absolute value expression on one side of the equation: $|A| = B$.

❷ Write the equation as the two equivalent equations $A = B$ and $A = -B$.

❸ Solve each equation.

❹ Check for extraneous solutions.

CAUTION

When B is a multiterm expression, be sure to distribute the negative in $A = -B$ to each term in B.

EXAMPLE 7   Solving an Absolute Value Equation

Solve each equation.

A. $|4x - 2| - 6 = 0$

B. $1 = \left|\dfrac{x - 7}{5}\right| + 4$

C. $\left|\dfrac{6}{x + 4}\right| - 9 = -6$

SOLUTION

A. Add 6 to both sides to isolate the absolute value expression $|4x - 2|$. Then write and solve the two equations.

$$|4x - 2| - 6 = 0$$
$$|4x - 2| = 6 \qquad \text{\textit{Isolate the absolute value expression.}}$$
$$4x - 2 = 6 \quad \text{or} \quad 4x - 2 = -6 \qquad \text{\textit{Write } } |A| = B \text{ \textit{as} } A = B \text{ \textit{or as} } A = -B.$$
$$x = 2 \qquad\qquad x = -1 \qquad \text{\textit{Solve each equation.}}$$

Substitute to check for extraneous solutions.

$$|4(2) - 2| - 6 = |6| - 6 = 0 \ \checkmark$$
$$|4(-1) - 2| - 6 = |-6| - 6 = 0 \ \checkmark$$

Therefore, the solutions are $x = -1$ and $x = 2$.

B. Subtracting 4 from both sides to isolate the absolute value expression gives $-3 = \left|\dfrac{x - 7}{5}\right|$.

The absolute value of a number cannot equal a negative number, so there is no solution.

C. Add 9 to both sides to isolate the absolute value expression, then write and solve the two equations. Notice that the resulting equations will be rational and therefore should be solved using one of the techniques for solving rational equations.

$$\left|\frac{6}{x+4}\right| - 9 = -6$$

$$\left|\frac{6}{x+4}\right| = 3 \qquad\qquad \textit{Isolate the absolute value expression.}$$

$$\frac{6}{x+4} = 3 \quad \text{or} \quad \frac{6}{x+4} = -3 \qquad\qquad \textit{Write } |A| = B \textit{ as } A = B \textit{ or as } A = -B.$$

$$
\begin{aligned}
6 = 3(x+4) \qquad & 6 = -3(x+4) \qquad && \textit{Multiply both sides by } x+4. \\
6 = 3x + 12 \qquad & 6 = -3x - 12 \qquad && \textit{Distribute.} \\
-2 = x \qquad & -6 = x \qquad && \textit{Solve each equation for x.}
\end{aligned}
$$

Check for extraneous solutions. Substituting $x = -2$ into the original equation results in a true statement, as does substituting $x = -6$, so the solutions are $x = -6$ and $x = -2$.

SECTION P.8 EXERCISES

Warm Up

1. Simplify. $-|8 - 3(-5 + 2)|$

2. Evaluate $\dfrac{3x + 4}{x + 1} + \dfrac{x}{5}$ for $x = 1$.

3. Factor. $6x^2 - 5x - 4$

Just the Facts

Fill in the blanks.

4. The equation $a_n x^n + a_{n-1} x^{n-1} + \cdots + a_2 x^2 + a_1 x + a_0 = 0$ is a(n) _____ equation written in general form.

5. If a radical equation contains two square root expressions and at least one additional term, then the equation can be _____ twice to find solutions.

6. An equation that contains a radical where the radicand includes a variable is called a(n) _____ equation.

7. Always check for _____ solutions when solving a radical equation because they can occur when the equation's domain is not all real numbers.

8. An expression with a(n) _____ exponent can be written as a radical where the _____ is the index of the radical.

9. When solving an absolute value equation, isolate the _____ expression on one side of the equation, then write the two equations $A = B$ and _____.

10. The denominators in a rational equation can be cleared by _____.

Essential Skills

In Exercises 1–60, solve each equation.

1. $2x^6 + 3x^5 - 7x^4 - 2x^6 + 15x^5 + 9x^4 = 0$

2. $6x^5 + 40x^4 + 20x^3 = 4x^4 - 28x^3$

3. $6x^6 + 33x^5 - 133x^4 = 9x^5 - 7x^4$

4. $3t^5 + 3t^4 - 79t^3 - 9t^4 = -7t^3$

5. $5r^7 + 40r^6 + 35r^5 - 10r^6 = -5r^5$

6. $3r^9 + 15r^8 - 60r^7 = 6r^8 - 6r^7$

7. $5x^3 + 7x^2 - 27x + 15 = 2x^3 + 6x^2 + 24$

8. $2x^3 - x^2 - x = 2x^2 + x - 3$

9. $3a^3 + 4a^2 - 80a + 50 = 6a^2 - 5a$

10. $5b^3 + 3b^2 - 130b = 5b^2 - 5b - 50$

11. $4m^3 + 2m^2 - 102m + 75 - 5m^2 = -2m$

12. $2x^3 + 3x^2 - 22x + 27 = 6x^2 - 4x$

13. $\sqrt{z + 10} = 2$

14. $\sqrt{3w + 14} + 6 = 3w$

15. $\sqrt{15a + 10} = 5a - 6$

16. $6 - 7w = -\sqrt{21w + 10}$

17. $4y + 1 = \sqrt{4y + 7}$

18. $\sqrt{14x + 12} + 6 = 7x$

19. $\sqrt{x} = \sqrt{x + 5} - 1$

20. $\sqrt{8x + 4} = \sqrt{2x + 1} + 3$

21. $\sqrt{3z} + 1 = 3 + \sqrt{2z - 8}$

22. $\sqrt{a + 1} = 3 - \sqrt{4 - a}$

23. $\sqrt{2x - 11} - \sqrt{3x + 6} = -3$

24. $\sqrt{22w + 4} - 1 = \sqrt{4w + 1} + 2$

25. $(x^2 - 4x + 3)^{\frac{1}{3}} = x^{\frac{2}{3}}$

26. $(y + 3)^{\frac{1}{2}} = 2y^{\frac{1}{4}}$

27. $(2k - 1)^{\frac{1}{5}} = k^{\frac{2}{5}}$

28. $(17d^2 - 16)^{\frac{1}{4}} = d$

29. $(w - 1)^{\frac{2}{3}} = (w^2 - 4w)^{\frac{1}{3}}$

30. $(z + 8)^{\frac{1}{2}} = 3z^{\frac{1}{4}}$

31. $\dfrac{x}{4} + \dfrac{2x + 3}{x - 2} = \dfrac{3x + 1}{x - 2}$

32. $\dfrac{x + 4}{x + 1} + \dfrac{x}{5} = \dfrac{2x + 5}{x + 1}$

33. $\dfrac{1}{2} - \dfrac{2}{x - 1} = -\dfrac{3}{2x - 2}$

34. $\dfrac{5}{4} - \dfrac{1}{t + 2} = \dfrac{1}{t - 1}$

35. $\dfrac{5}{2g + 6} + \dfrac{1}{g - 2} = \dfrac{3}{g + 3}$

36. $\dfrac{32}{d^2 - 25} = \dfrac{2}{d - 5} + \dfrac{4}{d + 5}$

37. $y^6 + 16y^3 + 64 = 0$

38. $z^{10} - 6z^5 = 2z^5 - 15$

39. $81b^8 + 80b^4 + 64 = 65$

40. $27b^6 + 19b^3 = 8$

41. $25c^4 + 10 = -46c^2 + 18$

42. $a^6 - 4a^3 + 20 = 5a^3$

43. $2x^{\frac{2}{5}} - x^{\frac{1}{5}} - 1 = 0$

44. $(x+2)^{\frac{1}{2}} + 4 = 5(x+2)^{\frac{1}{4}}$

45. $(n-3)^{\frac{2}{3}} - 3(n-3)^{\frac{1}{3}} + 2 = 0$

46. $(2x-1)^{\frac{2}{5}} - 2(2x-1)^{\frac{1}{5}} + 1 = 0$

47. $(b+2)^{\frac{1}{2}} - 5(b+2)^{\frac{1}{4}} = -4$

48. $(w+6)^{\frac{1}{2}} + 8 = 6(w+6)^{\frac{1}{4}}$

49. $|5a+2| = -1$

50. $5 = |6x+4|$

51. $7 = |2p+5|$

52. $|9t+4| = 8$

53. $|5m-14| - 6 = 0$

54. $8 + |-3x+9| = 0$

55. $\left|\dfrac{3}{b+1}\right| = 2$

56. $\left|\dfrac{5}{x+2}\right| = 7$

57. $10 + \left|\dfrac{4}{p+6}\right| = 16$

58. $6 - \left|\dfrac{2}{k-5}\right| = 1$

59. $\left|\dfrac{w+5}{2}\right| - 7 = 9$

60. $4 - \left|\dfrac{a-2}{3}\right| = 10$

Extensions

In Exercises 61–64, use techniques for solving quadratic equations to solve each equation for the indicated variable.

61. $(y+2)^2 = 3x - 5$ for y

62. $0 = (-3+x)^2 - 8z$ for x

63. $5cp - 6ap^2 + cp = 0$ for p

64. $x + 2hm = 7rm^2 + hm$ for m

In Exercises 65–69, solve each equation.

65. $\sqrt{1 - \sqrt{x-1}} + x - 1 = 1$

66. $\dfrac{1}{x-1} + \dfrac{2}{x-5} = \dfrac{4}{x+2}$

67. $|3x-4| = |5x+2|$

68. $9x^4 + 3\sqrt{7}x^3 + 4x^2 = 2x^4 - 11\sqrt{7}x^3 - 45x^2$

69. $6x^{-2} + 11x^{-1} = 10$

70. In still water, a barge travels at an average of 8 miles per hour. The barge travels 60 miles up the Mississippi River and 60 miles down the river in 16.5 hours. What is the average speed of the current in miles per hour? Round to the nearest tenth of a mile per hour.

71. A woman spends her morning kayaking on a river. She travels 6 miles upstream and 6 miles downstream in 4.5 hours. In still water, she averages 3 miles per hour. What is the average speed of the current in miles per hour? Round to the nearest mile per hour.

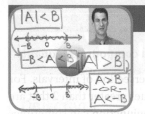

P.9.3   Solving Absolute Value Inequalities

Recall that an absolute value equation is solved by isolating the absolute value expression and then writing $|A| = B$ as two equivalent equations: $A = B$ and $A = -B$. A similar procedure is used for solving **absolute value inequalities**.

Absolute Value Inequalities

If A and B are some numbers or algebraic expressions such that

- $|A| < B$, then $-B < A < B$,
- $|A| \leq B$, then $-B \leq A \leq B$,
- $|A| > B$, then $A > B$ or $A < -B$, and
- $|A| \geq B$, then $A \geq B$ or $A \leq -B$.

CAUTION

If B represents a number such that B < 0 (i.e., B is negative), then
$|A| < B$ *and* $|A| \leq B$ *have no solutions.*

So, a *less than* absolute value inequality ($|A| < B$ or $|A| \leq B$) can be written as an "and" compound inequality, and a *greater than* absolute value inequality ($|A| > B$ or $|A| \geq B$) can be written as an "or" compound inequality. In each case, the resulting inequality (which does not contain an absolute value expression) can be solved using the techniques for solving compound inequalities.

Steps for Solving an Absolute Value Inequality

❶ Isolate the absolute value expression on one side of the inequality.

❷ Write the absolute value inequality as the equivalent compound inequality.

❸ Solve the compound inequality.

EXAMPLE 3   Solving an Absolute Value Inequality

Solve each inequality. Express each solution set in interval notation.

A. $12 > |9 - 3x|$ 　　　　　　　　**B.** $|x - 7| - 1 > 5$

SOLUTION

A. Reverse the inequality so that the absolute value expression is on the left side.

$$12 > |9 - 3x| \implies |9 - 3x| < 12$$

Express the absolute value inequality as a compound inequality using $|A| < B \implies -B < A < B$, then solve the double inequality by applying each solving step to all three sides.

$$-12 < 9 - 3x < 12$$
$$-21 < -3x < 3 \qquad \textit{Subtract 9 from each side.}$$
$$7 > x > -1 \qquad \textit{Divide each side by -3 and reverse both inequality symbols.}$$

The inequality $7 > x > -1$ should be written as $-1 < x < 7$. The solution set is $(-1, 7)$.

B. Add 1 to each side to isolate the absolute value expression on the left side.

$$|x - 7| - 1 > 5 \implies |x - 7| > 6$$

Express the absolute value inequality as a compound inequality using $|A| > B \implies A < B$ or $A < -B$, and then solve each inequality individually.

$$x - 7 > 6 \implies x > 13 \qquad \text{or} \qquad x - 7 < -6 \implies x < 1$$

The solution set of $x > 13$ or $x < 1$ is $(-\infty, 1) \cup (13, \infty)$.

P.9.4 Solving Absolute Value Inequalities: Another Example

When solving an absolute value inequality, be sure to isolate the absolute value expression on one side of the inequality (typically the left side) and simplify the absolute value expression before writing the compound inequality.

EXAMPLE 4   Solving an Absolute Value Inequality

Solve $18 - 5|2 - (3x - 5)| \geq -37$. Express the solution set in interval notation.

SOLUTION

Simplify the absolute value expression, then isolate the expression on the left side.

$$18 - 5|2 - (3x - 5)| \geq -37$$
$$18 - 5|2 - 3x + 5| \geq -37 \qquad \textit{Distribute.}$$
$$18 - 5|-3x + 7| \geq -37 \qquad \textit{Combine the like terms.}$$
$$-5|-3x + 7| \geq -55 \qquad \textit{Subtract 18 from each side.}$$
$$|-3x + 7| \leq 11 \qquad \textit{Divide each side by } -5 \textit{ and reverse the inequality symbol.}$$

Express the absolute value inequality as a compound inequality using $|A| \leq B \implies -B \leq A \leq B$, and then solve the double inequality by applying each solving step to all three sides.

$$-11 \leq -3x + 7 \leq 11$$
$$-18 \leq -3x \leq 4 \qquad \textit{Subtract 7 from each side.}$$
$$6 \geq x \geq -\frac{4}{3} \qquad \textit{Divide each side by } -3 \textit{ and reverse both inequality symbols.}$$

The inequality $6 \geq x \geq -\dfrac{4}{3}$ should be written as $-\dfrac{4}{3} \leq x \leq 6$. The solution set is $\left[-\dfrac{4}{3}, 6 \right]$.

WHAT'S THE BIG IDEA?

Explain why $|A| < B$ can be written equivalently as $-B < A < B$.

P.9.5 Solving Quadratic Inequalities

When an inequality is linear and has a solution set, its solution set is a single interval of real numbers. For example, the solution set of the linear inequality $x - 1 > 0$ is all real numbers x in the interval $(1, \infty)$. Notice that the solution of the *related equation* $x - 1 = 0$ (i.e., $x = 1$) gives the interval's endpoint.

If a solution set exists for a **quadratic inequality,** it can consist of one or two intervals of real numbers where each endpoint (other than $-\infty$ and ∞) is a solution of the *related equation* (i.e., the equation given by replacing the inequality symbol with an equals sign).

$$x^2 - 4x + 3 = 0$$
$$(x - 1)(x - 3) = 0$$
$$x - 1 = 0 \text{ or } x - 3 = 0$$
$$x = 1 \qquad x = 3$$

For example, consider the quadratic inequality $x^2 - 4x + 3 > 0$. The related equation $x^2 - 4x + 3 = 0$ has solutions $x = 1$ and $x = 3$. So, the solution set for $x^2 - 4x + 3 > 0$ (if one exists) is all real numbers x in one or more of the intervals $(-\infty, 1)$, $(1, 3)$, and $(3, \infty)$.

P.9.6 Solving Quadratic Inequalities: Another Example

The first step in solving the four inequalities in **Example 5** was to find the solutions of the related equation. Notice that each inequality was given in general form. If the inequality is not given in general form, begin by rewriting the inequality so that one side is 0.

EXAMPLE 6   Solving a Quadratic Inequality

Solve $84 \leq 4x^2 + 16x$. Express the solution set in interval notation.

SOLUTION

❶ Rewriting the inequality gives $-4x^2 - 16x + 84 \leq 0$.

The related equation is $-4x^2 - 16x + 84 = 0$. Solve by factoring.

$$-4(x^2 + 4x - 21) = 0 \qquad \textit{Factor out } -4.$$

$$-4(x + 7)(x - 3) = 0 \qquad \textit{Factor the trinomial.}$$

The solutions of $-4x^2 - 16x + 84 = 0$ are $x = -7$ and $x = 3$.

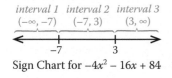

interval 1   interval 2   interval 3
$(-\infty, -7)$ $(-7, 3)$ $(3, \infty)$

$-7 \qquad 3$

Sign Chart for $-4x^2 - 16x + 84$

❷ Note the solutions on a sign chart as the endpoints of the test intervals.

❸ Substitute a value from each test interval into $-4x^2 - 16x + 84$ and complete the sign chart.

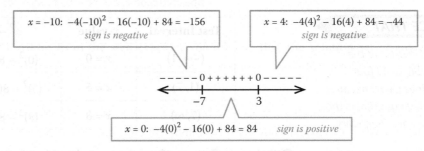

$x = -10$: $-4(-10)^2 - 16(-10) + 84 = -156$
sign is negative

$x = 4$: $-4(4)^2 - 16(4) + 84 = -44$
sign is negative

$- - - - - 0 + + + + + + 0 - - - - -$

$-7 \qquad 3$

$x = 0$: $-4(0)^2 - 16(0) + 84 = 84$ sign is positive

Test Interval	x-value	$-4x^2 - 16x + 84$	Sign
$(-\infty, -7)$	$x = -10$	$-4(-10)^2 - 16(-10) + 84 = -156$	negative
$(-7, 3)$	$x = 0$	$-4(0)^2 - 16(0) + 84 = 84$	positive
$(3, \infty)$	$x = 4$	$-4(4)^2 - 16(4) + 84 = -44$	negative

❹ The solution set of $-4x^2 - 16x + 84 \leq 0$ includes all x-values where $-4x^2 - 16x + 84$ is *less than or equal to* 0. Since $-4x^2 - 16x + 84$ is negative in $(-\infty, -7)$ and $(3, \infty)$, and $-4x^2 - 16x + 84 = 0$ when $x = -7$ and 3, the solution set is $(-\infty, -7] \cup [3, \infty)$.

WHAT'S THE BIG IDEA?

Explain the purpose of the sign chart when solving a quadratic inequality.

P.9.7 Solving a Polynomial Inequality

A sign chart can be used to find the solution set of a **polynomial inequality**. However, if the degree of the polynomial is greater than 2 (i.e., the polynomial inequality is not linear or quadratic), then the sign chart may have more than three test intervals. When substituting a value from each test interval into the polynomial expression to determine its sign, keep in mind that the value can be substituted into the factored form of the polynomial. Doing so almost always makes the calculations easier.

EXAMPLE 7   Solving a Polynomial Inequality

Solve $x^3 + 2x^2 > 18 + 9x$. Express the solution set in interval notation.

SOLUTION

❶ Rewriting the inequality gives $x^3 + 2x^2 - 9x - 18 > 0$.

The related equation is $x^3 + 2x^2 - 9x - 18 = 0$. Solve by factoring.

$$x^3 + 2x^2 - 9x - 18 = 0$$

$$x^2(x + 2) - 9(x + 2) = 0 \quad \textit{Factor by grouping.}$$

$$(x + 2)(x^2 - 9) = 0 \quad \textit{Factor (x + 2) from each term.}$$

$$(x + 2)(x - 3)(x + 3) = 0 \quad \textit{Factor the difference of two squares.}$$

The solutions of $x^3 + 2x^2 - 9x - 18 = 0$ are $x = -3$, $x = -2$, and $x = 3$.

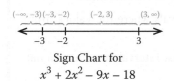

$(-\infty, -3)$ $(-3, -2)$ $(-2, 3)$ $(3, \infty)$

Sign Chart for
$x^3 + 2x^2 - 9x - 18$

❷ Note the solutions on a sign chart as the endpoints of the test intervals.

❸ Substitute a value from each test interval into $x^3 + 2x^2 - 9x - 18$. Complete the sign chart.

Here, the factored form, $(x + 2)(x - 3)(x + 3)$, is used to simplify the calculations.

Test Interval	x-value	$(x + 2)(x - 3)(x + 3)$	Sign
$(-\infty, -3)$	$x = -4$	$(-4 + 2)(-4 - 3)(-4 + 3)$ $(-) \quad (-) \quad (-) = \textit{negative}$	negative
$(-3, -2)$	$x = -\dfrac{5}{2}$	$\left(-\dfrac{5}{2} + 2\right)\left(-\dfrac{5}{2} - 3\right)\left(-\dfrac{5}{2} + 3\right)$ $(-) \quad (-) \quad (+) = \textit{positive}$	positive
$(-2, 3)$	$x = 0$	$(0 + 2)(0 - 3)(0 + 3)$ $(+) \quad (-) \quad (+) = \textit{negative}$	negative
$(3, \infty)$	$x = 4$	$(4 + 2)(4 - 3)(4 + 3)$ $(+) \quad (+) \quad (+) = \textit{positive}$	positive

$$-- 0 ++ 0 ------- 0 ++$$

$-3 \quad\quad -2 \quad\quad\quad\quad 3$

❹ The solution set of $x^3 + 2x^2 - 9x - 18 > 0$ includes all values where $x^3 + 2x^2 - 9x - 18$ is *greater than* 0 (but not equal to 0). Since $(x + 2)(x - 3)(x + 3)$ is positive in $(-3, -2)$ and $(3, \infty)$, the solution set of $x^3 + 2x^2 > 18 + 9x$ is $(-3, -2) \cup (3, \infty)$.

TIP

The actual value of the expression is not important; only the sign is needed. So, determine whether each factor is positive or negative, and then use those signs to determine the sign of the expression, instead of simplifying and finding the exact value.

P.9.9 Solving Rational Inequalities: Another Example

In **Example 8**, the rational expression had a linear numerator and a linear denominator. Therefore, there was one value that made the expression 0 and one value that made the expression undefined, resulting in three possible solution intervals on the sign chart. However, a sign chart for a rational inequality may be divided into more than three test intervals when the degree of the polynomial in the numerator or denominator is greater than 1.

EXAMPLE 9   Solving a Rational Inequality with Common Denominators

Solve $\dfrac{x^2-7}{x-6} < \dfrac{9}{x-6}$. Express the solution set in interval notation.

SOLUTION

❶ Rewrite the rational inequality.

$$\frac{x^2-7}{x-6} - \frac{9}{x-6} < 0 \qquad \textit{Subtract } \frac{9}{x-6} \textit{ from each side.}$$

$$\frac{x^2-16}{x-6} < 0 \qquad \textit{Combine the numerators.}$$

Determine the values where the rational expression $\dfrac{x^2-16}{x-6}$ is a) 0, and b) undefined.

a) $x^2 - 16 = 0$ **b)** $x - 6 = 0$
     $(x+4)(x-4) = 0$ $x = 6$
      $x = -4$ or $x = 4$ *The denominator is 0 when x is 6.*
    The numerator is 0 when x is −4 or 4.

So, the rational expression is 0 when $x = -4$ or 4 and undefined when $x = 6$.

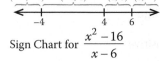

Sign Chart for $\dfrac{x^2-16}{x-6}$

❷ Note the values on a sign chart to denote the test intervals.

❸ Substitute a value from each test interval into $\dfrac{x^2-16}{x-6}$ and complete the sign chart.

Test Interval	x-value	$\dfrac{x^2-16}{x-6}$	Sign
$(-\infty, -4)$	$x = -5$	$\dfrac{(-5)^2 - 16}{-5-6} = \dfrac{pos}{neg} = \textit{negative}$	negative
$(-4, 4)$	$x = 0$	$\dfrac{(0)^2 - 16}{0-6} = \dfrac{neg}{neg} = \textit{positive}$	positive
$(4, 6)$	$x = 5$	$\dfrac{(5)^2 - 16}{5-6} = \dfrac{pos}{neg} = \textit{negative}$	negative
$(6, \infty)$	$x = 7$	$\dfrac{(7)^2 - 16}{7-6} = \dfrac{pos}{pos} = \textit{positive}$	positive

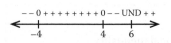

❹ The solution set of $\dfrac{x^2-16}{x-6} < 0$ includes all values where $\dfrac{x^2-16}{x-6}$ is *less than* 0. Since $\dfrac{x^2-16}{x-6}$ is negative in $(-\infty, -4)$ and $(4, 6)$, the solution set is $(-\infty, -4) \cup (4, 6)$.

SECTION P.9 EXERCISES

Warm Up

Write each set using interval notation.

1. all numbers greater than 5

2. all numbers excluding 0

3. $\{x|\ -2 \le x \le 70\}$

Just the Facts

Fill in the blanks.

4. The _____ symbol must be reversed when an inequality is _____ or _____ by a _____ number.

5. The phrase "x is at least y" can be represented by the inequality _____.

6. The phrase "x is no more than y" can be represented by the inequality _____.

7. When two inequalities are connected by the word "and" or "or", the inequality is called a _____.

8. A *less than* absolute value inequality can be rewritten as a compound inequality using the word _____. A *greater than* absolute value inequality can be rewritten as a compound inequality using the word _____.

9. The solution sets for the inequalities $ax^2 + bx + c$ _____ 0 and $ax^2 + bx + c$ _____ 0 do not include the solutions of the related equation $ax^2 + bx + c = 0$.

10. The solution sets for the inequalities $ax^2 + bx + c$ _____ 0 and $ax^2 + bx + c$ _____ 0 include the solutions of the related equation $ax^2 + bx + c = 0$.

Essential Skills

In Exercises 1–6, write the solution set of each inequality using interval notation.

1. $8h + 3 \le 4h - 21$

2. $-5x + 3 \ge 6(x - 5)$

3. $3(1 + 2b) > 2 - b$

4. $6x - 14 < 4(x - 6)$

5. $5(d - 2) \ge -(8d - 3)$

6. $-2(5a + 1) > 7(4 - 3a)$

In Exercises 7–66, write the solution set of each inequality using interval notation. If there is no solution, write the empty set, ø.

7. $3x \le 6$ or $3x \ge 21$

8. $5 - 3x \le -7$ or $x + 8 \le -1$

9. $-2a + 1 \ge 9$ or $5a + 2 \ge -28$

10. $4 - 10x \le 10$ or $x + 16 \le 14$

11. $9 - 7h \le -12$ or $h + 9 < 4$

12. $2d - 6 < -8$ or $-5d + 7 \le -13$

13. $-9 \le -3x + 6 \le 0$

14. $-7 \le -13 - 2x \le 15$

15. $16 < -2 + 3d \le 34$

16. $12 \le 7w - 2 < 40$

17. $-4 \le -3a - 16 < 5$

18. $-5 \le -9 - 2y \le 3$

19. $|3 - 2y| > 5$

20. $8 > |3 - x|$

21. $|22 + 4q| < 2$

22. $|36 + 8p| \le 4$

23. $6 \ge |6b + 24|$

24. $9 > |12 - 2z| - 1$

25. $4 > |8 - 2f|$

26. $|2 - 4x| \ge 6$

27. $1 + |12 + 2c| \ge 5$

28. $2 < |14 + 2y| - 2$

29. $|-2v + 7| - 2 > 1$

30. $|-8z + 44| + 1 \ge 13$

31. $12 \le 3|2 - (3x - 6)|$

32. $30 - 4|2 - (3d - 4)| \ge -6$

33. $27 - 9|1 - 2(c - 1)| < 108$

34. $40 + 4|3 - 3(p - 3)| < 100$

35. $18 - 5|2 - (3w - 5)| \ge -37$

36. $15 - 3|-3(x + 2) + 2| \ge -12$

37. $3k^2 - 14k + 8 < 0$

38. $5x^2 + 7x - 6 > 0$

39. $5a^2 + 39a - 8 \le 0$

40. $2z^2 - 3z - 14 \ge 0$

41. $6m^2 + 7m - 20 \ge 0$

42. $3p^2 + 2p - 8 \le 0$

43. $-10x + 12 \ge -4x^2 + 9x$

44. $6z^2 - 1 \le z^2 - 17z - 7$

45. $x^2 - 27 \ge -3x - x^2$

46. $7x^2 - 28 > x^2 - 17x$

47. $5b^2 - 13b + 12 \geq b^2 + 6b$

48. $7a^2 - 6a + 4 < a^2 + 10 - a$

49. $x^3 - 3x^2 < 9x - 27$

50. $x^3 + 7x^2 > 49x + 343$

51. $a^3 + 2a^2 + 3 \leq 4a + 11$

52. $p^3 + 8p^2 - 16p \leq 4p^2 + 64$

53. $c^3 + 6c^2 > -2c^2 + 64c + 512$

54. $y^3 + 4y^2 - 4y \leq 2y^2 + 8$

55. $\dfrac{x+1}{2x-7} \geq 0$

56. $\dfrac{4x-3}{x+4} < 1$

57. $\dfrac{x+3}{2x-5} \leq 0$

58. $\dfrac{6x-6}{x+6} \geq 1$

59. $\dfrac{3x+7}{5x-4} > 0$

60. $\dfrac{7y-5}{y+7} < 2$

61. $\dfrac{3x-2}{x-1} < \dfrac{6}{x-1}$

62. $\dfrac{x^2-3}{x+6} \geq \dfrac{1}{x+6}$

63. $\dfrac{3}{d+5} \leq \dfrac{d^2-1}{d+5}$

64. $\dfrac{y^2-2}{y+4} \geq \dfrac{2}{y+4}$

65. $\dfrac{7x-2}{x+2} \geq \dfrac{3}{x+2}$

66. $\dfrac{t^2-1}{t+7} < \dfrac{24}{t+7}$

Extensions

In Exercises 67–70, write the solution set of each inequality using interval notation. If there is no solution, write the empty set, ø.

67. $5 - |x - 12| + |2x + 4| > 0$

68. $\dfrac{2x^3 + 4x^2 - 30x}{x^2 + 3x - 4} < 0$

69. $\dfrac{3+x}{3-x} - \dfrac{3-x}{3+x} < -6$

70. $\dfrac{2x^2 + 5x - 3}{x^2 + 8x + 15} > 0$

71. The two shorter sides of a right triangle are x and $3 - x$, where $x > 0$. For which values of x will the hypotenuse be less than $\sqrt{15}$?

72. The sum of the first n natural numbers is given by $1 + 2 + 3 + \ldots + n = \dfrac{n(n+1)}{2}$. For which values of n will the sum be less than 36?

73. A college student earns \$20 per lawn mowing lawns in his neighborhood. If he pays \$350 per month in rent, what is the minimum number of lawns that he must mow each month to be able to pay the rent?

74. At a rental car company, the total price for a rental car is either \$100 per week plus \$0.20 per mile driven or \$50 per week plus \$0.30 per mile driven. For what number of miles per week is the total price for the first option less than the total price for the second option?

75. The high-school marching band is selling boxes of candy bars to earn money for new uniforms. The uniforms will cost \$12,000, but the band already has \$4800. If they profit \$4 from each box of candy sold, what is the minimum number of boxes they must sell in order to have enough money to buy the uniforms?

76. A yo-yo factory has fixed operating costs that add up to \$450,000 per year. In addition to the fixed costs, the cost to produce one yo-yo is \$1.20. The yo-yo company sells the yo-yos to a distributor for \$4.80 each. How many yo-yos must the factory sell to the distributor in a year in order to earn a profit of at least \$100,000?

CHAPTER P REVIEW EXERCISES

Section P.1 Real Numbers

1. Evaluate $3a - 4ab^2 - 6(10 + b) - a^2$ for $a = 3$ and $b = -2$.

2. Write the solution set for $-10 < x \leq -7$ using interval notation.

3. Write the inequality with solution set $[-1, \infty)$.

4. Express the interval $(-\infty, 2] \cup (3, 5)$ on a number line.

5. Simplify. $-4|7 - 12| + |-18|$

Section P.2 Integer Exponents

In Exercises 6–8, simplify each expression. Include only positive exponents in simplified expressions.

6. $(-5a^2bc)(3a^4b)^2$

7. $\dfrac{(-2g^3)^2}{16g^2(g^5)}$

8. $(2^{-3})\left(\dfrac{4}{3}\right)^{-2}$

9. Write 0.0000047 in scientific notation.

10. Simplify. Write the answer in scientific notation.
$$\frac{(3 \times 10^7)(6.4 \times 10^{-4})}{7.5 \times 10^{-3}}$$

Section P.3 Rational Exponents and Radicals

In Exercises 11–15, simplify. Do not use a calculator. Rationalize the denominator as necessary. Assume all variables represent positive numbers.

11. $2\sqrt{18} + \sqrt{60} + \sqrt{72} - \sqrt{135}$

12. $\dfrac{-5}{\sqrt{6} + 7}$

13. $\left(\dfrac{27}{64}\right)^{-\frac{2}{3}}$

14. $\sqrt{12b^3c^2d^{11}}$

15. $\sqrt{\dfrac{100x^9y^2z^6}{4x^6y^3}}$

Section P.4 Polynomials

In Exercises 16–18, simplify each expression. Write the polynomial answer in standard form. Then identify the leading coefficient and classify it according to its degree and number of terms.

16. $[2x^2 - (7x + 6)] + [-(5x^3 - 8x^2) - 14x]$

17. $(3x + 5)(2x - 3)$

18. $(x - 5)(x^2 + 3x - 1 + x)$

In Exercises 19–20, expand each expression.

19. $(c^2 + 2d)(c^2 - 2d)$

20. $(6x - 5y)^3$

Section P.5 Factoring

In Exercises 21–25, factor each polynomial completely.

21. $6a^2 + 4a - 10$

22. $25n^6 - 1$

23. $3x^3 - 8y - 2x^2y + 12x$

24. $8c^3d^{12} + 1$

25. $4z^5 - 4z^3 - 4z^2 + 4$

Section P.6 Rational Expressions

In exercises 26-27, simplify each expression and state any excluded values of the variable.

26. $\dfrac{-x^2 + 2x + 35}{7 - x}$

27. $\dfrac{x^3 + 27}{x^2 - x - 12}$

In Exercises 28–30, simplify. Assume that all variables result in nonzero denominators.

28. $\dfrac{4k^2 - k - 3}{k^2 + 6k + 5} \div \dfrac{9 - 16k^2}{2k^2 + 2k}$

29. $\dfrac{1}{x^2 - 4x + 3} - \dfrac{3}{x^2 - 9}$

30. $\dfrac{\dfrac{5}{2x^2 - 6x}}{\dfrac{2}{x} - \dfrac{1}{x - 3}}$

Section P.7
Solving Linear and Quadratic Equations

In Exercises 31–37, solve each equation.

31. $9(x - 1) + 3x = -9x + 5$

32. $4 - \dfrac{x}{2} = \dfrac{2(x+1)}{5}$

33. $\dfrac{2}{5x - 1} = \dfrac{6}{2x - 3}$

34. $\dfrac{z - 4}{z + 1} = -\dfrac{24}{11}$

35. $8x^2 - 17x - 14 = 21 + x$

36. $x^2 - 6x = 2$

37. $6x^2 - \sqrt{7}x + 3 = 0$

38. Two cars leave an intersection at the same time. One travels east $5(x + 1)$ miles while the other travels south $6(x - 1)$ miles. At that point, the cars are $2(4x - 3)$ miles apart. How many miles did the eastbound car travel?

Section P.8 Other Types of Equations

In Exercises 39–42, solve each equation. Rationalize the denominator when necessary.

39. $\left| \dfrac{8}{5x - 3} \right| = \left| \dfrac{6}{2x + 7} \right|$

40. $(y - 3)^{\frac{1}{2}} = (-2y + 5)^{\frac{1}{4}}$

41. $\sqrt{2x + 10} = \sqrt{2x - 6} + 4$

42. $2x^3 + 2x^2 = x + 1$

Section P.9 Inequalities

In Exercises 43–46, write the solution set of each inequality using interval notation. If there is no solution, write the empty set, ø.

43. $-9 \leq \dfrac{2x + 6}{4} < 4$

44. $\left| \dfrac{1 - 3x}{8} \right| \geq 3$

45. $3x^2 - 7x - 6 \leq 0$

46. $\dfrac{x - 7}{5x - 1} + 4 \leq \dfrac{9x + 5}{5x - 1}$

TRIGONOMETRY

FUNCTIONS AND THEIR GRAPHS

1.1 COORDINATES AND GRAPHS

OBJECTIVES

- Graph points on a coordinate plane.
- Use the Distance and Midpoint Formulas.
- Graph equations by plotting points.
- Find and plot the *x*- and *y*-intercepts of an equation.
- Graph circles in a coordinate plane.
- Write the equation of a circle.
- Determine types of symmetry from equations.

PREREQUISITE VOCABULARY TERMS

absolute value equation

completing the square

inequality

linear equation

perfect-square trinomial

Pythagorean Theorem

quadratic equation

square root

1.1.1 Using the Cartesian System

Introduction to the Coordinate Plane

A **Cartesian plane** or **coordinate plane** is formed by two perpendicular number lines (one horizontal and the other vertical), intersecting at 0 on each. A coordinate plane has seven basic parts: the two axes, the origin, and four quadrants. The number lines are the **axes**, and the point at which the axes intersect is the **origin**, *O*. Specifically, the horizontal axis is called the ***x*-axis**, and the vertical axis is called the ***y*-axis**. The axes divide a coordinate plane into four **quadrants**, labeled I, II, III, and IV (Figure 1.1a).

Recall that each point on a real number line corresponds to a unique real number. Similarly, each point *P* on a coordinate plane corresponds to a unique pair of real numbers called an **ordered pair**. In any ordered pair (a, b), the first number, *a*, is the ***x*-coordinate**, corresponding to a location indicated by the *x*-axis, and the second number, *b*, is the ***y*-coordinate**, corresponding to a location indicated by the *y*-axis. Therefore, ordered pairs are often referred to generally as (x, y). For example, the ordered pair $(1, 6)$ corresponds to 1 on the *x*-axis and 6 on the *y*-axis.

Many aspects of algebra, such as ordered pairs (Figure 1.1b), equations (Figure 1.1c), and inequalities (Figure 1.1d), can be visualized by representations on the coordinate plane.

> **TIP**
>
> Ordered pairs are also referred to as points or coordinate pairs.

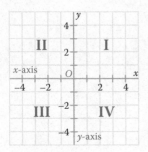

Figure 1.1a

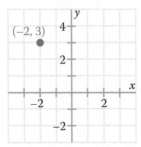

Figure 1.1b

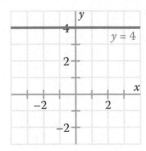

Figure 1.1c

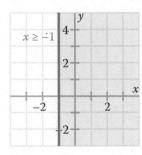

Figure 1.1d

Plotting a Point on a Coordinate Plane

To graph (or plot) an ordered pair on a coordinate plane, start at the position on the x-axis indicated by the x-coordinate. From that position on the x-axis, move up or down the number of units indicated by the y-coordinate. Move up if the y-coordinate is positive, or down if the y-coordinate is negative. Note that if the ordered pair's x-coordinate is 0, then the point is located on the y-axis. Similarly, if the ordered pair's y-coordinate is 0, then the point is located on the x-axis. The ordered pair $(0, 0)$ is the origin.

EXAMPLE 1   Plotting Points

Identify the location of $A(3, -1)$, $B(0, 2)$, and $C(-4.5, 0)$.

SOLUTION

Plot each point on a coordinate plane.

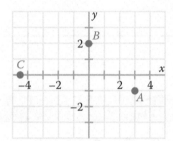

The x-coordinate of point C is −4.5, so the position on the x-axis is halfway between −4 and −5.

Point A is in quadrant IV, point B is on the y-axis, and point C is on the x-axis.

Tables and Ordered Pairs

Lists of ordered pairs can be written in a table that has either two rows or two columns. For a two-column table (a vertical table), the first column contains the x-coordinates, and the second column contains the y-coordinates (Figure 1.1e). Similarly, for a two-row table (a horizontal table), the first row contains the x-coordinates, and the second row contains the y-coordinates (Figure 1.1f).

x	y
−3	1
−1	0
0	−2
2	4

x	−3	−1	0	2
y	1	0	−2	4

Both tables list the points (−3, 1), (−1, 0), (0, −2), and (2, 4).

Figure 1.1e   Figure 1.1f

EXAMPLE 2	Plotting Points from a Table

Plot the points from the table on a coordinate plane.

x	0	−1	−3	3
y	4	1	−2	−1

SOLUTION

The table lists four ordered pairs:
(0, 4), (−1, 1), (−3, −2), and (3, −1).

Plot each point on a coordinate plane.

1.1.2   The Distance and Midpoint Formulas

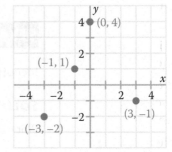

Finding the Distance between Two Points

The distance between two points on a coordinate plane can be found using the **Distance Formula**.

> **The Distance Formula**
>
> The distance d between two points (x_1, y_1) and (x_2, y_2) on a coordinate plane is $d = \sqrt{(x_2 - x_1)^2 + (y_2 - y_1)^2}$.

The Distance Formula is derived by using the Pythagorean Theorem, $a^2 + b^2 = c^2$, with two general points on a coordinate plane, (x_1, y_1) and (x_2, y_2), where the distance between the two points is the length of the hypotenuse of a right triangle.

Steps for Finding the Distance between Two Points

❶ Decide which of the two points will be the first point, (x_1, y_1), and which will be the second point, (x_2, y_2).

❷ Substitute the coordinates from the two points, x_1, x_2, y_1, and y_2, into the Distance Formula.

❸ Simplify the radicand, and then find the square root. If the radicand is not a perfect square, write the square root as a decimal (using a calculator) or in simplest radical form.

EXAMPLE 3	**Finding the Distance between Two Points**

Determine the distance between $A(8, -10)$ and $B(0, 5)$.

SOLUTION

Let $B(0, 5)$ be (x_1, y_1), and let $A(8, -10)$ be (x_2, y_2). $x_1 = 0, x_2 = 8, y_1 = 5, y_2 = -10$

Substitute the coordinates into the Distance Formula and simplify.

$$d = \sqrt{(8-0)^2 + (-10-5)^2} \qquad \textit{Substitute.}$$

$$= \sqrt{(8)^2 + (-15)^2} \qquad \textit{Subtract within the parentheses.}$$

$$= \sqrt{64 + 225} \qquad \textit{Evaluate the powers.}$$

$$= \sqrt{289} \qquad \textit{Add.}$$

$$= 17 \qquad \textit{Evaluate the square root.}$$

The distance between points A and B is 17 units.

ALTERNATIVE METHOD

Graph the two points, and then sketch a triangle where the distance between the two points is the hypotenuse.

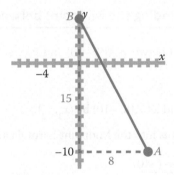

The length of the horizontal leg is 8 units since $|8 - 0| = 8$.

The length of the vertical leg is 15 units since $|-10 - 5| = 15$.

Use the Pythagorean Theorem to find the length of the hypotenuse AB.

$$a^2 + b^2 = c^2$$
$$8^2 + 15^2 = c^2 \qquad \textit{Substitute the lengths of the legs.}$$
$$64 + 225 = c^2 \qquad \textit{Evaluate the powers.}$$
$$289 = c^2 \qquad \textit{Add.}$$
$$17 = c \qquad \textit{Take the square root of each side.}$$

The length of the hypotenuse AB (the distance between points A and B) is 17 units.

WHAT'S THE BIG IDEA?

Plot the points $(0, 0)$, (x_1, y_1), and (x_2, y_2), where (x_1, y_1) and (x_2, y_2) are in quadrant I. Then use the distance between these points to explain the relationship between the Pythagorean Theorem and the Distance Formula.

Finding the Midpoint between Two Points

The midpoint between two points on a coordinate plane can be found using the **Midpoint Formula**.

TIP

As with the Distance Formula, either of the two points can be designated as (x_1, y_1) when using the Midpoint Formula. Furthermore, the x-coordinates and the y-coordinates can be added in any order in each coordinate's numerator, because addition is commutative.

> ### The Midpoint Formula
>
> The midpoint between two points (x_1, y_1) and (x_2, y_2) on a coordinate plane is $M = \left(\dfrac{x_1 + x_2}{2}, \dfrac{y_1 + y_2}{2}\right)$.

Steps for Finding the Midpoint between Two Points

❶ Decide which of the two points will be the first point, (x_1, y_1), and which will be the second point, (x_2, y_2).

❷ Substitute the coordinates from the two points, x_1, x_2, y_1, and y_2, into the Midpoint Formula.

❸ Simplify each coordinate.

EXAMPLE 4   Finding the Midpoint between Two Points

Determine the midpoint between $A(8, -10)$ and $B(0, 5)$.

SOLUTION

TIP

The same midpoint will be found if $A(8, -10)$ is (x_1, y_1) and $B(0, 5)$ is (x_2, y_2).

Let $B(0, 5)$ be (x_1, y_1), and let $A(8, -10)$ be (x_2, y_2). $x_1 = 0, x_2 = 8, y_1 = 5, y_2 = -10$

Substitute the coordinates into the Midpoint Formula and simplify.

$$\left(\frac{0+8}{2}, \frac{5+(-10)}{2}\right) \quad \text{Substitute.}$$

$$= \left(\frac{8}{2}, \frac{-5}{2}\right) \quad \text{Simplify the numerators.}$$

$$= \left(4, -\frac{5}{2}\right) \quad \text{Simplify the fraction.}$$

The midpoint between points A and B is $\left(4, -\dfrac{5}{2}\right)$.

1.1.3 Finding the Second Endpoint of a Segment

If one endpoint and the midpoint of a segment are known, the midpoint formula can be used to find the segment's other endpoint.

Equation for the Midpoint's x-coordinate	Equation for the Midpoint's y-coordinate
$$x_M = \frac{x_1 + x_2}{2}$$	$$y_M = \frac{y_1 + y_2}{2}$$
x_1 and x_2 are the x-coordinates of the endpoints, and x_M is the x-coordinate of the midpoint.	y_1 and y_2 are the y-coordinates of the endpoints, and y_M is the y-coordinate of the midpoint.

EXAMPLE 5   Finding the Coordinates of the Second Endpoint

$C(4, 3)$ is the midpoint between $A(x, y)$ and $B(11, 7)$. Find the coordinates of A.

SOLUTION

TIP

The x-coordinate from the midpoint must be substituted for x_M, but the x-coordinate of the endpoint can be substituted for either x_1 or x_2.

Substitute the x-coordinate from the midpoint and the x-coordinate from B into $x_M = \frac{x_1 + x_2}{2}$, and solve to find the x-coordinate of A.

$$4 = \frac{x + 11}{2} \qquad \textit{Substitute.}$$

$$8 = x + 11 \qquad \textit{Multiply both sides by 2.}$$

$$-3 = x \qquad \textit{Subtract 11 from each side.}$$

TIP

The y-coordinate from the midpoint must be substituted for y_M, but the y-coordinate of the endpoint can be substituted for either y_1 or y_2.

Substitute the y-coordinate from the midpoint and the y-coordinate from B into $y_M = \frac{y_1 + y_2}{2}$, and solve to find the y-coordinate of A.

$$3 = \frac{y + 7}{2} \qquad \textit{Substitute.}$$

$$6 = y + 7 \qquad \textit{Multiply both sides by 2.}$$

$$-1 = y \qquad \textit{Subtract 7 from each side.}$$

TIP

The answer can be checked by finding the midpoint between (−3, −1) and (11, 7).

Therefore, the coordinates of A are $(-3, -1)$.

WHAT'S THE BIG IDEA?

Explain why each coordinate in a midpoint is found by adding the coordinates from the endpoints and dividing by 2.

be substituted into the equation. Again, −1, 0, 1, and 2 are chosen here for the *x*-values.

x	y
−1	2
0	1
1	2
2	5

$y = 1 + x^2$

$y = 1 + (-1)^2 = 1 + 1 = 2$

$y = 1 + (0)^2 = 1 + 0 = 1$

$y = 1 + (1)^2 = 1 + 1 = 2$

$y = 1 + (2)^2 = 1 + 4 = 5$

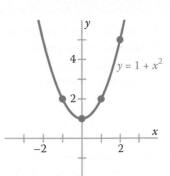

Plot each ordered pair solution from the table, and then draw a U-shaped graph (because the equation is quadratic) through the points.

C. This equation is not solved for *x* or *y*. Finding the ordered pair solutions is easier when the equation is solved for one of the variables, so solve the equation for *y* first, and then make the table.

$$\left|\frac{x}{2}\right| = y - 1 \implies y = \left|\frac{x}{2}\right| + 1$$

Here, −2, 0, 2, and 4 are chosen for the *x*-values. Plot each ordered pair solution from the table, and then draw a V-shaped graph (because the equation is an absolute value equation) through the points.

> **IMPORTANT**
>
> *Even x-values are chosen for the table so that the resulting y-values will be integers, making the points easier to plot.*

x	y
−2	2
0	1
2	2
4	3

$y = \left|\frac{x}{2}\right| + 1$

$y = \left|\frac{-2}{2}\right| + 1 = |-1| + 1 = 2$

$y = \left|\frac{0}{2}\right| + 1 = |0| + 1 = 1$

$y = \left|\frac{2}{2}\right| + 1 = |1| + 1 = 2$

$y = \left|\frac{4}{2}\right| + 1 = |2| + 1 = 3$

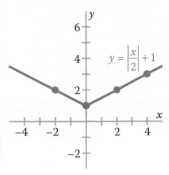

D. This equation is solved for *x*, so choose *y*-values for the table. Here, −1, 0, 1, and 2 are chosen for the *y*-values.

> **IMPORTANT**
>
> *Since y is the squared variable, y-values are chosen and listed in the second column of the table. Next, each y-value is substituted into the equation for y to find the corresponding x-value in each ordered pair solution. Those x-values are then listed in the first column of the table.*

x	y
0	−1
0	0
2	1
6	2

$x = y^2 + y$

$x = (-1)^2 + (-1) = 1 - 1 = 0$

$x = (0)^2 + 0 = 0$

$x = (1)^2 + 1 = 1 + 1 = 2$

$x = (2)^2 + 2 = 4 + 2 = 6$

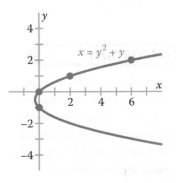

Plot each ordered pair solution from the table, and then draw a U-shaped graph (because the equation is quadratic) through the points.

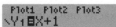

Figure 1.1i

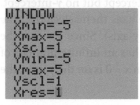

Figure 1.1j

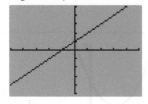

Figure 1.1k

```
TABLE SETUP
 TblStart=-5
 ΔTbl=2
```

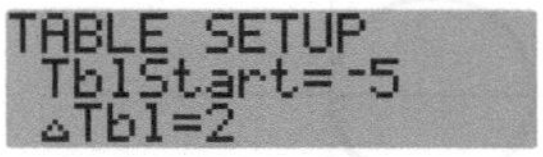

Figure 1.1l

Table for $y = x + 1$

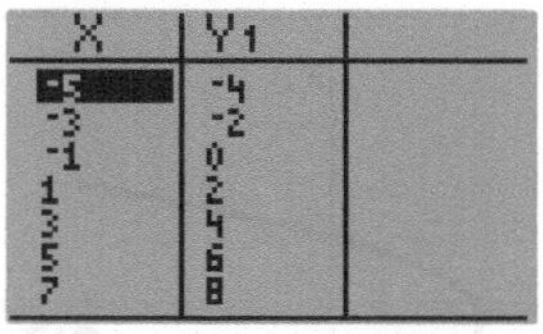

Figure 1.1m

WHAT'S THE BIG IDEA?

Describe the relationship between an equation in two variables, a table of ordered pairs defined by the equation, and the graph of the equation.

Using a Graphing Calculator to Graph an Equation

Once an equation is solved for y, the equation can be graphed using a graphing calculator. Use the following steps to graph an equation using a graphing calculator.

Steps for Graphing an Equation Using a Graphing Calculator

❶ Solve the equation for y.

❷ Using a graphing calculator, go to the Y= window and enter the expression for y.

❸ Adjust the viewing window (WINDOW) as needed.

❹ View the graph (GRAPH).

For example, to graph the equation $y = x + 1$ (the equation is already solved for y), enter "$x + 1$" in the Y= window, as shown in Figure 1.1i. Then adjust the WINDOW as needed. The window in Figure 1.1j is set to ±5 on the x- and y-axes, with a scale of 1 on both axes. Then view the graph, as shown in Figure 1.1k.

After an equation is entered into a graphing calculator, a corresponding table of ordered pairs can be viewed by using the table function (TABLE). Most graphing calculators also have a function for setting the first value seen in the table, as well as the interval for the change in the x-values. For example, to view a table starting with $x = -5$ where the x-values increase by 2 (i.e., the x-values are $-5, -3, -1, 1, 3 \ldots$), set the start value to -5 and the interval (often denoted by Δ) to 2, as shown in Figures 1.1l and 1.1m.

1.1.7   Finding the x- and y-Intercepts of an Equation

Another method for graphing an equation in two variables is to find and plot the **x-** and **y-intercepts** (the points at which the equation's graph crosses the x- and y-axes). The equation's graph can be sketched by drawing a line or curve through the x- and y-intercepts, keeping in mind the general shape of the graph (e.g., a line for a linear equation, a parabola for a quadratic equation, etc.). Some additional points on the graph are often needed to reveal the shape of the graph.

TIP

An x-intercept is a point at which a graph crosses the x-axis, and a y-intercept is a point at which a graph crosses the y-axis.

DEFINITION

An **x-intercept** of an equation is a point at which the equation's graph intersects the x-axis. The y-coordinate of an x-intercept is always 0.

A **y-intercept** of an equation is a point at which the equation's graph intersects the y-axis. The x-coordinate of a y-intercept is always 0.

$$x\text{-intercept: } (x, 0) \qquad y\text{-intercept: } (0, y)$$

Steps for Writing the Equation of a Circle in Standard Form

❶ Group the x-terms together and the y-terms together, both on one side of the equation, and move the constant term to the other side.

❷ Complete the square as needed to write a perfect-square trinomial with the x-terms and with the y-terms.

❸ Factor each trinomial.

EXAMPLE 12   Writing the Equation of a Circle in Standard Form

Write $x^2 + y^2 - 8x + 12y + 34 = 0$ in the standard form of a circle. Then identify the circle's center and radius.

SOLUTION

Grouping the x-terms and the y-terms and moving the constant term to the right side gives $(x^2 - 8x) + (y^2 + 12y) = -34$. Complete the square twice to write the x-terms as a perfect-square trinomial and the y-terms as a perfect-square trinomial.

$$(x^2 - 8x) + (y^2 + 12y) = -34$$

$$(x^2 - 8x + 16) + (y^2 + 12y + 36) = -34 + 16 + 36 \quad \text{Complete the square twice.}$$

$$(x - 4)^2 + (y + 6)^2 = 18 \quad \text{Factor each perfect-square trinomial and simplify the right side.}$$

The standard form equation is $(x - 4)^2 + (y + 6)^2 = 18$.

From the equation, $h = 4$, $k = -6$, and $r^2 = 18$, so $r = 3\sqrt{2}$. So, the circle's center is at $(4, -6)$, and the radius is $3\sqrt{2}$ units.

> **REMEMBER**
>
> *To complete the square for $x^2 + bx$, add the square of half of b to each side of the equation. Then the perfect-square trinomial $x^2 + bx + \left(\frac{b}{2}\right)^2$ can be written as $\left(x + \frac{b}{2}\right)^2$.*

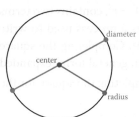

1.1.11 Writing the Equation of a Circle: Another Example

Any segment that passes through the center of a circle with endpoints on the circle is called a **diameter** of the circle. The length of a diameter is equal to twice the length of the circle's radius, and the midpoint of any diameter is the center of the circle, as shown in Figure 1.1p.

When a circle is graphed on a coordinate plane, the Distance Formula can be used to find the length of the circle's diameter (the distance between a diameter's endpoints, which are two specific points on the circle). The Distance Formula can also be used to find the length of the circle's radius (the distance between the circle's center and any point on the circle). The Midpoint Formula can be used to find the coordinates of the circle's center, which is the midpoint of a diameter.

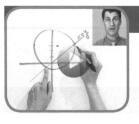

Figure 1.1p

EXAMPLE 13	**Writing the Equation of a Circle Given the Endpoints of a Diameter**

Write the equation of the circle where $A(0, 0)$ and $B(4, 6)$ are the endpoints of a diameter.

SOLUTION

To write the equation of a circle, find the radius r and the coordinates of the center (h, k), then substitute those values into the standard form equation of a circle, $(x - h)^2 + (y - k)^2 = r^2$.

Find the radius.

The line segment AB is a diameter, so the length of the circle's radius is half of the length of AB.

Use the Distance Formula to find the length of AB.

Let $A(0, 0)$ be (x_1, y_1), and let $B(4, 6)$ be (x_2, y_2). $x_1 = 0, x_2 = 4, y_1 = 0, y_2 = 6$

Distance Formula ▶

$$d = \sqrt{(x_2 - x_1)^2 + (y_2 - y_1)^2}$$

Substitute the coordinates into the Distance Formula and simplify.

$$AB = \sqrt{(4 - 0)^2 + (6 - 0)^2} \qquad \textit{Substitute.}$$

$$= \sqrt{(4)^2 + (6)^2} \qquad \textit{Subtract within the parentheses.}$$

$$= \sqrt{16 + 36} \qquad \textit{Evaluate the powers.}$$

$$= \sqrt{52} \qquad \textit{Add.}$$

$$= 2\sqrt{13} \qquad \textit{Simplify the square root.}$$

The length of the circle's diameter is $2\sqrt{13}$ units, so the length of its radius is $\frac{2\sqrt{13}}{2} = \sqrt{13}$ units.

Find the center.

Since the line segment AB is a diameter, the midpoint of AB is the circle's center.

Use the Midpoint Formula to find the midpoint of AB.

Again, let $A(0, 0)$ be (x_1, y_1), and let $B(4, 6)$ be (x_2, y_2). $x_1 = 0, x_2 = 4, y_1 = 0, y_2 = 6$

Midpoint Formula ▶

$$M = \left(\frac{x_1 + x_2}{2}, \frac{y_1 + y_2}{2} \right)$$

Substitute the coordinates into the Midpoint Formula and simplify.

$$\left(\frac{0 + 4}{2}, \frac{0 + 6}{2} \right) = (2, 3)$$

The midpoint between points A and B is $(2, 3)$, so the circle's center is at $(2, 3)$.

Alternative Method ▶
Find the circle's center first (the midpoint between A and B), and then find the circle's radius (the distance between the center and either A or B).

Write the equation.

Substitute $r = \sqrt{13}$, $h = 2$, and $k = 3$ into the equation of a circle with center at (h, k), $(x - h)^2 + (y - k)^2 = r^2$, and simplify.

$$(x - 2)^2 + (y - 3)^2 = (\sqrt{13})^2 \;\Rightarrow\; (x - 2)^2 + (y - 3)^2 = 13$$

1.1.12 Testing for Symmetry

A circle is a figure with perfect **symmetry**, because any line drawn through the center of the circle divides the circle into two parts that are **reflections** of each other. A line that divides a figure so that one side is a reflection of the other is called a **line of symmetry**. So, a circle has an infinite number of lines of symmetry.

EXAMPLE 15 | Using Symmetry to Graph an Equation

Use symmetry and intercepts to sketch the graph of $y = |x| - 2$.

SOLUTION

Test the equation for each type of symmetry.

With Respect to the x-Axis	With Respect to the y-Axis	With Respect to the Origin
$-y = |x| - 2$	$y = |-x| - 2$	$-y = |-x| - 2$
$y = -|x| + 2$	$y = |x| - 2$	$y = -|x| + 2$
Not equivalent to $y = |x| - 2$	*Equivalent to $y = |x| - 2$*	*Not equivalent to $y = |x| - 2$*

So, the graph $y = |x| - 2$ is symmetric with respect to the y-axis.

Find the intercepts.

> **TIP**
>
> The equation
> $0 = |x| - 2$ is an
> absolute value equation,
> so solve using $A = |B|$
> $\Rightarrow$ $A = B$ or $A = -B$.

x-intercept: $0 = |x| - 2$ $\Rightarrow$ $x = 2$ or $x = -2$ *Substitute 0 for y and solve for x.*
y-intercept: $y = |0| - 2 = -2$ *Substitute 0 for x and simplify to find y.*

So, the graph $y = |x| - 2$ crosses the x-axis at $(2, 0)$ and $(-2, 0)$, and the y-axis at $(0, -2)$.

Find some additional points on the graph on one side of the y-axis (the line of symmetry). Organize these points in a table.

x	1	3	4	5
y	−1	1	2	3

Choose four x-values. Substitute each into the equation to find the corresponding y-value.

The graph is symmetric with respect to the y-axis, so for each (x, y) on the graph, $(-x, y)$ is also on the graph. Use this fact to find additional points on the graph. Organize these points in a table.

> **TIP**
>
> The x-value 2 is not
> included in the table
> because the point on
> the graph where x = 2 is
> already known; it is the
> x-intercept.

x	−1	−3	−4	−5
y	−1	1	2	3

Replace x with −x for each value in the table.

Plot the intercepts and all of the points from the tables on a coordinate plane, and sketch the graph.

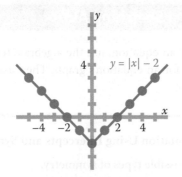

The graph is symmetric with respect to the y-axis, so each of the graph's points on the left side of the y-axis is a reflection of a point on the graph on the right side of the y-axis.

WHAT'S THE BIG IDEA?

How does the fact that the graph of an equation is symmetric with respect to the origin help when graphing the equation?

SECTION 1.1 EXERCISES

Warm Up

1. Simplify. $\sqrt{(4-(-3))^2+(-5-3)^2}$

2. Simplify. $\left(\dfrac{-6+4}{2},\dfrac{3-9}{2}\right)$

3. Factor. x^2-4x+4

Just the Facts

Fill in the blanks.

4. The Cartesian plane has these basic parts: the two _____, the _____ quadrants, and the _____.

5. The point (2, 4) is located in quadrant _____ , the point (−3, 1) is located in quadrant _____ , and the point (−5, −8) is located in quadrant _____.

6. The formula $d=\sqrt{(x_2-x_1)^2+(y_2-y_1)^2}$ represents the _____ between two points _____ and _____.

7. If A is (x_1, y_1), B is (x_2, y_2), and $C=\left(\dfrac{x_1+x_2}{2},\dfrac{y_1+y_2}{2}\right)$, then C is the _____ between _____ and _____.

8. If point G is between points A and E and $AG+GE=AE$, then the three points are _____.

9. To find the x-intercept of $y=ax+b$ (where a and b are real numbers), substitute 0 for _____ and solve for _____. Similarly, to find the y-intercept, substitute _____ for _____ and solve for _____.

10. The graph of the equation $x^2+y^2=100$ is a(n) _____ with center _____ and radius _____.

Essential Skills

In Exercises 1–6, identify the quadrant or axis that contains each point.

1. (8, 6)
2. (−7, −3)
3. (0, −9)
4. (−2, 4)
5. (2.5, −4)
6. (−3, 0)

In Exercises 7–8, graph the points from each table in a coordinate plane.

7.
x	1	5	−4	−3
y	−1	1	2	−3

8.
x	y
0	4
3	1
−2	0
1	−1

In Exercises 9–14, determine the distance between each pair of points. Round to the nearest hundredth, as needed.

9. (−2, 5) and (−7, −3)
10. (11, −4) and (5, 12)
11. (−10, 14) and (3, −8)
12. (−2, −3) and (3, 4)
13. (3.1, 1.6) and (−1.4, 5.3)
14. (−2.5, 3.8) and (−1.2, −7.2)

In Exercises 15–20, determine the midpoint between each pair of points.

15. $G(4, 7)$ and $Q(-6, 6)$
16. $A(-8, 6)$ and $B(2, -3)$
17. $Y(-2, -5)$ and $Z(4, -8)$
18. $E(-1, 3)$ and $F(7, 8)$
19. $\left(-\dfrac{1}{10},\dfrac{3}{8}\right)$ and $\left(\dfrac{1}{4},-\dfrac{1}{4}\right)$
20. $\left(-\dfrac{3}{8},-\dfrac{1}{4}\right)$ and $\left(\dfrac{2}{3},-\dfrac{5}{6}\right)$

In Exercises 21–26, determine the unknown endpoint of each segment.

21. $P(-6, 3)$ is the midpoint between $F(x, y)$ and $T(-2, 5)$. Find the coordinates of F.

22. $M(3, -4)$ is the midpoint between $R(x, y)$ and $S(6, 0)$. Find the coordinates of R.

23. $K(-7, -5)$ is the midpoint between $M(x, y)$ and $P(-1, -3)$. Find the coordinates of M.

24. $T(-1, 2)$ is the midpoint between $S(x, y)$ and $U(4, 10)$. Find the coordinates of S.

25. $D(-3.6, -7.1)$ is the midpoint between $F(x, y)$ and $B(2.8, -2.7)$. Find the coordinates of F.

26. $G(8.3, -1.4)$ is the midpoint between $B(x, y)$ and $L(-5.9, 8)$. Find the coordinates of B.

In Exercises 27–30, determine whether each set of points is collinear.

27. $M(-2, 3)$, $N(-3, 8)$, and $P(1, -6)$

28. $A(-5, 20)$, $B(6, -13)$, and $C(-2, 11)$

29. $J(3, -10)$, $K(-1, 2)$, and $L(-7, 20)$

30. $A(4, 8)$, $B(7, 13)$, and $C(16, 23)$

In Exercises 31–38, classify the figure formed by each set of points.

31. $A(6, -2)$, $B(4, 3)$, and $C(-1, 5)$

32. $X(-3, 1)$, $Y(5, 3)$, and $Z(6, -1)$

33. $E(3, 17)$, $F(-16, 5)$, and $G(4, 4)$

34. $K(-2, -1)$, $L(12, -1)$, and $M(-2, 13)$

35. $A(-1, 0)$, $B(2, -3\sqrt{3})$, and $C(5, 0)$

36. $P(-1, 3)$, $Q(13, -3)$, and $R(-1, 24)$

37. $U(-15, 12)$, $V(-13, 6)$, and $W(-12, 3)$

38. $A(-6, 4)$, $B(-2, 4)$, and $C(-4, 4 - 2\sqrt{3})$

In Exercises 39–42, sketch the graph of each equation by plotting points.

39. $y = |x - 3| - 2$

40. $y = 1 + 2x$

41. $y^2 = 4x + 1$

42. $y - 5 = -x^2$

In Exercises 43–46, use the intercepts to sketch the graph of each equation.

43. $-4 = -x + y$

44. $2x + y = 2$

45. $y - 9 = -x^2$

46. $y = 2x^2 + x - 15$

In Exercises 47–52, write the equation of each circle.

47. radius 7 and center at the origin

48. radius 11 and center at the origin

49. radius 6 and center at $(-4, -3)$

50. radius 15 and center at $(0, -9)$

51. radius 1/2 and center at $(7, 2)$

52. radius 5 and center $(-5, 3)$

In Exercises 53–54, graph each circle, and identify its center and radius.

53. $x^2 + (y + 4)^2 = 25$

54. $(x + 3)^2 + (y - 3)^2 = 144$

In Exercises 55–60, write each equation in the standard form of a circle. Then identify the circle's center and radius.

55. $x^2 - 2x + y^2 + 10y - 170 = 0$

56. $x^2 + y^2 - 8x + 4y - 205 = 0$

57. $x^2 + 12x + y^2 - 14y - 204 = 0$

58. $x^2 + y^2 - 6x - 2y - 26 = 0$

59. $x^2 + y^2 - 8x + 16y + 16 = 0$

60. $x^2 - 4x + y^2 + 4y - 28 = 0$

In Exercises 61–66, write the equation of each circle where the given coordinates are the endpoints of a diameter.

61. $A(3, 4)$ and $B(-5, 6)$

62. $Q(1, -4)$ and $R(-7, 8)$

63. $C(-2, -6)$ and $D(8, 10)$

64. $P(6, 4)$ and $Q(-4, 8)$

65. $H(-3, -2)$ and $F(7, 4)$

66. $S(9, 10)$ and $V(-1, 4)$

In Exercises 67–70, identify the type of symmetry, if any, for the graph of each equation.

67. $y = 3x^2 - 4$

68. $y = 2x^3$

69. $y = -x^6 + 4x^4 + 5$

70. $y = 2x^4 + 3x$

In Exercises 71–72, use symmetry and intercepts to sketch each graph.

71. $y^2 = x + 4$

72. $y = 2|x| + 4$

Extensions

73. Complete the square for both x and y, and write the equation in the standard form of a circle.

$$x^2 + 6\sqrt{2}x + y^2 + 4\sqrt{2}y = 2$$

74. Use the Midpoint Formula to find the points that divide the line segment with endpoints $(10, 2)$ and $(-2, 6)$ into 8 equal parts.

75. True or False? The points in the table form a regular hexagon.

x	5	-5	2.5	-2.5	2.5	-2.5
y	0	0	$2.5\sqrt{3}$	$2.5\sqrt{3}$	$-2.5\sqrt{3}$	$-2.5\sqrt{3}$

In Exercises 76–78, find m and n so that the graph of $y = mx^3 - nx^2 + mx$ has the type of symmetry indicated.

76. symmetry with respect to the x-axis

77. symmetry with respect to the y-axis

78. symmetry with respect to the origin

79. True or False? The Midpoint Formula must be used 12 times to divide a line segment into 12 equal parts.

80. Solve the Distance Formula for x_1.

81. Write the equation in the standard form of a circle.

$$16x^2 + 16y^2 - 32x + 64y + 64 = 80$$

1.2 LINES

OBJECTIVES

- Find the slope of a line.
- Graph lines using the slope and a point on the line.
- Graph lines given point-slope, slope-intercept, and standard form equations.
- Write the equations of lines in point-slope and slope-intercept form.
- Write the equations of parallel and perpendicular lines.
- Model with linear equations.

PREREQUISITE VOCABULARY TERMS

coordinate plane

linear equation

ordered pair

x-**axis** and y-**axis**

x-**intercept**

y-**intercept**

1.2.1 Finding the Slope of a Line from Two Points

The **slope** of a line between two points (a measure of the line's steepness) is equal to the vertical change between the points divided by the corresponding horizontal change. Slope is a constant value for any line, because the steepness of a line does not change between any two points on the line. It follows that the slope of a line can be determined between any two points on the line.

In a coordinate plane, the slope of a line between two points (x_1, y_1) and (x_2, y_2) is the change in the y-coordinates divided by the change in the x-coordinates. The change in the y-coordinates between two points (the vertical change) is called the "rise" or "change in y" (Δy), and the change in the x-coordinates between two points is called the "run" or "change in x" (Δx).

DEFINITION

The **slope** m of a line that passes through the points (x_1, y_1) and (x_2, y_2), where $x_1 \neq x_2$, is the quotient of the vertical change (rise) and the horizontal change (run) between those two points.

$$m = \frac{\text{rise}}{\text{run}} = \frac{y}{x} = \frac{y_2 - y_1}{x_2 - x_1}$$

When $x_1 = x_2$, the line is vertical and the slope is undefined.

A line that increases (heads upward from left to right) has a positive slope (Figure 1.2a), and a line that decreases (heads downward from left to right) has a negative slope (Figure 1.2b).

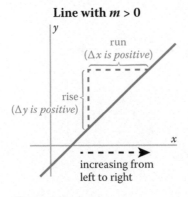

Figure 1.2a

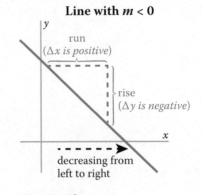

Figure 1.2b

Steps for Finding the Slope of a Line

❶ Identify any two points on the line. Designate one point (either point) to be (x_1, y_1) and the other to be (x_2, y_2).

❷ Substitute the coordinates from the two points into $m = \dfrac{y_2 - y_1}{x_2 - x_1}$ and simplify.

IMPORTANT

If A and B are two points on a line, then the slope from A to B is the same as the slope from B to A. So, when using the slope formula to find the slope of a line, it doesn't matter which of the two points is (x_1, y_1).

EXAMPLE 1   Finding the Slope of a Line

Find the slope of the line.

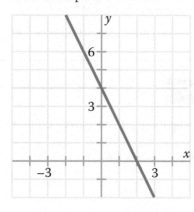

SOLUTION

∑ Identify any two points on the line, such as (0, 4) and (2, 0) (the intercepts). Let (0, 4) be (x_1, y_1) and (2, 0) be (x_2, y_2).

∏ Substitute the coordinates into the slope formula and simplify.

$$m = \frac{0 - 4}{2 - 0} = \frac{-4}{2} = -2$$

The line's slope is –2.

IMPORTANT

The slope is –2 regardless of which two points on the line are used to find the slope. For example, substitute (–1, 6) and (2, 0) into the slope formula.

$$m = \frac{0 - 6}{2 - (-1)} = \frac{-6}{3} = -2$$

1.2.2   Graphing a Line Using a Point and the Slope

There are an infinite number of lines that have any one particular slope. For example, each of the lines in Figure 1.2c has a slope equal to 2. So, knowing the slope of a line is not sufficient information for sketching the graph of the line. However, there is only one line with a specific slope that passes through a specific point. So, when the slope of a line is given, along with a point that the line passes through, the graph of the line can be sketched.

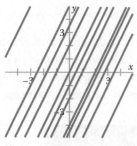

Figure 1.2c

Steps for Graphing a Line Using a Point and the Slope

❶ Plot the point.

❷ Using the slope, identify the rise (numerator) and run (denominator) values.

❸ Starting at the point, move up (for positive slope) or down (for negative slope) the number of units indicated by the slope's rise value.

❹ Move to the right the number of units indicated by the slope's run value (run is always to the right when using this method) and plot a second point.

❺ Write any powers with rational exponents that are proper fractions in radical notation.Sketch the line through the two points.

EXAMPLE 2   **Graphing a Line Using the Slope and a Point on the Line**

Graph the line with slope −3 that passes through the point (2, −1).

SOLUTION

❶ Plot the point (2, −1).

❷ The line's slope is −3, which is equivalent to $\frac{-3}{1}$, so the rise value is −3 and the run value is 1.

❸ From (2, −1), move down (since the slope is negative) 3 units. (Do not plot the point yet.)

❹ From 3 units below (2, −1), move to the right 1 unit, which is the point (3, −4). Plot the second point at (3, −4).

❺ Sketch the line through the two points, (2, −1) and (3, −4).

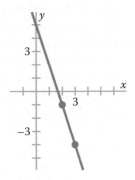

TIP

3 units down and 1 unit to the right of (2, −1) is (2 + 1, −1 − 3), or (3, −4).

WHAT'S THE BIG IDEA?

When graphing a line using its slope and a given point, why is the point plotted before the slope is used?

1.2.3   Introduction to Slope-Intercept Form

Previously, a linear equation in one variable was defined to be any equation that can be written in the form $ax + b = 0$, where a and b are real numbers. The definition of a linear equation will now be extended to include equations with two variables.

TIP

In a linear equation, the term Ax is referred to as the "linear x-term," the term By as the "linear y-term," and the term C as the "constant term."

DEFINITION

A **linear equation** is an equation that can be written in the general form $Ax + By + C = 0$, where A, B, and C are real numbers, and A and B cannot both be 0.

The graph of every linear equation is a line, and the equation of every line is a linear equation.

There are several forms of a linear equation from which information about the equation's graph (a line) can be deduced and then used to graph the line. These forms of a linear equation can be used to write the equation of a given line. One form of a linear equation (the equation of a line) is **slope-intercept form**. The "intercept" in slope-intercept form refers to the line's y-intercept.

Slope-Intercept Form of the Equation of a Line

The equation of the line with slope m and y-intercept b is $y = mx + b$.

When a linear equation is written in slope-intercept form, the slope and y-intercept can be deduced from the equation (and then used to graph the equation). Conversely, when the slope and y-intercept of a line are known, the corresponding linear equation can be written by substituting those values into slope-intercept form.

Steps for Writing the Equation of a Line in Slope-Intercept Form

❶ Identify the line's slope m and y-intercept b.

❷ Substitute the m- and b-values into $y = mx + b$, and simplify.

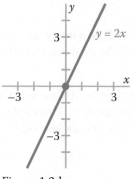

Figure 1.2d

EXAMPLE 3   Writing the Equation of a Line

Write the slope-intercept form equation of the line with slope 2 that passes through $(0, 0)$.

SOLUTION

❶ A line that passes through the origin has y-intercept at $(0, 0)$. So, $m = 2$ and $b = 0$.

❷ Substitute these values into the slope-intercept form of the equation of a line, $y = mx + b$, and simplify.

$$y = mx + b \implies y = 2x + 0 \implies y = 2x$$

So, the equation of the line with slope 2 that passes through the origin is $y = 2x$ (Figure 1.2d).

Recall that the line through some point with some slope can be graphed by plotting the point and then using the slope to find a second point on the line. It follows that since the slope and y-intercept (a point) can be deduced from an equation in slope-intercept form, a slope-intercept equation can be graphed without making a table of values or using any of the other techniques previously used for graphing an equation.

Steps for Graphing an Equation in Slope-Intercept Form

❶ Identify the slope m and the y-intercept b from the equation.

❷ Plot the y-intercept (on the y-axis).

❸ Use the rise and run values from the slope to find a second point on the line.

❹ Sketch the line through the two points.

EXAMPLE 4   Graphing a Slope-Intercept Equation

Graph $4 - \frac{7}{3}x = y$.

SOLUTION

❶ From the equation, $m = \frac{-7}{3}$ and $b = 4$.

❷ Plot the y-intercept, $(0, 4)$.

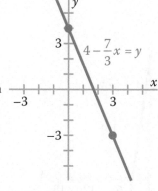

❸ The line's slope is $\frac{-7}{3}$, so the rise value is -7 and the run value is 3. So, from $(0, 4)$, move down (since the slope is negative) 7 units, and then to the right 3 units, and plot the second point at $(3, -3)$.

❹ Sketch the line through the two points, $(0, 4)$ and $(3, -3)$.

IMPORTANT

When using the slope to find a second point on a line, remember that this method defines the rise to be up or down (depending on the sign of the slope), but the run is always to the right.

1.2.4 Writing the Equation of a Line

It is easy to write the equation of a line when the slope and y-intercept are known: just substitute the m- and b-values into the slope-intercept form of a linear equation, $y = mx + b$, and simplify. The equation of any line can also be written when the slope and y-intercept are *not* known, as long as two points on the line are known.

One method for writing the equation of a line on a coordinate plane is to identify the slope and y-intercept by looking at the graph, and then substitute those m- and b-values into $y = mx + b$. For example, the slope of the line shown in Figure 1.2e is observed to be $\frac{2}{5}$ (by counting the rise and the run), and the y-intercept is at 2, so the equation of the line is $y = \frac{2}{5}x + 2$.

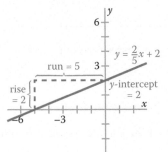

Figure 1.2e

This method works well as long as the y-intercept is an integer. However, if the y-intercept is not an integer, an algebraic method for finding the equation of the line should be used to ensure that the exact slope and y-intercept are found.

The algebraic method for writing the equation of a line involves using the slope formula to find the slope of the line and then algebraically finding the b-value by solving an equation. This method can be used to find the equation of any line when at least two points on the line are known.

Steps for Writing the Equation of a Line in Slope-Intercept Form Algebraically

❶ Use the slope formula to find the slope m.

❷ To find b, substitute the x- and y-coordinates from *any* point on the line and the m-value into $y = mx + b$, and solve for b.

❸ Substitute the m- and b-values into the slope-intercept form equation, $y = mx + b$, and simplify.

EXAMPLE 5   **Writing the Equation of a Line Algebraically**

Write the slope-intercept form equation of the line that passes through (2, 10) and (4, −4).

SOLUTION

❶ Substitute the coordinates from each point into the slope formula and simplify.

$$m = \frac{-4 - 10}{4 - 2} = \frac{-14}{2} = -7 \quad \text{The line's slope is } -7.$$

❷ Substitute the m-value and the x- and y-coordinates from *either* one of the points into $y = mx + b$, and solve for b. Here, (2, 10) is used, so 2 is substituted for x and 10 is substituted for y.

$y = mx + b$	
$10 = (-7)(2) + b$	*Substitute.*
$10 = -14 + b$	*Multiply.*
$24 = b$	*Add 14 to each side to solve for b.*

The line's y-intercept is at (0, 24).

❸ Substitute $m = -7$ and $b = 24$ into $y = mx + b$.

$$y = mx + b \implies y = -7x + 24$$

So, the equation of the line that passes through (2, 10) and (4, −4) is $y = -7x + 24$ (Figure 1.2f).

TIP

It doesn't matter which point is used as (x_1, y_1) or (x_2, y_2).

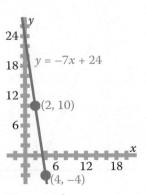

Figure 1.2f

1.2.5 Introduction to Point-Slope Form

Another form of a linear equation is **point-slope form**.

> ### *Point-Slope Form of the Equation of a Line*
>
> The equation of the line with slope m that passes through (x_1, y_1) is $y - y_1 = m(x - x_1)$.

When a linear equation is written in point-slope form, the slope and a point on the line can be deduced from the equation, which can then be used to graph the equation. Conversely, when the slope and the coordinates of a point on the line are known, then the corresponding linear equation can be written by substituting those values into point-slope form.

> **Steps for Writing the Equation of a Line in Point-Slope Form**
> ❶ Find the slope m and a point on the line (x_1, y_1).
> ❷ Substitute the values of m, x_1, and y_1 into the point-slope form equation, $y - y_1 = m(x - x_1)$.

To convert an equation that is in point-slope form to slope-intercept form, distribute m to $(x - x_1)$ and then add y_1 to each side to solve for y. For example, to write the point-slope form equation $y - 2 = 3(x - 5)$ in slope-intercept form, distribute 3 to $(x - 5)$ and then add 2 to each side to solve for y.

$$y - 2 = 3(x - 5) \;\Rightarrow\; y - 2 = 3x - 15 \;\Rightarrow\; y = 3x - 13$$
$$\textit{point-slope form} \qquad\qquad\qquad \textit{slope-intercept form}$$

EXAMPLE 6   Writing the Equation of a Line Using the Slope and a Point

Write the equation of the line that passes through $(-2, 3)$ with slope 5 in point-slope form and in slope-intercept form.

SOLUTION

Substitute $m = 5$, $x_1 = -2$, and $y_1 = 3$ into the point-slope form of the equation of a line.

$$y - y_1 = m(x - x_1) \;\Rightarrow\; y - 3 = 5(x - (-2)) \;\Rightarrow\; y - 3 = 5(x + 2)$$

Simplify and solve the equation for y to write the equation in slope-intercept form, $y = mx + b$.

$$y - 3 = 5x + 10 \quad \textit{Distribute.}$$
$$y = 5x + 13 \quad \textit{Add 3 to both sides.}$$

So, the point-slope equation is $y - 3 = 5(x + 2)$, and the slope-intercept equation is $y = 5x + 13$.

WHAT'S THE BIG IDEA?

Explain the relationship between the point-slope form of a linear equation and the slope formula.

1.2.6 Vertical and Horizontal Lines

All points on any horizontal line on a coordinate plane have equal y-coordinates. For example, consider the horizontal line shown in Figure 1.2g. The y-coordinate of every point on this line is 2. The x-coordinate of any point on the line in Figure 1.2g could be any real number. Therefore, either of the following tables is a corresponding table of ordered pairs for the line given in Figure 1.2g.

x	-2	-1	0	1
y	2	2	2	2

x	1	2	3	4
y	2	2	2	2

The slope of a horizontal line is 0 because the change in y between any two points on a horizontal line is 0. Substituting $m = 0$ into slope-intercept form gives the general equation of a horizontal line.

$$y = mx + b \implies y = (0)x + b \implies y = b$$

So, the equation of any horizontal line is $y = b$, where b is the line's y-intercept. Therefore, the equation of the line in Figure 1.2g is $y = 2$.

Similarly, all points on a vertical line have equal x-coordinates. The horizontal change between points with equal x-coordinates is 0. So, the slope of any line through points with equal x-coordinates must be undefined (since the change in x, the denominator of slope, is 0). Therefore, the slope of any vertical line is undefined. The equation of any vertical line is $x = c$, where c is the line's x-intercept.

Figure 1.2g

	Horizontal Line	Vertical Line
Slope	0	undefined
Equation	$y = b$ b is the y-intercept.	$x = c$ c is the x-intercept.

Horizontal and Vertical Lines

TIP

On a coordinate plane, horizontal lines do not intersect the x-axis, so they have no x-intercept; vertical lines do not intersect the y-axis, so they have no y-intercept. The only exceptions are the axes. The equation of the line formed by the y-axis is x = 0, and the equation of the line formed by the x-axis is y = 0.

EXAMPLE 7 **Graphing Horizontal and Vertical Lines**

Graph $y = -1$ and $x = 4$ on a coordinate plane.

SOLUTION

The graph of $y = -1$ is a horizontal line with y-intercept at $(0, -1)$.

The graph of $x = 4$ is a vertical line with x-intercept at $(4, 0)$.

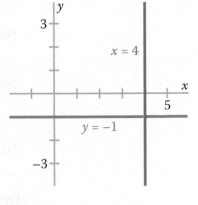

1.2.7 Graphing a Standard Form Linear Equation

Recall the two forms of the equation of a line discussed so far in this section.

Slope-Intercept Form: $y = mx + b$ *The line's slope and y-intercept are m and b.*

Point-Slope Form: $y - y_1 = m(x - x_1)$ *The line has slope m and passes through (x_1, y_1).*

A third form of a linear equation (the equation of a line) is the **standard form**.

Standard Form of the Equation of a Line

The equation of the line can be written in the form $Ax + By = C$, where A, B, and C are real numbers, and A and B are not both 0.

There are many ways to graph a linear equation in standard form, including the two methods described here.

Graphing a Linear Equation in Standard Form

Method 1: Use the Intercepts
Find and plot the x- and y-intercepts. Then draw a line through those two points.

Method 2: Use Slope-Intercept Form
Write the equation in slope-intercept form (by solving for y), and then use the slope and y-intercept from the equation to draw the line.

EXAMPLE 8   Graphing a Standard Form Linear Equation

Graph $3x - 4y = -8$ on a coordinate plane.

SOLUTION

Solve the equation for y to write the equation in slope-intercept form.

$$3x - 4y = -8$$

$$-4y = -8 - 3x$$

$$y = \frac{-8 - 3x}{-4}$$

$$y = 2 + \frac{3}{4}x$$

From the equation, $m = \frac{3}{4}$ and $b = 2$.

Plot the y-intercept, then use the slope to find a second point on the line.

Sketch the line through the two points.

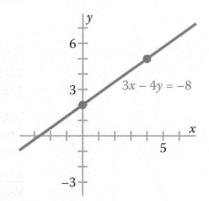

ALTERNATIVE METHOD

Find the x- and y-intercepts. Substitute 0 for y and solve for x to find the x-intercept.

$$3x - 4(0) = -8$$

$$3x = -8$$

$$x = -\frac{8}{3}$$

Substitute 0 for x and solve for y to find the y-intercept.

$$3(0) - 4y = -8$$

$$-4y = -8$$

$$y = 2$$

Plot the x-intercept at $-\frac{8}{3}$ (i.e., $-2\frac{2}{3}$) and the y-intercept at 2, then sketch the line through the two intercepts.

1.2.8   Equations of Parallel and Perpendicular Lines

Parallel lines never intersect, and **perpendicular lines** intersect at a 90° angle. There are many facts regarding the slopes of parallel and perpendicular lines that can be applied when writing the equations of or graphing lines that are parallel or perpendicular to each other.

> **IMPORTANT**
>
> *Lines with the same slope and the same y-intercept are not parallel, because they form the same line.*

Parallel and Perpendicular Lines

- Parallel lines have equal slopes.
- Perpendicular lines have slopes that are opposite reciprocals of one another.
- The product of the slopes of two perpendicular lines is equal to −1.
- All vertical lines are parallel.
- All horizontal lines are parallel.
- A vertical line is perpendicular to any horizontal line.
- A horizontal line is perpendicular to any vertical line.

EXAMPLE 9   Writing the Equations of Parallel Lines

> **IMPORTANT**
>
> *The notation $l \parallel p$ means that line l is parallel to line p.*

Line l passes through (4, 5), and line p is the graph of $y - 3 = 2(x + 7)$. If $l \parallel p$, what is the slope-intercept form equation of l?

SOLUTION

Since line l is parallel to line p, the two lines must have the same slope. So, the slope of line l is 2, because the slope of line p is 2 (from the equation of line p).

Substitute the slope of line l, 2, and the coordinates from the point on line l, (4, 5), into the point-slope form equation to write the equation of line l.

$$y - y_1 = m(x - x_1) \implies y - 5 = 2(x - 4)$$

Simplify and solve for y to write the equation of line l in slope-intercept form.

$$y - 5 = 2(x - 4) \implies y - 5 = 2x - 8 \implies y = 2x - 3$$

So, the slope-intercept form equation of line l is $y = 2x - 3$.

CHECK
The answer can be checked graphically or algebraically.

Graphically
Graph the equations for l and p. Visually confirm that the lines are parallel and that l passes through (4, 5) (Figure 1.2h).

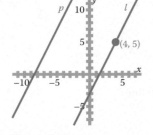

Figure 1.2h

Algebraically
Verify that l and p are parallel using the equations, and then verify that (4, 5) is on l algebraically.

From the equations for l and p, $y = 2x - 3$ and $y - 3 = 2(x + 7)$, the slopes of l and p are equal (both 2).

Substituting $x = 4$ and $y = 5$ into the equation of l results in $5 = 2(4) - 3$, which is a true statement. So, (4, 5) is a solution to $y = 2x - 3$.

Lines l and p are parallel. ✔

Line l contains (4, 5). ✔

EXAMPLE 10 | **Writing the Equations of Perpendicular Lines**

Line l passes through (–5, 2), and line p is the graph of $2x - y = 1$. If $l \perp p$, what is the slope-intercept form equation of l?

SOLUTION

Since line l is perpendicular to line p, the two lines must have slopes that are opposite reciprocals of one another. Find the slope of line p by writing the equation of p in slope-intercept form.

$$2x - y = 1 \Rightarrow -y = -2x + 1 \Rightarrow y = 2x - 1 \qquad \text{So, the slope of line } p \text{ is 2.}$$

The opposite reciprocal of 2 is $-\frac{1}{2}$, so the slope of l is $-\frac{1}{2}$.

To write the equation of line l, substitute the slope of l, $-\frac{1}{2}$, and the coordinate from the point on line l, (–5, 2), into the point-slope form equation.

$$y - y_1 = m(x - x_1) \Rightarrow y - 2 = -\frac{1}{2}(x - (-5)) \Rightarrow y - 2 = -\frac{1}{2}(x + 5)$$

Simplify and solve for y to write the equation of line l in slope-intercept form.

$$y - 2 = -\frac{1}{2}(x + 5) \Rightarrow y - 2 = -\frac{1}{2}x - \frac{5}{2} \Rightarrow y = -\frac{1}{2}x - \frac{1}{2}$$

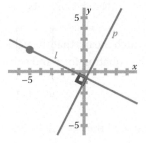

Figure 1.2i

So, the slope-intercept form equation of line l is $y = -\frac{1}{2}x - \frac{1}{2}$.

As in **Example 9**, the answer can be checked graphically (Figure 1.2i) or algebraically.

1.2.9 Modeling Rate of Change with Linear Equations

A linear equation (and its corresponding line) can model a relationship between two real quantities, such as the relationship between the number of hours traveled and the total distance traveled, or the relationship between the number of days worked and the total pay earned. The two quantities are represented in the equation by the two variables. The slope of the equation can be interpreted as the **rate of change** of one quantity in relation to the other—specifically, the rate of change in the y-variable in relation to the change in the x-variable (since slope is $\frac{\Box y}{\Box x}$).

For example, the line shown in Figure 1.2j models the relationship between the total pay (in dollars) and time worked (in hours) for a person paid by the hour. The equation of the line is $y = 12x$, so the line's slope is 12. Considered as a rate of change, a slope of 12 in this situation means that the rate of pay is 12 dollars per hour ($12/h).

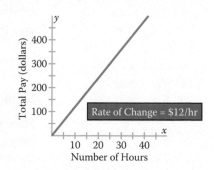

Figure 1.2j

The Units Used with Slope

When slope is interpreted as a rate of change, the units are the y-variable's units divided by the x-variable's units (because slope is the ratio of the change in y to the change in x). For example, in the linear equation $y = 60x + 500$, if x represents the number of hours (time) traveled and y represents the number of miles (distance) traveled, then the slope, 60, can be interpreted as the rate of change "60 miles per hour."

If the units of x and y are the same, then the units for slope cancel out, and the slope is just a number with no units.

EXAMPLE 11 Modeling Change in Value with a Linear Equation

The estimated value of a used car x years after purchase can be represented by $y = 15{,}000 - 750x$. Explain the significance of the line's slope, y-intercept, and x-intercept within the context of the situation.

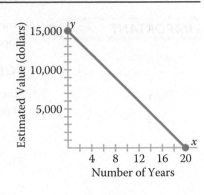

SOLUTION

From the equation, the slope is -750 and the y-intercept is 15,000. The y-intercept is the value of the car at year 0. So, the y-intercept indicates that the initial value of the car (the value at time of purchase) was \$15,000.

TIP

The slope is negative, so the value of the car is decreasing. In finance, a decrease in value is called "depreciation."

The slope is the rate of change in the value of the car (y) per year (x), which means that the value of the car is depreciating at a rate of \$750 per year. Substitute 0 into the equation for y and solve for x to find the x-intercept.

$$0 = 15{,}000 - 750x \;\Rightarrow\; 750x = 15{,}000 \;\Rightarrow\; x = 20$$

So, the x-intercept is 20 years, which means that after 20 years, the value of the car will be \$0.

EXAMPLE 12 Modeling Change in Temperature with a Linear Equation

After a constant heat source was applied to it for 3 minutes, the temperature of a substance was found to be 170° F. After 7 minutes, the temperature was 210° F. Assuming a linear equation can be used to model the change in heat over time between $x = 3$ minutes and $x = 7$ minutes, write this linear model in slope-intercept form. Explain the significance of the slope and y-intercept in the context of this situation. Then predict the temperature of the substance after 15 minutes and the number of minutes it will take for the substance to reach 400° F using this linear model.

SOLUTION

IMPORTANT

When an equation is modeled involving time and some other quantity, time is usually the x-variable (independent variable), and the other quantity is the y-variable (dependent variable).

This situation involves two variables: the time (in minutes) that the substance has been heated, and the temperature of the substance (in ° F). Let x be the number of minutes that the substance is heated, and let y be the temperature of the substance after x minutes.

The two given pairs of corresponding x- and y-values can be written as ordered pairs: (3, 170) and (7, 210). Write the equation of the line through these two points.

Find the slope.

$$m = \frac{210 - 170}{7 - 3} = \frac{40}{4} = 10$$

Write the equation of the line.

$y - y_1 = m(x - x_1)$ *Substitute $m = 10$, $x_1 = 3$, and $y_1 = 170$*

$y - 170 = 10(x - 3)$ *into the point-slope form equation.*

So, the equation of the line is $y - 170 = 10(x - 3)$, or $y = 10x + 140$ in slope-intercept form.

Slope is the rate of change, so the temperature is increasing at a rate of 10° F per minute. Since the y-intercept (140) is the temperature that corresponds to time 0, the starting temperature of the substance was 140° F.

Use the slope-intercept form equation, $y = 10x + 140$, to make the predictions.

According to the model, the substance will be $10(15) + 140 = 290$° F after 15 minutes.

TIP

Substitute 15 for x and simplify to predict the temperature after 15 minutes.

Substitute 400 for y and solve for x to predict the time it takes for the substance to reach 400° F.

$$400 = 10x + 140 \;\Rightarrow\; 260 = 10x \;\Rightarrow\; 26 = x$$

According to the model, 26 minutes after the heat source is applied, the substance will be 400° F.

SECTION 1.2 EXERCISES

Warm Up

1. Simplify. $\dfrac{-4-6}{7-(-1)}$

2. Solve for y. $y - 20 + 8x = -5x + 6$

3. What is the opposite reciprocal of 2/3?

Just the Facts

Fill in the blanks.

4. The _____ of a line is a measure of the line's steepness. It is equal to the _____ change divided by the _____ change.

5. To find the slope of the line that passes through (2, 6) and (0, 5), use the formula _____. It doesn't matter which point is chosen for _____ or _____.

6. $y = mx + b$ is the _____ form of the equation of a line. $y - y_1 = m(x - x_1)$ is the _____ form of the equation of a line, where m is the _____, b is the _____, and (x_1, y_1) is a(n) _____ on the line.

7. Vertical lines have a slope that is _____, because the horizontal change between any two y-coordinates is _____; _____ lines have slope equal to 0, since the _____ change between any two x-coordinates is 0.

8. _____ is the standard form equation of a line.

9. Parallel lines have the _____ slope, while _____ lines have slopes that are _____. The symbol for _____ is ||, and the symbol for perpendicular is _____.

10. If the equation of a line is $y - p = q(x - r)$, then the slope of the line is _____, and the line passes through the point _____.

Essential Skills

In Exercises 1–8, find the slope of each line.

1. passes through (3, 5) and (−3, −11)

2.
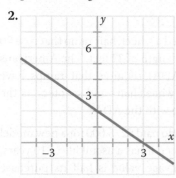

3. passes through (−5, 8) and (4, 2)

4. passes through (−2, 7) and (−2, −6)

5. passes through (−13, 9) and (−4, 3)

6. passes through (1, −2) and (−3, 6)

7. passes through (−5, −6) and (0, −6)

8. passes through (−7, 3) and (8, 15)

In Exercises 9–10, graph each line using the given slope and point.

9. slope 2/3, passes through (0, −2)

10. slope −1, passes through (−1, 2)

In Exercises 11–16, write the slope-intercept form equation of each line.

11. slope 2, passes through (0, 1)

12. slope −1, passes through (0, −5)

13. slope 3/5, passes through (0, 4)

14. slope −7/6, passes through (0, −2)

15. slope 9/4, passes through (0, 0)

16. slope −8/3, passes through (0, 7)

In Exercises 17–18, graph each equation.

17. $-x + 1 = y$

18. $y = 3x - 4$

In Exercises 19–28, write the slope-intercept form equation of each line.

19. passes through (5, −6) and (9, −2)

20. passes through (1, −8) and (−5, −20)

21. passes through (4, 7) and (0, 5)

22. passes through (7, −2) and (0, 2)

23. passes through (−2, −15) and (−1, 7)

24. passes through (−5, 8) and (−2, −4)

25. passes through (3, −5) and (−1, 6)

26. passes through (−1, 4) and (2, 0)

27. passes through (2, 5) and (8, 3)

28. passes through (−6, 8) and (9, −3)

In Exercises 29–36, write the point-slope form and the slope-intercept form equation of each line.

29. slope 4, passes through (5, −3)

30. slope −2/5, passes through (−5, 7)

31. slope 1/2, passes through (−6, 5)

32. slope −5, passes through (−1/2, 1)

33. slope 6, passes through (8, 3)

34. slope 7/8, passes through (−4, 1)

35. slope −4/5, passes through (10, 7)

36. slope −3/2, passes through (−8, −6)

In Exercises 37–42, write the equation of each line.

37. passes through (4, −5) and (10, −5)

38. passes through (−1, 6) and (−1, −4)

39. passes through (−3, 9) and (−8, 9)

40. passes through (6, −5) and (6, 3)

41. passes through (2, −8) and (2, 7)

42. passes through (−5, −4) and (−6, −4)

In Exercises 43–48, find the slope and *y*-intercept of the graph of each equation.

43. $8 = 3x − 2y$

44. $5x − 2y = 14$

45. $3x + 4y = 3$

46. $−11 = 8x + 2y$

47. $5 = 2x − 3y$

48. $−2x − 7y = −6$

In Exercises 49–56, if *l* ∥ *p*, what is the slope-intercept form equation of *l*?

49. Line *l* passes through (9, 4), and line *p* is the graph of $y + 5 = −(x + 2)$. ▶

50. Line *l* passes through (1, −5), and line *p* is the graph of $y − 2 = −3(x + 6)$.

51. Line *l* passes through (4, 6), and line *p* is the graph of $y − 13 = −5(x − 1)$.

52. Line *l* passes through (−3, −1), and line *p* is the graph of $y + 4 = −2(x − 9)$.

53. Line *l* passes through (7, −2), and line *p* is the graph of $y − 1 = \frac{3}{4}(x + 5)$.

54. Line *l* passes through (2, 3), and line *p* is the graph of $y + 8 = \frac{4}{9}(x − 2)$.

55. Line *l* passes through (−4, 1), and line *p* is the graph of $y + 3 = −\frac{2}{3}(x − 7)$.

56. Line *l* passes through (3, −5), and line *p* is the graph of $y − 4 = −\frac{7}{2}(x + 4)$.

In Exercises 57–64, if *l* ⊥ *p*, what is the slope-intercept form equation of *l*?

57. Line *l* passes through (−5, 2), and line *p* is the graph of $y = 2x − 1$.

58. Line *l* passes through (−4, −3), and line *p* is the graph of $5x − 6y = 24$.

59. Line *l* passes through (6, −1), and line *p* is the graph of $y = −3x + 5$.

60. Line *l* passes through (−3, 8), and line *p* is the graph of $y = 4x − 7$.

61. Line *l* passes through (2, 7), and line *p* is the graph of $y = −\frac{1}{5}x − 9$.

62. Line *l* passes through (−4, −2), and line *p* is the graph of $y = \frac{8}{3}x + 2$.

63. Line *l* passes through (6, 1), and line *p* is the graph of $5x − 6y = 24$.

64. Line *l* passes through (9, −5), and line *p* is the graph of $3x − 5y = 6$.

In Exercises 65–67, use the following information.

A woman drove 800 miles to Dallas. She traveled 292 miles in 4 hours, and after 9 hours, she had traveled 657 miles.

65. Assuming a linear equation can be used to model the change in distance traveled over time between $x = 4$ hours and $x = 9$ hours, write this linear model in slope-intercept form.

66. Explain the significance of the slope in the context of this situation.

67. Determine how long it took to complete the trip to Dallas. Round to the nearest minute, if necessary.

In Exercises 68–70, use the following information.

After 2 minutes, an ant had traveled 100 meters, and after 6 minutes, the ant had traveled 220 meters.

68. Assuming a linear equation can be used to model the change in distance traveled over time between $x = 2$ minutes and $x = 6$ minutes, write this linear model in slope-intercept form.

69. Explain the significance of the slope in the context of this situation.

70. Using the linear model, predict the distance that the ant will travel after 10 minutes and the number of minutes it will take for the ant to travel 400 meters.

Extensions

71. A local restaurant installed a wheelchair ramp that rose 20 inches over a horizontal length of 22 feet. The Americans with Disabilities Act (ADA) requires that ramps have at least a 1:12 slope for wheelchairs and scooters. Is the restaurant in compliance with the ADA?

72. The HSBC Arena in Buffalo paid $225,000 for a new model 700 Zamboni ice resurfacer. It has a useful life of 10 years, after which time the salvage value is half its purchase price. Write a linear equation that describes the value of the Zamboni each year. What is the value after 3 years?

73. A computer salesman earns a monthly salary of $2250 plus 5% commission when his total monthly sales are under $10,000, 10% commission when his total monthly sales are between $10,000 and $14,999, and 12% commission when his total monthly sales are between $15,000 and $17,999. Write three separate linear equations representing the salesman's monthly wage W in terms of the monthly sales S. What is his monthly salary if he sold 16,000 dollars' worth of computer equipment in the month of July?

74. Show that the slope between the points $(x + 2, (x + 2)^2)$ and $(2, 4)$ is $x + 4$.

In Exercises 75–77, use the following information.

In 2007, Apple opened its 200th store, and in 2011, they had 357 stores in ten countries.

75. Assuming a linear equation can be used to model the change in stores over time between 2007 and 2011, write this linear model in slope-intercept form. Use $t = 7$ to represent the year 2007.

76. Use the linear model to predict the number of stores that Apple had in 1998. Is the answer reasonable? Explain.

77. Use the linear model to predict the number of stores that Apple had in 2009. Is the answer reasonable? Explain.

In Exercises 78–81, use the following information.

A landscaping contractor purchased a dump truck for $21,900. The contractor pays a dump truck driver $10.75 per operating hour and the truck costs the contractor an average of $4.20 per operating hour for fuel and maintenance.

78. Write a linear equation giving the average total cost C of operating the dump truck for t hours, including the purchase price.

79. The contractor charges customers $23.75 per hour for the services of the truck and driver. Write an equation for the revenue R for t hours of use.

80. Use $P = R - C$, the formula for profit, to write an equation for the profit earned from t hours of use.

81. After how many hours will the contractor break even?

1.3 VARIATION

PREREQUISITE VOCABULARY TERMS

linear equation
proportion
rational equation
slope

1.3.1 Direct Variation

A situation involving two variables x and y that can be modeled by an equation of the form $y = kx$, where k is some nonzero constant, is called a **direct variation**.

DEFINITION

> If two quantities x and y are related by the equation $y = kx$, where k, the **constant of variation,** is some constant such that $k \neq 0$, then the relationship between x and y is a **direct variation** where y varies directly as x.

A direct variation is also called a **direct proportion**. If y varies directly as x, then it can also be said that y is directly proportional to x or that y is proportional to x. The k-value in a direct variation equation is also called the **constant of proportionality**.

Recall that the equation of any line can be written as $y = mx + b$ (slope-intercept form), where m and b are the line's slope and y-intercept, respectively. The direct variation equation, $y = kx$, is a linear equation in slope-intercept form where $m = k$ and $b = 0$. Any line with a y-intercept equal to 0 passes through the origin. Therefore, a direct variation equation, $y = kx$, describes a line with slope k that passes through the origin.

IMPORTANT

The x- and y-intercepts of $y = kx$ are both 0.

Steps for Writing and Using an Equation When y Varies Directly as x

❶ Substitute the given corresponding x- and y-values into $y = kx$ and solve for k.

❷ Write the direct variation equation by substituting the k-value into $y = kx$. (Be sure to leave x and y as variables.)

❸ Find an unknown value by substituting the corresponding known value into the direct variation equation (from step ❷) and solving for the unknown.

EXAMPLE 1 **Writing a Direct Variation Equation**

Write the variation equation for x and y, if y varies directly as x, and $y = 8$ when $x = 12$. Then find y when $x = 45$ and find x when $y = 50$.

SOLUTION

Since y varies directly as x, the relationship between x and y is a direct variation, and the equation $y = kx$ models the situation.

❶ Substitute the given corresponding x- and y-values, $x = 12$ and $y = 8$, into $y = kx$ and solve for k.

$$y = kx \implies 8 = k(12) \implies k = \frac{2}{3} \quad \textit{The constant of variation is 2/3.}$$

❷ Substitute $k = \frac{2}{3}$ into $y = kx$. The direct variation equation is $y = \frac{2}{3}x$.

❸ Use $y = \frac{2}{3}x$ to find y when $x = 45$ and x when $y = 50$.

Find y when $x = 45$.   Find x when $y = 50$.

$$y = \frac{2}{3}(45) = 30 \qquad\qquad 50 = \frac{2}{3}x \implies x = \frac{3}{2}(50) = 75$$

Direct Variation as a Proportion

Solving $y = kx$ for k gives $k = \dfrac{y}{x}$. It follows that y/x will be equal for all corresponding x- and y-values in a direct variation. Therefore, two pairs of x- and y-values from a direct variation can be written as a proportion: $\dfrac{y_1}{x_1} = \dfrac{y_2}{x_2}$.

> **TIP**
>
> *From this proportion, it follows that $x_2 y_1 = x_1 y_2$ for any two ordered pairs in a direct variation.*

The relationship given in **Example 1** ("y varies directly as x, and $y = 8$ when $x = 12$") can be written as a proportion to find y when $x = 45$ and to find x when $y = 50$.

Find y when $x = 45$.   Find x when $y = 50$.

$$\frac{8}{12} = \frac{y}{45} \implies 12y = 8(45) \implies y = 30 \qquad \frac{8}{12} = \frac{50}{x} \implies 8x = 50(12) \implies x = 75$$

1.3.2   Modeling with Direct Variation

EXAMPLE 2   **Modeling a Direct Variation**

The dosage of a medication in milligrams varies directly as the weight of the patient in kilograms. A 50-kilogram patient receives 2000 milligrams of the medication. Find the constant of variation, write the variation equation, and find the amount of medication that a patient weighing 60 kilograms should receive.

SOLUTION

❶ Since the dosage (milligrams) varies directly as the patient's weight (kilograms), let x be the weight of the patient in kilograms, and let y be the dosage of the medication in milligrams. (So, $y = kx$.)

Find the constant of variation using $x = 50$ and $y = 2000$.

$$2000 = k(50) \implies k = 40 \qquad \textit{The constant of variation is 40.}$$

❷ So, the direct variation equation is $y = 40x$.

❸ Use the equation to find the amount of medication needed for a 60-kilogram patient.

$$y = 40(60) = 2400 \text{ mg} \qquad \text{The 60 kg patient requires 2400 mg of the medication.}$$

1.3.3 Inverse Variation

A situation involving two variables x and y that can be modeled by an equation of the form $y = \dfrac{k}{x}$, where k is some nonzero constant and $x \neq 0$, is called an **inverse variation**.

> **IMPORTANT**
>
> *An inverse variation is also called an inverse proportion.*

DEFINITION

If two quantities x and y are related by the equation $y = \dfrac{k}{x}$, where $x \neq 0$ and k is some constant such that $k \neq 0$, then the relationship between x and y is an **inverse variation** where y varies inversely as x.

> **NOTICE THAT**
>
> *Since $x \neq 0$ in an inverse variation, the graph has no x-intercept. Furthermore, since $k \neq 0$ in an inverse variation, the graph has no y-intercept.*

The general shape of a rational equation of the form $y = \dfrac{k}{x}$ is two curves.

- When $k > 0$, one curve is in quadrant I and the other is in quadrant III (Figure 1.3a).
- When $k < 0$, one curve is in quadrant II and the other is in quadrant IV (Figure 1.3b).

Steps for Writing and Using an Equation When y Varies Inversely as x

❶ Substitute the given corresponding x- and y-values into $y = \dfrac{k}{x}$ and solve for k.

❷ Write the inverse variation equation by substituting the k-value into $y = \dfrac{k}{x}$. (Be sure to leave x and y as variables.)

❸ Find an unknown value by substituting the corresponding known value into the inverse variation equation (from step ❷) and solving for the unknown.

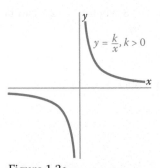

Figure 1.3a

Figure 1.3b

EXAMPLE 3   Writing an Inverse Variation Equation

Write the variation equation for x and y, if y varies inversely as x, and $y = 1$ when $x = 10$. Then find y when $x = 5$, and find x when $y = -10$.

SOLUTION

Since y varies inversely as x, the relationship between x and y is an inverse variation, and the equation $y = \dfrac{k}{x}$ models the situation.

❶ Substitute $x = 10$ and $y = 1$, into $y = \dfrac{k}{x}$, then solve for k.

$$y = \frac{k}{x} \implies 1 = \frac{k}{10} \implies k = 10 \quad \textit{The constant of variation is 10.}$$

❷ Substitute $k = 10$ into $y = \dfrac{k}{x}$. The inverse variation equation is $y = \dfrac{10}{x}$.

❸ Use $y = \dfrac{10}{x}$ to find y when $x = 5$, and to find x when $y = -10$.

Find y when $x = 5$.   Find x when $y = -10$.

$$y = \frac{10}{5} = 2 \qquad\qquad\qquad -10 = \frac{10}{x} \implies x = -1$$

Alternative Method: Inverse Variation as Products of Coordinates

Solving the general inverse variation equation $y = \dfrac{k}{x}$ for k gives $k = xy$. It follows that for all corresponding x- and y-values in an inverse variation, the value of xy must be the same (and equal to k). Therefore, for any two pairs of x- and y-values from an inverse variation, $x_1 y_1 = x_2 y_2$.

Consider the relationship given in **Example 3**: y varies inversely as x, and $y = 1$ when $x = 10$. Since the relationship between x and y is an inverse variation, the fact that $x_1 y_1 = x_2 y_2$ can be used to find y when $x = 5$, as well as to find x when $y = -10$.

<table>
<tr><td>**Find y when $x = 5$.**</td><td></td><td>**Find x when $y = -10$.**</td><td></td></tr>
<tr><td>$10(1) = 5y$</td><td>$x_1 y_1 = x_2 y_2$</td><td>$10(1) = x(-10)$</td><td>$x_1 y_1 = x_2 y_2$</td></tr>
<tr><td>$y = 2$</td><td>*Solve for y.*</td><td>$x = -1$</td><td>*Solve for x.*</td></tr>
</table>

1.3.4   Modeling with Inverse Variation

Variation equations may involve powers of the quantities in the relationship. For example, if y varies inversely as the cube of x, then $y = \dfrac{k}{x^3}$.

EXAMPLE 4   Modeling an Inverse Variation

In order for all of the cylindrical cans produced by a manufacturer to have a constant volume, the height of each can must vary inversely as the square of the diameter of the can's base. One type of can produced has a diameter of 3 inches and a height of 4 inches. Find the constant of variation, write the variation equation, and find the diameter for a can with height 9 inches.

SOLUTION

Since a can's height varies inversely as the square of the base's diameter, let x be the diameter and let y be the height. Then $y = \dfrac{k}{x^2}$.

Use $x = 3$ and $y = 4$ to find k. $4 = \dfrac{k}{3^2} \;\Rightarrow\; k = 4(3^2) = 36$ *The constant of variation is 36.*

So, the inverse variation equation is $y = \dfrac{36}{x^2}$.

Use the equation to find the diameter of a can with height 9 inches.

$$9 = \dfrac{36}{x^2} \;\Rightarrow\; 9x^2 = 36 \;\Rightarrow\; x^2 = 4 \;\Rightarrow\; x = 2$$

IMPORTANT

Since x represents a length, x must be positive. So, only the positive square root is needed.

The diameter of a can must be 2 inches when the height is 9 inches.

A variation equation can also be used to determine how a specific change in one variable, such as doubling the variable, affects the other variable. In this case, specific x- and y-values are not substituted into the variation equation. Instead, an expression for one of the variables is substituted into the general variation equation. For example, to determine how y is affected if x is doubled when x and y are inversely related, substitute $2x$ into the general inverse variation equation, $y = \dfrac{k}{x}$. This procedure is demonstrated in **Example 5**.

EXAMPLE 5   **Modeling an Inverse Variation**

At some constant temperature, the volume V of a gas varies inversely as the pressure P. How does the volume of the gas change if the pressure is tripled?

SOLUTION

Since the volume V varies inversely as the pressure P, $V_1 = \dfrac{k}{P_1}$, where V_1 and P_1 represent the original volume and pressure (i.e., the volume and pressure before the pressure is tripled).

To find the effect of tripling the pressure on the volume, substitute $3P_1$ for P_1 in the variation equation, and let V represent the volume of the gas *after the pressure is tripled.*

$$V = \frac{k}{3P_1}$$

From the original variation equation, $V_1 = \dfrac{k}{P_1}$. So, substitute V_1 into $V = \dfrac{k}{3P_1}$ for $\dfrac{k}{P_1}$.

$$V = \frac{k}{3P_1} = \frac{1}{3} \cdot \frac{k}{P_1} = \frac{1}{3}V_1$$

After the pressure is tripled, the volume, V, is equal to one-third of the original volume, $\dfrac{1}{3}V_1$. In other words, tripling the pressure results in one-third of the original volume.

1.3.5 Joint Variation

A situation involving three variables, x, y, and z, which can be modeled by an equation of the form $y = kxz$, where k is some nonzero constant, is called a **joint variation**.

DEFINITION

If three quantities x, y, and z are related by the equation $y = kxz$, where k is some constant such that $k \neq 0$, then the relationship between x, y, and z is a **joint variation** where y varies jointly as x and z.

A joint variation may involve powers of x or z. Specifically, x, y, and z are related by an equation of the form $y = kx^n z^m$ when y varies jointly as x to the nth power and z to the mth power. For example, the equation $y = kxz^2$ describes a variation where y varies jointly as x and the square of z.

The steps for writing a joint variation equation are the same as those for writing any other type of variation equation, except that the values of the variables are substituted into $y = kxz$ for a joint variation.

Steps for Writing and Using an Equation When *y* Varies Jointly as *x* and *z*

❶ Substitute the given corresponding *x*-, *y*-, and *z*-values into $y = kxz$ and solve for *k*.

❷ Write the joint variation equation by substituting the *k*-value into $y = kxz$. (Be sure to leave *x*, *y*, and *z* as variables.)

❸ Find an unknown value by substituting the corresponding known values into the joint variation equation (from step ❷) and solving for the unknown.

EXAMPLE 6   **Writing a Joint Variation Equation**

The volume *V* of a rectangular pyramid varies jointly as the area of the base *B* and the height *h*. The volume of a rectangular pyramid is 56 cubic meters when the area of its base is 24 square meters and its height is 7 meters. Find the constant of variation, write the variation equation, and find the area of a rectangular pyramid's base when its volume is 81 cubic meters and its height is 9 meters.

SOLUTION

Since *V* varies jointly as *B* and *h*, the relationship between *V*, *B*, and *h* is a joint variation, and the equation $V = kBh$ models the situation.

❶ Substitute the given corresponding *V*-, *B*-, and *h*-values, $V = 56$, $B = 24$, and $h = 7$, into $V = kBh$, and solve for *k*.

$$V = kBh \implies 56 = k(24)(7) \implies k = \frac{1}{3} \quad \textit{The constant of variation is 1/3.}$$

❷ Substitute $k = \frac{1}{3}$ into $V = kBh$. The direct variation equation is $V = \frac{1}{3}Bh$, or $V = \frac{Bh}{3}$.

❸ Use $V = \frac{Bh}{3}$ to find *B* when $V = 81$ and $h = 9$.

When $V = 81$ and $h = 9$, $81 = \frac{B(9)}{3}$, and so $B = \frac{81(3)}{9} = 27$.

So, the area of a rectangular pyramid's base is 27 square meters when its volume is 81 cubic meters and its height is 9 meters.

WHAT'S THE BIG IDEA?

How is a joint variation similar to a direct variation?

1.3.6 Modeling with Combined Variation

$$V = \frac{KT}{P} \Rightarrow V = \frac{T}{100P}$$
$$4 = \frac{K\,200}{0.5}$$
$$\frac{2}{200} = \frac{200\,K}{200}$$
$$\frac{1}{100} = K$$
$$6.5 = \frac{320}{100P}$$
$$6.5\,P = 32$$
$$P = \frac{32}{65} \approx 0.49 \text{ atm}$$

A **combined variation** is a relationship between three or more variables that combines both direct and inverse variation. In a combined variation, the constant of variation *k* is multiplied by a ratio of variables where quantities that vary directly are in the numerator of the ratio and quantities that vary inversely are in the denominator of the ratio.

DEFINITION

If three (or more) quantities x, y, and z are related by the equation $y = \dfrac{kx}{z}$, where $z \neq 0$ and k is some constant such that $k \neq 0$, then the relationship between x, y, and z is a **combined variation** where y varies directly as x and inversely as z.

The steps for writing a combined variation equation are the same as those for writing any other type of variation equation, except that the values of the variables are substituted into $y = \dfrac{kx}{z}$ for a combined variation.

Steps for Writing and Using an Equation When y Varies Directly as x and Inversely as z

❶ Substitute the given corresponding x-, y-, and z-values (where x represents the variable(s) that vary directly as y, and z represents the variable(s) that vary inversely as y) into $y = \dfrac{kx}{z}$ and solve for k.

❷ Write the combined variation equation by substituting the k-value into $y = \dfrac{kx}{z}$. (Be sure to leave x, y, and z as variables.)

❸ Find an unknown value by substituting the corresponding known values into the combined variation equation (from step ❷) and solving for the unknown.

EXAMPLE 7   **Modeling a Combined Variation Equation**

The pressure P of a gas varies directly as the temperature T and inversely as the volume V, and 100 liters (L) of the gas exerts a pressure of 33.2 kilopascal (kPa) when its temperature is 400 Kelvins (K). Find the constant of variation, write the variation equation, and find the pressure for 80 L of the gas at 500 K.

SOLUTION

Since P varies directly as T and inversely as V, the relationship between P, T, and V is a combined variation, and the equation $P = \dfrac{kT}{V}$ models the situation.

❶ Substitute $P = 33.2$, $T = 400$, and $V = 100$ into $P = \dfrac{kT}{V}$, and solve for k.

$$P = \frac{kT}{V} \quad \Rightarrow \quad 33.2 = \frac{k(400)}{100} \quad \Rightarrow \quad k = 8.3 \quad \textit{The constant of variation is 8.3.}$$

❷ Substitute $k = 8.3$ into $P = \dfrac{kT}{V}$. The combined variation equation is $P = \dfrac{8.3T}{V}$.

❸ Use $P = \dfrac{8.3T}{V}$ to find P when $V = 80$ and $T = 500$. $P = \dfrac{8.3(500)}{80} = 51.875$

So, the pressure of the gas is 51.875 kPa when its volume is 80 L and its temperature is 500 K.

SECTION 1.3 EXERCISES

Warm Up

Solve each equation.

1. $5y = (10)(8)$

2. $(7)(6)(3)k = 20$

3. $75 = \dfrac{A(5)}{3}$

Just the Facts

Fill in the blanks.

4. For $k > 0$, if y varies directly with x, then when x _____, y decreases, and when x increases, y _____.

5. The four types of variation situations are _____, _____, _____, and _____.

6. $y = kx$ is a(n) _____ variation equation where the graph passes through the _____ and the slope is _____.

7. An inverse variation where y varies inversely as x is written _____, where _____ $\neq 0$.

8. "P is jointly proportional to r and the third power of m" is written as $P =$ _____.

9. The equation $y = kmn$ is a(n) _____ variation equation where y varies _____ with _____, _____, and _____, which is some nonzero constant.

10. Mathematical models that involve both direct and inverse variation are said to have a(n) _____ variation.

Essential Skills

In Exercises 1–10, write the direct variation equation and find the specified values.

1. Two values, d and g, are directly proportional. If $d = 16$ when $g = 14$, what is the value of g when d is 25?

2. Suppose y varies directly with x, and $y = 18$ when $x = 30$. Find y when $x = 60$, and find x when $y = 3$.

3. Suppose t varies directly with s, and $t = 8$ when $s = 14$. Find t when $s = 21$, and find s when $t = 20$.

4. Suppose z varies directly with g, and $z = 36$ when $g = 30$. Find z when $g = 54$, and find g when $z = 60$.

5. Two values, p and q, are directly proportional. If $p = 4.8$ when $q = 2.8$, what is the value of q when p is 3.6?

6. Suppose b varies directly with a, and $b = 6.2$ when $a = 1.5$. Find b when $a = 7.4$, and find a when $b = 9.6$.

7. Suppose u varies directly with v, and $u = -12$ when $v = 8.4$. Find v when $u = 9.2$ and find u when $v = 4.9$.

8. Suppose m varies directly with n, and $m = 11.6$ when $n = -2.4$. Find n when $m = -29$, and find m when $n = 22.5$.

9. Suppose w varies directly with r, and $w = 14/3$ when $r = -5/6$. Find w when $r = -10/3$, and find r when $w = 7/4$.

10. Suppose p varies directly with l, and $p = -7/8$ when $l = -5/2$. Find p when $l = 2/3$, and find l when $p = -4/5$.

In Exercises 11–13, use the following information.

A kite company produces kites whose lengths vary directly with their widths.

11. If a kite with length 80 centimeters has width 65 centimeters, what is the width of a 96-centimeter-long kite?

12. If a kite with length 63 inches has width 48 inches, what is the length of a 40-inch-wide kite?

13. If a kite with length 3.4 feet has width 2.5 feet, what is the width of a 5.1-foot-long kite?

In Exercises 14–16, use the following information.

If income tax varies directly with income and a person earning \$30,000 per year pays \$8,400 in taxes, how much will a person earning each of the following amounts pay?

14. \$42,000 per year

15. \$136,000 per year

16. \$78,500 per year

In Exercises 17–24, write the inverse variation equation and find the specified values.

17. Suppose $x = 8.4$ when $y = 1$, and x varies inversely with y. Find x when $y = 4$.

18. Suppose y varies inversely with x, and $y = 1/2$ when $x = 8$. Find y when $x = -1$, and find x when $y = 1$.

19. Suppose a varies inversely with b, and $b = 3/8$ when $a = 61$. Find b when $a = 1/3$, and find a when $b = 15$.

20. Suppose t varies inversely with u, and $u = 3.7$ when $t = 14$. Find u when $t = 7.5$, and find t when $u = 40$.

21. Suppose y varies inversely with x, and $y = 12$ when $x = -3/4$. Find y when $x = 6/11$, and find x when $y = -3/2$.

22. Suppose $n = -15/16$ when $p = 8$, and n varies inversely with p. Find n when $p = -4/3$, and find p when $n = 1/6$.

23. Suppose c varies inversely with d, and $c = -7/4$ when $d = -6/5$. Find d when $c = -9/10$, and find c when $d = 3/8$.

24. Suppose w varies inversely with z, and $w = 3/10$ when $z = -5/9$. Find z when $w = -2/7$, and find w when $z = -13/2$.

In Exercises 25–27, use the following information.

The number of days needed to harvest a wheat field varies inversely with the number of people harvesting the field.

25. If it takes 13 days for 12 people to harvest the field, how many days would it take for 4 people to harvest the field?

26. If it takes 24 days for 8 people to harvest the field, how many days would it take for 10 people to harvest the field?

27. If it takes 9 days for 27 people to harvest the field, how many days would it take for 45 people to harvest the field?

In Exercises 28–30, use the following information.

Power in an electric circuit varies inversely with the resistance.

28. If the power is 1200 watts when the resistance is 12 ohms, find the resistance when the power is 2400 watts.

29. If the power is 1700 watts when the resistance is 25 ohms, find the resistance when the power is 5000 watts.

30. If the power is 625 watts when the resistance is 15 ohms, find the power when the resistance is 12 ohms.

In Exercises 31–33, use the following information.

The illumination, measured in candelas, from a light bulb varies inversely with the square of the distance d from the light bulb. Round to the nearest tenth, as needed.

31. If the illumination is 85 candelas at 5 meters, what is the illumination at 15 meters?

32. If the illumination is 78 candelas at 6 meters, what is the illumination at 20 meters?

33. If the illumination is 56 candelas at 12 meters, what is the distance away from the light bulb if the illumination is 42 candelas?

In Exercises 34–36, use the following information.

The frequency of the oscillations of a pendulum varies inversely with the square root of the length of the pendulum.

34. How does the frequency change if the pendulum's length is increased to 4 times the original length?

35. How does the frequency change if the pendulum's length is increased to 9 times the original length?

36. How does the frequency change if the pendulum's length is decreased to one-sixteenth of the original length?

In Exercises 37–39, use the following information.

The area A of a triangle varies jointly with the base b and height h.

37. Suppose $A = 24$ square inches when $b = 6$ inches, and $h = 8$ inches. Find h when $A = 100$ square inches and $b = 10$ inches.

38. Suppose $A = 18$ square inches when $b = 2$ inches, and $h = 3$ inches. Find b when $A = 72$ square inches and $h = 8$ inches.

39. Suppose $A = 124$ square feet when $b = 9$ feet, and $h = 12$ feet. Find A when $b = 5$ feet and $h = 27$ feet.

In Exercises 40–42, use the following information.

The volume V of a cone varies jointly with the area of the base B and the height h.

40. If $V = 32$ cubic centimeters when $B = 16$ square centimeters, and $h = 6$ centimeters, what is h when $V = 60$ cubic centimeters and $B = 20$ square centimeters?

41. If $V = 138$ cubic inches when $B = 23$ square inches, and $h = 18$ inches, what is h when $V = 57$ cubic inches and $B = 19$ square inches?

42. If $V = 144$ cubic millimeters when $B = 12$ square millimeters, and $h = 36$ millimeters, what is h when $V = 240$ cubic millimeters and $B = 64$ square millimeters?

43. The amount of light E provided by a light bulb is inversely proportional to the square of the distance d in meters from the bulb. When a person is 3 meters from the bulb, the amount of light is 5.9 lux. Write the variation equation.

44. The resistance R of a wire varies directly with its length L and inversely with the square of its diameter D. Write an equation for the constant of variation in terms of R, L, and D.

In Exercises 45–47, use the following information.

The number of vibrations n per second of a nylon guitar string varies directly with the square root of the tension T and inversely with the length L of the string. Round to the nearest kilogram, as needed.

45. If the tension is 400 kilograms when the number of vibrations per second is 12 and the length is 0.7 meters, find the tension when the length is 0.4 meters and the number of vibrations is 8.

46. If the tension is 256 kilograms when the number of vibrations per second is 15 and the length is 0.6 meters, find the tension when the length is 0.3 meters and the number of vibrations is 12.

47. If the tension is 324 kilograms when the number of vibrations per second is 14 and the length is 0.8 meters, find the tension when the length is 0.2 meters and the number of vibrations is 12.

In Exercises 48–50, use the following information.

The power P that must be delivered by a car's engine varies directly with the distance d that the car moves and inversely with the time t required to move that distance. Round to the nearest foot, as needed.

48. To move the car 2000 feet in 75 seconds, the engine must deliver 152 kilowatts of power. Find the distance (in feet) the car moves when 189 kilowatts of power is delivered for 90 seconds.

49. To move the car 600 feet in 60 seconds, the engine must deliver 56 kilowatts of power. Find the distance (in feet) the car moves when 79 kilowatts of power is delivered for 80 seconds.

50. To move the car 1800 feet in 90 seconds, the engine must deliver 114 kilowatts of power. Find the distance (in feet) the car moves when 140 kilowatts of power is delivered for 110 seconds.

Extensions

In Exercises 51–53, use the following information.

At Chapel Hill Tubal Reversal Center, patients are required to have a body mass index (BMI) of less than 37 at least three weeks prior to the date of any scheduled tubal reversal surgery. This policy is in place to ensure optimal patient safety when undergoing this elective, outpatient surgery. A person's BMI is directly proportional to their weight (w) in pounds, and inversely proportional to the square of their height (h) in inches. A person who is 65 inches tall and weighs 130 pounds has a BMI of 21.6 pounds per square inch.

51. Would a person 5 feet 3 inches tall weighing 180 pounds be allowed to have the surgery? Depending upon the result, what amount is the person over/under? Round to the nearest tenth.

52. Would a person 6 feet 4 inches tall weighing 290 pounds be allowed to have the surgery? Depending upon the result, what amount is the person over/under? Round to the nearest tenth.

53. What is the most that a person 5 feet 8 inches tall could weigh and still have the surgery? Round to the nearest pound.

54. In photography, the luminance L varies directly as the square of the f-stop f and inversely as the product of the film ISO number s and the exposure time t. An ISO 100 film has a luminance of 14 candelas per square meter when shot for 1 second at an f-stop of 8. Write the equation. What is the f-stop of an ISO 400 film with a luminance of 22 candelas per square meter when shot for 1.3 seconds?

55. Suppose b varies directly as the cube of w and inversely as the square of h. If w is doubled and h is halved, what happens to b?

56. If x varies directly as a^2 and h^4, and a doubles while h triples, what happens to x?

57. The force needed to keep a car from skidding on a curve varies inversely as the radius r of the curve and jointly as the weight w of the car and the square of the speed s. If an 1800-pound car traveling 20 miles per hour takes a force of 3600 pounds to keep from skidding on a curve of radius 600 feet, what force would be required to prevent the same car from skidding at the same curve traveling 15 miles per hour faster? Write the variation equation.

58. Write a sentence using variation terminology to describe the formula $E = mc^2$ where E is energy, m is mass, and c is the speed of light.

1.4 FUNCTIONS

OBJECTIVES

- Identify functions graphically.
- Identify functions algebraically.
- Understand and use function notation.
- Evaluate a piecewise-defined function.
- Model with functions.
- Find the domain of a function.

PREREQUISITE VOCABULARY TERMS

coordinate plane

domain

equation

formula

ordered pair

1.4.1   Functions and the Vertical Line Test

A **relation** is any relationship between two quantities (variables, such as x and y) or sets. A special kind of relation where each item from one set, the **domain**, corresponds to exactly one item from a second set, the **range**, is called a **function**.

> ### DEFINITION
>
> A **relation** that assigns each element in a set A to exactly one element in a set B is a **function** from A to B. The set A is the **domain**, or set of allowable input values, and the set B is the **range**, or set of corresponding output values.

There are many ways to express a function, including as a set of ordered pairs. For example, the set of ordered pairs $\{(1, 2), (2, 4), (3, 6), (4, 8)\}$ expresses a function from A to B where set A is $\{1, 2, 3, 4\}$ and set B is $\{2, 4, 6, 8\}$. Notice that each element in A is assigned to exactly one element in B.

Another way to express a function is a **mapping diagram** (also known as an **arrow diagram**). The mapping diagram in Figure 1.4a expresses the function $\{(1, 1), (6, 36), (5, 25), (3, 9)\}$. The domain is the set A, $\{1, 3, 5, 6\}$, and the range is the set B, $\{1, 9, 25, 36\}$. In a mapping diagram, a function will show one arrow from each element in set A pointing to exactly one element in set B. The following mapping diagrams show examples of relations that are functions and relations that are not functions.

```
1 ──────▶ 1
6         9
5         25
3 ──────▶ 36
Set A    Set B
```

Figure 1.4a

Mapping Diagrams			
Functions		**Not Functions**	
$x_1 \rightarrow y_1$ $x_2 \rightarrow y_2$ $x_3 \rightarrow y_3$ $x_4 \rightarrow y_4$ Set A Set B	$x_1, x_2 \rightarrow y_1$ $x_3, x_4 \rightarrow y_2$ Set A Set B	$x_1 \rightarrow y_1, y_2$ $x_2 \rightarrow y_3$ $x_3 \rightarrow y_4$ Set A Set B	$x_1 \rightarrow y_1$ $x_2 \rightarrow y_2$ $x_3 \rightarrow y_3$ x_4 Set A Set B
Each x is mapped to exactly one y.	*Each x is mapped to exactly one y. More than one x can be mapped to the same y.*	*Not a function because x_1 is mapped to more than one y.*	*Not a function because x_3 is not mapped to any y.*

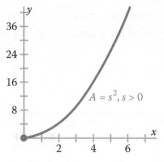

Figure 1.4b

A function can also be represented by an equation (or formula), or by a graph in a coordinate plane. For example, the relationship between the length s of the side of a square and the area A of the square is a function, where the area of the square *is a function of* the length of its side. In this case, the s-values are the input (domain) and the A-values are the output (range). This function can be expressed by the equation $A = s^2$, or by the graph in Figure 1.4b.

Determining Whether a Graph Represents a Function

A function must assign each value in its domain to exactly one value in its range. Therefore, if a graph on a coordinate plane is a function, then the graph contains points where each x-coordinate (domain value) is assigned to exactly one y-coordinate (range value). In other words, a graph that is a function *cannot* contain two points with the same x-value and different y-values. A test for determining whether a graph is a function follows from this statement.

The Vertical Line Test

If any vertical line intersects a graph more than once, then the graph is not a function.

For example, consider a graph that contains the points (3, 2) and (3, 5). We know that this graph cannot be a function because the x-coordinate 3 is assigned to two y-coordinates, 2 and 5. Additionally, by the Vertical Line Test, this graph cannot be a function because the vertical line $x = 3$ intersects the two points (3, 5) and (3, 2).

EXAMPLE 1   Using the Vertical Line Test

Use the Vertical Line Test to determine whether each graph represents a function.

A.

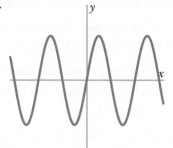

B.

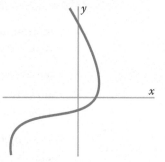

SOLUTION

A. The graph passes the Vertical Line Test because no vertical line intersects the graph more than once. Therefore, the graph is a function.

B. The graph fails the Vertical Line Test because there are many vertical lines that will intersect the graph more than once. One such vertical line is shown in Figure 1.4c. Therefore, the graph is not a function.

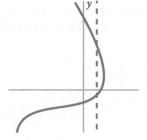

Figure 1.4c

1.4.2   Identifying Functions Algebraically

To determine algebraically whether an equation in x and y is a function, solve the equation for y and then analyze the expression for y to determine whether there could possibly be more than one y-value for any x-value in the equation's domain.

For example, the equation $2x^2 + y = 1$ is a function. Solving for y gives $y = 1 - 2x^2$. Notice that any substituted x-value will result in only one y-value.

However, the equation $2x + y^2 = 1$ is not a function. Solving for y gives $y = \pm\sqrt{1 - 2x}$. Notice that when $x = 0$, the corresponding y-values are -1 and 1. So, there is at least one x-value in the equation's domain with more than one corresponding y-value.

EXAMPLE 2 **Identifying Functions Algebraically**

Determine algebraically whether each equation represents a function.

A. $x + 2y = 0$ **B.** $x^2 + y^2 = 16$

SOLUTION

Solve each equation for y.

A. $x + 2y = 0 \implies y = -\dfrac{x}{2}$

Each x-value has one corresponding y-value: $-\dfrac{x}{2}$. So, $x + 2y = 0$ is a function.

B. $x^2 + y^2 = 16 \implies y = \pm\sqrt{16 - x^2}$

Each x-value has two corresponding y-values: $\sqrt{16 - x^2}$ and $-\sqrt{16 - x^2}$. So, $x^2 + y^2 = 16$ is not a function.

1.4.3 Function Notation and Finding Function Values

Function notation can be used to write the equation of a function where the output value, y, is replaced with $f(x)$, which is read as "f of x". This notation

- names the function with a letter (usually f, but other letters can be used),
- shows the input value (usually x, but other letters can be used), and
- shows the rule described by the function.

For example, $f(x) = 2x + 1$ is the function notation for $y = 2x + 1$, where $y = f(x)$. This function could also be written as $g(x) = 2x + 1$ or $p(x) = 2x + 1$ (all are equivalent functions). The two variables in $f(x) = 2x + 1$ are x and $f(x)$, where x is the input and $f(x)$ is the output. Two additional examples of functions written using function notation follow.

Example function: $f(x) = x^2$
- The function is named f.
- The input is x.
- The rule is x^2.
- The output is $f(x)$.
- Equivalent to $y = x^2$.
- f is a quadratic function.

Example function: $r(a) = |4 - a|$
- The function is named r.
- The input is a.
- The rule is $|4 - a|$.
- The output is $r(a)$.
- Equivalent to $y = |4 - a|$.
- r is an absolute value function.

When the variable is replaced by a number (or by another variable or expression) in function notation, it denotes evaluation. For example, if $f(x) = 2x + 1$, then $f(5)$ means to evaluate the function f for $x = 5$. So, $f(5) = 2(5) + 1 = 11$.

Additionally, $f(b + 1)$ means to evaluate the function f for $x = b + 1$.

$$f(b + 1) = 2(b + 1) + 1 = 2b + 3$$

EXAMPLE 3   **Evaluating a Function**

If $h(x) = x + 3x^2$, find $h(4)$, $h(-1)$, and $h(a + 1)$.

SOLUTION

Substitute each given input value into the function and simplify.

$$h(4) = (4) + 3(4)^2 = 4 + 3(16) = 4 + 48 = 52$$
$$h(-1) = (-1) + 3(-1)^2 = -1 + 3(1) = -1 + 3 = 2$$

$$
\begin{aligned}
h(a + 1) &= (a + 1) + 3(a + 1)^2 && \textit{Substitute a + 1 for x.} \\
&= a + 1 + 3(a + 1)(a + 1) && \textit{Expand the power.} \\
&= a + 1 + 3(a^2 + 2a + 1) && \textit{FOIL} \\
&= a + 1 + 3a^2 + 6a + 3 && \textit{Distribute.} \\
&= 3a^2 + 7a + 4 && \textit{Combine the like terms.}
\end{aligned}
$$

So, $h(4) = 52$, $h(-1) = 2$, and $h(a + 1) = 3a^2 + 7a + 4$.

1.4.4   Evaluating Piecewise-Defined Functions

A **piecewise-defined function** is a combination of two or more functions. There are specific values of the domain that correspond to each piece (part) of the function. The values from the domain that correspond to each of the function's pieces are written in an inequality (or equation) to the right of that piece. For example, $f(x)$ is a piecewise-defined function with the domain divided into three parts: values less than 0, values between 0 and 4 (including 0 and 4), and values greater than 4.

$$
f(x) = \begin{cases}
5 - x & \text{if } x < 0 & \textit{Piece 1: For domain values less than 0, } f(x) = 5 - x. \\
2x & \text{if } 0 \leq x \leq 4 & \textit{Piece 2: For domain values from 0 to 4, } f(x) = 2x. \\
(3 + x)^2 & \text{if } x > 4 & \textit{Piece 3: For domain values greater than 4, } f(x) = (3 + x)^2.
\end{cases}
$$

To evaluate a piecewise-defined function for some domain value x, first determine which piece of the function corresponds to that domain value. Then substitute the x-value into just that piece of the function. For example, to evaluate $f(3)$ using $f(x)$ given above, substitute 3 into $f(x) = 2x$ (since $x = 3$ is a solution to the inequality $0 \leq x \leq 4$): $f(3) = 2(3) = 6$.

EXAMPLE 4   **Evaluating a Piecewise-Defined Function**

Given $g(x) = \begin{cases} x^2 - 3x & \text{if } x \leq -3 \\ 7 & \text{if } -3 < x \leq 1 \\ 5x & \text{if } x > 1 \end{cases}$, find $g(-5)$ and $g(1)$.

SOLUTION

Identify the piece of the function that corresponds to each given x-value. Then substitute that x-value into that piece of the function and simplify.

Evaluate $g(-5)$ by substituting -5 into $g(x) = x^2 - 3x$ (since $-5 \leq -3$).

$$g(-5) = (-5)^2 - 3(-5) = 25 - (-15) = 40$$

Evaluate $g(1)$ by substituting 1 into $g(x) = 7$ (since $-3 < 1 \leq 1$).

$$g(1) = 7$$

So, $g(-5) = 40$ and $g(1) = 7$.

1.4.5 Finding Specific Function Values

So far in this section, all functions have been evaluated for some particular x-value (domain value). So, the corresponding range value has been found for some specific domain value. It is also possible to find a corresponding domain value when a range value is given. For example, suppose $f(x) = 2x + 1$. To find the domain value that corresponds to the range value 9, substitute 9 for $f(x)$ and solve for x. So, if $f(x) = 2x + 1$ and $f(x) = 9$, then $9 = 2x + 1$, and thus $x = 4$.

When a function is set equal to 0 (i.e., $f(x) = 0$) and solved for x, the resulting x-values (the solutions) are called the **roots of the function** or the **zeros of the function**. Since these x-values correspond to where $y = 0$, these x-values are also the x-intercepts of the function's graph.

EXAMPLE 5   **Finding Values for Which a Function is Equal to 0**

Find all real x-values such that $r(x) = 0$.

A. $r(x) = 5x + 10$ $\qquad\qquad$ **B.** $r(x) = x^2 - 13x + 30$

SOLUTION

For each function, substitute 0 for $r(x)$ and then solve for x.

A. $\quad 0 = 5x + 10$
$\quad -10 = 5x \quad$ *Subtract 10 from each side.*
$\quad\; -2 = x \quad$ *Divide each side by 5.*

So, if $r(x) = 5x + 10$,
then $r(x) = 0$ when $x = -2$.

B. $\; 0 = x^2 - 13x + 30$
$\quad 0 = (x - 3)(x - 10) \qquad$ *Factor.*
$\quad x - 3 = 0 \;$ or $\; x - 10 = 0 \quad$ *Set each factor equal to 0.*
$\quad\quad x = 3 \qquad\qquad x = 10 \quad$ *Solve each equation.*

So, if $r(x) = x^2 - 13x + 30$,
then $r(x) = 0$ when $x = 3$ or $x = 10$.

The x-values found in **Example 5** correspond to where $r(x) = 0$, so these x-values are the roots, zeros, or solutions of the functions. These x-values are also the x-intercepts of the function, as shown in Figures 1.4d and 1.4e.

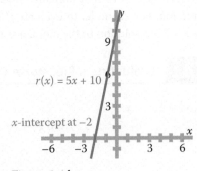

Figure 1.4d

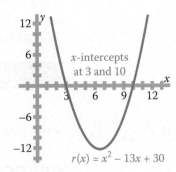

Figure 1.4e

WHAT'S THE BIG IDEA?

If $p(a)$ is some function, explain the meaning of $p(0)$ and $p(a) = 0$.

Values of x for Which Two Functions are Equal

Two functions f and g can be set equal to each other to find the x-values where the functions are equal. So, these x-values correspond to the points (x, y) that are the same on both functions. Graphically, these are the points at which the two functions intersect each other.

| **EXAMPLE 6** | **Finding Values for Which Two Functions are Equal** |

If $g(x) = x + 12$ and $h(x) = x^2$, find all real x-values such that $g(x) = h(x)$.

SOLUTION

> **TIP**
>
> *Any x-value that makes $g(x) = h(x)$ is an x-value that corresponds to the same y-value for both functions.*

To find the x-value(s) for which $g(x) = h(x)$, set the expression for $g(x)$, $x + 12$, equal to the expression for $h(x)$, x^2, and then solve for x.

$$g(x) = h(x)$$
$$x + 12 = x^2 \qquad \text{\textit{Substitute } } x + 12 \text{ \textit{for} } g(x) \text{ \textit{and} } x^2 \text{ \textit{for} } h(x).$$
$$0 = x^2 - x - 12 \qquad \text{\textit{Subtract } } x \text{ \textit{and 12 from each side.}}$$
$$0 = (x - 4)(x + 3) \qquad \text{\textit{Factor.}}$$
$$x - 4 = 0 \quad \text{or} \quad x + 3 = 0 \qquad \text{\textit{Set each factor equal to 0.}}$$
$$x = 4 \qquad\qquad x = -3 \qquad \text{\textit{Solve each equation.}}$$

So, if $g(x) = x + 12$ and $h(x) = x^2$, then $g(x) = h(x)$ when $x = 4$ or $x = -3$.

CHECK

Check the answer by evaluating $g(4)$ and $h(4)$, and then evaluating $g(-3)$ and $h(-3)$.

$$g(4) = 4 + 12 = 16 \qquad\qquad g(-3) = -3 + 12 = 9$$
$$h(4) = 4^2 = 16 \qquad\qquad h(-3) = (-3)^2 = 9$$

So, when $x = 4$, $g(x) = 16$ and $h(x) = 16$, and when $x = -3$, $g(x) = 9$ and $h(x) = 9$. ✔

Figure 1.4f shows the graphs of functions g and h from **Example 6**. Notice that the functions intersect at the points $(4, 16)$ and $(-3, 9)$.

Figure 1.4f

1.4.6 Modeling with Functions

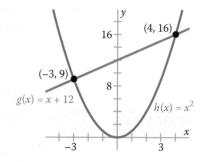

Independent and Dependent Variables

A function's x-variable is also called the **independent variable,** and its y-variable is also called the **dependent variable**, since the y-value depends on the x-value. The function's domain and range are the sets of all values for the independent and dependent variables, respectively.

When modeling, the relationship between two variables A and B can be stated as "A is a function of B." From this statement, it can be determined that B is the independent variable (x) and A is the dependent variable (y).

$$A \text{ is a function of } B \implies f(B) = A \qquad y \text{ is a function of } x \implies f(x) = y$$

1.4.7 Satisfying the Domain of a Function

Recall that the domain of an expression in one variable is all allowable values for that variable (i.e., values that result in a real number when substituted into the expression). For example, the domain of $5 + x^2$ is all real numbers, because the result is always a real number when any real number is substituted into the expression. The domain of $\sqrt{x+3}$ is all real x-values such that $x \geq -3$ (i.e., $[-3, \infty)$), because substituting any number that is greater than or equal to -3 results in a real number, but substituting numbers less than -3 results in a negative radicand, which is not a real number.

> **REMEMBER**
>
> *The set of all real numbers can be represented using the symbol $\mathbb{R}$ or in interval notation as $(-\infty, \infty)$.*

The domain of a function is the domain of the expression used to define the function. For example, the domain of $f(x) = 5 + x^2$ is all real numbers, because the domain of $5 + x^2$ is all real numbers. So, to find the domain of a function, simply find the domain of the related expression.

As with expressions, the domains of functions do not include values that result in a 0 denominator or in a negative radicand.

EXAMPLE 9 Finding the Domain of a Function

Find the domain of each function.

A. f: {$(-2, -3), (0, -1), (1, 0), (5, 4)$} **B.** $g(x) = \sqrt{4 - x}$ **C.** $p(x) = \dfrac{x^2}{4x^2 - 1}$

SOLUTION

A. The domain of f is the set of all x, which is the first coordinate in each ordered pair.

Domain of f: {$-2, 0, 1, 5$}

B. The domain of g is all real numbers except those x-values that make the radicand < 0. So, set the expression in the radicand ≥ 0 and solve for x.

$4 - x \geq 0 \implies x \leq 4$ *Reverse the inequality symbol when dividing by -1.*

Domain of g: $(-\infty, 4]$ *The domain is all real numbers less than or equal to 4.*

C. The domain of p is all real numbers except those x-values that make the denominator 0. So, set the expression in the denominator equal to 0 and solve for x.

$4x^2 - 1 = 0 \implies (2x - 1)(2x + 1) = 0 \implies x = \dfrac{1}{2}$ or $x = -\dfrac{1}{2}$

> **IMPORTANT**
>
> *The set of "all real numbers except $\frac{1}{2}$ or $-\frac{1}{2}$" can be expressed as $\mathbb{R} \backslash \{\frac{1}{2}, -\frac{1}{2}\}$.*

Domain of p: {$x \mid x \neq \frac{1}{2}, x \neq -\frac{1}{2}$}

WHAT'S THE BIG IDEA?

Explain the differences between $y = 3x + 1$, $f(x) = 3x + 1$, and $3x + 1$.

SECTION 1.4 EXERCISES

Warm Up

1. Given $x - 5 = y$, find y when $x = -4$.

2. Given $m = 3n^2 - n + 2$, find m when $n = 3$.

3. Given $y = 4x^3 + 9x$, find y when $x = 2$.

Just the Facts

Fill in the blanks.

4. The set of ordered pairs $\{(2, -3), (4, -7), (-3, 7), (0, 1)\}$ represent a(n) _____ because each x-value corresponds to only one _____.

5. To determine graphically whether a relation is a function, draw a(n) _____. If it intersects the graph _____, it is a(n) _____.

6. $f(x)$ is just another name for _____, the dependent variable. The equation $y = 2x + 1$ would be rewritten using function notation as _____.

7. To find where two functions intersect, set the functions _____ to one another and solve.

8. The domain of $g(x) = 6x + 1$ is _____.

9. The four ways to express a function are _____, _____, _____, and _____. A list of ordered pairs is an example of expressing a function _____.

10. A combination of two or more functions in which each part has its own domain is a(n) _____-defined function. To evaluate, identify the part that corresponds to that _____ value, substitute that value, and _____.

Essential Skills

In Exercises 1–2, determine whether each graph represents a function.

1.

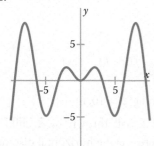

2.

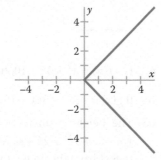

In Exercises 3–10, determine whether each equation represents a function.

3. $3 = |x - 6| + y$

4. $x^2 + 5 - y = 1$

5. $x^2 + 5 - y = 1$

6. $x - 6 + 8y^2 = 9$

7. $-4x^3 + x^2 + 3x = y$

8. $x^2 + 4y^2 = 36$

9. $y^2 = x - 2$

10. $y = 1$

In Exercises 11–28, evaluate.

11. If $f(x) = 2x^2 - x - 8$, find $f(-4)$ and $f(1)$.

12. If $g(x) = 2x - |5 + x|$, find $g(10)$ and $g(-7)$.

13. If $w(x) = 3x - |4 + x|$, find $w(3)$ and $w(-3)$.

14. If $r(x) = 6x^2 - 6x + 4$, find $r(2)$ and $r(-6)$.

15. If $t(x) = -x^3 + 2x$, find $t(-1)$ and $t(-4)$.

16. If $q(x) = x^4 - 5x^3 - 3x$, find $q(-3)$ and $q(1)$.

17. If $p(x) = |4x - 3|$, find $p(m - 7)$.

18. If $h(x) = x^2 - 2x$, find $h(3 + c)$.

19. If $j(x) = -3x^2 + 2x$, find $j(r - 5)$.

20. If $d(x) = -x^2 + 4x - 9$, find $d(s - 2)$.

21. If $b(x) = 2x^2 - 3x + 5$, find $b(4 + z)$.

22. If $v(x) = 4x^2 - 2x + 1$, find $v(1 - t)$.

23. If $f(x) = \begin{cases} -2x + 7 & \text{if } x < -8 \\ 3x^2 + x & \text{if } -8 \le x < -1 \\ -6x - 1 & \text{if } x \ge -1 \end{cases}$, find $f(-9)$ and $f(0)$.

24. If $p(x) = \begin{cases} 1 & \text{if } x \le -5 \\ |7 - 2x| & \text{if } -5 < x < 0 \\ x^2 & \text{if } x \ge 0 \end{cases}$, find $p(0)$ and $p(-12)$.

25. If $u(x) = \begin{cases} (2 - x)^2 & \text{if } x < -9 \\ -x^2 & \text{if } -9 \le x \le -2 \\ 8 - x & \text{if } x > -2 \end{cases}$, find $u(-10)$ and $u(-2)$.

26. If $k(x) = \begin{cases} 4 - 3x & \text{if } x \le 1 \\ -(3 - x)^2 & \text{if } 1 < x \le 4 \\ 5x & \text{if } x > 4 \end{cases}$, find $k(1)$ and $k(4)$.

27. If $c(x) = \begin{cases} 2 & \text{if } x \le -11 \\ |6x - 2| & \text{if } -11 < x < 5 \\ 6x^2 + 6 & \text{if } x \ge 5 \end{cases}$, find $c(6)$ and $c(-14)$.

28. If $n(x) = \begin{cases} 3x - 7 & \text{if } x < -4 \\ -x^2 + 5x & \text{if } -4 \le x < 3 \\ -4x - 2 & \text{if } x \ge 3 \end{cases}$, find $n(-4)$ and $n(3)$.

In Exercises 29–36, find the real x-value(s) such that the function equals 0.

29. $q(x) = 7x - 8$

30. $f(x) = 3x^2 + 13x - 10$

31. $v(x) = -\dfrac{2}{3}x - 14$

32. $h(x) = 16 - 9x$

33. $m(x) = 4x^2 - 17x - 15$

34. $w(x) = 18 - \dfrac{12}{5}x$

35. $p(x) = 5x^3 - 7x^2 - 6x$

36. $g(x) = 2x^3 + 3x^2 - 20x$

In Exercises 37–44, find the real x-value(s) so that the two functions are equal.

37. $g(x) = 10x - 9$ and $f(x) = -8x + 6$

38. $p(x) = 2 + 40x - x^2$ and $q(x) = 4x^2 + 6x - 5$

39. $m(x) = 4x + 13$ and $n(x) = x^2 - 8$

40. $d(x) = x^2 - 2x + 7$ and $c(x) = 29 - 14x + x^2$

41. $s(x) = 3x^2 - 9x$ and $t(x) = -7x - 2x + 3x^2$

42. $h(x) = 2x^2 - x - 15$ and $k(x) = 21 - x - 2x^2$

43. $j(x) = x^3 - 11x^2 + 3$ and $l(x) = -8x^2 + 18x + 3$

44. $u(x) = -2x^3 + 23x^2 - 8x$ and $v(x) = 2x^3 - 3x^2 + 4x$

In Exercises 45–46, express each function with an equation, table, and graph.

45. At the local department store, the average pay is $9 per hour. The total pay p an employee earns is a function of the number of hours h they work.

46. If a person drives 400 miles at an average of 50 miles per hour, then their distance d from the destination (in miles) is a function of the number of hours h driven.

In Exercises 47–49, use the following information.

Use a function to find the perimeter of a rectangle with the given area and length.

47. area: 20 square feet; length: 5 feet

48. area: 36 square feet; length: 4 feet

49. area: 313.5 square feet; length: 19 feet

In Exercises 50–52, use the following information.

A piece of rope is cut into two pieces. One piece is used to form a circle, and the other is used to form a square. Use the given length to write a function f representing the area of the circle as a function of the length of one side of the square s. Then write a function g representing the area of the square as a function of the radius of the circle r. Hint: If C is the circumference of the circle and P is the perimeter of the square, then the length equals $C + P$.

50. length: 20 feet

51. length: 12 feet

52. length: 36 feet

In Exercises 53–60, find the domain of each function.

53. $\{(2, -4), (4, 0), (-3, -14), (0, -8)\}$

54. $f(x) = \sqrt{-2x + 8}$

55. $v(x) = \sqrt{63 - 7x}$

56. $w(x) = \sqrt{11 + 5x}$

57. $p(x) = \dfrac{x}{x^2 - 10x - 24}$

58. $q(x) = \dfrac{x - 3}{x^2 + x - 12}$

59. $h(x) = \dfrac{x + 6}{x^2 - 36}$

60. $d(x) = \dfrac{x - 4}{x^2 + 3x - 40}$

Extensions

61. Find the domain of $f(x) = \dfrac{\sqrt{x^2 - 9}}{x^2 - 5x - 6}$.

62. True or False? The following graph is a function.

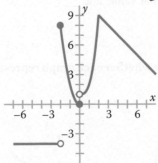

63. For $f(x) = x^2 + 3x - 10$, find $\dfrac{f(x + h) - f(x)}{h}$.

64. If $g(x) = -5x^2 - 3kx + 15$ and $g(2) = 10$, find k.

65. The height y (in feet) of a ball thrown by a child is $y = -0.083x^2 + 2x + 4$, where x is the horizontal distance in feet from the point at which the ball is thrown. Will the ball fly over the head of a 4-foot-tall child trying to catch the ball 24 feet away?

66. Will the graphs of $f(x) = \sqrt{2x^2 + x - 6}$ and $g(x) = x - 2$ intersect?

1.5 GRAPHS OF FUNCTIONS

OBJECTIVES

- Identify the domain and range of functions.
- Graph common types of functions.
- Graph piecewise-defined functions.
- Graph and use greatest integer (step) functions.
- Find the real zeros of functions.
- Identify intervals where functions are strictly increasing or decreasing.
- Find the maximum or minimum value(s) of functions.

PREREQUISITE VOCABULARY TERMS

absolute value equation
domain
function
linear equation
piecewise-defined function
quadratic equation
range

1.5.1 Finding the Domain and Range

Recall that the domain of a function is all allowable input values (x-values) and that the range of a function is all possible output values (y-values). The domain and range of a function can be identified visually from a graph of the function. A function's graph is the collection of ordered pairs (x, y) such that x is in the function's domain and y is in the function's range.

If function notation is used, then the ordered pairs can be expressed as $(x, f(x))$ or as (x, y). Since $f(x) = y$, each point on a function's graph is located x units from the y-axis and $f(x)$ units from the x-axis, as shown in Figure 1.5a.

Both the domain and range of the function shown in Figure 1.5a are all real numbers. It is assumed that the graph extends infinitely at both ends, unless the graph shows an open or closed point at one end.

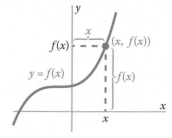

Figure 1.5a

Recall that an open point (open circle) indicates that the point is *not* included on a graph, and a closed point (closed circle) indicates that the point is included on a graph.

Evaluating a Function Graphically

Recall that a function can be evaluated algebraically for x by substituting the given x-value into the equation and simplifying to find the corresponding y-value (i.e., $f(x)$-value). For example, to evaluate $f(x) = 2x - 3$ for $x = 1$, substitute 1 into the function for x and simplify.

$$f(1) = 2(1) - 3 = -1$$

So, when $x = 1, f(x) = -1$ for $f(x) = 2x - 3$.

> **TIP**
>
> *The statement $f(x) = -1$ is equivalent to $y = -1$.*

These corresponding x and $f(x)$ values are an ordered pair on the graph of f. Specifically, the ordered pair $(1, -1)$ is a point on the graph of $f(x) = 2x - 3$. It follows that a function can also be evaluated by using the graph of the function. To evaluate a function for x using the graph, identify the point on the graph with this x-coordinate. The corresponding y-value from this point on the graph is the $f(x)$-value. This method for evaluating a function is demonstrated in **Example 1**.

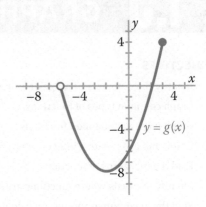

EXAMPLE 1   **Finding the Domain and Range of a Function**

Identify the domain and range of g. Then, using the graph, find $g(0)$, $g(3)$, and all x such that $g(x) = 0$.

SOLUTION

The graph of g has a point at each end. Therefore, it does not continue infinitely on either end (i.e., to ∞ or $-\infty$). Because the graph contains an open point at $(-6, 0)$, this point is not included on the graph. Because the graph contains a closed point at $(3, 4)$, this point is included on the graph.

Domain of g

The points on the graph includee all x-values between -6 and 3, not including -6 (because there is an open point where $x = -6$). So, the domain is all x-values such that $-6 < x \leq 3$.

$\qquad$ Domain of g: $(-6, 3]$ *The domain is all x-values between -6 and 3, not including -6.*

Range of g

The points on the graph include all y-values between -8 and 4. So, the range is all y-values such that $-8 \leq y \leq 4$.

$\qquad$ Range of g: $[-8, 4]$ *The range is all y-values between -8 and 4.*

Find $g(0)$, $g(3)$, and x such that $g(x) = 0$

Use the graph to find the coordinates that correspond to $x = 0$, $x = 3$, and $y = 0$.

$\qquad g(0) = -6$ $\qquad$ *The graph passes through $(0, -6)$, so when $x = 0$, $g(x) = -6$.*

$\qquad g(3) = 4$ $\qquad$ *The graph passes through $(3, 4)$, so when $x = 3$, $g(x) = 4$.*

The graph includes the point $(2, 0)$, and this is the only point on the graph where $y = 0$. So, $g(2) = 0$. Therefore, $g(x) = 0$ only when $x = 2$.

1.5.2   Graphing Some Important Functions

Several general types of equations and their graphs were demonstrated previously, including linear, quadratic, and absolute value equations. The graph of a function can be sketched using the general shape of a type of function and a few points on the function. Recall that an equation in two variables can be graphed by making a table (i.e., listing several chosen x-values and the corresponding y-value for each in a table) and then plotting the points from that table. Additionally, recall that the x- and y-intercepts (the points on the graph where $y = 0$ and $x = 0$, respectively) are also good points to find when graphing.

The following table shows the basic function for several function types. All functions of the same type will have a similarly shaped graph. For example, all absolute value functions will have the general V-shape, but the V may point up or down (or be wider or more narrow than the graph of $f(x) = |x|$), depending on the specific equation.

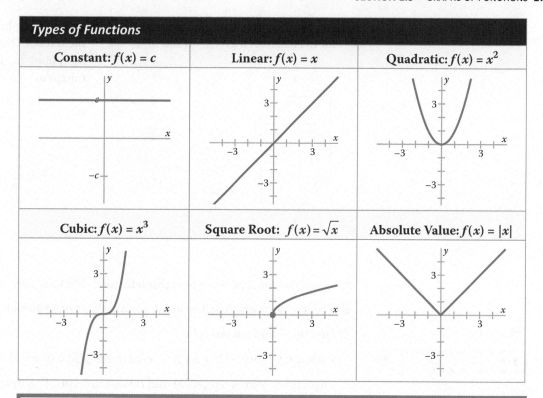

Types of Functions

Constant: $f(x) = c$	Linear: $f(x) = x$	Quadratic: $f(x) = x^2$
Cubic: $f(x) = x^3$	Square Root: $f(x) = \sqrt{x}$	Absolute Value: $f(x) = |x|$

Steps for Graphing a Function

❶ Identify the type of function and the general shape of the function's graph.

❷ Find the y-intercept(s) by evaluating $f(0)$, and the x-intercept(s) by solving $f(x) = 0$. Plot these points.

❸ Make a table of points by choosing several allowable values for x and finding the corresponding $f(x)$-value. Plot each ordered pair $(x, f(x))$ on a coordinate plane.

❹ Connect the points with a straight line or smooth curve, corresponding to the general shape of the graph defined by the function type.

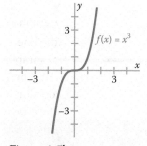

Figure 1.5b

EXAMPLE 2   **Graphing Functions by Plotting Points**

Find the intercepts, make a table, and sketch a graph for each function.

A. $f(x) = x^3 - 1$ **B.** $f(x) = -|x| + 2$

SOLUTION

A. Notice that the function type is cubic. The basic cubic function is $f(x) = x^3$.

❶ The function's graph will be in the general shape of a cubic function (Figure 1.5b).

❷ Find the x- and y-intercepts.

y-intercept: $f(0) = (0)^3 - 1 = -1$ x-intercept: $f(x) = 0 \Rightarrow 0 = x^3 - 1 \Rightarrow x = 1$

There is one y-intercept, $(0, -1)$, and one x-intercept, $(1, 0)$.

❸ Choose x-values near the x-intercept for the table, such as -2, -1, and 2.

❹ Plot the intercepts and the points fr the table. Then sketch a curve through the points in the general shape of a cubic function.

x	$f(x)$
-2	-9
-1	-2
2	7

$f(-2) = (-2)^3 - 1 = -9$

$f(-1) = (-1)^3 - 1 = -2$

$f(2) = (2)^3 - 1 = 7$

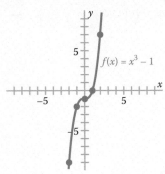

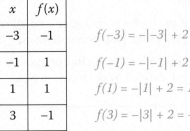

Figure 1.5c

TIP

Solve $0 = -|x| + 2$ by isolating the absolute value expression, then writing the two equations. Remember, if $|A| = B$, then $A = B$ or $A = -B$.

$0 = -|x| + 2$

$-|x| + 2 = 0$

$-|x| = -2$

$|x| = 2$

$x = 2$ or $x = -2$

NOTICE THAT

The graph is symmetric with respect to the y-axis.

B. Notice that the function type is absolute value. The basic absolute value function is $f(x) = |x|$.

❶ The function's graph will be in the general shape of an absolute value function (Figure 1.5c).

❷ Find the x- and y-intercepts.

y-intercept: $f(0) = -|0| + 2 = 2$ x-intercept: $f(x) = 0 \Rightarrow 0 = -|x| + 2 \Rightarrow x = 2$ or $x = -2$

There is one y-intercept, $(0, 2)$, and two x-intercepts, $(-2, 0)$ and $(2, 0)$.

❸ Choose x-values near the x-intercepts for the table, such as -3, -1, 1, and 3.

❹ Plot the intercepts and the points from the table. Then sketch the graph through the points in the general shape of an absolute value function.

x	$f(x)$
-3	-1
-1	1
1	1
3	-1

$f(-3) = -|-3| + 2 = -1$

$f(-1) = -|-1| + 2 = 1$

$f(1) = -|1| + 2 = 1$

$f(3) = -|3| + 2 = -1$

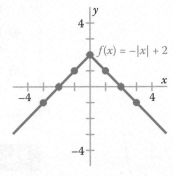

1.5.3 Graphing Piecewise-Defined Functions

Recall that a piecewise-defined function is a combination of two or more functions where a specific interval from the domain corresponds to each of the function's pieces. The graph of a piecewise-defined function is also divided into separate pieces.

| **EXAMPLE 3** | **Graphing a Piecewise-Defined Function** |

Sketch the graph of $f(x) = \begin{cases} 1-x & \text{if } x < -3 \\ 3 & \text{if } -3 \leq x < 0 \\ 2x+1 & \text{if } x \geq 0 \end{cases}$.

IMPORTANT

When graphing each piece of a piecewise-defined function, be sure to use an open point (open circle) for any endpoint when the corresponding x-value is not included in the domain.

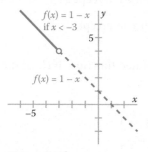

Figure 1.5d

SOLUTION

Graph the three pieces for the specific corresponding domain values. Notice that all three pieces are linear functions, so the graph of each piece is a line.

Function Piece	**Domain**	**Graph Description**
$f(x) = 1 - x$	$\{x \mid x < -3\}$	line with slope -1 and y-intercept 1
$f(x) = 3$	$\{x \mid -3 \leq x < 0\}$	horizontal line with y-intercept 3
$f(x) = 2x + 1$	$\{x \mid x \geq 0\}$	line with slope 2 and y-intercept 1

$\underline{f(x) = 1 - x \text{ if } x < -3}$

Sketch the line $y = 1 - x$, then remove the section of the line where $x \geq -3$. Since $x = -3$ is not included in the domain of this piece, use an open point where $x = -3$, which is $(-3, 4)$, as shown in Figure 1.5d.

$\underline{f(x) = 3 \text{ if } -3 \leq x < 0}$

Sketch the horizontal line $y = 3$ starting where $x = -3$ and ending where $x = 0$. Since -3 is included in the domain of this piece, use a closed point at $(-3, 3)$. Since 0 is not included in the domain of this piece, use an open point at $(0, 3)$.

$\underline{f(x) = 2x + 1 \text{ if } x \geq 0}$

Sketch the line $y = 2x + 1$, then remove the section of the line where $x < 0$. Since $x = 0$ is included in the domain of this piece, use a closed point where $x = 0$, which is $(0, 1)$.

NOTICE THAT

If both points where $x = -3$ were closed points, then the graph would not be a function. Similarly, if both points where $x = 0$ were closed points, then the graph would not be a function.

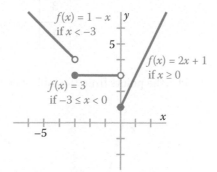

$g(x) = \begin{cases} x+2 & \text{if } x < -1 \\ x^2 & \text{if } -1 \leq x \leq 2 \\ x & \text{if } x > 2 \end{cases}$

1.5.4   Using a Table to Graph Piecewise-Defined Functions

The piecewise-defined function in the preceding example contained three pieces where each piece was a linear function, and so the graph of each piece was a line. Any type of function can be included in a piecewise-defined function. In the case where a piece is not linear, graph the piece by making a table of values and noting the general shape of the graph, as demonstrated in **Example 4**.

EXAMPLE 4 Graphing a Piecewise-Defined Function by Using a Table

Sketch the graph of $f(x) = \begin{cases} 0.5x^2 & \text{if } x \le 0 \\ -x & \text{if } 0 < x < 2. \\ |x| + 1 & \text{if } x \ge 2 \end{cases}$

SOLUTION

Graph the three pieces for the specific corresponding domain values.

Function Piece	Domain	Graph Description
$f(x) = 0.5x^2$	$\{x \mid x \le 0\}$	parabola with y-intercept 0
$f(x) = -x$	$\{x \mid 0 < x < 2\}$	line with slope -1 and y-intercept 0
$f(x) = \mid x \mid + 1$	$\{x \mid x \ge 2\}$	V-shaped graph with y-intercept 1

Since each piece is not a line, use a table to graph the piecewise-defined function. Include the endpoints of the domain intervals in the x-values for the table.

TIP

The entire table does not need to be completed. Substitute the x-values from the table into only the corresponding piece of the function. If a domain interval's endpoint is included for more than one piece (as is the case with $x = 0$ and $x = 2$), evaluate that endpoint value in both applicable functions.

x	$f(x) = 0.5x^2$	$f(x) = -x$	$f(x) = \mid x \mid + 1$
-4	8		
-2	2		
0	0	0	
1		-1	
2		-2	3
3			4
4			5

Plot the points from the table, keeping in mind the general shape of each piece.

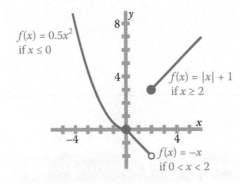

(0, 0) is included in the graph of $f(x) = 0.5x^2$, so a closed circle is used for the point.

WHAT'S THE BIG IDEA?

Explain the instances where open and closed points are used in the graph of a piecewise-defined function.

1.5.5   Modeling with Piecewise-Defined Functions

A piecewise-defined function will be used to model a situation when the independent variable (domain) is divided into parts. For example, suppose a person earns $30 for mowing a yard if it takes him between 0 and 2 hours. He earns $50 if it takes him longer than 2 hours. This situation's independent variable (the domain), the amount of time spent mowing a yard, is divided into two parts: 1) between 0 and 2 hours, and 2) more than 2 hours.

This situation is modeled by the piecewise-defined function shown in Figure 1.5e, where $f(x)$, the total pay, is a function of x, the number of hours spent mowing.

$$f(x) = \begin{cases} 30 & \text{if } 0 < x \le 2 \\ 50 & \text{if } x > 2 \end{cases}$$

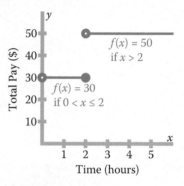

Figure 1.5e

EXAMPLE 5   **Modeling a Piecewise-Defined Function**

A freelance designer earns $200 per project for the first 5 projects, $250 per project for the next 10 projects, and $350 per project for any additional projects he completes. Write a piecewise-defined function for his total pay.

SOLUTION

The domain is the number of projects completed. So, write a function for the total pay, $f(x)$, as a function of the number of projects completed, x (where x is a whole number).

The domain is divided into 3 parts: the first 5 projects, the next 10 projects (the 6th through the 15th projects), and all additional projects (all projects after the 15th project).

Domain Parts: $x \le 5$, $5 < x \le 15$, and $x > 15$

Determine how the total pay is calculated for each piece.

Domain	Pay Description	Function Piece
$\{x \mid x \le 5\}$	$200 per project for projects 1 through 5	$f(x) = 200x$
$\{x \mid 5 < x \le 15\}$	$250 per project for projects 6 though 15	$f(x) = 250x - 250$
$\{x \mid x > 15\}$	$350 per project for projects 16 and greater	$f(x) = 350x - 1750$

The piecewise-defined function for his total pay is $f(x) = \begin{cases} 200x & \text{if } x \le 5 \\ 250x - 250 & \text{if } 5 < x \le 15 \\ 350x - 1750 & \text{if } x > 15 \end{cases}$.

CAUTION

It may seem that the function for projects 6 through 15 should be $f(x) = 250x$ (since the pay for projects 6 through 15 is $250/project). However, if the designer completed 8 projects, he would not earn $250(8) = $2000. Instead, he would earn $200(5) + $250(3) = $1750 ($200(5) for the first 5 projects and $250(3) for projects 6, 7, and 8).

The function corresponding to projects 6 through 15 must take into account that the pay rate is \$200 per project for projects 1 through 5. So, if he completes between 6 and 15 projects, the total pay can be calculated by adding \$200(5) and \$250(x – 5), where \$200(5) is the pay for the first 5 projects and \$250(x – 5) is the pay for projects over 5.

$$f(x) = 200(5) + 250(x - 5) = 1000 + 250x - 1250 = 250x - 250$$

Similarly, the function for 16 or more projects must take into account that the pay rate for projects 1 through 5 and for projects 6 through 15 was not \$350 per project. The function for 16 or more projects can be found by adding \$200(5), \$250(10), and \$350(x – 15), where \$200(5) is the pay for the first 5 projects, \$250(10) is the pay for projects 6 through 15, and \$350(x – 15) is the pay for projects over 15.

$$f(x) = 200(5) + 250(10) + 350(x - 15) = 1000 + 2500 + 350x - 5250 = 350x - 1750$$

1.5.6 The Greatest Integer Function

The **greatest integer function**, denoted as $[[x]]$, is a piecewise-defined function. The output of the greatest integer function is the greatest integer that is less than or equal to the input value. So, $[[x]]$ represents the greatest integer that is less than or equal to x. The greatest integer function is an example of a **step function**, which is a function where the graph is a series of disconnected horizontal line segments resembling a staircase.

EXAMPLE 6   Evaluating the Greatest Integer Function

Evaluate $[[16.9]]$, $[[405.111]]$, $[[3]]$, $[[-5.7]]$, and $[[-9(2)]] - [[0.4]] + [[-0.82]]$.

SOLUTION

Determine the greatest integer that is less than or equal to each input value. If the input value x is an integer, then the output is the same integer. If the input value x is not an integer, then $[[x]]$ is the greatest integer less than x.

$[[16.9]] = 16$	*16 is the greatest integer less than 16.9.*
$[[405.111]] = 405$	*405 is the greatest integer less than 405.111.*
$[[3]] = 3$	*3 is equal to 3.*
$[[-5.7]] = -6$	*–6 is the greatest integer less than –5.7.*

The next expression involves addition and subtraction. The greatest integer function acts like grouping symbols in the order of operations.

$$[[-9(2)]] - [[0.4]] + [[-0.82]] = [[-18]] - [[0.4]] + [[-0.82]] \quad \textit{Multiply.}$$
$$= -18 - 0 + (-1) \quad \textit{Evaluate each function.}$$
$$= -19 \quad \textit{Simplify.}$$

1.5.7 Graphing the Greatest Integer Function

The domain of the greatest integer function is all real numbers. The range of the greatest integer function is only integers because the output of the function is always an integer. Therefore, non-integer y-values are not represented on the graph of $f(x) = [[x]]$, and so the graph is a series of horizontal line segments.

EXAMPLE 7   **Graphing the Greatest Integer Function**

Sketch the graph of $y = [[x]]$.

SOLUTION

Make a table to locate some points on the graph. Use some x-values that are not integers in the table.

x	−2.5	−2	−1.5	−1	−0.5	0	0.5	1	1.5	2	2.5
$f(x)$	−3	−2	−2	−1	−1	0	0	1	1	2	2

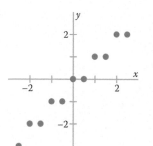

Figure 1.5f

Plot these points (Figure 1.5f) and look for a pattern.

Notice the pattern with the x-values ≥ 0.   Similarly, for x-values < 0, the pattern continues.

$$0 \leq x < 1 \;\Rightarrow\; y = 0 \qquad\qquad -1 \leq x < 0 \;\Rightarrow\; y = -1$$
$$1 \leq x < 2 \;\Rightarrow\; y = 1 \qquad\qquad -2 \leq x < -1 \;\Rightarrow\; y = -2$$
$$2 \leq x < 3 \;\Rightarrow\; y = 2 \qquad\qquad -3 \leq x < -2 \;\Rightarrow\; y = -3$$

> **TIP**
>
> *The x-intervals and corresponding y-values can be written in a table.*
>
> | x | y |
> |------|-----|
> | $-3 \leq x < -2$ | -3 |
> | $-2 \leq x < -1$ | -2 |
> | $-1 \leq x < 0$ | -1 |
> | $0 \leq x < 1$ | 0 |
> | $1 \leq x < 2$ | 1 |
> | $2 \leq x < 3$ | 2 |

The pattern forms a piecewise-defined function. Since all of the x-values between two consecutive integer x-values correspond to a single range value, the graph is a series of horizontal line segments. Since only the smaller of the two consecutive integer x-values is included in the domain of that interval, the graph includes a closed point on the left end and an open point on the right end of each horizontal line segment.

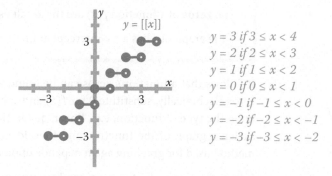

$$y = 3 \text{ if } 3 \leq x < 4$$
$$y = 2 \text{ if } 2 \leq x < 3$$
$$y = 1 \text{ if } 1 \leq x < 2$$
$$y = 0 \text{ if } 0 \leq x < 1$$
$$y = -1 \text{ if } -1 \leq x < 0$$
$$y = -2 \text{ if } -2 \leq x < -1$$
$$y = -3 \text{ if } -3 \leq x < -2$$

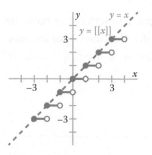

Figure 1.5g

The horizontal line segments in the graph of $y = [[x]]$ occur where the range values are integers. Notice that the line $y = x$ (the related line to $y = [[x]]$) passes through the left endpoint of each line segment in the graph of $y = [[x]]$, as shown in Figure 1.5g. This is not a coincidence. For all greatest integer functions where the expression is linear, the related line passes through the endpoints of the line segments. This fact can be used to graph a greatest integer function where the expression is linear.

EXAMPLE 8 **Graphing the Greatest Integer Function**

Sketch the graph of $y = [[2x + 1]]$.

SOLUTION

Sketch the related line, $y = 2x + 1$ (slope 2 and y-intercept 1), using a dashed line.

Then draw a horizontal line segment starting at each point on the line with an integer y-value. End each line segment at the x-value that corresponds to the next point with an integer y-value.

TIP

Make a table of points if this process is difficult to visualize.

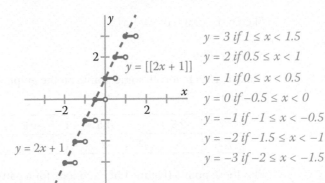

$y = 3$ if $1 \le x < 1.5$
$y = 2$ if $0.5 \le x < 1$
$y = 1$ if $0 \le x < 0.5$
$y = 0$ if $-0.5 \le x < 0$
$y = -1$ if $-1 \le x < -0.5$
$y = -2$ if $-1.5 \le x < -1$
$y = -3$ if $-2 \le x < -1.5$

1.5.8 Finding Zeros of a Function

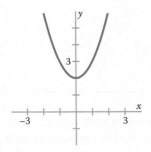

Recall that a zero of a function is an x-value such that $f(x) = 0$. Furthermore, a zero of a function is the x-coordinate of an x-intercept of the function.

DEFINITION

The **zeros** of a function $f(x)$ are the x-values where $f(x) = 0$.

If the graph of f has an x-intercept at $(a, 0)$, then a is a zero of f.

It follows that a function's zeros can be found algebraically or graphically. To find a function's zeros algebraically, substitute 0 for $f(x)$ and solve for x. (The method used for solving depends upon the type of function, e.g., linear, quadratic, cubic.) To find a function's zeros graphically, sketch a graph of the function and then identify the x-coordinate of any x-intercepts. (The method used for graphing again depends upon the type of function.)

Just as the graph of a function can have any number of x-intercepts, a function can have any number of zeros, including no zeros. Since it is possible for a graph of a function to not intersect the x-axis, as is the case in Figure 1.5h, the graph of a function can have no x-intercepts, and will then also have no zeros.

Figure 1.5h

EXAMPLE 9 **Finding the Real Zeros of a Function**

Find the real zeros of each function.

A. $f(x) = 2x^3 + 5x^2 - 2x - 5$ **B.** $g(x) = 2\sqrt{x^2 + 9}$ **C.** $h(x) = \dfrac{2 - x}{3x + 5}$

SOLUTION

To find a function's zero(s), substitute 0 for the range value and find the corresponding domain value(s), if any.

A. The function is a polynomial function, so solve by factoring.

$$f(x) = 2x^3 + 5x^2 - 2x - 5$$
$$0 = 2x^3 + 5x^2 - 2x - 5 \qquad \text{Substitute 0 for } f(x).$$
$$0 = x^2(2x + 5) - (2x + 5) \qquad \text{Factor by grouping.}$$
$$0 = (2x + 5)(x^2 - 1) \qquad \text{Factor } (2x + 5) \text{ from each term.}$$
$$2x + 5 = 0 \quad \text{or} \quad x^2 - 1 = 0 \qquad \text{Set each factor equal to 0.}$$
$$2x = -5 \qquad\qquad x^2 = 1 \qquad \text{Solve each equation for } x.$$
$$x = -\frac{5}{2} \qquad\qquad x = \pm 1$$

REMEMBER

Take ± the square root of each side to solve $x^2 = 1$.

So, $f(x) = 2x^3 + 5x^2 - 2x - 5$ has zeros at $x = -\frac{5}{2}, -1,$ and 1.

Use a graphing calculator to graph the function and check the answer.

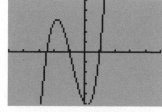

The function's graph has x-intercepts at $\left(-\frac{5}{2}, 0\right)$, $(-1, 0)$, and $(1, 0)$.

B. The function is a square root function, so solve by isolating the radical expression on one side of the equation and then squaring both sides.

$$g(x) = 2\sqrt{x^2 + 9}$$
$$0 = 2\sqrt{x^2 + 9} \qquad \text{Substitute 0 for } g(x).$$
$$0 = \sqrt{x^2 + 9} \qquad \text{Divide each side by 2 to isolate the radical.}$$
$$(0)^2 = \left(\sqrt{x^2 + 9}\right)^2 \qquad \text{Square each side.}$$
$$0 = x^2 + 9 \qquad \text{Simplify.}$$
$$-9 = x^2 \qquad \text{Subtract 9 from each side.}$$
$$\pm\sqrt{-9} = x \qquad \text{Take ± the square root of each side.}$$

The x-values are not real numbers, so the function has no real zeros. Notice that the graph of the function, as shown in Figure 1.5i, does not intersect the x-axis.

C. The function is a rational function, so solve by setting the expression in the numerator equal to zero and solving for x.

$$h(x) = \frac{2 - x}{3x + 5}$$
$$0 = \frac{2 - x}{3x + 5} \qquad \text{Substitute 0 for } h(x).$$
$$2 - x = 0 \qquad \text{Set the expression in the numerator equal to 0.}$$
$$x = 2 \qquad \text{Solve for } x.$$

So, $h(x) = \frac{2 - x}{3x + 5}$ has one zero at $x = 2$. Notice that the graph of the function, as shown in Figure 1.5j, intersects the x-axis only at $(2, 0)$.

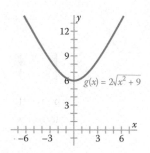

Figure 1.5i

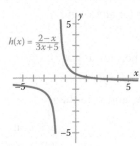

Figure 1.5j

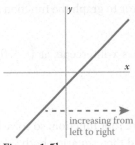

WHAT'S THE BIG IDEA?

Explain the relationship between a function's zero and the graph of a function, as well as the relationship between a function's zero and the equation of a function.

1.5.9 Determining Intervals Over Which a Function Is Increasing

Recall that a line with positive slope increases from left to right, as shown in Figure 1.5k, and a line with negative slope decreases from left to right, as shown in Figure 1.5l. So, we say that a linear function with a positive slope is **increasing** for all domain values, and a linear function with a negative slope is **decreasing** for all domain values.

Linear Function with Positive Slope   **Linear Function with Negative Slope**

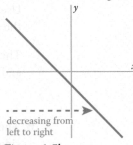

Figure 1.5k   Figure 1.5l

The third possibility for a linear function is the horizontal line, where the slope is 0. A linear function with slope 0 (a constant function) is **constant** for all domain values. Since a line has a constant rate of change, a linear function is either only increasing, only decreasing, or only constant for all domain values.

Graphs of nonlinear functions may not have a constant slope. In the case where the slope is not constant, the function may be **strictly increasing** on some intervals (i.e., some interval of domain values), **strictly decreasing** on some other intervals, and **constant** on some intervals.

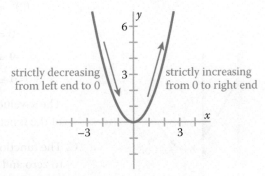

For example, consider the graph of the quadratic function $f(x) = x^2$ (Figure 1.5m). This function is strictly decreasing on the interval $(-\infty, 0)$ and strictly increasing on the interval $(0, \infty)$.

Figure 1.5m

Increasing, Decreasing, and Constant Functions

A function f is **strictly increasing** on an open interval when for any x_1 and x_2 in the interval where $x_1 < x_2$, it is also true that $f(x_1) < f(x_2)$.

A function f is **strictly decreasing** on an open interval when for any x_1 and x_2 in the interval where $x_1 < x_2$, it is also true that $f(x_1) > f(x_2)$.

A function f is **constant** on an open interval when for any x_1 and x_2 in the interval, it is true that $f(x_1) = f(x_2)$.

EXAMPLE 10	**Identifying a Function's Strictly Increasing and Strictly Decreasing Intervals**

Identify the intervals on which each function is strictly increasing, strictly decreasing, or constant.

A.

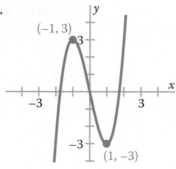

B.

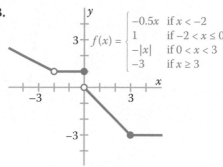

$$f(x) = \begin{cases} -0.5x & \text{if } x < -2 \\ 1 & \text{if } -2 < x \le 0 \\ -|x| & \text{if } 0 < x < 3 \\ -3 & \text{if } x \ge 3 \end{cases}$$

SOLUTION

A. Starting on the left end, the function is strictly increasing on the interval $(-\infty, -1)$, strictly decreasing on the interval $(-1, -1)$, and strictly increasing again on the interval $(1, \infty)$.

B. Starting on the left end, the function is strictly decreasing on the interval $(-\infty, -2)$, constant on the interval $(-2, 0)$, strictly decreasing again on the interval $(0, 3)$, and constant on the interval $(3, \infty)$.

1.5.10 Relative Minimums and Maximums

Some functions have a **minimum** y-value, a **maximum** y-value, or both a minimum and a maximum y-value, but not all functions do. A minimum is the y-value of the point on a function with the least y-value, and a maximum is the y-value of the point on a function with the greatest y-value. Consider the graph of a linear function that is not horizontal. Regardless of the slope, this function has no maximum or minimum y-value because the line continues infinitely in both directions. Consider the graph of the parabola shown in Figure 1.5m. This graph has a minimum y-value at $(0, 0)$. However, it has no maximum y-value because the graph extends infinitely in an upward direction.

A point on the graph of a function such that the graph is increasing on one side and decreasing on the other is a **relative maximum** or **relative minimum** (also called a **local maximum** or **minimum**). For example, the graph in **Example 10A** contains one relative maximum point at $(-1, 3)$, so the relative maximum y-value is 3. This graph also contains one relative minimum point at $(1, -3)$, so the relative minimum y-value is -3.

A function may have any number of relative maximum or minimum y-values. These values can be identified by graphing the function. If the relative maximum or minimum points do not have integer coordinates, then they can be approximated by using the TRACE function on a graphing calculator.

EXAMPLE 11 Identifying Relative Maximum and Minimum Values

Identify the relative maximum and minimum values of $y = -x^3 + 5x + 1$, if any.

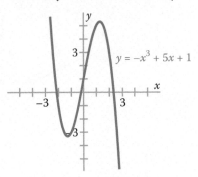

SOLUTION

From the graph, the function has a relative minimum between $x = -2$ and $x = 0$, and a relative maximum between $x = 0$ and $x = 2$.

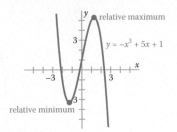

The exact coordinates of the minimum and maximum points cannot be determined from this graph. So, enter the function into a graphing calculator and use the TRACE function to approximate the coordinates of the minimum and maximum points.

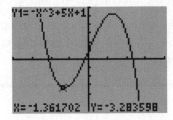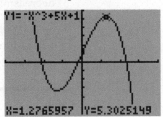

From the calculator, the function has a relative minimum at approximately $(-1.4, -3.3)$, and a relative maximum at approximately $(1.3, 5.3)$.

SECTION 1.5 EXERCISES

Warm Up

Describe the shape of the graph of each function.

1. $y = 2|x + 6|$

2. $x^2 = y$

3. $y = 2x + 9$

Just the Facts

Fill in the blanks.

4. To indicate that the point (a, b) is not included on the graph of a function, use a(n) _____ point at (a, b).

5. The greatest integer function, denoted as _____, is an example of a(n) _____ function.

6. The _____ of a function f are the values of x for which $f(x) = 0$. Graphically, they are the _____.

7. A function f is strictly decreasing on an interval when, for any x_1 and x_2 in the interval where $x_1 < x_2$, it is also true that $f(x_1)$ _____ $f(x_2)$.

8. If a function is increasing on one side of a point and decreasing on the other side of the point, then the y-coordinate of that point is a relative _____ or _____ value.

9. If the domain of a function f is [3, 5), then the graph of f will contain a(n) _____ point at $(3, f(5))$ and a(n) _____ point at $(5, f(5))$.

10. An absolute value function will always have one interval where the function is _____ and one interval where the function is _____, because its graph is _____-shaped.

Essential Skills

In Exercises 1–8, write the domain and range of each function. Use interval notation when possible; otherwise, use set-builder notation.

1.

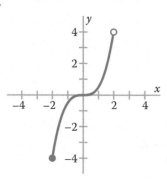

2.

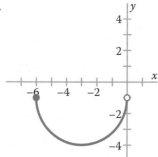

3.

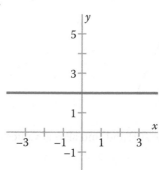

4.

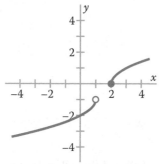

5.

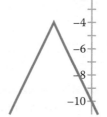

6.

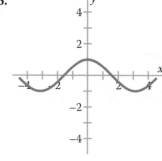

64.

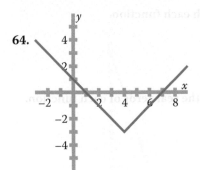

65.

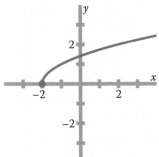

66.

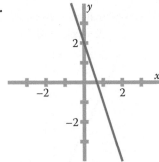

67.

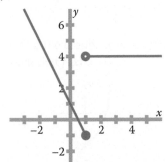

68.

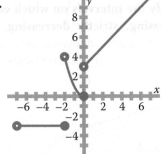

69.

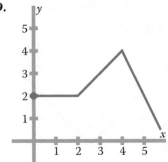

70.

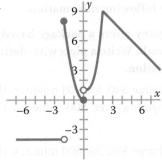

In Exercises 71–72, identify the relative maximum and relative minimum points on each graph, if any. Round to the nearest tenth.

71.

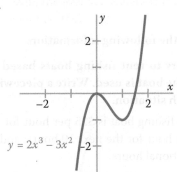

$y = 2x^3 - 3x^2$

72.

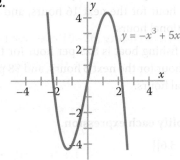

$y = -x^3 + 5x$

Extensions

In Exercises 73–76, identify the domain and range of the following functions. Then identify the intervals on which each function is strictly increasing, strictly decreasing, or constant.

73. $f(x) = \dfrac{1}{10}x - 6$

74. $h(x) = -2x^2 + 5$

75. $t(x) = |4x - 3| - 2$

76. $q(x) = -\sqrt{x - 5}$

77. The cost of sending an overnight package from Texas to Massachusetts is $100.42 for a package weighing up to and including 1 pound, plus an additional $6.42 for each additional pound or portion of a pound. Use the greatest integer function to create a model for the cost c of overnight delivery of a package weighing p pounds. Then graph the function.

78. Write the piecewise-defined function for the graph.

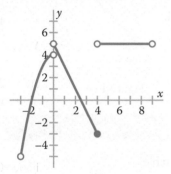

79. Credit card companies base the minimum payment due on the amount owed. The following rules apply: For a bill less than $20, the entire amount is due. For a bill of at least $20 but less than $1000, the minimum payment due is $20. On a bill of at least $1000 but less than $3000, a minimum of $50 is due. Additionally, there is a minimum of $100 due on bills of $3000 and over. Write the function $p(x)$ that describes the minimum payment due on a bill of x dollars (where x is a whole number).

80. A car rental company offers a midsize car for $130 per week. Extra days cost $30 per day until the rate exceeds the quoted weekly rate, in which case the weekly rate applies. Write a piecewise-defined function for the cost c of renting a midsize car as a function of the number of days x, where $0 < x \le 20$.

81. Solve $h(x) = -7x^3 + 35x^2 - 5x + 25$. How many real zeros does the function have?

82. True or False? A function that has three relative maximums must have three relative minimums.

83. Sketch the graph with the following properties: zeros at 2 and −4, y-intercept at 4, a relative maximum at $(-2, 8)$, a relative minimum at $(2, 0)$, strictly increasing from $(-\infty, -2)$ and $(2, \infty)$, strictly decreasing from $(-2, 2)$, with a domain and range of all real numbers.

1.6 TRANSFORMATIONS OF FUNCTIONS

OBJECTIVES

- Graph functions using translations.
- Graph functions using reflections.
- Stretch graphs of functions.
- Determine whether functions are even or odd.
- Identify symmetry of functions.

PREREQUISITE VOCABULARY TERMS

domain

function

range

reflection

symmetry

A **transformation** is an operation that changes the graph of an equation. The original graph is called the **pre-image**, and the transformed graph is called the **image**.

One type of transformation is called a **translation**, which is a shift of a graph horizontally or vertically. For example, Figure 1.6a shows the graphs of $y = x$ and $y = x + 5$. Notice that shifting the graph of $y = x$ upward 5 units forms the graph of $y = x + 5$. So, we can say that the graph of $y = x + 5$ is the result of translating the graph of $y = x$ upward 5 units. In this case, the graph of $y = x$ is the pre-image and the graph of $y = x + 5$ is the image.

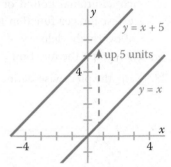

Figure 1.6a

1.6.1 Translating Functions

The graphs of six basic functions are shown in the following table.

Basic Functions		
Constant: $f(x) = c$	**Linear:** $f(x) = x$	**Quadratic:** $f(x) = x^2$
Cubic: $f(x) = x^3$	**Square Root:** $f(x) = \sqrt{x}$	**Absolute Value:** $f(x) = |x|$

When the equation of one of the basic functions is modified by adding or subtracting a number, the graph of that basic function is translated either horizontally or vertically.

Generally, suppose $g(x)$ and $f(x)$ are some functions and $c > 0$.

- If $g(x) = f(x) + c$, then the graph of $g(x)$ is the image of $f(x)$ after a vertical translation of c units upward. So, every point (x, y) on $f(x)$ corresponds to a point $(x, y + c)$ on $g(x)$.

- If $g(x) = f(x) - c$, then the graph of $g(x)$ is the image of $f(x)$ after a vertical translation of c units downward. So, every point (x, y) on $f(x)$ corresponds to a point $(x, y - c)$ on $g(x)$.

- If $g(x) = f(x + c)$, then the graph of $g(x)$ is the image of $f(x)$ after a horizontal translation of c units to the left. So, every point (x, y) on $f(x)$ corresponds to a point $(x - c, y)$ on $g(x)$.

- If $g(x) = f(x - c)$, then the graph of $g(x)$ is the image of $f(x)$ after a horizontal translation of c units to the right. So, every point (x, y) on $f(x)$ corresponds to a point $(x + c, y)$ on $g(x)$.

Steps for Graphing a Function $g(x)$ by Using Translations Where $c > 0$

❶ Identify the basic type of function, $f(x)$, that $g(x)$ is based on.

❷ Identify any horizontal and/or vertical translations from the equation of $g(x)$.
  - $g(x) = f(x) + c \implies f(x)$ is shifted c units upward $\implies (x, y) \to (x, y + c)$
  - $g(x) = f(x) - c \implies f(x)$ is shifted c units downward $\implies (x, y) \to (x, y - c)$
  - $g(x) = f(x + c) \implies f(x)$ is shifted c units to the left $\implies (x, y) \to (x - c, y)$
  - $g(x) = f(x - c) \implies f(x)$ is shifted c units to the right $\implies (x, y) \to (x + c, y)$

❸ Apply these translations to the graph of $f(x)$, resulting in the graph of $g(x)$.

EXAMPLE 1 **Graphing a Function by Using Vertical and Horizontal Translations**

Sketch the graph of each function by using a translation of the corresponding basic function.

A. $g(x) = x^2 - 3$ **B.** $h(x) = (x + 1)^3 + 2$

SOLUTION

A. The function $g(x) = x^2 - 3$ corresponds to the basic quadratic function $f(x) = x^2$.

So, $g(x) = f(x) - 3$, where $f(x) = x^2$.

Therefore, the graph of $g(x)$ is the image of $f(x) = x^2$ after a vertical translation downward 3 units.

To complete this translation of $f(x) = x^2$, shift each point (x, y) on $f(x) = x^2$ to $(x, y - 3)$.

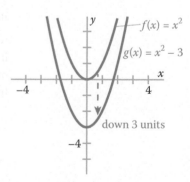

$f(x) \to g(x)$
$(-1, 1) \to (-1, -2)$
$(0, 0) \to (0, -3)$
$(1, 1) \to (1, -2)$

For example, the points $(-1, 1)$, $(0, 0)$, and $(1, 1)$ are on the graph of $f(x) = x^2$. So, the points $(-1, -2)$, $(0, -3)$, and $(1, -2)$ are on the graph of $g(x) = x^2 - 3$.

B. The function $h(x) = (x + 1)^3 + 2$ corresponds to the basic cubic function $f(x) = x^3$.

So, $h(x) = f(x + 1) + 2$, where $f(x) = x^3$.

Therefore, the graph of $h(x)$ is the image of $f(x) = x^3$ after a vertical translation upward 2 units and a horizontal translation to the left 1 unit.

To complete this translation of $f(x) = x^3$, shift each point (x, y) on $f(x) = x^3$ to $(x - 1, y + 2)$.

For example, the points $(-1, -1)$, $(0, 0)$, and $(1, 1)$ are on the graph of $f(x) = x^3$. So, the points $(-2, 1)$, $(-1, 2)$, and $(0, 3)$ are on the graph of $h(x) = (x + 1)^3 + 2$.

$f(x) \rightarrow h(x)$
$(-1, -1) \rightarrow (-2, 1)$
$(0, 0) \rightarrow (-1, 2)$
$(1, 1) \rightarrow (0, 3)$

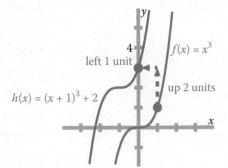

1.6.2 Reflecting Functions

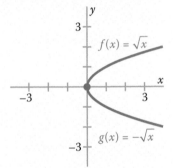

A reflection is another type of transformation. In Figure 1.6b, the graph of $g(x) = -\sqrt{x}$ is a reflection of the graph of $f(x) = \sqrt{x}$ over the x-axis. Generally, if $g(x) = -f(x)$, then the graph of $g(x)$ is a reflection of the graph of $f(x)$ over the x-axis. Thus, every point (x, y) on $f(x)$ corresponds to a point $(x, -y)$ on $g(x)$.

Figure 1.6b

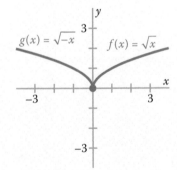

In Figure 1.6c, notice that the graph of $g(x) = \sqrt{-x}$ is a reflection of the graph of $f(x) = \sqrt{x}$ over the y-axis. Generally, if $g(x) = f(-x)$, then the graph of $g(x)$ is a reflection of the graph of $f(x)$ over the y-axis. So, every point (x, y) on $f(x)$ corresponds to a point $(-x, y)$ on $g(x)$.

Figure 1.6c

Steps for Graphing a Function $g(x)$ by Using Reflections

❶ Identify the basic type of function, $f(x)$, that $g(x)$ is based on.

❷ Identify any reflections from the equation of $g(x)$.

- $g(x) = -f(x) \Rightarrow f(x)$ is reflected over the x-axis $\Rightarrow (x, y) \rightarrow (x, -y)$
- $g(x) = f(-x) \Rightarrow f(x)$ is reflected over the y-axis $\Rightarrow (x, y) \rightarrow (-x, y)$

❸ Apply the reflection to the graph of $f(x)$, resulting in the graph of $g(x)$.

Reflections can also be combined with translations to graph a function.

EXAMPLE 2 — Graphing a Function by Using a Reflection

Sketch the graph of each function by using a reflection or translation of the corresponding basic function.

A. $g(x) = -x^2$ **B.** $h(x) = (-x)^3 - 2$

SOLUTION

A. The function $g(x) = -x^2$ corresponds to the basic quadratic function $f(x) = x^2$.

So, $g(x) = -f(x)$, where $f(x) = x^2$.

Therefore, the graph of $g(x)$ is the image of $f(x) = x^2$ after a reflection over the x-axis.

To complete this reflection of $f(x) = x^2$, reflect each point (x, y) on $f(x) = x^2$ to $(x, -y)$.

For example, the points $(-1, 1)$, $(0, 0)$, and $(1, 1)$ are on the graph of $f(x) = x^2$. So, the points $(-1, -1)$, $(0, 0)$, and $(1, -1)$ are on the graph of $g(x) = -x^2$.

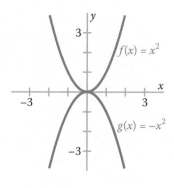

$f(x) \to g(x)$
$(-1, 1) \to (-1, -1)$
$(0, 0) \to (0, 0)$
$(1, 1) \to (1, -1)$

B. The function $h(x) = (-x)^3 - 2$ corresponds to the basic cubic function $f(x) = x^3$.

So, $h(x) = f(-x) - 2$, where $f(x) = x^3$.

Therefore, the graph of $h(x)$ is the image of $f(x) = x^3$ after a reflection over the y-axis and a vertical translation downward 2 units.

To complete this translation of $f(x) = x^3$, shift each point (x, y) on $f(x) = x^3$ to $(-x, y - 2)$.

For example, the points $(-1, -1)$, $(0, 0)$, and $(1, 1)$ are on the graph of $f(x) = x^3$. So, the points $(1, -3)$, $(0, -2)$, and $(-1, -1)$ are on the graph of $h(x) = (-x)^3 - 2$.

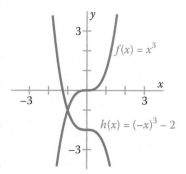

$f(x) \to h(x)$
$(-1, -1) \to (1, -3)$
$(0, 0) \to (0, -2)$
$(1, 1) \to (-1, -1)$

WHAT'S THE BIG IDEA?

Describe the graph of $g(x) = -(x - h)^2 + k$, where $h > 0$ and $k > 0$, as compared to the graph of $f(x) = x^2$.

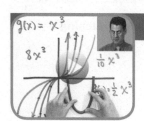

1.6.3 Stretching Functions

When the graph of a function is translated or reflected, the position of the graph changes, but the shape of the graph remains the same. So, translations and reflections are **rigid transformations**. A **nonrigid transformation** is a change to the graph that results in a change in the shape of the graph. One example of a nonrigid transformation is a vertical **stretch**, where the graph of a function either widens or narrows.

If $g(x)$ and $f(x)$ are some functions such that $g(x) = cf(x)$, where c is some positive number, then the graph of $g(x)$ is the image of $f(x)$ after a vertical stretch by a factor of c.

• If $c > 1$, then the vertical stretch narrows the graph of $f(x)$.
• If $0 < c < 1$, then the vertical stretch widens the graph of $f(x)$.

In either case, every point (x, y) on $f(x)$ corresponds to a point (x, cy) on $g(x)$.

Steps for Graphing a Function $g(x)$ by Stretching

❶ Identify the basic type of function, $f(x)$, that $g(x)$ is based on.

❷ Identify any stretch from the equation of $g(x)$.

❸ Apply the stretch to the graph of $f(x)$, resulting in the graph of $g(x)$.

Reflections and translations can be combined with a stretch to graph a function.

EXAMPLE 3   **Graphing a Function by Using a Stretch**

Sketch the graph of $g(x) = 2|x|$ by stretching the corresponding basic function.

SOLUTION

The function $g(x) = 2|x|$ corresponds to the basic absolute value function $f(x) = |x|$.

So, $g(x) = 2f(x)$ where $f(x) = |x|$.

Therefore, the graph of $g(x)$ is the image of $f(x) = |x|$ after a vertical stretch by a factor of 2.

To complete this stretch of $f(x) = |x|$, change each point (x, y) on $f(x) = |x|$ to $(x, 2y)$.

$f(x) \rightarrow g(x)$
$(-1, 1) \rightarrow (-1, 2)$
$(0, 0) \rightarrow (0, 0)$
$(1, 1) \rightarrow (1, 2)$

▶ For example, the points $(-1, 1)$, $(0, 0)$, and $(1, 1)$ are on the graph of $f(x) = |x|$. So, the points $(-1, 2)$, $(0, 0)$, and $(1, 2)$ are on the graph of $g(x) = 2|x|$.

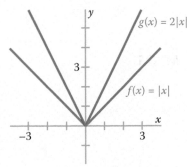

1.6.4   Using Patterns to Graph Functions

Translations, reflections, and stretches can be combined to sketch the graph of a function.

Steps for Graphing a Function $g(x)$ by Translating, Reflecting, and Stretching

❶ Identify the basic type of function, $f(x)$, that $g(x)$ is based on.

❷ Identify any reflection from the equation of $g(x)$.

❸ Identify any stretch from the equation of $g(x)$.

❹ Identify any translation(s) (shifts) from the equation of $g(x)$.

❺ Apply the transformations to the graph of $f(x)$, resulting in the graph of $g(x)$.

EXAMPLE 4   **Graphing a Function by Using Patterns**

Sketch the graph of $g(x) = -\frac{1}{2}|x+1| - 4$.

SOLUTION

The function $g(x) = -\frac{1}{2}|x+1| - 4$ corresponds to the basic absolute value function $f(x) = |x|$.

Identify any reflections, stretches, or translations to the graph of $f(x) = |x|$ from the equation of $g(x)$.

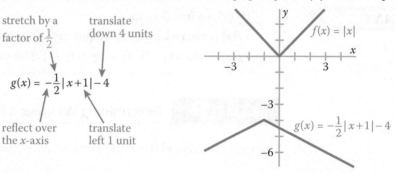

stretch by a factor of $\frac{1}{2}$ translate down 4 units

$$g(x) = -\frac{1}{2}|x+1| - 4$$

reflect over the x-axis   translate left 1 unit

$f(x) = |x|$

$g(x) = -\frac{1}{2}|x+1| - 4$

Apply these changes to the graph of $f(x) = |x|$. The changes are applied to three points on $f(x)$ in the following table.

$f(x)$	→	reflect over x-axis	→	stretch by factor of $\frac{1}{2}$	→	translate left 1 unit	→	translate downard 4 units
(x, y)	→	$(x, -y)$	→	$\left(x, -\frac{1}{2}y\right)$	→	$\left(x-1, -\frac{1}{2}y\right)$	→	$\left(x-1, -\frac{1}{2}y-4\right)$
$(-2, 2)$	→	$(-2, -2)$	→	$(-2, -1)$	→	$(-3, -1)$	→	$(-3, -5)$
$(0, 0)$	→	$(0, 0)$	→	$(0, 0)$	→	$(-1, 0)$	→	$(-1, -4)$
$(2, 2)$	→	$(2, -2)$	→	$(2, -1)$	→	$(1, -1)$	→	$(1, -5)$

1.6.5   Even and Odd Functions

Recall that the graph of an equation (which may or may not be a function) can be symmetric with respect to the x-axis, the y-axis, or the origin, as summarized in the following table.

Symmetry and Points on a Graph

Symmetric with respect to the origin	Symmetric with respect to the x-axis	Symmetric with respect to the y-axis
For every (x, y) on the graph, $(-x, -y)$ is also on the graph.	For every (x, y) on the graph, $(x, -y)$ is also on the graph.	For every (x, y) on the graph, $(-x, y)$ is also on the graph.

Functions that are symmetric with respect to the *y*-axis are called **even functions**. Functions that are symmetric with respect to the origin are called **odd functions**. So, whether a function is even or odd can be determined by analyzing the graph of the function. This can also be determined algebraically by substituting −*x* for *x* in the function, as was done previously to determine the type of symmetry. When −*x* is substituted for *x* in an even function $f(x)$, the result is $f(x)$. When −*x* is substituted for *x* in an odd function $f(x)$, the result is $-f(x)$.

Even and Odd Functions

If $f(x)$ is a function, then
- $f(x)$ is even when $f(-x)$ is equal to $f(x)$ for every *x* in the domain of $f(x)$, and
- $f(x)$ is odd when $f(-x)$ is equal to $-f(x)$ for every *x* in the domain of $f(x)$.

IMPORTANT

Since many functions are not symmetric with respect to the origin or the y-axis, many functions are neither even nor odd.

EXAMPLE 5 **Determining Whether a Function Is Even or Odd**

Determine whether $p(x) = x - x^3$ is even, odd, or neither.

SOLUTION

Substitute −*x* for *x* and simplify.

$$p(-x) = (-x) - (-x)^3$$
$$= (-x) - (-x^3) \qquad (-x)^3 = -x^3$$
$$= -x + x^3 \qquad \textit{Subtracting a negative can be written as addition.}$$
$$= -(x - x^3) \qquad \textit{Factor −1 from each term.}$$
$$= -p(x) \qquad \textit{Substitute } p(x) \textit{ for } x - x^3.$$

Since $p(-x) = -p(x)$, $p(x)$ is odd. (The graph of $p(x)$ is shown in Figure 1.6d.)

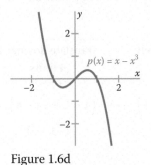

Figure 1.6d

The function is odd, so the graph is symmetric with respect to the origin.

WHAT'S THE BIG IDEA?

How can knowing that a function is even or odd be useful when graphing a function?

SECTION 1.6 EXERCISES

Warm Up

True or False?

1. The graph of $f(x) = x^2 + c$, where c is any real number, is always symmetric with respect to the y-axis.

2. A square root function will sometimes have a domain restriction.

3. Zeros of a function are also called y-intercepts.

Just the Facts

Fill in the blanks.

4. _____ and _____ are rigid transformations in which the shape of the graph _____ change, whereas transformations that cause a distortion of shape are called _____ transformations.

5. If the point (x, y) on the pre-image corresponds to the point $(x - c, y)$ on the image, then the coordinate has been shifted _____.

6. If $g(x) = -f(x)$, then the graph of $g(x)$ is a(n) _____ of the graph of $f(x)$ over the _____.

7. When $g(x) = cf(x)$, where $0 < c < 1$, the graph of $g(x)$ is _____ than the graph of $f(x)$.

8. The image of the point $(2, 0)$ after a reflection across the y-axis and a shift down 4 units is _____.

9. $g(x) = (x + 5)^2 - 3$ is a shift of $f(x) =$ _____ to the _____ 5 units and _____ 3 units.

10. If for all (a, b) on the graph of $f(x)$, $(-a, b)$ is also on the graph of $f(x)$, then $f(x)$ is a(n) _____ function.

Essential Skills

In Exercises 1–30, sketch the graph of each function.

1. $f(x) = x^2 + 1$

2. $g(x) = (x - 2)^3$

3. $h(x) = |x - 4|$

4. $q(x) = \sqrt{x - 3}$

5. $p(x) = (x - 1)^2 - 2$

6. $g(x) = \sqrt{x + 5} - 7$

7. $w(x) = |x - 3| - 2$

8. $s(x) = (x + 4)^3 + 5$

9. $f(x) = (x + 1)^4 - 1$

10. $c(x) = \sqrt{x - 6} - 3$

11. $f(x) = (x - 5)^2 + 8$

12. $w(x) = |x + 3| + 7$

13. $p(x) = -x^3 - 2$

14. $g(x) = -|x + 6|$

15. $k(x) = -x^2 + 9$

16. $d(x) = -\sqrt{x} - 4$

17. $h(x) = -|x| + 3$

18. $b(x) = -(x - 1)^2$

19. $m(x) = -x^5 + 2$

20. $t(x) = -\sqrt{x + 3}$

21. $g(x) = 2\sqrt{x}$

22. $g(x) = \dfrac{1}{2}x^3$

23. $f(x) = 3x^2$

24. $v(x) = \dfrac{1}{4}|x|$

25. $f(x) = (x + 3)^2 + 1$

26. $p(x) = -2(x - 10)^3 + 9$

27. $g(x) = 2\sqrt{x + 3} - 4$

28. $h(x) = -|x - 5| - 2$

29. $q(x) = \dfrac{1}{3}(x + 6)^2 + 1$

30. $c(x) = -4\sqrt{x - 1} + 2$

In Exercises 31–36, determine whether each function is even, odd, or neither.

31. $f(x) = x^2 - 1$

32. $r(x) = 2x^5 - x^3$

33. $k(x) = 7x^6 - x^4 + 3$

34. $m(x) = -3|x| + 9$

35. $p(x) = 4x^5 + 2x^4 - x^3 - 2$

36. $h(x) = -x^3 + x + 5$

Extensions

In Exercises 37–41, use the following information.

Given that f is an odd function, determine whether g is even, odd, or neither.

37. $g(x) = f(-x)$

38. $g(x) = -f(-x)$

39. $g(x) = f(x + 3)$

40. $g(x) = -f(x)$

41. $g(x) = (f(x))^2$

42. Write the equation of $g(x)$ if g is the image of the basic cubic function after a reflection across the x-axis and translations right 2 units, down 5 units.

43. Write the equation of $h(x)$ if h is the image of the basic absolute value function after a reflection across the x-axis and translations left 1 unit, up 2 units.

44. Write the equation of the graph.

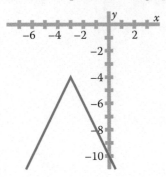

45. True or False? It is possible to have an even function with a domain of $[0, \infty)$.

46. Complete the graph of h given that it is an odd function.

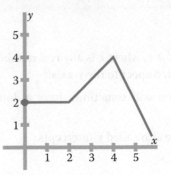

1.7 COMBINING FUNCTIONS

OBJECTIVES

- Perform arithmetic with functions.
- Calculate the difference quotient for functions and average rates of change.
- Compose functions and evaluate compositions of functions.
- Express functions as a composite of functions.
- Model with compositions of functions.

PREREQUISITE VOCABULARY TERMS

domain
function
rate of change
slope

1.7.1 Using Operations with Functions

Two functions can be combined by adding, subtracting, multiplying, or dividing to form a new function. There are no new rules or processes for combining functions because the same properties used for performing operations with real numbers and algebraic expressions are utilized. However, there is some new notation for combining functions, as summarized in the following table.

Arithmetic with Functions $f(x)$ and $g(x)$	
Sum of Functions $(f+g)(x) = f(x) + g(x)$	Difference of Functions $(f-g)(x) = f(x) - g(x)$
Product of Functions $(fg)(x) = f(x)g(x)$	Quotient of Functions $\left(\dfrac{f}{g}\right)(x) = \dfrac{f(x)}{g(x)}$ (when $g(x) \neq 0$)

The Domain of a Combination of Functions

The domain of a combination of functions f and g is all real numbers that are in both the domain of f and the domain of g. For example, if the domain of f is all real numbers x such that $x > 2$, and the domain of g is all real numbers x such that $x < 5$, then the domain of f combined with g (by using addition, subtraction, or multiplication) is the intersection of the domain of f and g, or $\{x \mid 2 < x < 5\}$. Additionally, in the case of a quotient of functions f/g, the domain is further restricted so that $g(x) \neq 0$.

EXAMPLE 1   Combining Functions

Given $p(x) = 1 - 5x^2$ and $r(x) = 2 - x$, find $(p+r)(x)$, $(r-p)(x)$, and $(pr)(x)$.

SOLUTION

Find the sum $(p+r)(x)$ by adding the two functions.

$(p+r)(x) = p(x) + r(x) = 1 - 5x^2 + 2 - x = -5x^2 - x + 3$ *Combine the like terms.*

Find the difference $(r-p)(x)$ by subtracting $p(x)$ from $r(x)$.

$(r-p)(x) = r(x) - p(x) = 2 - x - (1 - 5x^2) = 2 - x - 1 + 5x^2 = 5x^2 - x + 1$

Find the product $(pr)(x)$ by multiplying the two functions.

$(pr)(x) = p(x)r(x) = (1 - 5x^2)(2 - x) = 2 - x - 10x^2 + 5x^3 = 5x^3 - 10x^2 - x + 2$ *FOIL the binomials.*

IMPORTANT

Place the subtracted function, $p(x)$, within parentheses.

Evaluating a Combination of Functions

A combination of two or more functions can be evaluated for a given number by either

- evaluating each function for the given number and then combining the results, or
- combining the functions and then evaluating the combination for the given number.

For example, consider $(f+g)(2)$ when $f(x) = 5x$ and $g(x) = 3x$. One method for evaluating $(f+g)(2)$ is to evaluate each function for $x = 2$ first, and then combine (in this case add) those values.

$$(f+g)(2) = f(2) + g(2) = 5(2) + 3(2) = 16$$

The other method for evaluating $(f+g)(2)$ is to combine (add) the functions first, and then evaluate the combination for $x = 2$.

$$(f+g)(x) = f(x) + g(x) = 5x + 3x = 8x \quad \textit{Add the functions.}$$
$$(f+g)(2) = 8(2) = 16 \quad \textit{Evaluate the combination for x = 2.}$$

EXAMPLE 2   Evaluating a Combination of Functions

Given $p(x) = 1 - 5x^2$ and $r(x) = 2 - x$, find $\left(\dfrac{p}{r}\right)(-1)$.

SOLUTION

Find the quotient by dividing $p(-1)$ by $r(-1)$.

$$\left(\frac{p}{r}\right)(-1) = \frac{p(-1)}{r(-1)} = \frac{1-5(-1)^2}{2-(-1)} = \frac{1-5(1)}{2-(-1)} = \frac{-4}{3} = -\frac{4}{3}$$

ALTERNATIVE METHOD

Find the quotient $\left(\dfrac{p}{r}\right)(x)$ first, then evaluate the quotient for $x = -1$.

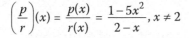

$$\left(\frac{p}{r}\right)(x) = \frac{p(x)}{r(x)} = \frac{1-5x^2}{2-x}, x \neq 2 \qquad \left(\frac{p}{r}\right)(-1) = \frac{1-5(-1)^2}{2-(-1)} = \frac{1-5(1)}{2-(-1)} = \frac{-4}{3} = -\frac{4}{3}$$

IMPORTANT

Exclude 2 from the rational expression's domain because the denominator is 0 when x = 2.

1.7.2   The Difference Quotient

Recall that the slope of a line is the ratio of the change in y to the change in x, $\dfrac{y_2 - y_1}{x_2 - x_1}$, and that slope is also the average rate of change of y with respect to x.

Similarly with functions, the average rate of change in the value of a function f between two domain values x_1 and x_2 is given by the ratio of

- the change in f between $f(x_1)$ and $f(x_2)$, and
- the change in x between x_1 and x_2.

Let h be the difference between the two domain values x_1 and x_2 (where $x_1 < x_2$). Then, if $x_1 = a$, it follows that $x_2 = a + h$. In this case, the change in f between $f(x_1)$ and $f(x_2)$ is $f(a+h) - f(a)$.

So, the ratio of the change in f to the change in x is given by $\dfrac{f(a+h) - f(a)}{h}$, which is known as the **difference quotient**.

DEFINITION

The **difference quotient**,

$$\frac{f(a+h) - f(a)}{h},$$

gives the average rate of change in f between the two domain values a and $a + h$.

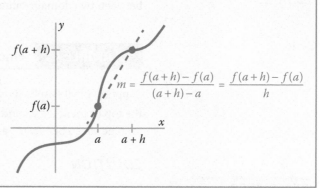

$$m = \frac{f(a+h) - f(a)}{(a+h) - a} = \frac{f(a+h) - f(a)}{h}$$

EXAMPLE 3   **Simplifying the Difference Quotient**

Simplify the difference quotient for each function.

A. $f(x) = 2 - 5x$ **B.** $f(x) = x^2 + 6x + 2$

SOLUTION

The difference quotient $\dfrac{f(a+h) - f(a)}{h}$ is the difference of $f(a + h)$ and $f(a)$ divided by h. So, use each given function to evaluate $f(a + h)$ and $f(a)$, subtract, and then divide by h.

TIP

$f(a + h) = 2 - 5(a + h)$
   $= 2 - 5a - 5h$

$f(a) = 2 - 5(a)$
   $= 2 - 5a$

A.
$$\frac{f(a+h) - f(a)}{h} = \frac{2 - 5(a+h) - (2 - 5(a))}{h} \qquad \textit{Evaluate } f(a + h) \textit{ and } f(a).$$

$$= \frac{2 - 5a - 5h - 2 + 5a}{h} \qquad \textit{Distribute.}$$

$$= \frac{-5h}{h} \qquad \textit{Combine the like terms.}$$

$$= -5 \qquad \textit{Divide } -5h \textit{ by } h.$$

TIP

$f(a + h) =$
$(a + h)^2 + 6(a + h) + 2 =$
$a^2 + 2ah + h^2 + 6a + 6h + 2$

$f(a) = (a)^2 + 6(a) + 2$
   $= a^2 + 6a + 2$

B.
$$\frac{f(a+h) - f(a)}{h} = \frac{(a+h)^2 + 6(a+h) + 2 - ((a)^2 + 6(a) + 2)}{h} \qquad \textit{Evaluate } f(a + h) \textit{ and } f(a).$$

$$= \frac{a^2 + 2ah + h^2 + 6a + 6h + 2 - a^2 - 6a - 2}{h} \qquad \textit{FOIL and distribute.}$$

$$= \frac{2ah + h^2 + 6h}{h} \qquad \textit{Combine the like terms.}$$

$$= 2a + h + 6 \qquad \textit{Divide each term in the numerator by } h.$$

Examining the Difference Quotients (Rates of Change) in Example 3

Notice that the difference quotient for $f(x) = 2 - 5x$ is the constant -5. So, the rate of change between any two domain values for $f(x) = 2 - 5x$ will always be -5. This is to be expected since the rate of change (slope) of any line is constant and the slope of $f(x) = 2 - 5x$ is -5. Generally, since the rate of change for any linear function $f(x) = mx + b$ is the constant value m, the difference quotient of any linear function $f(x) = mx + b$ is also the constant m.

IMPORTANT

The difference quotient is equal to the slope of the line for any linear function.

The difference quotient for $f(x) = x^2 + 6x + 2$ is $2a + h + 6$, which is not a constant value. This is also to be expected, because the graph of $f(x)$ is not a line. The graph of $f(x)$ is a parabola, which does not have a constant rate of change between any two domain values on the parabola. In other words, the rate of change between domain values x_1 and x_2 is *not* equal to the rate of change between domain values x_3 and x_4 for all domain values. Instead, the rate of change between any two domain values on $f(x) = x^2 + 6x + 2$ is given by $2a + h + 6$, where a is the first domain value and h is the difference between the two domain values.

In the following example, the difference quotient will be used to find the average rate of change between two domain values on a nonlinear function.

EXAMPLE 4   Finding the Average Rate of Change

Suppose a ball is released from the top of a hill. The distance (in feet) that the ball rolls from the top of the hill t seconds after it is let go is given by the function $d(t) = 5.7t^2$. Find the ball's average speed between 7 and 12 seconds.

SOLUTION

The average rate of change in the function is the ratio of the change in d, the distance, to the change in t, the time, or d/t. Since $d/t = r$ (where r is the average rate or speed), the average rate of change in the function gives the ball's average speed. So, use the difference quotient to find the average rate of change in d.

$$\frac{d(a+h) - d(a)}{h} = \text{the ball's average speed between } t = a \text{ and } t = a + h$$

The domain values are 7 and 12. Since $12 = 7 + 5$, it follows that $a = 7$, $a + h = 12$, and $h = 5$.

$$\frac{d(12) - d(7)}{5} = \frac{5.7(12)^2 - 5.7(7)^2}{5} = \frac{820.8 - 279.3}{5} = \frac{541.5}{5} = 108.3$$

So, the ball's average speed between 7 and 12 seconds is 108.3 feet per second.

WHAT'S THE BIG IDEA?

How is the difference quotient related to slope?

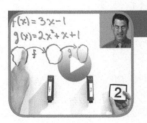

1.7.3 Composition of Functions

Another way of combining two functions to form a new function is to **compose** the two functions (i.e., to form the **composition** of the two functions). Two functions are composed when one function is evaluated for another function.

Recall that the notation $f(3)$ means to evaluate f for 3, or to substitute 3 into f for x. It follows that $f(g(3))$ (read as "f of g of 3") means to evaluate f for $g(3)$, or to substitute the value of $g(3)$ into f for x.

For example, suppose $f(x) = 5x + 3$ and $g(x) = x^2$. To find $f(g(3))$, first evaluate $g(3)$, then use that number to evaluate f.

$$\begin{aligned} f(g(3)) &= f(9) && \textit{Evaluate } g(3)\text{: } g(3) = 3^2 = 9. \\ &= 5(9) + 3 && \textit{Evaluate } f \textit{ for } g(3)\text{, or evaluate } f(9). \\ &= 48 && \textit{Simplify.} \end{aligned}$$

DEFINITION

The **composition** of the function f with the function g, $f(g(x))$, is the result of evaluating f for g.

$$f(g(x)) = (f \circ g)(x)$$

The domain of $f \circ g$ is the set of all x in the domain of g such that $g(x)$ is in the domain of f.

EXAMPLE 5 Composition of Functions

Given $p(x) = 1 - 5x^2$ and $r(x) = 2 - x$, find $(p \circ r)(3)$ and $(r \circ p)(3)$.

SOLUTION

To find $(p \circ r)(3)$, evaluate $r(3)$, and then evaluate p for $r(3)$.

ALTERNATIVE METHOD

Evaluate r(3) first.
$$r(3) = 2 - 3 = -1$$
Now evaluate p(−1).
$$p(-1) = 1 - 5(-1)^2$$
$$= 1 - 5(1)$$
$$= -4$$

$(p \circ r)(3) = p(r(3))$	*Write p composed with r(3).*
$= p(2 - 3)$	*Evaluate r(3) by substituting 3 into r(x) = 2 − x for x.*
$= p(-1)$	*Subtract.*
$= 1 - 5(-1)^2$	*Evaluate p(−1) by substituting −1 into p(x) = 1 − 5x² for x.*
$= 1 - 5(1)$	*Evaluate the power.*
$= -4$	*Simplify.*

To find $(r \circ p)(3)$, evaluate $p(3)$, and then evaluate r for $p(3)$.

NOTICE THAT

Since (p ∘ r)(3) = −4 and (r ∘ p)(3) = 46, (p ∘ r)(3) ≠ (r ∘ p)(3). It follows that for any functions f and g, (f ∘ g) is not necessarily equivalent to (g ∘ f).

$(r \circ p)(3) = r(p(3))$	*Write r composed with p(3).*
$= r(1 - 5(3)^2)$	*Evaluate p(3) by substituting 3 into p(x) = 1 − 5x² for x.*
$= r(-44)$	*Simplify: 1 − 5(3)² = 1 − 5(9) = 1 − 45 = −44.*
$= 2 - (-44)$	*Evaluate r(−44) by substituting −44 into r(x) = 2 − x for x.*
$= 46$	*Simplify.*

So, $(p \circ r)(3) = -4$ and $(r \circ p)(3) = 46$.

1.7.4 Composition of Functions: Another Example

In the previous topic, a composition of two functions was evaluated for a given number, for example, $(p \circ r)(3)$. In this topic, a function will be composed with itself, and then evaluated for some given number, for example, $(f \circ f)(5)$.

Additionally, a function will be composed with a function that is not evaluated for a number, for example, $(f \circ g)(x)$. The notation $(f \circ g)(x)$ means to evaluate f for g, or to substitute $g(x)$ into the function f for x. For example, suppose $f(x) = 5x + 3$ and $g(x) = x^2$. Since $g(x) = x^2$, the x in $f(x) = 5x + 3$ is replaced by x^2 when evaluating $(f \circ g)(x)$.

$$\text{Evaluate } f \text{ for } g \ \Rightarrow \ (f \circ g)(x) = f(g(x)) = 5(g(x)) + 3 = 5x^2 + 3$$

So, the new function formed by the composition of f and g is $(f \circ g)(x) = 5x^2 + 3$.

EXAMPLE 6 Composition of Functions

Given $r(x) = 2 - x$ and $p(x) = 1 - 5x^2$, find $(r \circ r)(3)$ and $(p \circ r)(x)$.

SOLUTION

To find $(r \circ r)(3)$, evaluate $r(3)$, and then evaluate r for $r(3)$.

$(r \circ r)(3) = r(r(3))$	*Write r composed with r(3).*
$= r(2 - 3)$	*Evaluate r(3) by substituting 3 into r(x) = 2 − x for x.*
$= r(-1)$	*Subtract.*
$= 2 - (-1)$	*Evaluate r(−1) by substituting −1 into r(x) = 2 − x for x.*
$= 3$	*Simplify.*

To find $(p \circ r)(x)$, evaluate p for $r(x)$.

$$
\begin{aligned}
(p \circ r)(x) &= p(r(x)) && \textit{Write p composed with r(x).}\\
&= p(2 - x) && \textit{Substitute } 2 - x \textit{ for } r(x).\\
&= 1 - 5(2 - x)^2 && \textit{Substitute } 2 - x \textit{ into } p(x) = 1 - 5x^2 \textit{ for } x.\\
&= 1 - 5(2 - x)(2 - x) && \textit{Evaluate the power.}\\
&= 1 - 5(4 - 4x + x^2) && \textit{FOIL the binomials.}\\
&= 1 - 20 + 20x - 5x^2 && \textit{Distribute } -5.\\
&= -5x^2 + 20x - 19 && \textit{Combine the like terms.}
\end{aligned}
$$

WHAT'S THE BIG IDEA?

Explain the difference between $(f \circ g)(x)$ and $(g \circ f)(x)$.

1.7.5 Finding Functions That Form a Given Composite

Sometimes a given function can be written as a composition of two functions. The process of finding two functions that can be composed to form a given function is called **decomposing**.

To decompose a function, analyze the function, considering its parts, until a possibility for two functions has been determined. Then compose these two functions to check that they do form the given composite. There is often more than one way to decompose a composite function.

EXAMPLE 7   Decomposing a Composite Function

Write $p(x) = \dfrac{9}{2(1 - x)^3}$ as a composition of two functions in two different ways.

SOLUTION

Notice that the expression $(1 - x)$ is cubed and multiplied by 2, and that 9 is divided by that result. Breaking this into parts reveals that if $f(x) = 1 - x$ and $g(x) = \dfrac{9}{2x^3}$, then $g(f(x)) = p(x)$. Compose g with f to confirm.

$$
g(f(x)) = g(1 - x) = \dfrac{9}{2(1 - x)^3} = p(x)
$$

Again, breaking the expression for $p(x)$, $\dfrac{9}{2(1 - x)^3}$, into parts reveals that if $f(x) = 2(1 - x)^3$ and $g(x) = \dfrac{9}{x}$, then $g(f(x)) = p(x)$. Compose g with f to confirm.

$$
g(f(x)) = g(2(1 - x)^3) = \dfrac{9}{2(1 - x)^3} = p(x)
$$

IMPORTANT

There are other ways to write $p(x)$ as a composite of two functions.

CAUTION

Notice that in the previous example, writing $p(x)$ as the composition $g(f(x))$ where $f(x) = 2(1 - x)$ and $g(x) = \dfrac{9}{x^3}$ would not be correct, because the coefficient of 2 in $f(x) = 2(1 - x)$ must also be cubed when evaluating the composite.

$$g(f(x)) = g(2(1 - x)) = \frac{9}{(2(1 - x))^3} = \frac{9}{8(1 - x)^3} \neq p(x)$$

Therefore, $p(x) \neq g(f(x))$ when $f(x) = 2(1 - x)$ and $g(x) = \dfrac{9}{x^3}$.

1.7.6   Modeling with Composite Functions

A composite function can be used to model a situation where one quantity is dependent on two different quantities (i.e., one quantity is a function of two different quantities). For example, suppose there are two discounts on the price of an item. In this case, the sale price of the item is a function of the price after the second discount, which is a function of the price after the first discount. A multiple-discount situation is modeled with a composition of functions in the following example.

EXAMPLE 8   **Modeling with a Composite Function**

A cell phone company offers a $100 discount on the price of a phone for customers signing a two-year contract. The same company is offering a 15% discount on their phones for customers during a holiday weekend. Let x represent the regular price of a phone. Write two composite functions: one to represent the sale price of the phone if the 15% discount is applied after the $100 discount, and one to represent the sale price of the phone if the 15% discount is applied before the $100 discount. Which is the better deal for the customer?

SOLUTION

Write a function for each discount. Let the 15% discount be represented by the function f, and let the $100 discount be represented by the function g.

$$f(x) = x - 0.15x = 0.85x \qquad\qquad g(x) = x - 100$$

15% discount applied
after the $100 discount
$f(g(x)) = 0.85(x - 100) = 0.85x - 85$

15% discount applied
before the $100 discount
$g(f(x)) = 0.85x - 100$

Notice that both compositions start with $0.85x$, or 85% of the original price. When the $100 discount is applied first (as in $(f \circ g)(x)$), the sale price is $85 less than 85% of the original price. When the $100 discount is applied second (as in $(g \circ f)(x)$), the sale price is $100 less than 85% of the original price. So, applying the 15% discount first and the $100 discount second results in the better deal for the customer.

SECTION 1.7 EXERCISES

Warm Up

Find the x- and y-intercepts of each function.

1. $y = 2x - 1$

2. $g(x) = 3x^2 - 27$

3. $p(x) = \sqrt{x + 1}$

Just the Facts

Fill in the blanks.

4. Two functions g and h can be combined by the arithmetic operations of _____, _____, _____, and _____ to form new functions.

5. The _____ of the function g with f is $(g \circ f)(x) = (g(f(x)))$.

6. The domain of $(g + f)$ is all real numbers that are in both the domain of _____ and the domain of _____.

7. The difference quotient of any linear function $y = mx + b$ is always _____.

8. The _____ gives the average rate of change in f between two domain values such that the difference in the domain values is _____.

9. _____ is the process of finding two functions that can be composed to form a given function.

10. The quotient $\left(\dfrac{g}{h}\right)(x)$ is defined only when _____ does not equal 0.

Essential Skills

In Exercises 1–32, use the given functions to complete each operation.

1. $p(x) = -2x$ and $r(x) = x + 4$; $(p + r)(x)$

2. $f(x) = 1 + x^2$ and $g(x) = 3x^2 + 5$; $(f + g)(x)$

3. $g(x) = x^2 + 1$ and $h(x) = -x^2 - 5$; $(g - h)(x)$

4. $r(x) = 6x - 2$ and $t(x) = 4x^2 + 23$; $(r - t)(x)$

5. $s(x) = 11 + 4x^2$ and $t(x) = 3x^2 - 11x + 4$; $(s + t)(x)$

6. $r(x) = 9x^2 + 8x - 5$ and $w(x) = x^2 - 7x + 3$; $(r - w)(x)$

7. $c(x) = 3 - x - 6x^2$ and $d(x) = -2x^2 + x - 4$; $(c - d)(x)$

8. $p(x) = -4x^2 - 15x$ and $q(x) = 8x^2 + 3x - 9$; $(p + q)(x)$

9. $u(x) = \dfrac{2}{x}$ and $v(x) = \dfrac{3}{x - 1}$; $(u + v)(x)$

10. $b(x) = -\dfrac{4}{x + 3}$ and $n(x) = \dfrac{x}{x - 2}$; $(b - n)(x)$

11. $k(x) = \dfrac{x + 1}{x - 5}$ and $h(x) = -\dfrac{2x + 3}{x^2 - 25}$; $(k + h)(x)$

12. $f(x) = \dfrac{3x - 5}{x^2 + x - 20}$ and $g(x) = \dfrac{2x - 1}{x + 5}$; $(f - g)(x)$

13. $h(x) = 2x + 1$ and $g(x) = -x + 8$; $(hg)(x)$

14. $f(x) = 5 - x^2$ and $g(x) = 6 - x$; $(fg)(x)$

15. $p(x) = x + 7$ and $r(x) = x^2 + 14x + 49$; $\left(\dfrac{p}{r}\right)(x)$

16. $h(x) = 5 + x$ and $g(x) = 25 - x^2$; $\left(\dfrac{g}{h}\right)(x)$

17. $k(x) = 3x - 8$ and $l(x) = 8 + 3x^2$; $(kl)(x)$

18. $m(x) = x^2 - 19x + 78$ and $n(x) = x - 6$; $\left(\dfrac{m}{n}\right)(x)$

19. $u(x) = 5x^2 - 20$ and $v(x) = 2 + x$; $\left(\dfrac{u}{v}\right)(x)$

20. $s(x) = 2x^2 - x$ and $t(x) = x^2 - 4$; $(st)(x)$

21. $q(x) = -\dfrac{5x}{x + 4}$ and $r(x) = \dfrac{x + 2}{x - 3}$; $(qr)(x)$

22. $g(x) = \dfrac{4x - 1}{x - 6}$ and $t(x) = \dfrac{x + 7}{2x - 3}$; $(gt)(x)$

23. $f(x) = \dfrac{2x^2 - 2}{x + 3}$ and $h(x) = \dfrac{x^2 + 5x + 4}{x^2 - 9}$; $\left(\dfrac{f}{h}\right)(x)$

24. $w(x) = \dfrac{x^2 - 7x - 8}{x^2 + 3x - 18}$ and $z(x) = \dfrac{x^2 - 6x - 16}{x^2 + 2x - 24}$; $\left(\dfrac{w}{z}\right)(x)$

25. $g(x) = 3x + 2$ and $h(x) = -2x$; $(gh)(4)$

26. $f(x) = x^2$ and $g(x) = x + 1$; $(fg)(-3)$

27. $h(x) = -x^2 - 6$ and $k(x) = 9 - 4x$; $(h + k)(-2)$

28. $p(x) = 7 - 2x^2$ and $q(x) = -5x + 8$; $(p - q)(3)$

29. $b(x) = -4x^2 - 2$ and $c(x) = 2x + 5$; $(bc)(-1)$

30. $k(x) = 3x^2 - 5x$ and $n(x) = x - 9$; $(kn)(-6)$

31. $d(x) = \sqrt{1 - x}$ and $p(x) = \dfrac{2}{x - 7}$; $\left(\dfrac{d}{p}\right)(-3)$

32. $t(x) = \dfrac{3x}{x + 11}$ and $w(x) = \sqrt{x^2 - 7}$; $\left(\dfrac{t}{w}\right)(4)$

In Exercises 33–40, simplify the difference quotient for each function.

33. $g(x) = -3x + 8$

34. $f(x) = -x^2 + 7x + 3$

35. $r(x) = 9 - 2x^2$

36. $c(x) = 14 - 5x$

37. $k(x) = 6x^2 - 4x + 1$

38. $d(x) = -3x^2 - 2x + 7$

39. $m(x) = x^3 - 5x$

40. $n(x) = 4x^3 - x^2 + 1$

In Exercises 41–60, use the given functions to find each composite.

41. $(f \circ g)(9)$ for $f(x) = x + 4$ and $g(x) = 9x - 3$

42. $(g \circ f)(3)$ for $f(x) = -2x^2 + 5x + 7$ and $g(x) = 4x - 3$

43. $(g \circ f)(-2)$ for $f(x) = -4x + 1$ and $g(x) = -x^2 + 3x + 2$

44. $(f \circ g)(-1)$ for $f(x) = -3x^2 + x + 9$ and $g(x) = 2x^2 + x - 8$

45. $(g \circ f)(-4)$ for $f(x) = 8 - x^2$ and $g(x) = \dfrac{x}{x+1}$

46. $(f \circ g)(-4)$ for $f(x) = 8 - x^2$ and $g(x) = \dfrac{x}{x+1}$

47. $(g \circ g)(2)$ for $g(x) = 2x + 1$

48. $(f \circ f)(-2)$ for $f(x) = x^2 + 4x$

49. $(f \circ f)(-1)$ for $f(x) = 3x^2 + 4x - 2$

50. $(g \circ g)(3)$ for $g(x) = -x^2 - 2x + 5$

51. $(f \circ f)(8)$ for $f(x) = \dfrac{x-1}{2}$

52. $(g \circ g)(-5)$ for $g(x) = \dfrac{x+2}{x}$

53. $(g \circ f)(x)$ and $(f \circ g)(x)$ for $f(x) = 6 + 5x$ and $g(x) = 4x - 4$

54. $(f \circ g)(x)$ and $(g \circ f)(x)$ for $f(x) = 5 - 4x$ and $g(x) = x^2 - 4$

55. $(f \circ g)(x)$ and $(g \circ f)(x)$ for $f(x) = 2x - 4$ and $g(x) = \dfrac{1}{2}x + 2$.

56. $(g \circ f)(x)$ and $(f \circ g)(x)$ for $f(x) = \dfrac{3}{2}x - 6$ and $g(x) = \dfrac{2}{3}x + 4$.

57. $(f \circ g)(x)$ and $(g \circ f)(x)$ for $f(x) = 5x - 4$ and $g(x) = x^2 - 5x + 6$.

58. $(g \circ f)(x)$ and $(f \circ g)(x)$ for $f(x) = 3 - x$ and $g(x) = 2x^2 - x + 4$.

59. $(g \circ f)(x)$ and $(f \circ g)(x)$ for $f(x) = 2\sqrt{x}$ and $g(x) = x^2 + 3$.

60. $(f \circ g)(x)$ and $(g \circ f)(x)$ for $f(x) = 2x^2 + 1$ and $g(x) = \sqrt{x - 4}$.

In Exercises 61–62, find the function $f(x)$ that forms each given composite function with $g(x) = x^2$.

61. $(g \circ f)(x) = (-3x - 10)^2$

62. $(f \circ g)(x) = x^4 - 5x^2$

63. Find $f(x)$ such that $(f \circ g)(x) = 6x + 10$ and $g(x) = 3x + 2$.

64. Find $f(x)$ such that $(f \circ g)(x) = 8x + 22$ and $g(x) = 2x + 4$.

65. Find $g(x)$ such that $(f \circ g)(x) = 12x - 5$ and $f(x) = 4x - 1$.

66. Find $g(x)$ such that $(f \circ g)(x) = -7x + 9$ and $f(x) = -x - 3$.

67. Find $g(x)$ such that $(f \circ g)(x) = 2x^6 - 5x^3$ and $f(x) = 2x^2 - 5x$.

68. Find $f(x)$ such that $(f \circ g)(x) = 3x^8 - 6x^4$ and $g(x) = x^4$.

69. A department store offers their employees a 20% discount on all of their merchandise m. An employee has a coupon from the local paper for \$10 off any purchase. Write a function p for the cost of the merchandise after receiving only the employee discount. Write a function c for the cost of the merchandise after receiving only the coupon discount. Evaluate $(p \circ c)(m)$ and explain what the composition represents.

70. A car dealership offers a \$1500 factory rebate and a 10% discount off the price of a new car c. Write a function r for the cost of the car after receiving only the factory rebate. Write a function p for the cost of the car after receiving only the dealership discount. Evaluate $(r \circ p)(c)$ and explain what the composition represents.

Extensions

In Exercises 71–79, use the graphs of $f(x)$ and $g(x)$ to evaluate each expression.

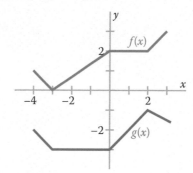

71. $(f + g)(0)$

72. $(f - g)(2)$

73. $(gf)(0)$

74. $(fg)(-3)$

75. $\left(\dfrac{f}{g}\right)(-4)$

76. $\left(\dfrac{g}{f}\right)(2)$

77. $(f \circ g)(0)$

78. $(g \circ f)(1)$

79. $(f \circ f)(-3)$

In Exercises 80–82, use the function $f(x) = 3x^2 - 2x + 1$ to find the average rate of change between each pair of values.

80. 4 and 7

81. 0 and 2

82. a and b

83. Let $f(m)$ be the number of full-time employees in a company in month m, and let $p(m)$ be the number of part-time employees in month m. Let $m = 1$ correspond to January. Find the function $t(m)$ that represents the total number of employees in the company. Then interpret the value $t(7)$.

84. A car salesman is paid an annual salary plus a bonus of 5% for sales over \$750,000. Given the two functions $g(x) = x - 750,000$ and $f(x) = 0.05x$, where x represents the sales over \$750,000, does $f(g(x))$ or $g(f(x))$ represent the bonus?

85. Given $h(x) = \dfrac{2}{x-5}$ and $g(x) = -3x + 8$, find $(h \circ g)(x)$ and $(g \circ h)(x)$. State the domain of each composite function.

In Exercises 86–92, given $f(x) = 3x^2$ and $g(x) = x^2$, describe the graph of the function.

86. $(f + g)(x)$

87. $(f - g)(x)$

88. $(g - f)(x)$

89. $(fg)(x)$

90. $\left(\dfrac{f}{g}\right)(x)$

91. $\left(\dfrac{g}{f}\right)(x)$

92. $(g \circ g)(x)$

1.8 INVERSE FUNCTIONS

OBJECTIVES

- Understand inverse functions and one-to-one functions.
- Use the Horizontal Line Test.
- Verify that two functions are inverses.
- Find the graph of an inverse function.
- Find the inverse function of a function algebraically.

PREREQUISITE VOCABULARY TERMS

domain

function

function composition

Vertical Line Test

1.8.1 Introduction to Inverse Functions

Recall that inverse operations are two operations that undo one another. For example, the inverse operation of multiplication is division, because when a number a is multiplied by a nonzero number b and then divided by b, the result is a ($a \cdot b \div b = a$). The same result occurs when a is divided by a nonzero number b and then multiplied by b ($a \div b \cdot b = a$).

Two functions can be **inverses** as well. If f is a function with domain A and range B, then the inverse function of f is a function g with range A and domain B such that for each point (c, d) on the graph of f there is a point (d, c) on the graph of g. In this way, the inverse function of a function *undoes* the original function.

DEFINITION

If two functions f and g are **inverse functions** then
- for every x in the domain of f, $g(f(x)) = x$, and
- for every x in the domain of g, $f(g(x)) = x$.

The domain of f must be equal to the range of g, and the domain of g must be equal to the range of f.

The relationship between the domain and range of two inverse functions f and g is shown in Figure 1.8a.

Figure 1.8a

Consider the function $f(x) = x - 3$. When the input is 5, the output is 2, since $f(5) = 5 - 3 = 2$ (i.e., $(5, 2)$ is a point on the graph of f). So, the inverse function of $f(x) = x - 3$ must take 2 as an input value and return 5 as the output value (i.e., $(2, 5)$ must be a point on the inverse of f). The inverse function of $f(x) = x - 3$ must be a function that *undoes* subtracting 3 from the domain value. Since addition and subtraction are inverse operations, it seems reasonable to expect that the inverse function of $f(x) = x - 3$ is $g(x) = x + 3$.

By the definition of inverse functions, we know that if f and g are inverse functions, then $g(f(x)) = x$ and $f(g(x)) = x$. Notice that composing the functions $f(x) = x - 3$ and $g(x) = x + 3$ results in x.

$$g(f(x)) = (x - 3) + 3 = x \qquad\qquad f(g(x)) = (x + 3) - 3 = x$$

Therefore, $f(x) = x - 3$ and $g(x) = x + 3$ are inverse functions, as expected.

EXAMPLE 1	Verifying Inverse Functions

Use $(f \circ g)$ and $(g \circ f)$ to confirm that $f(x) = 5x$ and $g(x) = \dfrac{x}{5}$ are inverse functions.

SOLUTION

Evaluate each composition.

$$(f \circ g)(x) = f(g(x)) = f\left(\frac{x}{5}\right) = 5 \cdot \frac{x}{5} = x$$

$$(g \circ f)(x) = g(f(x)) = g(5x) = \frac{5x}{5} = x$$

So, since $(f \circ g)(x) = x$ and $(g \circ f)(x) = x$, f and g are inverse functions.

EXAMPLE 2	Evaluating with Inverse Functions

Suppose that g and h are inverse functions, and that $h(1) = 3$, $g(-4) = 10$, and $h(0) = -2$.
Use the given information to evaluate $h(10)$, $g(-2)$, and $g(1)$, if possible.

SOLUTION

Since g and h are inverse functions, we know that if $g(a) = b$, then $h(b) = a$. So, $h(10) = -4$ because $g(-4) = 10$.

Additionally, since g and h are inverse functions, we know that if $h(a) = b$, then $g(b) = a$. So, $g(-2) = 0$ because $h(0) = -2$.

We are not given a domain value for h that results in a range value of 1. Therefore, $g(1)$ cannot be evaluated using the given information.

1.8.2	The Horizontal Line Test

Recall that there are some graphs that are not functions. The Vertical Line Test is used to determine whether a graph is a function. When any vertical line intersects a graph no more than one time, then the graph passes the Vertical Line Test and therefore is a function.

Similarly, there are some functions that do not have inverse functions. The **Horizontal Line Test** is used to determine whether a function has an inverse function.

Horizontal Line Test

A function f has an inverse function if any possible horizontal line can intersect the graph of f at most once.

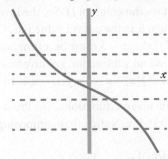

Passes the Horizontal Line Test

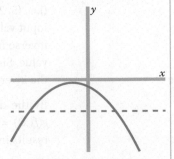

Fails the Horizontal Line Test

When a function passes the Horizontal Line Test, each of its domain values corresponds to exactly one range value.

DEFINITION

A function f that has exactly one range value corresponding to each of its domain values is a **one-to-one function**. In other words, $f(x_1) = f(x_2)$ if and only if $x_1 = x_2$.

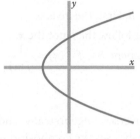

Figure 1.8b

A one-to-one function will always pass the Horizontal Line Test because it has no more than one point on its graph for any y-value in its range. Therefore, a one-to-one function will always have an inverse function.

CAUTION

Figure 1.8b shows a graph that no horizontal line will intersect more than once, so it may appear to pass the Horizontal Line Test. However, this is not the graph of a one-to-one function because it is not the graph of a function (i.e., it does not pass the Vertical Line Test).

EXAMPLE 3   **Using the Horizontal Line Test**

Use the Horizontal Line Test to determine whether each graph is a one-to-one function with an inverse function.

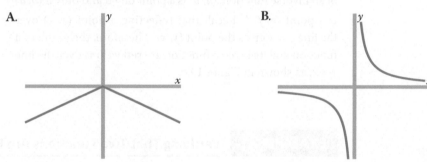

A.

B.

SOLUTION

A. The graph fails the Horizontal Line Test because at least one horizontal line will intersect the graph at more than one point. Therefore, the graph is not a one-to-one function and does not have an inverse function.

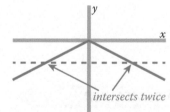

intersects twice

B. The graph passes the Horizontal Line Test because any horizontal line will intersect the graph at most once. Therefore, the graph is a one-to-one function, and the function has an inverse function.

1.8.3   Verifying That Functions Are Inverses

Inverse Function Notation

If f is a one-to-one function, then the inverse function of f is denoted f^{-1} (read as "f-inverse") or $f^{-1}(x)$.

CAUTION

There are two common misconceptions with inverse function notation. First, the inverse function of f is *not* denoted as $f(x)^{-1}$. Instead, the superscript −1 must follow the f, not the x. Second, the superscript −1 in inverse function notation is not an exponent. So, $f^{-1}(x) \neq \dfrac{1}{f(x)}$.

Verifying Inverse Functions

There are two methods for verifying that two functions are inverses: algebraically and graphically. The algebraic method, which was demonstrated previously, uses the compositions of the two functions. When two functions are inverses, their compositions are equal to x.

$$f^{-1}(f(x)) = x \quad \text{and} \quad f(f^{-1}(x)) = x$$

The other method for verifying that two functions are inverses utilizes the graphs of the functions. By the definition of an inverse function, (a, b) is a point on f if and only if (b, a) is a point on f^{-1}. Recall that reflecting a point (x, y) over the line $y = x$ gives the point (y, x). Therefore, the graph of a function and its inverse function are reflections over the line $y = x$, as shown in Figure 1.8c.

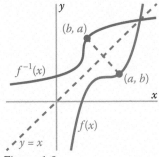

Figure 1.8c

EXAMPLE 4   Verifying That Two Functions Are Inverse Functions

Show graphically and algebraically that $f(x) = 3x + 6$ and $g(x) = \dfrac{x}{3} - 2$ are inverse functions.

SOLUTION

<u>Graphically</u>

$f(x) = 3x + 6$ is a line with slope 3 and y-intercept 6.

$g(x) = \dfrac{x}{3} - 2$ is a line with slope $\dfrac{1}{3}$ and y-intercept −2.

The lines are reflections over the line $y = x$.

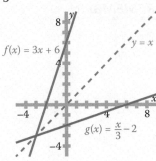

> ### REMEMBER
> *When two graphs are reflections over the line $y = x$, then for each point (a, b) on one graph, the point (b, a) is on the other graph.*

<u>Algebraically</u>

Verify that $g(f(x)) = x$ and $f(g(x)) = x$.

$$g(f(x)) = \frac{3x + 6}{3} - 2 = (x + 2) - 2 = x \qquad f(g(x)) = 3\left(\frac{x}{3} - 2\right) + 6 = (x - 6) + 6 = x$$

Since $g(f(x)) = x$ and $f(g(x)) = x$, the functions are inverses.

1.8.4 Finding the Inverse of a Function Graphically

The graph of a function can be used to determine whether the function has an inverse function and to find the graph of that inverse function when it exists. Recall that if the graph of a function passes the Horizontal Line Test, then it is a one-to-one function and it does have an inverse function. So, by applying the Horizontal Line Test, the existence of an inverse function can be determined. Also recall that functions are inverses when their graphs are reflections over the line $y = x$. So, when the graph of a function passes the Horizontal Line Test, then the inverse function of this function can be graphed by reflecting the function's graph over the line $y = x$.

| EXAMPLE 5 | Finding the Graph of an Inverse Function |

Graph the inverse function of f, if it exists.

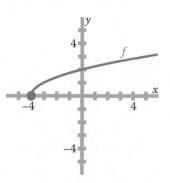

SOLUTION

The function f passes the Horizontal Line Test, so it is a one-to-one function and has an inverse function.

Reflect f over the line $y = x$ to graph the inverse function of f.

Since the graph of f passes through the line $y = x$, the graph of f^{-1} must also pass through this same point on $y = x$. Find additional points on the graph of f^{-1} by identifying points on f and then reversing the coordinates. For example, since $(-4, 0)$ and $(0, 2)$ are points on f, $(0, -4)$ and $(2, 0)$ must be points on f^{-1}.

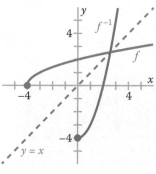

So, to graph f^{-1}, sketch a curve that passes through $(0, -4)$, $(2, 0)$, and the point at which f intersects the line $y = x$.

1.8.5 Finding the Inverse of a Function Algebraically

The inverse function of simple functions can be determined visually or by considering how the operations in the function can be undone. A more systematic algebraic method should be used to find the inverse function of a complicated function.

Steps for Finding the Inverse Function of a Function f

❶ Use the Horizontal Line Test to verify that the inverse function of f exists.

❷ If the equation is in function notation, replace $f(x)$ with y.

❸ Interchange x and y in the equation, and then solve for y.

❹ Replace y with f^{-1} in the equation from step ❸.

| EXAMPLE 6 | Finding the Equation of an Inverse Function Algebraically |

Find the inverse function of each function, if it exists.

A. $f(x) = \dfrac{3x-2}{5}$ 　　　　　　　　　　　**B.** $g(x) = \sqrt{4x+1}$

SOLUTION

A. Since f is a linear equation, the graph of f is a line. The line is not horizontal, because the equation contains x. Any nonhorizontal line passes the Horizontal Line Test, so f is a one-to-one function and has an inverse function.

To find the inverse function of f, replace $f(x)$ with y, interchange x and y, then solve for y.

$$f(x) = \frac{3x-2}{5} \qquad \text{\textit{Write the function.}}$$

$$y = \frac{3x-2}{5} \qquad \text{\textit{Replace $f(x)$ with y.}}$$

$$x = \frac{3y-2}{5} \qquad \text{\textit{Interchange x and y.}}$$

$$5x = 3y - 2 \qquad \text{\textit{Multiply both sides by 5.}}$$

$$5x + 2 = 3y \qquad \text{\textit{Add 2 to each side.}}$$

$$\frac{5x+2}{3} = y \qquad \text{\textit{Divide each side by 3.}}$$

Replace y with f^{-1} to write the inverse function's equation: $f^{-1}(x) = \dfrac{5x+2}{3}$.

The inverse function can be checked by confirming that $f^{-1}(f(x)) = x$ and $f(f^{-1}(x)) = x$, or by graphing the functions and verifying that the graphs are reflections over the line $y = x$, as shown in Figure 1.8d.

B. Graph g with a graphing calculator, as shown in Figure 1.8e. The graph passes the Horizontal Line Test, so the function is one-to-one and has an inverse function.

The domain of g is the interval $\left[-\dfrac{1}{4}, \infty\right)$, so the range of g^{-1} must also be $\left[-\dfrac{1}{4}, \infty\right)$. Furthermore, the range of g is the interval $[0, \infty)$, so the domain of g^{-1} must also be $[0, \infty)$.

To find the inverse function of g, replace $g(x)$ with y, interchange x and y, then solve for y.

$$g(x) = \sqrt{4x+1} \qquad \text{\textit{Write the function.}}$$

$$y = \sqrt{4x+1} \qquad \text{\textit{Replace $g(x)$ with y.}}$$

$$x = \sqrt{4y+1} \qquad \text{\textit{Interchange x and y.}}$$

$$x^2 = 4y + 1 \qquad \text{\textit{Square both sides.}}$$

$$\frac{x^2-1}{4} = y \qquad \text{\textit{Subtract 1 from both sides and divide each side by 4 to solve for y.}}$$

Replace y with g^{-1} to write the inverse function's equation: $g^{-1}(x) = \dfrac{x^2-1}{4}, x \geq 0$.

The graphs of g and g^{-1} are shown in Figure 1.8f.

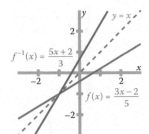
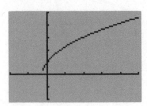

Figure 1.8d

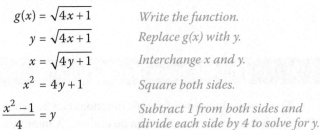

Figure 1.8e

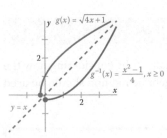

Figure 1.8f

WHAT'S THE BIG IDEA?

Explain the relationship between a function, its inverse function, and the line $y = x$.

SECTION 1.8 EXERCISES

Warm Up

Write the domain of each function using interval notation.

1. $g(x) = -3x + 2$

2. $f(x) = \sqrt{9 - x^2}$

3. $p(x) = \dfrac{1}{x + 3}$

Just the Facts

Fill in the blanks.

4. A function and its inverse function, when graphed, will always be symmetric with respect to the line _____.

5. If (x, y) is a point on the graph of $f(x)$, then _____ is a point on the graph of $f^{-1}(x)$.

6. Functions that pass the _____ are one-to-one functions and they have _____ functions.

7. If $x > 9$ is the domain of f, then the range of f^{-1} is _____.

8. If $(f \circ g)(x) = x$ and $(g \circ f)(x) = x$, then f and g are _____ functions.

9. The function $g(x) = -3|x + 2|$ does not have an inverse function because the graph of g does not pass the _____.

10. If $g(x) = x + 1$, its inverse function will be $g^{-1}(x) = x - 1$, since the addition is undone by the _____

Essential Skills

In Exercises 1–6, evaluate, if possible, given that p and q are inverse functions.

1. If $q(3) = 5$, what is $p(5)$?

2. If $p(9) = -4$, what is $q(-4)$?

3. If $q(-1) = 8$, what is $p(-8)$?

4. If $q(2) = -7$, what is $p(-7)$?

5. If $p(-0.6) = -1.3$, what is $q(-1.3)$?

6. If $p(1.8) = 0.5$, what is $q(1.8)$?

In Exercises 7–12, use the Horizontal Line Test to determine whether each graph is a one-to-one function with an inverse function.

7.

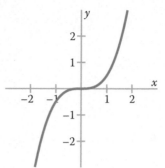

8.

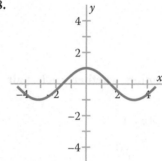

9.

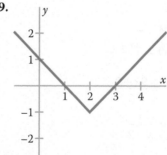

10.

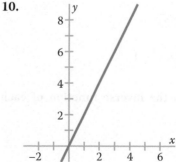

11.

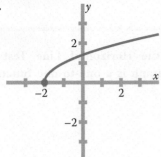

12.

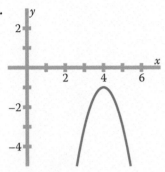

In Exercises 13–22, determine whether each pair of functions are inverses.

13. $g(x) = 4x + 1$ and $f(x) = -4x - 1$

14. $f(x) = \dfrac{2x + 5}{3}$ and $g(x) = \dfrac{3x - 5}{2}$

15. $g(x) = x$ and $f(x) = -x$

16. $g(x) = x + 2$ and $f(x) = -x - 2$

17. $f(x) = \dfrac{9x - 13}{3}$ and $g(x) = \dfrac{3x + 13}{9}$

18. $g(x) = \dfrac{5x + 2}{9}$ and $f(x) = \dfrac{9x + 2}{5}$

19. $g(x) = \dfrac{1}{x} + 2$ and $f(x) = \dfrac{1}{x - 2}$

20. $f(x) = \dfrac{1}{2(x - 5)}$ and $g(x) = \dfrac{1}{2x} + 5$

21. $g(x) = \dfrac{x^3}{8}$ and $f(x) = \sqrt[3]{2x}$

22. $f(x) = \sqrt[3]{x + 1}$ and $g(x) = x^3 - 1$

In Exercises 23–24, graph the inverse function of each function, if it exists.

23.

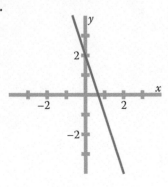

24.

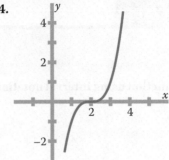

In Exercises 25–42, find the inverse function of each function, if it exists.

25. $g(x) = -x + 3$

26. $f(x) = \dfrac{5 + 7x}{2}$

27. $p(x) = 6x - 1$

28. $q(x) = \dfrac{4}{5}x - 3$

29. $t(x) = \dfrac{11 + 9x}{2}$

30. $r(x) = \dfrac{-3x + 6}{13}$

31. $g(x) = \sqrt{x + 4}$

32. $f(x) = \sqrt{3x - 6}$

33. $h(x) = \sqrt{2x - 1}$

34. $j(x) = \sqrt{8 - 5x}$

35. $w(x) = (x + 3)^2$

36. $d(x) = x^2 - 7$

37. $k(x) = \dfrac{1}{x + 6}$

38. $c(x) = \dfrac{1}{x} - 8$

39. $m(x) = \dfrac{1}{x - 4} + 2$

40. $v(x) = -\dfrac{1}{x + 1} - 3$

41. $s(x) = \sqrt[3]{2x + 7}$

42. $n(x) = x^3 - 4$

Extensions

43. $f(x) = x^2 - 9$ is not a one-to-one function and therefore the inverse function of f does not exist. However, if the domain of f is restricted in a particular way (so that f passes the Horizontal Line Test), then $f^{-1}(x)$ exists. State the domain values over which $f^{-1}(x)$ exists.

In Exercises 44–50, use the following information.

Find the indicated value or expression, if it exists, given that $f(x) = x + 5$ and $g(x) = 2x - 1$.

44. $(f^{-1} \circ g)(4)$

45. $(f^{-1} \circ g^{-1})(0)$

46. $(g^{-1} \circ g^{-1})(2)$

47. $(f^{-1} \circ f^{-1})(9)$

48. $(f^{-1} \circ g)(x)$

49. $(g^{-1} \circ f^{-1})(x)$

50. $(g^{-1} \circ g^{-1})(x)$

51. Find the value of k such that $f(x) = kx^3 + kx + 6k$ has an inverse function and $f^{-1}(8) = -1$.

52. Always, sometimes, or never? If f is an odd function, then f^{-1} exists.

53. Find the inverse function of $g(x) = (x - 3)(x^2 + 3x + 9)$, if it exists.

CHAPTER 1 REVIEW EXERCISES

Section 1.1 Coordinates and Graphs

1. Given points $A(1, 3)$, $B(-1, -3)$, and $C(3, 9)$, find the length of the segments AB, AC, and BC and determine whether the points are collinear.

2. Write the equation $9x^2 + 9y^2 + 36x - 90y + 117 = 0$ in the standard form of a circle. Then identify the circle's center and radius, and graph the circle.

3. Use intercepts to sketch the graph of $y = x^2 + 5x + 6$.

4. Write the equation of the circle where $A(-2, -3)$ and $B(6, -3)$ are the endpoints of a diameter.

5. Use symmetry and intercepts to sketch the graph of $y = -|x| + 3$.

Section 1.2 Lines

6. Write the slope-intercept form equation of the line with slope 3 that passes through $(-2, 4)$. Graph the line.

7. Write the slope-intercept form equation of the line that passes through $(-1, 7)$ and $(-2, -15)$.

8. Find the slope and y-intercept of the graph of $4 + 2y = -5x$.

9. Line l passes through $(7, -2)$ and line p is the graph of $y - 1 = \frac{3}{4}(x + 5)$. If $l \parallel p$, what is the point-slope form equation of l?

10. Line l passes through $(4, -2)$ and line p is the graph of $y = \frac{4}{3}x - 1$. If $l \perp p$, what is the slope-intercept form equation of l?

Section 1.3 Variation

11. The pressure P exerted by a force varies inversely as the area A on which the force is applied. If 16 newtons per square feet of pressure are exerted by a force on an area of 3 square feet, what is the pressure exerted by the same force on an area of 6 square feet?

12. The number of chocolate bunnies that can be eaten varies directly with the number of people eating them and the time taken to eat them. If 39 chocolate bunnies can be eaten in 10 minutes by 3 people, how many chocolate bunnies can be eaten in 30 minutes by 4 people?

13. A satellite orbiting Earth has a period of 21 hours when its average distance is 3.8×10^7 meters. Find the orbital period of a satellite when the average distance is 5.1×10^7 meters. Use the law that the square of the time of orbit varies directly with the average radius cubed. Round to the nearest tenth, if necessary.

14. If a pendulum with length 81 centimeters has a frequency of 1/10 hertz, find the frequency of a 36-centimeter pendulum, given that frequency varies inversely with the square root of length.

15. The gravitational force F in newtons between two objects, having mass m_1 and m_2 respectively, varies jointly with respect to m_1 and m_2 and inversely with respect to the square of the distance d between the two objects. If the gravitational force between Earth (mass 5.98×1024 kilograms, radius 6.38×10^6 meters) and a math student (mass 65 kilograms) is 637.227 newtons, find the gravitational force F between Earth and a football player who weighs 90 kilograms. Round to the nearest thousandth.

Section 1.4 Functions

16. Use the Vertical Line Test to determine whether the graph represents a function.

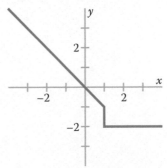

17. If $g(x) = x^2 - 5x + 1$, find $g(2)$, $g(-5)$, and $g(a - 2)$.

18. Given an equilateral triangle with side s, write a function for the area of the triangle in terms of s.

19. If $g(x) = 2x^2 + 3x - 1$ and $h(x) = -x + 5$, find all real x-values such the $g(x) = h(x)$.

20. Find the domain of $f(x) = \dfrac{x^2}{x^2 - 2x - 3}$.

Section 1.5 Graphs of Functions

21. Given the graph of function $h(x)$, use the graph to identify the domain and range of h, then evaluate $h(-1)$, $h(2)$, and find all x such that $h(x) = 0$.

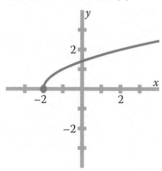

22. Graph. $k(x) = \begin{cases} -x - 4 & \text{if } x \le -1 \\ 2x + 1 & \text{if } -1 < x \le 2 \\ -4 & \text{if } x > 2 \end{cases}$

23. Graph. $r(x) = 4[[x - 1]]$

24. Find the real zeros of the function $m(x) = x^3 + 2x^2 - 36x - 72$.

25. Identify the intervals over which the function is strictly increasing, strictly decreasing, or constant.

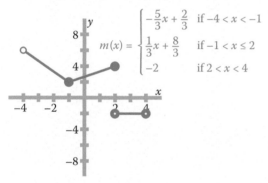

$$m(x) = \begin{cases} -\dfrac{5}{3}x + \dfrac{2}{3} & \text{if } -4 < x < -1 \\ \dfrac{1}{3}x + \dfrac{8}{3} & \text{if } -1 < x \le 2 \\ -2 & \text{if } 2 < x < 4 \end{cases}$$

Section 1.6 Transformations of Functions

In Exercises 26–28, sketch the graph of each function.

26. $g(x) = (x - 6)^2 - 4$

27. $f(x) = 3|x + 1|$

28. $h(x) = -\sqrt{x - 1}$

In Exercises 29–30, determine whether each function is even, odd, or neither.

29. $m(x) = 5|x| + 2$

30. $p(x) = 7(x + 6)^3$

Section 1.7 Combining Functions

31. Given $f(x) = 4x^2 - 3x + 3$ and $g(x) = 5 - 2x + x^2$, find $(f - g)(x)$ and $(f + g)(4)$.

32. Given $m(x) = x - 8$ and $n(x) = x + 1$, find $(mn)(x)$ and $\left(\dfrac{m}{n}\right)(x)$.

33. Simplify the difference quotient for $f(x) = -3x^2 + 5x - 6$.

34. Given $p(x) = x^2 - x - 5$ and $r(x) = 2x - 1$, find $(p \circ r)(x)$ and $(p \circ r)(3)$.

35. Find the function $g(x)$ that forms the composite $(f \circ g)(x) = (7x - 4)^2$ with $f(x) = x^2$.

Section 1.8 Inverse Functions

36. Suppose that p and g are inverse functions, and that $p(-5) = 8$, $g(6) = 0$, and $p(9) = 11$. Use the given information to evaluate $g(8)$, $p(0)$, and $p(11)$, if possible.

37. Use the Horizontal Line Test to determine whether the graph is a one-to-one function with an inverse function.

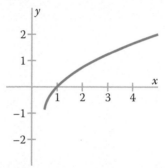

38. Determine whether $f(x) = 4x + \dfrac{1}{4}$ and $g(x) = \dfrac{1}{4}x - \dfrac{1}{16}$ are inverses of each other.

39. Graph the inverse function, if it exists.

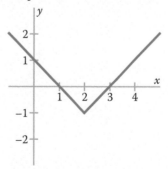

40. Find the inverse of $k(x) = 3\sqrt{x - 5}$, if it exists.

TRIGONOMETRIC FUNCTIONS

2.1 ANGLES AND THEIR MEASURE

OBJECTIVES

- Draw an angle in standard position in a coordinate plane.
- Identify coterminal angles.
- Find the supplement and complement of an angle.
- Measure angles in degrees and radians.
- Use the arc length formula and the formula for the area of a sector of a circle.
- Find linear speed and angular speed.

PREREQUISITE VOCABULARY TERMS

circle

circumference

coordinate plane

degrees

quadrants

radius

2.1.1 Measuring Angles Using Degrees

A **ray** is a line with one endpoint. Two rays with a common endpoint define an **angle**, which is formed by rotating one ray about its endpoint. The ray in the starting position is called the **initial side**, and the ray in the ending position (i.e., the position after the rotation) is called the **terminal side**. The endpoint is called the angle's **vertex** (Figure 2.1a).

We have seen angles measured using degrees. For example, a right angle (i.e., the angle formed by two perpendicular rays) measures 90°. Note that a fraction of 1° can be expressed using a decimal (e.g., $\frac{1}{2}(1°) = 0.5°$). Alternatively, a fraction of 1° can be expressed in **minutes** and **seconds**, where 1 minute is defined as 1/60 of 1°, and 1 second is defined as 1/60 of 1 minute.

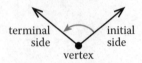

terminal side | initial side
vertex

Figure 2.1a

A Fraction of a Degree

1 minute = $1' = \frac{1}{60}(1°) \approx 0.01667°$ *Use ′ (prime) to denote minutes.*

1 second = $1'' = \frac{1}{60}(1') = \frac{1}{3600}(1°) \approx 0.0002778°$ *Use ″ (double prime) to denote seconds.*

For example, 10 degrees, 5 minutes, and 80 seconds is denoted 10° 5′ 80″. To find the approximate degree value of 10° 5′ 80″, convert the minutes and the seconds to degrees, then add the three degree values. Since $10 + \frac{5}{60} + \frac{80}{3600} \approx 10.10556$, 10° 5′ 80″ is approximately 10.10556°.

Angles in a Coordinate Plane

Consider a coordinate plane, as shown in Figure 2.1b. Recall that the *x*- and *y*-axes are perpendicular lines that divide the plane into four quadrants. Since the axes intersect at right angles (which measure 90°), the sum of the measures of the four angles formed by the intersections of the axes a is 4(90°) = 360°.

An angle in a coordinate plane with its vertex at the origin and its initial side on the positive *x*-axis is said to be in **standard position**. The terminal side of an angle in standard position may lie in one of the four quadrants or on either the positive or negative *x*- or *y*-axis.

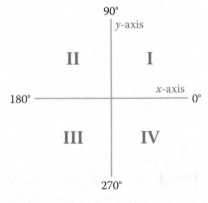

Figure 2.1b

Angles with Positive Measure

Angles with positive measure are formed by rotating the terminal side in a counterclockwise direction, as shown in Figures 2.1c and 2.1d. Angle θ in Figure 2.1c is called an **acute angle** because $0° < \theta < 90°$. Angle θ in Figure 2.1d is called an **obtuse angle** because $90° < \theta < 180°$.

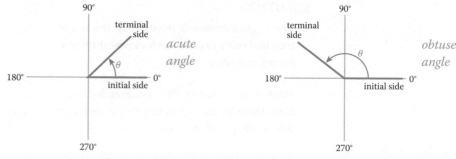

Figure 2.1c   Figure 2.1d

IMPORTANT

Greek letters, such as θ (theta), are often used to represent the measure of an angle.

Consider an angle in standard position. If the angle measures 90°, then the terminal side is on the positive y-axis (Figure 2.1e). As we have seen, angles measuring 90° are called right angles. If the angle measures 180°, then the terminal side is on the negative x-axis (Figure 2.1f). Angles measuring 180° are called **straight angles**. If the angle measures 360°, then the terminal side is on the positive x-axis (Figure 2.1g). In this case, the terminal side is in the same position as the initial side.

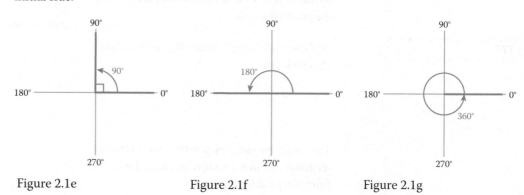

Figure 2.1e   Figure 2.1f   Figure 2.1g

2.1.2   Drawing an Angle in Standard Position

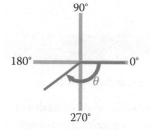

To draw an angle in standard position, first draw the initial side on the positive x-axis, then rotate the terminal side from this position. For angles with positive measure, rotate the terminal side in a *counterclockwise* direction, using the angle's measure at each axis as a guide.

For angles with negative measure, rotate the terminal side in a *clockwise* direction (Figure 2.1h), again using the angle's measure at each axis as a guide. The terminal side of the angle in Figure 2.1h is rotated clockwise from the positive x-axis, through the negative y-axis, to a position between the negative y-axis and the negative x-axis (i.e., in quadrant III). So, its measure must be between $-90°$ and $-180°$.

Angles with measure greater than 360° (or less than $-360°$) are formed by rotating the terminal side more than one full rotation around the axes. For example, a 380° angle is formed by rotating the terminal side 20° beyond the positive x-axis (i.e., beyond 360°). Note that the terminal side of a 20° angle is in the same position as the terminal side of a 380° angle, and this is true for any two angles which differ by a multiple of 360°.

θ is a negative angle.

Figure 2.1h

EXAMPLE 1   Drawing an Angle in Standard Position

Draw each angle in standard position.

A. 160°   **B.** −45°   **C.** 400°

SOLUTION

A. The angle measure is positive, so rotate the terminal side in a counterclockwise direction from the positive *x*-axis.

Note that rotating 90° counterclockwise from the positive *x*-axis brings the terminal side to the positive *y*-axis.

To draw a 160° angle, rotate the terminal side counterclockwise 70° past the positive *y*-axis because 90° + 70° = 160°.

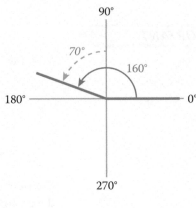

B. The angle measure is negative, so rotate the terminal side in a clockwise direction from the positive *x*-axis.

To draw a −45° angle, rotate the terminal side 45° clockwise.

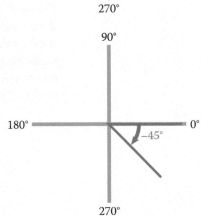

C. The angle measure is positive, so rotate the terminal side in a counterclockwise direction from the positive *x*-axis.

Note that rotating 360° counterclockwise from the positive *x*-axis returns the terminal side to the positive *x*-axis.

To draw a 400° angle, make a full counterclockwise rotation of the terminal side (i.e., rotate 360°) and then rotate 40° past the positive *x*-axis because 360° + 40° = 400°.

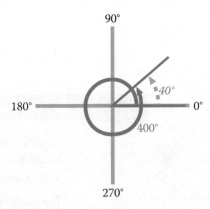

2.1.3   Finding the Quadrant in Which an Angle Lies

From here forward, assume that all angles in a coordinate plane are in standard position.

An angle in standard position where the terminal side is on the *x*- or *y*-axis is called a **quadrantal angle**. If an angle is not a quadrantal angle, then its terminal side lies in a quadrant. An angle is said to lie in a particular quadrant when its terminal side lies in that quadrant. For example, a 100° angle lies in quadrant II because its terminal side lies in quadrant II.

| **EXAMPLE 2** | **Finding the Quadrant in Which an Angle Lies** |

Identify the quadrant in which each angle lies, if any.

A. 190°   **B.** −120°   **C.** −800°

SOLUTION

A. A 190° angle is formed by rotating the terminal side counterclockwise because its measure is positive. The terminal side of a 190° angle is rotated 10° beyond the negative *x*-axis because 180° + 10° = 190°. Since the angle's terminal side is between the negative *x*-axis and the negative *y*-axis, a 190° angle lies in quadrant III.

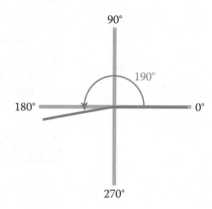

B. A −120° angle is formed by rotating the terminal side clockwise because its measure is negative. The terminal side of a −120° angle is rotated −30° beyond the negative *y*-axis because −90° + (−30°) = −120°. Since the angle's terminal side is between the negative *x*-axis and the negative *y*-axis, a −120° angle lies in quadrant III.

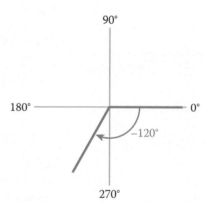

C. A −800° angle is formed by rotating the terminal side clockwise because its measure is negative. The terminal side of a −800° angle is rotated −80° beyond the positive *x*-axis because −360° + (−360°) + (−80°) = −800°. Since the angle's terminal side is between the positive *x*-axis and the negative *y*-axis, a −800° angle lies in quadrant IV.

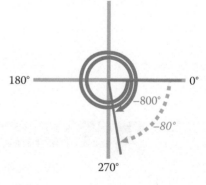

2.1.4 Finding Coterminal Angles

Since rotating the terminal side of an angle 360° clockwise or counterclockwise is a full rotation around the plane, adding (or subtracting) a multiple of 360° to the measure of any angle results in an angle whose terminal side is in the same position as the original angle.

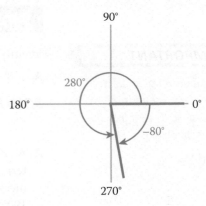

Angles in standard position with common terminal sides are called **coterminal angles**. For example, angles measuring −80° and 280° are coterminal (Figure 2.1i).

All angles that are coterminal with a given angle can be identified by adding (or subtracting) multiples of 360° to the angle's measure. The difference of two coterminal angles is always a multiple of 360°.

Figure 2.1i

TIP

Multiples of 360°:
. . . −1080°, −720°,
−360°, 0°, 360°, 720°,
1080°, . . .

EXAMPLE 3 **Identifying Coterminal Angles**

Determine whether angles measuring −1180° and 20° are coterminal with θ if θ = −460°. Then find the smallest positive angle that is coterminal with θ, and find the negative angle closest to 0° that is coterminal with θ.

SOLUTION

ALTERNATIVE METHOD

Sketch the two angles in a coordinate plane to determine whether or not the angles are coterminal.

Angles measuring −1180° and 20° are coterminal with θ if the difference between each measure and θ is a multiple of 360°.

−1180° − (−460°) = −720° ✔ *The difference is a multiple of 360°, so the angles are coterminal.*

20° − (−460°) = 480° ✖ *The difference is not a multiple of 360°, so the angles are not coterminal.*

Adding (or subtracting) multiples of 360° to the measure of θ gives the measures of the angles coterminal with θ. The measure of the smallest positive angle that is coterminal with θ is between 0° and 360°. The measure of the negative angle closest to 0° that is coterminal with θ is between 0° and −360°.

−460° + 360° = −100°   The negative angle closest to 0° that is coterminal with θ is −100°.

−100° + 360° = 260°   The smallest positive angle that is coterminal with θ is 260°.

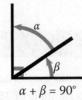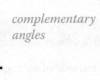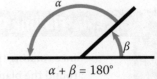

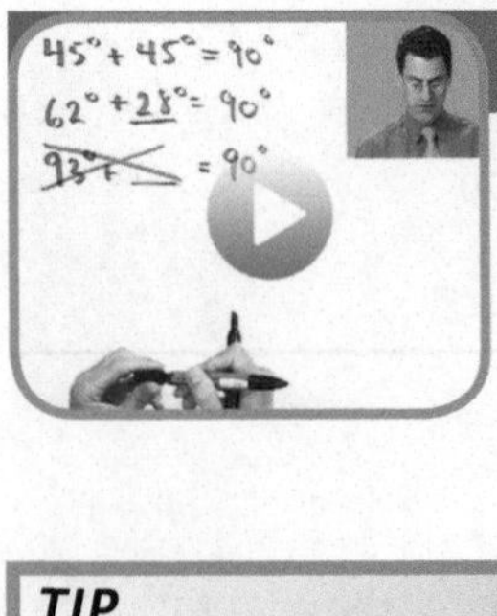

2.1.5 Finding the Complement and Supplement of an Angle

Two positive angles are **complementary** if the sum of their measures is 90° (Figure 2.1j), or **supplementary** if the sum of their measures is 180° (Figure 2.1k). When two angles are complementary, each angle is the **complement** of the other. When two angles are supplementary, each angle is the **supplement** of the other.

TIP

The Greek letters α (alpha) and β (beta) represent the measures of the angles.

complementary angles

α + β = 90°

Figure 2.1j

supplementary angles

α + β = 180°

Figure 2.1k

Since the sum of the measures of complementary angles is 90°, only acute angles have complements, and the complement of the angle is also acute. Since the sum of supplementary angles is 180°, an angle and its supplement may both be right angles, or one angle may be acute and the other obtuse.

IMPORTANT

Complementary and supplementary angles must be positive angles.

EXAMPLE 4   Finding Complementary and Supplementary Angles

For each angle, identify the complement and supplement, if it exists.

A. 15°   **B.** 129°   **C.** 200°

SOLUTION

Let θ be the measure of the given angle.

- If $0 < \theta < 90$, then θ has a complement given by x in the equation $\theta + x = 90$.
- If $0 < \theta < 180$, then θ has a supplement given by y in the equation $\theta + y = 180$.

IMPORTANT

If $\theta > 90°$, then θ has no complement.
If $\theta > 180°$, then θ has no complement or supplement.

A. Since 15° < 90° and 15° < 180°, 15° has a complement and a supplement.

$15° + x = 90° \implies x = 75°$ The complement of 15° is 75°.

$15° + y = 180° \implies y = 165°$ The supplement of 15° is 165°.

B. Since 129° < 180°, 129° has a supplement. However, since 129° > 90°, 129° has no complement.

$129° + y = 180° \implies y = 51°$ The supplement of 129° is 51°.

C. Since 200° > 180°, 200° has neither a complement nor a supplement.

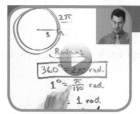

2.1.6   Converting between Degrees and Radians

Introduction to Radians

We have seen that an angle can be measured in degrees, and that this degree measure indicates the amount of rotation from the angle's initial side to its terminal side. An amount of rotation can also be measured in **radians**.

DEFINITION

> **Radians** are a unit of angular measure defined such that 2π radians = 360°.

When the amount of rotation from the initial side to the terminal side forms a complete circle, the angle's measure is 360°. If the radius of this complete circle is 1 unit, then the circumference of this circle (i.e., the length around the circle) is 2π. It follows that radians relate the length around a circle to the angle forming the circle (Figure 2.1l).

REMEMBER

The formula for the circumference of a circle is $C = 2\pi r$.

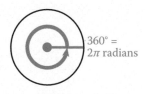

$360° = 2\pi$ radians

one complete rotation

Figure 2.1l

When the amount of rotation from the initial side to the terminal side forms a semicircle, the angle's measure is 180° because 360°/2 = 180°. This amount of rotation is equal to π radians (Figure 2.1m) because 2π/2 = π. Therefore, π radians = 180°.

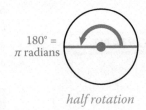

180° = π radians

half rotation

Figure 2.1m

The radian measures of additional common angles are shown in the following table. Notice that a 90° angle (a right angle) is 1/4 of a complete rotation, so the radian measure of a right angle is 2π/4 radians, that is, π/2 radians. Alternatively, a 90° angle is 1/2 of π radians, that is, π/2 radians. Additionally, a 45° angle is 1/2 of π/2 radians, that is, π/4 radians.

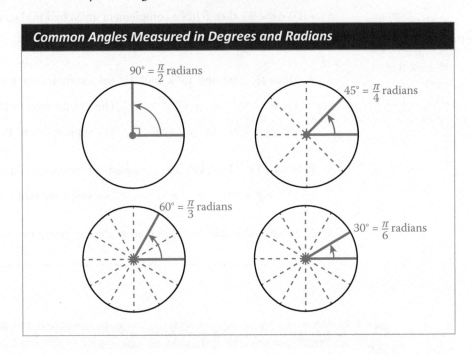

Common Angles Measured in Degrees and Radians

$90° = \frac{\pi}{2}$ radians

$45° = \frac{\pi}{4}$ radians

$60° = \frac{\pi}{3}$ radians

$30° = \frac{\pi}{6}$ radians

II · I

$\frac{\pi}{2} < \theta < \pi$ · $0 < \theta < \frac{\pi}{2}$

$\frac{\pi}{2}$

π ——————— 0

$\pi < \theta < \frac{3\pi}{2}$ · $\frac{3\pi}{2} < \theta < 2\pi$

$\frac{3\pi}{2}$

III · IV

Figure 2.1n

Figure 2.1n shows the range of radian measures for an angle θ within each quadrant (when $0 < \theta < 2\pi$).

Converting between Degree and Radian Measures

Since π radians is equal to 180°, it follows that $\frac{\pi \text{ radians}}{180°} = 1$ and $\frac{180°}{\pi \text{ radians}} = 1$. Therefore, multiplying the degree measure of an angle by $\frac{\pi \text{ radians}}{180°}$ will convert the degree measure into radians. Similarly, multiplying the radian measure of an angle by $\frac{180°}{\pi \text{ radians}}$ will convert the radian measure into degrees.

Converting between Degrees and Radians	
Degrees to Radians	**Radians to Degrees**
Multiply the degrees by $\frac{\pi \text{ radians}}{180°}$.	Multiply the radians by $\frac{180°}{\pi \text{ radians}}$.

| **EXAMPLE 5** | **Converting from Degrees to Radians** |

Convert each degree measure to radian measure.

A. 225° **B.** −420°

SOLUTION

Multiply each degree measure by $\dfrac{\pi \text{ radians}}{180°}$.

A. $225° = (225°)\left(\dfrac{\pi \text{ radians}}{180°}\right) = \dfrac{225\pi}{180} \text{ radians} = \dfrac{5\pi}{4} \text{ radians}$

B. $-420° = (-420°)\left(\dfrac{\pi \text{ radians}}{180°}\right) = \dfrac{-420\pi}{180} \text{ radians} = -\dfrac{7\pi}{3} \text{ radians}$

ALTERNATIVE METHOD

IMPORTANT

*Since 180° = π radians,
1° = π/180 radians.*

Multiply each side of the equation $1° = \dfrac{\pi}{180}$ radians by the given degree measure.

A. Multiply each side by 225.

$(225)1° = \dfrac{\pi}{180} \text{ radians}(225)$

$225° = \dfrac{225\pi}{180} \text{ radians}$

$225° = \dfrac{5\pi}{4} \text{ radians}$

B. Multiply each side by −420.

$(-420)1° = \dfrac{\pi}{180} \text{ radians}(-420)$

$-420° = \dfrac{-420\pi}{180} \text{ radians}$

$-420° = -\dfrac{7\pi}{3} \text{ radians}$

| **EXAMPLE 6** | **Converting from Radians to Degrees** |

Convert each radian measure to degree measure.

A. 3π radians **B.** $-5\pi/6$ radians

SOLUTION

Multiply each radian measure by $\dfrac{180°}{\pi \text{ radians}}$.

A. $3\pi \text{ radians} = (3\pi \text{ radians})\left(\dfrac{180°}{\pi \text{ radians}}\right) = \dfrac{3\pi(180°)}{\pi} = 540°$

B. $-\dfrac{5\pi}{6} \text{ radians} = \left(-\dfrac{5\pi}{6} \text{ radians}\right)\left(\dfrac{180°}{\pi \text{ radians}}\right) = \dfrac{-5\pi(180°)}{6\pi} = -150°$

ALTERNATIVE METHOD

IMPORTANT

*Since 180° = π radians,
180°/π = 1 radian.*

Multiply each side of the equation $\dfrac{180°}{\pi} = 1$ radian by the given radian measure.

A. Multiply each side by 3π.

$(3\pi)\dfrac{180°}{\pi} = 1 \text{ radian}(3\pi)$

$(3)(180°) = 3\pi \text{ radians}$

$540° = 3\pi \text{ radians}$

B. Multiply each side by $-\dfrac{5\pi}{6}$.

$\left(-\dfrac{5\pi}{6}\right)\dfrac{180°}{\pi} = 1 \text{ radian}\left(-\dfrac{5\pi}{6}\right)$

$-\dfrac{5(180°)}{6} = -\dfrac{5\pi}{6} \text{ radians}$

$-150° = -\dfrac{5\pi}{6} \text{ radians}$

2.1.7 Using the Arc Length Formula

Figure 2.1o shows a circle where **central angle** θ defines **arc** s.

DEFINITION

An **arc** is a portion of the circumference of a circle.

A **central angle** is an angle within a circle where the angle's vertex is at the circle's center.

The **arc length formula** gives the measure of an arc as a length.

Figure 2.1o

The Arc Length Formula

If a central angle θ (measured in radians) intercepts an arc of length s in a circle with radius r, then $s = r\theta$.

> **NOTICE THAT**
>
> *If $r = 1$, then the radian measure of θ is equal to the length of the arc.*
>
> $s = (1)\theta = \theta$

EXAMPLE 7   Finding the Length of an Arc

Suppose an arc on a circle with a radius of 5 meters is intercepted by a 90° angle. Find the length of the arc to the nearest hundredth of a meter.

SOLUTION

Substitute the measure of the central angle (in radians) and the radius of the circle into the arc length formula $s = r\theta$, and then round the answer to the nearest hundredth of a meter.

The measure of the central angle is 90°, so substitute $\pi/2$ for θ (since 90° = $\pi/2$ radians).

> **NOTICE THAT**
>
> *A 90° central angle corresponds to 1/4 of a circle, so the length of its intercepted arc is 1/4 of the circumference of the circle ($C = 2\pi r$).*
>
> $s = C/4 = 2\pi(5)/4 = 5\pi/2$

$$s = r\theta = (5)\left(\frac{\pi}{2}\right) = \frac{5\pi}{2} \approx 7.85 \text{ meters}$$

Therefore, the length of the arc is approximately 7.85 meters.

Using the Arc Length Formula to Approximate a Distance

If a central angle is very small, then the length of the intercepted arc can be used to approximate the subtended distance perpendicular to the angle's initial side, as shown in **Example 8**.

| **EXAMPLE 8** | **Using the Arc Length Formula to Approximate a Distance** |

A tower 2500 feet from an observer subtends a 2.5° angle, as shown in the picture. Use the arc length formula to approximate the height of the tower to the nearest foot.

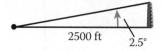

2500 ft 2.5°

SOLUTION

The height of the tower is approximately equal to the length of the intercepted arc of a circle, where the central angle is 2.5° and the radius is 2500 feet.

IMPORTANT

The measure of an angle used in the arc length formula must be in radians, not degrees.

Convert the angle measure from degrees to radians.

$$2.5° = (2.5°)\left(\frac{\pi \text{ radians}}{180°}\right) = \frac{2.5\pi}{180}\text{ radians} = \frac{\pi}{72}\text{ radians}$$

Substitute the measure of the central angle and the radius of the circle into the arc length formula and round to the nearest foot.

$$s = r\theta = (2500)\left(\frac{\pi}{72}\right) \approx 109 \text{ feet}$$

The height of the tower is approximately 109 feet.

2.1.8 Finding Linear and Angular Speeds

As an object travels along a circular path (i.e., along an arc) at a constant speed, the central angle changes uniformly. The rate at which the central angle is changing is the object's **angular speed** ω. The object's **linear speed** v is the rate at which the object is moving along the arc.

> ### Formulas for Linear and Angular Speed
>
> Suppose an object travels at a constant speed along an arc on a circle with radius r. If s is the length of the arc traveled in time t and the corresponding central angle is θ (in radians), then
>
> $$\pi = \frac{\theta}{t} \text{ and } v = \frac{s}{t}.$$

| **EXAMPLE 9** | **Finding Linear and Angular Speed** |

IMPORTANT

One complete revolution is 2π radians.

The blades on a ceiling fan are 3 feet long. When set to medium speed, the blades rotate at 12 revolutions per second. Find the linear speed of the end of a blade in feet per second and the angular speed of a blade in radians per second, each to the nearest whole number.

SOLUTION

In 1 second, a blade completes 12 revolutions. So, when $t = 1$ second, $\theta = 12(2\pi) = 24\pi$ radians.

Find the linear speed.

$$v = \frac{s}{t} = \frac{r\theta}{t} = \frac{3(24\pi)}{1} = 72\pi \text{ ft/s} \approx 226 \text{ ft/s}$$

Find the angular speed.

$$\pi = \frac{\theta}{t} = \frac{24\pi}{1} = 24\pi \text{ rad/s} \approx 75 \text{ rad/s}$$

2.1.9   Finding the Area of a Sector of a Circle

A **sector** of a circle is the interior portion of a circle defined by a central angle θ (i.e., the portion of the circle enclosed by two radii and their intercepted arc) where θ is between 0 and 2π radians, as shown in Figure 2.1p.

The **area of a sector** of a circle is a fraction of the circle's area. This fraction of the circle's area is given by $\theta/2\pi$. For example, the area of a sector defined by a central angle θ of π radians is 1/2 the area of the circle because $\pi/2\pi = 1/2$. Therefore, since the area of a circle with radius r is πr^2, the area of a sector of a circle with radius r and angle θ is $\dfrac{\theta}{2\pi} \cdot \pi r^2$, which simplifies to $\dfrac{1}{2}r^2\theta$.

Figure 2.1p

> ### The Area of a Sector of a Circle
>
> The area of a sector of a circle defined by central angle θ is given by
> $$A = \frac{1}{2}r^2\theta$$
> where r is the circle's radius and θ is measured in radians.

NOTICE THAT

If $\theta = 2\pi$, then the sector is the entire circle. In this case, the formula gives

$A = \dfrac{1}{2}r^2(2\pi) = \pi r^2$,

which is the area of an entire circle.

EXAMPLE 10   Finding the Radius of a Circle

Find the radius of a circle to the nearest tenth of a centimeter if the area of a sector defined by a 120° central angle is 54.8 square centimeters.

SOLUTION

Convert the angle measure to radians.

$$120° = (120°)\left(\frac{\pi \text{ radians}}{180°}\right) = \frac{120\pi}{180} \text{ radians} = \frac{2\pi}{3} \text{ radians}$$

Substitute the given angle and area into the formula, then solve for r.

REMEMBER

Since a radius is a length, r must be positive.

$$54.8 = \frac{1}{2}r^2\left(\frac{2\pi}{3}\right) \Rightarrow 54.8 = r^2\left(\frac{\pi}{3}\right) \Rightarrow \frac{(3)(54.8)}{\pi} = r^2 \Rightarrow r = \sqrt{\frac{(3)(54.8)}{\pi}} \approx 7.2 \text{ cm}$$

SECTION 2.1 EXERCISES

Warm Up

1. Find the circumference and area of a circle with a radius of 15 centimeters. Round each answer to the nearest tenth.

2. Identify the quadrant or axis in which each point lies: (−2, 3), (5, 9), (7, 0), (5, −4), and (−10, −9).

3. Convert 158 inches to feet.

Just the Facts

Fill in the blanks.

4. An angle in standard position has its initial side on the positive _____ and its _____ at the origin. To graph an angle in standard position that has a measure of −81°, rotate 81 degrees in the _____ direction, starting from the _____ x-axis.

5. A straight angle has a measure of _____, a(n) _____ angle has a measure of 90°, and a(n) _____ angle has a measure between 0° and 90°.

6. Angles whose difference is a multiple of 360° are _____.

7. An angle whose measure is 250° is located in quadrant _____ and is _____ with −110°. The measure of 250° in radians is _____.

8. A nail moving at a rate of 145 feet per second in a wheel of a car is an example of the nail's _____.

9. An angle that is its own complement has a measure of _____. An angle that is its own supplement has a measure of _____.

10. To convert $-\dfrac{10\pi}{3}$ radians to degrees, multiply by _____, and the result is _____. This angle is located in quadrant _____.

Essential Skills

In Exercises 1–12, draw an angle with each given measure in standard position.

1. 100°
2. 240°
3. 59°
4. 319°
5. −80°
6. −210°
7. −155°
8. −320°
9. 420°
10. −840°
11. −630°
12. 910°

In Exercises 13–16, choose which angle(s) lies in the indicated quadrant.

13. quadrant III
    A. 45°   B. 195°   C. −20°

14. quadrant IV
    A. 280°   B. 175°   C. −70°   D. −120°   E. 10°

15. quadrant II
    A. 455°   B. 175°   C. −181°   D. −275°   E. 1100°

16. quadrant I
    A. 1105°   B. 775°   C. −710°   D. −320°   E. 91°

In Exercises 17–24, identify the quadrant in which each angle lies.

17. 380°
18. 1150°
19. 1349°
20. 650°
21. −445°
22. −1100°
23. −1650°
24. −938°

In Exercises 25–30, choose all angles that are coterminal with each given angle θ.

25. θ = 70°
    A. −70°   B. 430°   C. −290°   D. −430°   E. 790°

26. θ = 200°
    A. −160°   B. 160°   C. 560°   D. −200°   E. −520°

27. θ = −300°
    A. 60°   B. −60°   C. 560°   D. −1020°   E. 420°

28. θ = −140°
    A. 260°   B. −400°   C. 220°   D. −500°   E. 580°

29. θ = 150°
    A. −110°   B. 1230°   C. 410°   D. −210°   E. −570°

30. θ = 340°
    A. −20°   B. −700°   C. 700°   D. −380°   E. −1100°

In Exercises 31–42, find the smallest positive angle and the negative angle closest to 0° that are coterminal with each given angle (other than itself).

31. 240°
32. 655°
33. 1020°
34. 981°
35. 158°
36. 556°
37. −170°
38. −795°
39. −642°
40. −287°
41. −1033°
42. −714°

In Exercises 43–46, find the measure of the complementary angle, if it exists, for the angle with each given measure.

43. 7°   44. 103°

45. 90.5°   46. 22.7°

In Exercises 47–50, find the measure of the supplementary angle, if it exists, for the angle with each given measure.

47. 75°   48. 58°

49. 144°   50. 280°

In Exercises 51–56, convert each degree measure to radian measure.

51. 45°   52. 132°

53. −201°   54. −94°

55. −355°   56. 314°

In Exercises 57–62, convert each radian measure to degree measure. Round to the nearest degree.

57. $\frac{\pi}{6}$ radians   58. $\frac{5\pi}{12}$ radians

59. $-\frac{11\pi}{3}$ radians   60. −2.4 radians

61. 4.7 radians   62. $\frac{3\pi}{8}$ radians

63. What is the length of the arc intercepted by an angle of 10° on a circle with a radius of 10 meters? Round the answer to the nearest hundredth of a meter.

64. A tree 1200 yards from an observer subtends an angle of 1.5°. Use the arc length formula to estimate the height of the tree to the nearest yard.

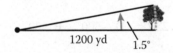

65. What is the length of the arc intercepted by an angle of 324° on a circle with a radius of 47.2 feet? Round the answer to the nearest tenth of a foot.

66. A flagpole 1600 yards from an observer subtends an angle of 3°. Use the arc length formula to estimate the height of the flagpole to the nearest yard.

67. What is the length of the arc intercepted by an angle of 115° on a circle with a radius of 7 inches? Round the answer to the nearest hundredth of an inch.

68. A telephone mast 1300 yards from an observer subtends an angle of 1.5°. Use the arc length formula to estimate the height of the telephone mast to the nearest yard.

69. Find the radius of the circle to the nearest unit.

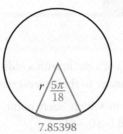

70. A 50-foot radio tower r feet from an observer subtends an angle of 0.75°. Use the arc length formula to estimate r (the distance between the observer and the radio tower) to the nearest foot.

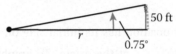

71. Find the radius of the circle to the nearest tenth of an inch.

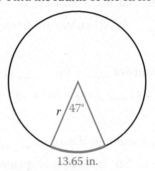

72. A 65-foot flagpole r feet from an observer subtends an angle of 3.5°. Use the arc length formula to estimate r (the distance between the observer and the flagpole) to the nearest foot.

73. Find the radius of the circle to the nearest tenth of a meter.

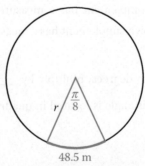

74. A 50-foot building r feet from an observer subtends an angle of 3.25°. Use the arc length formula to estimate r (the distance between the observer and the building) to the nearest foot.

75. An object is traveling around a circle of radius 13 centimeters at a constant speed. If in 10 seconds the object travels 27 centimeters, what is its linear speed in centimeters per second? Round to the nearest whole number.

76. A wheel with diameter 24 inches completes 2 revolutions in 0.5 seconds. Find the linear speed of the edge of the wheel in inches per second. Round to the nearest whole number.

77. An object is traveling around a circle of radius 74 millimeters at a constant speed. If in 36 seconds the object travels 137 millimeters, what is its linear speed in millimeters per second? Round to the nearest tenth.

78. A wheel with diameter 32 inches completes 4 revolutions in 0.5 seconds. Find the linear speed of the edge of the wheel in inches per second. Round to the nearest whole number.

79. An object is traveling around a circle at a constant speed. If in 4 seconds the object travels 29 inches, what is its linear speed in inches per second? Round to the nearest whole number.

80. A wheel with diameter 9 inches completes 10 revolutions in 2.5 seconds. Find the linear speed of the edge of the wheel in inches per second. Round to the nearest whole number.

81. The original Ferris wheel, built in Chicago in 1893, completed 4 revolutions in 40 minutes. Find the angular speed of the Ferris wheel in radians per minute. Leave the answer in terms of π.

82. If a 5-foot blade on a propeller completes 20 revolutions per second, find the angular speed of the blade in radians per second. Round to the nearest hundredth.

83. A small pulley is turning at 145 revolutions per minute. Find the angular speed of the pulley in radians per second. Round to the nearest tenth.

84. If a 9-foot blade on a propeller completes 38 revolutions in 16 seconds, find the angular speed of the blade in radians per second. Round to the nearest hundredth.

85. The average speed in professional bike racing is 30 miles per hour. The bicycles' wheels have a diameter of 24.5 inches. Find the angular speed of the wheels in radians per hour. Round to the nearest tenth. Hint: 1 mile = 5280 feet.

86. If a 3-foot blade on a propeller completes 10 revolutions in 42 seconds, find the angular speed of the blade in radians per second. Round to the nearest hundredth.

87. Find the area of a sector of a circle with a radius of 7 millimeters and a central angle of $\frac{2\pi}{3}$ radians. Round to the nearest square millimeter.

88. When a sprinkler is set to full rotation, the water covers a circular section of a garden with a radius of 22 feet. If the sprinkler is set to rotate back and forth through an angle of 100°, find the area of the garden that is covered by the sprinkler to the nearest square foot.

89. Find the area of a sector of a circle with a radius of 22 millimeters and a central angle of 210°. Round to the nearest square millimeter.

90. When a sprinkler is set to full rotation, the water covers a circular section of a front yard with a radius of 30 feet. If the sprinkler is set to rotate back and forth through an angle of $\frac{9\pi}{5}$ radians, find the area of the front yard that is covered by the sprinkler to the nearest square foot.

91. If an 18-inch windshield wiper rotates at an angle of 115°, find the area covered by the wiper to the nearest tenth of an inch.

92. Find the area of a sector of a circle with a radius of 65 meters and a central angle of 10°. Round to the nearest square meter.

93. A speedometer needle covers an area of approximately 40 square centimeters when it rotates at an angle of $\frac{\pi}{5}$ radians. Find the length of the speedometer needle to the nearest centimeter.

94. If a windshield wiper covers an area of approximately 200 square inches when it rotates at an angle of 98°, find the length of the wiper to the nearest tenth of an inch.

95. Find the radius of a circle to the nearest hundredth of an inch if the area of a sector defined by a 302° central angle is 214.5 square inches.

96. An area of approximately 180 square inches is covered when a rear windshield wiper rotates at an angle of $\frac{11\pi}{8}$ radians. Find the length of the wiper to the nearest tenth of an inch.

97. Find the radius of a circle to the nearest tenth of a meter if the area of a sector defined by a central angle of $\frac{\pi}{3}$ radians is 456.8 square meters.

98. The second hand of a clock covers an area of approximately 50 square centimeters when it rotates at an angle of 215°. Find the length to the nearest hundredth of a centimeter of the second hand.

Extensions

99. Find the measure of an angle y, in degrees, if its complement and supplement can be represented by $6x$ and $12x + 4$, respectively.

100. A wall clock reads exactly four o'clock. What is the radian measure of the acute angle formed by the hour and minute hands of the clock?

101. The cities of Cape Town and Stockholm are located at the same longitude (the angular distance of a place on Earth measured east or west of a north-south line called the Prime Meridian), but at different latitudes (the angular distance of a place on Earth measured north or south of the equator). Lines of longitude are circles on Earth's surface that go through both poles. Cape Town is at latitude 34° S, while Stockholm is at 59° N. Ignoring topographic features such as mountains and valleys, what is the distance (along Earth's surface) between the two cities? Assume that Earth is perfectly round and that its radius is 3959 miles. Round to the nearest mile.

102. An arc that is 3/8 the circumference of a circle subtends what central angle in radians? in degrees?

In Exercises 103–105, use the following information.

A van is moving at a rate of 62 miles per hour, and the circumference of its wheels is approximately 7.5 feet. Round each answer to the nearest tenth.

103. Find the linear speed of the wheels in feet per second.

104. Find the angular speed of the wheels in radians per second.

105. Find the number of revolutions that the wheels are rotating per second.

106. Find the area of the yellow region to the nearest square centimeter if the diameter of the larger circle is 12 centimeters and the radius of the red circle is 2/3 of the larger circle's radius.

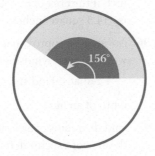

107. Which is the larger angle, 1.2 radians or 68° 45′ 13″? Explain.

108. Suppose a sector comprises 32% of the area of a circle. If the circle has a diameter of 34.6 centimeters, what is the area of the sector to the nearest square centimeter?

109. The wheels on a child's bicycle have a radius of 50 centimeters. The child rides her bicycle so that its wheels rotate at 1.2 revolutions per second. How fast is she riding in meters per second? Round to the nearest tenth.

110. At a birthday party, a circular cake with a diameter of 14 inches is cut into 16 equal pieces. What is the length to the nearest hundredth of an inch of the curved end of each piece of cake?

111. The clock in the tower of City Hall has a circular face that measures 15 feet in diameter. What is the arc length to the nearest thousandth of a foot of the smaller arc between the number 3 and the number 8?

In Exercises 112–115, use the following information.

A pepper shaker is sitting 4.5 inches from the center of a rotating tray. A woman spins the tray through an angle of 132°. Round each answer to the nearest tenth.

112. Through how many radians does the shaker turn?

113. What distance in inches does the shaker travel?

114. If the woman turned the rotating tray 42° in a half second, what was the angular speed of the shaker in radians per second?

115. What was the linear speed of the shaker in inches per second?

2.2 RIGHT ANGLE TRIGONOMETRY

OBJECTIVES

- Write trigonometric ratios.
- Evaluate trigonometric functions of acute angles.
- Use trigonometric functions to find the length of a side of a right triangle.
- Use trigonometric functions to model situations with angles of elevation and depression.

PREREQUISITE VOCABULARY TERMS

acute angle	Pythagorean Theorem
equilateral triangle	reciprocal
hypotenuse	right triangle
isosceles triangle	similar triangles
perpendicular bisector	vertex (of a polygon)

Trigonometry is the study of angles and the relationships between angles and sides in triangles. The discussion of trigonometry in this course begins with the relationships between angles and sides in right triangles.

Review of Right Triangles

> **IMPORTANT**
>
> *A length of a side of a triangle may be referenced by naming the side (e.g., "the length of the hypotenuse" will often be referred to as "the hypotenuse"). Similarly, the measure of an angle may be referenced by naming the angle.*

A right triangle has one right angle and two acute angles. The side opposite the right angle is called the hypotenuse. The other two sides (opposite of the acute angles) are called the legs. The hypotenuse is always the longest side of a right triangle because it is opposite the triangle's largest angle. The Pythagorean Theorem, $a^2 + b^2 = c^2$, relates the lengths of the sides of a right triangle, where c is the length of the hypotenuse, and a and b are the lengths of the legs.

There are two **special right triangles**: the 45°-45°-90° triangle (a right triangle with two equal legs, called an isosceles right triangle) and the 30°-60°-90° triangle. These two triangles are referenced often in trigonometry, so the relationship between the lengths of their sides should be memorized. For example, in a 30°-60°-90° triangle, the ratio of the short side (i.e., the side opposite the 30° angle) to the hypotenuse is always equal to 1/2, and in a 45°-45°-90° triangle, the ratio of either leg to the hypotenuse is always equal to $\frac{1}{\sqrt{2}}$.

Special Right Triangles: 45°-45°-90° and 30°-60°-90°

The sides of each special right triangle are expressed in terms of a (a positive real number).

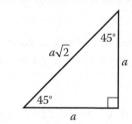

45°-45°-90° Triangle

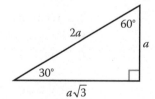

30°-60°-90° Triangle

> **IMPORTANT**
>
> *If a = 1, then the side lengths of a 45°-45°-90° triangle are 1, 1, and $\sqrt{2}$, and the side lengths of a 30°-60°-90° triangle are 1, $\sqrt{3}$, and 2. Special right triangles with these specific side lengths will be referenced often in this chapter.*

Note that an equilateral triangle is divided into two 30°-60°-90° triangles by a perpendicular bisector (as shown by the dashed line in Figure 2.2a), which bisects both the angle and the opposite side. In Figure 2.2a, the equilateral triangle's sides have length 2. Therefore, each 30°-60°-90° triangle has side lengths 1, $\sqrt{3}$, and 2.

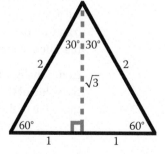

An equilateral triangle is divided into two 30°-60°-90° triangles by a perpendicular bisector.

Figure 2.2a

2.2.1   Introduction to the Trigonometric Functions

Consider a right triangle where one of the acute angles is identified as θ. Then the leg opposite θ is called the **opposite side** and the leg next to θ is called the **adjacent side**. Note that the opposite and the adjacent sides of a right triangle are identified as such only in relation to angle θ (Figures 2.2b and 2.2c).

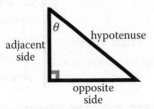

Figure 2.2b

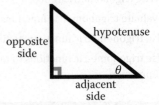

Figure 2.2c

The six **trigonometric functions** of θ are **sine θ**, **cosine θ**, **tangent θ**, **cosecant θ**, **secant θ**, and **cotangent θ**, abbreviated as sin θ, cos θ, tan θ, csc θ, sec θ, and cot θ, respectively. If θ is an acute angle, then each of the trigonometric functions of θ is a ratio of the lengths of two sides of a right triangle, as defined below. Again, θ is an acute angle, so $0° < \theta < 90°$.

The Trigonometric Functions of Acute Angle θ	
sine θ = sin θ = $\dfrac{\text{opp}}{\text{hyp}}$	cosecant θ = csc θ = $\dfrac{\text{hyp}}{\text{opp}}$
cosine θ = cos θ = $\dfrac{\text{adj}}{\text{hyp}}$	secant θ = sec θ = $\dfrac{\text{hyp}}{\text{adj}}$
tangent θ = tan θ = $\dfrac{\text{opp}}{\text{adj}}$	cotangent θ = cot θ = $\dfrac{\text{adj}}{\text{opp}}$

The ratio for the cosecant of θ is the reciprocal of the ratio for the sine of θ. Furthermore, the ratios for cosine and secant of θ are reciprocals, and the ratios for the tangent and cotangent of θ are reciprocals. The cosecant, secant, and cotangent functions are called the **reciprocal trigonometric functions**.

The reciprocal relationship can be used to evaluate a trigonometric function. For example, if sin θ = 1/2, then csc θ = 2, because sine and cosecant are reciprocal functions, and 2 is the reciprocal of 1/2.

The Value of the Sine or Cosine of an Acute Angle θ

Since the length of the hypotenuse is always greater than the length of the side opposite of or adjacent to an acute angle θ in a right triangle, the ratio opp/hyp must always be a value between 0 and 1. For the same reason, the ratio adj/hyp must also be a value between 0 and 1. Therefore, the value of the sine or cosine of an acute angle θ will always be between 0 and 1.

Additionally, since cosecant is the reciprocal of sine, and $0 < \sin \theta < 1$ (where θ is an acute angle), the value of the cosecant of an acute angle θ will always be greater than 1. The same is true for the value of the secant of an acute angle θ.

| **EXAMPLE 1** | **Evaluating the Trigonometric Functions of an Unknown Angle** |

Find the sine, cosine, tangent, cosecant, secant, and cotangent of θ in each triangle.

A. 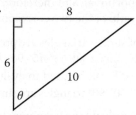   **B.** 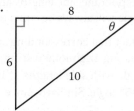   **C.**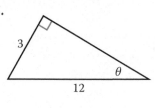

SOLUTION

A. The hypotenuse is 10, the side opposite θ is 8, and the side adjacent to θ is 6.

$$\sin\theta = \frac{\text{opp}}{\text{hyp}} = \frac{8}{10} = \frac{4}{5} \qquad \cos\theta = \frac{\text{adj}}{\text{hyp}} = \frac{6}{10} = \frac{3}{5} \qquad \tan\theta = \frac{\text{opp}}{\text{adj}} = \frac{8}{6} = \frac{4}{3}$$

$$\csc\theta = \frac{\text{hyp}}{\text{opp}} = \frac{10}{8} = \frac{5}{4} \qquad \sec\theta = \frac{\text{hyp}}{\text{adj}} = \frac{10}{6} = \frac{5}{3} \qquad \cot\theta = \frac{\text{adj}}{\text{opp}} = \frac{6}{8} = \frac{3}{4}$$

> **NOTICE THAT**
>
> *Since cosecant is the reciprocal of sine, $\csc\theta$ can be determined by just finding the reciprocal of $\sin\theta$. Similarly, $\cos\theta$ and $\sec\theta$ are reciprocals, as well as $\tan\theta$ and $\cot\theta$.*

B. The triangles given in **A** and **B** are the same, but the angle identified as θ is different. Therefore, the hypotenuse is again 10, but here the side opposite θ is 6, and the side adjacent to θ is 8.

$$\sin\theta = \frac{\text{opp}}{\text{hyp}} = \frac{6}{10} = \frac{3}{5} \qquad \cos\theta = \frac{\text{adj}}{\text{hyp}} = \frac{8}{10} = \frac{4}{5} \qquad \tan\theta = \frac{\text{opp}}{\text{adj}} = \frac{6}{8} = \frac{3}{4}$$

$$\csc\theta = \frac{\text{hyp}}{\text{opp}} = \frac{10}{6} = \frac{5}{3} \qquad \sec\theta = \frac{\text{hyp}}{\text{adj}} = \frac{10}{8} = \frac{5}{4} \qquad \cot\theta = \frac{\text{adj}}{\text{opp}} = \frac{8}{6} = \frac{4}{3}$$

> *Pythagorean Theorem* ▶
> $$a^2 + b^2 = c^2$$

C. Let b represent the side adjacent to θ. Use the Pythagorean Theorem to find b.

$$b = \sqrt{12^2 - 3^2} = \sqrt{135} = 3\sqrt{15}$$

Thus, the side adjacent to θ is $3\sqrt{15}$. From the triangle, the hypotenuse is 12 and the side opposite θ is 3.

$$\sin\theta = \frac{\text{opp}}{\text{hyp}} = \frac{3}{12} = \frac{1}{4} \qquad \cos\theta = \frac{\text{adj}}{\text{hyp}} = \frac{3\sqrt{15}}{12} = \frac{\sqrt{15}}{4} \qquad \tan\theta = \frac{\text{opp}}{\text{adj}} = \frac{3}{3\sqrt{15}} = \frac{1}{\sqrt{15}}$$

Use the reciprocals of $\sin\theta$, $\cos\theta$, and $\tan\theta$ to find $\csc\theta$, $\sec\theta$, and $\cot\theta$.

$$\csc\theta = 4 \qquad\qquad \sec\theta = \frac{4}{\sqrt{15}} \qquad\qquad \cot\theta = \sqrt{15}$$

Rationalizing the Denominator

Recall from Section P.3 that when a fractional expression contains a radical in the denominator, we can rationalize the denominator, and thus write the fractional expression as an equivalent expression in which the denominator does not contain a radical. For example, the value of $\tan\theta$ from **Example 1C** can be rationalized and written equivalently as $\tan\theta = \dfrac{\sqrt{15}}{15}$ because

$$\tan\theta = \frac{1}{\sqrt{15}} = \frac{1}{\sqrt{15}} \cdot \frac{\sqrt{15}}{\sqrt{15}} = \frac{1 \cdot \sqrt{15}}{\sqrt{15} \cdot \sqrt{15}} = \frac{\sqrt{15}}{15}. \text{ Since } \frac{1}{\sqrt{15}} = \frac{\sqrt{15}}{15}, \text{ either answer is acceptable.}$$

*From here forward, many denominators in **Examples** will remain irrational, but all answers to Section Exercises and Chapter Review Exercises will be given with a rationalized denominator.*

Using Similar Triangles to Evaluate Trigonometric Functions

If the measures of the angles in a triangle are equal to the measures of the corresponding angles in another triangle, then the two triangles are similar. When triangles are similar, the corresponding side lengths are proportional, and therefore, the ratio of any two sides from one triangle will always be equal to the ratio of the two corresponding sides from the other triangle.

The fact that corresponding sides of similar triangles are proportional can be very helpful when evaluating trigonometric functions. Since all 45°-45°-90° triangles are similar, a 45°-45°-90° triangle with side lengths 1, 1, and $\sqrt{2}$ can be used to evaluate the trigonometric functions of any 45° angle. Similarly, since all 30°-60°-90° triangles are similar, a 30°-60°-90° triangle with side lengths 1, $\sqrt{3}$, and 2 can be used to evaluate the trigonometric functions of any 30° angle or any 60° angle.

EXAMPLE 2 **Evaluating the Trigonometric Functions of an Angle in a Special Right Triangle**

Find the sine, cosine, and tangent of π/3 radians.

SOLUTION

Recall that π/3 radians = 60° and a 60° angle is the angle opposite the longer leg in a 30°-60°-90° triangle. So, use the 60° angle in a 30°-60°-90° triangle to evaluate the trigonometric functions of π/3 radians.

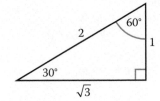

From the 30°-60°-90° triangle, the hypotenuse is 2, the side opposite the 60° angle is $\sqrt{3}$, and the side adjacent to the 60° angle is 1.

$$\sin\frac{\pi}{3} = \frac{\text{opp}}{\text{hyp}} = \frac{\sqrt{3}}{2} \qquad \cos\frac{\pi}{3} = \frac{\text{adj}}{\text{hyp}} = \frac{1}{2} \qquad \tan\frac{\pi}{3} = \frac{\text{opp}}{\text{adj}} = \frac{\sqrt{3}}{1} = \sqrt{3}$$

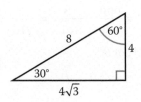

Figure 2.2d

To confirm that the 60° angle in any 30°-60°-90° triangle can be used to evaluate the trigonometric functions of π/3 radians, evaluate the functions again using a 30°-60°-90° triangle where the side lengths are something other than 1, 2, and $\sqrt{3}$. For example, use a triangle with side lengths of 4, 8, and $4\sqrt{3}$, as shown in Figure 2.2d. In this case, the hypotenuse is 8, the side opposite the 60° angle is $4\sqrt{3}$, and the side adjacent to the 60° angle is 4.

$$\sin\frac{\pi}{3} = \frac{\text{opp}}{\text{hyp}} = \frac{4\sqrt{3}}{8} = \frac{\sqrt{3}}{2} ✔ \qquad \cos\frac{\pi}{3} = \frac{\text{adj}}{\text{hyp}} = \frac{4}{8} = \frac{1}{2} ✔ \qquad \tan\frac{\pi}{3} = \frac{\text{opp}}{\text{adj}} = \frac{4\sqrt{3}}{4} = \sqrt{3} ✔$$

2.2.2 Evaluating Trigonometric Functions

Knowing the value of one trigonometric function of an acute angle θ is sufficient for evaluating the rest of the trigonometric functions. For example, suppose θ is an acute angle such that $\cos\theta = 5/13$. Then θ can be drawn as an acute angle in a right triangle where the ratio of the side adjacent to θ to the hypotenuse is 5/13 (since cos θ = adj/hyp). If the Pythagorean Theorem is used to find the length of the side opposite θ in this right triangle, then the rest of the trigonometric functions can be evaluated, as demonstrated in **Example 3**.

| **EXAMPLE 3** | **Using the Value of One Trigonometric Function to Evaluate the Rest of the Trigonometric Functions** |

Suppose that θ is an acute angle such that $\tan \theta = 1/3$. Use a right triangle to find $\sin \theta$ and $\sec \theta$.

SOLUTION

Draw a right triangle where θ is an acute angle, the side opposite θ is 1, and the side adjacent to θ is 3 ($\tan \theta = 1/3 = $ opp/adj).

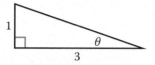

Use the Pythagorean Theorem to find the hypotenuse c of this right triangle.

$$c = \sqrt{1^2 + 3^2} = \sqrt{10} \qquad \sin \theta = \frac{\text{opp}}{\text{hyp}} = \frac{1}{\sqrt{10}} \qquad \sec \theta = \frac{\text{hyp}}{\text{adj}} = \frac{\sqrt{10}}{3}$$

2.2.3 Finding an Angle Measure in a Special Right Triangle Using the Value of a Trigonometric Function

In **Example 3**, the value of a given trigonometric function of an acute angle θ and a right triangle were used to find the values of other trigonometric functions of θ. In that example, the value of θ could not be determined using only the given information. However, if the value of a given trigonometric function of an acute angle θ can be used to form a *special* right triangle, then the value of the angle θ can be determined. In this case, we must recognize the right triangle formed from the given information as a special right triangle.

| **EXAMPLE 4** | **Using a Special Right Triangle to Find the Measure of an Acute Angle** |

Suppose that θ is an acute angle such that $\csc \theta = \dfrac{8\sqrt{128}}{64}$.

Use a right triangle to find the measure of θ in radians and in degrees.

SOLUTION

Simplify.　　$\csc \theta = \dfrac{8\sqrt{128}}{64} = \dfrac{64\sqrt{2}}{64} = \sqrt{2}$

Draw a right triangle where θ is an acute angle. Since $\csc \theta = $ hyp/opp, the hypotenuse is $\sqrt{2}$ and the side opposite θ is 1.

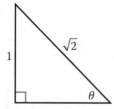

You should recognize that this is a 45°-45°-90° triangle. Use the Pythagorean Theorem to confirm that this is an isosceles right triangle. Let b represent the unknown leg.

$b = \sqrt{\sqrt{2}^2 - 1^2} = \sqrt{2-1} = 1$

Since both legs have length 1, the triangle is a 45°-45°-90° triangle.

Therefore, when θ is an acute angle such that $\csc \theta = \sqrt{2}$, $\theta = 45° = \pi/4$ radians.

2.2.4 Using Trigonometric Functions to Find Unknown Sides of Right Triangles

The value of a trigonometric function of a given angle (in degrees or radians) can be determined using a calculator, as demonstrated in **Example 5**. The calculator must be set to degree mode or radian mode, depending on whether the given angle is measured in degrees or radians.

EXAMPLE 5   Using a Calculator to Evaluate a Trigonometric Function of a Given Angle Measured in Degrees or Radians

TIP

The default setting of a calculator is typically radian mode.

Use a calculator to evaluate each trigonometric function.

A. tan 50° **B.** cos $(\pi/7)$

SOLUTION

The expressions can be entered directly as "tan 50" and "cos $(\pi/7)$", followed by ⎡ENTER⎤ when using a graphing calculator. However, when using some scientific calculators, the angle measure must be entered first. The following directions are for this type of scientific calculator.

A. To calculate tan 50°, set your calculator to degree mode, enter 50, then press ⎡ TAN ⎤.

$$\tan 50° = 1.1917535\ldots$$

IMPORTANT

When an angle measure does not include a degree symbol, assume that the measure is in radians.

B. To calculate cos $(\pi/7)$, set your calculator to radian mode, then use the keystrokes ⎡ π ⎤, ⎡ / ⎤, ⎡ 7 ⎤, ⎡ENTER⎤, and then press ⎡ COS ⎤.

$$\cos (\pi/7) = 0.9009688\ldots$$

When the length of one side and the measure of one acute angle in a right triangle are known, the length of either of the other two sides can be found by solving an equation that involves a trigonometric function.

EXAMPLE 6   Finding the Length of the Sides of a Right Triangle Given One Acute Angle Measure and One Side Length

IMPORTANT

Be sure to set your calculator to radian mode or degree mode as needed.

Use the given information to find the length of the indicated unknown side of each right triangle. Round to the nearest hundredth as needed.

A. Find the length of the side opposite a 52° angle if its adjacent side has length 14.

B. Find the length of the side adjacent to an angle measuring $2\pi/5$ radians if the hypotenuse is 3.7.

SOLUTION

A. Draw the right triangle.

Write an equation using one of the trigonometric functions. Since the equation should include the sides opposite and adjacent to the known angle, use $\tan \theta = \dfrac{\text{opp}}{\text{adj}}$.

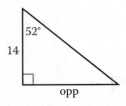

$$\tan 52° = \frac{\text{opp}}{14} \quad \Rightarrow \quad \text{opp} = 14 \tan 52° \approx 17.92$$

Multiply both sides by 14.
Use a calculator to evaluate tan 52°.
Round to the nearest hundredth.

B. Draw the right triangle.

Write an equation using one of the trigonometric functions. Since the equation should include the side adjacent to the known angle and the hypotenuse, use $\cos \theta = \dfrac{\text{adj}}{\text{hyp}}$.

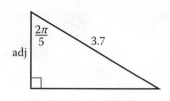

$$\cos \frac{2\pi}{5} = \frac{\text{adj}}{3.7} \implies \text{adj} = 3.7 \cos \frac{2\pi}{5} \approx 1.14$$

Multiply both sides by 3.7.
Use a calculator to evaluate cos 2π/5.
Round to the nearest hundredth.

ALTERNATIVE METHOD

In **Example 6A**, the cotangent function cot θ = adj/opp can be used to write the equation because, like tangent, cotangent relates the sides opposite of and adjacent to an angle.

Similarly, in **Example 6B**, the secant function sec θ = hyp/adj can used to write the equation because, like cosine, secant relates the hypotenuse and the side adjacent to an angle.

2.2.5   Using Trigonometric Functions to Determine a Length

EXAMPLE 7   **Using a Trigonometric Function to Determine a Length**

A 27-foot support wire attached to the top of a pole makes a 65° angle with the ground. Find the height of the pole to the nearest hundredth of a foot.

SOLUTION

The pole forms a right angle with the ground. The wire and the pole are therefore two sides of a right triangle, where the length of the wire is the hypotenuse and the height of the pole is the side opposite the 65° angle.

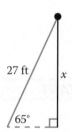

Let x be the height of the pole.

Since the hypotenuse is known and the side opposite the known angle is x, use $\sin \theta = \dfrac{\text{opp}}{\text{hyp}}$ to write an equation.

$$\sin 65° = \frac{x}{27} \implies x = 27 \sin 65° \qquad \textit{Multiply both sides by 27 to solve for x.}$$

Use a calculator to evaluate sin 65°.

$$x = 27 \sin 65° \approx 24.47 \qquad \textit{Round to the nearest hundredth.}$$

Therefore, the height of the pole is approximately 24.47 feet.

2.2.6 Using Trigonometric Functions with an Angle of Elevation or Depression

Angles of **elevation** or **depression** are formed with a horizontal line. The horizontal line is often the ground or a horizontal line at the eye level of an observer. An angle of elevation is measured *up* from this horizontal line and an angle of depression is measured *down* from this horizontal line (Figure 2.2e).

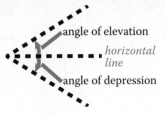

Figure 2.2e

EXAMPLE 8   **Using a Trigonometric Function to Determine a Length**

An observer stands on a platform that is 100 feet from a building. The angle of depression formed by the observer's line of sight to the base of the building is 13°, and the angle of elevation formed by the observer's line of sight to the top of the building is 51°. Find the height of the building to the nearest hundredth of a foot.

SOLUTION

The height of the building is divided into two parts. Let x be the upper part and let y be the lower part, as shown in the drawing.

Two right triangles can be formed. In each triangle, the side adjacent to the known acute angle is 100 feet, and the side opposite the known acute angle is part of the height of the building (i.e., x or y).

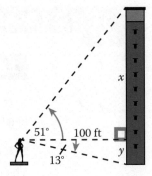

Since tangent relates the side opposite an acute angle to the side adjacent to an acute angle, use tangent to write two equations.

$\tan 51° = \dfrac{x}{100} \quad \Rightarrow \quad x = 100 \tan 51°$ *Multiply each side by 100 to solve for x.*

$\tan 13° = \dfrac{y}{100} \quad \Rightarrow \quad y = 100 \tan 13°$ *Multiply each side by 100 to solve for y.*

Therefore, the height of the building is approximately $100 \tan 51° + 100 \tan 13° \approx 146.58$ feet.

IMPORTANT

Set your calculator to degree mode. Alternatively, convert the degree measures to radians and use radian mode.

SECTION 2.2 EXERCISES

Warm Up

1. Classify each angle according to its measure: 150° 15′ 22″, 32°, 90°, 180°, and 47.325°.

2. Find the length of the hypotenuse of an isosceles right triangle if each leg has length 10 feet.

3. Find the height of an equilateral triangle if a side has length 24 centimeters.

Just the Facts

Fill in the blanks.

4. In any triangle, the longest side is opposite the _____ angle. In a right triangle, this side is called the _____, and it is opposite the _____ angle. The other two sides of a right triangle are called the _____.

5. In the two special right triangles, the 30°-60°-90° triangle has sides of length _____, _____, and _____. The 45°-45°-90° triangle has sides of length _____, _____, and _____.

6. When the lengths of the opposite and adjacent sides to angle θ are known, the trigonometric functions _____ or _____ may be used to find θ.

7. The values of sine and _____ of acute angle θ will always be between _____ and 1.

8. The reciprocal function of cosine is _____, of cotangent is _____, and of cosecant is _____.

9. When a radical is eliminated from the denominator of a fractional expression, that is called _____ the denominator.

10. The angle of _____ is always measured up from a horizontal line, and the angle of _____ is always measured _____ from a horizontal line.

Essential Skills

In Exercises 1–6, find the sine, cosine, tangent, cosecant, secant, and cotangent of θ.

1.
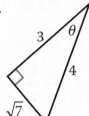

2.

3.
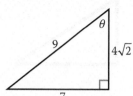

4.
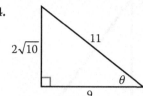

5.
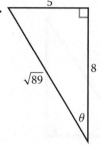

6.
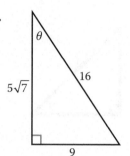

In Exercises 7–12, find the sine, cosine, and tangent of θ.

7.
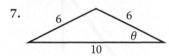

8.
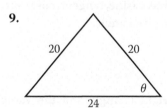

9.
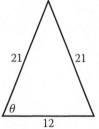

10.

11.
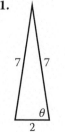

12.
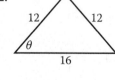

In Exercises 13–18, find the cosecant, secant, and cotangent of θ.

13.
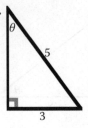

14.
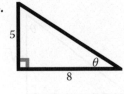

15.
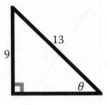

16.
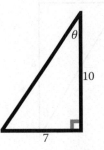

17.
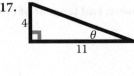

18.
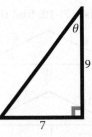

In Exercises 19–20, find the sine, cosine, tangent, cosecant, secant, and cotangent of each given angle.

19. 45°

20. π/6 radians

In Exercises 21–26, use a right triangle and the value of each trigonometric function to find all other trigonometric functions of acute angle θ.

21. $\cos \theta = 5/12$

22. $\sin \theta = 4/9$

23. $\cos \theta = \dfrac{9}{\sqrt{85}}$

24. $\tan \theta = \dfrac{4\sqrt{65}}{65}$

25. $\sec \theta = \dfrac{\sqrt{51}}{7}$

26. $\csc \theta = \dfrac{2\sqrt{55}}{11}$

In Exercises 27–34, use a right triangle to find the exact measure of each acute angle θ in radians and degrees.

27. $\cos \theta = \dfrac{\sqrt{3}}{2}$

28. $\sin \theta = \dfrac{\sqrt{12}}{4}$

29. $\csc \theta = \sqrt{2}$

30. $\cot \theta = \sqrt{3}$

31. $\cos \theta = 19/38$

32. $\sec \theta = \dfrac{12}{\sqrt{72}}$

33. $\csc \theta = \dfrac{8}{\sqrt{32}}$

34. $\tan \theta = \dfrac{\sqrt{108}}{18}$

In Exercises 35–40, use a calculator to evaluate each trigonometric function. Round to the nearest thousandth as needed.

35. sin (π/13) radians

36. tan 75°

37. csc 259°

38. tan 0.42 radians

39. sec 312.6°

40. cos 1.26 radians

In Exercises 41–52, round the unknown side of each right triangle to the nearest hundredth as needed.

41. Find the length of the side opposite a 20° angle if its hypotenuse has length 25.

42. Find the length of the side adjacent to a 38° angle if its opposite side has length 7.

43. Find the length of the side adjacent to a 75° angle if its hypotenuse has length 18.

44. Find the length of the side opposite a 35° angle if its hypotenuse has length 10.

45. Find the length of the side opposite a 52° angle if its adjacent side has length 32.

46. Find the length of the side adjacent to a 46° angle if its opposite side has length 13.

47. Find the length of the side opposite an angle measuring π/5 radians if its hypotenuse has length 14.

48. Find the length of the side opposite an angle measuring 2π/5 radians if its hypotenuse has length 12.

49. Find the length of the side adjacent to an angle measuring π/11 radians if its opposite side has length 25.2.

50. Find the length of the side adjacent to an angle measuring 2π/21 radians if its hypotenuse has length 13.6.

51. Find the length of the side opposite an angle measuring $\pi/25$ radians if its adjacent side has length 148.

52. Find the length of the side opposite an angle measuring $\pi/7$ radians if its adjacent side has length 15.74. .

53. The angle of elevation from the foot of an observer to the basket of a hot air balloon is 30 degrees. Find the height of the balloon. Round to the nearest foot.

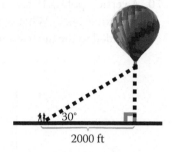

2000 ft

54. For safety reasons, the angle a ladder makes with the ground should be no greater than 70°. Find the length to the nearest foot of the shortest ladder that will safely reach a roof that is 25 feet high.

55. If the distance between a kicking tee and a goalpost is 63 yards and a football is kicked from this tee at an angle of 40°, how far to the nearest tenth of a yard will the football have traveled when it passes through the goalpost? Assume the effects of gravity are negligible and that the ball travels in a straight line.

40°

63 yd

56. A 50-foot ladder is set against a wall so that the top of the ladder makes a 20° angle with the wall. How high up the wall to the nearest tenth of a foot does the ladder reach?

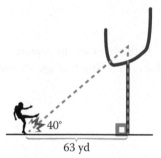

50 ft 20°

57. Find the distance to the nearest foot from the lighthouse to the boat.

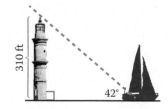

310 ft

42°

58. A hiker is hiking up a 14° slope. If she hikes at a constant rate of 2 miles per hour, how much altitude to the nearest hundredth of a mile does she gain in 4 hours of hiking?

14°

59. A 60-foot ladder is set against a wall so that the top of the ladder makes a 15° angle with the wall. How high up the wall does the ladder reach? Round to the nearest ten-thousandth of a foot.

60. A holiday tree is formed by extending single strands of lights from the top of a pole to an anchor point on the ground. Each strand's anchor point is on the circumference of a circle with radius 60 feet, where the bottom of the pole is the center of the circle. If the angle formed between the ground and a strand of lights is $7\pi/18$ radians, find the length of a single strand of lights to the nearest hundredth of a foot.

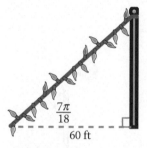

$\frac{7\pi}{18}$

60 ft

61. Find the height x of the indicated mountain to the nearest hundredth of a mile.

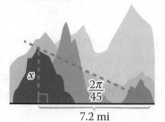

x

$\frac{2\pi}{45}$

7.2 mi

62. Find the height of the building to the nearest hundredth of a foot.

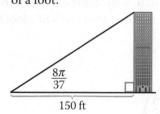

$\frac{8\pi}{37}$

150 ft

63. A moat surrounds a castle. A knight wants to extend a ladder from one side of the moat to a window 45 feet above ground level on the other side of the moat so he can rescue a princess. How long must the ladder be to the nearest tenth of a foot?

64. Find the height of the hot air balloon to the nearest tenth of a foot.

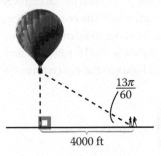

65. A telephone pole casts an 18-foot-long shadow. If the angle of elevation from the ground to the sun is 68°, what is the height of the pole? Round to the nearest hundredth of a foot. ▶

66. The height of a tower is 50 feet, and the height of a building is 20 feet. If the angle of depression from the top of the tower to the top of the building is 32.8°, what is the horizontal distance between the two buildings to the nearest foot?

67. A blimp is flying at an elevation of 6000 feet. The camera under the blimp has to swivel up 58° from the vertical to focus on the football stadium. What is the distance x from the blimp to the stadium to the nearest tenth of a foot?

68. Two buildings are 200 feet apart. If the angle of elevation from the top of the shorter building to the top of the taller building is 8°, what is the difference in the heights of the two buildings to the nearest foot?

69. The height of a building is 40 feet, and the height of a tree is 20 feet. If the angle of depression from the top of the building to the top of the tree is 12.3°, what is the horizontal distance between the two to the nearest tenth of a foot?

70. A vertical pole is 15 feet high and the angle of elevation of the sun is 36.9°. What is the length of the pole's shadow rounded to the nearest tenth of a foot?

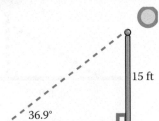

71. When observed from the top of a 250-foot-tall lighthouse, the angle of depression of an approaching ship is 50°. Identify the horizontal distance from the lighthouse to the ship rounded to the nearest foot.

72. A man standing on a lighthouse of height 162 feet sights two boats directly in front of him. One is at an angle of depression of 50°, and the other is at an angle of depression of 45°. Identify the distance between the two boats rounded to the nearest foot.

Extensions

73. Suppose that $\tan \theta = 4$. If the area of the square is 25 square inches, what is the area of the triangle shown in the picture?

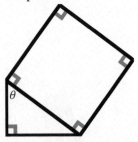

74. Suppose C is the center of the circle. What is the value of $\cos \theta$?

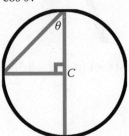

75. If $\tan \pi = \dfrac{2}{7}$, what is the area of the triangle?

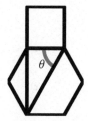

76. Suppose the square has a side length 2 and the hexagon is regular, having all equal sides and angles, what is the value of $\sin \theta$?

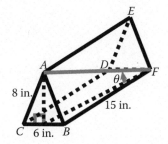

77. From a point on the North Rim of the Grand Canyon to a point on the South Rim, a surveyor measures an angle of depression of $\pi/179$ radians. From an aerial photograph, she determines that the horizontal distance is 20 miles. How many feet is the South Rim below the North Rim? Round to the nearest tenth of a foot.

78. Suppose θ is the angle between AF and the rectangular base $BCDF$. What is the value of $\cos \theta$?

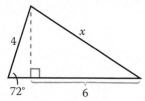

79. Suppose that $\tan \theta = \dfrac{3421}{\sqrt{11703241}}$. What is the value of θ in degrees? Assume that θ is an acute angle in a right triangle.

80. Given that $\sin 72° \approx 0.95$, what is the value of x?

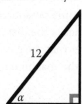

81. An isosceles triangle has a base of length 5. The angle opposite the base measures $\pi/5$ radians. What are the lengths of the two equal sides? Round to the nearest tenth.

82. A person is walking towards a billboard sign directly in front of him. The angle of elevation from his position to the top of the billboard is 10.7°. After he walks 10 more feet, the angle of elevation increases by 5°. Approximate the height of the billboard sign to the nearest tenth of a foot.

83. A surveillance camera is mounted in a pawn shop on a ceiling that is 12 feet high. Is an angle of depression of 12.3° sufficient if the camera needs to focus on the cash register, which is 17 feet from the camera and 4 feet above the floor?

84. A bird is fluttering 30 feet above the ground. At an angle of depression of 35°, it notices a cockroach. At that moment, what is the shortest distance to the nearest tenth of a foot the bird must travel to reach the cockroach?

85. A neap tide occurs when the positions of the sun, moon, and Earth form a right triangle in which Earth is at the vertex of the right angle and the moon is at the vertex of an angle that measures approximately 89.8528 degrees. Find the distance to the nearest kilometer from Earth to the sun at neap tide, given that the distance from the moon to Earth at this time is 381,550 kilometers.

86. Use the triangle to prove that $(\tan \theta)^2 + 1 = (\sec \theta)^2$.

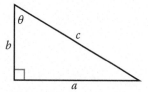

87. A submarine at the surface of the Atlantic Ocean makes an emergency dive at an angle of 39° 10′ 25″ with the surface of the water. How deep will it be if it goes for 700 meters along its path? What is the submarine's horizontal distance from its starting point? How much farther does it need to dive along its path to reach a depth of 1200 meters? Round all answers to the nearest tenth of a meter.

88. An observer 6 kilometers away from the launching pad observes a space shuttle ascend at an angle of elevation of 24° 5′. After 6 seconds, the angle has increased by 12° 10′. How far did the space shuttle travel to the nearest hundredth of a kilometer during the 6-second interval? What was its average speed during that interval?

89. Commercial airliners typically fly at an altitude of 10.9728 kilometers. They start descending toward the airport when they are far away so that they will not have to dive at a steep angle. If the pilot wants the plane's path to make an angle of 2° 15′ 39″ with the ground, what horizontal distance to the nearest tenth of a kilometer from the airport must she start descending?

90. A beam of gamma rays is used to treat a tumor that is 4.6 centimeters beneath the patient's skin. To avoid damaging a vital organ, the radiologist aims the gamma ray source at an angle of depression of 39° 1′ 2″. What is the distance to the nearest hundredth of a centimeter that the gamma ray has to travel to reach the tumor, if the machine is 11 centimeters above the patient?

2.3 THE TRIGONOMETRIC FUNCTIONS IN THE COORDINATE PLANE

OBJECTIVES

- Evaluate the trigonometric functions of an angle in standard position in a coordinate plane.
- Use a reference angle to evaluate the trigonometric functions.
- Use the value of a given trigonometric function and the sign of another to evaluate other trigonometric functions.
- Evaluate and memorize the trigonometric functions of important angles.

PREREQUISITE VOCABULARY TERMS

coordinate plane

degrees

radians

special right triangles

standard position

trigonometric functions

2.3.1 Evaluating Trigonometric Functions of an Angle in the Coordinate Plane

In Section 2.2, the trigonometric functions of an *acute* angle θ ($0° < \theta < 90°$) were evaluated using a right triangle (Figure 2.3a). In this section, the trigonometric functions of angles of *any measure* will be evaluated by using a related right triangle graphed on a coordinate plane (Figure 2.3b).

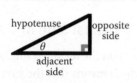

Figures 2.3a

Figure 2.3b

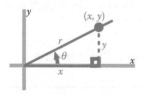

Figure 2.3c

Suppose (x, y) is a point on the terminal side of an angle θ in standard position. A right triangle can be formed with the x-axis where the legs have lengths $|x|$ and $|y|$. The hypotenuse r is given by the Pythagorean Theorem, $r = \sqrt{x^2 + y^2}$ such that $r > 0$ (Figure 2.3c). The signed side lengths of this triangle (x, y, and r) can be used to evaluate the trigonometric functions of θ. For example, since $\sin \theta = \text{opp/hyp}$, using the right triangle in Figure 2.3c gives since $\sin \theta = \text{opp/hyp} = y/r$. The definitions of the trigonometric functions in terms of x, y, and r are given in the following table.

IMPORTANT

*These definitions of the trigonometric functions can be used for any angle θ. However, θ is an angle in the triangle with sides x, y, and r **only** when $0° < \theta < 90°$ (i.e., when (x, y) is in quadrant I).*

The Trigonometric Functions of Angle θ

If (x, y) is a point on the terminal side of an angle θ in standard position and r is the distance from the origin to (x, y) such that $r = \sqrt{x^2 + y^2} \neq 0$, then the trigonometric functions of θ can be defined in terms of x, y, and r.

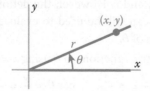

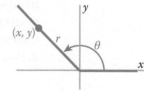

$$\sin \theta = \frac{y}{r} \qquad \cos \theta = \frac{x}{r} \qquad \tan \theta = \frac{y}{x}, x \neq 0$$

$$\csc \theta = \frac{r}{y}, y \neq 0 \qquad \sec \theta = \frac{r}{x}, x \neq 0 \qquad \cot \theta = \frac{x}{y}, y \neq 0$$

EXAMPLE 1 **Evaluating Trigonometric Functions Given a Point on the Terminal Side of θ in Quadrant I**

Find the sine, cosine, tangent, cosecant, secant, and cotangent of θ, given that θ is an angle in standard position and (6, 8) is a point on the terminal side of θ.

SOLUTION

Sketch angle θ in standard position with its terminal side passing through the point (6, 8). Then draw a line perpendicular to the x-axis through the point to form a right triangle where r is the hypotenuse.

Since the terminal side of θ passes through (6, 8), $x = 6$, $y = 8$, and $r = \sqrt{6^2 + 8^2} = \sqrt{100} = 10$.

Use the definitions of the trigonometric functions of θ where $x = 6$, $y = 8$, and $r = 10$ to evaluate each function.

$$\sin \theta = \frac{y}{r} = \frac{8}{10} = \frac{4}{5} \qquad \cos \theta = \frac{x}{r} = \frac{6}{10} = \frac{3}{5} \qquad \tan \theta = \frac{y}{x} = \frac{8}{6} = \frac{4}{3}$$

$$\csc \theta = \frac{r}{y} = \frac{10}{8} = \frac{5}{4} \qquad \sec \theta = \frac{r}{x} = \frac{10}{6} = \frac{5}{3} \qquad \cot \theta = \frac{x}{y} = \frac{6}{8} = \frac{3}{4}$$

NOTICE THAT

The point on the terminal side of θ is in quadrant I, and the value of each trigonometric function of θ is positive.

When the Point on the Terminal Side of θ Is Not in Quadrant I

We have seen that if a point (x, y) on the terminal side of angle θ is in quadrant I, then the values of both x and y are positive, which means that the values of all six trigonometric functions of θ are positive. However, if a point (x, y) on the terminal side of angle θ is in quadrant II, III, or IV, then the values of some of the trigonometric functions of θ are negative because at least one of x and y is negative (depending on the quadrant of the terminal side). For example, if (x, y) is in quadrant II, then $\tan \theta < 0$ because $x < 0$ and $y > 0$ in quadrant II and $\tan \theta = y/x$.

NOTICE THAT

If a point (x, y) on the terminal side of θ is in quadrant II, then $x < 0$, $y > 0$, and $r > 0$ (r is always positive). Thus, $\sin \theta = y/r > 0$, $\cos \theta = x/r < 0$, and $\tan \theta = y/x < 0$.

EXAMPLE 2 **Evaluating Trigonometric Functions Given a Point on the Terminal Side of θ in Quadrant II**

Find the sine, cosine, tangent, cosecant, secant, and cotangent of θ, given that θ is an angle in standard position and (−4, 2) is a point on the terminal side of θ.

SOLUTION

Since the terminal side of θ passes through (−4, 2), $x = -4$, $y = 2$, and $r = \sqrt{(-4)^2 + 2^2} = \sqrt{20} = 2\sqrt{5}$.

Since (x, y) is not in quadrant I, θ is not an angle in the triangle with sides x, y, and r. However, the definitions in terms of x, y, and r can still be used to evaluate the trigonometric functions of θ.

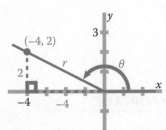

Evaluate the trigonometric functions of θ using $x = -4$, $y = 2$, and $r = 2\sqrt{5}$.

$$\sin \theta = \frac{y}{r} = \frac{2}{2\sqrt{5}} = \frac{1}{\sqrt{5}} \qquad \cos \theta = \frac{x}{r} = \frac{-4}{2\sqrt{5}} = -\frac{2}{\sqrt{5}} \qquad \tan \theta = \frac{y}{x} = \frac{2}{-4} = -\frac{1}{2}$$

$$\csc \theta = \frac{r}{y} = \frac{2\sqrt{5}}{2} = \sqrt{5} \qquad \sec \theta = \frac{r}{x} = \frac{2\sqrt{5}}{-4} = -\frac{\sqrt{5}}{2} \qquad \cot \theta = \frac{x}{y} = \frac{-4}{2} = -2$$

2.3.2 Evaluating Trigonometric Functions of an Angle in the Coordinate Plane: Another Example

The sign of each trigonometric function of θ depends on the quadrant in which θ lies. For example, if an angle θ is in quadrant III and (x, y) is on the terminal side of θ, then $x < 0$ and $y < 0$. Therefore, $y/r < 0$ and $x/r < 0$, but $y/x > 0$. It also follows that $\sin \theta < 0$ and $\cos \theta < 0$, but $\tan \theta > 0$. As a result, only $\tan \theta$ and its reciprocal, $\cot \theta$, are positive when θ lies in quadrant III.

Similarly, only $\sin \theta$, and its reciprocal $\csc \theta$, are positive when θ lies in quadrant II, and only $\cos \theta$, and its reciprocal, $\sec \theta$, are positive when θ lies in quadrant IV.

Use the phrase "all students take calculus" to remember the correspondence between the quadrant containing θ and the sign of the trigonometric function of θ.
- "All" (quadrant I): if θ is in quadrant I, then *all* trigonometric functions of θ are positive.
- "Students" (quadrant II): if θ is in quadrant II, then only $\sin \theta$ and $\csc \theta$ are positive.
- "Take" (quadrant III): if θ is in quadrant III, then only $\tan \theta$ and $\cot \theta$ are positive.
- "Calculus" (quadrant IV): if θ is in quadrant IV, then only $\cos \theta$ and $\sec \theta$ are positive.

REMEMBER

$r > 0$, regardless of the quadrant in which θ is located.

TIP

*students (**s**ine)*
*take (**t**angent)*
*calculus (**c**osine)*

IMPORTANT

Reciprocals have the same sign, so cosecant is positive in the same quadrants as sine, cosine is positive in the same quadrants as secant, and tangent is positive in the same quadrants as cotangent.

Signs of the Trigonometric Functions of Angle θ			
II $\sin \theta$: + $\cos \theta$: – $\tan \theta$: –	I $\sin \theta$: + $\cos \theta$: + $\tan \theta$: +	"students" *Sine and cosecant are positive.*	"all" *All trigonometric functions are positive.*
III $\sin \theta$: – $\cos \theta$: – $\tan \theta$: +	IV $\sin \theta$: – $\cos \theta$: + $\tan \theta$: –	"take" *Tangent and cotangent are positive.*	"calculus" *Cosine and secant are positive.*

EXAMPLE 3 — Evaluating Trigonometric Functions Given a Point on the Terminal Side of θ in Quadrant III

Suppose θ is an angle in standard position such that its terminal side passes through $(-2, -5)$. Determine the signs of $\sin \theta$, $\cos \theta$, and $\tan \theta$, and then evaluate each function.

SOLUTION

Since θ lies in quadrant III, only tangent and cotangent will be positive. Therefore, $\sin \theta < 0$, $\cos \theta < 0$, and $\tan \theta > 0$.

Use the definitions of the trigonometric functions of θ to evaluate $\sin \theta$, $\cos \theta$, and $\tan \theta$.

Find x, y, and r. Since the terminal side of θ passes through $(-2, -5)$, $x = -2$, $y = -5$, and $r = \sqrt{(-2)^2 + (-5)^2} = \sqrt{29}$.

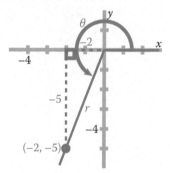

$$\sin \theta = \frac{y}{r} = \frac{-5}{\sqrt{29}} = -\frac{5}{\sqrt{29}} \qquad \cos \theta = \frac{x}{r} = \frac{-2}{\sqrt{29}} = -\frac{2}{\sqrt{29}} \qquad \tan \theta = \frac{y}{x} = \frac{-5}{-2} = \frac{5}{2}$$

2.3.3 Evaluating Trigonometric Functions Using the Reference Angle

If θ is a standard position angle that is *not a quadrantal angle*, then the positive acute angle formed by the terminal side of θ and the x-axis is called the **reference angle** of θ, denoted θ'. In Figure 2.3d we see $\theta = 150°$ and its reference angle $\theta' = 30°$. Note that θ' is not in standard position. Other examples of θ and the corresponding reference angle θ' are shown below.

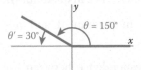

Figure 2.3d

Reference Angles

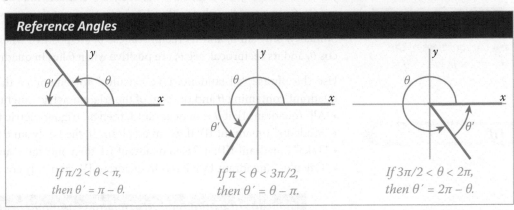

If $\pi/2 < \theta < \pi$, then $\theta' = \pi - \theta$.   *If $\pi < \theta < 3\pi/2$, then $\theta' = \theta - \pi$.*   *If $3\pi/2 < \theta < 2\pi$, then $\theta' = 2\pi - \theta$.*

The value of a trigonometric function of θ' is the absolute value of the same trigonometric function of θ (e.g., $\sin \theta' = |\sin \theta|$). It follows that the value of a trigonometric function of θ can be determined by applying the appropriate sign (as given by the quadrant containing θ) to the trigonometric function of θ', as demonstrated in **Example 4**.

EXAMPLE 4 — Evaluating a Trigonometric Function by Using a Reference Angle and a Special Right Triangle

Use a reference angle to evaluate each trigonometric function.

A. $\sec (3\pi/4)$ **B.** $\cos (-120°)$

SOLUTION

A. If $\theta = 3\pi/4$, then $\theta' = \pi/4$.

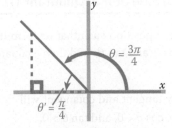

Evaluate $\sec \theta'$. Since $\pi/4$ is an angle in a special right triangle, use a 45°-45°-90° triangle to evaluate $\sec (\pi/4)$.

$$\sec \frac{\pi}{4} = \frac{\text{hyp}}{\text{adj}} = \frac{\sqrt{2}}{1} = \sqrt{2}$$

Apply the appropriate sign. Since θ is in quadrant III, $\sec \theta < 0$. So, $\sec \dfrac{3\pi}{4} = -\left(\sec \dfrac{\pi}{4}\right) = -\sqrt{2}$.

B. θ is in quadrant III, but $\theta' \neq \theta - \pi$ because θ is not between π and $3\pi/2$. However, θ' is equal to the reference angle for the smallest positive angle coterminal with θ, which is 240°.

So, $\theta' = 240° - \pi = 240° - 180° = 60°$. Now evaluate $\cos \theta'$ using a 30°-60°-90° triangle.

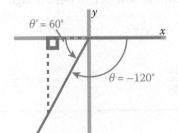

$$\cos 60° = \frac{\text{adj}}{\text{hyp}} = \frac{1}{2}$$

Apply the appropriate sign. Since θ is in quadrant III, $\cos \theta < 0$. So, $\cos (-120°) = -(\cos 60°) = -1/2$.

2.3.4 Using Values of Trigonometric Functions to Find the Value of Another Trigonometric Function

If θ is a non-quadrantal angle, then the value of one trigonometric function of θ and the sign of a second trigonometric function of θ (that is not the reciprocal of the first) can be used to find the values of all other trigonometric functions of θ. Two methods for doing this are demonstrated in **Example 5**.

EXAMPLE 5	**Evaluating Trigonometric Functions by Using the Value of One Trigonometric Function and the Sign of Another**

Find $\cos \theta$ and $\cot \theta$, given that $\sin \theta = \dfrac{4}{\sqrt{65}}$ and $\tan \theta < 0$.

SOLUTION

REMEMBER

To evaluate a trigonometric function of θ using its reference angle θ', first evaluate the trigonometric function of θ'. Then apply the appropriate sign, which depends on the quadrant that contains θ.

Method 1: Use the Reference Angle

Use the signs of both trigonometric functions to identify the quadrant containing θ. Then, use the x-axis to draw a right triangle in the quadrant corresponding to θ, where one angle is θ' and two sides are given by the value of the known trigonometric function.

Since $\sin \theta > 0$ and $\tan \theta < 0$, θ is in quadrant II.

Draw the right triangle in quadrant II.

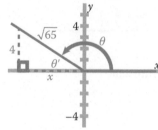

Since $\sin \theta = \dfrac{4}{\sqrt{65}} = \dfrac{\text{opp}}{\text{hyp}}$, the side opposite θ' is 4 and the hypotenuse is $\sqrt{65}$.

REMEMBER

x is a length, so only the positive square root is needed.

Use the Pythagorean Theorem to find the unknown side x. $x^2 + 16 = 65 \Rightarrow x^2 = 49 \Rightarrow x = 7$

Use the triangle to evaluate $\cos \theta'$ and $\cot \theta'$.

$$\cos \theta' = \text{adj/hyp} = 7/\sqrt{65} \qquad \cot \theta' = \text{adj/opp} = 7/4$$

Since cosine and cotangent are both negative in quadrant II, $\cos \theta = -7/\sqrt{65}$ and $\cot \theta = -7/4$.

Method 2: Use the Definitions of the Trigonometric Functions of θ

Let (x, y) be a point on the terminal side of θ. Since $\sin \theta > 0$ and $\tan \theta < 0$, θ is in quadrant II. Therefore, $x < 0$ and $y > 0$.

REMEMBER

$r > 0$, regardless of the signs of x and y.

Since $\sin \theta = \dfrac{4}{\sqrt{65}} = \dfrac{y}{r}$, $y = 4$ and $r = \sqrt{65}$.

Use $r = \sqrt{x^2 + y^2}$ to find x. $\sqrt{65} = \sqrt{x^2 + 4^2} \Rightarrow 65 = x^2 + 16 \Rightarrow x^2 = 49 \Rightarrow x = \pm 7$

However, since $x < 0$ in quadrant II, $x = -7$.

Use the definitions of the trigonometric functions of θ where $x = -7$, $y = 4$, and $r = \sqrt{65}$ to evaluate $\cos \theta$ and $\cot \theta$.

$$\cos \theta = \frac{x}{r} = \frac{-7}{\sqrt{65}} = -\frac{7}{\sqrt{65}} \qquad\qquad \cot \theta = \frac{x}{y} = \frac{-7}{4} = -\frac{7}{4}$$

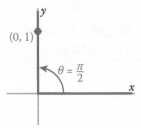

2.3.5 Trigonometric Functions of Important Angles

If $\theta = \pi/2$ radians (i.e, $\theta = 90°$) and $r = 1$, then $x = 0$ and $y = 1$ (Figure 2.3e). If $\theta = 0$ radians (i.e, $\theta = 0°$) and $r = 1$, then $x = 1$ and $y = 0$ (Figure 2.3f). These values can be used to evaluate the trigonometric functions of the quadrantal angles $\pi/2$ radians and 0 radians.

The Trigonometric Functions of $\pi/2$ and 0 Radians (90° and 0°)		
$\sin \dfrac{\pi}{2} = 1$ $sin\,\dfrac{\pi}{2} = \dfrac{y}{r} = \dfrac{1}{1} = 1$		$\sin 0 = 0$ $sin\,0 = \dfrac{y}{r} = \dfrac{0}{1} = 0$
$\cos \dfrac{\pi}{2} = 0$ $cos\,\dfrac{\pi}{2} = \dfrac{x}{r} = \dfrac{0}{1} = 0$		$\cos 0 = 1$ $cos\,0 = \dfrac{x}{r} = \dfrac{1}{1} = 1$
$\tan \dfrac{\pi}{2}$ is undefined $tan\,\dfrac{\pi}{2} = \dfrac{y}{x} = \dfrac{1}{0}$		$\tan 0 = 0$ $tan\,0 = \dfrac{y}{x} = \dfrac{0}{1} = 0$

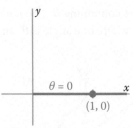

Figure 2.3e

Figure 2.3f

From the special right triangles, we know the values of $\sin \theta$, $\cos \theta$, and $\tan \theta$ when $\theta = \pi/6$ radians, $\theta = \pi/4$ radians, and $\theta = \pi/3$ radians (i.e. when $\theta = 30°$, $\theta = 45°$, and $\theta = 60°$). The values of $\sin \theta$, $\cos \theta$, and $\tan \theta$ for these angle values, along with $\theta = \pi/2$ radians and $\theta = 0$ radians, are listed in the following chart for reference.

The Trigonometric Functions of Important Angles				
θ (deg)	θ (rad)	$\sin \theta$	$\cos \theta$	$\tan \theta$
0°	0	0	1	0
30°	$\dfrac{\pi}{6}$	$\dfrac{1}{2}$	$\dfrac{\sqrt{3}}{2}$	$\dfrac{1}{\sqrt{3}}$
45°	$\dfrac{\pi}{4}$	$\dfrac{\sqrt{2}}{2}$	$\dfrac{\sqrt{2}}{2}$	1
60°	$\dfrac{\pi}{3}$	$\dfrac{\sqrt{3}}{2}$	$\dfrac{1}{2}$	$\sqrt{3}$
90°	$\dfrac{\pi}{2}$	1	0	und

> **TIP**
>
> *Memorize each of these values.*

EXAMPLE 6 Evaluating Trigonometric Functions of Important Angles without Using a Calculator

Evaluate each trigonometric function without using a calculator.

A. $\cos 90°$

B. $\cot \dfrac{\pi}{3}$ radians

SOLUTION

A. From the chart, $\cos 90° = 0$.

B. From the chart, $\tan \dfrac{\pi}{3} = \sqrt{3}$.

Cotangent is the reciprocal of tangent, so $\cot \dfrac{\pi}{3} = \dfrac{1}{\tan \dfrac{\pi}{3}} = \dfrac{1}{\sqrt{3}}$.

SECTION 2.3 EXERCISES

Warm Up

1. Convert 135°, 240°, 90°, and 330° to radian measure.

2. Convert $2\pi/3$, $5\pi/4$, $\pi/5$, and $3\pi/2$ radians to degree measure.

3. Draw 135°, 240°, 90°, and 180° in standard position.

Just the Facts

Fill in the blanks.

4. When the lengths of any two sides in a right triangle are given, the length of the third side can be found using the _____ Theorem.

5. If (x, y) is a point on the terminal side of an angle θ in standard position, and r is the distance from the origin to (x, y) such that $r = \sqrt{x^2 + y^2} \neq 0$, then the trigonometric functions of θ can be defined in terms of x, y, and r. The trigonometric function defined as x/r is _____, y/x is _____, and r/y is _____. All the values of the trigonometric functions are _____ in quadrant I. Only the values of _____ and _____ are positive in quadrant III.

6. If $\tan\theta < 0$ and $\csc\theta > 0$, θ must lie in quadrant _____.

7. A reference angle, usually denoted by _____, is the positive _____ angle formed by the _____ side of θ and the _____.

8. If $\theta = 325°$, then the reference angle is _____.

9. The phrase "All Students Take Calculus" is useful for recalling in which quadrants the trigonometric functions are _____. When $x < 0$ and $y > 0$, _____ and its reciprocal function _____ are positive. The word _____ in the phrase indicates this fact.

10. If $\cos\theta = 1/2$, θ is either in the first or _____ quadrant.

Essential Skills

In Exercises 1–16, find the sine, cosine, tangent, cosecant, secant, and cotangent of θ, given that θ is an angle in standard position and the given point is on the terminal side of θ.

1. $(4, 7)$ 2. $(5, 3)$

3. $(1, 2)$ 4. $(9, 7)$

5. $(-3, 5)$ 6. $(-1, 4)$

7. $(-6, 3)$ 8. $(-4, 9)$

9. $(-1, -2)$ 10. $(-4, -5)$

11. $(-2, -6)$ 12. $(-9, -7)$

13. $(5, -12)$ 14. $(7, -3)$

15. $(3.4, -5.1)$ 16. $(5, -7)$

In Exercises 17–28, evaluate each trigonometric function without using a calculator.

17. $\sin 150°$ 18. $\sec 240°$

19. $\cot 315°$ 20. $\csc 300°$

21. $\tan(-120°)$ 22. $\cos 135°$

23. $\cot \dfrac{5\pi}{6}$ 24. $\sin\left(-\dfrac{\pi}{3}\right)$

25. $\sec \dfrac{4\pi}{3}$ 26. $\csc \dfrac{3\pi}{4}$

27. $\cos\left(-\dfrac{5\pi}{6}\right)$ 28. $\tan \dfrac{11\pi}{6}$

In Exercises 29–46, evaluate the trigonometric functions.

29. Find $\sec\theta$ and $\cot\theta$, given that $\sin\theta = -5/13$ and $\sec\theta < 0$.

30. Find $\sin\theta$ and $\tan\theta$, given that $\cos\theta = -3/5$ and $\sin\theta > 0$.

31. Find $\sin\theta$ and $\cot\theta$, given that $\cos\theta = -24/25$ and $\tan\theta < 0$.

32. Find $\sec\theta$ and $\csc\theta$, given that $\tan\theta = 12/5$ and $\cos\theta > 0$.

33. Find $\cos\theta$ and $\csc\theta$, given that $\sin\theta = \dfrac{\sqrt{5}}{7}$ and $\sec\theta > 0$.

34. Find $\sec\theta$ and $\csc\theta$, given that $\tan\theta = -24/7$ and $\cos\theta > 0$.

35. Find $\sin\theta$ and $\tan\theta$, given that $\cos\theta = -\dfrac{4\sqrt{3}}{9}$ and $\csc\theta > 0$.

36. Find $\sin\theta$ and $\cos\theta$, given that $\tan\theta = -24/7$ and $\sin\theta < 0$.

37. Find $\cos\theta$ and $\cot\theta$, given that $\sin\theta = -\dfrac{\sqrt{6}}{3}$ and $\tan\theta < 0$.

38. Find $\sec\theta$ and $\csc\theta$, given that $\cos\theta = -24/25$ and $\sin\theta > 0$.

39. Find $\cos\theta$ and $\cot\theta$, given that $\tan\theta = -2/3$ and $\csc\theta < 0$.

40. Find $\sin\theta$ and $\tan\theta$, given that $\cos\theta = 3/5$ and $\sin\theta < 0$.

41. Find $\sec\theta$ and $\csc\theta$, given that $\cot\theta = 7/5$ and $\sin\theta < 0$.

42. Find $\cos\theta$ and $\tan\theta$, given that $\csc\theta = -8/5$ and $\sec\theta > 0$.

43. Find $\cos\theta$ and $\sin\theta$, given that $\cot\theta = -9/4$ and $\sin\theta < 0$.

44. Find $\csc\theta$ and $\cot\theta$, given that $\sec\theta = -25/7$ and $\csc\theta < 0$.

45. Find $\tan \theta$ and $\csc \theta$, given that $\sec \theta = -\dfrac{5\sqrt{7}}{4}$ and $\tan \theta > 0$.

46. Find $\cos \theta$ and $\tan \theta$, given that $\csc \theta = 12/7$ and $\sec \theta < 0$.

In Exercises 47–64, evaluate each trigonometric function without using a calculator.

47. $\tan 60°$ **48.** $\cos 45°$

49. $\sin 30°$ **50.** $\cos 60°$

51. $\tan 0°$ **52.** $\sin 90°$

53. $\cos (\pi/4)$ **54.** $\sin (\pi/3)$

55. $\tan (\pi/6)$ **56.** $\sin (\pi/4)$

57. $\cos (\pi/6)$ **58.** $\tan (\pi/4)$

59. $\csc (\pi/6)$ **60.** $\cot (\pi/6)$

61. $\sec (\pi/4)$ **62.** $\csc (\pi/3)$

63. $\cot (\pi/2)$ **64.** $\sec (\pi/6)$

Extensions

In Exercises 65–68, simplify the expression without using a calculator.

65. $\left(\sin \dfrac{\pi}{6} \right)^2 + \left(\cos \dfrac{\pi}{4} \right)^2 + \left(\tan \left(-\dfrac{5\pi}{3} \right) \right)^2$

66. $\cos \dfrac{5\pi}{6} - \sin \left(-\dfrac{\pi}{3} \right) + \cot \dfrac{\pi}{2}$

67. $\left(\cos \pi \right)^2 \left[\left(\csc \dfrac{5\pi}{4} \right)^2 + \cos \left(-\dfrac{\pi}{2} \right) + \left(\sin \dfrac{\pi}{4} \right)^2 \right]$

68. $\dfrac{\left(\sec \dfrac{\pi}{4} \right)\left(\cot \dfrac{\pi}{6} \right)^2}{\left(\cos \dfrac{5\pi}{6} \right)^2 + \left(\tan \dfrac{5\pi}{3} \right)^2 + \left(\sin \dfrac{2\pi}{3} \right)^2}$

69. Suppose that $\sin \theta < 0$ and $\cos \theta = a$, where $0 < a < 1$. Find the value of $\csc \theta$ in terms of a.

70. Suppose that $\tan \theta < 0$ and $\sin \theta = a$, where $0 < a < 1$. Find the value of $\cot \theta$ in terms of a.

In Exercises 71–73, use the following information.

The angular position x and velocity x' with respect to a crank angle for a piston engine are given by

$$x = r \cos A + \sqrt{l^2 - r^2 (\sin A)^2} \quad \text{and}$$

$$x' = -r \sin A - \frac{r^2 \sin A \cos A}{\sqrt{l^2 - r^2 (\sin A)^2}} \text{, respectively, where } r \text{ is}$$

the crank radius, A is the crank angle, l is the rod length, x is the position of the piston pin from the crank center, and x' is the velocity of the piston pin. Determine the position and velocity of the piston pin in each of the following situations. Leave answers in simplified radical form.

71. $r = 4$ inches, $A = 30°$, $l = 15$ inches

72. $r = 6$ inches, $A = 60°$, $l = 11$ inches

73. $r = 2$ inches, $A = 45°$, $l = 5$ inches

In Exercises 74–76, use the following information.

The acceleration a of a block sliding down a plane is represented by the function $a = g \cos \theta(\tan \theta - \mu_k)$, where g is the acceleration due to gravity, θ is the angle of elevation of the plane, and μ_k is the kinetic friction coefficient. Use $g \approx 32$ feet per second squared to determine the acceleration in each of the following situations. Leave answers in simplified radical form.

74. $\theta = 30°$, $\mu_k = 0.4$

75. $\theta = 45°$, $\mu_k = 0.5$

76. $\theta = 60°$, $\mu_k = 0.3$

In Exercises 77–80, determine the smallest possible positive value in radians to make each statement true.

77. $\sin x = \cos \dfrac{\pi}{3}$ **78.** $\sin \dfrac{\pi}{2} = \cos x$

79. $\tan \dfrac{\pi}{6} = \cot x$ **80.** $\cos 0 = \sin x$

81. Explain why a reference angle cannot be used to evaluate the trigonometric functions of θ when θ is a quadrantal angle.

2.4 UNIT CIRCLE TRIGONOMETRY

OBJECTIVES

- Find points on a unit circle.
- Evaluate the trigonometric functions using the unit circle.
- Define the period and domain of sine and cosine functions.
- Use the domain and period to evaluate sine and cosine functions.
- Use the even and odd identities to evaluate the trigonometric functions.

PREREQUISITE VOCABULARY TERMS

central angle

domain

radians

radius

trigonometric functions

2.4.1 The Unit Circle

The **unit circle** is the circle on a coordinate plane with center at (0, 0) and radius 1, as shown in Figure 2.4a. Therefore, the equation of the unit circle is $x^2 + y^2 = 1$.

Since the equation of a unit circle is $x^2 + y^2 = 1$, any point (x, y) in the plane such that $x^2 + y^2 = 1$ is on the unit circle. And for any such point (x, y), a corresponding right triangle can be formed with legs of length $|x|$ and $|y|$ and hypotenuse of length 1 (Figure 2.4b).

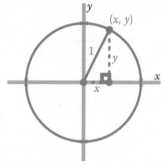

Figure 2.4b

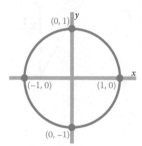

Figure 2.4a

Recall that the length of a circular arc s intercepted by a central angle θ is given by $s = r\theta$. Since the radius of a unit circle is 1, the length of any arc on the unit circle is equal to the measure of the intercepting central angle. Therefore, $s = \theta$ for the unit circle.

Let t represent the radian measure of a central angle in standard position of the unit circle. Then t is also equal to the length of the intercepted arc on the unit circle (i.e., $s = t$). Every t-value has a corresponding point (x, y) on the unit circle that satisfies the equation $x^2 + y^2 = 1$.

If t is a multiple of $\pi/6$ or $\pi/4$, then the coordinates of the corresponding point (x, y) on the unit circle can be determined using special right triangles. The unit circle in Figure 2.4c shows the point (x, y) corresponding to each t that is a multiple of $\pi/6$ or $\pi/4$ such that $0 \le t < 2\pi$.

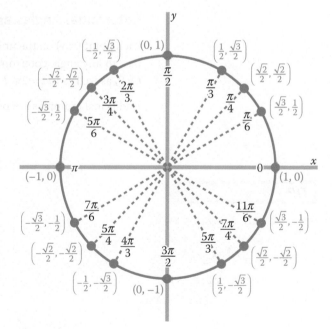

Figure 2.4c

NOTICE THAT

The important angles discussed in Topic 2.3.5 (0, π/6, π/4, π/3, and π/2) are t-values in this unit circle.

Determining the x- and y-Coordinates of Points on the Unit Circle

Each point on the unit circle in Figure 2.4c corresponds to a t-value that is a multiple of either $\pi/6$ or $\pi/4$ (i.e., 30° and 45°). It follows that the coordinates of each point (x, y) can be determined by using a special right triangle.

For example, consider the point (x, y) corresponding to $t = 5\pi/3$. Since the measure of the reference angle for $5\pi/3$ is 60°, the x- and y-coordinates of this point are the signed lengths of the legs of a 30°-60°-90° triangle formed with the x-axis, as shown in Figure 2.4d. The triangle's hypotenuse is a radius of the unit circle, so the length of the hypotenuse must be 1.

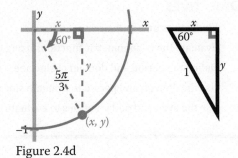

Figure 2.4d

NOTICE THAT

In (x, y), x is the signed length of the side opposite the 30° angle, and y is the signed length of the side opposite the 60° angle.

Recall that the sides of a 30°-60°-90° triangle can be expressed as a, $a\sqrt{3}$, and $2a$, where, a is the side opposite the 30° angle, $a\sqrt{3}$ is the side opposite the 60° angle, and $2a$ is the hypotenuse. The hypotenuse of this 30°-60°-90° triangle is 1, so $2a = 1$. Thus, $a = 1/2$. It follows that the side opposite the 30° angle is 1/2, and the side opposite the 60° angle is $\sqrt{3}/2$.

TIP

If $a = 1/2$, then
$$a\sqrt{3} = \left(\frac{1}{2}\right)\left(\sqrt{3}\right) = \frac{\sqrt{3}}{2}.$$

The point (x, y) is in quadrant IV, so $x > 0$ and $y < 0$.

Therefore, as shown in Figure 2.4e, the point on the unit circle that corresponds to

$$t = \frac{5\pi}{3} \text{ is } \left(\frac{1}{2}, -\frac{\sqrt{3}}{2}\right).$$

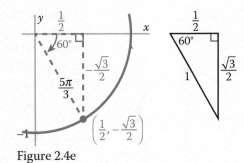

Figure 2.4e

Coterminal Angles and the Unit Circle

Each point (x, y) on the unit circle corresponds not only to the given t-value, but also to $t + 2\pi n$ (i.e., to any angle coterminal with t), where n is an integer. For example, $(1, 0)$ corresponds to $t = 0$, as well as to $t = 2\pi$, $t = 4\pi$, $t = 6\pi$, . . ., and to $t = -2\pi$, $t = -4\pi$, ...

Additional examples are provided in the following table.

TIP

$\pi/2 + 2\pi = \pi/2 + 4\pi/2 = 5\pi/2$

$\pi/2 + 4\pi = \pi/2 + 8\pi/2 = 9\pi/2$

$\pi/2 - 2\pi = \pi/2 - 4\pi/2 = -3\pi/2$

$\pi/2 - 4\pi = \pi/2 - 8\pi/2 = -7\pi/2$

$\pi/2 - 6\pi = \pi/2 - 12\pi/2 = -11\pi/2$

(x, y)	t (radians)
$(0, 1)$	$\pi/2, 5\pi/2, 9\pi/2, \ldots$ $-3\pi/2, -7\pi/2, -11\pi/2, \ldots$
$(-1, 0)$	$\pi, 3\pi, 5\pi, \ldots$ $-\pi, -3\pi, -5\pi, \ldots$
$\left(\frac{1}{2}, \frac{\sqrt{3}}{2}\right)$	$\pi/3, 7\pi/3, 13\pi/3, \ldots$ $-5\pi/3, -11\pi/3, -17\pi/3, \ldots$

| **EXAMPLE 1** | **Identifying a Point on the Unit Circle** |

Identify the point (x, y) on the unit circle that corresponds to each given real number t.

A. $3\pi/2$ **B.** $-2\pi/3$ **C.** $19\pi/4$

SOLUTION

Use the unit circle in Figure 2.4c to find the point that corresponds to each t-value.

A. From the unit circle, $t = 3\pi/2$ corresponds to $(0, -1)$.

> **TIP**
>
> *All angles coterminal to $3\pi/2$ also correspond to $(0, -1)$.*

B. $t = -2\pi/3$ is not shown on the unit circle. However, since $-\dfrac{2\pi}{3} + 2\pi = \dfrac{4\pi}{3}$, the angles measuring $-2\pi/3$ and $4\pi/3$ are coterminal. So, the point corresponding to $t = -2\pi/3$ also corresponds to $t = 4\pi/3$, which is $\left(-\dfrac{1}{2}, -\dfrac{\sqrt{3}}{2}\right)$.

> **IMPORTANT**
>
> *If $t > 2\pi$, subtract a multiple of 2π from t to produce a value between 0 and 2π, then find its corresponding point on the unit circle.*

C. $t = 19\pi/4$ is not shown on the unit circle. However, since $\dfrac{19\pi}{4} - 4\pi = \dfrac{3\pi}{4}$, the angles measuring $19\pi/4$ and $3\pi/4$ are coterminal. So, the point corresponding to $t = 19\pi/4$ also corresponds to $t = 3\pi/4$, which is $\left(-\dfrac{\sqrt{2}}{2}, \dfrac{\sqrt{2}}{2}\right)$.

2.4.2   Using the Unit Circle to Evaluate Trigonometric Functions

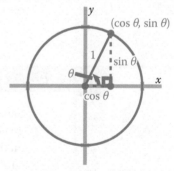

Recall from Section 2.3 that $\sin\theta = y/r$ and $\cos\theta = x/r$.

Since $r = 1$ on a unit circle, if (x, y) is a point on a unit circle, then $\sin\theta = y$ and $\cos\theta = x$. Therefore, any point (x, y) on a unit circle can be expressed as $(\cos\theta, \sin\theta)$ (Figure 2.4f).

The following definitions of the trigonometric functions follow from the definitions given in Section 2.3, here using $r = 1$.

Figure 2.4f

The Trigonometric Functions of Real Number t on the Unit Circle

Let t be a real number and let (x, y) be a point on the unit circle corresponding to t.

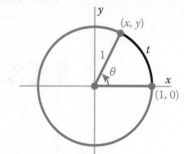

$\sin t = y$ $\csc t = \dfrac{1}{y}, y \neq 0$

$\cos t = x$ $\sec t = \dfrac{1}{x}, x \neq 0$

$\tan t = \dfrac{y}{x}, x \neq 0$ $\cot t = \dfrac{x}{y}, y \neq 0$

| EXAMPLE 2 | **Using the Unit Circle to Evaluate the Trigonometric Functions** |

Evaluate the sine, cosine, tangent, cosecant, secant, and cotangent of each real number.

A. $t = 7\pi/6$ **B.** $t = -7\pi/6$

SOLUTION

A. On the unit circle, $t = \dfrac{7\pi}{6}$ corresponds to the point $\left(-\dfrac{\sqrt{3}}{2}, -\dfrac{1}{2}\right)$. So, $x = -\dfrac{\sqrt{3}}{2}$ and $y = -\dfrac{1}{2}$.

$$\sin\frac{7\pi}{6} = y = -\frac{1}{2} \qquad \cos\frac{7\pi}{6} = x = -\frac{\sqrt{3}}{2} \qquad \tan\frac{7\pi}{6} = \frac{y}{x} = \frac{-\frac{1}{2}}{-\frac{\sqrt{3}}{2}} = \frac{1}{\sqrt{3}}$$

$$\csc\frac{7\pi}{6} = \frac{1}{y} = \frac{1}{-\frac{1}{2}} = -2 \qquad \sec\frac{7\pi}{6} = \frac{1}{x} = \frac{1}{-\frac{\sqrt{3}}{2}} = -\frac{2}{\sqrt{3}} \qquad \cot\frac{7\pi}{6} = \frac{x}{y} = \frac{-\frac{\sqrt{3}}{2}}{-\frac{1}{2}} = \sqrt{3}$$

B. On the unit circle, $t = -\dfrac{7\pi}{6}$ corresponds to the point $\left(-\dfrac{\sqrt{3}}{2}, \dfrac{1}{2}\right)$ because $-\dfrac{7\pi}{6} + 2\pi = \dfrac{5\pi}{6}$.

So, $x = -\dfrac{\sqrt{3}}{2}$ and $y = \dfrac{1}{2}$.

$$\sin\left(-\frac{7\pi}{6}\right) = y = \frac{1}{2} \qquad \cos\left(-\frac{7\pi}{6}\right) = x = -\frac{\sqrt{3}}{2} \qquad \tan\left(-\frac{7\pi}{6}\right) = \frac{y}{x} = \frac{\frac{1}{2}}{-\frac{\sqrt{3}}{2}} = -\frac{1}{\sqrt{3}}$$

Using reciprocals gives $\csc\left(-\dfrac{7\pi}{6}\right) = 2$, $\sec\left(-\dfrac{7\pi}{6}\right) = -\dfrac{2}{\sqrt{3}}$, and $\cot\left(-\dfrac{7\pi}{6}\right) = -\sqrt{3}$.

2.4.3 The Domain and Period of Sine and Cosine

Since the input, t, can be any angle, the domains of $\sin t$ and $\cos t$ consist of all of real numbers. To determine the ranges of $\sin t$ and $\cos t$, consider the unit circle. Since $-1 \le x \le 1$ and $-1 \le y \le 1$ on the unit circle, and since $\sin t = y$ and $\cos t = x$ by definition, it follows that $-1 \le \sin t \le 1$, and $-1 \le \cos t \le 1$. Therefore, the ranges of $\sin t$ and $\cos t$ are the interval $[-1, 1]$.

Periodic Functions

Recall that a complete rotation around a circle measures 2π radians. So, $\sin 0 = \sin 2\pi = \sin 4\pi \ldots$, since adding or subtracting 2π from any t-value completes another rotation around the unit circle. This is true not only for $\sin 0$, but also for the sine of any angle. Thus, for any integer n, $\sin t = \sin(t + 2\pi n)$, and $\cos t = \cos(t + 2\pi n)$. When the value of a function is cyclic (i.e., repeated regularly), as is the case for sine and cosine, the function is called a **periodic function**.

DEFINITION

A function f is a **periodic function** if there exists a positive real number c such that $f(t) = f(t + c)$ for all t in the domain of f. The smallest value of c for which f is periodic is called the **period** of f.

Since the period of a function is the smallest number for which the function is periodic, the periods of $\sin t$ and $\cos t$ are 2π.

2.4.4 Even and Odd Trigonometric Functions

Recall that if f is an even function (for all x in the domain of f), then $f(-x) = f(x)$, and if f is an odd function, then $f(-x) = -f(x)$. These definitions apply to the trigonometric functions as well. Cosine and its reciprocal function, secant, are even functions. For example, recall that $\cos(\pi/3) = 1/2$, and $\cos(-\pi/3) = 1/2$. Therefore, $\cos(-\pi/3) = \cos(\pi/3)$, since cosine is an even function. The remaining trigonometric functions are all odd functions.

Even and Odd Trigonometric Functions		
$\sin(-t) = -\sin t$	$\cos(-t) = \cos t$	$\tan(-t) = -\tan t$
$\csc(-t) = -\csc t$	$\sec(-t) = \sec t$	$\cot(-t) = -\cot t$

EXAMPLE 3 — Using Properties of Even and Odd Functions to Evaluate Trigonometric Functions

Evaluate the sine and cosine of $t = -3\pi/4$.

SOLUTION

Since sine is an odd function, $\sin(-t) = -\sin t$. Therefore, $\sin\left(-\dfrac{3\pi}{4}\right) = -\sin\dfrac{3\pi}{4}$. And since cosine is an even function, $\cos(-t) = \cos t$. Therefore, $\cos\left(-\dfrac{3\pi}{4}\right) = \cos\dfrac{3\pi}{4}$.

So, $t = \dfrac{3\pi}{4}$ can be used to evaluate $\sin\left(-\dfrac{3\pi}{4}\right)$ and $\cos\left(-\dfrac{3\pi}{4}\right)$.

From the unit circle, $t = \dfrac{3\pi}{4}$ corresponds to the point $\left(-\dfrac{\sqrt{2}}{2}, \dfrac{\sqrt{2}}{2}\right)$. So, $x = -\dfrac{\sqrt{2}}{2}$ and $y = \dfrac{\sqrt{2}}{2}$.

$$\sin\left(-\frac{3\pi}{4}\right) = -\sin\frac{3\pi}{4} = -\left(\frac{\sqrt{2}}{2}\right) = -\frac{\sqrt{2}}{2} \qquad \cos\left(-\frac{3\pi}{4}\right) = \cos\frac{3\pi}{4} = -\frac{\sqrt{2}}{2}$$

> **REMEMBER**
>
> *If (x, y) is a point on the unit circle corresponding to t, then $\cos t = x$, and $\sin t = y$.*

EXAMPLE 4 — Using Properties of Even and Odd Functions to Evaluate Trigonometric Functions

If $\tan t = -1/5$, evaluate $\tan(-t)$ and $\cot(-t)$.

SOLUTION

Use the fact that $\tan(-t) = -\tan t$ (i.e., tangent is an odd function) to evaluate $\tan(-t)$.

$$\tan(-t) = -\tan t = -\left(-\frac{1}{5}\right) = \frac{1}{5}$$

Cotangent is the reciprocal of tangent, so $\cot(-t) = \dfrac{1}{\tan(-t)} = \dfrac{1}{\frac{1}{5}} = 5$.

SECTION 2.4 EXERCISES

Warm Up

1. Find the values of tan 60°, cos 45°, sin 60°, sec 30°, and cot 45° without using a calculator.

2. Identify the quadrant in which cot $\theta < 0$ and csc $\theta > 0$.

3. If csc $\theta = 7/5$, evaluate sin θ.

Just the Facts

Fill in the blanks.

4. The equation of the unit circle is _____ with center _____ and radius _____.

5. On the unit circle, the coordinates _____ correspond to $t = \dfrac{7\pi}{4}$, the coordinates $\left(-\dfrac{1}{2}, -\dfrac{\sqrt{3}}{2}\right)$ correspond to $t =$ _____, and the coordinates of the point on the negative x-axis (i.e., $(-1, 0)$) correspond to $t =$ _____.

6. The range of sine and cosine is _____, since the least value that is possible is _____, and the greatest value possible is _____.

7. A function that repeats its values in regular intervals is called a(n) _____ function. The _____ of sine and cosine is 2π.

8. For a(n) even function, $f(-x) =$ _____, and for an odd function, $f(-x) =$ _____. Cosine and secant are examples of _____ functions.

9. Since the radius on the unit circle is _____, the length of any arc on the unit circle is _____ to the measure of its corresponding central angle.

10. A full rotation around a circle is _____ radians, and every additional full rotation in either a(n) _____ or a(n) _____ direction is a multiple of _____.

Essential Skills

In Exercises 1–18, identify the point (x, y) on the unit circle that corresponds to each given real number t.

1. $\dfrac{3\pi}{4}$

2. $\dfrac{7\pi}{6}$

3. $\dfrac{2\pi}{3}$

4. $\dfrac{3\pi}{2}$

5. $\dfrac{5\pi}{6}$

6. $\dfrac{7\pi}{4}$

7. $-\pi$

8. $-\dfrac{4\pi}{3}$

9. $-\dfrac{11\pi}{6}$

10. $-\dfrac{3\pi}{2}$

11. $-\dfrac{2\pi}{3}$

12. $-\dfrac{3\pi}{4}$

13. $\dfrac{21\pi}{2}$

14. $-\dfrac{13\pi}{6}$

15. $\dfrac{15\pi}{4}$

16. $\dfrac{17\pi}{3}$

17. $-\dfrac{29\pi}{6}$

18. $-\dfrac{19\pi}{2}$

In Exercises 19–42, evaluate the sine, cosine, tangent, cosecant, secant, and cotangent of each real number.

19. $t = \dfrac{4\pi}{3}$

20. $t = \dfrac{3\pi}{4}$

21. $t = \dfrac{5\pi}{6}$

22. $t = \dfrac{3\pi}{2}$

23. $t = \dfrac{11\pi}{4}$

24. $t = \dfrac{5\pi}{3}$

25. $t = \pi$

26. $t = \dfrac{11\pi}{6}$

27. $t = \dfrac{2\pi}{3}$

28. $t = \dfrac{5\pi}{4}$

29. $t = \dfrac{\pi}{2}$

30. $t = \dfrac{7\pi}{6}$

31. $t = -\dfrac{\pi}{6}$

32. $t = -\dfrac{5\pi}{3}$

33. $t = -\dfrac{5\pi}{4}$

34. $t = -\dfrac{3\pi}{2}$

35. $t = -\dfrac{2\pi}{3}$

36. $t = -\dfrac{7\pi}{4}$

37. $t = -\dfrac{\pi}{2}$

38. $t = -\dfrac{11\pi}{6}$

39. $t = -\dfrac{3\pi}{4}$

40. $t = -\dfrac{\pi}{3}$

41. $t = -\dfrac{5\pi}{6}$

42. $t = -\dfrac{\pi}{4}$

43. Evaluate the cotangent and tangent of $t = -\dfrac{5\pi}{3}$.

44. Evaluate the cosecant and secant of $t = -\dfrac{7\pi}{6}$.

45. Evaluate the sine and cosine of $t = -\dfrac{5\pi}{6}$.

46. Evaluate the cotangent and tangent of $t = -\dfrac{7\pi}{4}$.

47. Evaluate the cosecant and secant of $t = -\dfrac{3\pi}{4}$.

48. Evaluate the sine and cosine of $t = -\dfrac{2\pi}{3}$.

49. If $\sin t = -4/9$, evaluate $\sin (-t)$ and $\csc (-t)$.

50. If $\cos t = -2/7$, evaluate $\cos (-t)$ and $\sec (-t)$.

51. If $\tan t = 3/5$, evaluate $\tan (-t)$ and $\cot (-t)$.

52. If $\sec t = 10/3$, evaluate $\sec (-t)$ and $\cos (-t)$.

53. If $\csc t = -5/4$, evaluate $\csc (-t)$ and $\sin (-t)$.

54. If $\cot t = -12/11$, evaluate $\cot (-t)$ and $\tan (-t)$.

Extensions

55. If $\tan t = \dfrac{\sqrt{3}}{3}$ and $\sin t = 1/2$, what is the smallest positive value of t?

56. True or False? If $\sin x = 0$, then $\cos x =$ undefined.

57. If $\cos t = -3/5$ and t is in quadrant II, evaluate
$\cos (-t) + \sec (-t) - \sin (-t) + \csc (-t) - \tan (-t) + \cot (-t)$.

In Exercises 58–60, evaluate without using a calculator.

58. $\cos \dfrac{4001\pi}{2}$

59. $\sin 15{,}000\pi$

60. $\left(\sin \left(-\dfrac{\pi}{2}\right)\right)\left(\cos \dfrac{29\pi}{6}\right)\left(\sec \left(-\dfrac{17\pi}{3}\right)\right)\left(\tan \dfrac{76\pi}{4}\right)$

In Exercises 61–64, use the given function $f(x)$ and the given value of $f(t)$ to find the exact value of $f(-t)$, $f(-t) + f(t + 2\pi)$, and $f(t) + f(t + 4\pi) + f(-t)$ without using a calculator.

61. $f(x) = \sin x, f(t) = -2/3$

62. $f(x) = \cos x, f(t) = -1/4$

63. $f(x) = \sec x, f(t) = -11/3$

64. $f(x) = \csc x, f(t) = -7/4$

In Exercises 65–66, use the given function $f(x)$ and the given value of $f(t)$ to find the exact value of $f(-t)$, $f(-t) + f(t + \pi)$, and $f(t) + f(t + 2\pi) + f(-t)$ without using a calculator.

65. $f(x) = \cot x, f(t) = -2$

66. $f(x) = \tan x, f(t) = -5/8$

In Exercises 67–72, determine whether each statement is true or false.

67. $\left(\sin \dfrac{2\pi}{3}\right)^2 + \left(\cos \dfrac{2\pi}{3}\right)^2 = 1$

68. $\left(\tan \dfrac{5\pi}{4}\right)^2 = 1 - \left(\sec \dfrac{5\pi}{4}\right)^2$

69. $\left(\tan \dfrac{\pi}{3}\right)^2 = \dfrac{1 - \cos\left(2 \cdot \dfrac{\pi}{3}\right)}{1 + \cos\left(2 \cdot \dfrac{\pi}{3}\right)}$

70. $\sin \dfrac{\pi}{2} + \sin \pi = 2 \sin \dfrac{1}{2}\left(\dfrac{\pi}{2} + \pi\right) \cos \dfrac{1}{2}\left(\dfrac{\pi}{2} + \pi\right)$

71. $\cos \dfrac{5\pi}{6} \sin \dfrac{\pi}{3} = \dfrac{1}{2}\left[\sin \left(\dfrac{5\pi}{6} + \dfrac{\pi}{3}\right) - \cos \left(\dfrac{5\pi}{6} - \dfrac{\pi}{3}\right)\right]$

72. $\tan \left(2 \cdot \dfrac{5\pi}{3}\right) = \dfrac{2 \tan \dfrac{5\pi}{3}}{1 + \left(\tan \dfrac{5\pi}{3}\right)^2}$

2.5 GRAPHING SINE AND COSINE FUNCTIONS

OBJECTIVES

- Graph the basic sine function and the basic cosine function.
- Use the amplitude and period to graph sine and cosine functions.
- Use translations to graph sine and cosine functions.
- Use a graph to find minimum and maximum values of sine and cosine functions.
- Use a graph to find the zeros of sine and cosine functions.

PREREQUISITE VOCABULARY TERMS

cosine

maximum and minimum

period

sine

translation

zero (of a function)

2.5.1 Introduction to the Graphs of the Sine and Cosine Functions

In Chapter 1, we used various methods to graph functions such as $y = x + 1$ and $f(x) = x^2$. In one method, we made a table of ordered pairs representing points on the graph of the function, plotted the points on a coordinate plane, and then connected them using a smooth line or curve.

This procedure can also be used to graph trigonometric functions, such as the basic sine and cosine functions, $y = \sin x$ and $y = \cos x$, where x represents an angle (or a real number). First, choose several x-values (multiples of $\pi/4$ or $\pi/6$) for the table, then find each corresponding y-value (i.e., the values of $\sin x$ and $\cos x$). To make the points easier to plot, choose multiples of $\pi/2$ as x-values so that each corresponding y-value is −1, 0, or 1.

IMPORTANT

Choosing multiples of π/4 or π/6 as x-values (in radians) for the table ensures that exact values of sin x and cos x (i.e., the y-values) can be found using the unit circle, a special right triangle, or a reference angle.

$y = \sin x$	
x	y
0	0
$\pi/2$	1
π	0
$3\pi/2$	−1
2π	0
$5\pi/2$	1

$y = \cos x$	
x	y
0	1
$\pi/2$	0
π	−1
$3\pi/2$	0
2π	1
$5\pi/2$	0

From the tables, we see that the graph of $y = \sin x$ passes through the points $(0, 0)$, $(\pi/2, 1)$, $(\pi, 0)$, $(3\pi/2, −1)$, $(2\pi, 0)$, and $(5\pi/2, 1)$, and the graph of $y = \cos x$ passes through the points $(0, 1)$, $(\pi/2, 0)$, $(\pi, −1)$, $(3\pi/2, 0)$, $(2\pi, 1)$, and $(5\pi/2, 0)$. Plot the points on a coordinate plane where the scale on the x-axis is $\pi/2$ and the scale on the y-axis is 1.

Since the sine and cosine functions are periodic, the graphs continue to follow the patterns established by these points. The change in the y-coordinate between these points is gradual, resulting in the smooth curves shown here.

NOTICE THAT

The graph of y = sin x is symmetric about the origin and the graph of y = cos x is symmetric about the y-axis (confirming that sin x is an odd function and cos x is an even function). The range of both functions is the interval [−1, 1].

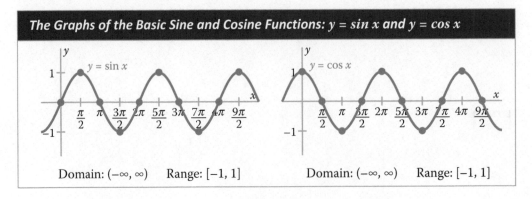

The Graphs of the Basic Sine and Cosine Functions: $y = \sin x$ and $y = \cos x$

Domain: $(−\infty, \infty)$ Range: $[−1, 1]$

Domain: $(−\infty, \infty)$ Range: $[−1, 1]$

Recall from Section 5.4 that the period of $\sin \theta$ and $\cos \theta$ is 2π. When a function's period is 2π, the graph of the function will repeat itself every 2π radians. Figure 2.5a shows the graph of $y = \sin x$ over four periods.

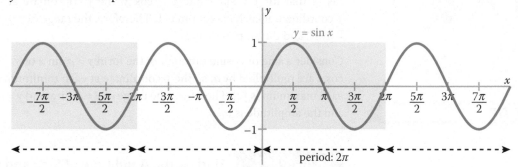

Figure 2.5a

The Amplitude, Zeros, Minimums, and Maximums of $y = \sin x$ and $y = \cos x$

The **amplitude** of sine and cosine functions is half the distance between the minimum y-value and the maximum y-value. For the graph of $y = \sin x$, the minimum y-value is -1 and the maximum y-value 1. Therefore, the amplitude of the graph of $y = \sin x$ is 1 because $|-1 - 1|/2 = 1$. Similarly, the amplitude of the graph of $y = \cos x$ is also 1.

Within each period of $y = \sin x$ and $y = \cos x$ there are two zeros, one minimum, and one maximum. Since $y = \sin x$ and $y = \cos x$ are periodic functions, each function has an infinite number of zeros, minimums, and maximums, each occurring at regular intervals.

The zeros of $y = \sin x$ and $y = \cos x$ occur every π units. The minimums (points where $y = -1$) and the maximums (points where $y = 1$) of $y = \sin x$ and $y = \cos x$ occur every 2π units

Specifically, the zeros of $y = \sin x$ occur when $x = \ldots -\pi, 0, \pi, 2\pi, \ldots$, that is, at multiples (positive and negative) of π. If we let n be any integer, then the *general equation* of the zeros of $y = \sin x$ is $x = \pi n$. Additionally, if n is an integer, then the general equations for the minimums and maximums of $y = \sin x$ are $x = \dfrac{3\pi}{2} + 2\pi n$ and $x = \dfrac{\pi}{2} + 2\pi n$, respectively.

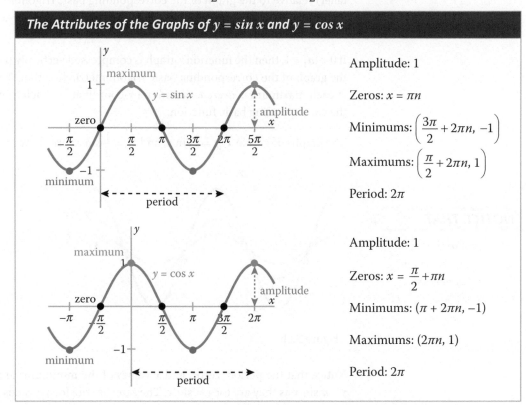

The Attributes of the Graphs of $y = \sin x$ and $y = \cos x$

Amplitude: 1

Zeros: $x = \pi n$

Minimums: $\left(\dfrac{3\pi}{2} + 2\pi n, -1 \right)$

Maximums: $\left(\dfrac{\pi}{2} + 2\pi n, 1 \right)$

Period: 2π

Amplitude: 1

Zeros: $x = \dfrac{\pi}{2} + \pi n$

Minimums: $(\pi + 2\pi n, -1)$

Maximums: $(2\pi n, 1)$

Period: 2π

2.5.2   Changing the Amplitude of Sine and Cosine Functions

Recall that for $y = \sin x$ and $y = \cos x$, the y-coordinate at each minimum is -1, and the y-coordinate at each maximum is 1. Therefore, the range of $y = \sin x$ and $y = \cos x$ is the interval $[-1, 1]$, and the amplitude is 1.

Consider a sine or cosine function of the form $y = a \sin x$ or $y = a \cos x$. The values of $\sin x$ and $\cos x$ are multiplied by a, so the y-coordinate at each minimum is $-|a|$, and the y-coordinate at each maximum is $|a|$. Therefore, the range of $y = a \sin x$ and $y = a \cos x$ is the interval $[-|a|, |a|]$, and the amplitude is $|a|$.

> **TIP**
>
> *Since the amplitude is half the distance between the minimum and maximum y-values, the amplitude of $y = a \sin x$ and $y = a \cos x$ is*
>
> $$\frac{\||a| - (-|a|)\|}{2} = \frac{|2|a\||}{2},$$
>
> *that is, $|a|$.*

EXAMPLE 1   **Finding the Amplitude of Sine and Cosine Functions**

Find the amplitude of each function.

A. $y = \dfrac{1}{3} \sin x$ **B.** $y = -4 \cos x$

SOLUTION

The amplitude of $y = a \sin x$ and $y = a \cos x$ is $|a|$.

A. The amplitude of $y = \dfrac{1}{3} \sin x$ is $\dfrac{1}{3}$ because $a = \dfrac{1}{3}$ and $\left|\dfrac{1}{3}\right| = \dfrac{1}{3}$.

B. The amplitude of $y = -4 \cos x$ is 4 because $a = -4$ and $|-4| = 4$.

The Graphs of $y = a \sin x$ and $y = a \cos x$ When $a > 0$

The coefficient a of the trigonometric functions $y = a \sin x$ and $y = a \cos x$ is a scale factor that applies either a vertical stretch or a vertical compression to the graph of the corresponding basic trigonometric function. If $|a| > 1$, then the function's graph is stretched vertically (i.e., becomes taller) relative to the graph of the corresponding basic trigonometric function. This is because, relative to the corresponding basic function, the y-coordinate at each maximum is increased, and the y-coordinate at each minimum is decreased.

If $0 < |a| < 1$, then the function's graph is compressed vertically (i.e., becomes shorter) relative to the graph of the corresponding basic trigonometric function. This is because the y-coordinate at each maximum is *decreased* and the y-coordinate at each minimum is *increased*, relative to the corresponding basic function.

The graphs of $y = \sin x$, $y = 2 \sin x$, and $y = \dfrac{1}{2} \sin x$ are shown in Figure 2.5b for comparison.

> **NOTICE THAT**
>
> *Compared to the graph of $y = \sin x$, the graph of $y = 2 \sin x$ appears stretched, and the graph of $y = \dfrac{1}{2} \sin x$ appears compressed.*

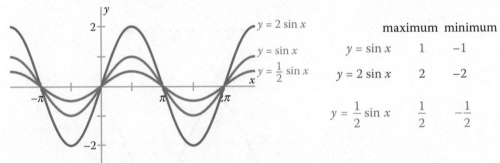

Figure 2.5b

	maximum	minimum
$y = \sin x$	1	-1
$y = 2 \sin x$	2	-2
$y = \dfrac{1}{2} \sin x$	$\dfrac{1}{2}$	$-\dfrac{1}{2}$

Notice that the period, zeros, and x-values of the minimums and maximums are the same for $y = a \sin x$ as they are for $y = \sin x$. The same is true for $y = a \cos x$ and $y = \cos x$.

The Graphs of $y = a \sin x$ and $y = a \cos x$, $a > 0$

$y = a \sin x$, $a > 0$

Domain: $(-\infty, \infty)$

Range: $[-a, a]$

Amplitude: a

Zeros: $x = \pi n$

Period: 2π

Maximums:
$$\left(\frac{\pi}{2} + 2\pi n, a \right)$$

Minimums:
$$\left(\frac{3\pi}{2} + 2\pi n, -a \right)$$

$y = a \cos x$, $a > 0$

Domain: $(-\infty, \infty)$

Range: $[-a, a]$

Amplitude: a

Zeros: $x = \frac{\pi}{2} + \pi n$

Period: 2π

Maximums:
$$(2\pi n, a)$$

Minimums:
$$(\pi + 2\pi n, -a)$$

The Graphs of $y = a \sin x$ and $y = a \cos x$ ($a < 0$ and $a > 0$)

If $a < 0$, then the graph of $y = a \sin x$ is a reflection of the graph of $y = |a| \sin x$ over the x-axis. Similarly, if $a < 0$, then the graph of $y = a \cos x$ is a reflection of the graph of $y = |a| \cos x$ over the x-axis. For example, the graphs of $y = \sin x$ and $y = -\sin x$ are reflections over the x-axis, as shown in Figure 2.5c. Notice that these graphs have the same amplitude, because $|-1| = |1|$. Furthermore, notice that the y-values for the minimums and maximums have switched.

To graph $y = a \sin x$ when $a > 0$, use the graph of $y = \sin x$ to identify the zeros. Then change the y-coordinates of the minimums and maximums of $y = \sin x$ from -1 and 1 to $-a$ and a, respectively. When $a < 0$, graph $y = |a| \sin x$ first, then reflect that graph over the x-axis to graph $y = a \sin x$. Follow the same general procedure to graph $y = a \cos x$.

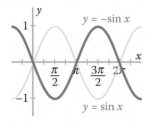

Figure 2.5c

Graphing Sine and Cosine Functions: Amplitude Is Not 1

Graph at least two periods of each function.

A. $y = \dfrac{1}{3} \sin x$

B. $y = -4 \cos x$

SOLUTION

A. To graph $y = \dfrac{1}{3} \sin x$, first sketch the graph of the basic sine function $y = \sin x$, then compare the period, zeros, maximums, and minimums of the two functions. Since the equation is of the form $y = a \sin x$, the period and the zeros are not changed (i.e., the period is 2π and the zeros occur at $x = \pi n$ for both graphs). Furthermore, the minimums and maximums of both graphs occur at the same x-values, but the y-values at those points are not the same. Instead, since the amplitude of $y = \dfrac{1}{3} \sin x$ is 1/3, the range is $\left[-\dfrac{1}{3}, \dfrac{1}{3} \right]$ and the y-coordinates at the maximums and minimums are 1/3 and $-1/3$, respectively.

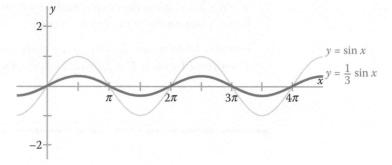

Confirm several points on the graph by making a table, as shown here. Note that multiplying each value of sin x by 1/3 gives the corresponding y-coordinate for the point on the graph of $y = \dfrac{1}{3} \sin x$.

From the table, we see that the graph passes through $(0, 0)$, $(\pi/2, 1/3)$, $(\pi, 0)$, $(3\pi/2, -1/3)$, $(2\pi, 0)$, and $(5\pi/2, 1/3)$.

x	$\sin x$	$\dfrac{1}{3}\sin x$
0	0	0
$\pi/2$	1	1/3
π	0	0
$3\pi/2$	-1	$-1/3$
2π	0	0
$5\pi/2$	1	1/3

IMPORTANT

If a < 0, then the graph of y = a cos x is a reflection of the graph of y = |a| cos x over the x-axis.

B. Since $a < 0$, sketch the graph of $y = 4 \cos x$ first, then reflect that graph over the x-axis.

Since $y = 4 \cos x$ is of the form $y = a \cos x$, the period is 2π and the zeros occur at $x = \dfrac{\pi}{2} + \pi n$ (like $y = \cos x$).

Furthermore, the minimums and maximums of $y = 4 \cos x$ and $y = \cos x$ occur at the same x-values, but the y-values at those points are not the same. Instead, since the amplitude of $y = 4 \cos x$ is 4, the range is $[-4, 4]$ and the y-coordinates at the maximums and minimums are 4 and -4, respectively.

Reflect the graph of $y = 4 \cos x$ over the x-axis to graph $y = -4 \cos x$.

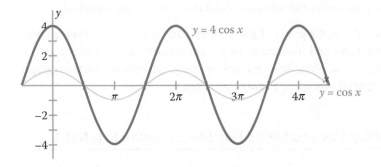
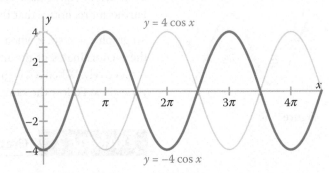

Notice that the point where $x = 0$ is a minimum on the graph of $y = -4 \cos x$, but a maximum on the graph of $y = 4 \cos x$.

Also, notice that the point where $x = \pi$ is a maximum on the graph of $y = -4 \cos x$, but a minimum on the graph of $y = 4 \cos x$.

In general, any x-value that corresponds to a minimum on the graph of $y = 4 \cos x$ also corresponds to a maximum on the graph of $y = -4 \cos x$, and any x-value that corresponds to a maximum on the graph of $y = 4 \cos x$ also corresponds to a minimum on the graph of $y = -4 \cos x$.

Confirm several points on the graph by making a table, as shown here. Note that multiplying each value of cos x by -4 gives the corresponding y-coordinate for the point on the graph of $y = -4 \cos x$.

From the table, we see that the graph passes through $(0, -4)$, $(\pi/2, 0)$, $(\pi, 4)$, $(3\pi/2, 0)$, $(2\pi, -4)$, and $(5\pi/2, 0)$.

x	$\cos x$	$-4 \cos x$
0	1	-4
$\pi/2$	0	0
π	-1	4
$3\pi/2$	0	0
2π	1	-4
$5\pi/2$	0	0

2.5.3 Changing the Period of Sine and Cosine Functions

Recall that the period of $y = \sin x$ and $y = \cos x$ is 2π. Note that the coefficient of x in each function is 1. If the coefficient of x is not 1, then the period is not 2π, and the function's graph will appear either horizontally stretched or horizontally compressed because the periods of sine and cosine functions are affected by changes to the coefficient of the independent variable (in this case x). In general, the period of $y = a \sin bx$ and $y = a \cos bx$ is $\dfrac{2\pi}{|b|}$.

EXAMPLE 3   **Finding the Period of Sine and Cosine Functions**

Find the period of each function.

A. $y = 2 \sin \dfrac{1}{2}x$

B. $y = -\cos 2x$

SOLUTION

The period of $y = a \sin bx$ and $y = a \cos bx$ is $\dfrac{2\pi}{|b|}$.

A. The period of $y = 2 \sin \dfrac{1}{2}x$ is 4π because $b = \dfrac{1}{2}$ and $\dfrac{2\pi}{\left|\dfrac{1}{2}\right|} = 2\pi(2) = 4\pi$.

B. The period of $y = -\cos 2x$ is π because $b = 2$ and $\dfrac{2\pi}{|2|} = \pi$.

The Graphs of $y = a \sin bx$ and $y = a \cos bx$

If $b \neq 1$, then the graphs of $y = a \sin bx$ and $y = a \sin x$ have the same amplitude (and thus the same range), but differ in their periods and zeros. The same is true for $y = a \cos bx$ and $y = a \cos x$.

REMEMBER

n is an integer.

The zeros of $y = a \sin bx$ and $y = a \cos bx$ occur at $x = \dfrac{\pi}{|b|}n$ and $x = \dfrac{\pi}{2|b|} + \dfrac{\pi}{|b|}n$, respectively.

To graph $y = a \sin bx$, make a table of ordered pairs to identify several points on the graph. Then sketch the curve with amplitude $|a|$ through those points (and through the function's zeros), following the general curve of a $\sin x$ graph.

Follow the same general process to graph $y = a \cos bx$.

Note that since the period of $y = a \sin bx$ and $y = a \cos bx$ is $2\pi/|b|$, each function's graph completes one cycle between 0 and $2\pi/|b|$.

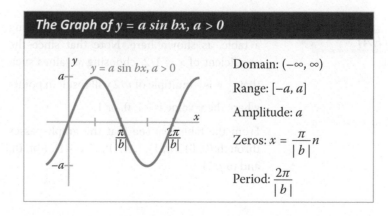

The Graph of $y = a \sin bx$, $a > 0$

Domain: $(-\infty, \infty)$

Range: $[-a, a]$

Amplitude: a

Zeros: $x = \dfrac{\pi}{|b|}n$

Period: $\dfrac{2\pi}{|b|}$

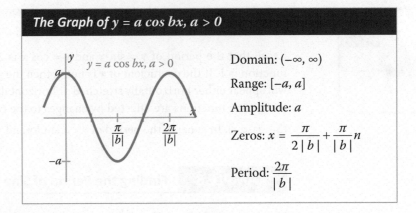

The Graph of $y = a \cos bx$, $a > 0$

Domain: $(-\infty, \infty)$

Range: $[-a, a]$

Amplitude: a

Zeros: $x = \dfrac{\pi}{2|b|} + \dfrac{\pi}{|b|}n$

Period: $\dfrac{2\pi}{|b|}$

EXAMPLE 4   **Graphing Sine and Cosine Functions When the Period Is Not 2π**

Graph at least one period of each function.

A. $y = \sin \dfrac{1}{2}x$ 　　　　　　　　　　　　**B.** $y = \cos 2x$

SOLUTION

A. The function is of the form $y = a \sin bx$, so the amplitude a is 1 and the range is the interval $[-1, 1]$. Since the period is $\dfrac{2\pi}{|1/2|} = 2\pi(2) = 4\pi$, the graph completes one cycle in 4π radians.

When $x = 0$, $y = \sin 0 = 0$. Thus, the graph passes through the origin $(0, 0)$. Since the period is 4π, the graph also passes through $(4\pi, 0)$.

The period of $y = \sin \dfrac{1}{2}x$ is twice the period of $y = \sin x$, so its graph is the graph of $y = \sin x$ stretched horizontally by a factor of 2.

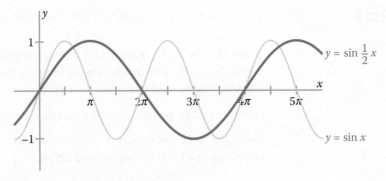

NOTICE THAT

If each $\dfrac{1}{2}x$-value is a multiple of $\pi/2$, then each corresponding y-value (i.e., each value of $\sin \dfrac{1}{2}x$) is either −1, 0, or 1.

Confirm several points on the graph by making a table, as shown here. Note that since the coefficient of x is 1/2, choosing x-values such that $\dfrac{1}{2}x$ is a multiple of $\pi/2$ will result in points where the y-value is −1, 0, or 1.

From the table, we see that the graph passes through $(0, 0)$, $(\pi, 1)$, $(2\pi, 0)$, $(3\pi, −1)$, $(4\pi, 0)$, and $(5\pi, 1)$.

x	$\dfrac{1}{2}x$	$\sin \dfrac{1}{2}x$
0	0	0
π	$\pi/2$	1
2π	π	0
3π	$3\pi/2$	−1
4π	2π	0
5π	$5\pi/2$	1

B. The function is of the form $y = a \cos bx$ and the amplitude a is 1, so the range is the interval $[-1, 1]$. The period is $2\pi/|2| = \pi$, so the function completes one cycle in π radians.

The period of $y = \cos 2x$ is $1/2$ the period of $y = \cos x$, so its graph is the graph of $y = \cos x$ stretched by a factor of $1/2$ (resulting in a horizontal compression).

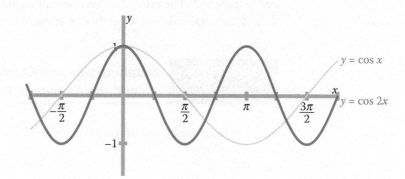

If each 2x-value is a multiple of π/2, then each corresponding y-value (i.e., each value of cos 2x) is either −1, 0, or 1. This makes the graph easier to sketch.

Confirm several points on the graph by making a table, as shown here. Note that since the coefficient of x is 2, choosing x-values such that $2x$ is a multiple of $\pi/2$ will result in points where the y-value is −1, 0, or 1.

x	$2x$	$\cos 2x$
0	0	1
$\pi/4$	$\pi/2$	0
$\pi/2$	π	−1
$3\pi/4$	$3\pi/2$	0
π	2π	1
$5\pi/4$	$5\pi/2$	0

So, the graph passes through $(0, 1)$, $\left(\dfrac{\pi}{4}, 0\right)$, $\left(\dfrac{\pi}{2}, -1\right)$, $\left(\dfrac{3\pi}{4}, 0\right)$, $(\pi, 1)$, and $\left(\dfrac{5\pi}{4}, 0\right)$.

The Zeros of $y = \cos 2x$

The zeros of $y = \cos 2x$ can be found using the b-value 2.
$$x = \frac{\pi}{2\,|2|} + \frac{\pi}{|2|}n = \frac{\pi}{4} + \frac{\pi}{2}n$$

This general equation of the zeros of $y = \cos 2x$ can be confirmed using the graph of $y = \cos 2x$ from **Example 4B**, where we see that the x-intercepts of the graph of $y = \cos 2x$ occur at $x = -\pi/4$, $x = \pi/4$, $x = 3\pi/4$, and $x = 5\pi/4$, or generally at $x = \dfrac{\pi}{4} + \dfrac{\pi}{2}n$, as expected.

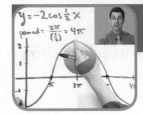

2.5.4 Changing the Amplitude and Period of Sine and Cosine Functions

Each sine and cosine function graphed in the preceding topic had a period other than 2π, but had amplitude 1. The procedure for graphing a sine (or cosine) function when the period is not 2π and the amplitude is not 1 is demonstrated in **Example 5**.

EXAMPLE 5 **Graphing Sine and Cosine Functions When the Period Is Not 2π and the Amplitude Is Not 1**

Graph at least one period of $y = -5\sin\dfrac{1}{3}x$.

SOLUTION

The function is of the form $y = a\sin bx$ and the amplitude is 5, so the range is the interval $[-5, 5]$.

The period is 6π, so the function will complete one cycle in 6π radians.

Since $a = -5$, the graphs of $y = -5\sin\dfrac{1}{3}x$ and $y = 5\sin\dfrac{1}{3}x$ are reflections over the x-axis.

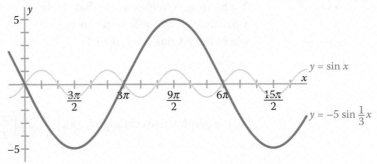

Make a table to confirm several points on the graph.

Choose x-values such that $\dfrac{1}{3}x$ is a multiple of $\pi/2$ because the coefficient of x is 1/3.

Multiply each value of $\sin\dfrac{1}{3}$ by -5 to find the corresponding y-value.

x	$\dfrac{1}{3}x$	$\sin\dfrac{1}{3}x$	$-5\sin\dfrac{1}{3}x$
0	0	0	0
$3\pi/2$	$\pi/2$	1	-5
3π	π	0	0
$9\pi/2$	$3\pi/2$	-1	5
6π	2π	0	0
$15\pi/2$	$5\pi/2$	1	-5

So, the graph passes through $(0, 0)$, $\left(\dfrac{3\pi}{2}, -5\right)$, $(3\pi, 0)$, $\left(\dfrac{9\pi}{2}, 5\right)$, $(6\pi, 0)$, and $\left(\dfrac{15\pi}{2}, -5\right)$.

2.5.5 Finding Maximum and Minimum Values and Zeros of Sine and Cosine

We have seen that functions of the form $y = a \sin bx$ and $y = a \cos bx$ are periodic, each having an infinite number of minimums, maximums, and zeros, all of which occur at regular intervals. More specifically, the x-coordinates of the minimums, maximums, or zeros of the functions of these forms occur at $x = r + pn$, where p is the function's period, r is the x-coordinate of any minimum, maximum, or zero, and n is any integer.

EXAMPLE 6	Finding the Minimums, Maximums, and Zeros of Sine and Cosine Functions

Write the general equations for the x-values of all minimums, maximums, and zeros of $y = -5 \sin \dfrac{1}{3}x$. (This function was graphed in **Example 5**).

SOLUTION

Use the graph of from **Example 5** to identify the smallest positive x-value corresponding to a minimum, a maximum, and a zero. Note that the function's period is 6π.

The smallest positive minimum occurs at $x = \dfrac{3\pi}{2}$, so the minimums occur at $x = \dfrac{3\pi}{2} + 6\pi n$.

The smallest positive maximum occurs at $x = \dfrac{9\pi}{2}$, so the maximums occur at $x = \dfrac{9\pi}{2} + 6\pi n$.

The smallest positive zero occurs at $x = 0$, so the zeros occur at $x = 0 + \dfrac{6\pi}{2}n = 0 + 3\pi n = 3\pi n$.

Substitute the n-values and compare the x-values to the graph to confirm the general equations.

<u>Zeros</u>

$x = -6\pi$	$3\pi(-2)$	$x = 0$	$3\pi(0)$	$x = 6\pi$	$3\pi(2)$
$x = -3\pi$	$3\pi(-1)$	$x = 3\pi$	$3\pi(1)$	$x = 9\pi$	$3\pi(3)$

<u>Minimums</u>		<u>Maximums</u>	
$x = -\dfrac{9\pi}{2}$	$\dfrac{3\pi}{2} + 6\pi(-1) = \dfrac{3\pi}{2} - 6\pi = -\dfrac{9\pi}{2}$	$x = -\dfrac{3\pi}{2}$	$\dfrac{9\pi}{2} + 6\pi(-1) = \dfrac{9\pi}{2} - 6\pi = -\dfrac{3\pi}{2}$
$x = \dfrac{3\pi}{2}$	$\dfrac{3\pi}{2} + 6\pi(0) = \dfrac{3\pi}{2} + 0 = \dfrac{3\pi}{2}$	$x = \dfrac{9\pi}{2}$	$\dfrac{9\pi}{2} + 6\pi(0) = \dfrac{9\pi}{2} + 0 = \dfrac{9\pi}{2}$
$x = \dfrac{15\pi}{2}$	$\dfrac{3\pi}{2} + 6\pi(1) = \dfrac{3\pi}{2} + 6\pi = \dfrac{15\pi}{2}$	$x = \dfrac{21\pi}{2}$	$\dfrac{9\pi}{2} + 6\pi(1) = \dfrac{9\pi}{2} + 6\pi = \dfrac{21\pi}{2}$
$x = \dfrac{27\pi}{2}$	$\dfrac{3\pi}{2} + 6\pi(2) = \dfrac{3\pi}{2} + 12\pi = \dfrac{27\pi}{2}$	$x = \dfrac{33\pi}{2}$	$\dfrac{9\pi}{2} + 6\pi(2) = \dfrac{9\pi}{2} + 12\pi = \dfrac{33\pi}{2}$

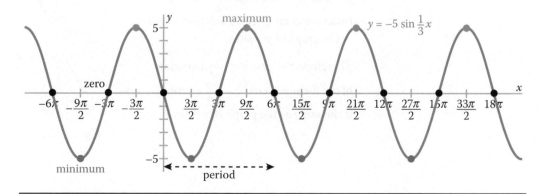

2.5.6 Graphing Sine and Cosine Functions with Phase Shifts

Functions of the form $y = \sin(x - c)$ and $y = \cos(x - c)$, where c is any real number, can be graphed by horizontally translating the graph of the corresponding basic trigonometric function. Specifically, the graph of $y = \sin(x - c)$ is the graph of $y = \sin x$ shifted c units to the right if $c > 0$ or c units to the left if $c < 0$. The graphs of cosine functions behave in the same way.

The horizontal translation applied to the graph of $y = \sin x$ when graphing a function of the form $y = \sin(x - c)$ is also called a **phase shift**. If the graph of $y = \sin x$ is horizontally translated c units to the right, then the phase shift is c. If the graph of $y = \sin x$ is horizontally translated c units to the left, then the phase shift is $-c$.

When the Phase Shift Is $2\pi n$

Since the period of $y = \sin x$ and $y = \cos x$ is 2π, shifting the graph of $y = \sin x$ or $y = \cos x$ to the left or right 2π units does not change the appearance of the graph of the function. Furthermore, shifting the graph of $y = \sin x$ or $y = \cos x$ to the left or right of any multiple of 2π units does not change the resulting graph of the function. For example, $y = \sin x$, $y = \sin(x + 2\pi)$, $y = \sin(x + 4\pi)$, and $y = \sin(x - 4\pi)$ all result in the same graph.

When the Phase Shift Is $\pi/2$

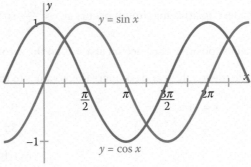

Figure 2.5d

Figure 2.5d shows the graphs of $y = \sin x$ and $y = \cos x$. Notice that each graph is a horizontal translation of the other. Specifically, if the graph of $y = \cos x$ is shifted $\pi/2$ units to the right, then the resulting graph is the same as the graph of $y = \sin x$, as shown in Figure 2.5e. Therefore, the graphs of $y = \cos\left(x - \dfrac{\pi}{2}\right)$ and $y = \sin x$ are the same.

Furthermore, shifting the graph of $y = \cos x$ to the right $\dfrac{\pi}{2} + 2\pi n$ units (where n is an integer) will also result in the graph of $y = \sin x$.

Therefore, the graph of any equation of the form $y = \cos\left(x - \left(\dfrac{\pi}{2} + 2\pi n\right)\right)$ is the same as the graph of $y = \sin x$.

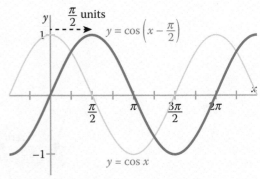

Figure 2.5e

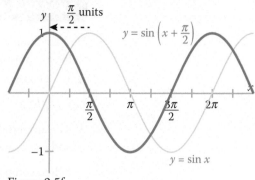

Figure 2.5f

Shifting the graph of y = sin x to the left π/2 + 2πn units (where n is an integer) will also result in the graph of y = cos x.

If the graph of $y = \sin x$ is shifted $\pi/2$ units to the left, the resulting graph is the same as the graph of $y = \cos x$, as shown in Figure 2.5f. So, $y = \cos x$ and $y = \sin\left(x + \dfrac{\pi}{2}\right)$ have the same graph.

EXAMPLE 7 | **Graphing Sine and Cosine Functions with a Phase Shift**

Graph at least two periods of $y = \cos(x + \pi)$ and identify all zeros, if any.

SOLUTION

Since $y = \cos(x + \pi)$ is of the form $y = \cos(x - c)$ where $c = -\pi$ (i.e., π is added to x), the graph of $y = \cos(x + \pi)$ is the graph of $y = \cos x$ shifted π units to the left. From the graph, we see that $y = \cos(x + \pi)$ and $y = \cos x$ have the same zeros.

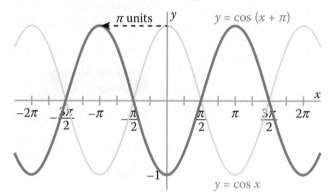

Therefore, the zeros of $y = \cos(x + \pi)$ occur at $x = \dfrac{\pi}{2} + \pi n$.

2.5.7 Graphing All Types of Sine and Cosine Functions

Functions of the form $y = \sin x + d$ and $y = \cos x + d$ (i.e., where a constant d is added to the trigonometric function $\sin x$ or $\cos x$) can be graphed by translating the graph of $y = \sin x$ or $y = \cos x$ vertically d units (upward if $d > 0$ or downward if $d < 0$).

Note that a vertical shift of d units affects a function's range. The amplitude of $y = a \sin x + d$ is still $|a|$, but the range is not $[-|a|, |a|]$ unless $d = 0$. For example, consider the function $y = 5 \sin x + 1$. The amplitude is 5 and the vertical shift is 1 unit up. Therefore, the function's range is $[-4, 6]$, as shown in Figure 2.5g.

Figure 2.5g

The Graphs of $y = a \sin b(x - c) + d$ **and** $y = a \cos b(x - c) + d$

- The amplitude is $|a|$.
- The phase shift is c units right if $c > 0$, or left if $c < 0$.

- The period is $\dfrac{2\pi}{|b|}$.
- The vertical shift is d units upward if $d > 0$, or downward if $d < 0$.

| EXAMPLE 8 | Describing the Attributes of Sine and Cosine Functions |

Find the amplitude and period of each function. Then describe any phase shifts or vertical shifts, as compared to the corresponding basic trigonometric function.

A. $y = 2 \cos 4(x - \pi) + 3$ **B.** $y = 0.5 \sin 2x - 1$

SOLUTION

A. The amplitude of $y = a \cos b(x - c) + d$ is $|a|$ and the period is $2\pi/|b|$. Therefore, since $a = 2$ and $b = 4$, the amplitude of the graph of $y = 2 \cos 4(x - \pi) + 3$ is 2 and its period is $\pi/2$.

When compared to $y = \cos x$, the graph has a phase shift of π units to the right (because π is subtracted from x), and a vertical shift 3 units upward (because 3 is added to y).

B. The amplitude of $y = a \sin b(x - c) + d$ is $|a|$ and the period is $2\pi/|b|$. Therefore, since $a = 0.5$ and $b = 2$, the amplitude of the graph of $y = 0.5 \sin 2x - 1$ is 0.5 and its period is π.

When compared to $y = \sin x$, the graph has no phase shift (because nothing is added to or subtracted from x). However, the graph of $y = 0.5 \sin 2x - 1$ does have a vertical shift 1 unit downward (because 1 is subtracted from y).

> **CAUTION**
>
> $y = 0.5 \sin 2x - 1$
> is equivalent to
> $y = -1 + 0.5 \sin 2x$.
> but is not equivalent
> to $y = 0.5 \sin (2x - 1)$,
> because
> $\sin 2x - 1 \neq \sin (2x - 1)$.

| EXAMPLE 9 | Graphing Sine and Cosine Functions |

Graph at least two periods of each function.

A. $y = 2 \cos 4(x - \pi) + 3$ **B.** $y = 0.5 \sin 2x - 1$

SOLUTION

A. As shown in **Example 8**, the amplitude of the graph $y = 2 \cos 4(x - \pi) + 3$ is 2, its period is $\pi/2$, and, when compared to $y = \cos x$, the graph has a phase shift π units to the right and a vertical shift 3 units upward.

First, graph $y = 2 \cos 4x$ (i.e., $y = \cos x$ but with amplitude 2 and period $\pi/2$.)

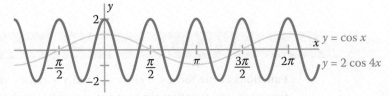

> **NOTICE THAT**
>
> The phase shift does not change the appearance of the graph, because the phase shift is a multiple of the period.

Apply the phase shift, π units to the right.

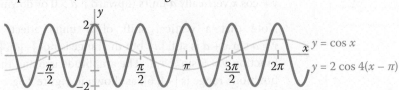

> **NOTICE THAT**
>
> The function
> $y = 2 \cos 4(x - \pi) + 3$
> has no zeros.

Apply the vertical shift, 3 units upward.

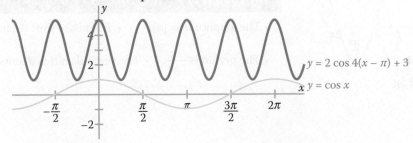

B. From **Example 8**, the amplitude of the graph of $y = 0.5 \sin 2x - 1$ is 0.5, its period is π, and as compared to $y = \sin x$, the graph has a vertical shift 1 unit downward (but no phase shift).

First, graph $y = 0.5 \sin 2x$ (i.e., $y = \sin x$ but with amplitude 0.5 and period π.)

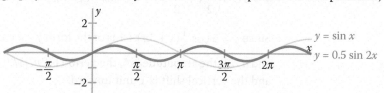

Apply the vertical shift, 1 unit downward.

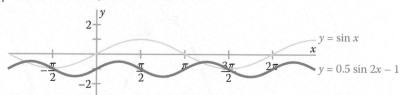

NOTICE THAT

The function
$y = 0.5 \sin 2x - 1$
has no zeros.

2.5.8   Modeling with Sine and Cosine Functions

If a trigonometric function of a binomial contains a coefficient of the independent variable that is not equal to 1, then the coefficient must be factored from the terms in the binomial before determining the period or any horizontal shifts. This is demonstrated in **Example 10**.

EXAMPLE 10   Graphing Sine and Cosine Functions

Graph at least one period of each function.

A. $y = \sin (2x - \pi)$

B. $y = 5 \cos \left(\dfrac{1}{2} x + \dfrac{3\pi}{2} \right) + 1$

SOLUTION

A. First, factor 2 from $2x - \pi$, then graph the resulting function.

$$y = \sin (2x - \pi) = \sin 2\left(x - \frac{\pi}{2} \right)$$

IMPORTANT

The phase shift is not π
units. The coefficient 2
must be factored from
$2x - \pi$ before the phase
shift is identified.

Since $y = \sin 2\left(x - \dfrac{\pi}{2} \right)$ is of the form $y = a \sin b(x - c)$, where $a = 1$, $b = 2$, and $c = \pi/2$, the amplitude is 1, the period is $2\pi/|2| = \pi$, and the phase shift is $\pi/2$ units to the right.

Graph $y = \sin 2x$ (i.e., $y = \sin x$ but with period π).

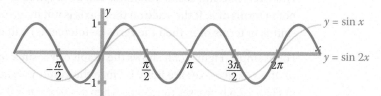

NOTICE THAT

The zeros of
$y = \sin (2x - \pi)$
occur at $x = \dfrac{\pi}{2} n$.

Apply the phase shift, $\pi/2$ units to the right.

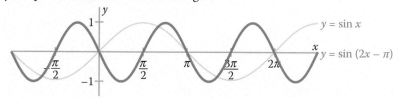

B. First, factor $\frac{1}{2}$ from $\frac{1}{2}x + \frac{3\pi}{2}$, then graph the resulting function.

$$y = 5\cos\left(\frac{1}{2}x + \frac{3\pi}{2}\right) + 1 = 5\cos\frac{1}{2}(x + 3\pi) + 1$$

Since $y = 5\cos\frac{1}{2}(x + 3\pi) + 1$ is of the form $y = a\cos b(x - c) + d$, where $a = 5$, $b = \frac{1}{2}$, $c = -3\pi$, and $d = 1$, the amplitude is 5, the period is $2\pi/|1/2| = 4\pi$, the phase shift is 3π units to the left, and the vertical shift is 1 unit upward.

Graph $y = 5\cos\frac{1}{2}x$ (i.e., $y = \cos x$ but with amplitude 5 and period 4π).

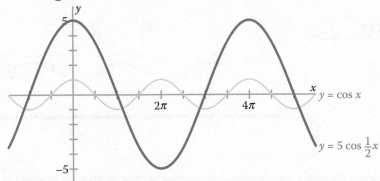

Apply the phase shift, 3π units to the left, and the vertical shift, 1 unit upward.

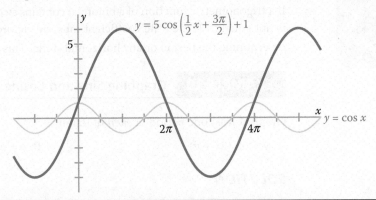

Graphs Where the Scale on the x-Axis Is Not in Terms of π

Thus far in Section 2.5, all of the sine and cosine functions have been graphed on a coordinate plane in which the scale on the x-axis is in terms of π. This type of graph is useful when the period or phase shift of the function is in terms of π.

However, sine and cosine functions can be graphed on a coordinate plane in which the x-axis is not in terms of π. If the scale on the x-axis is not in terms of π, but the function's period or phase shift is in terms of π, then the zeros (x-intercepts) will need to be approximated.

For example, Figure 2.5h shows the graph of $y = \sin x$ on a coordinate plane in which the scales on the x- and y-axes are both 1. Since the graph $y = \sin x$ has zeros at multiples of π, the graph in Figure 2.5.h crosses the x-axis when $x = 0$, $x = \pi \approx 3.1$, $x = 2\pi \approx 6.3$, and so on.

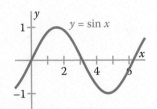

Figure 2.5h

EXAMPLE 11 | **Modeling with a Sine Function**

A windmill takes 6 seconds to make one complete rotation. The height y in feet above the ground of the tip of one blade can be modeled by $y = 40 \sin\left(\dfrac{\pi}{3}x - \dfrac{1.5\pi}{3}\right) + 60$, where x is the time in seconds. Graph at least two periods of the function and find the maximum height of the tip of the blade.

SOLUTION

First, factor $\dfrac{\pi}{3}$ from $\dfrac{\pi}{3}x - \dfrac{1.5\pi}{3}$, then graph the resulting function.

$$y = 40 \sin\left(\frac{\pi}{3}x - \frac{1.5\pi}{3}\right) + 60 = 40 \sin \frac{\pi}{3}(x - 1.5) + 60$$

The equation $y = 40 \sin \dfrac{\pi}{3}(x - 1.5) + 60$ is of the form $y = a \sin b(x - c) + d$, where $a = 40$, $b = \pi/3$, $c = 1.5$, and $d = 60$. So, the phase shift is 1.5 units to the right, the vertical shift is 60 units upward, the amplitude is 40, and the period is 6 (because $\dfrac{2\pi}{\left|\dfrac{\pi}{3}\right|} = 2\pi\left(\dfrac{3}{\pi}\right) = 6$).

Graph $y = 40 \sin \dfrac{\pi}{3}x$ (i.e., $y = \sin x$, but with amplitude 40 and period 6.) Since the period is not in terms of π, make the scale used on the x-axis some whole number (i.e., not in terms of π).

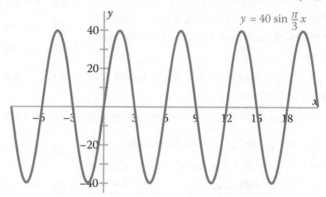

Apply the phase shift, 1.5 units to the right, and the vertical shift, 60 units upward.

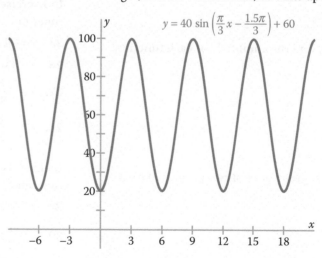

NOTICE THAT

The period of the function corresponds to the number of seconds needed for the blade to make one complete rotation. The vertical shift relates to the height of the center axis that turns the blades, and the phase shift relates to the starting position of the blade, which happens to be at the lowest point of the rotation. The amplitude represents the radius of the windmill.

The curve represents the height of the tip of the blade of the windmill after x seconds, and so the graph's maximum and minimum represent the high and low positions of the tip of the blade. Therefore, from the graph, the maximum height of a tip of the blade is 100 feet.

SECTION 2.5 EXERCISES

Warm Up

Identify the real number(s) t that satisfy each equation.

1. $\cos t = 0$

2. $\sin t = 1$

3. $\cos t = -1$

Just the Facts

Fill in the blanks.

4. The distance from the minimum y-value to the maximum y-value divided by _____ is called the _____ of the sine and cosine functions.

5. Due to the periodic nature of the sine and _____ functions, the x-intercepts, or _____, occur at regular intervals, as do the _____ and minimums.

6. The range of $y = 10 \sin x$ is _____.

7. One major difference between $y = 2 \cos x$ and $y = \cos x$ is the _____ of the cosine functions, which affects the range of the functions.

8. When the graph of $y = a \sin x$ is shifted $\pi/2$ units left, the resulting graph is the same as _____.

9. The period of $y = a \cos bx$ is _____. Therefore, the graph of $y = -4 \cos \frac{1}{4} x$ has period _____ and amplitude _____.

10. A sine function of the form $y = a \sin b(x - c) + d$ has a phase shift to the right when _____, and to the left when _____.

Essential Skills

In Exercises 1–4, find the amplitude of each function.

1. $y = \frac{1}{2} \sin x$

2. $y = 3 \cos x$

3. $y = -5 \cos x$

4. $y = -11 \sin x$

In Exercises 5–12, graph at least two periods of each function.

5. $y = 4 \cos x$

6. $y = \frac{1}{2} \sin x$

7. $y = \frac{3}{4} \cos x$

8. $y = 3 \sin x$

9. $y = -5 \sin x$

10. $y = -3 \cos x$

11. $y = -\frac{1}{4} \sin x$

12. $y = -\frac{1}{3} \cos x$

In Exercises 13–16, find the period of each function.

13. $y = -6 \sin \pi x$

14. $y = 2 \cos 4x$

15. $y = \frac{1}{3} \cos \frac{3}{4} x$

16. $y = -\frac{1}{2} \sin \frac{1}{4} x$

In Exercises 17–24, graph at least two periods of each function.

17. $y = \cos 4x$

18. $y = \sin 8x$

19. $y = \sin 3x$

20. $y = \cos 2x$

21. $y = \sin \frac{1}{3} x$

22. $y = \cos \frac{1}{2} x$

23. $y = \cos \frac{2}{3} x$

24. $y = \sin \frac{3}{4} x$

In Exercises 25–28, find the period and amplitude of each function.

25. $y = -4 \cos 3x$

26. $y = 3 \sin 5x$

27. $y = -\frac{1}{2} \sin \frac{1}{4} \pi x$

28. $y = -\frac{2}{3} \cos \frac{3}{5} x$

In Exercises 29–36, graph at least two periods of each function.

29. $y = 2 \cos 2x$

30. $y = \frac{1}{2} \sin 3x$

31. $y = -\frac{1}{4} \sin \frac{1}{3} x$

32. $y = -3 \cos \frac{1}{2} x$

33. $y = 4 \sin \frac{1}{4} x$

34. $y = -2 \sin 2x$

35. $y = -\dfrac{3}{4} \cos \dfrac{3}{4} x$

36. $y = \dfrac{1}{3} \cos 4x$

In Exercises 37–44, find all *x*-values for the maximums, minimums, and zeros of each function.

37. $y = \dfrac{1}{4} \sin \dfrac{1}{2} x$

38. $y = -5 \sin 3x$

39. $y = -2 \sin 4x$

40. $y = \dfrac{1}{3} \sin \dfrac{2}{3} x$

41. $y = \dfrac{1}{2} \cos 2x$

42. $y = 3 \cos \dfrac{1}{2} x$

43. $y = -4 \cos \dfrac{1}{3} x$

44. $y = -\dfrac{1}{3} \cos 3x$

In Exercises 45–48, graph at least two periods of each function and identify all zeros, if any.

45. $y = \cos\left(x + \dfrac{\pi}{2}\right)$

46. $y = \sin\left(x - \dfrac{\pi}{4}\right)$

47. $y = \sin\left(x + \dfrac{2\pi}{3}\right)$

48. $y = \cos\left(x - \dfrac{\pi}{6}\right)$

In Exercises 49–52, find the amplitude and period of each function. Then describe any phase shifts or vertical shifts, as compared to the corresponding basic trigonometric function.

49. $y = 2 \sin\left(x - \dfrac{\pi}{3}\right) + 1$

50. $y = -3 \cos\left(x + \dfrac{\pi}{6}\right) + 2$

51. $y = -\dfrac{3}{4} \cos\left(x + \pi\right) - 5$

52. $y = \dfrac{2}{5} \sin\left(x - \dfrac{\pi}{4}\right) - 3$

In Exercises 53–60, graph at least two periods of each function.

53. $y = 2 \sin\left(x - \dfrac{\pi}{6}\right)$

54. $y = 3 \cos\left(x + \dfrac{\pi}{6}\right)$

55. $y = -\dfrac{1}{2} \cos\left(x + \dfrac{\pi}{4}\right)$

56. $y = -\dfrac{3}{4} \sin\left(x + \pi\right)$

57. $y = 2 \cos\left(x + \dfrac{\pi}{3}\right) - 1$

58. $y = 3 \sin\left(x - \dfrac{\pi}{6}\right) + 2$

59. $y = -\dfrac{4}{5} \sin\left(x - \pi\right) + 3$

60. $y = -\dfrac{1}{3} \cos\left(x + \dfrac{\pi}{4}\right) - 2$

In Exercises 61–64, find the amplitude and period of each function. Then describe any phase shifts or vertical shifts, as compared to the corresponding basic trigonometric function.

61. $y = 2 \sin\left(x - \dfrac{\pi}{3}\right) + 1$

62. $y = -2 \cos\left(2x + \dfrac{\pi}{3}\right) + 3$

63. $y = -\dfrac{1}{4} \cos\left(\dfrac{1}{2} x + \dfrac{\pi}{2}\right) - 1$

64. $y = -\dfrac{4}{7} \sin\left(\dfrac{1}{3} x - \dfrac{\pi}{2}\right) - 2$

In Exercises 65–76, graph at least two periods of each function.

65. $y = -\sin \dfrac{1}{2} x + 3$

66. $y = -2 \cos 2\left(x + \dfrac{\pi}{4}\right) - 1$

67. $y = \dfrac{1}{3} \cos\left(x - \dfrac{\pi}{6}\right) - 1$

68. $y = \dfrac{1}{2} \sin\left(x - \dfrac{\pi}{3}\right) + 2$

69. $y = \dfrac{1}{2} \cos\left(4x + \pi\right)$

70. $y = 4 \sin\left(2x - \dfrac{\pi}{2}\right)$

71. $y = -2 \sin\left(3x - 2\pi\right)$

72. $y = -\dfrac{2}{3} \cos\left(2x - \dfrac{\pi}{3}\right)$

73. $y = 4 \sin\left(\dfrac{1}{2} x - \dfrac{\pi}{4}\right)$

74. $y = -2 \cos\left(\dfrac{1}{3} x + \dfrac{\pi}{6}\right)$

75. $y = 3 \cos\left(\dfrac{1}{4} x - \dfrac{\pi}{12}\right)$

76. $y = \dfrac{1}{2} \sin\left(\dfrac{2}{3} x - \dfrac{\pi}{4}\right)$

77. The height h of a seat above ground on a Ferris wheel at time t is given by $h(t) = 30 \sin \frac{\pi}{10} t + 35$, where $t \geq 0$ seconds and h is in feet. Graph the function for two periods and find the maximum height of the seat.

78. The current I, in amperes, flowing through an alternating circuit at time t, in seconds, is given by $I(t) = 65 \sin\left(20\pi t - \frac{\pi}{6}\right)$, where $t \geq 0$. Graph the function for two periods and find the maximum current flowing through the circuit.

79. A person's blood pressure, $P(t)$, in millimeters of mercury, is modeled by the function $P(t) = 20 \cos \frac{7\pi}{3} t + 85$, where t is the time in seconds. Graph the function for two periods and find the maximum blood pressure.

80. The height h of a seat above ground on a Ferris wheel at time t is given by $h(t) = 45 \cos \frac{\pi}{6} t + 50$, where $t \geq 0$ seconds and h is in feet. Graph the function for two periods and find the maximum height of the seat.

81. The current I, in amperes, flowing through an alternating circuit at time t, in seconds, is given by $I(t) = 200 \sin\left(45\pi t - \frac{\pi}{3}\right)$, where $t \geq 0$. Graph the function for two periods and find the maximum current flowing through the circuit.

82. A person's blood pressure, $P(t)$, in millimeters of mercury, is modeled by the function $P(t) = -20 \cos \frac{5\pi}{3} t + 90$, where t is the time in seconds. Graph the function for two periods and find the maximum blood pressure.

Extensions

83. In a particular wildlife refuge the variation in the total number of white spotted owls can be described by the formula $P(t) = 15 \sin \frac{\pi}{6} t + 20$, where P is the population and t is the time in months since January 1, 1991. What is the maximum population of white spotted owls in the wildlife refuge?

In Exercises 84–87, determine whether the statements are true or false. If false, explain why.

84. $\sin 9\pi = \sin \pi$

85. $\cos \frac{210\pi}{2} = \sin(-52.5\pi)$

86. The graph of $y = \cos\left(x - \frac{\pi}{2}\right)$ is identical to the graph of $y = \sin\left(x + \frac{\pi}{2}\right)$.

87. The function $y = \sin \frac{1}{3} x$ has a period that is one-third that of its corresponding basic trigonometric function.

88. A group of scientists conducting a statistical survey found that traffic in a local mall over the course of a day could be estimated by the equation $P(t) = -3500 \cos \frac{\pi}{5} t + 3500$, where P is the population and t is the time in hours after the mall opens. After the mall opens, how many hours pass before the number of people in the mall reaches its maximum? What is the maximum number of people?

89. The temperature of a patient ranges from 96° Fahrenheit to 100° Fahrenheit as modeled by $T(t) = 2 \sin \frac{\pi}{14} t + C$. What is the value of C?

In Exercises 90–93, use the given amplitude, period, phase shift, and vertical shift to write the equation for the function $y = a \sin b(x - c) + d$.

	Amplitude	Period	Phase Shift	Vertical Shift
90.	3	8π	$\pi/6$ left	6 down
91.	4	6	3 right	7 up
92.	1/2	$3\pi/2$	none	1 up
93.	15	$\pi/3$	$4\pi/5$ left	30 down

94. A Ferris wheel ride at the local carnival lasts 4 minutes, during which time the Ferris wheel makes 8 revolutions. Patrons get on the ride from a platform that is 5 feet above the ground, and after 15 seconds they reach a maximum height of 60 feet. Write the trigonometric function that models this situation.

In Exercises 95–98, graph at least two periods of each function.

95. $y = -15 \sin\left(4\pi x - \frac{2}{3}\right) + 5$

96. $y = -4 \cos\left(\frac{3\pi}{4} x + \frac{4}{5}\right) - 2$

97. $y = 3 + 8 \cos\left(\frac{\pi}{2} x + \frac{\pi}{8}\right)$

98. $y = 7 + 2 \sin\left(2\pi x - \frac{7\pi}{4}\right)$

2.6 GRAPHING OTHER TRIGONOMETRIC FUNCTIONS

OBJECTIVES

- Graph the basic tangent and cotangent functions.
- Graph the basic cosecant and secant functions.
- Use the period to graph cosecant and secant functions.
- Use the period and stretches to graph tangent and cotangent functions.
- Find the vertical asymptotes of cosecant, secant, tangent, and cotangent functions.
- Use a graph to find the zeros of tangent and cotangent functions.
- Use translations to graph cosecant, secant, tangent, and cotangent functions.
- Match graphs of trigonometric functions to their equations.

PREREQUISITE VOCABULARY TERMS

cosecant
cotangent
maximum
minimum
period
phase shift
secant
tangent
zero (of a function)

2.6.1 Introduction to the Graph of the Tangent Function

Recall from Section 2.4 that tangent is an odd function. Therefore, since all odd functions are symmetric with respect to the origin, the graph of $y = \tan x$ must also be symmetric with respect to the origin.

Points on the graph of $y = \tan x$ can be determined by considering the relationship between the tangent function and the sine and cosine functions. Recall the definitions of sine, cosine, and tangent for any angle θ from Section 2.4.

$$\sin \theta = \frac{y}{r} \qquad \cos \theta = \frac{x}{r} \qquad \tan \theta = \frac{y}{x}$$

Notice that the result of dividing $\sin \theta$ by $\cos \theta$ is equal to $\tan \theta$. $\dfrac{\sin \theta}{\cos \theta} = \dfrac{\frac{y}{r}}{\frac{x}{r}} = \dfrac{y}{r} \cdot \dfrac{r}{x} = \dfrac{y}{x} = \tan \theta$

So, $\tan \theta = \dfrac{\sin \theta}{\cos \theta}$ and similarly, $\cot \theta = \dfrac{\cos \theta}{\sin \theta}$.

Therefore, the graph of $y = \tan x$ is the same as the graph of $y = \dfrac{\sin x}{\cos x}$. It follows that for all (x, y) on the graph of $y = \tan x$, the y-coordinate is equal to $\sin x$ divided by $\cos x$.

From this definition of tangent (where $\cos x$ is in the denominator), we see that $\tan x$ is undefined for all x such that $\cos x = 0$. Therefore, the graph of $y = \tan x$ has a vertical asymptote at each zero of $y = \cos x$. From Section 2.5, we know that the zeros of $y = \cos x$ occur when $x = \pi/2 + \pi n$ (where n is an integer). Thus, the graph of $y = \tan x$ has a vertical asymptote at each $x = \pi/2 + \pi n$.

IMPORTANT

Unless otherwise stated, assume that n represents any integer.

Similarly, $y = \tan x = \dfrac{\sin x}{\cos x} = 0$ for all x such that $\sin x = 0$. Since the zeros of $y = \sin x$ occur where $x = \pi n$ (where n is an integer), the equation $x = \pi n$ gives the zeros of $y = \tan x$.

To graph the basic tangent function $y = \tan x$, it is convenient to use a coordinate plane in which the scale on the x-axis is $\pi/4$ and the scale on the y-axis is 1 (since $\tan x$ is equal to -1, 0, or 1 when x is a multiple of $\pi/4$). As shown in Figure 2.6a, use a table to list the values of $\tan x$, where x is a multiple of $\pi/4$.

x	$\tan x$
$-5\pi/4$	-1
$-\pi$	0
$-3\pi/4$	1
$-\pi/2$	undefined
$-\pi/4$	-1
0	0
$\pi/4$	1
$\pi/2$	undefined
$3\pi/4$	-1
π	0
$5\pi/4$	1

Figure 2.6a

We have now seen that tangent is undefined at $x = \pi/2 + \pi n$, and equal to 0 at $x = \pi n$. Therefore, the graph of $y = \tan x$ has a vertical asymptote at $x = -3\pi/2$, $x = -\pi/2$, $x = \pi/2$, $x = 3\pi/2$, $x = 5\pi/2$, and so on (to the left and to the right), and x-intercepts at $x = -\pi$, $x = 0$, $x = \pi$, $x = 2\pi$, and so on (to the left and to the right).

Consider the shape and behavior of the graph of $y = \tan x$ between pairs of consecutive vertical asymptotes. From the table, we see that between the asymptotes at $x = -3\pi/2$ and $x = -\pi/2$, the graph of $y = \tan x$ passes through the points $(-5\pi/4, -1)$, $(-\pi, 0)$, and $(-3\pi/4, 1)$. And between the asymptotes at $x = -\pi/2$ and $x = \pi/2$, the graph of $y = \tan x$ passes through the points $(-\pi/4, -1)$, $(0, 0)$, and $(\pi/4, 1)$. These y-coordinates are repeated between the interval made by each pair of asymptotes. Therefore, the tangent function is periodic and the graph continues to the left and right following this pattern.

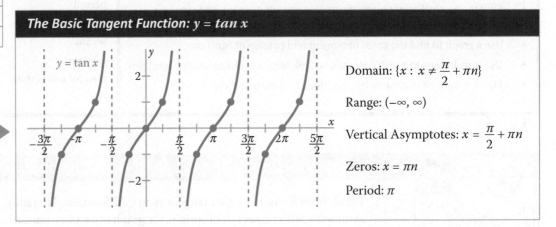

The Basic Tangent Function: $y = \tan x$

Domain: $\{x : x \neq \frac{\pi}{2} + \pi n\}$

Range: $(-\infty, \infty)$

Vertical Asymptotes: $x = \frac{\pi}{2} + \pi n$

Zeros: $x = \pi n$

Period: π

NOTICE THAT

The graph of $y = \tan x$ is symmetric about the origin. The graph has no minimums or maximums.

The same curve is repeated between each pair of consecutive vertical asymptotes. Therefore, the period of $y = \tan x$ is π.

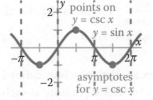

2.6.2 Introduction to the Graphs of the Cosecant and Secant Functions

Recall that the cosecant function is the reciprocal of the sine function, and the secant function is the reciprocal of the cosine function. This reciprocal relationship can be used to graph the basic cosecant function $y = \csc x$ and the basic secant function $y = \sec x$ by first considering the graphs of $y = \sin x$ and $y = \cos x$.

Generally, if (x, y) is a point on the graph of $y = \sin x$ such that $y \neq 0$, then $(x, 1/y)$ is a point on the graph of $y = \csc x$ because the functions are reciprocals of one another. The same relationship exists between the points on the graphs of $y = \cos x$ and $y = \sec x$ as these functions are reciprocals as well.

Figure 2.6b

Since the reciprocal of 0 is undefined, $y = \csc x$ is undefined at each x-value where $y = \sin x$ has a zero. Recall that the zeros of $y = \sin x$ are at $x = \pi n$ (i.e., when x is a multiple of π). Therefore, $y = \csc x$ is undefined at $x = \pi n$, so the graph of $y = \csc x$ has vertical asymptotes when $x = \pi n$.

Similarly, since the zeros of $y = \cos x$ are at $x = \pi/2 + \pi n$, these x-values give the equations of the vertical asymptotes on the graph of $y = \sec x$. The vertical asymptotes at the zeros are shown in Figures 2.6b and 2.6c.

Figure 2.6c

Since the reciprocal of 1 is 1, and the reciprocal of -1 is -1, the points on the graph of $y = \sin x$, where $y = 1$ or $y = -1$, are also on the graph of $y = \csc x$. Similarly, the points on the graph of $y = \cos x$, where $y = 1$ or $y = -1$, are also on the graph of $y = \sec x$. These common points are shown in red in Figures 2.6b and 2.6c.

The behavior of the graphs of $y = \csc x$ and $y = \sec x$ between the asymptotes can be determined by generalizing the relationship between reciprocals. If a value is between 0 and 1, then its reciprocal is greater than 1.

Moreover, the closer the value is to 0, the greater its reciprocal is. Therefore, for each (x, y) on the graph of $y = \sin x$ such that $0 < y < 1$, there is a point on the graph of $y = \csc x$ with the same x-coordinate, and a y-coordinate that is greater than 1. In addition, as the value of the y-coordinate for $y = \sin x$ decreases toward 0, the value of the y-coordinate on the graph of $y = \csc x$ increases.

This also describes the relationship between the points on the graphs of $y = \cos x$ and $y = \sec x$.

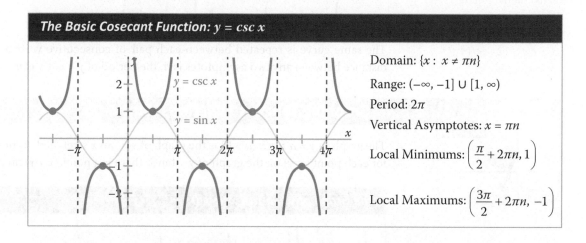

The Basic Cosecant Function: $y = \csc x$

Domain: $\{x : x \neq \pi n\}$

Range: $(-\infty, -1] \cup [1, \infty)$

Period: 2π

Vertical Asymptotes: $x = \pi n$

Local Minimums: $\left(\dfrac{\pi}{2} + 2\pi n, 1 \right)$

Local Maximums: $\left(\dfrac{3\pi}{2} + 2\pi n, -1 \right)$

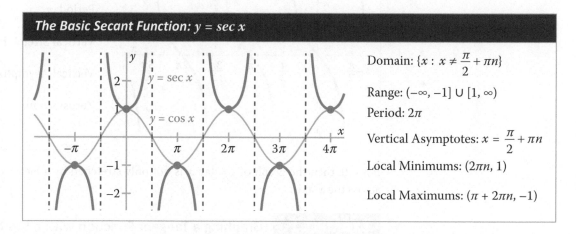

The Basic Secant Function: $y = \sec x$

Domain: $\{x : x \neq \dfrac{\pi}{2} + \pi n\}$

Range: $(-\infty, -1] \cup [1, \infty)$

Period: 2π

Vertical Asymptotes: $x = \dfrac{\pi}{2} + \pi n$

Local Minimums: $(2\pi n, 1)$

Local Maximums: $(\pi + 2\pi n, -1)$

Notice that each local maximum of $y = \sin x$ is a local minimum of $y = \csc x$, and each local minimum of $y = \sin x$ is a local maximum of $y = \csc x$. The relationship is the same for $y = \cos x$ and $y = \sec x$. From the graph, the period of $y = \csc x$ and $y = \sec x$ is 2π.

2.6.3 Introduction to the Graph of the Cotangent Function

The basic cotangent function $y = \cot x$ can be graphed by again using the relationship between reciprocals and the graph of $y = \tan x$ because the cotangent function is the reciprocal of the tangent function. Generally, if (x, y) is a point on the graph of $y = \tan x$ such that $y \neq 0$, then $(x, 1/y)$ is a point on the graph of $y = \cot x$.

Again, where the graph of $y = \tan x$ has zeros, the graph of $y = \cot x$ will have asymptotes. And, all points on the graph of $y = \tan x$ where $y = 1$ and where $y = -1$ will also be points on the graph of $y = \cot x$, because the reciprocal of 1 is 1 and the reciprocal of -1 is -1.

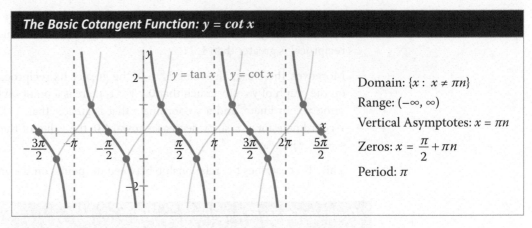

The Basic Cotangent Function: $y = \cot x$

Domain: $\{x : x \neq \pi n\}$

Range: $(-\infty, \infty)$

Vertical Asymptotes: $x = \pi n$

Zeros: $x = \dfrac{\pi}{2} + \pi n$

Period: π

NOTICE THAT

Like the graph of $y = \tan x$, the graph of $y = \cot x$ is symmetric about the origin, and has no minimums or maximums. Where the graph of $y = \tan x$ has zeros, the graph of $y = \cot x$ has vertical asymptotes.

The same curve is repeated between each pair of consecutive vertical asymptotes. Since the distance between any two asymptotes is π, the period of $y = \cot x$ is π.

2.6.4   Graphing Tangent Functions: Stretches

The graph of $y = a \tan x$ ($a > 0$) is the graph of $y = \tan x$ stretched vertically by a factor of a. So, for each point (x, y) on the graph of $y = \tan x$, there is a point (x, ay) on the graph of $y = a \tan x$.

The Graph of $y = a \tan x$, $a > 0$

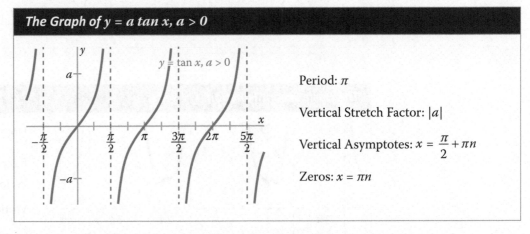

Period: π

Vertical Stretch Factor: $|a|$

Vertical Asymptotes: $x = \dfrac{\pi}{2} + \pi n$

Zeros: $x = \pi n$

If $a < 0$, then the graph of $y = \tan x$ is not only stretched by a factor of $|a|$, but also reflected across the x-axis.

EXAMPLE 1   Graphing a Tangent Function with a Stretch

IMPORTANT

All functions of the form $y = a \tan x$ will have the same zeros, vertical asymptotes, and period as $y = \tan x$.

Graph at least two periods of $y = 2 \tan x$, $y = \dfrac{1}{2} \tan x$, and $y = -2 \tan x$. Write the general equation of all vertical asymptotes and zeros of each function, if any.

SOLUTION

Find several points on the graph by making a table. Begin with the table for $y = \tan x$, then multiply each value in the $\tan x$ column by 2, 1/2, and -2 to find the corresponding y-values for the points on the graphs of $y = 2 \tan x$, $y = \dfrac{1}{2} \tan x$, and $y = -2 \tan x$, respectively.

x	$\tan x$	$2 \tan x$	$\dfrac{1}{2} \tan x$	$-2 \tan x$
$-\pi$	0	0	0	0
$-3\pi/4$	1	2	1/2	-2
$-\pi/4$	-1	-2	$-1/2$	2
0	0	0	0	0
$\pi/4$	1	2	1/2	-2
$3\pi/4$	-1	-2	$-1/2$	2
π	0	0	0	0

From the table, the graphs of all three functions pass through $(-\pi, 0)$, $(0, 0)$, and $(\pi, 0)$ as expected, since graphs of functions of the form $y = a \tan x$ have the same zeros.

Since $y = 2 \tan x$, $y = \frac{1}{2} \tan x$, and $y = -2 \tan x$ are of the form $y = a \tan x$, each graph has vertical asymptotes at $x = \frac{\pi}{2} + \pi n$, zeros at $x = \pi n$, and a period of π, like $y = \tan x$.

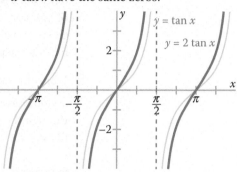

Because each equation has a coefficient of $\tan x$ that is not equal to 1 (or -1), each graph appears stretched or shrunk vertically as compared to the graph of $y = \tan x$.

> **NOTICE THAT**
>
> *The graphs of $y = 2 \tan x$ and $y = -2 \tan x$ are reflections of each other over the x-axis.*

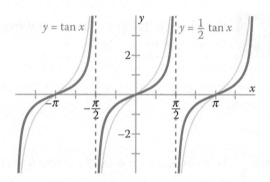

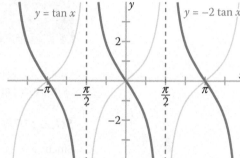

2.6.5 Graphing Tangent and Cotangent Functions: Stretches and Changes to the Period

In Section 2.5, we saw that the period of $y = \sin x$ and $y = \cos x$ is 2π, and that the period of $y = a \sin bx$ and $y = a \cos bx$ can be found by dividing 2π by $|b|$. The period of tangent and cotangent functions of the form $y = a \tan bx$ and $y = a \cot bx$ can be found in a similar way. Since the period of $y = \tan x$ and $y = \cot x$ is π, the period of $y = a \tan bx$ and $y = a \cot bx$ is $\frac{\pi}{|b|}$.

EXAMPLE 2   **Graphing a Tangent Function When the Period Is Not π**

Graph at least two periods of $y = \tan 2x$. Write the general equation of all vertical asymptotes and zeros, if any.

SOLUTION

Since $y = \tan 2x$ is of the form $y = \tan bx$ where $b = 2$, the function's period is $\pi/2$, and the graph has vertical asymptotes at $x = \frac{\pi}{4}$ and $x = -\frac{\pi}{4}$, and a zero at 0.

Sketch the tangent curve between those asymptotes.

The tangent function is periodic, so the graph repeats itself between each pair of consecutive vertical asymptotes, which occur every $\pi/2$ radians.

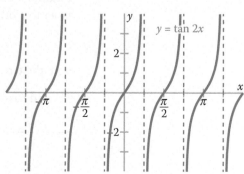

From the graph, the vertical asymptotes are at $x = \frac{\pi}{4} + \frac{\pi}{2} n$ and the zeros are at $x = \frac{\pi}{2} n$.

Confirm several points on the graph by making a table. Since tan x is equal to $-1, 0, 1,$ or undefined at multiples of $\pi/4$, and since the coefficient of x in $y = \tan 2x$ is 2, choose x-values such that $2x$ is a multiple of $\pi/4$ (thus making the points easier to plot).

From the table, the graph of $y = \tan 2x$ has vertical asymptotes at $x = \dfrac{\pi}{4}$ and $x = -\dfrac{\pi}{4}$, a zero at 0, and passes through the points $(-3\pi/8, 1)$, $(-\pi/8, -1)$, $(\pi/8, 1)$, and $(3\pi/8, -1)$.

x	$2x$	$\tan 2x$
$-3\pi/8$	$-3\pi/4$	1
$-\pi/4$	$-\pi/2$	undefined
$-\pi/8$	$-\pi/4$	-1
0	0	0
$\pi/8$	$\pi/4$	1
$\pi/4$	$\pi/2$	undefined
$3\pi/8$	$3\pi/4$	-1

EXAMPLE 3   **Graphing a Tangent Function with a Stretch and a Reflection When the Period Is Not π**

Graph at least two periods of $y = -2 \tan \dfrac{1}{2}x$. Write the general equation of all vertical asymptotes and zeros, if any.

SOLUTION

Since $y = -2 \tan \dfrac{1}{2}x$ is of the form $y = a \tan bx$ where $b = 1/2$, the graph of the function is horizontally stretched by a factor of 2 and the period is $\pi/|1/2| = 2\pi$.

Therefore, the graph has vertical asymptotes at $x = \pi$ and $x = -\pi$, and a zero at 0.

Sketch the tangent curve between the asymptotes. Note that the tangent curve is

• stretched by a factor of 2 because $|a| = 2$ and
• reflected over the x-axis because $a < 0$.

Since the tangent function is periodic, the graph repeats itself between each pair of consecutive vertical asymptotes, which occur every 2π radians.

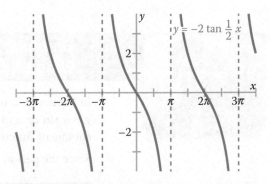

From the graph, the vertical asymptotes are at $x = \pi + 2\pi n$, and the zeros are at $x = 2\pi n$.

Confirm several points on the graph by making a table. Since the coefficient of x is 1/2, choose x-values such that $\dfrac{1}{2}x$ is a multiple of $\pi/4$ (thus making the points easier to plot).

x	$\dfrac{1}{2}x$	$\tan \dfrac{1}{2}x$	$-2 \tan \dfrac{1}{2}x$
$-3\pi/2$	$-3\pi/4$	1	-2
$-\pi$	$-\pi/2$	undefined	undefined
$-\pi/2$	$-\pi/4$	-1	2
0	0	0	0
$\pi/2$	$\pi/4$	1	-2
π	$\pi/2$	undefined	undefined
$3\pi/2$	$3\pi/4$	-1	2

From the table, the graph of $y = -2 \tan \dfrac{1}{2}x$ has vertical asymptotes at $x = \pi$ and $x = -\pi$, a zero at 0, and passes through the points $(-3\pi/2, -2)$, $(-\pi/2, 2)$, $(\pi/2, -2)$, and $(3\pi/2, 2)$.

Graphing $y = a \cot bx$

The strategies used for graphing tangent functions can also be applied to graphing cotangent functions.

EXAMPLE 4 — **Graphing a Cotangent Function with a Stretch and a Reflection When the Period Is Not π**

Graph at least two periods of $y = -3 \cot \frac{1}{4}x$. Write the general equation of all vertical asymptotes and zeros, if any.

SOLUTION

Since $y = -3 \cot \frac{1}{4}x$ is of the form $y = a \cot bx$ where $b = 1/4$, the graph of the function is horizontally stretched by a factor of 4 and the period is $\pi/|1/4| = 4\pi$. Therefore, the graph has vertical asymptotes at $x = -4\pi$, $x = 0$, and $x = 4\pi$, and zeros at $x = -2\pi$ and $x = 2\pi$ (i.e., the midpoints on the x-axis between the vertical asymptotes).

Draw the vertical asymptotes, then sketch the cotangent curve between each pair of consecutive asymptotes.

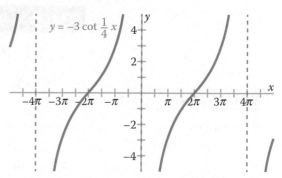

Note that the cotangent curve is
- stretched vertically by a factor of 3 because $|a| = 3$ and
- reflected over the x-axis because $a < 0$.

From the graph, the vertical asymptotes are at $x = 4\pi n$, and the zeros are at $x = 2\pi + 4\pi n$.

TIP

Since cot x is equal to –1, 0, 1, or undefined at multiples of π/4, choosing x-values such that $\frac{1}{4}x$ is a multiple of π/4 makes the graph easier to sketch.

Confirm several points on the graph by making a table. Since the coefficient of x is $1/4$, choose x-values such that $\frac{1}{4}x$ is a multiple of $\pi/4$.

Multiply each value of $\cot \frac{1}{4}x$ by -3 to find the corresponding y-values.

x	$\frac{1}{4}x$	$\cot \frac{1}{4}x$	$-3 \cot \frac{1}{4}x$
-3π	$-3\pi/4$	1	-3
-2π	$-\pi/2$	0	0
$-\pi$	$-\pi/4$	-1	3
0	0	undefined	undefined
π	$\pi/4$	1	-3
2π	$\pi/2$	0	0
3π	$3\pi/4$	-1	3

From the table, the graph of $y = -3 \cot \frac{1}{4}x$ has a vertical asymptotes at $x = 0$, zeros at $x = -2\pi$ and $x = 2\pi$, and passes through the points $(-3\pi, -3)$, $(-\pi/2, 3)$, $(\pi, -3)$, and $(3\pi, 3)$.

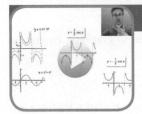

2.6.6   Graphing Cosecant and Secant Functions

Recall that the amplitudes of $y = a \sin x$ and $y = a \cos x$ is $|a|$, so the vertical distance between the local minimums and maximums is $2|a|$. Similarly, the vertical distance between the local minimums and maximums of a graph of a function of the form $y = a \csc x$ or $y = a \sec x$ is $2|a|$.

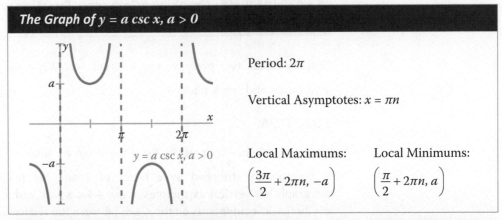

The Graph of $y = a \csc x$, $a > 0$

$y = a \csc x$, $a > 0$

Period: 2π

Vertical Asymptotes: $x = \pi n$

Local Maximums:
$\left(\dfrac{3\pi}{2} + 2\pi n, -a\right)$

Local Minimums:
$\left(\dfrac{\pi}{2} + 2\pi n, a\right)$

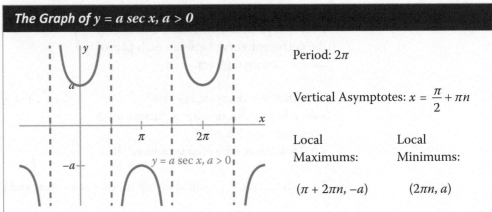

The Graph of $y = a \sec x$, $a > 0$

$y = a \sec x$, $a > 0$

Period: 2π

Vertical Asymptotes: $x = \dfrac{\pi}{2} + \pi n$

Local Maximums:
$(\pi + 2\pi n, -a)$

Local Minimums:
$(2\pi n, a)$

> **NOTICE THAT**
>
> *The graphs of $y = a \csc x$ and $y = a \sec x$ have no zeros.*

Note that the graph of $y = a \csc x$ is very similar to the graph of $y = \csc x$. They have the same vertical asymptotes, the same period, and when $a > 0$, the same x-values corresponding to the local minimums and local maximums (though not the same y-values). The same is true for the graphs of $y = a \sec x$ as compared to $y = \sec x$.

The Graphs of $y = a \csc x$ and $y = a \sec x$ When $a < 0$

Figure 2.6d shows the graphs of $y = \sec x$ and $y = -\sec x$. Notice that the graphs are reflections over the x-axis. Generally (as with $y = a \sin x$ and $y = a \cos x$), if $a < 0$, then the graph of $y = a \sec x$ is a reflection of the graph of $y = |a| \sec x$ across the x-axis. Similarly, if $a < 0$, then the graph of $y = a \csc x$ is a reflection of the graph of $y = |a| \csc x$ across the x-axis.

Figure 2.6d

Graphing $y = a \csc x$ and $y = a \sec x$

Functions of the form $y = a \csc x$ and $y = a \sec x$ can be graphed by transforming the corresponding basic trigonometric function.

Alternatively, to graph $y = a \csc x$ when $a \neq 1$, first graph the corresponding reciprocal function $y = \sin x$ and sketch vertical asymptotes through the zeros of $y = \sin x$. Then multiply the y-coordinates at the local minimums and maximums of $y = \sin x$ by $|a|$. The resulting points are the local maximums and minimums of $y = |a| \csc x$. Sketch the graph of $y = |a| \csc bx$ using these local minimum and local maximum points between the vertical asymptotes. If $a < 0$, reflect the graph of $y = |a| \csc x$ over the x-axis, resulting in the graph of $y = a \csc x$.

The process is the same for graphing $y = a \sec x$ when $a \neq 1$, but begin by graphing the corresponding reciprocal function $y = \cos x$ (instead of $y = \sin x$).

| EXAMPLE 5 | **Graphing Cosecant and Secant Functions** |

Graph at least one period of each function and write the general equation of all vertical asymptotes and zeros, if any.

A. $y = \dfrac{1}{2} \sec x$ 　　　　　　　**B.** $y = -2 \csc x$

SOLUTION

A. Graph the corresponding reciprocal function $y = \cos x$. Draw vertical asymptotes through the zeros. For each maximum on the graph of $y = \cos x$, there is a local minimum with $1/2$ of the y-coordinate on the graph of $y = \dfrac{1}{2} \sec x$. For each minimum on the graph of $y = \cos x$, there is a local maximum with $1/2$ of the y-coordinate on the graph of $y = \dfrac{1}{2} \sec x$.

NOTICE THAT

The function is of the form $y = a \sec x$ where $a = 1/2$, so:
- *the period is 2π,*
- *the vertical asymptotes are at $x = \dfrac{\pi}{2} + \pi n$,*
- *$y = 1/2$ at the local minimums, and*
- *$y = -1/2$ at the local maximums.*

Graph $y = \dfrac{1}{2} \sec x$ using these points and the vertical asymptotes.

The zeros of $y = \cos x$ occur at $x = \dfrac{\pi}{2} + \pi n$, so the vertical asymptotes of $y = \dfrac{1}{2} \sec x$ occur at $x = \dfrac{\pi}{2} + \pi n$.

Like $y = \sec x$, $y = \dfrac{1}{2} \sec x$ has no zeros.

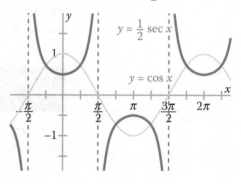

B. Graph the corresponding reciprocal function $y = \sin x$. Draw vertical asymptotes at the zeros.

For each maximum on the graph of $y = \sin x$, there is a local minimum with 2 times the y-coordinate on the graph of $y = 2 \csc x$. For each minimum on the graph of $y = \sin x$, there is a local maximum with 2 times the y-coordinate on the graph of $y = 2 \sin x$.

Graph $y = 2 \csc x$ using these points and the vertical asymptotes.

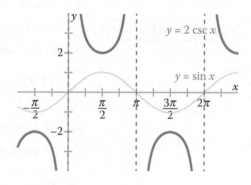

NOTICE THAT

The function is of the form $y = a \csc x$ where $a = -2$, so:
- *the period is 2π,*
- *the vertical asymptotes are at $x = \pi n$,*
- *$y = 2$ at the local minimums, and*
- *$y = -2$ at the local maximums.*

Reflect the graph of $y = 2 \csc x$ over the x-axis to graph $y = -2 \csc x$.

The zeros of $y = \sin x$ occur at $x = \pi n$, so the vertical asymptotes of $y = -2 \csc x$ occur at $x = \pi n$.

Like $y = \csc x$, $y = -2 \csc x$ has no zeros.

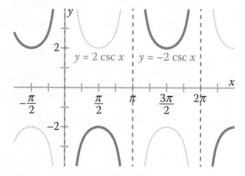

2.6.7 Graphing Cosecant and Secant Functions: Changes to the Period

Recall that the period of $y = a \sin bx$ and $y = a \cos bx$ is $2\pi/|b|$. Since the period of a function and its reciprocal is the same, the period of functions of the form $y = a \csc bx$ and $y = a \sec bx$ is also $2\pi/|b|$. Then, if $b \neq 1$, the period of $y = a \csc bx$ and $y = a \sec bx$ is not 2π.

Graphing $y = \csc bx$ and $y = \sec bx$

To graph $y = \csc bx$, first graph the corresponding reciprocal function $y = \sin bx$ and sketch vertical asymptotes through the zeros of $y = \sin bx$. Each maximum on the graph of $y = \sin bx$ is a local minimum on the graph of $y = \csc bx$. Each minimum on the graph of $y = \sin bx$ is a local maximum on the graph of $y = \csc bx$. Sketch the graph of $y = \csc bx$ using these local minimum and local maximum points between the vertical asymptotes.

The process is the same for graphing $y = \sec bx$, but begin by graphing the corresponding reciprocal function $y = \cos bx$ (instead of $y = \sin bx$).

EXAMPLE 6 **Graphing Cosecant and Secant Functions When the Period Is Not 2π**

Graph at least one period of each function and write the general equation of all vertical asymptotes and zeros, if any.

A. $y = \csc \dfrac{1}{2}x$ **B.** $y = \sec 3x$

SOLUTION

A. Graph the corresponding reciprocal function $y = \sin \dfrac{1}{2}x$ with a period of 4π. Draw vertical asymptotes at the zeros.

NOTICE THAT

Since the function is of the form $y = a \csc bx$ where $b = 1/2$, the period is 4π.

Each maximum and minimum on the graph of $y = \sin \dfrac{1}{2}x$ is a local minimum or local maximum, respectively, on the graph of $y = \csc \dfrac{1}{2}x$.

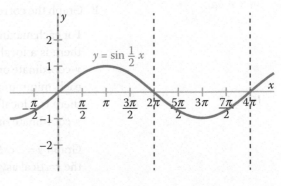

Graph $y = \csc \dfrac{1}{2}x$ using these points and the vertical asymptotes.

The zeros of $y = \sin \dfrac{1}{2}x$ occur at $x = 2\pi n$, so the vertical asymptotes of $y = \csc \dfrac{1}{2}x$ occur at $x = 2\pi n$.

Like $y = \csc x$, $y = \csc \dfrac{1}{2}x$ has no zeros.

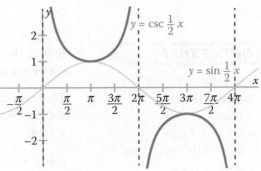

B. Graph the corresponding reciprocal function $y = \cos 3x$, which has a period of $2\pi/3$. Draw vertical asymptotes through the zeros.

Each maximum and minimum on the graph of $y = \cos 3x$ is a local minimum or local maximum, respectively, on the graph of $y = \sec 3x$.

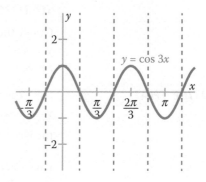

Graph $y = \sec 3x$ using these points and the vertical asymptotes.

The zeros of $y = \cos 3x$ occur at $x = \dfrac{\pi}{6} + \dfrac{\pi}{3}n$, as do the vertical asymptotes of $y = \sec 3x$.

Like $y = \sec x$, $y = \sec 3x$ has no zeros.

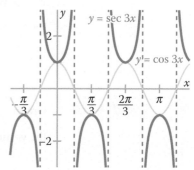

2.6.8 Graphing Cosecant and Secant Functions: Another Example

Graphing $y = a \csc bx$ and $y = a \sec bx$

To graph $y = a \csc bx$ when $a \neq 1$ and $b \neq 1$, first graph the corresponding reciprocal function $y = \sin bx$ and sketch vertical asymptotes through the zeros of $y = \sin bx$. Then multiply the y-coordinates at the minimums and maximums of $y = \sin bx$ by $|a|$. The resulting points are the local maximums and local minimums of $y = |a| \csc bx$. Sketch the graph of $y = |a| \csc bx$ using these local minimum and local maximum points between the vertical asymptotes. If $a < 0$, reflect the graph of $y = |a| \csc bx$ over the x-axis, resulting in the graph of $y = a \csc bx$.

The process is the same for graphing $y = a \sec bx$ when $b \neq 1$, but begin by graphing the corresponding reciprocal function $y = \cos bx$ (instead of $y = \sin bx$).

EXAMPLE 7 **Graphing Cosecant and Secant Functions When the Period Is Not 2π**

Graph at least two periods of $y = -\dfrac{1}{2} \csc 3x$. Write the general equation of all vertical asymptotes and zeros, if any.

SOLUTION

Graph the corresponding reciprocal function $y = \sin 3x$. Draw vertical asymptotes at the zeros.

For each maximum on the graph of $y = \sin 3x$, there is a local minimum with 1/2 of the y-coordinate on the graph of $y = \frac{1}{2} \csc 3x$.

For each minimum on the graph of $y = \sin 3x$, there is a local maximum with 1/2 of the y-coordinate on the graph of $y = \frac{1}{2} \csc 3x$.

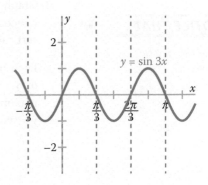

Graph $y = \frac{1}{2} \csc 3x$ using these points and the vertical asymptotes.

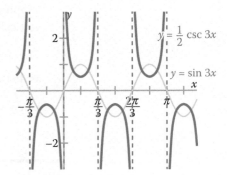

Reflect the graph of $y = \frac{1}{2} \csc 3x$ over the x-axis to graph $y = -\frac{1}{2} \csc 3x$.

The zeros of $y = \sin 3x$ occur at $x = \frac{\pi}{3}n$, as do the vertical asymptotes of $y = -\frac{1}{2} \csc 3x$.

Like $y = \csc x$, $y = -\frac{1}{2} \csc 3x$ has no zeros.

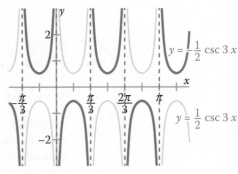

2.6.9 Shifting the Graphs of Other Trigonometric Functions

Graphing $y = \tan (x - c)$ and $y = \cot (x - c)$

Recall from Section 2.5 that a phase shift is a horizontal shift of a trigonometric function.

Functions of the form $y = \tan (x - c)$ and $y = \cot (x - c)$, where c is any real number, can be graphed by horizontally translating the graph of the corresponding basic trigonometric function. Specifically, the graph of $y = \tan (x - c)$ is the graph of $y = \tan x$ shifted c units to the right if $c > 0$, or c units to the left if $c < 0$.

The graphs of cotangent functions behave in the same way.

EXAMPLE 8   Graphing Tangent and Cotangent Functions with a Phase Shift

Graph at least two periods of $y = \cot \left(x - \frac{\pi}{3} \right)$. Write the general equation of all vertical asymptotes and zeros, if any.

SOLUTION

Graph the corresponding basic trigonometric function $y = \cot x$.

Recall that the zeros occur at $x = \dfrac{\pi}{2} + \pi n$ and the vertical asymptotes at $x = \pi n$.

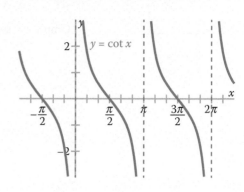

TIP

Since the phase shift is π/3, and the zeros of y = cot x occur at $x = \dfrac{\pi}{2} + \pi n$, graph y = cot x using an interval of π/6 on the x-axis.

The graph of $y = \cot\left(x - \dfrac{\pi}{3}\right)$ is the graph of $y = \cot x$ shifted $\pi/3$ units to the right.

Thus, the zeros occur at
$$x = \left(\dfrac{\pi}{2} + \pi n\right) + \dfrac{\pi}{3} = \dfrac{5\pi}{6} + \pi n,$$

and the vertical asymptotes occur at
$$x = (\pi n) + \dfrac{\pi}{3} = \dfrac{\pi}{3} + \pi n.$$

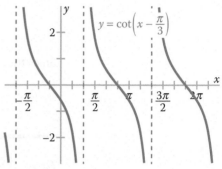

Graphing $y = \csc(x - c)$ and $y = \sec(x - c)$

Trigonometric functions of the form $y = \csc(x - c)$ and $y = \sec(x - c)$ can also be graphed by horizontally translating the graph of the corresponding basic trigonometric function. However, an alternative method is demonstrated in **Example 9**, where the corresponding reciprocal function is graphed first.

EXAMPLE 9 **Graphing Cosecant and Secant Functions with a Phase Shift**

Graph at least two periods of $y = \sec\left(x + \dfrac{3\pi}{2}\right)$. Write the general equation of all vertical asymptotes and zeros, if any.

SOLUTION

Graph the corresponding reciprocal function $y = \cos\left(x + \dfrac{3\pi}{2}\right)$ by shifting the graph of $y = \cos x$ left $3\pi/2$ units.

Draw vertical asymptotes at the zeros.

Since $a = 1$, each maximum and minimum on the graph of $y = \cos\left(x + \dfrac{3\pi}{2}\right)$ is a local minimum or local maximum, respectively, on the graph of $y = \sec\left(x + \dfrac{3\pi}{2}\right)$.

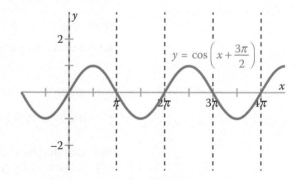

REMEMBER

Horizontally shifting the graph of y = cos x $\dfrac{\pi}{2} + 2\pi n$ units will result in the graph of y = sin x. Therefore, the graph of $y = \cos\left(x + \dfrac{3\pi}{2}\right)$ is the same as the graph of y = sin x.

Graph $y = \sec\left(x + \dfrac{3\pi}{2}\right)$ using these points and the vertical asymptotes.

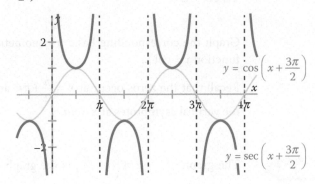

Since the zeros of $y = \cos\left(x + \dfrac{3\pi}{2}\right)$ occur at $x = \pi n$, the vertical asymptotes of $y = \sec\left(x + \dfrac{3\pi}{2}\right)$ occur at $x = \pi n$. Like $y = \sec x$, $y = \sec\left(x + \dfrac{3\pi}{2}\right)$ has no zeros.

Graphing $y = a \tan (bx - c)$ and $y = a \cot (bx - c)$

To graph a function of the form $y = a \tan (bx - c)$ or $y = a \cot (bx - c)$, first factor the b-value from $bx - c$, then graph the resulting function, as demonstrated in **Example 10**.

EXAMPLE 10 **Graphing Tangent and Cotangent Functions with a Phase Shift When the Period Is Not π**

Graph at least two periods of $y = -\tan (3x + 2\pi)$. Write the general equation of all vertical asymptotes and zeros, if any.

SOLUTION

First, factor 3 from $3x + 2\pi$.

$$y = -\tan (3x + 2\pi) = -\tan 3\left(x + \dfrac{2\pi}{3}\right)$$

First, graph $y = -\tan 3x$, which is the reflection of $y = \tan 3x$ over the x-axis.

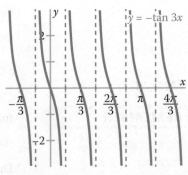

Note that since $b = 3$, the period is $\pi/3$ and the asymptotes are located at $x = \dfrac{\pi}{6} + \dfrac{\pi}{3}n$.

Now graph $y = -\tan 3\left(x + \dfrac{2\pi}{3}\right)$, which is the graph of $y = -\tan 3x$ shifted $2\pi/3$ units to the left.

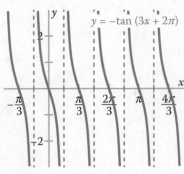

Note that the phase shift $2\pi/3$ is a multiple of the period of $y = -\tan 3x$, $\pi/3$. So the graph of $y = -\tan (3x + 2\pi)$ is the same graph as $y = -\tan 3x$.

The zeros occur at $x = \dfrac{\pi}{3}n$, and the vertical asymptotes occur at $x = \dfrac{\pi}{6} + \dfrac{\pi}{3}n$.

Graphing $y = a \csc (bx - c)$ and $y = a \sec (bx - c)$

To graph $y = a \csc (bx - c)$ or $y = a \sec (bx - c)$, first factor the b-value from $bx - c$, then graph the resulting function, as demonstrated in **Example 11**.

> **EXAMPLE 11** **Graphing Cosecant and Secant Functions with a Phase Shift When the Period Is Not 2π**

Graph at least two periods of $y = 3 \sec \left(\dfrac{1}{2}x - \dfrac{\pi}{4} \right)$. Write the general equation of all vertical asymptotes and zeros, if any.

SOLUTION

First, factor $\dfrac{1}{2}$ from $\dfrac{1}{2}x - \dfrac{\pi}{4}$. $\quad y = 3 \sec \left(\dfrac{1}{2}x - \dfrac{\pi}{4} \right) = 3 \sec \dfrac{1}{2}\left(x - \dfrac{\pi}{2} \right)$

Graph the corresponding reciprocal function $y = \cos \dfrac{1}{2}\left(x - \dfrac{\pi}{2} \right)$. Since $b = 1/2$, the period is 4π.

Draw vertical asymptotes through the zeros.

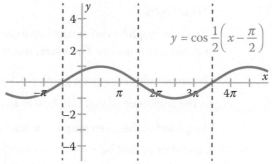

For each maximum on the graph of $y = \cos \dfrac{1}{2}\left(x - \dfrac{\pi}{2} \right)$, there is a local minimum with 3 times the y-coordinate on the graph of $y = 3 \sec \dfrac{1}{2}\left(x - \dfrac{\pi}{2} \right)$. For each minimum on the graph of $y = \cos \dfrac{1}{2}\left(x - \dfrac{\pi}{2} \right)$, there is a local maximum with 3 times the y-coordinate on the graph of $y = 3 \sec \dfrac{1}{2}\left(x - \dfrac{\pi}{2} \right)$. Graph $y = 3 \sec \dfrac{1}{2}\left(x - \dfrac{\pi}{2} \right)$ (i.e., graph $y = 3 \sec \left(\dfrac{1}{2}x - \dfrac{\pi}{4} \right)$) using these points and the vertical asymptotes.

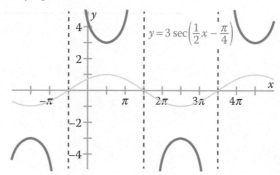

Since the zeros of $y = \cos \dfrac{1}{2}\left(x - \dfrac{\pi}{2} \right)$ occur at $x = \dfrac{3\pi}{2} + 2\pi n$, the vertical asymptotes of $y = 3 \sec \left(\dfrac{1}{2}x - \dfrac{\pi}{4} \right)$ occur at $x = \dfrac{3\pi}{2} + 2\pi n$.

Like $y = \sec x$, $y = 3 \sec \left(\dfrac{1}{2}x - \dfrac{\pi}{4} \right)$ has no zeros.

2.6.10 Identifying the Equation of a Trigonometric Function from Its Graph

EXAMPLE 12 Using the Attributes of the Graph of a Trigonometric Function to Identify Its Equation

Choose the equation that corresponds to the graph.

A. $y = 3 \sec\left(x - \dfrac{\pi}{2}\right)$ **B.** $y = 2 \sin\left(2x - \dfrac{\pi}{2}\right)$

C. $y = -3 \sin\left(2x - \dfrac{\pi}{2}\right)$ **D.** $y = -3 \cos\left(x - \dfrac{\pi}{4}\right)$

E. $y = -3 \tan\left(2x - \dfrac{\pi}{4}\right)$ **F.** $y = 3 \csc\left(x - \dfrac{\pi}{2}\right)$

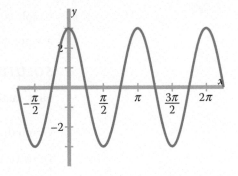

SOLUTION

The given graph has no vertical asymptotes, so the graph cannot be a cosecant, secant, tangent, or cotangent function. Therefore, the graph must be a sine or cosine function.

The amplitude of the given graph is 3, so the equation of the graph cannot be $y = 2 \sin\left(2x - \dfrac{\pi}{2}\right)$ (as the amplitude of that function is 2).

The period of the given graph is π. So, the coefficient of x in the sine or cosine function must be 2, and thus cannot be $y = -3 \cos\left(x - \dfrac{\pi}{4}\right)$.

So, the equation of the given graph must be $y = -3 \sin\left(2x - \dfrac{\pi}{2}\right)$.

Verify that the equation corresponds to the given graph.

First, factor 2 from $2x - \dfrac{\pi}{2}$. $y = -3 \sin\left(2x - \dfrac{\pi}{2}\right) = -3 \sin 2\left(x - \dfrac{\pi}{4}\right)$

The graph of this equation is a sine function with an amplitude of 3, a period of π, and a phase shift of $\pi/4$, all of which match the given graph.

SECTION 2.6 EXERCISES

Warm Up

1. Identify the domain and range of $y = \cos x$.

2. Identify the zeros of $y = \sin x$.

3. Identify the values for which the function $y = \tan x$ is undefined.

Just the Facts

Fill in the blanks.

4. Unlike the graphs of $y = \sin x$ and $y = \cos x$, the graph of _____ has _____ asymptotes at $\frac{\pi}{2} + \pi n$ radians, where _____ is an integer.

5. The reciprocal of the sine function is the _____ function, and the reciprocal of the _____ function is the secant function.

6. The reciprocal of the _____ function is the cotangent function. Both functions have a period of _____. When $y = a \tan bx$ or $y = a \cot bx$, the _____ stretch is _____ and the period is _____. When _____ is negative, the graph is reflected across the x-axis.

7. The graph of $y = \tan x$ is identical to the graph of $y = \cot x$ if the cotangent graph is shifted _____ units to the _____ or _____, and is reflected across the _____.

8. In the graphs of the cosecant and _____ functions, there are _____ asymptotes, since where sine and cosine are 0 the cosecant and _____ functions are undefined.

9. The graph of $y = \csc(x + c)$ has a phase shift left c units if _____. When c is a multiple of _____, the graph of $y = \csc(x + c)$ is identical to $y = \csc x$.

10. To graph an equation when of the form $y = a \csc(bx + c)$, first factor out the _____.

Essential Skills

In Exercises 1–32, graph each function and identify all vertical asymptotes and zeros, if any.

1. $y = 3 \tan x$

2. $y = \frac{1}{4} \tan x$

3. $y = -\frac{2}{3} \tan x$

4. $y = -4 \tan x$

5. $y = \tan 3x$

6. $y = \tan \frac{1}{2} x$

7. $y = \tan \frac{1}{4} x$

8. $y = \tan 5x$

9. $y = \frac{1}{4} \tan 2x$

10. $y = 3 \tan 4x$

11. $y = 5 \tan \frac{1}{3} x$

12. $y = -\frac{1}{2} \tan 3x$

13. $y = -\frac{3}{4} \tan 4x$

14. $y = 2 \tan \frac{2}{3} x$

15. $y = \cot \frac{1}{2} x$

16. $y = \cot 3x$

17. $y = \cot 2x$

18. $y = \cot \frac{1}{3} x$

19. $y = -\frac{1}{2} \cot 4x$

20. $y = 2 \cot \frac{1}{4} x$

21. $y = \frac{1}{4} \cot 3x$

22. $y = -\frac{1}{3} \cot 2x$

23. $y = 3 \cot \frac{1}{2} x$

24. $y = -\frac{3}{4} \cot \frac{1}{3} x$

25. $y = \frac{1}{2} \csc x$

26. $y = -3 \csc x$

27. $y = -4 \csc x$

28. $y = \frac{1}{4} \csc x$

29. $y = -2 \sec x$

30. $y = \frac{3}{4} \sec x$

31. $y = \frac{1}{3} \sec x$

32. $y = -3 \sec x$

In Exercises 33–36, find the period of each function.

33. $y = \csc \frac{1}{2} x$

34. $y = \sec 3x$

35. $y = \sec \frac{2}{5} x$

36. $y = \csc 6x$

In Exercises 37–66, graph each function and identify all vertical asymptotes and zeros, if any.

37. $y = \csc 3x$

38. $y = \sec 4x$

39. $y = \sec 2x$

40. $y = \csc 2x$

41. $y = \sec \frac{1}{3} x$

42. $y = \csc \frac{1}{4} x$

43. $y = \csc \frac{3}{4} x$

44. $y = \sec \frac{1}{2} x$

45. $y = \frac{1}{2} \csc 3x$

46. $y = -2 \sec \frac{1}{3} x$

47. $y = -3 \sec 2x$

48. $y = \frac{1}{4} \csc 4x$

49. $y = -\frac{3}{4} \csc \frac{1}{2} x$

50. $y = -\frac{2}{3} \sec \frac{2}{3} x$

51. $y = \cot \left(x + \frac{\pi}{6} \right)$

52. $y = \tan \left(x - \frac{\pi}{8} \right)$

53. $y = \tan \left(x + \frac{\pi}{4} \right)$

54. $y = \cot \left(x - \frac{\pi}{3} \right)$

55. $y = \csc \left(x - \frac{\pi}{4} \right)$

56. $y = \sec \left(x + \frac{3\pi}{2} \right)$

57. $y = \sec \left(x - \frac{\pi}{6} \right)$

58. $y = \csc \left(x + \frac{2\pi}{3} \right)$

59. $y = -2 \tan (3x - \pi)$

60. $y = 3 \cot \left(\frac{1}{2} x + \frac{\pi}{3} \right)$

61. $y = \frac{1}{2} \cot (4x - \pi)$ **62.** $y = -\frac{3}{4} \tan \left(\frac{1}{3}x + \frac{\pi}{6} \right)$

63. $y = 2 \sec \left(2x + \frac{\pi}{3} \right)$ **64.** $y = -4 \csc \left(\frac{1}{4}x - \frac{\pi}{6} \right)$

65. $y = \frac{1}{3} \csc (3x + \pi)$ **66.** $y = -\frac{1}{2} \sec \left(\frac{1}{2}x - \frac{\pi}{6} \right)$

In Exercises 67–70, choose the equation from the following list that corresponds to each graph.

A. $y = \sin \frac{1}{2} \left(x - \frac{\pi}{4} \right)$ **B.** $y = -\cos \frac{1}{3} \left(x - \frac{\pi}{3} \right)$

C. $y = -\sin 3 \left(x - \frac{\pi}{3} \right)$ **D.** $y = -\sin \frac{1}{2} \left(x - \frac{\pi}{4} \right)$

E. $y = \cos 2 \left(x + \frac{\pi}{6} \right)$ **F.** $y = \sin 4 \left(x - \frac{\pi}{6} \right)$

67.
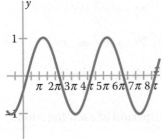

68.
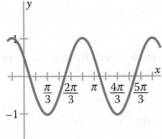

69.
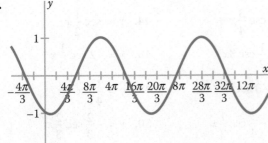

70.
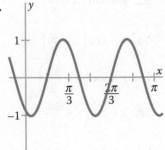

In Exercises 71–74, choose the equation from the following list that corresponds to each graph.

A. $y = \cot \frac{1}{4} \left(x + \frac{\pi}{3} \right)$ **B.** $y = -\cot 3 \left(x + \frac{\pi}{4} \right)$

C. $y = -\tan \frac{1}{2} \left(x + \frac{\pi}{6} \right)$ **D.** $y = \cot \frac{1}{4} \left(x - \frac{\pi}{3} \right)$

E. $y = \tan \frac{1}{2} \left(x - \frac{\pi}{3} \right)$ **F.** $y = \tan 2 \left(x - \frac{\pi}{3} \right)$

71.
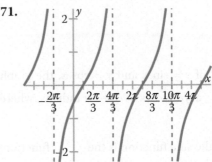

72.
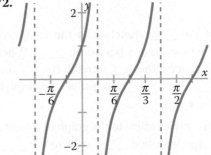

73.
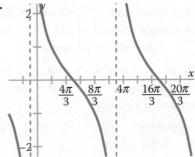

74.
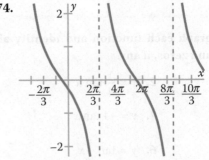

In Exercises 75–78, choose the equation from the following list that corresponds to each graph.

A. $y = \sec 2\left(x - \dfrac{\pi}{4}\right)$

B. $y = -\csc 4\left(x + \dfrac{\pi}{2}\right)$

C. $y = -\csc 3\left(x + \dfrac{\pi}{6}\right)$

D. $y = \sec 2\left(x + \dfrac{\pi}{3}\right)$

E. $y = \csc 2\left(x + \dfrac{\pi}{4}\right)$

F. $y = \sec \dfrac{1}{2}\left(x - \dfrac{\pi}{3}\right)$

75.

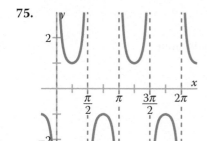

76.

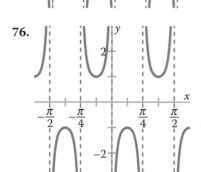

77.

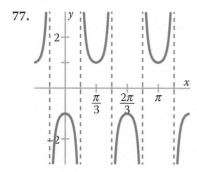

78.

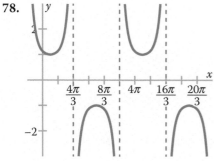

Extensions

79. How does the graph of $y = 2 \cot \pi x$ differ from the graph of $y = \cot x$?

80. Identify the vertical stretch, period, phase shift, and reflection, if any, of the graph of $y = -5 \sec\left(\dfrac{2}{3}x + \dfrac{\pi}{4}\right)$, as compared to the corresponding basic trigonometric function. Graph.

81. True or False? When the phase shift of any trigonometric function is a multiple of its period, the graph is identical to the graph of the same function without the phase shift.

82. Graph. $y = 2 \csc\left(\dfrac{\pi}{3}x - \dfrac{\pi}{6}\right)$

83. Write the equation of the tangent function that has period $\pi/4$, vertical stretch 5, phase shift $\pi/5$ radians to the left, and a reflection across the x-axis.

84. Identify any similarities between the graphs of

$$y = -2 \csc(2x - 2\pi) \text{ and } y = -2 \sec 2\left(x - \dfrac{\pi}{4}\right).$$

In Exercises 85–86, write the equation for the function $y = a \tan b(x - c)$ with the given characteristics.

85. vertical asymptotes: $x = \dfrac{\pi}{6} + \dfrac{\pi}{3}n$

zeros: $x = \dfrac{\pi}{3}n$

vertical stretch: 4

phase shift: none

reflection over the x-axis: none

86. period: 6π

vertical stretch: 2/3

phase shift: $\pi/4$ units left

reflection over the x-axis: yes

In Exercises 87–88, write the equation for the function $y = a \cot b(x - c)$ with the given characteristics.

87. period: $3\pi/2$

vertical stretch: 5

phase shift: $\pi/6$ units right

reflection over the x-axis: yes

88. vertical asymptotes: $x = -\dfrac{\pi}{4} + 3\pi n$

zeros: $x = \dfrac{5\pi}{4} + 3\pi n$

vertical stretch: 4

phase shift: none

reflection over the x-axis: none

In Exercises 89–90, write the equation for the function $y = a\,\csc b(x - c)$ **with the given characteristics.**

89. vertical asymptotes: $x = -\dfrac{\pi}{6} + \dfrac{3\pi}{2}n$

zeros: none

vertical stretch: 1/2

phase shift: $\pi/6$ units left

reflection over the x-axis: yes

90. period: $\pi/2$

vertical stretch: 2

phase shift: none

reflection over the x-axis: yes

In Exercises 91–92, write the equation for the function $y = a\,\sec b(x - c)$ **with the given characteristics.**

91. period: $\pi/4$

vertical stretch: 8

phase shift: $2\pi/5$ units right

reflection over the x-axis: yes

92. vertical asymptotes: $x = \dfrac{\pi}{8} + \dfrac{\pi}{4}n$

zeros: none

vertical stretch: 4

phase shift: none

reflection over the x-axis: none

2.7 INVERSE TRIGONOMETRIC FUNCTIONS

OBJECTIVES

- Define the inverse of the sine, cosine, tangent, cosecant, secant, and cotangent functions.
- Find exact values of inverse trigonometric functions.
- Use a calculator to evaluate inverse trigonometric functions.
- Evaluate the composition of a trigonometric function and its inverse.
- Evaluate the composition of a trigonometric function and the inverse of another trigonometric function.

PREREQUISITE VOCABULARY TERMS

composition (of functions)
domain
Horizontal Line Test
inverse function
one-to-one function
range
trigonometric functions

Review of Inverse Functions

REMEMBER

If any horizontal line would intersect the graph of a function f at most once, then the inverse function of f exists.

Recall from Section 1.8 that if a function f passes the Horizontal Line Test, then f is a one-to-one function and f has an inverse function, denoted f^{-1} or $f^{-1}(x)$, with the following properties.

1. For all x in the domain of f and f^{-1}: $f^{-1}(f(x)) = x = f(f^{-1}(x))$.
2. The graphs of f and f^{-1} are reflections of each other over the line $y = x$.
3. The domain of f is the range of f^{-1}, and the domain of f^{-1} is the range of f.

2.7.1 An Introduction to Inverse Trigonometric Functions

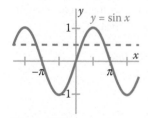

The Inverse Sine Function

In Figure 2.7a, we see that the graph of $y = \sin x$ does not pass the Horizontal Line Test, and so its inverse function does not exist. However, when the domain of $y = \sin x$ is restricted to the interval $\left[-\frac{\pi}{2}, \frac{\pi}{2}\right]$ (Figure 2.7b), the graph of $y = \sin x$ does pass the Horizontal Line Test. On this restricted domain (among others), its inverse function does exist. Note that the range of $y = \sin x$ is still $[-1, 1]$ within this interval.

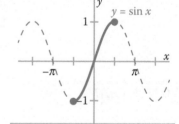

$y = \sin x$ has an inverse function on the interval $-\frac{\pi}{2} \leq x \leq \frac{\pi}{2}$.

Figure 2.7b

Figure 2.7a

Therefore, $y = \sin x$ with domain $-\frac{\pi}{2} \leq x \leq \frac{\pi}{2}$ is a one-to-one function which has an inverse function. Though there are other intervals of x-values where $y = \sin x$ is a one-to-one function, such as $\frac{\pi}{2} \leq x \leq \frac{3\pi}{2}$, we will use $-\frac{\pi}{2} \leq x \leq \frac{\pi}{2}$ to define the **inverse sine function**.

TIP

Think of $sin^{-1} x$ as "the angle (or real number) in the interval $[-\pi/2, \pi/2]$ whose sine is x."

DEFINITION

The **inverse sine function**, denoted $y = \sin^{-1} x$ or $y = \arcsin x$, is the inverse function of $y = \sin x$ with restricted domain $\left[-\frac{\pi}{2}, \frac{\pi}{2}\right]$.

$$y = \sin^{-1} x \iff \sin y = x \text{ where } -1 \leq x \leq 1 \text{ and } -\frac{\pi}{2} \leq y \leq \frac{\pi}{2}$$

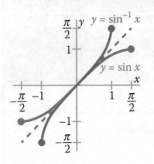

Figure 2.7c

Since $y = \sin x$ where $-\frac{\pi}{2} \le x \le \frac{\pi}{2}$ and $y = \sin^{-1} x$ are inverse functions, their graphs must be reflections over the line $y = x$, as shown in Figure 2.7c.

The Inverse Cosine Function

Like the graph of $y = \sin x$, the graph of $y = \cos x$ does not pass the Horizontal Line Test when the function is graphed over its entire domain (all real numbers), so its inverse function does not exist. However, if the domain of $y = \cos x$ is restricted to an interval where the function is either only increasing or only decreasing, such as $[0, \pi]$, then the graph does pass the Horizontal Line Test (Figure 2.7d), and then its inverse function does exist.

So, $y = \cos x$ with domain $0 \le x \le \pi$ is a one-to-one function which has an inverse function.

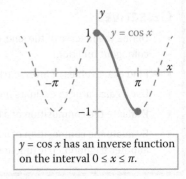

$y = \cos x$ has an inverse function on the interval $0 \le x \le \pi$.

Figure 2.7d

NOTICE THAT

The range of $y = \cos x$ does not change when its domain is restricted to $[0, \pi]$.

TIP

Think of $\cos^{-1} x$ as "the angle (or real number) in the interval $[0, \pi]$ whose cosine is x."

DEFINITION

The **inverse cosine function**, denoted $y = \cos^{-1} x$ or $y = \arccos x$, is the inverse function of $y = \cos x$ with restricted domain $[0, \pi]$.

$$y = \cos^{-1} x \iff \cos y = x \text{ where } -1 \le x \le 1 \text{ and } 0 \le y \le \pi$$

The Inverse Tangent Function

The graph $y = \tan x$ passes the Horizontal Line Test when the domain is restricted to $\left(-\frac{\pi}{2}, \frac{\pi}{2}\right)$, as shown in Figure 2.7e, and then its inverse function exists.

Note that within this restricted domain, the range of $y = \tan x$ is still $(-\infty, \infty)$.

So, $y = \tan x$ with domain $-\frac{\pi}{2} < x < \frac{\pi}{2}$ is a one-to-one function which has an inverse function.

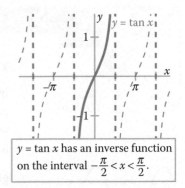

$y = \tan x$ has an inverse function on the interval $-\frac{\pi}{2} < x < \frac{\pi}{2}$.

Figure 2.7e

NOTICE THAT

The graph of $y = \tan x$ has vertical asymptotes at $x = -\pi/2$ and $x = \pi/2$, so those values are not in the restricted domain.

TIP

Think of $\tan^{-1} x$ as "the angle (or real number) in the interval $(-\pi/2, \pi/2)$ whose tangent is x."

DEFINITION

The **inverse tangent function**, denoted $y = \tan^{-1} x$ or $y = \arctan x$, is the inverse function of $y = \tan x$ with restricted domain $\left(-\frac{\pi}{2}, \frac{\pi}{2}\right)$.

$$y = \tan^{-1} x \iff \tan y = x \text{ where } -\infty < x < \infty \text{ and } -\frac{\pi}{2} < y < \frac{\pi}{2}$$

The Graphs of the Basic Inverse Trigonometric Functions

Recall that the domain of a function is the range of its inverse function, and the range of a function is the domain of its inverse function. So, the restricted domains of $y = \sin x$, $y = \cos x$, and $y = \tan x$ are the ranges of $y = \sin^{-1} x$, $y = \cos^{-1} x$, and $y = \tan^{-1} x$, respectively. Furthermore, the ranges $y = \sin x$, $y = \cos x$, and $y = \tan x$ are the domains of $y = \sin^{-1} x$, $y = \cos^{-1} x$, and $y = \tan^{-1} x$, respectively.

The following table shows the graphs of $y = \sin^{-1} x$, $y = \cos^{-1} x$, and $y = \tan^{-1} x$, along with the domain and range of each.

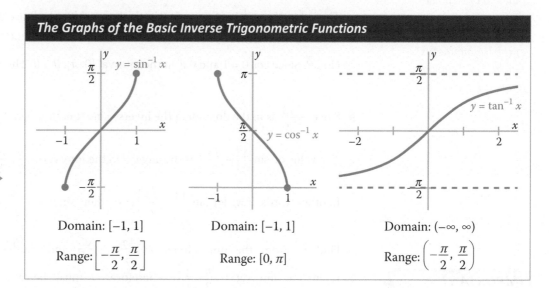

The Graphs of the Basic Inverse Trigonometric Functions

Domain: $[-1, 1]$
Range: $\left[-\dfrac{\pi}{2}, \dfrac{\pi}{2}\right]$

Domain: $[-1, 1]$
Range: $[0, \pi]$

Domain: $(-\infty, \infty)$
Range: $\left(-\dfrac{\pi}{2}, \dfrac{\pi}{2}\right)$

NOTICE THAT

The graph of $y = \tan x$ has vertical asymptotes at $x = \pm\pi/2$, so the graph of $y = \tan^{-1} x$ has horizontal asymptotes at $y = \pm\pi/2$.

CAUTION

Inverse function notation can easily be confused with exponential notation.

Recall that x^{-1} means the reciprocal of x (i.e., $x^{-1} = \dfrac{1}{x}$). Similarly,

- $\sin x^{-1}$ means the sine of the reciprocal of x (i.e., $\sin x^{-1} = \sin \dfrac{1}{x}$), and

- $(\sin x)^{-1}$ means the reciprocal of the sin of x (i.e., $(\sin x)^{-1} = \dfrac{1}{\sin x} = \csc x$).

However, $\sin^{-1} x$ means the inverse sine function of x (i.e., $\sin^{-1} x = \arcsin x$).

2.7.2 Evaluating Inverse Sine, Cosine, and Tangent Functions

When evaluating an inverse trigonometric function, that inverse function's domain and range must be considered. Recall that the domain of $y = \tan^{-1} x$ is all real numbers x, but the domains of $y = \sin^{-1} x$ and $y = \cos^{-1} x$ are limited to only those x-values in the interval $[-1, 1]$. Therefore, while the value of $\tan^{-1} x$ exists for any real number x, the values of $\sin^{-1} x$ and $\cos^{-1} x$ do not exist when $|x| > 1$.

REMEMBER

$|x| > 1 \implies x < -1 \text{ or } x > 1$
$|x| \leq 1 \implies -1 \leq x \leq 1$

Since an inverse function is a one-to-one function, each value in its domain corresponds to exactly one value in its range. For example, if $|x| \leq 1$ (which indicates that the value of $\cos^{-1} x$ exists), then $\cos^{-1} x$ is equal to exactly one value, and that value is in the interval $[0, \pi]$. In other words, when the value of $\cos^{-1} x$ exists for some given x-value, $\cos^{-1} x$ is equal to exactly one angle which is located either in quadrant I, quadrant II, on the positive y-axis, or on the x-axis.

EXAMPLE 1	Finding the Exact Value of an Inverse Sine, Inverse Cosine, or Inverse Tangent Function

Find the exact value of each inverse trigonometric function, if possible.

A. $\cos^{-1} 1$ **B.** $\sin^{-1}\left(-\dfrac{\sqrt{3}}{2}\right)$ **C.** $\tan^{-1}\left(-\sqrt{3}\right)$

SOLUTION

A. Since 1 is in the domain of the inverse cosine function, $\cos^{-1} 1$ exists.

The value of $\cos^{-1} 1$ is the angle θ in the interval $[0, \pi]$, whose cosine is 1.
In other words, if we let $\cos^{-1} 1 = \theta$, then $\cos \theta = 1$ when $0 \le \theta \le \pi$.

Find θ. Since $\cos 0 = 1$ and 0 is in the interval $[0, \pi]$, $\theta = 0$. Therefore $\cos^{-1} 1 = 0$.

B. Since $-\dfrac{\sqrt{3}}{2}$ is in the domain of the inverse sine function, $\sin^{-1}\left(-\dfrac{\sqrt{3}}{2}\right)$ exists.

The value of $\sin^{-1}\left(-\dfrac{\sqrt{3}}{2}\right)$ is the angle θ in the interval $\left[-\dfrac{\pi}{2}, \dfrac{\pi}{2}\right]$, whose sine is $-\dfrac{\sqrt{3}}{2}$.

In other words, if we let $\sin^{-1}\left(-\dfrac{\sqrt{3}}{2}\right) = \theta$, then $\sin \theta = -\dfrac{\sqrt{3}}{2}$ where $-\dfrac{\pi}{2} \le \theta \le \dfrac{\pi}{2}$.

Find θ. From the unit circle, $\sin\dfrac{4\pi}{3} = -\dfrac{\sqrt{3}}{2}$ and $\sin\dfrac{5\pi}{3} = -\dfrac{\sqrt{3}}{2}$, but neither angle

is in the interval $\left[-\dfrac{\pi}{2}, \dfrac{\pi}{2}\right]$. Therefore, θ must be coterminal with one of these angles. Specifically, since the interval includes quadrant IV, but not quadrant III, θ must be coterminal with $5\pi/3$, which is in quadrant IV. The angle in quadrant IV that is coterminal with $5\pi/3$ is $-\pi/3$. Thus, $\theta = -\pi/3$.

Therefore, $\sin^{-1}\left(-\dfrac{\sqrt{3}}{2}\right) = -\dfrac{\pi}{3}$.

C. Since $-\sqrt{3}$ is in the domain of the inverse tangent function, $\tan^{-1}\left(-\sqrt{3}\right)$ exists.

The value of $\tan^{-1}\left(-\sqrt{3}\right)$ is the angle θ in the interval $\left(-\dfrac{\pi}{2}, \dfrac{\pi}{2}\right)$, whose tangent is $-\sqrt{3}$.

In other words, if we let $\tan^{-1}\left(-\sqrt{3}\right) = \theta$, then $\tan \theta = -\sqrt{3}$ where $-\dfrac{\pi}{2} < \theta < \dfrac{\pi}{2}$.

Find θ. From the unit circle, $\tan\dfrac{2\pi}{3} = -\sqrt{3}$ and $\tan\dfrac{5\pi}{3} = -\sqrt{3}$, but neither angle is in the

interval $\left(-\dfrac{\pi}{2}, \dfrac{\pi}{2}\right)$. Therefore, θ must be coterminal with one of these angles. Specifically, since the interval includes quadrant IV, but not quadrant II, θ must be coterminal with $5\pi/3$, which is in quadrant IV. The angle in quadrant IV coterminal with $5\pi/3$ is $-\pi/3$. Thus, $\theta = -\pi/3$.

Therefore, $\tan^{-1}\left(-\sqrt{3}\right) = -\dfrac{\pi}{3}$.

| EXAMPLE 2 | Using a Calculator to Evaluate Inverse Sine, Cosine, and Tangent Functions |

Use a calculator to evaluate $\sin^{-1} x$, $\cos^{-1} x$, and $\tan^{-1} x$ for each given x-value, if possible. Round to the nearest thousandth.

A. 4

B. $-\dfrac{\sqrt{3}}{2}$

SOLUTION

The expressions can be entered directly (e.g., "$\tan^{-1}$ 4") followed by $\boxed{\textsf{ENTER}}$ when using a graphing calculator. However, when using a scientific calculator, first enter the value, and then press the button for the inverse trigonometric function. Be sure in either case to have the calculator set to radian mode.

A. Since 4 is not in the domain of the inverse sine function or the inverse cosine function, $\sin^{-1} 4$ and $\cos^{-1} 4$ do not exist. Entering either value into a calculator results in an error.

IMPORTANT

Unless otherwise stated, calculate the angle measure given by an inverse trigonometric function in radians.

To calculate $\tan^{-1} 4$ with a scientific calculator, press $\boxed{\textsf{4}}$, then press $\boxed{\textsf{TAN}^{-1}}$.

If using a graphing calculator, press $\boxed{\textsf{TAN}^{-1}}$, 4, then $\boxed{\textsf{ENTER}}$.

$$\tan^{-1} 4 \approx 1.326$$

B. Since $-1 \le -\dfrac{\sqrt{3}}{2} \le 1$, all three inverse trigonometric functions of $-\dfrac{\sqrt{3}}{2}$ exist.

For a scientific calculator, always enter $-\dfrac{\sqrt{3}}{2}$ first.

$\boxed{\textsf{3}}$, $\boxed{\sqrt{}}$, $\boxed{\textsf{—}}$, $\boxed{\textsf{/}}$, $\boxed{\textsf{2}}$, $\boxed{\textsf{ENTER}}$.

Then press the button for the appropriate inverse trigonometric function.

$$\sin^{-1}\left(-\frac{\sqrt{3}}{2}\right) \approx -1.047 \qquad \cos^{-1}\left(-\frac{\sqrt{3}}{2}\right) \approx 2.618 \qquad \tan^{-1}\left(-\frac{\sqrt{3}}{2}\right) \approx -0.714$$

TIP

While the value of any inverse trigonometric function that exists can be approximated using a calculator, the ability to find an exact value (i.e., without using a calculator) is important because recognizing exact values will simplify calculations involving more complicated inverse trigonometric functions.

The exact value of $\sin^{-1}\left(-\dfrac{\sqrt{3}}{2}\right)$ is $-\pi/3$ and its approximate value is -1.047 (as shown in **Example 1B** and **Example 2B**, respectively). The approximate value can be confirmed by finding the decimal approximation of $-\pi/3$.

$$\sin^{-1}\left(-\frac{\sqrt{3}}{2}\right) = -\frac{\pi}{3} \approx -1.047 \checkmark \qquad \textit{Divide $-\pi$ by 3 and round to the nearest thousandth.}$$

2.7.3 Evaluating a Composition Involving Inverse Trigonometric Functions

Recall from Section 1.7 that the composition of a function f with a function g, $f(g(x))$, is the result of evaluating f at g. In this case, the domain of $f(g(x))$ is the set of all x in the domain of g such that $g(x)$ is in the domain of f.

Compositions can involve trigonometric functions. For example, the composition $\cos(\tan \pi)$ is the result of evaluating the cosine function for the value of $\tan \pi$. Since $\tan \pi = 0$, $\cos(\tan \pi) = \cos 0 = 1$.

2.7.4 Inverse Cosecant, Secant, and Cotangent Functions

Like sine, cosine, and tangent, the cosecant, secant, and cotangent functions also have inverse functions when their domains are restricted.

The restricted domain of $y = \csc x$ is similar to that of $y = \sin x$ (i.e., $[-\pi/2, \pi/2]$), except 0 is excluded because $\csc 0$ is undefined. The restricted domain of $y = \csc x$ (and thus the range of $y = \csc^{-1} x$) is the union of the intervals $\left[-\dfrac{\pi}{2}, 0\right)$ and $\left(0, \dfrac{\pi}{2}\right]$.

The restricted domain of $y = \sec x$ is similar to that of $y = \cos x$ (i.e., $[0, \pi]$), except $\pi/2$ is excluded because $\sec \pi/2$ is undefined. The restricted domain of $y = \sec x$ (and thus the range of $y = \sec^{-1} x$) is the union of the intervals $\left[0, \dfrac{\pi}{2}\right)$ and $\left(\dfrac{\pi}{2}, \pi\right]$.

To define the inverse cotangent function, we restrict the domain of $y = \cot x$ to $(0, \pi)$. Thus, the range of $y = \cot^{-1} x$ is the interval $(0, \pi)$.

The graphs of the inverse cosecant, inverse secant, and inverse cotangent functions are reflections over the line $y = x$ of the graphs of the basic cosecant, secant, and cotangent functions, each over its respective restricted domain.

Inverse Cosecant, Secant, and Cotangent Functions

$y = \csc^{-1} x$ means that $\csc y = x$ | $y = \sec^{-1} x$ means that $\sec y = x$ | $y = \cot^{-1} x$ means that $\cot y = x$

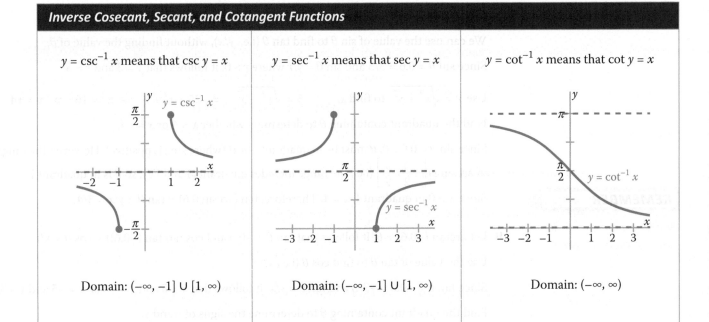

Domain: $(-\infty, -1] \cup [1, \infty)$ Domain: $(-\infty, -1] \cup [1, \infty)$ Domain: $(-\infty, \infty)$

Range: $\left[-\dfrac{\pi}{2}, 0\right) \cup \left(0, \dfrac{\pi}{2}\right]$ Range: $\left[0, \dfrac{\pi}{2}\right) \cup \left(\dfrac{\pi}{2}, \pi\right]$ Range: $(0, \pi)$

| EXAMPLE 5 | Finding the Exact Value of an Inverse Cosecant, Inverse Secant, or Inverse Cotangent Function |

Find the exact value of each inverse trigonometric function, if possible.

A. $\csc^{-1}(-1)$ **B.** $\sec^{-1}(-2)$ **C.** $\operatorname{arccot}\left(-\dfrac{1}{\sqrt{3}}\right)$

SOLUTION

A. The value of $\csc^{-1}(-1)$ is the angle θ in the interval $\left[-\dfrac{\pi}{2}, 0\right) \cup \left(0, \dfrac{\pi}{2}\right]$, whose cosecant is -1.

In other words, if we let $\csc^{-1}(-1) = \theta$, then $\csc\theta = -1$ where $-\dfrac{\pi}{2} \leq \theta < 0$ or $0 < \theta \leq \dfrac{\pi}{2}$.

Find θ. From the unit circle, we see that $\csc\dfrac{3\pi}{2} = -1$. However, since $\dfrac{3\pi}{2}$ is not in the interval $\left[-\dfrac{\pi}{2}, 0\right) \cup \left(0, \dfrac{\pi}{2}\right]$, θ must be an angle in this interval that is coterminal with $\dfrac{3\pi}{2}$. Thus, $\theta = -\dfrac{\pi}{2}$, and therefore $\csc^{-1}(-1) = -\dfrac{\pi}{2}$.

B. The value of $\sec^{-1}(-2)$ is the angle θ in the interval $\left[0, \dfrac{\pi}{2}\right) \cup \left(\dfrac{\pi}{2}, \pi\right]$, whose secant is -2.

In other words, if we let $\sec^{-1}(-2) = \theta$, then $\sec\theta = -2$ where $0 \leq \theta < \dfrac{\pi}{2}$ or $\dfrac{\pi}{2} < \theta \leq \pi$.

Find θ. From the unit circle, $\sec\dfrac{2\pi}{3} = -2$. Since $\dfrac{2\pi}{3}$ is in the interval $\left[0, \dfrac{\pi}{2}\right) \cup \left(\dfrac{\pi}{2}, \pi\right]$, $\theta = \dfrac{2\pi}{3}$. Therefore, $\sec^{-1}(-2) = \dfrac{2\pi}{3}$.

C. The value of $\operatorname{arccot}\left(-\dfrac{1}{\sqrt{3}}\right)$ is the angle in the interval $(0, \pi)$, whose cotangent is $-\dfrac{1}{\sqrt{3}}$.

From the unit circle, $\cot\dfrac{2\pi}{3} = -\dfrac{1}{\sqrt{3}}$. Since $0 < 2\pi/3 < \pi$, $\operatorname{arccot}\left(-\dfrac{1}{\sqrt{3}}\right) = \dfrac{2\pi}{3}$.

SECTION 2.7 EXERCISES

Warm Up

Determine whether each function has an inverse function. If so, write the equation of the inverse function.

1. $f(x) = 3x - 1$

2. $y = x^2$

3. $h(x) = \sqrt{2x+1}$

Just the Facts

Fill in the blanks.

4. A function f has an inverse function if any possible _____ line drawn through the graph touches the graph at most _____.

5. The graphs of a function and its inverse are _____ across the line _____.

6. The domains of the _____ trigonometric functions are restricted in order for the graphs to pass the _____ and thus have _____ that are functions.

7. The domain of $y = \sin x$ is restricted to _____ so it is a(n) _____ function with an inverse function. The range of the inverse sine function is _____ and its _____ is $[-1, 1]$.

8. The two ways to denote the inverse cosine function are $y = \cos^{-1} x$ and _____.

9. In order to define the inverse cosine function, the domain of the cosine function is restricted to _____.

10. The secant and _____ functions have undefined values at $\pi/2$ and _____. Therefore, the ranges of the inverse secant and inverse _____ functions are _____.

Essential Skills

In Exercises 1–8, find the exact value of $\sin^{-1} x$, $\cos^{-1} x$, and $\tan^{-1} x$ for each given x-value without using a calculator, if possible.

1. $\dfrac{\sqrt{2}}{2}$

2. $-\dfrac{\sqrt{2}}{2}$

3. 0

4. $-\dfrac{\sqrt{3}}{2}$

5. -1

6. $\dfrac{\sqrt{3}}{3}$

7. $\dfrac{\sqrt{3}}{2}$

8. $\sqrt{3}$

In Exercises 9–20, use a calculator to evaluate each inverse trigonometric function, if possible. Round to the nearest thousandth.

9. $\tan^{-1} 4.72$

10. $\sin^{-1}(-0.715)$

11. $\sin^{-1} 0.176$

12. $\cos^{-1}(-0.262)$

13. $\cos^{-1} 1.4411$

14. $\tan^{-1}(-10.619)$

15. $\cos^{-1} \dfrac{\sqrt{11}}{5}$

16. $\tan^{-1} 24.1$

17. $\sin^{-1} \dfrac{6\sqrt{3}}{17}$

18. $\cos^{-1}(-0.9)$

19. $\sin^{-1}(-0.068)$

20. $\tan^{-1}(-2.759)$

In Exercises 21–46, find the exact value of each composition, if possible.

21. $\sin^{-1}\left(\sin \dfrac{7\pi}{4}\right)$

22. $\sin^{-1}\left(\sin \dfrac{11\pi}{6}\right)$

23. $\sin^{-1}\left(\sin\left(-\dfrac{2\pi}{3}\right)\right)$

24. $\arcsin(\sin \pi)$

25. $\cos^{-1}\left(\cos \dfrac{5\pi}{6}\right)$

26. $\cos^{-1}\left(\cos \dfrac{5\pi}{4}\right)$

27. $\cos^{-1}\left(\cos\left(-\dfrac{\pi}{7}\right)\right)$

28. $\cos^{-1}\left(\cos\left(-\dfrac{7\pi}{3}\right)\right)$

29. $\tan^{-1}\left(\tan \dfrac{7\pi}{6}\right)$

30. $\tan^{-1}\left(\tan \dfrac{2\pi}{3}\right)$

31. $\tan^{-1}\left(\tan\left(-\dfrac{5\pi}{4}\right)\right)$

32. $\arctan(\tan \pi)$

33. $\tan\left(\cos^{-1} \dfrac{2}{5}\right)$

34. $\sin\left(\arctan \dfrac{2}{7}\right)$

35. $\cos\left(\sin^{-1} \dfrac{\sqrt{3}}{5}\right)$

36. $\cos\left(\tan^{-1} \dfrac{14}{5}\right)$

37. $\tan\left(\arcsin \dfrac{\sqrt{3}}{5}\right)$

38. $\sin\left(\cos^{-1} \dfrac{5}{7}\right)$

39. $\sin\left(\tan^{-1}\left(-\dfrac{15}{8}\right)\right)$

40. $\cos\left(\arcsin\left(-\dfrac{3}{8}\right)\right)$

41. $\sin\left(\arccos\left(-\dfrac{4}{5}\right)\right)$

42. $\tan\left(\cos^{-1}\left(-\dfrac{7}{9}\right)\right)$

43. $\cos\left(\tan^{-1}\left(-\dfrac{2}{5}\right)\right)$

44. $\tan\left(\sin^{-1}\left(-\dfrac{\sqrt{5}}{4}\right)\right)$

45. $\sin(\arctan(-5))$

46. $\sin\left(\cos^{-1}\left(-\dfrac{1}{3}\right)\right)$

In Exercises 47–50, find the exact value of $\csc^{-1}x$, $\sec^{-1}x$, and $\cot^{-1}x$ for each given x-value, if possible.

47. $\dfrac{2}{\sqrt{3}}$

48. $-\dfrac{2}{\sqrt{3}}$

49. 2

50. 1

In Exercises 51–56, find the exact value of each composition, if possible.

51. $\csc\left(\sec^{-1}\dfrac{5}{2}\right)$

52. $\cot\left(\sec^{-1}\left(-\dfrac{15}{2}\right)\right)$

53. $\sec\left(\cot^{-1}\left(-\dfrac{4}{7}\right)\right)$

54. $\sec\left(\csc^{-1}\dfrac{11}{5}\right)$

55. $\csc\left(\cot^{-1}\dfrac{12}{5}\right)$

56. $\cot\left(\csc^{-1}\left(-\dfrac{12}{11}\right)\right)$

Extensions

57. What is the domain of the function $f(t) = 3\sin^{-1}(2t)$?

58. Use a calculator to compute the smallest angle measure in a right triangle with side lengths 3, 4, and 5 in degrees to the nearest hundredth.

In Exercises 59–60, use the following information. A fighter jet cruises at an altitude of 10.32 miles toward a ship's landing deck. Consider θ and x as shown below.

59. Write θ as a function of x.

60. Find θ to the nearest tenth of a degree when $x = 4$ miles and when $x = 400$ feet.

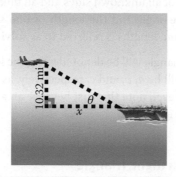

61. True or False? $\dfrac{5\pi}{4} = \arcsin\left(-\dfrac{\sqrt{2}}{2}\right)$

In Exercises 62–66, evaluate.

62. $\sin\left(\cos^{-1}\dfrac{\sqrt{3}}{2} - \sin^{-1}\left(-\dfrac{1}{2}\right)\right)$

63. $\cos(\arctan(-1) + \arccos(-1) + \arcsin 0)$

64. $\cot\left(\csc^{-1}\left(-2\right) - \sec^{-1}\left(-\sqrt{2}\right) + \arctan\left(-1\right)\right)$

65. $\tan^{-1}\left(\dfrac{\cos^{-1}\left(-\dfrac{1}{2}\right) + \sin^{-1}(-1)}{\cot^{-1}\sqrt{3}}\right)$

66. $\cot\left(\csc^{-1}\left(-\dfrac{7}{5}\right)\right) + \sec\left(\sin^{-1}\dfrac{6}{11}\right)$

2.8 APPLICATIONS OF TRIGONOMETRIC FUNCTIONS

OBJECTIVES

- Use the Triangle Sum Theorem to find the measure of an unknown angle in a right triangle.
- Use trigonometric functions to find the lengths of two unknown sides in a right triangle.
- Use trigonometric functions to find bearings and distance.
- Use trigonometric functions to find the frequency of harmonic motion.
- Introduction to damped harmonic motion.

PREREQUISITE VOCABULARY TERMS

acute angle

right angle

right triangle

trigonometric functions

2.8.1 Finding Unknown Sides and Angles in a Right Triangle

By the **Triangle Sum Theorem**, the sum of the measures of the three angles in a triangle must equal 180°. Therefore, if two angle measures are known, the measure of the third angle can be found by subtracting the sum of the two known angles' measure from 180°. It follows that if the measure of one acute angle in a right triangle is known, then the measure of the third angle can be found by subtracting the acute angle's measure from 90°.

These facts regarding the angles of a right triangle will be used, along with the trigonometric functions, to find the measures of all unknown sides and all unknown angles in a right triangle when the measure of one acute angle and the length of one side are given. This process of finding all unknown measures and lengths is referred to as **solving a triangle**.

In this section, the angles of a triangle will be denoted using the letters A, B, and C, and then the sides opposite of these angles will be a, b, and c, respectively, as shown in Figure 2.8a, where C represents the right angle. However, note that just because an angle is labeled C, this does not necessarily mean the angle is a right angle.

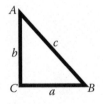

Figure 2.8a

EXAMPLE 1   Solving a Right Triangle

Suppose triangle ABC is a right triangle such that $B = 42°$, and $a = 12.5$. Solve the triangle for all unknown sides and angles. Round to the nearest tenth, as needed.

SOLUTION

Draw the right triangle where

- C is the right angle,
- B (one of the acute angles) is 42°, and
- a (the side opposite of A) is 12.5.

Since C is a right angle, the sum of angles A and B must be 90°, so $A = 90° - 42° = 48°$.

$$\tan 42° = \frac{b}{12.5} \implies b = 12.5(\tan 42°) \approx 11.3 \qquad \sin 48° = \frac{12.5}{c} \implies c = \frac{12.5}{\sin 48°} \approx 16.8$$

ALTERNATIVE METHOD

There are many alternative procedures for solving triangle *ABC* from **Example 1**.

For example, *c* can be found using $\cos\theta = \dfrac{\text{adj}}{\text{hyp}}$ where $\theta = B$.

$$\cos 42° = \frac{12.5}{c} \quad \Rightarrow \quad c = \frac{12.5}{\cos 42°} \approx 16.8$$

And instead of using another trigonometric function to find the third unknown side length (in this case *c*), the Pythagorean Theorem can be used.

$$c = \sqrt{12.5^2 + 11.3^2} = \sqrt{283.94} = 16.85\ldots \approx 16.9$$

However, the value of *c* obtained using a trigonometric function involving the given side length (12.5) is more precise than the value of *c* obtained using the Pythagorean Theorem because the Pythagorean Theorem used an approximate value for *b*, 11.3.

A more precise value of *c* can be obtained using the Pythagorean Theorem by using the exact value of *b*, 12.5(tan 42°), instead of the approximate value 11.3.

$$c = \sqrt{12.5^2 + (12.5(\tan 42°))^2} = 16.82\ldots \approx 16.8$$

2.8.2 Trigonometry and Bearings

A **bearing** measures the acute angle that a direct path (straight line) makes with a fixed, vertical north-south line. The graph of a bearing is the acute angle formed by rotating an initial side (where the bearing begins) clockwise or counterclockwise from either the north or south end of the north-south line, depending on the measure and direction of the bearing.

The notation for a bearing begins with either the letters N or S (representing north and south), followed by a degree value, and then by the letters E or W (representing east and west). N or S indicates whether the rotation begins from the north or south end of the north-south line, the degree value gives the amount of rotation, and E or W indicates whether the rotation is toward the east or west end of the east-west line.

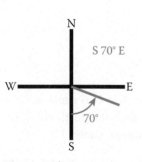

Figure 2.8b

For example, Figure 2.8b shows the graph of the bearing S 70° E. Notice that the terminal side is rotated counterclockwise from the south end of the north-south line a total of 70° toward the east end of the east-west line.

In **Example 2**, a bearing is used to find a distance between two points.

EXAMPLE 2	Using a Bearing to Find a Distance

A submarine departed from a naval base, traveled due west at 10 nautical miles per hour for 2 hours, and then traveled S 35° W at 20 nautical miles per hour for 1.5 hours. Find the distance (to the nearest tenth of a nautical mile) between the submarine and the base and find the submarine's bearing to the base at the end of the trip.

SOLUTION

Since the submarine traveled due west for 2 hours at 10 nautical miles per hour, it traveled 20 NM due west.

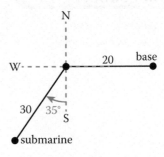

It then traveled along the S 35° W bearing for 1.5 hours at 20 nautical miles per hour, that is, a distance of 30 NM.

Draw a picture representing the submarine's path.

Now draw a right triangle where the distance between the submarine and the naval base is the hypotenuse c, as shown in the picture.

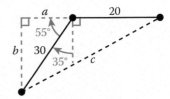

Let $a + 20$ and b represent the right triangle's legs.

Consider the smaller right triangle with hypotenuse 30 and legs a and b. Since angle B (the angle opposite of side b) is complementary with the 35° angle, it measures 90° − 35° = 55°.

Use cos 55° to find a and sin 55° to find b.

$$\cos 55° = a/30 \implies a = 30(\cos 55°) \qquad \sin 55° = b/30 \implies b = 30(\sin 55°)$$

So, the legs of the larger right triangle (with hypotenuse c) are 30(sin 55°) and 30(cos 55°) + 20 .

> **TIP**
>
> *The approximate values of a and b (17.2 and 24.6) can be used to find θ (instead of the exact values as seen here), but then the value of θ will not be as precise.*

Let θ be the angle opposite the naval base.

Since tan θ = opp/adj, $\tan\theta = \dfrac{30(\cos\ 55°) + 20}{30(\sin\ 55°)}$.

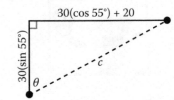

Use the inverse tangent function (and a calculator) to find θ.

$$\theta = \tan^{-1}\left(\frac{30(\cos\ 55°) + 20}{30(\sin\ 55°)}\right) \approx 56.6°$$

Now use a trigonometric function to find c.

$$\sin 56.6° = \frac{30(\cos\ 55°) + 20}{c} \implies c = \frac{30(\cos\ 55°) + 20}{\sin 56.6°} \approx 44.6 \text{ NM}$$

> **IMPORTANT**
>
> *A bearing measures an acute angle, so the bearing's degree measure must be less than 90°.*

Thus, the distance between the submarine and the base is approximately 44.6 nautical miles. The submarine's bearing with the naval base (the acute angle made with the north-south line and the line of sight between the submarine and the naval base) is approximately N 56.6° E.

ALTERNATIVE METHOD

As with **Example 1**, there are alternative ways to find the distance between the submarine and the naval base in **Example 2**. For example, the Pythagorean Theorem can be used to find c.

$$c = \sqrt{(30(\cos 55°) + 20)^2 + (30(\sin 55°))^2} \approx 44.6$$

2.8.3   Harmonic Motion

The motion of a point on an object that vibrates or rotates at a regular interval can often be modeled by a trigonometric function because the trigonometric functions are periodic, as is the motion of the point. For example, consider a point on an oscillating fan where the distance between the initial point, the **equilibrium point**, and the position at time t is d. At $t = 0$, $d = 0$. The distance then increases to some maximum displacement, decreases again back to 0, and then to some minimum displacement. Since d repeats at regular intervals of t, a function modeling this motion is therefore periodic. The total time needed for some point to complete a full cycle is the period, and the **frequency** is the number of cycles completed per unit of time.

Motion that can be modeled by a sine or cosine function of the form $d = a \sin \omega t$ or $d = a \cos \omega t$ is called **simple harmonic motion**.

Simple Harmonic Motion

If the distance d of a point from the origin at time t can be modeled by either

$$d = a \sin \omega t \qquad \text{or} \qquad d = a \cos \omega t$$

(where a and ω are real numbers with $\omega > 0$), then the motion of the point is called simple harmonic motion. In this case, the motion can be characterized by the following.

amplitude: $|a|$ period: $2\pi/\omega$ frequency: $\omega/2\pi$

IMPORTANT

If $d = 0$ at $t = 0$, then the simple harmonic motion can be modeled by $d = a \sin \omega t$.

If the initial motion is in the positive direction, then $a > 0$, but if the initial motion is in the negative direction, then $a < 0$.

EXAMPLE 3   **Modeling Simple Harmonic Motion**

A weight is attached to the bottom of a spring, and the top of the spring is attached to a surface such that the maximum distance d the weight can move up or down from its point of equilibrium (the point at which the spring is relaxed) is 8 inches, as shown in the picture. Suppose the weight begins from its equilibrium point at $t = 0$ seconds, moves to its maximum displacement above 0, to its minimum displacement below 0, and then back to equilibrium

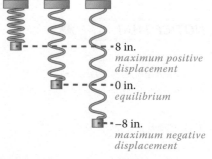

8 in.
maximum positive displacement

0 in.
equilibrium

−8 in.
maximum negative displacement

every 2 seconds (assume there is no air resistance, or friction). Model the weight's motion with a simple harmonic equation, find its frequency, and graph the model over at least two periods.

SOLUTION

Because the motion is harmonic and because $d = 0$ when $t = 0$ (i.e., the weight begins its motion at the point of equilibrium), use the sine equation $d = a \sin \omega t$. Since the weight completes 1 full cycle of its motion in 2 seconds, the period is 2 seconds.

Use the period to find ω. $2 = 2\pi/\omega \;\Rightarrow\; \omega = 2\pi/2 = \pi$

The displacement from the equilibrium point is 8, and the initial motion is up, so $a = 8$.

Using these values to write the equation gives $d = 8 \sin \pi t$.

The frequency is $\pi/2\pi$, that is, 1/2 cycle per second.

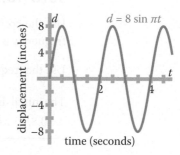

$d = 8 \sin \pi t$

2.8.4   Damped Harmonic Motion

The motion of the spring in **Example 3** continued regularly because the motion was not affected by gravity or friction. However, this is not a realistic situation as motion is typically affected by some sort of friction, and eventually slows until it stops. When the rate of harmonic motion decreases over time, the motion is called **damped harmonic motion**.

Damped Harmonic Motion

If the distance d of a point from the origin at time t can be modeled by either

$$d = ke^{-ct} \sin \omega t \quad \text{or} \quad d = ke^{-ct} \cos \omega t$$

(where k, ω, and c are real numbers with $\omega > 0$ and $c > 0$), then the motion of the point is called damped harmonic motion. In this case, the motion can be characterized by its:

initial amplitude: $|k|$ period: $2\pi/\omega$ damping constant: c

The simple and damped harmonic models are the same except for the coefficients of sine and cosine (a and ke^{-ct}). Recall that local minimums and local maximums of functions of the form $y = a \sin bx$ and $y = a \sin bx$ occur when its graph intersects the lines $y = -a$ and $y = a$ (i.e., the function's amplitude is $|a|$), as is the case for a simple harmonic model (Figure 2.8c). However, the relative minimums and maximums of a damped harmonic model occur when its graph intersects the curves $d = -ke^{-ct}$ and $d = ke^{-ct}$ (Figure 2.8d).

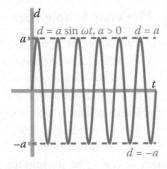

Figure 2.8c

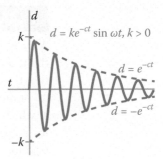

Figure 2.8d

EXAMPLE 4   Modeling Damped Harmonic Motion

Suppose a gust of wind causes a tree to sway (oscillate) back and forth with frequency 0.25 cycles per second. Assume that at the instant the wind stops, $t = 0$ seconds, the tree has reached its maximum displacement of 2 feet. Model the motion of the tree with a damped harmonic equation if the damping constant is 0.8.

SOLUTION

Use the cosine equation $d = ke^{-ct} \cos \omega t$ because in this equation $d = 2$ when $t = 0$. The tree's frequency is 0.25 (i.e., the tree completes one-quarter cycle of its motion every 1 second).

Use the frequency to find ω. $0.25 = \dfrac{\omega}{2\pi} \Rightarrow \omega = 2\pi(0.25) = 0.5\pi$

The initial displacement is 2, so $k = 2$. Using these values, along with the given damping constant $c = 0.8$, to write the equation gives $d = 2e^{-0.8t} \cos 0.5\pi t$.

SECTION 2.8 EXERCISES

Warm Up

In Exercises 1–3, translate the standard position angle into a bearing.

1. 150°

2. 40°

3. 290°

Just the Facts

Fill in the blanks.

4. When given the measures of two angles of a triangle, the third angle can be found by _____ the sum of the two angles from _____.

5. When the measure of an acute angle in a right triangle is known, the missing angle can be found by _____ the acute angle from _____.

6. When one angle and the hypotenuse of a triangle are known, either the _____ or _____ function can be used to find a missing side in a right triangle.

7. A bearing measures a(n) _____ angle. The first letter is always _____ or _____ to indicate whether the rotation begins from the _____ or _____ end of the north-south line.

8. The position where a spring is relaxed is called the _____ point.

9. The function $d = 6 \cos 9\pi t$ is an example of _____ harmonic motion. The frequency of the function is _____, and the period is _____.

10. Simple and damped harmonic motion models are the same except for the _____ of the sine and cosine models. With the simple harmonic model, the coefficient is _____. In the damped harmonic motion model, the coefficient is _____ because the motion is decreasing over time.

Essential Skills

In Exercises 1–6, use the given information for right triangle ABC to solve for all unknown sides and angles. Assume that C is the right angle. Round to the nearest tenth as needed.

1. $c = 12$, $B = 35°$

2. $b = 4$, $A = 20°$

3. $b = 7.2$, $A = 43°$

4. $a = 8$, $B = 16.2°$

5. $a = 24.3$, $B = 82°$

6. $c = 16.9$, $A = 54°$

In Exercises 7–10, use the following information.

A cellphone tower with height h feet must be secured with a guy-wire with length l feet such that θ is the angle of elevation of the wire as measured from the ground. Use the given information to find each indicated measure. Round to the nearest tenth as needed.

7. Find h if $l = 222.5$ feet and $\theta = 37°$.

8. Find l if $h = 150$ feet and $\theta = 22°$.

9. Find l if $h = 173$ feet and $\theta = 18°$.

10. Find h if $l = 89.2$ feet and $\theta = 46°$.

In Exercises 11–16, use the following information.

A firefighter is using a ladder to reach a person in a second-story window of a burning building. The window is h feet high, the ladder has length l feet, the firefighter is d feet away from the base of the building, and θ is the angle of elevation of the ladder. Use the given information to find each indicated measure. Round to the nearest tenth as needed.

11. Find h if $l = 46$ feet and $\theta = 15°$.

12. Find l if $d = 24$ feet and $\theta = 28°$.

13. Find d if $h = 28$ feet and $\theta = 32°$.

14. Find h if $d = 14$ feet and $\theta = 18°$.

15. Find l if $h = 50$ feet and $\theta = 36°$.

16. Find d if $l = 35$ feet and $\theta = 27°$.

In Exercises 17–22, use the following information.

A U.S. Coast Guard Response Boat leaves Charleston, South Carolina at time t heading due east. At time h, the boat changes course to bearing b. Find the boat's bearing and distance from Charleston, South Carolina (to the nearest hundredth of a unit) at the given time if it travels at an average of x knots (nautical miles per hour) for the entire trip.

17. at 6 p.m., if $t = 1$ p.m., $h = 4$ p.m., $b = $ N 24° W, $x = 35$ knots

18. at 8 p.m., if $t = 2$ p.m., $h = 5{:}30$ p.m., $b = $ N 16° E, $x = 42$ knots

19. at 9:30 a.m., if $t = 3{:}45$ a.m., $h = 6$ a.m., $b = $ S 18° E, $x = 28$ knots

20. at 11 a.m., if $t = 4$ a.m., $h = 8{:}30$ a.m., $b = $ S 11° W, $x = 24$ knots

21. at 7:45 p.m., if $t = 2{:}15$ p.m., $h = 3{:}30$ p.m., $b = $ N 32° E, $x = 20$ knots

22. at 10:30 a.m., if $t = 1{:}30$ a.m., $h = 7{:}30$ a.m., $b = $ S 26° E, $x = 38$ knots

In Exercises 23–28, find the frequency of each simple harmonic motion function.

23. $d = \dfrac{1}{3} \sin \dfrac{\pi}{4} t$

24. $d = 6 \cos 9\pi t$

25. $d = -2 \cos \dfrac{3\pi}{7} t$

26. $d = -\dfrac{4}{5} \sin \dfrac{6\pi}{11} t$

27. $d = 4 \sin \dfrac{8\pi}{17} t$

28. $d = 7 \cos \dfrac{4\pi}{5} t$

In Exercises 29–36, find a model for the displacement of a spring that exhibits simple harmonic motion that has displacement d_0 when $t = 0$, period p, and a maximum displacement m.

29. $d_0 = -12$ centimeters, $p = 16$ seconds, $m = 12$

30. $d_0 = 15$ inches, $p = 8$ seconds, $m = 15$

31. $d_0 = 0$, $p = 11$ seconds, $m = 23$

32. $d_0 = 0$, $p = 21$ seconds, $m = 8$

33. $d_0 = 0$, $p = 6$ seconds, $m = 22$

34. $d_0 = 37$ centimeters, $p = 25$ seconds, $m = 37$

35. $d_0 = -26$ centimeters, $p = 42$ seconds, $m = 26$

36. $d_0 = 0$, $p = 15$ seconds, $m = 43$

In Exercises 37–40, use the following information.

A string on a guitar is pulled a distance k above its rest position, then released and allowed to vibrate. Suppose that the note produced has a frequency of x cycles per second with a damping constant c. Find an equation that describes the motion of the point at which the string was pulled.

37. $k = 0.3$ millimeters, $c = 2$, $x = 261.63$

38. $k = 0.35$ millimeters, $c = 1.2$, $x = 293.665$

39. $k = 0.38$ millimeters, $c = 2$, $x = 293.665$

40. $k = 0.28$ millimeters, $c = 1.8$, $x = 329.628$

Extensions

41. A person sitting in a courtyard 50 feet from a building can see a flowerpot in a window as he looks up at an angle of $30° \, 24' \, 10''$. Looking directly above the flowerpot from the same position, he sees a dog in another window at an angle of $65° \, 55' \, 8''$. Find the distance between the dog and the flowerpot to the nearest hundredth of a foot.

42. A pilot spots a lake at an angle of depression from her line of sight of $20° \, 14' \, 53''$ while flying at an altitude of 15,000 feet. After two minutes, the angle of depression is $46° \, 5' \, 18''$. Find the horizontal distance the plane has traveled.

In Exercises 43–48, use the following information.

A point on the tip of a tuning fork vibrates in simple harmonic motion. Because the movement is short in duration, it is described by the equation $D = a \sin \omega t$. The velocity and acceleration are described by $V = \omega a \cos \omega t$ and $A = -\omega^2 a \sin \omega t$, respectively. Round each answer to the nearest tenth unless instructed otherwise.

43. Find the time t to the nearest millionth of a second at which the end of the prong has a displacement of 0.217 millimeters, frequency 1200 hertz (cycles per second), and amplitude 0.4944 millimeters.

44. Find the velocity at time t in Exercise 43.

45. Find the acceleration at time t in Exercise 43.

46. Find the displacement of the tuning fork that has a frequency of 800 hertz and an amplitude of 0.14 millimeters at 0.003 seconds. Round to the nearest thousandth of a millimeter.

47. Find the velocity at time t in Exercise 46.

48. Find the acceleration at time t in Exercise 46.

49. Find four possible models that relate the displacement d of an object that has 1.5 oscillations per second and a maximum displacement of 15 inches.

50. At the local carnival, a water gun is aimed at the mouth of a plastic clown in order to inflate a balloon until it bursts. Assuming the water is projected with enough pressure to reach the clown's mouth along a linear path, at what range of values for the angle of elevation can the water gun be positioned to ensure that the water goes through the clown's mouth? The clown's mouth is a circle of radius 1.75 inches, the distance between the water gun and the clown is 5 feet, and the clown's mouth is 7 inches higher than the water gun.

51. Solve for c in $d = ke^{-ct} \sin \omega t$.

52. A yacht and a sailboat leave the same port at the same time. The yacht travels at an average of 6 knots heading due east. The sailboat travels at an average of 5 knots heading due south. After 3 hours, what is the distance between the two boats, and what is the bearing of the yacht to the boat?

53. A buoy oscillates in simple harmonic motion as waves go past. At a given time, it is noted that the buoy moves a total of 4.5 feet from its low point to its high point, and that it completes a cycle every 2.4 seconds. Write an equation that describes the motion of the buoy if, at $t = 0$, it is at its high point.

54. A helicopter is hovering 300 feet over the finish line of a boat race. As Boats A and B approach the finish line (each traveling at a constant speed), the angle of elevation from Boat A to the helicopter is 3° at the same moment that the angle of elevation from Boat B to the helicopter is 3.5°. After 2 minutes, the angle of elevation from Boat A to the helicopter is 32°, and the angle of elevation from Boat B to the helicopter is 32.2°. If each boat maintains its constant speed, which boat will win the race and by how many seconds?

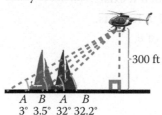

CHAPTER 2 REVIEW EXERCISES

Section 2.1 Angles and Their Measure

In Exercises 1–4, use each given angle θ.

• Identify the quadrant in which θ lies.

• Find the smallest positive angle and the negative angle closest to 0° that are coterminal with θ (other than itself).

• Find the complement of θ, if it exists.

• Find the supplement of θ, if it exists.

• Find the radian measure of θ.

1. $\theta = 45°$

2. $\theta = 160°$

3. $\theta = 715°$

4. $\theta = -400°$

5. When a sprinkler is set to full rotation, the water covers a circular section of a garden with a radius of 18.5 feet. The sprinkler is set to rotate back and forth through an angle of $11\pi/12$ radians. Find the area of the garden that is covered by the sprinkler, find the length of the outer edge of the area that the water covers, and convert the radian measure to degrees. Round to the nearest tenth, as necessary.

Section 2.2 Right Angle Trigonometry

6. Find the six trigonometric functions of θ, if θ is an angle in a right triangle where the hypotenuse is 10 and the side opposite θ is 7.

7. Find the length of the side adjacent to a 22.5° angle in a right triangle if its opposite side has length 19.2. Round to the nearest tenth.

8. Find the length of the side opposite an angle measuring $\pi/8$ radians in a right triangle if the hypotenuse has length 16. Round to the nearest tenth.

9. Find the length of the hypotenuse of a right triangle if the side adjacent to an angle measuring $\pi/5$ radians has length 4.5. Round to the nearest tenth.

10. When observed from the top of a 175-foot-tall lighthouse, the angle of depression of an approaching ship is 32°. Find the straight line distance from the lighthouse to the ship. Round to the nearest tenth of a foot.

Section 2.3 The Trigonometric Functions in the Coordinate Plane

In Exercises 11–12, find the sine, cosine, tangent, cosecant, secant, and cotangent of θ, given that θ is an angle in standard position and the given point is on the terminal side of θ.

11. $(-1, 5)$

12. $(-7, -3)$

In Exercises 13–14, find the six trigonometric functions of θ, if θ is a standard position angle.

13. $\theta = -225°$

14. $\theta = 7\pi/3$

15. Find $\sin \theta$ and $\cos \theta$, given that $\cot \theta = -5/2$ and $\sin \theta < 0$.

Section 2.4 Unit Circle Trigonometry

In Exercises 16–18, evaluate the six trigonometric functions of each real number.

16. $t = 7\pi/6$

17. $t = -\pi$

18. $t = 9\pi/2$

19. If $\csc t = -6/5$, evaluate $\csc (-t)$ and $\sin (-t)$.

20. If $\tan (-t) = 7/6$, evaluate $\tan t$ and $\cot t$.

Section 2.5 Graphing Sine and Cosine Functions

In Exercises 21–23, find each function's amplitude and period, describe any phase shifts or vertical shifts (as compared to the corresponding basic trigonometric function), and then graph at least two periods of the function. Identify the x-values of all maximums, minimums, and zeros.

21. $y = -2 \cos \pi x + 3$

22. $y = -\dfrac{1}{2} \sin \left(x + \dfrac{2\pi}{3} \right) + 1$

23. $y = \dfrac{2}{3} \cos \left(3x - 2\pi \right)$

24. Find the function's amplitude and period, describe any phase shift or vertical shift (as compared to $y = \sin x$), and then graph at least two periods of the function. Identify the x-values of all maximums and minimums.

$$y = 3 \sin \frac{\pi}{2}x - 1$$

25. The height h of a seat above ground on a ferris wheel at time t is given by $h(t) = 25 \sin\left(\frac{\pi}{6}t - \frac{5\pi}{6}\right) + 55$, where $t \geq 0$ seconds and h is in feet. Graph the function for two periods and find the maximum height of the seat.

Section 2.6 Graphing Other Trigonometric Functions

In Exercises 26–27, find each function's period, describe any phase shifts or vertical shifts (as compared to the corresponding basic trigonometric function), and then graph at least two periods of the function. Identify all vertical asymptotes and zeros, if any.

26. $y = \frac{1}{2} \tan\left(\frac{2}{3}x - \frac{\pi}{4}\right)$

27. $y = 4 \cot\left(\frac{1}{2}x + \frac{\pi}{2}\right)$

In Exercises 28–30, find each function's period, describe any phase shifts or vertical shifts (as compared to the corresponding basic trigonometric function), and then graph at least two periods of the function. Identify all vertical asymptotes.

28. $y = -\frac{1}{3} \csc(\pi x + 2\pi) - 2$

29. $y = 2 \sec\left(2x - \frac{\pi}{2}\right) + 1$

30. $y = -\frac{3}{4} \cot 2(x + \pi) - 1$

Section 2.7 Inverse Trigonometric Functions

In Exercises 31–35, find the exact value of each expression, if possible. If not possible, use a calculator to find the value of the expression to the nearest hundredth.

31. $\sin^{-1}(1/2)$

32. $\cos^{-1}(-0.882)$

33. $\arccos\left(\cos\left(-\frac{2\pi}{3}\right)\right)$

34. $\cos\left(\tan^{-1}\left(-\frac{\sqrt{6}}{7}\right)\right)$

35. $\csc\left(\cot^{-1}\left(-\frac{\sqrt{7}}{3}\right)\right)$

Section 2.8 Applications of Trigonometric Functions

36. In right triangle ABC with $a = 11.9$, $B = 36.2°$, and $C = 90°$, solve for the unknown sides and angle. Round to the nearest tenth, as needed.

37. A cat is trapped on a tree branch 12.3 feet above the ground. A nearby ladder is 13 feet long. If the ladder's tip is placed on the branch, what angle will the ladder make with the ground? Round to the nearest tenth of a degree.

38. An observer 75 feet above the surface of the water measures an angle of depression of 12° to a distant ship. How many feet to the nearest hundredth is the ship from the observer?

39. A ship leaves the port of Galveston with a bearing of S 68° E and a speed of 12 knots (nautical miles per hour). After 2 hours, the ship turns directly south. If the ship maintains its speed, what is the bearing of the ship relative to the port after 3 hours of travel? Round to the nearest hundredth of a degree.

40. A weight is attached to the bottom of a spring, and the top of the spring is attached to a surface so that the maximum distance d the weight can move vertically up or down from its point of equilibrium (the point at which the spring is relaxed) is 20 centimeters. Model the motion of the weight with a simple harmonic equation and find its frequency. Assume that the weight begins from its equilibrium point at $t = 0$ seconds and moves to its maximum displacement above 0, to its minimum displacement below 0, and then back to equilibrium every 1.5 seconds. Assume also that the weight is not affected by friction.

Group 2.9 Graphic Ideas of Trigonometry

Exercises

36. In right triangle ABC with $a = 11.9$, $B = 36.2°$, and $C = 90°$, solve for the unknown sides and angle. Round to the nearest tenth as needed.

37. A ladder is leaned against a tree branch 12.4 feet above the ground. A nearby ladder is 13.6 feet long. If the ladder is in place on the branch, what angle will the ladder make with the ground? Round to the nearest tenth of a degree.

38. An observer 75 feet above the surface of the water measures an angle of depression of 13° to a distant ship. How many feet to the nearest hundredth is the ship from the observer?

39. A ship leaves the port of Galveston with a bearing of S 68° E and a speed of 11.2 knots (nautical miles per hour). After 3 hours, the ship turns due south. If the ship maintains its speed, what is the bearing of the ship relative to the port after 3 hours of travel? Round to the nearest hundredth of a degree.

40. A weight is attached to the bottom of a spring and the top of the spring is attached to a surface so that the maximum distance it the weight can move vertically up or down from its point of equilibrium this point at which the spring is relaxed is 20 centimeters. Model the motion of the weight with a simple harmonic equation and find its frequency. Assume that the weight begins from its equilibrium point at $t = 0$ seconds and moves up to its maximum displacement score of 6 to its minimum displacement below 6, and then back to equilibrium every 1.5 seconds. Assume also that the weight is not affected by friction.

24. Find the function's amplitude and period. Describe any phase shift or vertical shift (as compared to $y = \sin x$) and then graph at least two periods of the function. Identify the x-values of all maximums and minimums.

$$y = 8 \sin\frac{\pi}{3}x - 2$$

25. The height h of a seat above ground on a Ferris wheel at time t is given by $h(t) = 26 \sin\left(\frac{3\pi}{5}t - \frac{5\pi}{6}\right) + 30$, where $t \geq 0$ seconds and h is in feet. Graph the function for two applications and find the maximum height of the seat.

Section 2.6 Graphing Other Trigonometric Functions

In Exercises 26–27, find each function's period, describe any phase shifts or vertical shifts (as compared to the corresponding basic trigonometric function) and then graph at least two periods of the function. Identify all vertical asymptotes and zeros, if any.

26. $y = \tan\left(\frac{2}{3}x - \pi\right)$

27. $y = 4 \cot\left(\frac{\pi}{2}x\right)$

In Exercises 28–30, find each function's period, describe any phase shifts or vertical shifts (as compared to the corresponding basic trigonometric function) and then graph at least two periods of the function. Identify all vertical asymptotes.

28. $y = \sec(\pi x + 2\pi) + 3$

29. $y = 2 \csc\left(3x - \frac{\pi}{2}\right) - 1$

30. $y = \frac{1}{3}\cot 2\left(x - \pi\right) - 1$

Section 2.7 Inverse Trigonometric Functions

In Exercises 31–35, find the exact value of each expression, if possible. If not possible, use a calculator to find the value of the expression to the nearest hundredth.

31. $\sin^{-1}(1/2)$

32. $\cos^{-1}(-0.882)$

33. $\arccos\left(\cos\frac{2\pi}{3}\right)$

34. $\cos\left[\tan^{-1}\left(-\frac{\sqrt{3}}{3}\right)\right]$

35. $\sin\left[\cos^{-1}\left(-\frac{\sqrt{2}}{2}\right)\right]$

ANALYTIC TRIGONOMETRY

3.1 FUNDAMENTAL TRIGONOMETRIC IDENTITIES

OBJECTIVES

- Use fundamental trigonometric identities to evaluate a trigonometric function.
- Use fundamental trigonometric identities to simplify or rewrite a trigonometric expression.
- Use fundamental trigonometric identities to factor a trigonometric expression.
- Prove a trigonometric identity.

PREREQUISITE VOCABULARY TERMS

binomial
Distributive Property
factors (of a polynomial)
Pythagorean Theorem
reciprocal
trigonometric functions

3.1.1 Fundamental Trigonometric Identities

An **identity** is an equation that is always true. For example, $1 + 2 = 3$ is a simple identity. If an identity contains variables, then the equation must be true for all values of the variables (within the equation's domain). For example, $2x + 6 = 2(x + 3)$ is an identity because any real number substituted for x results in a true statement.

Several groups of **fundamental trigonometric identities** will be presented in this topic. These identities can be used to simplify or rewrite a **trigonometric expression** (i.e., an expression involving at least one trigonometric function).

The **even-odd identities** were presented in Chapter 2.

Even-Odd Identities		
$\sin(-\theta) = -\sin\theta$	$\cos(-\theta) = \cos\theta$	$\tan(-\theta) = -\tan\theta$
$\csc(-\theta) = -\csc\theta$	$\sec(-\theta) = \sec\theta$	$\cot(-\theta) = -\cot\theta$

The rest of the fundamental trigonometric identities introduced in this topic will follow from the definitions of the trigonometric functions given in Chapter 2. Recall that if θ is an acute angle in a right triangle (Figure 3.1a), then

Figure 3.1a

$$\sin\theta = \frac{\text{opp}}{\text{hyp}}, \ \cos\theta = \frac{\text{adj}}{\text{hyp}}, \ \tan\theta = \frac{\text{opp}}{\text{adj}}, \ \csc\theta = \frac{\text{hyp}}{\text{opp}}, \ \sec\theta = \frac{\text{hyp}}{\text{adj}}, \text{ and } \cot\theta = \frac{\text{adj}}{\text{opp}}.$$

Recall that $\sin\theta$ and $\csc\theta$ are reciprocals. The same is true for $\cos\theta$ and $\sec\theta$, as well as for $\tan\theta$ and $\cot\theta$. The **reciprocal identities** follow from these reciprocal relationships.

Reciprocal Identities		
$\sin\theta = \dfrac{1}{\csc\theta}$	$\cos\theta = \dfrac{1}{\sec\theta}$	$\tan\theta = \dfrac{1}{\cot\theta}$
$\csc\theta = \dfrac{1}{\sin\theta}$	$\sec\theta = \dfrac{1}{\cos\theta}$	$\cot\theta = \dfrac{1}{\tan\theta}$

The next fundamental trigonometric identities are the **quotient identities**. Note that the quotient of $\sin \theta$ and $\cos \theta$ can be simplified, as shown here.

$$\frac{\sin \theta}{\cos \theta} = \frac{\dfrac{\text{opp}}{\text{hyp}}}{\dfrac{\text{adj}}{\text{hyp}}} = \frac{\text{opp}}{\text{hyp}} \cdot \frac{\text{hyp}}{\text{adj}} = \frac{\text{opp}}{\text{adj}} = \tan \theta$$

Therefore, $\tan \theta = \dfrac{\sin \theta}{\cos \theta}$. Furthermore, since $\tan \theta$ and $\cot \theta$ are reciprocals, $\cot \theta = \dfrac{\cos \theta}{\sin \theta}$.

NOTICE THAT

The same result is found when the definitions of the sine and cosine of any angle θ are used (i.e., sin θ = y/r and cos θ = x/r).

$$\frac{\sin \theta}{\cos \theta} = \frac{\dfrac{y}{r}}{\dfrac{x}{r}}$$
$$= \frac{y}{r} \cdot \frac{r}{x}$$
$$= \frac{y}{x}$$
$$= \tan \theta$$

Quotient Identities
$\tan \theta = \dfrac{\sin \theta}{\cos \theta} \qquad \cot \theta = \dfrac{\cos \theta}{\sin \theta}$

The **Pythagorean identities** are fundamental trigonometric identities following from the Pythagorean Theorem. To derive the first of the Pythagorean identities, consider the three sides of the right triangle in Figure 3.1a, which can be represented by opp, adj, and hyp. So, by the Pythagorean Theorem, $(\text{opp})^2 + (\text{adj})^2 = (\text{hyp})^2$. Dividing each side of the equation by $(\text{hyp})^2$ and simplifying gives the first Pythagorean identity.

IMPORTANT

$(\sin \theta)(\sin \theta) = (\sin \theta)^2 = \sin^2 \theta$
$(\sin \theta)(\sin \theta) \neq \sin \theta^2$

$$(\text{opp})^2 + (\text{adj})^2 = (\text{hyp})^2$$

$$\frac{(\text{opp})^2}{(\text{hyp})^2} + \frac{(\text{adj})^2}{(\text{hyp})^2} = \frac{(\text{hyp})^2}{(\text{hyp})^2} \qquad \textit{Divide each side by } (\text{hyp})^2.$$

$$\left(\frac{\text{opp}}{\text{hyp}}\right)^2 + \left(\frac{\text{adj}}{\text{hyp}}\right)^2 = 1 \qquad \textit{Simplify and use the Power of a Quotient Property.}$$

$$(\sin \theta)^2 + (\cos \theta)^2 = 1 \qquad \textit{Substitute } \sin \theta \textit{ for opp/hyp and } \cos \theta \textit{ for adj/hyp.}$$

$$\sin^2 \theta + \cos^2 \theta = 1 \qquad \textit{Write the square of } \sin \theta \textit{ and the square of } \cos \theta.$$

IMPORTANT

Pythagorean identities can be written in many forms. For example, $\sin^2 \theta + \cos^2 \theta = 1$ can be written as $\cos^2 \theta + \sin^2 \theta = 1$, $\cos^2 \theta = 1 - \sin^2 \theta$, or $\sin^2 \theta = 1 - \cos^2 \theta$.

Pythagorean Identities
$\sin^2 \theta + \cos^2 \theta = 1 \qquad \tan^2 \theta + 1 = \sec^2 \theta \qquad 1 + \cot^2 \theta = \csc^2 \theta$

The Pythagorean identities $1 + \tan^2 \theta = \sec^2 \theta$ and $1 + \cot^2 \theta = \csc^2 \theta$ can be derived using a number of methods. For example, dividing $\sin^2 \theta + \cos^2 \theta = 1$ by $\cos^2 \theta$ yields $\tan^2 \theta + 1 = \sec^2 \theta$.

$$\frac{\sin^2 \theta}{\cos^2 \theta} + \frac{\cos^2 \theta}{\cos^2 \theta} = \frac{1}{\cos^2 \theta} \quad \Rightarrow \quad \tan^2 \theta + 1 = \sec^2 \theta$$

The **cofunction identities** follow from the periodic nature of trigonometric functions.

Cofunction Identities		
$\sin\left(\dfrac{\pi}{2} - \theta\right) = \cos \theta$	$\cos\left(\dfrac{\pi}{2} - \theta\right) = \sin \theta$	$\tan\left(\dfrac{\pi}{2} - \theta\right) = \cot \theta$
$\csc\left(\dfrac{\pi}{2} - \theta\right) = \sec \theta$	$\sec\left(\dfrac{\pi}{2} - \theta\right) = \csc \theta$	$\cot\left(\dfrac{\pi}{2} - \theta\right) = \tan \theta$

3.1.2 Using Trigonometric Identities

In Section 2.3, the value of one trigonometric function of θ and the sign of another trigonometric function of θ (not the reciprocal of the first function) were used to evaluate all other trigonometric functions of θ. The first step in this procedure was to use the signs of the two trigonometric functions to determine the quadrant containing θ. Then a right triangle was drawn using the reference angle, and the Pythagorean Theorem was used to find this triangle's unknown side length. Finally, the lengths of the triangle's sides were used to evaluate the other trigonometric functions of θ.

Fundamental trigonometric identities can be used to evaluate all trigonometric functions of θ when the value of one trigonometric function of θ and the quadrant containing θ are known, as demonstrated in **Example 1**.

EXAMPLE 1   **Using Trigonometric Identities to Evaluate the Trigonometric Functions of θ**

IMPORTANT

If $\pi < \theta < 3\pi/2$, then θ is in quadrant III. In quadrant III, $\tan \theta > 0$ and $\cot \theta > 0$, but the rest of the trigonometric functions of θ are negative.

Evaluate $\sin \theta$, $\cos \theta$, $\tan \theta$, $\sec \theta$, and $\cot \theta$ if $\csc \theta = -2$ and $\pi < \theta < 3\pi/2$.

SOLUTION

Since $\csc \theta = -2$ and $\sin \theta = \dfrac{1}{\csc \theta}$ (reciprocal identity), $\sin \theta = \dfrac{1}{-2} = -\dfrac{1}{2}$.

Use the Pythagorean identity $1 + \cot^2 \theta = \csc^2 \theta$ to find $\cot \theta$.

$$1 + \cot^2 \theta = \csc^2 \theta \qquad \textit{Pythagorean Identity}$$
$$1 + \cot^2 \theta = (-2)^2 \qquad \textit{Substitute } -2 \textit{ for } \csc \theta.$$
$$1 + \cot^2 \theta = 4 \qquad \textit{Simplify.}$$
$$\cot^2 \theta = 3 \qquad \textit{Subtract 1 from each side.}$$
$$\cot \theta = \pm\sqrt{3} \qquad \textit{Take } \pm \textit{ the square root of each side.}$$

Since $\pi < \theta < 3\pi/2$, θ is in quadrant III, where cotangent is positive. Therefore, $\cot \theta = \sqrt{3}$.

Since $\cot \theta = \sqrt{3}$ and $\tan \theta = \dfrac{1}{\cot \theta}$ (reciprocal identity), $\tan \theta = \dfrac{1}{\sqrt{3}}$.

Use the quotient identity $\cot \theta = \dfrac{\cos \theta}{\sin \theta}$ to find $\cos \theta$.

$$\cot \theta = \frac{\cos \theta}{\sin \theta} \qquad \textit{Quotient Identity}$$
$$\sqrt{3} = \frac{\cos \theta}{-\dfrac{1}{2}} \qquad \textit{Substitute } \sqrt{3} \textit{ for } \cot \theta \textit{ and } -1/2 \textit{ for } \sin \theta.$$
$$\cos \theta = -\frac{1}{2} \cdot \sqrt{3} = -\frac{\sqrt{3}}{2} \qquad \textit{Multiply both sides by } -1/2 \textit{ and simplify.}$$

Since $\cos \theta = -\dfrac{\sqrt{3}}{2}$ and $\sec \theta = \dfrac{1}{\cos \theta}$ (reciprocal identity), $\sec \theta = \dfrac{1}{-\dfrac{\sqrt{3}}{2}} = -\dfrac{2}{\sqrt{3}}$.

ALTERNATIVE METHOD

There are many different ways to use the fundamental trigonometric identities to evaluate the trigonometric functions of θ. For example, the Pythagorean identity $\sin^2 \theta + \cos^2 \theta = 1$ can be used along with $\sin \theta = -1/2$ to find $\cos \theta$.

$$\sin^2 \theta + \cos^2 \theta = 1 \qquad \textit{Pythagorean Identity}$$

$$\left(-\frac{1}{2}\right)^2 + \cos^2 \theta = 1 \qquad \textit{Substitute } -1/2 \textit{ for sin } \theta.$$

$$\frac{1}{4} + \cos^2 \theta = 1 \qquad \textit{Simplify.}$$

$$\cos^2 \theta = \frac{3}{4} \qquad \textit{Subtract 1/4 from each side.}$$

$$\cos \theta = \pm\sqrt{\frac{3}{4}} = \pm\frac{\sqrt{3}}{2} \qquad \begin{array}{l}\textit{Take } \pm \textit{ the square root of each side and}\\ \textit{simplify the radical.}\end{array}$$

Again, since $\pi < \theta < 3\pi/2$, θ is in quadrant III. Cosine is negative in quadrant III, so $\cos \theta = -\dfrac{\sqrt{3}}{2}$.

3.1.3 Simplifying a Trigonometric Expression Using Trigonometric Identities

The fundamental trigonometric identities can be used to simplify trigonometric expressions. Note that you may need to manipulate the expression by applying a property of real numbers before substituting an expression from one of the fundamental trigonometric identities into the given trigonometric expression.

There will often be several possible procedures for simplifying a trigonometric expression, each resulting in an equivalent form of the expression when completed correctly.

EXAMPLE 2   Using Trigonometric Identities to Simplify an Expression

Simplify each expression.

A. $\sin^2 x + \tan^2 x + \cos^2 x$ **B.** $\cos^2 \theta \cdot \tan^2 \theta \cdot \csc \theta$

SOLUTION

REMEMBER

Commutative Property
$a + c + b = a + b + c$
$a \cdot c \cdot b = a \cdot b \cdot c$

Pythagorean Identity ▶
$1 + \tan^2 \theta = \sec^2 \theta$

A. Notice that the expression contains the terms $\sin^2 x$ and $\cos^2 x$. By the Commutative Property of Addition, $\sin^2 x + \tan^2 x + \cos^2 x$ can be written as $\sin^2 x + \cos^2 x + \tan^2 x$. The sin-cos Pythagorean identity states that $\sin^2 \theta + \cos^2 \theta = 1$. So, substitute 1 for $\sin^2 x + \cos^2 x$.

$$\sin^2 x + \tan^2 x + \cos^2 x = \sin^2 x + \cos^2 x + \tan^2 x \quad \textit{Commutative Property of Addition}$$

$$= 1 + \tan^2 x \qquad\qquad\qquad \textit{Substitute 1 for } \sin^2 x + \cos^2 x.$$

$$= \sec^2 x \qquad\qquad\qquad\quad \textit{Substitute } \sec^2 x \textit{ for } 1 + \tan^2 x.$$

So, $\sin^2 x + \tan^2 x + \cos^2 x = \sec^2 x$.

TIP

When simplifying, if an identity cannot be used immediately, it may be useful to first write all of the trigonometric functions in terms of $\sin\theta$ and $\cos\theta$.

B. Since no Pythagorean identities involve both $\cos^2 x$ and $\tan^2 x$, use identities to write the expression in terms of sine and cosine.

$$\cos^2\theta \cdot \tan^2\theta \cdot \csc\theta = \cos^2\theta \cdot (\tan\theta)^2 \cdot \csc\theta \qquad \text{\textit{tan}}^2\,\theta = (\tan\theta)^2$$

$$= \cos^2\theta \cdot \left(\frac{\sin\theta}{\cos\theta}\right)^2 \cdot \csc\theta \qquad \textit{Substitute } \sin\theta/\cos\theta \textit{ for } \tan\theta.$$

$$= \cos^2\theta \cdot \frac{\sin^2\theta}{\cos^2\theta} \cdot \frac{1}{\sin\theta} \qquad \textit{Power of a Quotient Property}$$

$$= \sin\theta \qquad \begin{array}{l}\textit{Simplify (remove the common factors}\\ \textit{from the numerator and denominator).}\end{array}$$

So, $\cos^2\theta \cdot \tan^2\theta \cdot \csc\theta = \sin\theta$.

3.1.4 Simplifying a Trigonometric Expression Using Trigonometric Identities: Another Example

EXAMPLE 3 Using Trigonometric Identities to Simplify an Expression

Simplify. $\dfrac{1}{\tan x + 1} + \dfrac{\cot x}{\tan x + 1}$

SOLUTION

$$\frac{1}{\tan x + 1} + \frac{\cot x}{\tan x + 1} = \frac{1 + \cot x}{\tan x + 1} \qquad \textit{Add the terms.}$$

Quotient Identities ▶

$\tan\theta = \dfrac{\sin\theta}{\cos\theta}$

$\cot\theta = \dfrac{\cos\theta}{\sin\theta}$

$$= \frac{1 + \dfrac{\cos x}{\sin x}}{\dfrac{\sin x}{\cos x} + 1} \qquad \begin{array}{l}\textit{Substitute } \sin x/\cos x \textit{ for } \tan x \textit{ and } \cos x/\\ \sin x \textit{ for } \cot x.\end{array}$$

$$= \frac{\dfrac{\sin x}{\sin x} + \dfrac{\cos x}{\sin x}}{\dfrac{\sin x}{\cos x} + \dfrac{\cos x}{\cos x}} \qquad \begin{array}{l}\textit{Write the terms with a common}\\ \textit{denominator.}\end{array}$$

$$= \frac{\sin x + \cos x}{\sin x} \cdot \frac{\cos x}{\sin x + \cos x} \qquad \begin{array}{l}\textit{Add the terms and multiply by the}\\ \textit{reciprocal.}\end{array}$$

$$= \frac{(\sin x + \cos x)(\cos x)}{(\sin x + \cos x)(\sin x)} \qquad \begin{array}{l}\textit{Multiply the numerators and the}\\ \textit{denominators.}\end{array}$$

$$= \frac{\cos x}{\sin x} \qquad \begin{array}{l}\textit{Simplify by removing common factor}\\ (\sin x + \cos x).\end{array}$$

$$= \cot x \qquad \textit{Substitute } \cot x \textit{ for } \cos x/\sin x.$$

So, $\dfrac{1}{\tan x + 1} + \dfrac{\cot x}{\tan x + 1} = \cot x$.

3.1.5 Simplifying Products of Binomials Involving Trigonometric Functions

Recall from Section P.4 that the FOIL method is a procedure for multiplying two binomials.

$$(a + b)(c + d) = ac + ad + bc + bd$$

Each letter in the word "FOIL" represents a multiplication step used in the procedure.

- F: multiply the *first* terms from each binomial
- O: multiply the *outer* terms from each binomial
- I: multiply the *inner* terms from each binomial
- L: multiply the *last* terms from each binomial

The FOIL method can also be used to multiply two binomials involving trigonometric functions. For example, the expansion of $(3 + \cos x)^2$ is shown here.

$$
\begin{aligned}
(3 + \cos x)^2 &= (3 + \cos x)(3 + \cos x) &&\textit{Write the power as a product of two factors.} \\
&= 9 + 3 \cos x + 3 \cos x + \cos^2 x &&\textit{FOIL} \\
&= 9 + 6 \cos x + \cos^2 x &&\textit{Combine the like terms.}
\end{aligned}
$$

If a trigonometric expression contains a product of two binomials, FOIL first and then use trigonometric identities to simplify, if possible.

EXAMPLE 4   Using Trigonometric Identities and FOIL to Simplify an Expression

Expand and simplify $(\sec x - 1)(\sec x + 1)$, if possible.

SOLUTION

FOIL the two binomials.

$$
\begin{aligned}
(\sec x - 1)(\sec x + 1) &= \sec^2 x + \sec x - \sec x - 1 &&\textit{FOIL} \\
&= \sec^2 x - 1 &&\textit{Simplify.} \\
&= \tan^2 x &&\textit{Pythagorean Identity}
\end{aligned}
$$

So, $(\sec x - 1)(\sec x + 1) = \tan^2 x$.

TIP

Subtracting 1 from both sides of the Pythagorean Identity $1 + \tan^2 \theta = \sec^2 \theta$ gives $\tan^2 \theta = \sec^2 \theta - 1$.

3.1.6 Simplifying Products of Binomials Involving Trigonometric Functions: Another Example

EXAMPLE 5 Using Trigonometric Identities and FOIL to Simplify an Expression

Expand and simplify $(\tan^2 x + 1)(1 - \cos^2 x)$, if possible.

SOLUTION

FOIL the two binomials.

$$(\tan^2 x + 1)(1 - \cos^2 x) = \tan^2 x + (\tan^2 x)(-\cos^2 x) + 1 - \cos^2 x \qquad \textit{FOIL}$$

$$= \tan^2 x - \tan^2 x \cos^2 x + 1 - \cos^2 x \qquad \textit{Simplify.}$$

$$= \tan^2 x - \tan^2 x \cos^2 x + (1 - \cos^2 x) \qquad \textit{Associative Property}$$

$$= \tan^2 x - \tan^2 x \cos^2 x + \sin^2 x \qquad \textit{Pythagorean Identity}$$

$$= \tan^2 x - \frac{\sin^2 x}{\cos^2 x} \cdot \cos^2 x + \sin^2 x \qquad \textit{Quotient Identity}$$

$$= \tan^2 x - \sin^2 x + \sin^2 x \qquad \textit{Simplify.}$$

$$= \tan^2 x \qquad \textit{Subtract the like terms.}$$

So, $(\tan^2 x + 1)(1 - \cos^2 x) = \tan^2 x$.

TIP

Subtracting $\cos^2 \theta$ from both sides of the Pythagorean identity $\sin^2 \theta + \cos^2 \theta = 1$ gives $\sin^2 \theta = 1 - \cos^2 \theta$.

ALTERNATIVE METHOD

Use an identity to simplify the expression in each binomial first.

$$(\tan^2 x + 1)(1 - \cos^2 x) = (\sec^2 x)(\sin^2 x) \qquad \textit{Pythagorean Identities}$$

$$= \left(\frac{1}{\cos^2 x}\right)(\sin^2 x) \qquad \textit{Reciprocal Identity}$$

$$= \frac{\sin^2 x}{\cos^2 x} \qquad \textit{Multiply.}$$

$$= \tan^2 x \qquad \textit{Quotient Identity}$$

3.1.7 Factoring Trigonometric Expressions

Factoring is another form of algebraic manipulation that may be helpful when simplifying trigonometric expressions. Factoring is used in the following example to demonstrate a third procedure for simplifying $(\tan^2 x + 1)(1 - \cos^2 x)$ (from **Example 5**).

EXAMPLE 6 Using Trigonometric Identities and Factoring to Simplify an Expression

Simplify. $(\tan^2 x + 1)(1 - \cos^2 x)$

SOLUTION

Suppose only the second binomial is simplified using a Pythagorean identity.

$$(\tan^2 x + 1)(1 - \cos^2 x) = (\tan^2 x + 1)(\sin^2 x) \qquad \textit{Pythagorean Identity}$$

The Distributive Property can now be used to expand the expression.

$$= \tan^2 x \cdot \sin^2 x + \sin^2 x \qquad \text{\textit{Distributive Property}}$$

$$= \frac{\sin^2 x}{\cos^2 x} \cdot \sin^2 x + \sin^2 x \qquad \text{\textit{Use a quotient identity to write the expression in terms of sine and cosine.}}$$

$$= \frac{\sin^4 x}{\cos^2 x} + \sin^2 x \qquad \text{\textit{Multiply.}}$$

$$= \frac{\sin^4 x}{\cos^2 x} + \frac{\sin^2 x \cos^2 x}{\cos^2 x} \qquad \text{\textit{Write the terms with a common denominator.}}$$

$$= \frac{\sin^4 x + \sin^2 x \cos^2 x}{\cos^2 x} \qquad \text{\textit{Add.}}$$

$$= \frac{\sin^2 x (\sin^2 x + \cos^2 x)}{\cos^2 x} \qquad \text{\textit{Factor } \sin^2 x \text{ from the numerator.}}$$

$$= \frac{\sin^2 x}{\cos^2 x} \qquad \text{\textit{Pythagorean Identity}}$$

$$= \tan^2 x \qquad \text{\textit{Quotient Identity}}$$

Pythagorean Identity ▶
$$\sin^2 \theta + \cos^2 \theta = 1$$

In addition to factoring a common factor from an expression (as seen in **Example 6**), simplification of trigonometric expressions may involve factoring a trinomial into two binomials. Factoring a trigonometric trinomial into two binomials is demonstrated in **Example 7**.

EXAMPLE 7   Factoring a Trigonometric Trinomial

IMPORTANT

Some trigonometric trinomials cannot be factored into two binomials, just like with polynomials.

Factor. $\cot^2 x - 7 \csc x + 11$

SOLUTION

Substitute $\csc^2 x - 1$ for $\cot^2 x$ (the Pythagorean identity) to write the expression in terms of cosecant.

$$\cot^2 x - 7 \csc x + 11 = (\csc^2 x - 1) - 7 \csc x + 11 \qquad \text{\textit{Pythagorean Identity}}$$

$$= \csc^2 x - 7 \csc x + 10 \qquad \text{\textit{Simplify.}}$$

$$= (\csc x - 5)(\csc x - 2) \qquad \text{\textit{Factor.}}$$

ALTERNATIVE METHOD

If factoring $\csc^2 x - 7 \csc x + 10$ into $(\csc x - 5)(\csc x - 2)$ is difficult because of the trigonometric terms, substitute S (or any variable) for the trigonometric function first and factor as usual. Then substitute the trigonometric function back into the expression.

$$\cot^2 x - 7 \csc x + 11 = (\csc^2 x - 1) - 7 \csc x + 11 \qquad \text{\textit{Pythagorean Identity}}$$

$$= \csc^2 x - 7 \csc x + 10 \qquad \text{\textit{Simplify.}}$$

$$= S^2 - 7S + 10 \qquad \text{\textit{Let } S = \csc x.}$$

$$= (S - 5)(S - 2) \qquad \text{\textit{Factor.}}$$

$$= (\csc x - 5)(\csc x - 2) \qquad \text{\textit{Substitute } \csc x \text{ for } S.}$$

Factoring a 4-term Expression

Recall that a polynomial expression containing four terms, such as $1 - a^2 + b^2 - a^2b^2$, can sometimes be factored into two binomials using the grouping method.

$$1 - a^2 + b^2 - a^2b^2$$
$$= (1 - a^2) + b^2(1 - a^2) \quad \textit{Group the first two terms and factor } b^2 \textit{ from the last two terms.}$$
$$= (1 - a^2)(1 + b^2) \quad \textit{Factor } 1 - a^2 \textit{ from each term.}$$

In **Example 8**, this grouping method is used to factor a 4-term trigonometric expression, and then the expression is simplified using trigonometric identities.

EXAMPLE 8 **Using Trigonometric Identities and Factoring to Simplify an Expression**

Simplify. $1 - \cos^2 x + \cot^2 x - \cos^2 x \cdot \cot^2 x$

SOLUTION

To make the possible factors easier to find, let a be $\cos^2 x$ and let b be $\cot^2 x$.

$$1 - \cos^2 x + \cot^2 x - \cos^2 x \cdot \cot^2 x = 1 - a^2 + b^2 - a^2b^2 \quad \textit{Substitute.}$$
$$= (1 - a^2)(1 + b^2) \quad \textit{Factor.}$$
$$= (1 - \cos^2 x)(1 + \cot^2 x) \quad \textit{Substitute.}$$
$$= (\sin^2 x)(\csc^2 x) \quad \textit{Pythagorean Identities}$$
$$= (\sin^2 x)\left(\frac{1}{\sin^2 x}\right) \quad \textit{Quotient Identity}$$
$$= \frac{\sin^2 x}{\sin^2 x} \quad \textit{Multiply.}$$
$$= 1 \quad \textit{Simplify.}$$

So, $1 - \cos^2 x + \cot^2 x - \cos^2 x \cdot \cot^2 x = 1$.

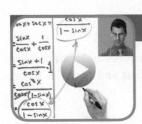

3.1.8 Proving an Identity

Recall that an identity is an equation that is true for all values of the variable within the equation's domain. So, an identity is an equality between two expressions (the two sides of the equation).

To prove that an equation is an identity, we can show that these two expressions are equivalent by simplifying each until both expressions are the same. If the two expressions cannot be written as the same expression, then the equation is not an identity.

Proving an identity may appear to be similar to solving an equation. However, solving an equation involves applying an operation to both sides of the equation (e.g., both sides of an equation might be divided by the coefficient of the variable), which is a strategy that cannot be used when proving an identity. To prove an identity, each side of the equation must be simplified separately (i.e., operations are not applied to both sides of the equation).

EXAMPLE 9   **Proving a Trigonometric Identity**

Determine whether $\dfrac{1+\csc^2 t + \cot^2 t}{(1+\sin t)(1-\sin t)} = \dfrac{2}{\sin^2 t \cdot \cos^2 t}$ is an identity or not.

SOLUTION

The expression on the right side appears to be simplified because it is written in terms of sine and cosine. So, simplify the left side. Keep in mind that the purpose of simplifying is to manipulate one side until it looks the same as the other side.

$$\frac{1+\csc^2 t + \cot^2 t}{(1+\sin t)(1-\sin t)} = \frac{\csc^2 t + (1+\cot^2 t)}{1-\sin^2 t}$$ *Use the Associative and Commutative Properties to group the terms in the numerator and use FOIL in the denominator.*

$$= \frac{\csc^2 t + \csc^2 t}{\cos^2 t}$$ *Pythagorean Identities*

$$= \frac{2\csc^2 t}{\cos^2 t}$$ *Combine the like terms.*

$$= \frac{2\left(\dfrac{1}{\sin^2 t}\right)}{\cos^2 t}$$ *Reciprocal Identity*

$$= 2\left(\frac{1}{\sin^2 t}\right)\cdot\left(\frac{1}{\cos^2 t}\right)$$ *Multiply by the reciprocal to divide.*

$$= \frac{2}{\sin^2 t \cdot \cos^2 t}$$ *Multiply.*

So, $\dfrac{1+\csc^2 t + \cot^2 t}{(1+\sin t)(1-\sin t)} = \dfrac{2}{\sin^2 t \cdot \cos^2 t}$ is an identity.

3.1.9   Proving an Identity: Another Example

If there are any x-values in an equation's domain that yield a false statement when substituted into the equation, then the equation is not an identity. In this case, any one of those x-values is a **counterexample**. One counterexample is sufficient evidence for concluding that an equation is not an identity.

For example, consider the equation $\sin x = \cos x$. We know that this equation is not an identity because there are many x-values for which $\sin x$ does not equal $\cos x$, such as $x = 0$.

$$\sin 0 \neq \cos 0$$
$$0 \neq 1$$

NOTICE THAT

The equation $\sin x = \cos x$ is true for some x-values, which are the solutions to the equation, but to be an identity the equation must be true for all values.

Therefore, $x = 0$ is a counterexample proving that $\sin x = \cos x$ is not an identity.

EXAMPLE 10 **Proving a Trigonometric Identity**

Determine whether $\dfrac{(\tan^2 t)^2}{\sec^4 t - 2\sec^2 t + 1} = \dfrac{\sin^2 t + \sin^2 t \cdot \cot^2 t}{\sin^2 t}$ is an identity or not.

SOLUTION

<table>
<tr><td>**IMPORTANT**</td></tr>
</table>

Simplify the left side of the equation.

$$\frac{(\tan^2 t)^2}{\sec^4 t - 2\sec^2 t + 1} = \frac{\tan^4 t}{(\sec^2 t - 1)(\sec^2 t - 1)} \qquad \begin{array}{l}\textit{Power of a Power}\\ \textit{Factor the denominator.}\end{array}$$

$$= \frac{\tan^4 t}{(\tan^2 t)(\tan^2 t)} \qquad \textit{Pythagorean Identity}$$

$$= \frac{\tan^4 t}{\tan^4 t} \qquad \textit{Simplify.}$$

$$= 1 \qquad \textit{Pythagorean Identity}$$

There are many ways to proceed, but do not apply any operation to both sides of this equation. For example, do not multiply both sides of the equation by $\sin^2 t$, as this is not allowed when proving an identity.

Now, simplify the right side of the equation.

$$\frac{\sin^2 t + \sin^2 t \cdot \cot^2 t}{\sin^2 t} = \frac{\sin^2 t(1 + \cot^2 t)}{\sin^2 t} \qquad \textit{Factor the numerator.}$$

$$= 1 + \cot^2 t \qquad \textit{Simplify.}$$

$$= \csc^2 t \qquad \textit{Pythagorean Identity}$$

Since $\csc^2 t \neq 1$ for all values of t, $\dfrac{(\tan^2 t)^2}{\sec^4 t - 2\sec^2 t + 1} = \dfrac{\sin^2 t + \sin^2 t \cdot \cot^2 t}{\sin^2 t}$ is not an identity.

While the equation given in **Example 10** is not an identity, it is however an equation that can be solved for t (i.e., there are t-values for which $\csc^2 t = 1$). Solving a trigonometric equation for a variable is covered in the next section.

A counterexample can also be used to prove that the equation is not an identity. Consider the equation when $t = \pi/4$.

$$\frac{\tan^2 \dfrac{\pi}{4}^2}{\sec^4 \dfrac{\pi}{4} - 2\sec^2 \dfrac{\pi}{4} + 1} \neq \frac{\sin^2 \dfrac{\pi}{4} + \sin^2 \dfrac{\pi}{4} \cot^2 \dfrac{\pi}{4}}{\sin^2 \dfrac{\pi}{4}} \qquad \textit{Substitute } \dfrac{\pi}{4} \textit{ for t.}$$

$$\frac{1}{4 - 4 + 1} \neq \frac{\dfrac{1}{2} + \dfrac{1}{2}}{\dfrac{1}{2}} \qquad \textit{Evaluate.}$$

$$1 \neq 2 \qquad \textit{Simplify.}$$

Therefore, $t = \pi/4$ is a counterexample proving that the equation is not an identity.

SECTION 3.1 EXERCISES

Warm Up

True or False?

1. $\cot 45° = 1$

2. $\sec 240° + 2 = \sec 120° + 2$

3. $2 \sin 150° = -1$

Just the Facts

Fill in the blanks.

4. An equation that is always true is an _____.

5. Writing $\sin (-50°)$ as $-\sin 50°$ and $\cos (-50°)$ as $\cos 50°$ is an application of the _____ identities.

6. $\sec^2 \theta - 1 = \tan^2 \theta$ is an example of a(n) _____ trigonometric identity.

7. The fundamental identities that follow from the periodic nature of trigonometric functions are the _____ identities.

8. In order for an equation to be an identity, _____ sides must be _____ for all values of the _____ in the equation's domain.

9. Replacing $\tan \theta$ with its quotient identity of _____ would simplify $\tan \theta \cdot \cos \theta$ to _____.

10. To show that an equation is not an identity, it is sufficient to provide a(n) _____.

Essential Skills

In Exercises 1–18, use the value of each given trigonometric function and quadrant to evaluate all other trigonometric functions.

1. $\sin \theta = -5/13$ and $3\pi/2 < \theta < 2\pi$

2. $\cos \theta = 1/4$ and $3\pi/2 < \theta < 2\pi$

3. $\cos \theta = 7/9$ and $0 < \theta < \pi/2$

4. $\sin \theta = 4/5$ and $\pi/2 < \theta < \pi$

5. $\sin \theta = -2/3$ and $\pi < \theta < 3\pi/2$

6. $\cos \theta = -3/8$ and $\pi < \theta < 3\pi/2$

7. $\tan \theta = 7/4$ and $0 < \theta < \pi/2$

8. $\cot \theta = -2$ and $\pi/2 < \theta < \pi$

9. $\cot \theta = -3$ and $3\pi/2 < \theta < 2\pi$

10. $\tan \theta = -5/6$ and $3\pi/2 < \theta < 2\pi$

11. $\tan \theta = -8$ and $\pi/2 < \theta < \pi$

12. $\cot \theta = 7/3$ and $\pi < \theta < 3\pi/2$

13. $\sec \theta = -3/2$ and $\pi < \theta < 3\pi/2$

14. $\csc \theta = 6$ and $\pi/2 < \theta < \pi$

15. $\csc \theta = -25/24$ and $\pi < \theta < 3\pi/2$

16. $\sec \theta = \dfrac{\sqrt{73}}{3}$ and $3\pi/2 < \theta < 2\pi$

17. $\sec \theta = 11/4$ and $3\pi/2 < \theta < 2\pi$

18. $\csc \theta = -\dfrac{\sqrt{290}}{13}$ and $\pi < \theta < 3\pi/2$

In Exercises 19–36, simplify.

19. $\tan^3 x \cdot \csc^3 x$

20. $\cot x \cdot \sec x \cdot \csc x \cdot \sin^2 x$

21. $\cos x \cdot \sin^3 x \cot^3 x \cdot \sec^2 x$

22. $\tan^3 x \cdot \cos^5 x \cdot \csc x \cdot \sec x$

23. $\sin x \cdot \tan x \cdot \csc x \cdot \cot x \cdot \cos x$

24. $\tan^6 x \cdot \csc^2 x \cdot \sin^2 x \cdot \cot^3 x$

25. $\sec x \cdot \cos x - \cos^2 x$

26. $\cot^2 x + \sin^2 x + \cos^2 x$

27. $\sec^2 x - \sin^2 x - \tan^2 x$

28. $\csc^2 x - \cot^2 x - \cos^2 x$

29. $\dfrac{\sin x \cdot \sec x}{\tan x}$

30. $\dfrac{\sec \theta \cdot \tan \theta}{\cot \theta \cdot \csc \theta}$

31. $\dfrac{\csc \theta \cdot \cot \theta}{\tan \theta \cdot \sec \theta}$

32. $\dfrac{\cos^4 x \cdot \tan^2 x}{\sin^3 x}$

33. $\dfrac{\cos x - 1}{\sin x} - \dfrac{\sin x}{\cos x - 1}$

34. $\dfrac{\sec^2 \theta - 1}{\cot^2 \theta} - \dfrac{1 + \tan^2 \theta}{\csc^2 \theta - 1}$

35. $\dfrac{\cos x}{1 + \sin x} + \dfrac{1 + \sin x}{\cos x}$

36. $\dfrac{1}{1 - \sec x} + \dfrac{1}{1 + \sec x}$

In Exercises 37–42, expand and simplify, if possible.

37. $(\sec x + \tan x)(\sec x - \tan x)$

38. $(1 + \sin^2 \theta)(1 + \cot^2 \theta)$

39. $(\tan x + \sin x)(\tan x - \sin x)$

40. $(\cos^2 x + \sec^2 x)(\cos^2 x - 2)$

41. $(3 \csc x + 3)(3 \csc x - 3)$

42. $(1 + \cos^2 \theta)(1 + \tan^2 \theta)$

In Exercises 43–48, expand and simplify, if possible.

43. $(\tan x + \cot x)^2$

44. $(\cot x - 1)^2$

45. $(\sin x + \cos x)^2$

46. $(\sec^2 \theta - 1)(\csc^2 \theta - 1)$

47. $(1 - \sin^2 \theta)(\cot^2 \theta + 1)$

48. $(\sin x - \csc x)^2$

In Exercises 49–52, factor and simplify, if possible.

49. $\sin^2 \theta + \cot^2 \theta \cdot \sin^2 \theta$

50. $\cot x \cdot \csc^2 x - \cot x$

51. $\tan^2 \theta - \tan^2 \theta \cdot \sin^2 \theta$

52. $\csc^5 x \cdot \cot^2 x + \csc^5 x$

In Exercises 53–58, factor.

53. $\sec^2 x + 6 \tan x + 4$

54. $\cot^2 x - 4 \csc x + 5$

55. $-2 \sin^2 \theta + 5 \cos \theta - 10$

56. $36 + 48 \cos t \cdot \sin t - 20 \sin^2 t$

57. $9 \sin^2 t + 42 \cos t \cdot \sin t + 49 \cos^2 t$

58. $\tan^2 x - 8 \sec x + 17$

In Exercises 59–62, factor and simplify, if possible.

59. $\cos^2 t \cdot \sin t - 2 \cos^4 t \cdot \sin t + \cos^6 t \cdot \sin t$

60. $1 - \sin^2 t + \tan^2 t - \sin^2 t \cdot \tan^2 t$

61. $\cos^4 t - \cos^4 t \cdot \sin^2 t + \cos^4 t \cdot \tan^2 t - \cos^4 t \cdot \tan^2 t \cdot \sin^2 t$

62. $\sin t - \sin t \cdot \cos^2 t + \sin t \cdot \cot^2 t - \sin t \cdot \cot^2 t \cdot \cos^2 t$

In Exercises 63–70, prove the identities.

63. $(\cos x - \sec x)^2 = \tan^2 x - \sin^2 x$

64. $\dfrac{1 - \cos t}{\sin t} + \dfrac{\sin t}{1 - \cos t} = 2 \csc t$

65. $\dfrac{1 - \sin t}{\cos t} + \dfrac{\cos t}{1 - \sin t} = 2 \sec t$

66. $\dfrac{1 + \cos t}{\sin t} + \dfrac{\sin t}{1 + \cos t} = 2 \csc t$

67. $\dfrac{1 + 2 \cot^2 x + \cot^4 x}{1 - \cot^2 x} = \dfrac{\csc^4 x}{1 - \cot^2 x}$

68. $\dfrac{\csc^4 x - 2 \csc^2 x + 1}{\cot^2 x} = \cot^2 x$

69. $\csc^2 x - \cos^2 x \times \csc^2 x = 1$

70. $\dfrac{1 - 2 \sin^2 x + \sin^4 x}{\cos^2 x} = \cos^2 x$

Extensions

In Exercises 71–74, evaluate without using a calculator.

71. $(\cos^2 (33°) + 4 + \sin^2 (33°))^3$

72. $\cot^2 (159°) - \csc^2 (159°)$

73. $5(\sec^2 (-221°) - \tan^2 (-221°)) + 7$

74. $-\sin^2 (317°) - \cos^2 (317°)$

In Exercises 75–80, prove the identities.

75. $\dfrac{1 + \sin x + \cos x}{1 - \sin x + \cos x} = \dfrac{1 + \sin x}{\cos x}$

76. $\dfrac{1}{(\csc x - \cot x)} = \dfrac{(1 + \cos x)}{\sin x}$

77. $\dfrac{\sec^3 \theta - \cos^3 \theta}{\sec \theta - \cos \theta} = \sec^2 \theta + \cos^2 \theta + 1$

78. $\csc^4 x - \cot^4 x = \dfrac{(1 + \cos^2 x)}{\sin^2 x}$

79. $(2 \sin x + 3 \cos x)^2 + (3 \sin x - 2 \cos x)^2 = 13$

80. $\dfrac{\sec^2 \theta - 6 \tan \theta + 7}{\sec^2 \theta - 5} = \dfrac{\tan \theta - 4}{\tan \theta + 2}$

81. Simplify. $(\tan x + \cos^2 x + \sin^2 x)(\tan x - \cos^2 x - \sin^2 x)$

82. Factor and simplify, if possible. $2 - \dfrac{\cos^2 x}{1 - \sin x}$

3.2 SOLVING TRIGONOMETRIC EQUATIONS

OBJECTIVES

- Use algebraic techniques to solve trigonometric equations.
- Use inverse trigonometric functions to solve trigonometric equations.
- Solve trigonometric equations of quadratic type.
- Solve trigonometric equations involving a multiple of an angle.
- Use fundamental identities to solve trigonometric equations.

PREREQUISITE VOCABULARY TERMS

fundamental trigonometric identities

inverse trigonometric functions

quadratic equation

Quadratic Formula

Zero-Product Property

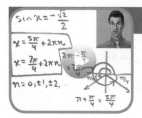

3.2.1 Solving Equations with a Single Trigonometric Function

The objective of solving a trigonometric equation is to find the values of the variable that make the equation true. These values are called the equation's solutions. Several procedures for solving trigonometric equations will be demonstrated in this section. Because trigonometric functions are periodic in nature, a trigonometric equation can have infinitely many solutions. These solutions can be expressed using general form equations, where each equation is the sum of a solution and all multiples of the function's period, as demonstrated in **Example 1**.

In some cases, all solutions within a given interval, such as $[0, 2\pi)$, are found. In these cases, the equation will either have no solution or a finite number of solutions.

Like the solutions of a polynomial equation, the solutions of a trigonometric equation can be determined (or checked) using a graph. For example, the equation $x + 1 = 4$ has solution $x = 3$, so graphically, the solution of $x + 1 = 4$ is the x-coordinate of the point of intersection of the graph of $y = x + 1$ and the graph of $y = 4$ (Figure 3.2a). The same relationship exists for the solutions of a trigonometric equation, as shown in **Example 1**.

Figure 3.2a

EXAMPLE 1   Solving a Basic Trigonometric Equation

Solve each equation.

A. $\sin x = 1$ **B.** $\tan x = 0$ **C.** $\sec x = -\sqrt{2}$

SOLUTION

Identify the solutions (if any) within one period. Then, if any solutions exist, add multiples of the function's period to each solution to write each solution in general form.

A. The period of $y = \sin x$ is 2π, so first identify all solutions within the interval $[0, 2\pi)$.

We know that $\sin \pi/2 = 1$ because $\pi/2$ is an important angle. From the graph, we see that $\pi/2$ is the only solution within the interval $[0, 2\pi)$. Since the period is 2π, add $2\pi n$ (where n is any integer) to $\pi/2$ to write the general form equation of all solutions.

$$x = \frac{\pi}{2} + 2\pi n$$

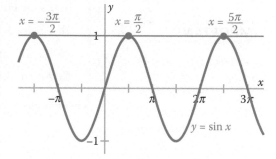

B. The period of $y = \tan x$ is π, so identify all solutions on the interval $[0, \pi)$.

We know that $\tan 0 = 0$ because 0 is an important angle. Notice that this is the only solution within the interval $[0, \pi)$.

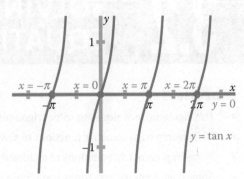

To write the general form equation of all solutions, add multiples of π (the period of $\tan x$) to 0.

$$x = 0 + \pi n = \pi n$$

Notice that the graph of $y = \tan x$ intersects the line $y = 0$ at $x = -\pi$, 0, π, and 2π.

IMPORTANT

Unless otherwise specified, n will always represent any integer in a general form equation.

C. The period of $y = \sec x$ is 2π, so identify all solutions on the interval $[0, 2\pi)$.

If $\sec x = -\sqrt{2}$, then $\cos x = -\dfrac{1}{\sqrt{2}} = -\dfrac{\sqrt{2}}{2}$ because secant and cosine are reciprocal functions.

Since $\cos x < 0$, all solutions must be in quadrants II and III (i.e., in quadrants where cosine is negative).

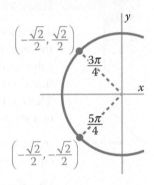

REMEMBER

cos t = x, where (x, y) is the point on the unit circle that corresponds to t.

Find all t-values in quadrants II and III on the unit circle such that $\cos x = -\dfrac{\sqrt{2}}{2}$.

$$\cos \frac{3\pi}{4} = -\frac{\sqrt{2}}{2} \text{ and } \cos \frac{5\pi}{4} = -\frac{\sqrt{2}}{2}$$

To write the general form equations of all solutions, add multiples of 2π to each solution.

$$x = \frac{3\pi}{4} + 2\pi n \text{ and } x = \frac{5\pi}{4} + 2\pi n$$

3.2.2 Solving Equations with a Single Trigonometric Function: Another Example

If a trigonometric equation is not solved for the trigonometric function, use the standard algebraic methods to isolate the trigonometric function on one side of the equation, and then find the solutions in one period.

IMPORTANT

Use algebraic methods (such as dividing both sides by a number, or taking ± the square root of both sides) to isolate the trigonometric function on one side of the equation.

Steps for Finding All Solutions for a Trigonometric Equation

❶ Isolate the trigonometric function on one side of the equation.

❷ Identify all solutions within one period.

❸ Add multiples of the period to each solution to write the general form of all solutions.

| **EXAMPLE 2** | **Solving a Trigonometric Equation** |

Solve each equation.

A. $3 = -2 \sin x + 1$ **B.** $3 \cot^2 x - 1 = 0$

SOLUTION

Use algebraic methods to isolate the trigonometric function in each equation.

A. Subtract 1 from each side and then divide each side by −2.

$$3 = -2 \sin x + 1 \Rightarrow 2 = -2 \sin x \Rightarrow -1 = \sin x$$

The period of $y = \sin x$ is 2π, so identify all solutions of $\sin x = -1$ on the interval $[0, 2\pi)$.

We know that $\sin 3\pi/2 = -1$ because $3\pi/2$ is an important angle. Notice that this is the only solution within the interval $[0, 2\pi)$.

To write the general form equation of all solutions, add multiples of 2π (the period of $\sin x$) to $3\pi/2$.

$$x = \frac{3\pi}{2} + 2\pi n$$

The graph of $y = \sin x$ confirms the solution.

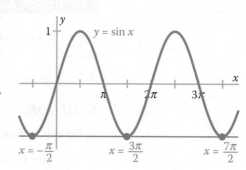

B. Add 1 to each side and then divide each side by 3.

$$3 \cot^2 x - 1 = 0 \Rightarrow 3 \cot^2 x = 1 \Rightarrow \cot^2 x = 1/3$$

Take the ± square root of each side. $\cot^2 x = 1/3 \Rightarrow \cot x = \pm\sqrt{\dfrac{1}{3}} = \pm\dfrac{1}{\sqrt{3}}$

The period of $y = \cot x$ is π, so identify all solutions of $\cot x = \pm\dfrac{1}{\sqrt{3}}$ on the interval $[0, \pi)$.

The equation $\cot x = \pm\dfrac{1}{\sqrt{3}}$ is equivalent to $\tan x = \pm\sqrt{3}$ because cotangent and tangent are reciprocal functions.

Since the value of $\tan x$ is both positive and negative, solutions are in all four quadrants.

Find all t-values on the unit circle within $[0, \pi)$ such that $\tan t = \sqrt{3}$ or $\tan t = -\sqrt{3}$.

$$\tan \frac{\pi}{3} = \sqrt{3} \text{ and } \tan \frac{2\pi}{3} = -\sqrt{3}$$

To write the general form equations of all solutions, add multiples of π (the period of $\cot x$) to each solution.

$$x = \frac{\pi}{3} + \pi n \text{ and } x = \frac{2\pi}{3} + \pi n$$

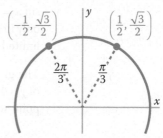

Since the period of $\cot x$ is π, identify the solutions within the interval $[0, \pi)$ (i.e., in quadrants I and II).

TIP

Substitute a variable for the trigonometric function, then solve. Let S represent sin x.
$3 = -2S + 1$
$2 = -2S$
$-1 = S$
So, $-1 = \sin x$.

TIP

Let S represent cot x.
$3S^2 - 1 = 0$
$3S^2 = 1$
$S^2 = 1/3$
$S = \pm\sqrt{\dfrac{1}{3}}$
So, $\cot x = \pm\sqrt{\dfrac{1}{3}}$.

REMEMBER

$\tan t = \sin t/\cos t = y/x$, where (x, y) is the point on the unit circle that corresponds to t.
$\tan \dfrac{\pi}{3} = \dfrac{y}{x} = \dfrac{\frac{\sqrt{3}}{2}}{\frac{1}{2}} = \sqrt{3}$

3.2.3   Solving Trigonometric Equations Using Inverse Functions

Recall from Section 2.7 that an inverse trigonometric function can be used to find the value of an angle in a trigonometric function. For example, the inverse sine function, $y = \sin^{-1} x$, means that $\sin y = x$. It follows that a trigonometric equation can be solved by using an inverse trigonometric function. For example, if $\sin x = 1$, then $x = \sin^{-1} 1$.

Inverse trigonometric functions can be evaluated using a calculator. However, if the angle is a multiple or combination of $\pi/6$ or $\pi/4$, then the solution should be expressed as an exact value instead of a decimal approximation.

IMPORTANT

The solutions obtained from using an inverse trigonometric function will be within the domain of the inverse function. Check the original function's graph to identify any additional solutions.

EXAMPLE 3   Solving a Trigonometric Equation Using an Inverse Function

Use an inverse trigonometric function to solve each equation. Round to the nearest tenth as needed.

A. $5 = 4 - \cos x$ **B.** $7 \csc x - 5 = 3 \csc x$ **C.** $6(\sec x + 1) = 2$

SOLUTION

A. Subtract 4 from each side and then divide each side by -1.

$$5 = 4 - \cos x \;\Rightarrow\; 1 = -\cos x \;\Rightarrow\; -1 = \cos x$$

If $\cos x = -1$, then $x = \cos^{-1}(-1)$. We know that $\cos \pi = -1$ because π is an important angle. Add multiples of 2π (the period of $\cos x$) to π to write the general form equation.

$$x = \pi + 2\pi n$$

IMPORTANT

The graph of $y = \cos x$ and $y = -1$ confirms that $x = \pi$ is the only solution of $-1 = \cos x$ within the interval $[0, 2\pi)$.

B. There is a cosecant term on each side of the equation, so subtract $3 \csc x$ from each side.

$$7 \csc x - 5 = 3 \csc x \;\Rightarrow\; 4 \csc x - 5 = 0 \;\Rightarrow\; 4 \csc x = 5 \;\Rightarrow\; \csc x = 5/4$$

If $\csc x = 5/4$, then $\sin x = 4/5$, because cosecant and sine are reciprocal functions. It follows that $x = \sin^{-1}(4/5)$.

$$x = \sin^{-1}(4/5) = 0.927\ldots \approx 0.9 \qquad \textit{Use a calculator to evaluate the inverse function.}$$

NOTICE THAT

The graph of $y = 4/5$ intersects the graph of $y = \sin x$ at two points between 0 and 2π. Thus, the equation $4/5 = \sin x$ has two solutions in the interval $[0, 2\pi)$.

Check the graph of $y = \sin x$ to identify any additional solutions within $[0, 2\pi)$. Because $\sin x = 4/5 > 0$, and because sine is positive only in quadrants I and II, the interval can be limited to $[0, \pi]$.

The graph of $y = \sin x$ intersects the graph of $y = 4/5$ when $x \approx 0.9$ and at one additional point within the interval $[0, 2\pi)$.

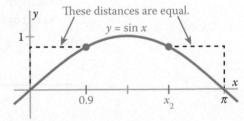

IMPORTANT

The graph of $y = \sin x$ is symmetric about $x = \pi/2$ within the interval $[0, \pi]$, so if (x_1, y) and (x_2, y) are points on $y = \sin x$ such that $x_2 > x_1$, then $x_2 = \pi - x_1$.

Let the x-coordinate of the second solution be x_2. Because of the symmetry of the graph of $y = \sin x$, the distance between 0 and $0.927\ldots$ (approximately 0.9) is equal to the distance between x_2 and π.

Therefore, $x_2 = \pi - 0.927\ldots \approx 2.2$.

So, within $[0, 2\pi)$, $x \approx 0.9$ and $x \approx 2.2$. Add multiples of 2π (the period of $\csc x$) to each solution to write the general form equations of all solutions.

$$x \approx 0.9 + 2\pi n \text{ and } x \approx 2.2 + 2\pi n$$

C. Divide each side by 6 and then subtract 1 from each side.

$$6(\sec x + 1) = 2 \implies \sec x + 1 = 1/3 \implies \sec x = -2/3$$

If $\sec x = -2/3$, then $\cos x = -3/2$. Recall that the range of cosine is $-1 \le y \le 1$. Since $y = -3/2$ is not in this interval, the equation has no real solution.

> **IMPORTANT**
>
> *If the y-value is not in the range of the trigonometric function, then the equation has no real solution.*

CHECK

Confirm that the equation has no solution by graphing $y = \cos x$.

The graph of $y = \cos x$ does not intersect the graph of $y = -3/2$, so $6(\sec x + 1) = 2$ has no real solution.

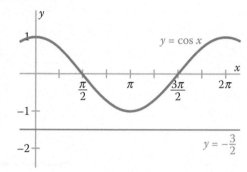

3.2.4 Solving Trigonometric Equations by Factoring

Recall from Section P.7 that the Zero-Product Property states that if $A \cdot B = 0$, then either $A = 0$ or $B = 0$. This property is applied to solve an equation in which a product of factors is equal to 0. For example, if $(x + 1)(x + 2) = 0$, then the equation's solutions are given by $x + 1 = 0$ or $x + 2 = 0$. The Zero-Product Property can be applied to trigonometric equations as well.

| EXAMPLE 4 | Solving a Trigonometric Equation by Factoring the GCF |

Find all solutions to $2 \cos^2 x \cdot \sin x = -\cos^2 x$ within the interval $[0, 2\pi)$.

SOLUTION

> **IMPORTANT**
>
> *When a solution interval is given, identify only specific solutions within that interval. If no solution interval is given, then all solutions should be expressed in the general form.*

Add $\cos^2 x$ to each side to get 0 on one side of the equation, then factor.

$$2 \cos^2 x \cdot \sin x = -\cos^2 x$$
$$2 \cos^2 x \cdot \sin x + \cos^2 x = 0 \qquad \textit{Add } \cos^2 x \textit{ to each side.}$$
$$\cos^2 x \,(2 \sin x + 1) = 0 \qquad \textit{Factor } \cos^2 x \textit{ from each term.}$$

By the Zero-Product Property, $\cos^2 x = 0$ or $2 \sin x + 1 = 0$. Solve each equation.

$$\cos^2 x = 0 \qquad\qquad\qquad 2 \sin x + 1 = 0$$
$$\cos x = 0 \quad \textit{Take } \pm \textit{ the square} \qquad 2 \sin x = -1 \quad \textit{Subtract 1 from each side.}$$
$$\textit{root of each side.} \qquad\qquad \sin x = -1/2 \quad \textit{Divide each side by 2.}$$

Find all solutions to $\cos x = 0$ and $\sin x = -1/2$ within the interval $[0, 2\pi)$. We know that $\cos x = 0$ exactly when $x = \pi/2$ and $x = 3\pi/2$ because $\pi/2$ and $3\pi/2$ are important angles.

Use the unit circle to solve $\sin x = -1/2$.

> **REMEMBER**
>
> *$\sin t = y$, where (x, y) is the point on the unit circle that corresponds to t.*

Since $\sin x < 0$, all solutions must be in quadrants III and IV (i.e., in quadrants where sine is negative).

Find all t-values on the unit circle in quadrants III and IV such that $\sin t = -1/2$.

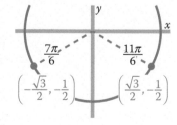

$$\sin \frac{7\pi}{6} = -\frac{1}{2} \text{ and } \sin \frac{11\pi}{6} = -\frac{1}{2}$$

Therefore, the solutions of $2 \cos^2 x \cdot \sin x = -\cos^2 x$ in $[0, 2\pi)$ are $x = \pi/2$, $7\pi/6$, $3\pi/2$, and $11\pi/6$.

CHECK

To confirm the solutions, graph $y = \cos x$ and $y = 0$, and graph $y = \sin x$ and $y = -1/2$, both on the interval on $[0, 2\pi)$.

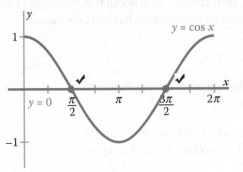 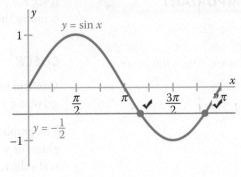

| EXAMPLE 5 | Solving a Trigonometric Equation by Factoring |

Solve. $2 - 2\sin^2 x = 1 + \cos x$

SOLUTION

Write the equation in general form.

$$2 - 2\sin^2 x = 1 + \cos x$$
$$-2\sin^2 x - \cos x + 1 = 0 \qquad \textit{Subtract 1 and cos x from each side.}$$

The expression $-2\sin^2 x - \cos x + 1$ cannot be factored. So, use the Pythagorean identity $\sin^2 x + \cos^2 x = 1$ to write the equation in terms of only cosine, and then factor (if possible).

$$-2(1 - \cos^2 x) - \cos x + 1 = 0 \qquad \textit{Substitute } 1 - \cos^2 x \textit{ for sin}^2 x.$$
$$-2 + 2\cos^2 x - \cos x + 1 = 0 \qquad \textit{Distribute } -2.$$
$$2\cos^2 x - \cos x - 1 = 0 \qquad \textit{Simplify.}$$
$$(2\cos x + 1)(\cos x - 1) = 0 \qquad \textit{Factor.}$$
$$2\cos x + 1 = 0 \quad \text{or} \quad \cos x - 1 = 0 \qquad \textit{Set each factor equal to 0.}$$
$$\cos x = -1/2 \qquad\qquad \cos x = 1 \qquad \textit{Solve each equation for cos x.}$$

Now solve each equation. We know that $\cos x = 1$ when $x = 0$ because 0 is an important angle.

> **TIP**
>
> Let S be $\cos x$.
> $2S^2 - S - 1 = 0$
> $(2S + 1)(S - 1) = 0$
> Substitute $\cos x$ for S.
> $(2\cos x + 1)(\cos x - 1) = 0$

Use the unit circle to solve $\cos x = -1/2$.

Since $\cos x < 0$, all solutions must be in quadrants II and III (i.e., in quadrants where cosine is negative).

> **REMEMBER**
>
> $\cos t = x$, where (x, y) is the point on the unit circle that corresponds to t.

Find all t-values on the unit circle in quadrants II and III such that $\cos t = -1/2$.

$$\cos \frac{2\pi}{3} = -\frac{1}{2} \text{ and } \cos \frac{4\pi}{3} = -\frac{1}{2}$$

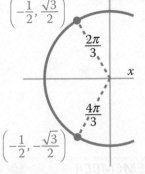

To write the general form equations of all solutions, add multiples of 2π (the period of $\cos x$) to each solution.

$$x = 2\pi n, \ x = \frac{2\pi}{3} + 2\pi n, \text{ and } x = \frac{4\pi}{3} + 2\pi n$$

3.2.5 Solving Trigonometric Equations Involving a Multiple of an Angle

If the angle of a trigonometric function has a coefficient (e.g., $\sin 2x$), then the trigonometric function involves a multiple of the angle.

The process for solving a trigonometric equation involving a multiple of an angle is demonstrated in **Example 6**.

EXAMPLE 6 **Solving a Trigonometric Equation Involving a Multiple Angle**

Find all solutions to $2 \sin 2x + \sqrt{3} = 0$ within the interval $[0, 2\pi)$.

SOLUTION

Isolate the trigonometric function.

> **TIP**
>
> *The solutions are all x-values within $[0, 2\pi)$ such that the sine of twice that value is equal to $-\sqrt{3}/2$.*

$$\sin 2x = -\frac{\sqrt{3}}{2} \qquad \textit{Subtract } \sqrt{3} \textit{ from each side and divide each side by 2.}$$

The coefficient of x is 2 and the given interval for the x-values is $0 \le x < 2\pi$, so the interval for the $2x$-values is $2(0) \le 2(x) < 2(2\pi)$, that is, $0 \le 2x < 4\pi$.

Find all $2x$-values within $[0, 4\pi)$ for which $\sin 2x = -\dfrac{\sqrt{3}}{2}$.

From the unit circle we know that $\sin \dfrac{4\pi}{3} = -\dfrac{\sqrt{3}}{2}$ and $\sin \dfrac{5\pi}{3} = -\dfrac{\sqrt{3}}{2}$.

Add 2π (the period of $\sin x$) to each $2x$-value.

> **NOTICE THAT**
>
> *Adding $2(2\pi)$ to either $4\pi/3$ or $5\pi/3$ results in a number greater than 4π, and thus not in the interval $[0, 4\pi)$.*

$$\frac{4\pi}{3} + 2\pi = \frac{4\pi}{3} + \frac{6\pi}{3} = \frac{10\pi}{3} < 4\pi$$

$$\frac{5\pi}{3} + 2\pi = \frac{5\pi}{3} + \frac{6\pi}{3} = \frac{11\pi}{3} < 4\pi$$

Therefore, $2x = \dfrac{4\pi}{3}, \dfrac{5\pi}{3}, \dfrac{10\pi}{3}, \dfrac{11\pi}{3}$.

Divide each $2x$-value by 2 to find the x-values.

$$x = \frac{2\pi}{3}, \frac{5\pi}{6}, \frac{5\pi}{3}, \frac{11\pi}{6}$$

So, $x = 2\pi/3, 5\pi/6, 5\pi/3$, and $11\pi/6$ are all of the solutions of $2 \sin 2x + \sqrt{3} = 0$ in $[0, 2\pi)$.

3.2.6 Solving Trigonometric Equations Involving a Multiple of an Angle: Another Example

| EXAMPLE 7 | Solving a Trigonometric Equation Involving a Multiple Angle |

Find all solutions to $\left(\sin\frac{1}{2}x\right) - \left(\tan\frac{1}{2}x\right)\left(\sin\frac{1}{2}x\right) = 0$ within the interval $[0, 10\pi)$.

SOLUTION

Factor $\sin\frac{1}{2}x$ from each term. $\qquad \left(\sin\frac{1}{2}x\right)\left(1 - \tan\frac{1}{2}x\right) = 0$

Set each factor equal to 0 and solve each equation for the trigonometric function.

$$\sin\frac{1}{2}x = 0 \quad \text{or} \quad 1 - \tan\frac{1}{2}x = 0 \;\Rightarrow\; \tan\frac{1}{2}x = 1 \qquad \textit{Subtract 1 from each side.}$$
$$\textit{Divide each side by } -1.$$

The coefficient of x is $1/2$ and the given interval for the x-values is $0 \le x < 10\pi$, so the interval for the $\frac{1}{2}x$-values is $\frac{1}{2}(0) \le \frac{1}{2}(x) < \frac{1}{2}(10\pi)$, that is, $0 \le \frac{1}{2}x < 5\pi$.

Find all $\frac{1}{2}x$-values within $[0, 5\pi)$ for which $\sin\frac{1}{2}x = 0$ or $\tan\frac{1}{2}x = 1$.

We know that $\sin 0 = 0$, $\sin \pi = 0$, and $\tan(\pi/4) = 1$ because 0, π, and $\pi/4$ are important angles. Furthermore, $x = 0$ and $x = \pi$ are the only solutions of $\sin\frac{1}{2}x = 0$ within one period of sine, $[0, 2\pi)$. And, $x = \pi/4$ is the only solution of $\tan\frac{1}{2}x = 1$ within the period of tangent, $[0, \pi)$.

IMPORTANT

To find all solutions in $[0, 5\pi)$, keep adding the period of sin x to 0 and π, and the period of tan x to $\pi/4$, until each sum is a value greater than or equal to 5π.

To find all $\frac{1}{2}x$-values within $[0, 5\pi)$ that are solutions for each equation, add positive multiples of each function's period to each solution. So, add 2π (the period of $\sin x$) to 0 and π to find all $\frac{1}{2}x$-values within $[0, 5\pi)$ for which $\sin\frac{1}{2}x = 0$.

$$0 + 2\pi = 2\pi \;{\scriptstyle <\, 5\pi} \qquad 0 + 2(2\pi) = 4\pi \;{\scriptstyle <\, 5\pi} \qquad 0 + 3(2\pi) = 6\pi \;{\scriptstyle >\, 5\pi}$$
$$\pi + 2\pi = 3\pi \;{\scriptstyle <\, 5\pi} \qquad \pi + 2(2\pi) = 5\pi \;{\scriptstyle =\, 5\pi} \qquad \pi + 3(2\pi) = 7\pi \;{\scriptstyle >\, 5\pi}$$

Add positive multiples of π (the period of $\tan x$) to $\pi/4$ to find all $\frac{1}{2}x$-values within $[0, 5\pi)$ for which $\tan\frac{1}{2}x = 1$.

$$\frac{\pi}{4} + \pi = \frac{\pi}{4} + \frac{4\pi}{4} = \frac{5\pi}{4} \;{\scriptstyle <\, 5\pi} \qquad\qquad \frac{\pi}{4} + 2\pi = \frac{\pi}{4} + \frac{8\pi}{4} = \frac{9\pi}{4} \;{\scriptstyle <\, 5\pi}$$
$$\frac{\pi}{4} + 3\pi = \frac{\pi}{4} + \frac{12\pi}{4} = \frac{13\pi}{4} \;{\scriptstyle <\, 5\pi} \qquad\qquad \frac{\pi}{4} + 4\pi = \frac{\pi}{4} + \frac{16\pi}{4} = \frac{17\pi}{4} \;{\scriptstyle <\, 5\pi}$$

IMPORTANT

Because the sum of 5π and $\pi/4$ is greater than 5π, it is clear that $17\pi/4$ is the greatest solution.

Therefore, $\frac{1}{2}x = 0, \frac{\pi}{4}, \pi, \frac{5\pi}{4}, 2\pi, \frac{9\pi}{4}, 3\pi, \frac{13\pi}{4}, 4\pi, \frac{17\pi}{4}$.

Multiply each $\frac{1}{2}x$-value by 2. $\qquad x = 0, \frac{\pi}{2}, 2\pi, \frac{5\pi}{2}, 4\pi, \frac{9\pi}{2}, 6\pi, \frac{13\pi}{2}, 8\pi, \frac{17\pi}{2}$

Therefore, $x = 0, \frac{\pi}{2}, 2\pi, \frac{5\pi}{2}, 4\pi, \frac{9\pi}{2}, 6\pi, \frac{13\pi}{2}, 8\pi$, and $\frac{17\pi}{2}$ are all of the solutions of $\left(\sin\frac{1}{2}x\right) - \left(\tan\frac{1}{2}x\right)\left(\sin\frac{1}{2}x\right) = 0$ within $[0, 10\pi)$.

3.2.7 Solving Trigonometric Equations of Quadratic Type

Recall from Section P.8 that an equation of quadratic type can be solved using a special substitution which results in a quadratic equation. Then the equation can be solved using one of the techniques for solving a quadratic equation, which include factoring and using the Quadratic Formula.

| **EXAMPLE 8** | **Solving a Trigonometric Equation by Factoring** |

Solve. $4\cos^4 x + 3 = 7\cos^2 x$

SOLUTION

Subtract $7\cos^2 x$ from each side so that the right side is 0.

$$4\cos^4 x + 3 = 7\cos^2 x \implies 4\cos^4 x - 7\cos^2 x + 3 = 0$$

Notice that substituting S for $\cos^2 x$ results in a quadratic equation in terms of S. Solve the quadratic equation.

$4S^2 - 7S + 3 = 0$	*Let $S = \cos^2 x$. Substitute.*
$(4S - 3)(S - 1) = 0$	*Factor.*
$4S - 3 = 0 \quad$ or $\quad S - 1 = 0$	*Set each factor equal to 0.*
$S = 3/4 \qquad\qquad S = 1$	*Solve each equation for S.*
$\cos^2 x = 3/4 \qquad \cos^2 x = 1$	*Substitute $\cos^2 x$ into each equation for S.*
$\cos x = \pm\dfrac{\sqrt{3}}{2} \qquad \cos x = \pm 1$	*Take $\pm$ the square root of each side.*

> **TIP**
>
> *If the quadratic expression cannot be factored, solve using the Quadratic Formula.*

Now solve each equation.

We know that $\cos x = 1$ when $x = 0$ because 0 is an important angle.

Additionally, we know that $\cos x = -1$ when $x = \pi$ because π is an important angle.

> **TIP**
>
> *Since $\cos x > 0$ and $\cos x < 0$, the solutions are in all four quadrants.*

Use the unit circle to solve $\cos x = \pm\dfrac{\sqrt{3}}{2}$. From the unit circle we know that

$$\cos\frac{\pi}{6} = \frac{\sqrt{3}}{2}, \cos\frac{11\pi}{6} = \frac{\sqrt{3}}{2}, \cos\frac{5\pi}{6} = -\frac{\sqrt{3}}{2}, \text{ and } \cos\frac{7\pi}{6} = -\frac{\sqrt{3}}{2}.$$

To write the general form equations of all solutions, add multiples of 2π (the period of $\cos x$) to each solution.

$$x = 2\pi n, x = \pi + 2\pi n, x = \frac{\pi}{6} + 2\pi n, x = \frac{5\pi}{6} + 2\pi n, x = \frac{7\pi}{6} + 2\pi n, \text{ and } x = \frac{11\pi}{6} + 2\pi n$$

Note that all solutions given by $x = \dfrac{\pi}{6} + 2\pi n$ and $x = \dfrac{7\pi}{6} + 2\pi n$ can be expressed as $x = \dfrac{\pi}{6} + \pi n$. Similarly, all solutions given by $x = \dfrac{5\pi}{6} + 2\pi n$ and $x = \dfrac{11\pi}{6} + 2\pi n$ can be expressed as $x = \dfrac{5\pi}{6} + \pi n$. In a similar way, the general forms $x = 2\pi n$ and $x = \pi + 2\pi n$ may be expressed as $x = \pi n$.

Therefore, $x = \pi n$, $x = \dfrac{\pi}{6} + \pi n$ and $x = \dfrac{5\pi}{6} + \pi n$ represent all the solutions of $4\cos^4 x + 3 = 7\cos^2 x$.

3.2.8 Solving Trigonometric Equations of Quadratic Type: Another Example

Recall that the three common methods for solving quadratic equations are factoring, completing the square, and using the Quadratic Formula, and that not all quadratic equations can be solved by factoring.

The Quadratic Formula will be used in **Example 9** to solve a trigonometric equation of quadratic type that cannot be factored.

EXAMPLE 9   Using the Quadratic Formula to Solve a Trigonometric Equation

---

Find all solutions to $\sin^2 x + \sin x = 1$. Round to the nearest thousandth as needed.

SOLUTION

Subtract 1 from each side so that the right side is 0.

$$\sin^2 x + \sin x = 1 \quad \Rightarrow \quad \sin^2 x + \sin x - 1 = 0$$

Notice that substituting S for $\sin x$ results in a quadratic equation in terms of S.

$$S^2 + S - 1 = 0 \qquad \textit{Substitute S for sin x.}$$

Solve the quadratic equation. The expression $S^2 + S - 1$ cannot be factored, so use the Quadratic Formula to solve the equation and then substitute $\sin x$ for S.

$$S = \frac{-1 \pm \sqrt{1^2 - 4(1)(-1)}}{2(1)} = \frac{-1 \pm \sqrt{5}}{2} \qquad \textit{Substitute a = 1, b = 1, and c = -1 into the Quadratic Formula to solve for S.}$$

$$\sin x = \frac{-1 + \sqrt{5}}{2} \quad \text{or} \quad \sin x = \frac{-1 - \sqrt{5}}{2} \qquad \textit{Substitute sin x for S.}$$

Next, use the inverse sine function to solve each equation, if possible.

However, note that $\sin^{-1}\left(\dfrac{-1 - \sqrt{5}}{2}\right)$ does not exist, because $\dfrac{-1 - \sqrt{5}}{2} < -1$.

Therefore, use the inverse sine function to solve $\sin x = \dfrac{-1 + \sqrt{5}}{2}$.

$$x = \sin^{-1}\left(\frac{-1 + \sqrt{5}}{2}\right) = 0.6662\ldots \approx 0.666 \qquad \textit{Use a calculator.}$$
$$\textit{Round to the nearest thousandth.}$$

Since $\sin x = \dfrac{-1 + \sqrt{5}}{2} > 0$ and $\sin x > 0$ in quadrants I and II, there is a solution in quadrant II.

$$x = \pi - 0.6662\ldots \approx 2.475 \qquad \textit{Subtract 0.6662\ldots from π to find the solution in quadrant II.}$$

To write the general form equations of all solutions, add multiples of 2π (the period of $\sin x$) to each solution.

$$x \approx 0.666 + 2\pi n \text{ and } x \approx 2.475 + 2\pi n$$

3.2.9   Solving Trigonometric Equations Using Fundamental Identities

Any of the fundamental trigonometric identities from Section 3.1 can be used to rewrite a trigonometric equation in a form that is easier to solve.

EXAMPLE 10   Using Identities to Solve a Trigonometric Equation

Find all solutions to $\sec^2 x + \tan x - 2 = \tan(-x)$ within the interval $[0, 2\pi]$. Round to the nearest thousandth as needed.

SOLUTION

Use an even-odd identity to write $\tan(-x)$ as a function of x (instead of $-x$), and use a Pythagorean identity to write the equation in terms of tangent only.

$$\sec^2 x + \tan x - 2 = \tan(-x)$$

$\sec^2 x + \tan x - 2 = -\tan x$	*Even-Odd Identity*
$\sec^2 x + \tan x - 1 - 1 = -\tan x$	*Express -2 as $-1 - 1$.*
$(\sec^2 x - 1) + \tan x - 1 = -\tan x$	*Associative and Commutative Properties*
$\tan^2 x + \tan x - 1 = -\tan x$	*Pythagorean Identity*
$\tan^2 x + 2\tan x - 1 = 0$	*Add $\tan x$ to each side.*
$S^2 + 2S - 1 = 0$	*Substitute S for $\tan x$.*

Pythagorean Identity ▶
$1 + tan^2\,\theta = sec^2\,\theta$

$$S = \frac{-2 \pm \sqrt{2^2 - 4(1)(-1)}}{2(1)} = \frac{-2 \pm 2\sqrt{2}}{2} = -1 \pm \sqrt{2} \qquad$$ *Substitute $a = 1$, $b = 2$, and $c = -1$ into the Quadratic Formula to solve for S.*

$$\tan x = -1 + \sqrt{2} \quad \text{or} \quad \tan x = -1 - \sqrt{2} \qquad$$ *Substitute $\tan x$ for S.*

Use the inverse tangent function to solve each equation.

$$x = \tan^{-1}\left(-1 + \sqrt{2}\right) = 0.3926\ldots \approx 0.393 \text{ or}$$

$$x = \tan^{-1}\left(-1 - \sqrt{2}\right) = -1.1780\ldots \approx -1.178$$

Use a calculator and round to the nearest thousandth.

Since $\tan x = -1 + \sqrt{2} > 0$ and $\tan x > 0$ in quadrants I and III, there is a solution in quadrant III.

$$x = \pi + 0.3926\ldots \approx 3.533 \qquad$$ *Add π to $0.3926\ldots$ to find the solution in quadrant III.*

Note that $x \approx -1.178$ is not in the interval $[0, 2\pi]$.

However, since $\tan x = -1 - \sqrt{2} < 0$ and $\tan x < 0$ in quadrants II and IV, use $x = -1.1780\ldots$ to find the solutions in quadrants II and IV.

$$x = \pi + (-1.1780\ldots) \approx 1.962 \qquad$$ *Add π to $-1.1780\ldots$ to find the solution in quadrant II.*

$$x = 2\pi + (-1.1780\ldots) \approx 5.102 \qquad$$ *Add 2π to $-1.1780\ldots$ to find the solution in quadrant IV.*

Therefore, $x \approx 0.393, 1.962, 3.533,$ and 5.102 are all of the solutions of $\sec^2 x + \tan x - 2 = \tan(-x)$ within the interval $[0, 2\pi]$.

3.2.10 Applications Involving Trigonometric Equations

EXAMPLE 11	Modeling with a Trigonometric Equation

Suppose the electromotive force E (in volts) in an electric circuit after t seconds is given by $E(t) = 2\cos 50\pi t$. Find the smallest positive t-value for which the electromotive force is 2 volts.

SOLUTION

Substitute 2 for $E(t)$ and solve for t.

$$2 = 2\cos 50\pi t \qquad \textit{Substitute 2 for E(t).}$$

$$1 = \cos 50\pi t \qquad \textit{Divide each side by 2.}$$

$$\cos^{-1}(1) = 50\pi t \qquad \textit{Take the inverse cosine of each side.}$$

We know that $\cos^{-1}(1) = 0$. Solving $0 = 50\pi t$ for t yields $t = 0$, so at time 0 (after 0 seconds) the electromotive force is 2 volts. However, the question asks for the smallest *positive* t-value. Since 0 is not positive, evaluate $\cos^{-1}(1)$ as the smallest *positive* angle with cosine equal to 1, which is 2π.

Substitute 2π for $\cos^{-1}(1)$ and solve for t.

$$2\pi = 50\pi t \qquad \textit{The smallest positive angle with cosine equal to 1 is } 2\pi.$$

$$t = 1/25 \qquad \textit{Divide each side by 50}\pi.$$

Thus, the electromotive force is 2 volts after 1/25 seconds.

SECTION 3.2 EXERCISES

Warm Up

Solve each equation by factoring.

1. $6x^2 + 7x = 3$

2. $20x = 4x^2$

3. $13x = -6 + 5x^2$

Just the Facts

Fill in the blanks.

4. Solutions to polynomial equations or trigonometric equations are the values that make the equations _____.

5. A trigonometric equation may have an infinite number of solutions due to its _____ nature.

6. To write the general form for all solutions to a trigonometric equation, _____ multiples of the _____ to the solutions found within one period.

7. Use _____ trigonometric functions to find the value of an angle.

8. If $y = f(x)$ is a trigonometric function and the y-value is not in the range of the trigonometric function, then the equation has _____.

9. Applying the even-odd identity, $\tan(-x) =$ _____.

10. Checking the _____ of the calculator is very important when solving for an angle.

Essential Skills

In Exercises 1–24, solve each equation.

1. $\sin x = \dfrac{\sqrt{3}}{2}$

2. $\sec x = -\dfrac{2}{\sqrt{3}}$

3. $\tan x = -1$

4. $\cos x = 1/2$

5. $\cot x = -\sqrt{3}$

6. $\csc x = -2$

7. $\sec x = 1$

8. $\csc x = -1$

9. $\cos x = 0$

10. $\cot x = 0$

11. $2\cos x - 3 = -4$

12. $2\sqrt{3} - \tan x = \sqrt{3}$

13. $2 = 4 + 2\cot x$

14. $4 + \sqrt{3}\sec x = 6$

15. $-3 = -5 + \sqrt{3}\csc x$

16. $7 + 2\sin x = 8$

17. $\tan^2 x = 3$

18. $2\csc^2 x = 4$

19. $-3 = -4\sin^2 x$

20. $10\cos^2 x = 5$

21. $\tan^2 x + 6 = 2\tan^2 x + 5$

22. $5\cos^2 x + 4 = 7 + \cos^2 x$

23. $2 + 7\csc^2 x = 8 + 4\csc^2 x$

24. $\sin^2 x + 6 = 5 + 5\sin^2 x$

In Exercises 25–28, using a calculator, find all solutions to each equation within the interval $[0, 2\pi)$ using inverse functions. Round each answer to the nearest thousandth.

25. $2\cos x + 1.3 = 2.06$

26. $3.6 - 1.6\sin x = 3.2$

27. $8.96 - 4.8\csc x = 3.4$

28. $0.96\cot x + 3.16 = 4.48$

In Exercises 29–68, find all solutions to each equation within the interval $[0, 2\pi)$, unless otherwise stated.

29. $\tan^2 x \cdot \csc x = \tan^2 x$

30. $2\sin x \cdot \cos x = \sin x$

31. $3\tan x = \tan^3 x$

32. $-5\sin^3 x = -5\sin x$

33. $\tan^2 x + \tan x = 0$

34. $\tan x \cdot \sec x = \tan x$

35. $2\sin^2 x + \sin x = 1$

36. $2\cos^2 x - 5\cos x = -2$

37. $4\csc^2 x + 4\csc x + 1 = 0$

38. $2\sec^2 x - 3\sec x = 2$

39. $2\cos^2 x + \cos x = 1$

40. $\sin^2 x + 5\sin x + 6 = 0$

41. $3 - 3\sin x = 2\cos^2 x$

42. $2\cos^2 x = 1 + \sin x$

43. $\tan^2 x - \sec x - 1 = 0$

44. $\sec^2 x = \left(\sqrt{3}+1\right)\tan x - \sqrt{3} + 1$

45. $\tan^5 x - 9\tan x = 0$

46. $3 - \cos^2 x + 3\sin x + 1 = \cos^2 x$

47. $2 \cot \dfrac{x}{2} = 2\sqrt{3}$

48. $\sec \dfrac{3\pi}{2} = -2$

49. $2 \cos 2x = 1$

50. $\tan 2\pi = \sqrt{3};\ [0, \pi)$

51. $3 \tan \dfrac{x}{2} + 3 = 0$

52. $\csc \dfrac{x}{2} = -\dfrac{2}{\sqrt{3}};\ [0, 4\pi)$

53. $\sin^2 2x = 1/4$

54. $4 \cos^2 2x - 4 \cos 2x + 1 = 0$

55. $\cos^2 2\theta = 1/4$

56. $\tan^2 2x - 2 \tan 2x + 1 = 0$

57. $\cos^2 2x - \sin^2 2x = 0$

58. $4 \csc^2 2x - 5 \csc 2x + 1 = 0$

59. $\sin 2x = 2 \tan 2x$

60. $\sin 3x \cdot \cos 2x = 0$

61. $\tan 3x + 1 = \sec 3x$

62. $\sec 3x \cdot \cos 2x = 0$

63. $\cos 3x \cdot \sin 2x = 0$

64. $\csc 5x \cdot \cos 2x = 0$

65. $\tan^4 x - 4 \tan^2 x + 3 = 0$

66. $8 \sin^4 \theta + 3 = 10 \sin^2 \theta$

67. $3 \csc^4 x - 16 \csc^2 x + 16 = 0$

68. $4 \cot^4 \theta - 3 = \cot^2 \theta$

In Exercises 69–78, find all solutions to each equation within the interval [0, 2π). Round each answer to the nearest thousandth.

69. $\cos^2 x - 3 \cos x + 1 = 0$

70. $5 \tan^2 x - 3 \tan x - 5 = 0$

71. $\csc^2 x - \csc x = 1$

72. $10 \sin^2 x - 3 \sin x - 2 = 0$

73. $\sin^2 2x - 3 \sin 2x + 1 = 0$

74. $2 \cos^2 3x + 6 \cos 3x = 3$

75. $\sin^2 \dfrac{x}{2} + 4 \sin \dfrac{x}{2} + 2 = 0$

76. $8 \sin^2 2x + 7 \sin 2x = 4$

77. $\cos x - \sin (-x) \cdot \tan x - 2 = 1$

78. $\dfrac{\cos (-x) + \cos x}{\sin x + 3 \sin (-x)} = \sqrt{3}$

In Exercises 79–88, find all solutions to each equation within the interval [0, 2π).

79. $\cos x(\sec x - \cos x) - 1 = 0$

80. $\cos x + \tan x \cdot \sin x = \dfrac{2}{\sqrt{3}}$

81. $\sin x \cdot \csc (-x) - \sec (-x) \cdot \cot (-x) = 0$

82. $\cot (-x) \cdot \tan (-x) + \sin (-x) \cdot \sin x = 2$

83. $\sec^2 x = \dfrac{1}{1 - \sin x} - \dfrac{1}{1 + \sin x}$

84. $\sec^2 x = 2 \tan x$

85. $\dfrac{\cos^2 x}{\sin x - 1} = -1$

86. $1 + \cos x = 2 - 2 \sin^2 x$

87. $\sec x = \tan x + \cot x$

88. $\csc^2 x = -2 \cot x$

In Exercises 89–94, use the following information.

A child is playing with a yo-yo. When the child does a certain trick, the yo-yo's position in feet relative to the ground is S(t), where t is the time in seconds. After how many seconds, to the nearest thousandth of a second, is the yo-yo first at the specified height?

89. $S(t) = -2 \sin 2\pi t + 2.2;\ 0.25$ feet

90. $S(t) = -2 \sin 2\pi t + 3;\ 1.5$ feet

91. $S(t) = -2.25 \sin 2\pi t + 2.26;\ 0.75$ feet

92. $S(t) = -1.75 \sin 2\pi t + 2;\ 0.25$ feet

93. $S(t) = -1.6 \sin 2\pi t + 2.9;\ 4.35$ feet

94. $S(t) = -2.25 \sin 2\pi t + 2.8;\ 0.5$ feet

Extensions

95. A weight is oscillating on the end of a spring. The position of the weight relative to the point of equilibrium is given by the equation $y = \dfrac{1}{12}(\sqrt{3} \cos 8t - 3 \sin 8t)$ where y is the displacement in meters and t is the time in seconds. Find the smallest positive value of t when the weight is at the point of equilibrium. Leave answer in terms of π.

96. An electric generator produces a 30-cycle alternating current described by the equation below.

$$I(t) = 40 \sin \left(60\pi \left(t - \dfrac{7}{72} \right) \right)$$

If $I(t)$ is the current measured in amperes at t seconds, find the smallest positive value of t for which the current is 20 amperes. Leave answer in terms of π.

SECTION 3.2 ~ SOLVING TRIGONOMETRIC EQUATIONS 359

97. In an electric circuit, the electromotive force is $E(t)$ volts where $E(t) = 2\cos 50\pi t$. Find the smallest positive value of t to the nearest thousandth of a second for which the electromotive force is 1.6 volts.

98. Verify $4\cos^2 2x - 4\cos 2x + 1 = 0$ when $x = 5\pi/6$.

99. Solve $\cos^2 \dfrac{x}{2} - \dfrac{1}{2}\cos \dfrac{x}{2} = \dfrac{1}{2}$ on the interval $[0, 10\pi)$.

100. Verify $3\csc^4 x - 16\csc^2 x + 16 = 0$ when $x = 7\pi/6$.

101. To the nearest hundredth of a degree, at what angle must a cannon ball be shot in order to hit a target 500 meters away, if the muzzle velocity V_0 is 150 meters per second and the horizontal distance r traveled is given by the equation $r = \dfrac{1}{9.8}V_0^2 \sin 2\pi$?

102. A baseball was thrown from first base at an angle θ with the horizontal and with an initial velocity V_0 of 80 feet per second. The ball was caught by the second-base player who was 100 feet away. Find θ if the horizontal distance covered by the ball, r, is given by the equation $r = \dfrac{1}{32}V_0^2 \sin 2\theta$.

103. Verify $\tan 3x - \sec 3x = -1$ when $x = 2\pi/3$, if possible.

104. Solve $10\sec^2 x - 10 = 7\tan x + 2$ on the interval $[0, 2\pi)$.

3.3 THE SUM AND DIFFERENCE FORMULAS

OBJECTIVES

- Use sum and difference formulas to evaluate trigonometric functions.
- Prove the cofunction identities using sum and difference formulas.
- Use sum and difference formulas to verify an identity.

PREREQUISITE VOCABULARY TERMS

cofunction identities

fundamental trigonometric identities

trigonometric functions

3.3.1 Introduction to the Sum and Difference Formulas

Consider the equation $\sin(\pi + \pi) = \sin \pi + \sin \pi$. This equation is a true statement because $\sin(\pi + \pi) = \sin 2\pi = 0$, $\sin \pi + \sin \pi = 0 + 0 = 0$, and, of course, $0 = 0$. Based on that result, we might wonder whether $\sin(x + y) = \sin x + \sin y$ is an identity (i.e., whether $\sin(x + y) = \sin x + \sin y$ is a true statement for all real numbers x and y). However, $x = \pi/2$ and $y = \pi$ provide a counterexample.

$$\sin(\pi/2 + \pi) = \sin(3\pi/2) = -1 \quad \text{and} \quad \sin(\pi/2) + \sin \pi = 1 + 0 = 1$$

Because $-1 \neq 1$, the equation $\sin(x + y) = \sin x + \sin y$ is not an identity.

However, identities for the sum of angles of trigonometric functions do exist. The following **sum and difference formulas** provide ways to express the sine, cosine, or tangent of a sum or a difference of angles θ_1 and θ_2. Each formula is an identity, so each is true for all values in the trigonometric function's domain.

Sum and Difference Formulas	
Sum of Angles Formulas	**Difference of Angles Formulas**
$\sin(\theta_1 + \theta_2) = \sin \theta_1 \cos \theta_2 + \cos \theta_1 \sin \theta_2$	$\sin(\theta_1 - \theta_2) = \sin \theta_1 \cos \theta_2 - \cos \theta_1 \sin \theta_2$
$\cos(\theta_1 + \theta_2) = \cos \theta_1 \cos \theta_2 - \sin \theta_1 \sin \theta_2$	$\cos(\theta_1 - \theta_2) = \cos \theta_1 \cos \theta_2 + \sin \theta_1 \sin \theta_2$
$\tan(\theta_1 + \theta_2) = \dfrac{\tan \theta_1 + \tan \theta_2}{1 - \tan \theta_1 \tan \theta_2}$	$\tan(\theta_1 - \theta_2) = \dfrac{\tan \theta_1 - \tan \theta_2}{1 + \tan \theta_1 \tan \theta_2}$

3.3.2 Using the Sum and Difference Formulas to Find Exact Values

Recall that if an angle θ is a multiple of $\pi/6$ or $\pi/4$ (i.e., 30° or 45°), then the exact value of a trigonometric function of θ can be determined using the function's graph, the unit circle, or a reference angle on a coordinate plane (among other methods). Otherwise (i.e., if θ is not a multiple of $\pi/6$ or $\pi/4$), a calculator has been used to find a decimal approximation of the trigonometric function of θ.

The sum and difference formulas provide methods for finding the exact value of a trigonometric function for values of θ such that $\theta = \theta_1 + \theta_2$ or $\theta = \theta_1 - \theta_2$, where θ_1 and θ_2 are multiples of $\pi/6$ or $\pi/4$. In other words, a sum formula or a difference formula gives the exact value of a trigonometric function of θ when θ can be expressed as a sum or as a difference of multiples of $\pi/6$ or $\pi/4$.

| **EXAMPLE 1** | **Using the Sum and Difference Formulas to Find the Exact Value of a Trigonometric Function** |

Find the exact value of each trigonometric function, if possible.

A. $\cos 105°$ **B.** $\tan 5\pi/12$

SOLUTION

Find two angles θ_1 and θ_2 (multiples of $\pi/6$ or $\pi/4$) such that their sum or difference is equal to the measure of the angle in the given trigonometric function. Then substitute the values of θ_1 and θ_2 into the corresponding sum or difference formula and simplify.

A. Notice that $105° = 150° - 45°$, $150°$ is a multiple of $30°$, and $45°$ is a multiple of $45°$. So, use the difference formula $\cos(\theta_1 - \theta_2) = \cos\theta_1 \cos\theta_2 + \sin\theta_1 \sin\theta_2$, where $\theta_1 = 150°$ and $\theta_2 = 45°$, to evaluate $\cos 105°$.

ALTERNATIVE METHOD

$60°$ is a multiple of $30°$, $45°$ is a multiple of $45°$, and $60° + 45° = 105°$, so the cosine of a sum formula can be used to evaluate $\cos 105°$, where $\theta_1 = 60°$ and $\theta_2 = 45°$ (or $\theta_1 = 45°$ and $\theta_2 = 60°$).

$$\cos 105° = \cos(150° - 45°)$$

$$= \cos 150° \cos 45° + \sin 150° \sin 45° \qquad \textit{Use the cosine of a difference formula.}$$

$$= -\frac{\sqrt{3}}{2} \cdot \frac{\sqrt{2}}{2} + \frac{1}{2} \cdot \frac{\sqrt{2}}{2} \qquad \textit{Evaluate each trigonometric function.}$$

$$= -\frac{\sqrt{6}}{4} + \frac{\sqrt{2}}{4} \qquad \textit{Multiply.}$$

$$= \frac{-\sqrt{6} + \sqrt{2}}{4} \qquad \textit{Add.}$$

B. Since $\dfrac{5\pi}{12} = \dfrac{3\pi}{12} + \dfrac{2\pi}{12} = \dfrac{\pi}{4} + \dfrac{\pi}{6}$, use the tangent of a sum formula, where $\theta_1 = \pi/4$ and $\theta_2 = \pi/6$, to evaluate $\tan 5\pi/12$.

ALTERNATIVE METHOD

The tangent of a difference formula can be used to evaluate $\tan 5\pi/12$, where $\theta_1 = 2\pi/3$ and $\theta_2 = \pi/4$.

$$\tan\frac{5\pi}{12} = \tan\left(\frac{\pi}{4} + \frac{\pi}{6}\right)$$

$$= \frac{\tan\dfrac{\pi}{4} + \tan\dfrac{\pi}{6}}{1 - \tan\dfrac{\pi}{4} \cdot \tan\dfrac{\pi}{6}} \qquad \textit{Use the tangent of a sum formula.}$$

$$= \frac{1 + \dfrac{1}{\sqrt{3}}}{1 - \dfrac{1}{\sqrt{3}}} \qquad \textit{Evaluate each trigonometric function.}$$

$$= \frac{\left(1 + \dfrac{1}{\sqrt{3}}\right)\sqrt{3}}{\left(1 - \dfrac{1}{\sqrt{3}}\right)\sqrt{3}} \qquad \textit{Multiply the numerator and denominator by $\sqrt{3}$ to simplify the complex fraction.}$$

$$= \frac{\sqrt{3} + 1}{\sqrt{3} - 1} \qquad \textit{Simplify.}$$

TIP

Rationalizing the denominator results in $\tan\dfrac{5\pi}{12} = 2 + \sqrt{3}$.

CHECK

Use a calculator to check each answer.

$$\cos 105° \approx -0.259 \text{ and } \frac{-\sqrt{6} + \sqrt{2}}{4} \approx -0.259 \checkmark \qquad\qquad \tan\frac{5\pi}{12} \approx 3.732 \text{ and } \frac{\sqrt{3} + 1}{\sqrt{3} - 1} \approx 3.732 \checkmark$$

3.3.3 Using the Sum and Difference Formulas to Find Exact Values: Another Example

If an expression is given in the expanded form of a sum or difference formula, then the expression can be simplified and written as the trigonometric function of the sum (or difference) of the angles, as demonstrated in **Example 2**. The exact value of the function can be determined if the sum (or difference) of those angles is a multiple of $\pi/6$ or $\pi/4$.

EXAMPLE 2   **Using the Sum and Difference Formulas to Simplify a Trigonometric Expression**

Find the exact value of $\cos \dfrac{\pi}{12} \cos \dfrac{5\pi}{12} + \sin \dfrac{\pi}{12} \sin \dfrac{5\pi}{12}$, if possible.

SOLUTION

The expression is in the expanded form of the cosine of a difference formula, $\cos \theta_1 \cos \theta_2 + \sin \theta_1 \sin \theta_2$, where $\theta_1 = \pi/12$ and $\theta_2 = 5\pi/12$. So, use this formula to simplify.

$$\cos \frac{\pi}{12} \cos \frac{5\pi}{12} + \sin \frac{\pi}{12} \sin \frac{5\pi}{12} = \cos\left(\frac{\pi}{12} - \frac{5\pi}{12}\right) \quad \textit{Use the cosine of a difference formula.}$$

$$= \cos\left(-\frac{4\pi}{12}\right) \quad \textit{Subtract.}$$

$$= \cos\left(-\frac{\pi}{3}\right) \quad \textit{Simplify.}$$

$$= \cos\frac{\pi}{3} \quad \textit{Even-Odd Identity}$$

$$= \frac{1}{2} \quad \textit{Evaluate the trigonometric function.}$$

> **REMEMBER**
>
> *Since cosine is an even function, $\cos(-x) = \cos x$.*

3.3.4 Using the Sum and Difference Formulas to Verify a Cofunction Identity

Verifying the Cofunction Identities

In this section we will establish a more formal proof of the cofunction identities that were introduced in Section 3.1.

Cofunction Identities		
$\sin\left(\dfrac{\pi}{2} - \theta\right) = \cos\theta$	$\cos\left(\dfrac{\pi}{2} - \theta\right) = \sin\theta$	$\tan\left(\dfrac{\pi}{2} - \theta\right) = \cot\theta$
$\csc\left(\dfrac{\pi}{2} - \theta\right) = \sec\theta$	$\sec\left(\dfrac{\pi}{2} - \theta\right) = \csc\theta$	$\cot\left(\dfrac{\pi}{2} - \theta\right) = \tan\theta$

Since each cofunction identity involves a trigonometric function of a difference of angles, the difference formulas can be used to expand the expression. Moreover, these identities can be proven using the difference formulas.

For example, expand $\sin\left(\dfrac{\pi}{2}-\theta\right)$ using the sine of a difference of angles formula, where $\theta_1 = \pi/2$ and $\theta_2 = \theta$, to verify that $\sin\left(\dfrac{\pi}{2}-\theta\right) = \cos\theta$ is an identity.

$$\sin\left(\frac{\pi}{2}-\theta\right) = \sin\frac{\pi}{2}\,\cos\theta - \cos\frac{\pi}{2}\,\sin\theta$$

$$= 1\cdot\cos\theta - 0\cdot\sin\theta$$

$$= \cos\theta \quad \checkmark$$

Therefore, $\sin\left(\dfrac{\pi}{2}-\theta\right) = \cos\theta$ is an identity.

A similar process can be used to verify the other five cofunction identities.

Deriving Additional Cofunction Identities

Additional identities can be derived using the sum and difference formulas. For example, suppose the difference of angles is $\theta - \pi/2$ (instead of $\pi/2 - \theta$). Then an identity involving $\sin\left(\theta - \dfrac{\pi}{2}\right)$ can be derived by using the sine of a difference of angles formula, where $\theta_1 = \theta$ and $\theta_2 = \pi/2$, as demonstrated in **Example 3**.

EXAMPLE 3   **Using the Sum and Difference Formulas to Derive a Cofunction Identity**

Complete the identity $\sin\left(\theta - \dfrac{\pi}{2}\right) = $ _____.

SOLUTION

$$\sin\left(\theta - \frac{\pi}{2}\right) = \sin\theta\,\cos\frac{\pi}{2} - \cos\theta\,\sin\frac{\pi}{2} \qquad \textit{Use the sine of a difference formula.}$$

$$= \sin\theta\cdot 0 - \cos\theta\cdot 1 \qquad \textit{Evaluate cos (π/2) and sin (π/2).}$$

$$= 0 - \cos\theta \qquad \textit{Simplify.}$$

$$= -\cos\theta \qquad \textit{Subtract.}$$

Therefore, $\sin\left(\theta - \dfrac{\pi}{2}\right) = -\cos\theta$ is an identity.

Identities for the other five trigonometric functions can be determined using a similar process.

Cofunction Identities ($\theta - \pi/2$)		
$\sin\left(\theta - \dfrac{\pi}{2}\right) = -\cos\theta$	$\cos\left(\theta - \dfrac{\pi}{2}\right) = \sin\theta$	$\tan\left(\theta - \dfrac{\pi}{2}\right) = -\cot\theta$
$\csc\left(\theta - \dfrac{\pi}{2}\right) = -\sec\theta$	$\sec\left(\theta - \dfrac{\pi}{2}\right) = \csc\theta$	$\cot\left(\theta - \dfrac{\pi}{2}\right) = -\tan\theta$

3.3.5 Using the Sum and Difference Formulas to Verify an Identity

EXAMPLE 4   **Proving a Trigonometric Identity**

Determine whether $\cos(x + y) \cos y + \sin(x + y) \sin y = \cos x$ is an identity or not.

SOLUTION

The expression on the right side is simplified. So, simplify the left side to determine whether or not it is equal to the right side.

The expression on the left side contains $\cos(x + y)$ and $\sin(x + y)$, so use the cosine of a sum formula to expand $\cos(x + y)$, and use the sine of a sum of angles formula to expand $\sin(x + y)$.

$\cos(x + y) \cos y + \sin(x + y) \sin y$

$= (\cos x \cos y - \sin x \sin y) \cos y + (\sin x \cos y + \cos x \sin y) \sin y$ *Expand.*

$= \cos x \cos^2 y - \sin x \sin y \cos y + \sin x \cos y \sin y + \cos x \sin^2 y$ *Distribute.*

$= \cos x \cos^2 y + \cos x \sin^2 y$ *Simplify.*

$= \cos x (\cos^2 y + \sin^2 y)$ *Factor out cos x.*

$= \cos x \,(1)$ *Pythagorean Identity*

$= \cos x$ ✔

So, $\cos(x + y) \cos y + \sin(x + y) \sin y = \cos x$ is an identity.

> **NOTICE THAT**
>
> *The sum of the second term ($-\sin x \sin y \cos y$) and the third term ($\sin x \cos y \sin y$) is 0.*

3.3.6 Using the Sum and Difference Formulas to Solve an Equation

Recall that an equation where the domain is not all real numbers may have an extraneous solution (i.e., a solution not in the equation's domain). So, if an equation's domain is not all real numbers, each possible solutions should be checked to confirm that it is in the equation's domain (and therefore not extraneous).

For example, consider the equation $\tan(x + \pi) = -2 \sin(x + \pi)$, as seen in **Example 5**. This equation contains the tangent of an unknown angle and the sine of an unknown angle. We know that sine is defined for all real numbers (because the domain of $\sin x$ is all real numbers). However, tangent is not defined for all real numbers (because the domain of $\tan x$ is all real numbers except all x such that $x = \pi/2 + \pi n$, where n is an integer). Therefore, extraneous solutions may be found when the equation is solved.

EXAMPLE 5   **Solving a Trigonometric Equation**

Find all solutions to $\tan(x + \pi) = -2\sin(x + \pi)$ within the interval $[0, 2\pi)$.

SOLUTION

The equation contains the tangent of a sum and the sine of a sum, so use the tangent and sine of a sum formulas to expand.

$$\tan(x + \pi) = -2\sin(x + \pi)$$

$$\frac{\tan x + \tan \pi}{1 - \tan x \, \tan \pi} = -2(\sin x \cos \pi + \cos x \sin \pi) \qquad \textit{Expand.}$$

$$\frac{\tan x + 0}{1 - \tan x \cdot 0} = -2(\sin x \cdot (-1) + \cos x \cdot 0) \qquad \textit{Evaluate the trigonometric functions.}$$

$$\tan x = -2(-\sin x) \qquad \textit{Simplify.}$$

$$\tan x = 2 \sin x \qquad \textit{Multiply.}$$

$$\tan x - 2 \sin x = 0 \qquad \textit{Subtract 2 sin x from each side.}$$

$$\frac{\sin x}{\cos x} - 2 \sin x = 0 \qquad \textit{Quotient Identity}$$

$$\frac{\sin x}{\cos x} - \frac{2 \sin x \cos x}{\cos x} = 0 \qquad \textit{Write the terms with a common denominator.}$$

$$\frac{\sin x - 2 \sin x \cos x}{\cos x} = 0 \qquad \textit{Subtract.}$$

Since the fraction is equal to 0, the numerator must also be equal to 0. Therefore, we can set the numerator equal to 0, and then solve the resulting equation. Note, however, that all values of x such that $\cos x = 0$ must be excluded from the equation's domain.

$$\sin x - 2 \sin x \cos x = 0 \qquad \textit{Set the numerator equal to 0.}$$

$$\sin x \, (1 - 2 \cos x) = 0 \qquad \textit{Factor out sin x.}$$

$$\sin x = 0 \quad \text{or} \quad 1 - 2 \cos x = 0 \qquad \textit{Set each factor equal to 0.}$$

$$\cos x = 1/2 \qquad \textit{Solve for cos x.}$$

Find all solutions to $\sin x = 0$ and $\cos x = 1/2$ within the interval $[0, 2\pi)$.

- $\sin 0 = 0$, so $x = 0$.
- $\sin \pi = 0$, so $x = \pi$.

- $\cos(\pi/3) = 1/2$, so $x = \pi/3$.
- $\cos(5\pi/3) = 1/2$, so $x = 5\pi/3$.

Check for extraneous solutions.

The equation's domain excludes
- all x-values such that $\cos x = 0$ (i.e., all x such that $x = \pi/2 + \pi n$) and
- all x-values for which $\tan(x + \pi)$ is undefined (i.e., all x such that $x = \pi/2 + \pi n$).

The solutions $x = 0$, $\pi/3$, π, and $5\pi/3$ are not excluded from the domain, so they are not extraneous solutions.

Therefore, $x = 0$, $\pi/3$, π, and $5\pi/3$ are all of the solutions of $\tan(x + \pi) = -2\sin(x + \pi)$ within the interval $[0, 2\pi)$.

SECTION 3.3 EXERCISES

Warm Up

Write a sum of multiples of π/6 or π/4 equal to each given angle.

1. $7\pi/12$

2. $75°$

3. $-105°$

Just the Facts

Fill in the blanks.

4. A(n) _____ is an equation that is true for all values in the trigonometric function's domain.

5. True or False? $\cos (A + B) = \cos A + \cos B$ is an identity.

6. By the tangent of a _____ formula, the expansion of $\tan(60° + 45°)$ is _____.

7. By the cosine of a _____ formula, the expansion of _____ is $\cos A \cos B - \sin A \sin B$.

8. By the sine of a _____ formula, the expansion of _____ is $\sin A \cos B - \cos A \sin B$.

9. When solving an equation that involves a trigonometric function that is not defined for all values of x, the solutions must be checked to ensure that there are no _____ solutions.

10. A sum or difference formula can be used to find an exact value of a trigonometric function of θ when θ can be expressed as a sum or _____ of multiples of $\pi/6$ or _____.

Essential Skills

In Exercises 1–4, write the sine, cosine, and tangent of each angle using a difference formula.

1. $75°$

2. $165°$

3. $7\pi/12$

4. $195°$

In Exercises 5–16, find the exact value of each trigonometric function, if possible.

5. $\sin 255°$

6. $\sin (7\pi/12)$

7. $\sin 195°$

8. $\sin (\pi/12)$

9. $\cos 165°$

10. $\cos (5\pi/12)$

11. $\cos 15°$

12. $\cos (11\pi/12)$

13. $\tan 165°$

14. $\tan (11\pi/12)$

15. $\tan (-\pi/12)$

16. $\tan (7\pi/12)$

In Exercises 17–24, find the exact value of each trigonometric expression, if possible.

17. $\cos 229° \cos 4° + \sin 229° \sin 4°$

18. $\dfrac{\tan 290° + \tan 10°}{1 - \tan 290° \tan 10°}$

19. $\dfrac{\tan 75° - \tan 15°}{1 + \tan 75° \tan 15°}$

20. $\sin 70° \cos 10° - \cos 70° \sin 10°$

21. $\sin \dfrac{11\pi}{8} \cos \dfrac{3\pi}{8} + \cos \dfrac{11\pi}{8} \sin \dfrac{3\pi}{8}$

22. $\cos \dfrac{5\pi}{12} \cos \dfrac{7\pi}{12} - \sin \dfrac{5\pi}{12} \sin \dfrac{7\pi}{12}$

23. $\sin \dfrac{\pi}{4} \cos \dfrac{\pi}{12} - \cos \dfrac{\pi}{4} \sin \dfrac{\pi}{12}$

24. $\dfrac{\tan \dfrac{7\pi}{12} - \tan \dfrac{5\pi}{12}}{1 + \tan \dfrac{7\pi}{12} \tan \dfrac{5\pi}{12}}$

In Exercises 25–30, complete each identity.

25. $\cos (\theta - 3\pi/2) =$

26. $\tan (\theta - \pi/2) =$

27. $\tan (4\pi - x) =$

28. $\sin (\theta + \pi) =$

29. $\sin (3\pi/2 - x) =$

30. $\cos (\theta + \pi/2) =$

In Exercises 31–34, determine whether each equation is an identity or not.

31. $\cos (x + \pi/6) + \sin (x - \pi/3) = 1$

32. $\cos (a + b) \cos (a - b) = \cos^2 a - \sin^2 b$

33. $\sin \left(\dfrac{\pi}{6} + x\right) = \dfrac{1}{2}\left(\cos x + \sqrt{3} \sin x\right)$

34. $\sin (a + b) \sin (a - b) = \sin^2 b - \cos^2 a$

In Exercises 35–38, find the exact value solutions to each equation on the interval $[0, 2\pi)$.

35. $\sin (x + \pi/3) + \sin (x - \pi/3) - 1 = 0$

36. $\tan (x - \pi) + 2 \sin (x - \pi) = 0$

37. $\cos (x + \pi/4) - \cos (x - \pi/4) = 1$

38. $\sin \left(x + \dfrac{\pi}{4} \right) + \sin \left(x - \dfrac{\pi}{4} \right) + \dfrac{\sqrt{6}}{2} = 0$ •

Extensions

In Exercises 39–44, find the exact value of each trigonometric function given that $\tan x = -5/12$, $\cos y = 4/5$, and both angles are in quadrant IV.

39. $\sin (x - y)$

40. $\sin (x + y)$

41. $\cos (x - y)$

42. $\cos (x + y)$

43. $\tan (x - y)$

44. $\tan (x + y)$

In Exercises 45–50, find the exact value of each trigonometric function given that $\tan x = 3/4$, $\sin y = -7/25$, and x and y are in quadrant III.

45. $\sin (x + y)$

46. $\sin (x - y)$

47. $\cos (x + y)$

48. $\cos (x - y)$

49. $\tan (x + y)$

50. $\tan (x - y)$

In Exercises 51–54, find the exact value of each trigonometric function, if possible.

51. $\sin (-7\pi/12)$

52. $\cos (-105°)$

53. $\tan (-13\pi/12)$

54. $\cot (19\pi/12)$

In Exercises 55–56, determine whether each equation is an identity or not.

55. $\tan \left(x + \dfrac{\pi}{4} \right) + 1 = 2 \cos x \sec \left(x + \dfrac{\pi}{4} \right)$

56. $(\cos B \cos C - \sin B \sin C)^2 + (\sin B \cos C + \cos B \sin C)^2 = 1$

3.4 DOUBLE-ANGLE, HALF-ANGLE, AND PRODUCT-SUM FORMULAS

OBJECTIVES

- Use double-angle formulas to simplify trigonometric expressions, evaluate trigonometric functions, and solve trigonometric equations.
- Use power-reducing formulas to simplify trigonometric expressions.
- Use half-angle formulas to evaluate trigonometric functions.
- Use product-sum formulas to expand a product of trigonometric functions and to simplify a sum of trigonometric functions.

PREREQUISITE VOCABULARY TERMS

fundamental trigonometric identities
Pythagorean Theorem
sum and difference formulas
trigonometric functions

3.4.1 Double-Angle Formulas

The sine of a sum formula and the cosine of a sum formula (introduced in Section 3.3) can each be simplified if we assume the condition that $\theta = \theta_1 = \theta_2$.

$$\sin (\theta_1 + \theta_2) = \sin \theta_1 \cos \theta_2 + \cos \theta_1 \sin \theta_2 \qquad \textit{Sine of a Sum Formula}$$

$$\sin (\theta + \theta) = \sin \theta \cos \theta + \cos \theta \sin \theta \qquad \textit{Substitute } \theta \textit{ for } \theta_1 \textit{ and } \theta_2$$

$$\sin 2\theta = 2 \sin \theta \cos \theta \qquad \textit{Simplify.}$$

$$\cos (\theta_1 + \theta_2) = \cos \theta_1 \cos \theta_2 - \sin \theta_1 \sin \theta_2 \qquad \textit{Cosine of a Sum Formula}$$

$$\cos (\theta + \theta) = \cos \theta \cos \theta - \sin \theta \sin \theta \qquad \textit{Substitute } \theta \textit{ for } \theta_1 \textit{ and } \theta_2$$

$$\cos 2\theta = \cos^2 \theta - \sin^2 \theta \qquad \textit{Simplify.}$$

Formulas for the sine, cosine, or tangent of twice an angle (such as $\sin 2\theta = 2 \sin \theta \cos \theta$ and $\cos 2\theta = \cos^2 \theta - \sin^2 \theta$) are called **double-angle formulas**.

Double-Angle Formulas	
$\sin 2\theta = 2 \sin \theta \cos \theta$	$\cos 2\theta = \cos^2 \theta - \sin^2 \theta$
$\tan 2\theta = \dfrac{2 \tan \theta}{1 - \tan^2 \theta}$	$= 1 - 2 \sin^2 \theta$
	$= 2 \cos^2 \theta - 1$

> **NOTICE THAT**
>
> *The additional forms of the cosine of a double-angle formula are given by substituting using the Pythagorean identity $\cos^2 \theta + \sin^2 \theta = 1$.*

EXAMPLE 1 Using a Double-Angle Formula to Evaluate a Trigonometric Function

Use a double-angle formula to evaluate $\sin (11\pi/3)$.

SOLUTION

Write $11\pi/3$ in the form 2θ. Note that $11\pi/3 = 2(1/2)(11\pi/3)$, and multiplying $1/2$ by $11\pi/3$ yields the double angle $2(11\pi/6)$. So, apply the sine of a double-angle formula where $\theta = 11\pi/6$.

> **NOTICE THAT**
>
> *$11\pi/3 = 2(1/2)(11\pi/3)$ because $2(1/2) = 1$.*

$$\sin \frac{11\pi}{3} = \sin 2\left(\frac{1}{2}\right)\left(\frac{11\pi}{3}\right) = \sin 2\left(\frac{11\pi}{6}\right) = 2 \sin \frac{11\pi}{6} \cos \frac{11\pi}{6} = 2\left(-\frac{1}{2}\right)\left(\frac{\sqrt{3}}{2}\right) = -\frac{\sqrt{3}}{2}$$

EXAMPLE 2   **Using a Double-Angle Formula to Simplify an Expression**

Use a double-angle formula to simplify each expression, if possible.

A. $3 \cos^2 t - 3 \sin^2 t$

B. 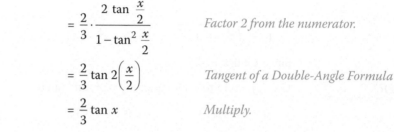 $\dfrac{4 \tan \frac{x}{2}}{3 - 3 \tan^2 \frac{x}{2}}$

SOLUTION

A. $3 \cos^2 t - 3 \sin^2 t = 3(\cos^2 t - \sin^2 t)$ *Factor 3 from each term.*

$\qquad\qquad\qquad = 3 \cos 2t$ *Cosine of a Double-Angle Formula*

B. $\dfrac{4 \tan \frac{x}{2}}{3 - 3 \tan^2 \frac{x}{2}} = \dfrac{4 \tan \frac{x}{2}}{3\left(1 - \tan^2 \frac{x}{2}\right)}$ *Factor 3 from each term in the denominator.*

$\qquad\qquad = \dfrac{2}{3} \cdot \dfrac{2 \tan \frac{x}{2}}{1 - \tan^2 \frac{x}{2}}$ *Factor 2 from the numerator.*

$\qquad\qquad = \dfrac{2}{3} \tan 2\left(\dfrac{x}{2}\right)$ *Tangent of a Double-Angle Formula*

$\qquad\qquad = \dfrac{2}{3} \tan x$ *Multiply.*

> **IMPORTANT**
>
> *In order to substitute using the tangent of a double-angle formula, the coefficient of tangent must be 2.*

3.4.2   Using Double-Angle Formulas

The double-angle formulas can be used to evaluate a trigonometric function of twice an angle (e.g., the value of $\tan 2\theta$), as demonstrated in **Example 3**.

EXAMPLE 3   **Using the Double-Angle Formulas**

Evaluate $\sin 2\theta$, $\cos 2\theta$, and $\tan 2\theta$.

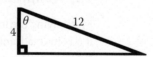

SOLUTION

Pythagorean Theorem ▶   Find the length of the side opposite of θ. $\text{opp} = \sqrt{12^2 - 4^2} = \sqrt{128} = 8\sqrt{2}$
$a^2 + b^2 = c^2$

So, $\sin \theta = \dfrac{8\sqrt{2}}{12} = \dfrac{2\sqrt{2}}{3}$, $\cos \theta = 4/12 = 1/3$, and $\tan \theta = \dfrac{8\sqrt{2}}{4} = 2\sqrt{2}$.

Substitute into the double angle formulas to evaluate $\sin 2\theta$, $\cos 2\theta$, and $\tan 2\theta$.

$$\sin 2\theta = 2 \sin \theta \cos \theta$$
$$= 2\left(\dfrac{2\sqrt{2}}{3}\right)\left(\dfrac{1}{3}\right)$$
$$= \dfrac{4\sqrt{2}}{9}$$

$$\cos 2\theta = 2\cos^2 \theta - 1$$
$$= 2\left(\dfrac{1}{3}\right)^2 - 1$$
$$= -\dfrac{7}{9}$$

$$\tan 2\theta = \dfrac{2 \tan \theta}{1 - \tan^2 \theta}$$
$$= \dfrac{2 \cdot 2\sqrt{2}}{1 - \left(2\sqrt{2}\right)^2}$$
$$= \dfrac{4\sqrt{2}}{1 - 8} = -\dfrac{4\sqrt{2}}{7}$$

EXAMPLE 4	Using the Double-Angle Formulas to Evaluate the Trigonometric Functions of a Double Angle

Evaluate each trigonometric function of 2θ if $\csc \theta = -13/12$ and $\pi < \theta < 3\pi/2$.

SOLUTION

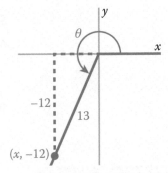

Let (x, y) be a point on the terminal side of θ.

The angle θ is in quadrant III (because $\pi < \theta < 3\pi/2$), so $x < 0$ and $y < 0$.

REMEMBER

r is the distance from the origin to the point (x, y) on the terminal side of the angle, so r > 0.

Since $\csc \theta = -13/12 = r/y$, $r = 13$ and $y = -12$.

Use $r = \sqrt{x^2 + y^2}$ to find x.

$$13 = \sqrt{x^2 + (-12)^2} \ \Rightarrow \ 169 = x^2 + 144 \ \Rightarrow \ x^2 = 25 \ \Rightarrow \ x = \pm 5$$

Since $x < 0$, $x = -5$.

REMEMBER

θ is in quadrant III, so $\sin \theta < 0$, $\cos \theta < 0$, and $\tan \theta > 0$.

Use x, y, and r to evaluate $\sin \theta$, $\cos \theta$, and $\tan \theta$.

$$\sin \theta = -12/13 \qquad \cos \theta = -5/13 \qquad \tan \theta = -12/(-5) = 12/5$$

Use the double-angle formulas to evaluate the trigonometric functions of 2θ.

$$\sin 2\theta = 2 \sin \theta \cos \theta = 2(-12/13)(-5/13) = 120/169$$

$$\cos 2\theta = 1 - 2 \sin^2 \theta = 1 - 2(-12/13)^2 = 1 - 2(144/169) = -119/169$$

$$\tan 2\theta = \frac{2 \tan \theta}{1 - \tan^2 \theta} = \frac{2(12/5)}{1 - (12/5)^2} = \frac{24/5}{1 - (144/25)} = \frac{24/5}{-119/25} = -\frac{120}{119}$$

By the reciprocal identities, $\csc 2\theta = 169/120$, $\sec 2\theta = -169/119$, and $\cot 2\theta = -119/120$.

The Quadrant of a Double Angle

Multiplying the interval of an angle θ by 2 gives the interval for the double angle 2θ. For example, if θ is in quadrant II, then the interval containing θ is $\pi/2 < \theta < \pi$. Multiplying the interval of θ by 2 gives the interval for 2θ.

$$2(\pi/2) < 2(\theta) < 2(\pi) \ \Rightarrow \ \pi < 2\theta < 2\pi$$

Therefore, if θ is in quadrant II, then 2θ is in either quadrant III or quadrant IV.

NOTICE THAT

In Example 4, sin 2x > 0, as expected, since x is in $(\pi, 3\pi/2)$ (quadrant III). Therefore, 2x is in $(2\pi, 3\pi)$ (quadrants I or II), where sine must be positive.

If the interval of 2θ is limited to two quadrants, then the sign of one of the trigonometric functions of 2θ can be determined. For example, if θ is in quadrant II (and so 2θ is in quadrant III or IV), then $\sin 2\theta < 0$ because sine is negative in quadrants III and IV. However, knowing that θ is in quadrant II does not provide conclusive information regarding the signs of cosine or tangent of 2θ because these functions are positive in one quadrant, but negative in the other.

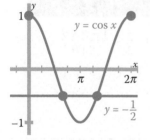

3.4.3   Using Double-Angle Formulas to Solve Equations

An equation involving trigonometric functions of a double angle (i.e., 2θ) can be solved by using algebraic techniques to isolate the trigonometric function and then using the inverse of the trigonometric function, as demonstrated in Section 3.2. An equation involving trigonometric functions of a single angle θ *and* of a double angle 2θ should first be rewritten using a double-angle formula, and then solved in a similar manner.

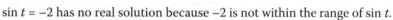

EXAMPLE 5	Solving a Trigonometric Equation Involving a Double Angle

REMEMBER

For sin x and cos x, the domain is $(-\infty, \infty)$, and the range is $[-1, 1]$.

Find all solutions to $\sin 2t + \sin t + 4 \cos t = -2$ within the interval $[0, 2\pi)$.

SOLUTION

The equation involves trigonometric functions of the single angle t and of the double angle $2t$. So, use the sine of a double-angle formula to write $\sin 2t$ as the sine of a single angle t, and then solve as usual.

$$\sin 2t + \sin t + 4 \cos t = -2$$
$$2 \sin t \cos t + \sin t + 4 \cos t = -2 \qquad \textit{Sine of a Double-Angle Formula}$$
$$2 \sin t \cos t + 4 \cos t + \sin t + 2 = 0 \qquad \textit{Add 2 to each side. Group the cosine terms.}$$
$$(2 \cos t)(\sin t + 2) + \sin t + 2 = 0 \qquad \textit{Factor 2 cos t from the first two terms.}$$
$$(\sin t + 2)(2 \cos t + 1) = 0 \qquad \textit{Factor out sin t + 2.}$$
$$\sin t + 2 = 0 \quad \text{or} \quad 2 \cos t + 1 = 0 \qquad \textit{Set each factor equal to 0.}$$
$$\sin t = -2 \qquad\qquad \cos t = -1/2 \qquad \textit{Solve for sin t and for cos t.}$$

$\sin t = -2$ has no real solution because -2 is not within the range of $\sin t$.

Solve the other equation $\cos t = -1/2$.

$\cos t = -1/2$ when $t = 2\pi/3$ or $t = 4\pi/3$.

Therefore, the solutions of $\sin 2t + \sin t + 4 \cos t = -2$ within $[0, 2\pi)$ are $t = 2\pi/3$ and $t = 4\pi/3$.

The graph $y = \cos t$ and $y = -1/2$ (Figure 3.4a) confirms that there are no additional solutions within $[0, 2\pi)$.

Figure 3.4a

3.4.4   Using a Power-Reducing Formula

We have seen that the double-angle formulas can be used to write a trigonometric function of a double angle 2θ as a trigonometric function of a single angle θ. Similarly, the **power-reducing formulas** (which are derived from the double-angle formulas) can be used to write an expression involving a power of a trigonometric function as an expression involving only powers of 1.

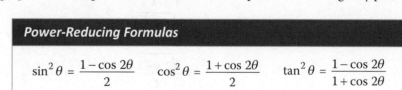

Power-Reducing Formulas		
$\sin^2 \theta = \dfrac{1 - \cos 2\theta}{2}$	$\cos^2 \theta = \dfrac{1 + \cos 2\theta}{2}$	$\tan^2 \theta = \dfrac{1 - \cos 2\theta}{1 + \cos 2\theta}$

| EXAMPLE 6 | Reducing a Power of a Trigonometric Function |

Write $\cos^3 x - \sin^3 x$ as an expression with only first powers.

SOLUTION

Write each term as a product containing a power of 2, then use a power-reducing formula.

$$\cos^3 x - \sin^3 x = \cos x \cos^2 x - \sin x \sin^2 x$$

$$= \cos x \, \frac{1 + \cos 2x}{2} - \sin x \, \frac{1 - \cos 2x}{2} \qquad \textit{Power-Reducing Formulas}$$

$$= \frac{\cos x + \cos x \cos 2x}{2} - \frac{\sin x - \sin x \cos 2x}{2} \qquad \textit{Multiply.}$$

$$= \frac{\cos x + \cos x \cos 2x - \sin x + \sin x \cos 2x}{2} \qquad \textit{Add.}$$

3.4.5   Using Half-Angle Formulas to Find Exact Values

The **half-angle formulas** are derived from the power-reducing formulas by replacing θ with $\theta/2$. These formulas can be used to write an expression involving a trigonometric function of a half of an angle as an expression involving the single angle.

> **Half-Angle Formulas**
>
> $$\sin \frac{\theta}{2} = \pm \sqrt{\frac{1 - \cos \theta}{2}} \qquad \cos \frac{\theta}{2} = \pm \sqrt{\frac{1 + \cos \theta}{2}} \qquad \tan \frac{\theta}{2} = \frac{1 - \cos \theta}{\sin \theta}$$
>
> *The signs of sin θ/2 and cos θ/2 depend on the quadrant containing the angle θ/2.*

| EXAMPLE 7 | Using a Half-Angle Formula |

Find the exact value of $\cos(-22.5°)$.

SOLUTION

Write $-22.5°$ as a half angle (i.e., as a fraction with denominator 2). $-22.5° = -45°/2$

Use the cosine of a half-angle formula to evaluate $\cos(-45°/2)$.

> **IMPORTANT**
>
> *$-22.5°$ is in quadrant IV, so $\cos(-22.5°) > 0$.*

$$\cos\left(-\frac{45°}{2}\right) = \sqrt{\frac{1 + \cos(-45°)}{2}} \qquad \textit{Cosine of a Half-Angle Formula}$$

$$= \sqrt{\frac{1 + \frac{\sqrt{2}}{2}}{2}} \qquad \textit{Evaluate cos (–45°).}$$

$$= \sqrt{\frac{2 + \sqrt{2}}{4}} \qquad \textit{Multiply by 2/2.}$$

$$= \frac{\sqrt{2 + \sqrt{2}}}{2} \qquad \textit{Simplify the radical.}$$

CHECK

IMPORTANT

The calculator must be in degree mode.

Use a calculator to evaluate $\cos(-22.5°)$ and to simplify $\dfrac{\sqrt{2+\sqrt{2}}}{2}$.

$$\cos(-22.5°) = 0.9238\ldots \qquad \frac{\sqrt{2+\sqrt{2}}}{2} = 0.9238\ldots \quad \checkmark$$

EXAMPLE 8	**Using a Half-Angle Formula and a Triangle to Evaluate the Trigonometric Functions of a Half Angle**

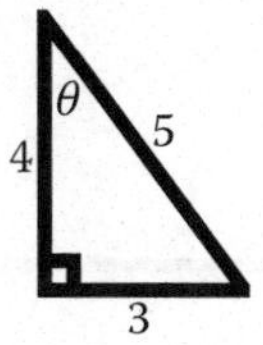

Suppose θ is an acute angle in a right triangle with an opposite side of length 3 and an adjacent side of length 4. Evaluate the trigonometric functions of $\theta/2$.

SOLUTION

By the Pythagorean Theorem, if the legs of a right triangle have lengths 3 and 4, then the hypotenuse is 5, as shown in Figure 3.4b.

Evaluate $\sin\theta$ and $\cos\theta$. $\quad \sin\theta = \text{opp/hyp} = 3/5 \quad \cos\theta = \text{adj/hyp} = 4/5$

Substitute these values into the half-angle formulas.

Since θ is an acute angle, $\theta/2$ is in quadrant I. Therefore, $\sin\theta > 0$ and $\cos\theta > 0$.

$$\sin\frac{\theta}{2} = \sqrt{\frac{1-\cos\theta}{2}} = \sqrt{\frac{1-4/5}{2}} = \sqrt{\frac{1/5}{2}} = \sqrt{\frac{1}{10}} = \frac{1}{\sqrt{10}}$$

$$\cos\frac{\theta}{2} = \sqrt{\frac{1+\cos\theta}{2}} = \sqrt{\frac{1+4/5}{2}} = \sqrt{\frac{9/5}{2}} = \sqrt{\frac{9}{10}} = \frac{3}{\sqrt{10}}$$

$$\tan\frac{\theta}{2} = \frac{1-\cos\theta}{\sin\theta} = \frac{1-4/5}{3/5} = \frac{1/5}{3/5} = \frac{1}{3}$$

By the reciprocal identities, $\csc\dfrac{\theta}{2} = \sqrt{10}$, $\sec\dfrac{\theta}{2} = \dfrac{\sqrt{10}}{3}$, and $\cot\dfrac{\theta}{2} = 3$.

Figure 3.4b

TIP

Only the values of $\sin\theta$ and $\cos\theta$ are needed to evaluate the sine, cosine, and tangent of $\theta/2$ using the half-angle formulas.

EXAMPLE 9	**Using a Half-Angle Formula**

Use a half-angle formula to evaluate $\sin t/2$, if $\sin t = -1/2$ and $-\dfrac{\pi}{2} < t < 0$.

SOLUTION

Use the sine of a half-angle formula $\sin\dfrac{\theta}{2} = \pm\sqrt{\dfrac{1-\cos\theta}{2}}$ to find $\sin t/2$.

First, evaluate $\cos t$.

Since $\sin t = -1/2 = y/r$, and $r > 0$, $y = -1$ and $r = 2$.

Use $r = \sqrt{x^2+y^2}$ to find x. Note that $x > 0$ because $-\dfrac{\pi}{2} < t < 0$ (i.e., t is in quadrant IV).

$$2 = \sqrt{x^2+(-1)^2} \ \Rightarrow\ 4 = x^2+1 \ \Rightarrow\ x = \sqrt{3}$$

Therefore, $\cos t = \dfrac{x}{r} = \dfrac{\sqrt{3}}{2}$.

Determine the sign of sin $(t/2)$.

Dividing the interval for t by 2 gives the interval for $t/2$.

$$-\frac{\pi}{2} < t < 0 \;\Rightarrow\; -\frac{\pi}{4} < \frac{t}{2} < 0$$

Therefore, $t/2$ is in quadrant IV and $\sin(t/2) < 0$.

Now evaluate $\sin(t/2)$.

Substitute the value of $\cos t$ into the sine of a half-angle formula, using only the negative square root, because $\sin(t/2) < 0$.

$$\sin\frac{t}{2} = -\sqrt{\frac{1 - \frac{\sqrt{3}}{2}}{2}} = -\sqrt{\frac{\frac{2 - \sqrt{3}}{2}}{2}} = -\sqrt{\frac{2 - \sqrt{3}}{4}} = -\frac{\sqrt{2 - \sqrt{3}}}{2}$$

ALTERNATIVE METHOD

The value of $\sin(t/2)$ can be found using a difference of angles formula instead of a half-angle formula, first by finding the exact value of $t/2$ using the fact that $\sin t = -1/2$ and $-\frac{\pi}{2} < t < 0$.

It is given that t is in quadrant IV. And in quadrant IV, $\sin t = -1/2$ when $t = 11\pi/6 + 2\pi n$. More specifically, we know that t is between $-\pi/2$ and 0. Therefore, $t = -\pi/6$. By dividing each side of $t = -\pi/6$ by 2, we see that $t/2 = -\pi/12$. Therefore, $\sin(t/2) = \sin(-\pi/12)$.

The value of $\sin(-\pi/12)$ can be found using the sine of a difference of angles formula.

$$\sin\left(-\frac{\pi}{12}\right) = \sin\left(\frac{\pi}{6} - \frac{\pi}{4}\right) = \sin\frac{\pi}{6}\cos\frac{\pi}{4} - \cos\frac{\pi}{6}\sin\frac{\pi}{4} = \frac{1}{2}\cdot\frac{\sqrt{2}}{2} - \frac{\sqrt{3}}{2}\cdot\frac{\sqrt{2}}{2} = \frac{\sqrt{2} - \sqrt{6}}{4}$$

Although the numbers $-\dfrac{\sqrt{2 - \sqrt{3}}}{2}$ and $\dfrac{\sqrt{2} - \sqrt{6}}{4}$ are equal, this may not be obvious visually.

TIP

The only value of
$11\pi/6 + 2\pi n$ that is
between $-\pi/2$ and 0 is
$-\pi/6$.
$11\pi/6 - 2\pi(1) = -\pi/6$

Determining the Equivalence of Numeric Expressions

Using a calculator to simplify each expression, we find that $-\dfrac{\sqrt{2 - \sqrt{3}}}{2} = -0.25881\ldots$ and $\dfrac{\sqrt{2} - \sqrt{6}}{4} = -0.25881\ldots$, so we can infer that $-\dfrac{\sqrt{2 - \sqrt{3}}}{2} = \dfrac{\sqrt{2} - \sqrt{6}}{4}$.

However, since it is possible that there could be some difference in decimal digits much further to the right, this does not prove that the two numbers are equal.

A more accurate numeric procedure for determining equivalence is to subtract the numbers (without using a calculator). If the difference of two numbers is 0, then the numbers are equal.

3.4.6 Using Product-Sum Formulas

Product-to-Sum Formulas

The **product-to-sum formulas** can be verified using the sum and difference formulas. These formulas can be used to simplify an expression involving a product of two trigonometric functions (sine or cosine).

Product-to-Sum Formulas

$$\sin \theta_1 \sin \theta_2 = \frac{1}{2}[\cos(\theta_1 - \theta_2) - \cos(\theta_1 + \theta_2)]$$

$$\cos \theta_1 \cos \theta_2 = \frac{1}{2}[\cos(\theta_1 - \theta_2) + \cos(\theta_1 + \theta_2)]$$

$$\sin \theta_1 \cos \theta_2 = \frac{1}{2}[\sin(\theta_1 + \theta_2) + \sin(\theta_1 - \theta_2)]$$

$$\cos \theta_1 \sin \theta_2 = \frac{1}{2}[\sin(\theta_1 + \theta_2) - \sin(\theta_1 - \theta_2)]$$

EXAMPLE 10   **Using a Product-to-Sum Formula**

Use a product-to-sum formula to rewrite each expression and simplify, if possible.

A. $\sin 6x \sin x$ **B.** $\sin 5t \cos 5t$

SOLUTION

A. Use the product-to-sum formula for $\sin \theta_1 \sin \theta_2$ where $\theta_1 = 6x$ and $\theta_2 = 6x$.

$$\sin 6x \sin x = \frac{1}{2}[\cos(6x - x) - \cos(6x + x)] \qquad \textit{Product-to-Sum Formula}$$

$$= \frac{1}{2}[\cos 5x - \cos 7x] \qquad \textit{Simplify (combine the like terms).}$$

$$= \frac{1}{2}\cos 5x - \frac{1}{2}\cos 7x \qquad \textit{Distribute.}$$

B. Use the product-to-sum formula for $\sin \theta_1 \cos \theta_2$, where $\theta_1 = 5t$ and $\theta_2 = 5t$.

$$\sin 5t \cos 5t = \frac{1}{2}[\sin(5t + 5t) + \sin(5t - 5t)] \qquad \textit{Product-to-Sum Formula}$$

$$= \frac{1}{2}[\sin 10t + \sin 0] \qquad \textit{Simplify (combine the like terms).}$$

$$= \frac{1}{2}[\sin 10t + 0] \qquad \textit{Evaluate sin 0.}$$

$$= \frac{1}{2}\sin 10t \qquad \textit{Multiply.}$$

Sum-to-Product Formulas

The **sum-to-product formulas** reverse the process and allow for a sum or difference of sine functions or cosine functions to be written as a product of sine or cosine functions.

Sum-to-Product Formulas

$$\sin \theta_1 + \sin \theta_2 = 2 \sin \left(\frac{\theta_1 + \theta_2}{2} \right) \cos \left(\frac{\theta_1 - \theta_2}{2} \right)$$

$$\sin \theta_1 - \sin \theta_2 = 2 \cos \left(\frac{\theta_1 + \theta_2}{2} \right) \sin \left(\frac{\theta_1 - \theta_2}{2} \right)$$

$$\cos \theta_1 + \cos \theta_2 = 2 \cos \left(\frac{\theta_1 + \theta_2}{2} \right) \cos \left(\frac{\theta_1 - \theta_2}{2} \right)$$

$$\cos \theta_1 - \cos \theta_2 = -2 \sin \left(\frac{\theta_1 + \theta_2}{2} \right) \sin \left(\frac{\theta_1 - \theta_2}{2} \right)$$

EXAMPLE 11 | **Using a Sum-to-Product Formula**

Use a sum-to-product formula to rewrite each expression and simplify, if possible.

A. $\sin 4t + \sin 6t$ **B.** $\cos x - \cos (-x)$

SOLUTION

A. Use the sum-to-product formula for $\sin \theta_1 + \sin \theta_2$, where $\theta_1 = 4t$ and $\theta_2 = 6t$.

$$\sin 4t + \sin 6t = 2 \sin \left(\frac{4t + 6t}{2} \right) \cos \left(\frac{4t - 6t}{2} \right) \qquad \textit{Sum-to-Product Formula}$$

$$= 2 \sin \left(\frac{10t}{2} \right) \cos \left(\frac{-2t}{2} \right) \qquad \textit{Simplify (combine the like terms).}$$

$$= 2 \sin 5t \cos (-t) \qquad \textit{Simplify (divide).}$$

$$= 2 \sin 5t \cos t \qquad \textit{cos} (-t) = \cos t$$

B. Use the product-to-sum formula for $\cos \theta_1 - \cos \theta_2$, where $\theta_1 = x$ and $\theta_2 = -x$.

$$\cos x - \cos (-x) = -2 \sin \left(\frac{x + (-x)}{2} \right) \sin \left(\frac{x - (-x)}{2} \right) \qquad \textit{Sum-to-Product Formula}$$

$$= -2 \sin \left(\frac{0}{2} \right) \sin \left(\frac{2x}{2} \right) \qquad \textit{Simplify (combine the like terms).}$$

$$= -2 \sin 0 \sin x \qquad \textit{Simplify (divide).}$$

$$= 0 \qquad \textit{Evaluate sin 0 and multiply.}$$

Note that the expression in **Example 11B** can be simplified using the fact that cosine is an even function, that is, $\cos (-x) = \cos x$.

$$\cos x - \cos (-x) = \cos x - \cos x = 0$$

SECTION 3.4 EXERCISES

Warm Up

Use Pythagorean identities to simplify each expression.

1. $3 \cos^2 x - 3 \sin^2 x - 3$

2. $\tan^2 x - \sec^2 x$

3. $5 \csc^2 x - 5 \cot^2 x$

Just the Facts

Fill in the blank to complete each formula.

4. $\sin 2\theta = $ _____

5. $1 - 2 \sin^2 \theta = $ _____

6. $\tan 2\theta = $ _____

7. $\dfrac{1 - \cos 2\theta}{1 + \cos 2\theta} = $ _____

8. $\sin (\theta/2) = $ _____

9. $\pm \sqrt{\dfrac{1 + \cos \theta}{2}} = $ _____

10. $\dfrac{1 - \cos 2\theta}{2} = $ _____

Essential Skills

each expression.

1. $\tan (5\pi/3)$

2. $\cos (7\pi/2)$

3. $\cos (5\pi/2)$

4. $\sin (7\pi/3)$

In Exercises 5–10, use a double-angle formula to rewrite each expression.

5. $20 \sin \theta \cos \theta$

6. $-8 + 16 \sin^2 \theta$

7. $10 \sin^2 \theta - 10 \cos^2 \theta$

8. $-7 + 7(\cos \theta - \sin \theta)^2$

9. $\dfrac{20 \tan \theta}{1 - \tan^2 \theta}$

10. $\dfrac{1}{\tan x - 1} + \dfrac{1}{\tan x + 1}$

In Exercises 11–14, evaluate the six trigonometric functions of 2θ.

11.

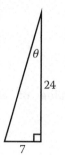

12.

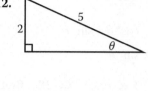

13.

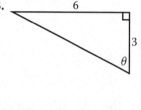

14.

In Exercises 15–20, evaluate the six trigonometric functions of 2θ with the given information.

15. $\sec \theta = 5/3$ and $3\pi/2 < \theta < 2\pi$

16. $\tan \theta = -6/5$ and $\pi/2 < \theta < \pi$

17. $\cot \theta = -8/7$ and $3\pi/2 < \theta < 2\pi$

18. $\sec \theta = -\dfrac{\sqrt{61}}{5}$ and $\pi < \theta < 3\pi/2$

19. $\sin \theta = 5/13$ and $\pi/2 < \theta < \pi$

20. $\csc \theta = -\dfrac{\sqrt{13}}{3}$ and $\pi < \theta < 3\pi/2$

In Exercises 21–28, find all exact solutions to each equation within the interval $[0, 2\pi)$.

21. $\sin 2x \sin x - \cos x = 0$

22. $\sin 2x = 2 \sin x$

23. $\sin 2x = -\cos x$

24. $\sin 2x = 3/2 \tan x$

25. $\cos 2x + 3 \sin x + 1 = 0$

26. $\cos 2x = \cos x$

27. $\cos 2x + \cos 4x = 0$

28. $\cos 2x = \sin x$

In Exercises 29–32, write each trigonometric expression with only first powers.

29. $\dfrac{\cos^4 t}{16}$

30. $\dfrac{\tan^4 t}{4}$

31. $\cos^4 \theta - \sin^4 \theta$

32. $\sin^6 \theta$

In Exercises 33–38, find the exact value of each trigonometric expression.

33. $\tan 105°$

34. $\cos 22.5°$

35. $\sin (-15°)$

36. $\sin 165°$

37. $\tan (-157.5°)$

38. $\cos (-67.5°)$

In Exercises 39–42, evaluate the six trigonometric functions of $\theta/2$ for each given triangle.

39.
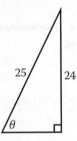

40.
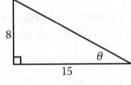

41.
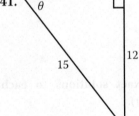

42.
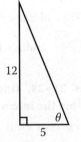

In Exercises 43–46, use a half-angle formula to evaluate the given trigonometric expression of $\theta/2$ using the given information.

43. $\sin (\theta/2)$, given $\tan \theta = -5/12$ and $\pi/2 < \theta < \pi$

44. $\cos (\theta/2)$, given $\cos \theta = -3/4$ and $\pi/2 < \theta < \pi$

45. $\tan (\theta/2)$, given $\sin \theta = -5/8$ and $3\pi/2 < \theta < 2\pi$

46. $\sin (\theta/2)$, given $\sec \theta = -7/4$ and $\pi < \theta < 3\pi/2$

In Exercises 47–56, use a product-to-sum formula to rewrite each expression and simplify, if possible.

47. $\sin 20x \cos 7x$

48. $\cos 3x \sin 5x$

49. $\cos 4x \cos 2x$

50. $\sin 11x \sin 6x$

51. $\cos 13x - \cos 3x$

52. $\sin 7x + \sin 3x$

53. $\cos 5x + \cos 3x$

54. $\cos 9x + \cos 3x$

55. $\sin x + \sin 5x$

56. $\sin 11x - \sin 3x$

Extensions

57. The area of a figure is given by the equation $A = \dfrac{1 + \cos 2\theta}{2}$. In the interval $0 \le \theta \le \pi$, at what value of θ is the area of the figure equal to 0?

58. Suppose (x, y) is a point on the circle with equation $x^2 + y^2 = 9$, then the points (x, y), $(-x, y)$, $(-x, -y)$, and $(x, -y)$ determine a rectangle. Also, for each value of θ, $x = 3 \cos \theta$ and $y = 3 \sin \theta$. Since the area of the rectangle pictured below is $2x \cdot 2y$, the area can be expressed in terms of θ as $18 \sin 2\theta$. In the interval $0 \le \theta \le \pi$, what is the value of θ that maximizes the area of the rectangle?

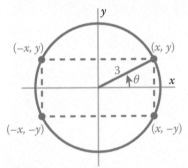

59. What is the area of the rectangle in the figure below in terms of r and θ?

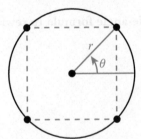

60. What is the difference in areas of squares $ABCD$ and $DEFG$ in the figure below in terms of h and θ?

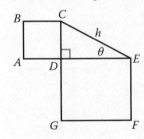

61. What is the area of an arbitrary right triangle in terms of the hypotenuse, c, and one acute angle, A?

In Exercises 62–64, write each trigonometric expression with only first powers.

62. $\tan^4 \theta$

63. $\tan^3 \theta$

64. $\sin^4 2\theta$

In Exercises 65–69, find all exact solutions to each equation within the interval $[0, 2\pi)$.

65. $\sin 2\theta + 4 \sin \theta + 2 \cos \theta = -4$

66. $8 \cos^4 \theta = \cos 4\theta + 4 \cos 2\theta + 3$

67. $\sec^4 2\theta = 4$

68. $\tan^2 2\theta - 1 = 0$

69. $\csc^4 2\theta - 4 = 0$

70. Suppose (x, y) is a point along the arc in the first quadrant of a circle represented by $x^2 + y^2 = 900$. At any location on the circle, a ray from the origin through (x, y) determines an angle θ with the x-axis. A right triangle is formed by a horizontal line through (x, y), a vertical line through (x, y), and a diameter of the circle. Find an expression for the area of the triangle in terms of $\cos \theta$ and $\sin \theta$.

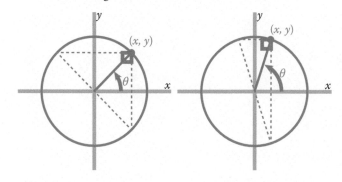

71. Suppose (x, y) is a point on the circle represented by $x^2 + y^2 = 100$. At any location on the circle, a ray from the origin through (x, y) determines an angle θ with the x-axis. The points (x, y), $(-x, y)$, $(-x, 0)$, and $(x, 0)$ determine a rectangle. Find an expression for the shaded portion of the circle in terms of θ.

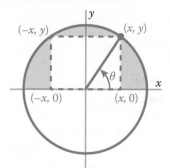

In Exercises 72–75, find all solutions to each equation within the interval $[0, 2\pi)$. Round each answer to the nearest hundredth.

72. $3 \sin 2\theta = 2 \cos \theta$

73. $5 \cos 2\theta + \sin^2 \theta = 0$

74. $6 \cos^2 \theta + 3 \cos 2\theta = 0$

75. $6 \sin 2\theta = -5 \sin \theta$

CHAPTER 3 REVIEW EXERCISES

Section 3.1 Fundamental Trigonometric Identities

1. Use $\csc \theta = -12/5$ and $\pi < \theta < 3\pi/2$ to evaluate all other trigonometric functions.

2. Expand and simplify, if possible.
$(\cot x - \csc x)(\cos x + 1)$

3. Factor and simplify, if possible.
$\tan x \sin x \cos x + \cot x \sin x \cos x$

4. Prove $\dfrac{\cos^2 x + \tan^2 x - 1}{\sin^2 x} = \tan^2 x$, if possible.

5. Prove $\dfrac{\sec x + \csc x}{\cot x + \tan x} = \cos x + \sin x$, if possible.

Section 3.2 Solving Trigonometric Equations

In Exercises 6–8, solve the equation.

6. $3 \tan (x/2) + 3 = 0$

7. $2 \sin^2 x - 5 \sin x + 2 = 0$

8. $\tan^3 x + \tan^2 x - 3 \tan x - 3 = 0$

In Exercises 9–10, find all solutions to the equation, within the interval $[0, 2\pi)$. Round to the nearest thousandth.

9. $3 \cos^2 x - 5 \cos x - 4 = 0$

10. $10 \sec^2 x - 10 = 7 \tan x + 2$

Section 3.3 The Sum and Difference Formulas

In Exercises 11–12, if possible, find the exact value of the trigonometric function.

11. $\tan 255°$

12. $\sin 11\pi/12$

13. Complete the identity.
$\cos (17\pi - x)$

14. Prove that $\sin (x + y) - \sin (x - y) = 2 \cos x \sin y$ is an identity, if possible.

15. Prove that $\dfrac{\sin (x + y) - \sin (x - y)}{\cos (x + y) + \cos(x - y)} = \tan y$ is an identity, if possible.

Section 3.4 Double-Angle, Half-Angle, and Product-Sum Formulas

16. Evaluate the six trigonometric functions of 2θ and $\theta/2$ using the given triangle.

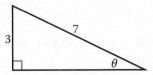

17. Evaluate the six trigonometric functions of 2θ and $\theta/2$, if $\cot \theta = -2/9$ and $\pi/2 < \theta < \pi$.

18. Find all exact solutions to $\sin 2x \cot x - 2 \sin^2 x = 1$ within the interval $[0, 2\pi)$.

19. Write $3 \cos^3 x \cos^2 x$ as an expression with only first powers.

20. Use a product-to-sum formula to rewrite $\cos 4x - \cos 6x$, and simplify, if possible.

APPLICATIONS OF TRIGONOMETRY

4.1 THE LAW OF SINES

OBJECTIVES

- Use the Law of Sines to solve an oblique triangle.
- Determine whether zero, one, or two triangles exist with given measurements.
- Find the area of an oblique triangle.

PREREQUISITE VOCABULARY TERMS

acute angle

obtuse angle

supplementary angles

Triangle Sum Theorem

trigonometric functions

The six trigonometric functions were used in Chapter 2 to determine side lengths and angle measures of right triangles. In this chapter, we will determine side lengths and angle measures of **oblique triangles**, which are triangles that have no right angles.

> **IMPORTANT**
>
> *An oblique triangle has no right angles, so the sides are not related by the Pythagorean Theorem (i.e., $a^2 + b^2 \neq c^2$), which holds only for right triangles.*

The angles of an oblique triangle will typically be represented by the Greek letters α (alpha), β (beta), and γ (gamma). The *corresponding opposite sides* in the oblique triangle will be represented by a, b, and c, respectively (Figure 4.1a). For any triangle with sides a, b, and c, and angles α, β, and γ, we can assume that side a is opposite angle α, side b is opposite angle β, and side c is opposite angle γ.

Oblique Triangle

Figure 4.1a

Note that the angle between two specific sides is called the **included angle** (e.g., the included angle for sides b and c is angle α). Similarly, the side between two specific angles is called the **included side** (e.g., the included side for angles α and γ is side b).

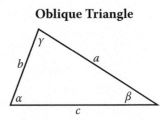

4.1.1 Using the Law of Sines Given Two Angles and One Side

For any oblique (or right) triangle, the ratio of the sine of an angle to its opposite side is equal to the ratio of the sine of another angle to that angle's opposite side, as stated in the **Law of Sines**.

> **The Law of Sines**
>
> For any triangle with sides a, b, and c, and respective opposite angles α, β, and γ, $\dfrac{\sin \alpha}{a} = \dfrac{\sin \beta}{b} = \dfrac{\sin \gamma}{c}$ and $\dfrac{a}{\sin \alpha} = \dfrac{b}{\sin \beta} = \dfrac{c}{\sin \gamma}$.

> **NOTICE THAT**
>
> *Each ratio is the sine of an angle to that angle's opposite side.*

The Law of Sines can be used to solve an oblique triangle (i.e., to find the unknown side and angle measures of an oblique triangle), given three specific measures of the triangle (either two sides and one angle or two angles and one side), as stated in the following cases.

- ASA (angle-side-angle): given two angles and the included side
- AAS (angle-angle-side): given two angles and the side opposite either given angle
- SSA (side-side-angle): given two sides and the angle opposite either given side

> **REMEMBER**
>
> *The Triangle Sum Theorem, $\alpha + \beta + \gamma = 180°$, gives the measure of a triangle's third angle when the two other angles are known.*

In other words, the Law of Sines gives the unknown measures in an oblique triangle when either two angles and *any* side (ASA or AAS), or two sides and the non-included angle (SSA) are given.

| EXAMPLE 1 | Using the Law of Sines to Solve a Triangle |

Use the Law of Sines to solve each triangle, if possible. Round the measures to the nearest hundredth, as needed.

A. $\beta = 18°$, $\gamma = 121°$, and $b = 60$ meters   **B.** $a = 10$ feet, $c = 14$ feet, and $\beta = 55°$

SOLUTION

A. Sketch the triangle.

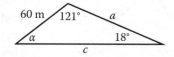

The measures of angle β and opposite side b, as well as angle γ, are given, so the AAS case applies to this triangle and the Law of Sines can be used to solve the triangle.

Use the Triangle Sum Theorem to find the unknown angle α. $\alpha = 180° - (121° + 18°) = 41°$

Write two equations using the Law of Sines, then solve each to find a and c.

$$\frac{a}{\sin\ \alpha} = \frac{b}{\sin\ \beta} \quad \Rightarrow \quad \frac{a}{\sin\ 41°} = \frac{60}{\sin\ 18°} \quad \Rightarrow \quad a = \frac{60\ \sin\ 41°}{\sin\ 18°} \approx 127.38\ m$$

$$\frac{c}{\sin\ \gamma} = \frac{b}{\sin\ \beta} \quad \Rightarrow \quad \frac{c}{\sin\ 121°} = \frac{60}{\sin\ 18°} \quad \Rightarrow \quad c = \frac{60\ \sin\ 121°}{\sin\ 18°} \approx 166.43\ m$$

> **IMPORTANT**
>
> *In each equation (proportion), one ratio must include an angle and its opposite side for which both measures are given (known).*

B. Sketch the triangle.

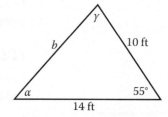

The measures of two sides, a and c, and the included angle β are given. However, since β is the included angle between the given sides (i.e., not the angle opposite one of the given sides), the Law of Sines cannot be used to solve this triangle.

Solving an oblique triangle where two sides and the included angle are given (the SAS case) will be discussed later in this chapter.

For any triangle, the smallest side must be opposite the smallest angle, and the largest side must be opposite the largest angle. Therefore, if a triangle's angles are related by the inequality $\beta < \gamma < \alpha$, then the triangle's sides must be related by the inequality $b < c < a$. These relationships should be confirmed after solving a triangle, as demonstrated below with the triangle solved in **Example 1A** (Figure 4.1b).

> **IMPORTANT**
>
> *Consistency of the inequalities of the sides and their opposite angles does not confirm that the measures are correct. However, if the sides are not consistent with their opposite angles, then at least one measure (side or angle) must be incorrect.*

From the triangle in Figure 4.1b:

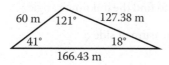

Figure 4.1b

• 60 is opposite the 18° angle,

• 127.38 is opposite the 41° angle, and

• 166.43 is opposite the 121° angle.

Sides from least to greatest: $60 < 127.38 < 166.43$

Angles from least to greatest: $18° < 41° < 121°$

Since the smallest side (60 m) is opposite the smallest angle (18°) and the largest side (166.43 m) is opposite the largest angle (121°), the lengths of the triangle's sides are consistent with their opposite angles.

4.1.2 Using the Law of Sines Given One Angle and Two Sides

Three side lengths uniquely determine a triangle, but three angle measures do not. For example, there is exactly one triangle with sides 4, 5, and 8 units, but there are an infinite number of triangles with angle measures 60°, 40°, and 80°.

If the measures of two angles and one side of an oblique triangle are given (i.e., the ASA or AAS case), then there is exactly one triangle that fits these criteria. For example, consider the oblique triangle given in Figure 4.1c, where one angle is 60°, another is 40°, and the included side has length 10 units (ASA). The lengths of sides a and b are unknown, but the point at which these two sides meet is determined by the given angles, thus setting the length of each unknown side. Therefore, exactly one triangle exists with the given angles and side shown in Figure 4.1c.

Figure 4.1c

If the measures of two sides and the non-included angle are given (i.e., the SSA case), there can be exactly one triangle, exactly two triangles, or zero triangles with the given measures. In both of the following SSA situations, exactly one triangle exists with the given measures.

The SSA cases where zero ▶ *or two triangles exist will be discussed further in Topic 4.1.3.*

1. The given angle is *obtuse* and its opposite side is greater than the other given side.
2. The given angle is *acute* and its opposite side is greater than or equal to the other given side.

EXAMPLE 2   Using the Law of Sines to Solve a Triangle

Use the Law of Sines to solve a triangle where a = 10 feet, b = 14 feet, and β = 55°. Round the measures to the nearest hundredth, as needed.

SOLUTION

Exactly one triangle with the given measures exists because the given angle is acute (β = 55° < 90°) and its opposite side is greater than the other given side ($b > a$).

Use the Law of Sines to find the measure of the unknown angle, opposite the given side.

IMPORTANT

For an SSA triangle, the measure of the unknown angle opposite the given side must be found first.

$$\frac{\sin \alpha}{a} = \frac{\sin \beta}{b} \qquad \textit{Law of Sines}$$

$$\frac{\sin \alpha}{10} = \frac{\sin 55°}{14} \qquad \textit{Substitute the given measures.}$$

$$\sin \alpha = \frac{10 \sin 55°}{14} \qquad \textit{Solve for sin } \alpha.$$

$$\alpha = \sin^{-1} \frac{10 \sin 55°}{14} \qquad \textit{Take the inverse sine of both sides to solve for } \alpha.$$

$$\alpha \approx 35.81° \qquad \textit{Use a calculator to evaluate the inverse sine function.}$$

Use the Triangle Sum Theorem to find the unknown angle γ. $\gamma \approx 180° - (55° + 35.81°) = 89.19°$

Use the Law of Sines find the measure of side c.

$$\frac{c}{\sin \gamma} = \frac{b}{\sin \beta}$$

$$\frac{c}{\sin 89.19°} \approx \frac{14}{\sin 55°}$$

TIP

Use b and sin β in one ratio (as opposed to a and sin α) because the exact values of β and b are known.

$$c \approx \frac{14 \sin 89.19°}{\sin 55°}$$

$$c \approx 17.09 \text{ ft}$$

Therefore, $a \approx 35.81°$, $\gamma \approx 89.19°$, and $c \approx 17.09$ feet.

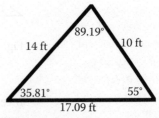

The side lengths in increasing order are consistent with their opposite angles in increasing order.

4.1.3   Using the Law of Sines: The Ambiguous Case

SSA is called the **ambiguous case** because the given measures (two side lengths and a non-included angle) might not correspond to exactly one triangle. Instead, zero, one, or even two triangles with the given measures can exist.

To determine whether zero or two triangles exist with the given measures, we compare the triangle's height (i.e., an altitude) to the side opposite the given angle. However, since the height of an oblique triangle is typically not given, we need an expression for the height in terms of a known side and a known angle to make this comparison.

REMEMBER

The base of a triangle can be any of its sides.

Recall that the height h of a triangle is the distance between a vertex and a line containing the opposite side (the triangle's base), as shown in Figure 4.1d.

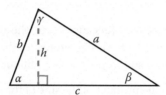

Figure 4.1d

Notice that h is a leg in the right triangle with hypotenuse b, where α is the angle opposite h. Therefore, $\sin \alpha = h/b$. Solving for h gives $h = b \sin \alpha$. Thus, the height of an oblique triangle is given by the expression $b \sin \alpha$.

The criteria for determining whether zero, one, or two triangles exists in an SSA case is summarized in the following tables. Note that α represents the given angle, and a and b represent the given sides, where a is the side opposite the given angle α.

NOTICE THAT

If $a = b \sin \alpha$, then a is the height of the triangle and the triangle is a right triangle.

SSA: The Ambiguous Case Given an Acute Angle α		
One Oblique Triangle	**Two Oblique Triangles**	**Zero Triangles**
$a \geq b$	$b \sin \alpha < a < b$	$a < b \sin \alpha$
The side opposite the given acute angle is greater than or equal to the other given side.	*The height ($b \sin \alpha$) is less than the side opposite the given acute angle, which is less than the other side.*	*The side opposite the given acute angle is less than the height ($b \sin \alpha$).*

SSA: The Ambiguous Case Given an Obtuse Angle α	
One Oblique Triangle	**Zero Triangles**
$a > b$	$a \leq b$
The side opposite the given acute angle is greater than the other given side.	*The side opposite the given acute angle is less than or equal to the other given side.*

EXAMPLE 3 — Determining the Number of Triangles that Exist (SSA)

Determine whether zero, one, or two triangles exist with the given measures.

A. $a = 12$, $c = 8$, $\alpha = 100°$ **B.** $a = 5$, $c = 7$, $\gamma = 25°$ **C.** $b = 4$, $c = 6$, $\beta = 51°$

SOLUTION

A. The given angle is obtuse. Since $a > c$ (because $12 > 8$), the side opposite the given angle (side a) is greater than the other given side (side c). Thus, there is exactly one oblique triangle with $a = 12$, $c = 8$, and $\alpha = 100°$.

> **IMPORTANT**
>
> *The given angle is γ, so c is the side opposite the given angle in this case.*

B. The given angle is acute. Since $c > a$ (because $7 > 5$), the side opposite the given angle (side c) is greater than the other given side (side a). Thus, there is exactly one oblique triangle with $a = 5$, $c = 7$, and $\gamma = 25°$.

C. The given angle is acute. Since $b < c$ (because $4 < 6$), the side opposite the given angle (side b) is less than the other given side (side c). Therefore, use the height of the triangle to determine whether the given measures result in zero or two oblique triangles.

The height of the triangle is the product of the sine of the given angle and the other given side (side c): $h = 6 \sin 51° \approx 4.7$. Since $b < c \sin \beta$ (because $4 < 4.7$), zero triangles exist with $b = 4$, $c = 6$, and $\beta = 51°$.

EXAMPLE 4 — Using the Law of Sines to Solve a Triangle

> **IMPORTANT**
>
> *Since α is an acute angle and $b > a$, either zero or two triangles exist with the given measures. Therefore, begin by finding $b \sin \alpha$.*

Use the Law of Sines to solve a triangle where $a = 7$, $b = 9$, and $\alpha = 40°$, if possible. Round the measures to the nearest hundredth, as needed. If two triangles exist, solve both triangles.

SOLUTION

Find $b \sin \alpha$. $b \sin \alpha = 9 \sin 40° \approx 5.79$

Since $5.79 < 7 < 9$ (i.e., $b \sin \alpha < a < b$), there are two oblique triangles with $a = 7$, $b = 9$, and $\alpha = 40°$. First, find the two possible measures of angle β (the angle opposite the given side). These angle measures are supplementary, so one possible measure of β is an acute angle and the other is an obtuse angle. Use the Law of Sines to find the acute measure of angle β.

$$\frac{\sin 40°}{7} = \frac{\sin \beta}{9} \quad \Rightarrow \quad \sin \beta = \frac{9 \sin 40°}{7} \quad \Rightarrow \quad \beta = \sin^{-1} \frac{9 \sin 40°}{7} \approx 55.73°$$

> **IMPORTANT**
>
> *The two possible measures of β are supplementary angles. Therefore, subtract the acute measure of β (given by using the Law of Sines) from 180° to find the obtuse measure of β.*
> $\beta \approx 180° - 55.73° = 124.27°$

Subtracting 55.73° from 180° gives the approximate measure of obtuse angle β. 124.27°.

Use the Triangle Sum Theorem to find the unknown angle γ in each triangle. Then use the Law of Sines to find the measure of side c in each triangle.

Triangle with Acute Angle β	Triangle with Obtuse Angle β
$\gamma \approx 180° - (40° + 55.73°) = 84.27°$	$\gamma \approx 180° - (40° + 124.27°) = 15.73°$
$\dfrac{c}{\sin 84.27°} \approx \dfrac{7}{\sin 40°}$	$\dfrac{c}{\sin 15.73°} \approx \dfrac{7}{\sin 40°}$
$c \approx \dfrac{7 \sin 84.27°}{\sin 40°}$	$c \approx \dfrac{7 \sin 15.73°}{\sin 40°}$
$c \approx 10.84$	$c \approx 2.95$

Thus, $\beta \approx 55.73°$, $\gamma \approx 84.27°$, and $c \approx 10.84$ in one triangle where $a = 7$, $b = 9$, and $\alpha = 40°$, and $\beta \approx 124.27°$, $\gamma \approx 15.73°$, and $c \approx 2.95$ in the other triangle where $a = 7$, $b = 9$, and $\alpha = 40°$.

4.1.4   Finding the Area of an Oblique Triangle

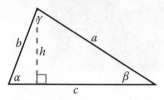

Recall that the area of a triangle is equal to 1/2 of the product of the triangle's base and height. The oblique triangle shown in Figure 4.1e has height h and base c. So, the area A of this triangle is given by the formula $A = \frac{1}{2}ch$.

Figure 4.1e

The formula for the area of an oblique triangle can also be written in terms of two sides and an angle. We saw in Topic 4.1.3 that $h = b \sin \alpha$. It follows that the area of an oblique triangle is given by the formula $A = \frac{1}{2}ch = \frac{1}{2}cb \sin \alpha$. Since α is the included angle between sides b and c, the area of an oblique triangle is half the product of two sides and the sine of the included angle.

This formula can be further generalized to include any two sides and the included angle.

The Area of an Oblique Triangle

For any oblique triangle with side lengths a, b, and c, and angle measures α, β, and γ, the area of the triangle is given by

$$A = \frac{1}{2}cb \sin \alpha = \frac{1}{2}ca \sin \beta = \frac{1}{2}ab \sin \gamma.$$

EXAMPLE 5   **Finding the Area of an Oblique Triangle**

Find the area of a triangle to the nearest hundredth of a square inch if $a = 56$ inches, $\alpha = 63°$, and $\gamma = 46°$.

SOLUTION

Sketch the triangle.

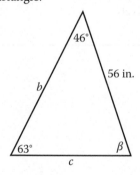

Two sides and the included angle must be known in order to use the formula for the area of an oblique triangle. Therefore, use the Triangle Sum Theorem to find β.

$$\beta \approx 180° - (63° + 46°) = 71°$$

Use the Law of Sines to find c (or b).

$$\frac{c}{\sin 46°} = \frac{56}{\sin 63°} \quad \Rightarrow \quad c = \frac{56 \sin 46°}{\sin 63°} \approx 45.21 \text{ in.} \quad \textit{Law of Sines}$$

IMPORTANT

Always use two sides and the included angle to evaluate the formula for the area of an oblique triangle.

Use the area formula $A = \frac{1}{2}ca \sin \beta$.

$$A \approx \frac{1}{2}(45.21)(56)(\sin 71°) \approx 1196.91 \text{ in}^2$$

4.1.5   The Law of Sines: An Application

> **EXAMPLE 6**   **Using the Law of Sines**

Suppose a pole is secured by two wires, where the longer wire forms a 20° angle with the ground, the shorter wire forms a 42° angle with the ground, and the distance between the point at which the two wires are attached to the ground is 28 meters, as shown in the picture.

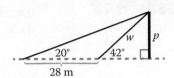

Assume that the pole forms a right angle with the ground. Find the length of the short wire w and the height of the pole p to the nearest tenth of a meter.

SOLUTION

Let α be the included angle between sides of lengths w and 28 meters, and let β be the third angle in the oblique triangle.

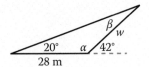

Since α and the 42° angle are supplementary angles, $\alpha = 180° - 42° = 138°$.

By the Triangle Sum Theorem, $\beta = 180° - (20° + 138°) = 22°$.

NOTICE THAT

The side opposite the 22° angle (28 meters) is longer than the side opposite the 20° angle (25.6 meters).

Use the Law of Sines to find w. $\dfrac{w}{\sin 20°} = \dfrac{28}{\sin 22°} \Rightarrow w = \dfrac{28 \sin 20°}{\sin 22°} \approx 25.6 \text{ m}$

Since the height of the pole p is a leg in a right triangle with hypotenuse approximately 25.6 meters, and the angle opposite p is 42°, we can use $\sin \theta = $ opp/hyp to find the approximate value of p.

$$\sin 42° \approx p/25.6 \Rightarrow p \approx 25.6 \sin 42° \approx 17.1 \text{ m}$$

Therefore, the height of the pole and the length of the short wire are approximately 17.1 meters and 25.6 meters, respectively.

SECTION 4.1 EXERCISES

Warm Up

Use the sine function, the given right triangle, and the given measures to find each indicated side or angle to the nearest hundredth, as needed.

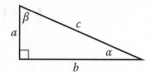

1. $\alpha = 15°$, $a = 25.86$; find c

2. $\beta = 21°$, $c = 22.55$; find b

3. $a = 73.5$, $c = 91$; find α

Just the Facts

Fill in the blanks.

4. A triangle where none of the angles is a right angle is called a(n) _____ triangle.

5. The Law of Sines states that for a triangle with sides a, b, c, and opposite angles α, β, γ, respectively, then _____ = _____ = _____.

6. The situation that applies to triangles for which two sides and the angle opposite one of them are known (SSA) is called the _____ case.

7. In an SSA triangle where α is given as an acute angle, if $a < b \sin \alpha$, then there are exactly _____ triangle(s) with the given measures.

8. In an SSA triangle where α is given as an acute angle, if $a = b \sin \alpha$, then exactly _____ triangle(s) exist with the given measures.

9. In an SSA triangle where α is given as an acute angle, if $a > b \sin \alpha$, and if $a < b$, then there are exactly _____ triangle(s) with the given measures.

10. Given a, c, and β, the area of an oblique triangle can be found using the formula $A =$ _____.

Essential Skills

In Exercises 1–16, use the Law of Sines to solve each triangle, if possible. Round each answer to the nearest hundredth, as needed.

1.
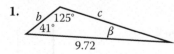

2.
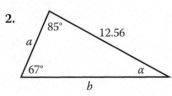

3.
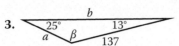

4.
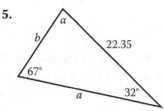

5.
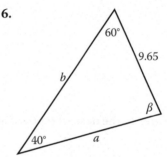

6.
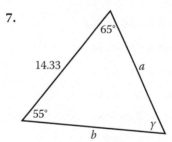

7.
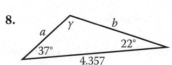

8.

9. $\alpha = 15°$, $\gamma = 127°$, $b = 25.86$

10. $\alpha = 75°$, $\beta = 60°$, $c = 15$

11. $\beta = 45°$, $\gamma = 120°$, $a = 12$

12. $\alpha = 24°$, $\beta = 37°$, $c = 5.192$

13. $\gamma = 122°$, $b = 128$, $c = 453$

14. $\gamma = 97°$, $b = 17.21$, $c = 27.32$

15. $\alpha = 39°$, $a = 91$, $b = 73.5$

16. $\beta = 110°$, $b = 22.55$, $c = 12$

In Exercises 17–20, determine whether exactly zero, one, or two triangles exist with the given measures.

17. $\beta = 30°$, $a = 10$, and $b = 9$

18. $\alpha = 35°$, $a = 7$, and $b = 9$

19. $\alpha = 70°$, $a = 7$, $c = 8$

20. $\gamma = 35°$, $a = 8$, and $c = 6$

In Exercises 21–24, use the Law of Sines to solve each triangle, if possible. Round answers to the nearest hundredth, as needed. If two triangles exist, solve both triangles.

21. $\alpha = 35°$, $a = 6$, and $b = 8$

22. $\alpha = 57°$, $a = 10.8$, and $b = 12.8$

23. $\gamma = 25°$, $a = 2$, and $c = 1$

24. $\alpha = 41°$, $a = 9.9$, and $b = 10.2$

In Exercises 25–28, use the given information to determine all measures for b that will result in zero, one, and two oblique triangles. Round b-values to the nearest hundredth, as needed.

25. $\alpha = 40°$ and $a = 11$

26. $\alpha = 35°$ and $a = 10$

27. $\gamma = 45°$ and $c = 8$

28. $\gamma = 50°$ and $c = 9$

In Exercises 29–36, find the area to the nearest tenth of an inch for each triangle.

29. $\beta = 49°$, $a = 115$ inches, and $c = 170$ inches

30. $\gamma = 119°$, $a = 10$ inches, and $b = 15$ inches

31. $\gamma = 124°$, $a = 17$ inches, and $b = 31$ inches

32. $\alpha = 10°$, $b = 14$ inches, and $c = 11$ inches

33. $\beta = 64°$, $b = 73$ inches, and $c = 68$ inches

34. $\gamma = 97°$, $b = 7$ inches, and $c = 12$ inches

35. $\alpha = 103°$, $a = 11$ inches, and $b = 9$ inches

36. $\alpha = 30°$, $a = 11$ inches, and $b = 9$ inches

37. Two wires help support a pole. One wire forms an angle of 48° with the ground and the other wire forms an angle of 72° with the ground. The wires are 20 meters apart. How tall is the pole to the nearest meter?

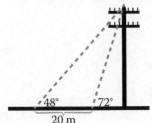

38. In a baseball game, a batter standing at home plate sees the second baseman standing on the baseline between 1st and 2nd base, as shown in the figure. How far is the second baseman from second base? Round to the nearest hundredth of a foot.

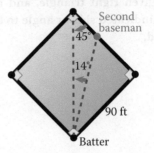

39. A person has a kite out on 1650 feet of string at an angle of 72° with the ground. An observer notes that the angle formed by the kite and the kite flier is 103°. Find the distance between the observer and the kite flier to the nearest foot.

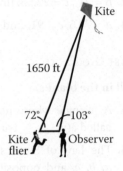

40. Two wires are part of the supports of a pole. One wire forms an angle of 53° with the ground and the other wire forms an angle of 78° with the ground. The distance between the wires on the ground is 25 meters. Find the height of the pole to the nearest tenth of a meter.

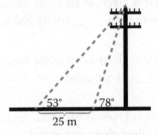

41. Troop A left base camp and hiked 6 hours at 4.4 mph. Troop B left the same camp and hiked 7 hours at 4.2 mph. That evening, Troop A noticed that the angle formed by beacons at the base camp and Troop B's camp was 87°. Find the distance to the nearest tenth of a mile between Troop A and Troop B.

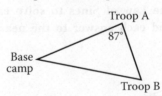

42. Two wireless telephone transmission centers are 35 km apart. A cell phone user is 19 km from one of the centers. At the cell phone user, the angle formed by the two centers is 101°. Find the distance to the nearest kilometer between the cell phone user and the other transmission center.

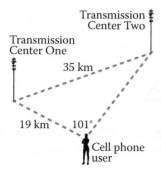

Extensions

43. In triangle *ABC*, *a* = 700 feet, *β* = 73° 39′, and *γ* = 37° 21′. If *M* is the midpoint of *c* (i.e., *M* is the midpoint of line segment *AB*), find the length of *AM* to the nearest hundredth of a foot.

44. Find the area of triangle *MNP* to the nearest tenth of a square unit.

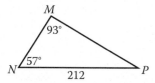

45. Suppose *AB* is a 652 foot line segment along a bank of a stream and *C* is a point on the opposite bank. If *A* = 50° and *B* = 48° in triangle *ABC* as shown in the picture, find the perpendicular distance from *C* to *AB* to the nearest hundredth of a foot.

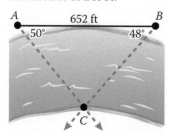

46. Suppose the ratio of the angles in a triangle are in a ratio of 4:5:8 and the shortest side of the triangle is 2.65 inches. Find the length of the longest side to the nearest hundredth of an inch.

47. A flagpole is leaning with the wind 8° from the vertical. 7 meters from the bottom of the flagpole, the angle of elevation to the top of the flagpole is 68°. How tall is the flagpole to the nearest hundredth of a meter?

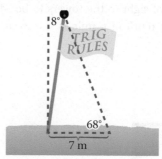

48. A person flying his jet airplane over Waikiki noticed a party on a yacht. His angle of depression to the yacht was 17.5°. Then he noticed the surfer on a huge pipeline wave. His angle of depression to the surfer was 24.167°. His navigation copilot told him he was 5120 feet from the yacht. How far to the nearest foot was he from the surfer?

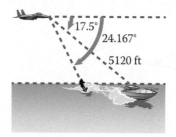

49. Two ships are 2 km apart. A submarine lies directly below the line passing through the two ships. From the submarine, the angle formed by the ships is 41°, while from ship A, the angle formed by ship B and the submarine is 97°. To the nearest hundredth of a kilometer, how much farther is ship B from the submarine than ship A?

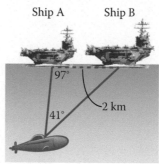

50. A park ranger standing on a hill can see two firewatch towers in the distance. She knows that the two towers are 8 miles from each other. She thinks she is approximately 4.8 miles from one tower. She roughly calculates the angle between her two lines of sight to the towers to be 34.6°. How far to the nearest tenth of a mile is she from the second tower?

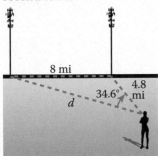

51. In the figure below, what is the measure of x to the nearest tenth of a unit?

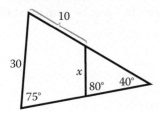

52. In the following triangles, $\alpha = 41°$, $b = 15.56$ mm, and $a = 13.05$ mm. Find the measures of γ_1 and γ_2 to the nearest degree.

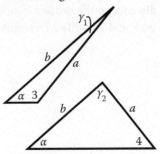

53. In the following triangles, $\alpha = 52°$, $b = 22.71$ cm, and $a = 18.95$ cm. Find the measures of β_1 and β_2 to the nearest degree.

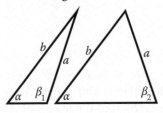

4.2 THE LAW OF COSINES

OBJECTIVES

- Use the Law of Cosines to find the angles of an oblique triangle given the lengths of three sides (SSS).
- Use the Law of Cosines to find the unknown angles and side of an oblique triangle given the lengths of two sides and the included angle (SAS).
- Use Heron's Formula to find the area and height of a triangle.

PREREQUISITE VOCABULARY TERMS

cosine

included angle

Law of Sines

oblique triangle

supplementary angles

4.2.1 The Law of Cosines

The **Law of Cosines** gives a relationship between the sides of an oblique triangle and one of its angles. Specifically, that the sum of the squares of two sides minus twice the product of the two sides and the cosine of the included angle is equal to the square of the third side.

NOTICE THAT

The included angle between b and c is α, the included angle between a and c is β, and the included angle between a and b is γ.

The Law of Cosines

For any triangle with sides a, b, and c, and opposite angles α, β, and γ, respectively,

$a^2 = b^2 + c^2 - 2bc \cos \alpha$,

$b^2 = a^2 + c^2 - 2ac \cos \beta$, and

$c^2 = a^2 + b^2 - 2ab \cos \gamma$.

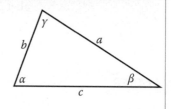

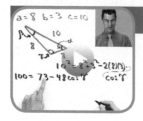

4.2.2 The Law of Cosines (SSS)

Use the Law of Cosines to solve an oblique triangle when three sides are given (SSS).

EXAMPLE 1   Using the Law of Cosines

Find the measures of the largest and smallest angles in a triangle where $a = 10$, $b = 14$, and $c = 6$.

SOLUTION

CAUTION

By the order of operations, the product 2ac cos β is subtracted from $a^2 + c^2$. So, do not subtract 2ac from $a^2 + c^2$.

A triangle's largest and smallest angles are opposite its longest and shortest sides, respectively. So, the largest angle is β (opposite $b = 14$) and the smallest angle is γ (opposite $c = 6$). Use the Law of Cosines to find β and γ.

$$b^2 = a^2 + c^2 - 2ac \cos \beta$$
$$14^2 = 10^2 + 6^2 - 2(10)(6) \cos \beta$$
$$196 = 136 - 120 \cos \beta$$
$$-1/2 = \cos \beta$$
$$\beta = \cos^{-1}(-1/2) = 120°$$

$$c^2 = a^2 + b^2 - 2ab \cos \gamma$$
$$6^2 = 10^2 + 14^2 - 2(10)(14) \cos \gamma$$
$$36 = 296 - 280 \cos \gamma$$
$$13/14 = \cos \gamma$$
$$\gamma = \cos^{-1}(13/14) \approx 21.79°$$

ALTERNATIVE METHOD

After finding β, γ can be found using the Law of Sines.

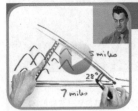

4.2.3 The Law of Cosines (SAS): An Application

The Law of Cosines can be used to solve an oblique triangle when the lengths of two sides and the measure of their included angle are known (SAS), as demonstrated in **Example 2**.

Remember, use the Law of Sines to find an unknown side length or angle measure of an oblique triangle given the lengths of two sides and the measure of their *nonincluded* angle (SSA).

EXAMPLE 2   **Using the Law of Cosines**

The obtuse angle formed by the intersection of Highway 1 and Highway 2 is 148°, as shown in the picture, where the points A, B, and C represent exits from the highways.

The distance between exit A and exit B is 47 miles and the distance between exit B and exit C is 55 miles. Find the shortest distance between exit A and exit C to the nearest hundredth of a mile.

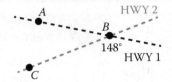

SOLUTION

Sketch a triangle.

Let b be the distance between A and C.

Then b is a side of triangle ABC, where the other two sides are 47 miles and 55 miles.

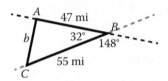

REMEMBER

The shortest distance between any two points is a straight line.

Angle B has supplement 148°, so
$B = 180° - 148° = 32°$.

Since two sides and their included angle are known (SAS), the Law of Cosines can be used to find the length of the triangle's remaining side (side b).

Use the Law of Cosines where $a = 55$ miles and $c = 47$ miles.

$$b^2 = a^2 + c^2 - 2ac \cos \beta \qquad \textit{Law of Cosines}$$
$$b^2 = 55^2 + 47^2 - 2(55)(47) \cos 32° \qquad \textit{Substitute.}$$
$$b^2 = 5234 - 5170 \cos 32° \qquad \textit{Simplify.}$$
$$b = \sqrt{5234 - 5170 \cos 32°} \qquad \textit{Take the positive square root of each side.}$$

TIP

Since b represents a distance, the square root must be positive.

$$b \approx 29.15 \qquad \textit{Use a calculator and round to the nearest hundredth.}$$

Therefore, the shortest distance between exit A and exit C is approximately 29.15 miles.

4.2.4   Heron's Formula

A formula for the area of an oblique triangle $A = \frac{1}{2}cb \sin \alpha$ was given in Section 4.1. Recall that in order to use this formula, the lengths of two sides and the measure of their included angle must be known.

The Law of Cosines can be used to derive a formula for the area of a triangle (oblique or right) in terms of only the triangle's side lengths in an expression known as **Heron's formula**. Note that the **semiperimeter** of a triangle is half the triangle's perimeter.

REMEMBER

The perimeter P of a polygon is the sum of the lengths of its sides. So, for triangle with sides a, b, and c, P = a + b + c.

> **Heron's Formula for the Area of a Triangle**
>
> The area of any triangle with sides a, b, and c, is given by $A = \sqrt{s(s-a)(s-b)(s-c)}$, where s is the semiperimeter, $s = \frac{1}{2}(a+b+c)$.

EXAMPLE 3   Using Heron's Formula to Find the Area of a Triangle

Find the area to the nearest tenth of a foot of the triangle with sides 10 feet, 12 feet, and 18 feet. Then, letting the triangle's base be 12 feet, find the triangle's height to the nearest tenth of a foot.

SOLUTION

Find the semiperimeter. $s = \frac{1}{2}(10 + 12 + 18) = \frac{1}{2}(40) = 20$ ft

Use Heron's formula to find the triangle's area.

NOTICE THAT

The triangle's exact area is $40\sqrt{2}$ ft².

$A = \sqrt{20(20-10)(20-12)(20-18)} = \sqrt{20(10)(8)(2)} = \sqrt{3200} = 40\sqrt{2} \approx 56.6 \text{ ft}^2$

Use the formula for the area of a triangle in terms of its height and base, $A = \frac{1}{2}bh$, to find the height of the triangle.

$40\sqrt{2} = \frac{1}{2}(12)h$ *Substitute 12 for b and $40\sqrt{2}$ for A.*

$h = \frac{40\sqrt{2}}{6} \approx 9.4 \text{ ft}$ *Solve for h. Use a calculator to simplify.*

Therefore, the area of the triangle is approximately 56.6 square feet and the height of the triangle (when the base is 12 feet) is approximately 9.4 feet.

SECTION 4.2 EXERCISES

Warm Up

1. Solve $c^2 = a^2 + b^2 - 2ab \cos \gamma$ for γ.

2. In the triangle where $a = 12$, $b = 17$, and $c = 15$, is α, β, or γ the smallest angle?

3. In the triangle where $a = 20.1$, $b = 20.12$, and $c = 20.01$, is α, β, or γ the largest angle?

Just the Facts

Fill in the blanks.

4. If three sides of a triangle are given, the Law of _____ is used to solve the triangle.

5. The Law of Cosines states that for any triangle with sides a, b, c, and opposite angles α, β, γ, respectively, $a^2 =$ _____, $b^2 =$ _____, and $c^2 =$ _____.

6. If one side and two angles of a triangle are given, the Law of _____ is used to solve the triangle.

7. If two sides and the included angle of a triangle are given, the Law of _____ is used to solve the triangle.

8. If two sides of a triangle and an angle opposite one of them are given, the Law of _____ is used to solve the triangle.

9. To find the area of a triangle if the three sides are known, _____ Formula can be used.

10. The area A of a triangle with given sides a, b, and c is $A =$ _____, where $s =$ _____.

Essential Skills

In Exercises 1–4, find the largest angle to the nearest thousandth of a degree in each triangle with the given sides.

1. 11, 6, 9

2. 50, 70, 85

3. 3, 8, 7

4. 42, 64, 77

In Exercises 5–8, find the smallest angle to the nearest thousandth of a degree in each triangle with the given sides.

5. 6, 9, 4

6. 40, 68, 83

7. 12, 17, 15

8. 38, 54, 71

9. Suppose two people stand 400 meters apart on one side of a river and a house is on the opposite side of the river. The people are 700 meters and 1065 meters from the house, as shown in the picture below. In the triangle formed by the two people and the house, what is the measure of the angle with vertex at the person 700 meters from the house? Round to the nearest degree.

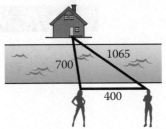

10. A Geiger counter is 4 stories (40 feet) above a sample of radium in a stairwell and 13 feet along the stairs away from directly above the substance. If based on the counter readings the radium is 42 feet away, find θ, as shown in the picture, to the nearest hundredth of a degree.

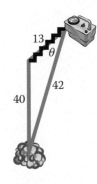

11. To straighten a tree, an 8.4 foot guy-wire is stretched from the top of the tree trunk (6.8 feet above the ground) to a stake in the ground that is 4.9 feet from the base of the tree. What is the angle to the nearest hundredth of a degree that the base of the tree makes with the ground?

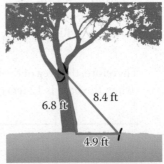

12. A 40-foot flag pole stands atop a hill. A woman stands at the base of the hill, 40 feet from the base of the flag pole, and 60 feet from the top. Find θ, as shown in the picture, to the nearest hundredth of a degree.

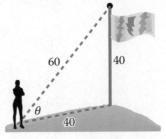

13. The sides of a parallelogram are 40 feet and 70 feet. The length of the longer diagonal is 105 feet. What is the measure of the smaller angle in the parallelogram? Round to the nearest tenth of a degree.

14. A Geiger counter is 3 stories (30 feet) above a sample of radium in a stairwell and 13 feet along the stairs away from being directly above the radium sample. If Geiger counter's readings indicate the radium is 37 feet away, θ, as shown in the picture, to the nearest hundredth of a degree.

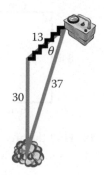

15. A blue boat and a red boat moored along the same side of a lake and are 18 miles apart. The blue boat is 30 miles from a lighthouse on the opposite side of the lake. The angle formed by the boats and the lighthouse, and whose vertex is the blue boat, measures 120°. Find the distance to the nearest mile from the red boat to the lighthouse.

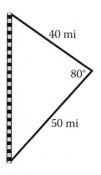

16. A man went off-roading in his Jeep. After driving 50 miles from the highway, he turned 80° to his left. After another 40 miles he reached the highway again. How much of the highway did he bypass? Round to the nearest hundredth of a mile.

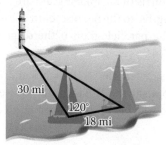

17. Two runners began running at the same time, but at a 25° angle from each other. One runner averages 7.5 mph, and the other averages 8 mph. How far apart are the runners after two hours? Round to the nearest tenth of a mile.

18. A piece of wire is bent into the shape of a triangle. Two sides have lengths of 18 inches and 22 inches. The angle between these two sides is 45°. What is the length of the third side to the nearest hundredth of an inch?

19. Determine the width of Lake Minnehaha to the nearest meter, given the following information. A surveyor standing at a point south of the lake is 2125 meters from the western end, and 3250 meters from the eastern end of the lake. The angle between the two lines-of-sight and either end of the lake is 77°.

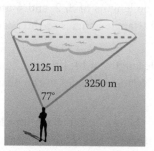

20. A man went off-roading in his jeep. He left the straight highway and drove 45 miles in a straight line away from the road. He then turned to the left 52 degrees and drove 65 miles in a straight line until he returned to the highway. How much of the highway did he bypass? Round to the nearest hundredth of a mile.

In Exercises 21–26, find the area of each triangle with the given lengths. Round each answer to the nearest tenth, as needed.

21. 4 inches, 6 inches, and 9 inches

22. 5.9 centimeters, 6.7 centimeters, and 10.3 centimeters

23. 35 feet, 45 feet, and 50 feet

24. 7 centimeters, 7.2 centimeters, and 9 centimeters

25. 3 inches, 2 inches, and 4 inches

26. 6.4 centimeters, 8.9 centimeters, and 9.4 centimeters

In Exercises 27–32, find the height of each triangle with the given sides. Round each answer to the nearest hundredth, as needed.

27. base 14 feet; sides 9 feet and 7 feet

28. base 6 inches; sides 3 inches and 5 inches

29. base 8 feet; sides 6 feet and 4 feet

30. base 12 inches; sides 6 inches and 7 inches

31. base 4 inches; sides 7 inches and 6 inches

32. base 9 inches; sides 3 inches and 7 inches

Extensions

33. Suppose a triangle has two sides with lengths of 4 units, and their included angle measures 110°. Find the unknown side to the nearest tenth of a unit for the triangle.

34. Suppose a triangle has side lengths of 3, 2, and 4 units. Find the measures of the triangle's angles to the nearest tenth of a degree.

35. Suppose a triangle has side lengths of 14, 12, and 17 units. Find the measures of the triangle's angles to the nearest tenth of a degree.

36. Two boats leave a dock at the same time. Each travels in a straight line. The angle between their courses measures 54° 10′ 15″. One boat travels at 36.2 kilometers per hour and the other travels at 45.6 kilometers per hour. How far apart, to the nearest tenth of a kilometer, will they be after 3 hours?

37. The perimeter of a triangle is 42 centimeters. Two sides of the triangle have lengths of 15 centimeters and 20 centimeters. What is the area of the triangle?

38. Find the area of quadrilateral *ABCD* to the nearest tenth of a square foot.

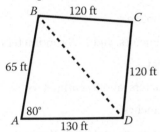

39. Find the area of the figure to the nearest tenth of a square foot.

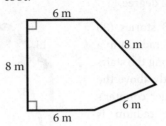

40. Find the area of the parallelogram to the nearest tenth of a square meter.

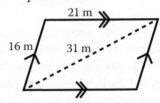

41. The lengths of the diagonals of a parallelogram are 8 feet and 12 feet. Find the lengths, to the nearest tenth of a foot, of the short sides of the parallelogram if the diagonals intersect at an angle of 24°.

42. Suppose a triangle has side lengths of 18 inches and 21.6 inches, and the angle opposite the 21.6 inch side measures 52°. Find the area of the triangle to the nearest tenth of a square inch.

4.3 VECTORS

OBJECTIVES

- Define a vector and the magnitude of a vector.
- Find the magnitude and direction of a vector.
- Multiply a vector by a scalar.
- Add and subtract vectors.
- Find the components of a vector.
- Find a unit vector.
- Write a vector as a linear combination of the standard unit vectors.
- Find the direction angle of a vector.

PREREQUISITE VOCABULARY TERMS

bearing
inverse trigonometric functions
parallelogram
Pythagorean Theorem
reference angle
trigonometric functions

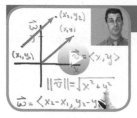

4.3.1   Introduction to Vectors

A **vector** is a quantity that has both **magnitude** (length) and direction. It can be represented graphically by a directed line segment. **Equivalent vectors** have the same magnitude and the same direction. The following table shows several pairs of equivalent vectors.

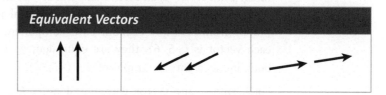

Equivalent Vectors

IMPORTANT

The equivalence of two vectors is determined by their direction and magnitude, not by their position. Equivalent vectors have the same slope.

Vectors are named using a single letter with a small arrow over the letter, or with a single boldface letter, such as $\vec{v}$ or $\boldsymbol{v}$ (both read as "vector v").

IMPORTANT

Two vectors may be equivalent even if their initial and terminal points differ. However, if two equivalent vectors have the same initial point, then they must have the same terminal point.

A vector is represented by a directed line segment on the coordinate plane, where the line segment's endpoints are called the vector's **initial point** and **terminal point**. An arrowhead on the segment indicates the direction of the vector. Figure 4.3a shows $\vec{v}$ with initial point at the origin and terminal point (x, y). A vector on the coordinate plane is said to be in **standard position** if its initial point is at the origin.

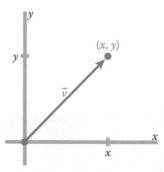

Figure 4.3a

If $\vec{v}$ is a vector on the coordinate plane with initial point at (x_1, y_1) and terminal point at (x_2, y_2), then the **component form** of $\vec{v}$ is $\vec{v} = \langle x_2 - x_1, y_2 - y_1 \rangle$. If a vector $\vec{v}$ is in standard position with terminal point at (x, y), then the component form of $\vec{v}$ is $\langle x, y \rangle$.

The two values in the component form of a vector are called the vector's **components**, specifically the **horizontal component** x and the **vertical component** y. The components indicate the change in x and the change in y from the initial point to the terminal point of a vector. The vector's components also indicate the coordinates of the terminal point of the vector in standard position.

| **EXAMPLE 1** | **Finding the Component Form of a Vector** |

Write the component form of each vector.

A. $\bar{v}$ with initial point $(0, 0)$ and terminal point $(-1, 3)$

B. $\bar{u}$ with initial point $(0, -4)$ and terminal point $(-5, 2)$

C. $\bar{w}$ with initial point $(-3, 1)$ and terminal point $(0, 0)$

SOLUTION

> **IMPORTANT**
>
> *The terminal point must be (x_2, y_2) and the initial point must be (x_1, y_1).*

A. $\bar{v} = \langle x_2 - x_1, y_2 - y_1 \rangle = \langle -1 - 0, 3 - 0 \rangle = \langle -1, 3 \rangle$ $\qquad x_1 = 0, y_1 = 0, x_2 = -1, y_2 = 3$

The component form of any vector with initial point at the origin and terminal point at (x, y) is $\langle x, y \rangle$. So, since $\bar{v}$ has initial point at $(0, 0)$ and terminal point at $(-1, 3)$, $\bar{v} = \langle -1, 3 \rangle$.

B. $\bar{u} = \langle x_2 - x_1, y_2 - y_1 \rangle = \langle -5 - 0, 2 - (-4) \rangle = \langle -5, 6 \rangle$ $\qquad x_1 = 0, y_1 = -4, x_2 = -5, y_2 = 2$

C. $\bar{w} = \langle x_2 - x_1, y_2 - y_1 \rangle = \langle 0 - (-3), 0 - 1 \rangle = \langle 3, -1 \rangle$ $\qquad x_1 = -3, y_1 = 1, x_2 = 0, y_2 = 0$

Equivalent Vectors

Two vectors are equivalent if and only if their respective components are equal. Specifically, $\bar{v} = \langle v_1, v_2 \rangle$ and $\bar{u} = \langle u_1, u_2 \rangle$ are equivalent if and only if $v_1 = u_1$ and $v_2 = u_2$.

Figure 4.3b shows the graphs of two vectors: one with initial point at $(0, -4)$ and terminal point at $(-5, 2)$, and the other with initial point at $(0, 0)$ and terminal point at $(-5, 6)$ (from **Example 1B**). Since the component form of each vector is $\langle -5, 6 \rangle$, they are equivalent vectors (i.e., both line segments are graphs of $\bar{u} = \langle -5, 6 \rangle$).

Furthermore, any vector with initial point (x_1, y_1) and terminal point (x_2, y_2) such that $\langle x_2 - x_1, y_2 - y_1 \rangle = \langle -5, 6 \rangle$ is equivalent to $\bar{u}$. For example, a vector with initial point $(5, -6)$ and terminal point $(0, 0)$ is also equivalent to $\bar{u}$.

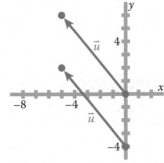

Figure 4.3b

It follows that there are an infinite number of directed line segments representing a vector with component form $\langle x, y \rangle$. Typically, the most convenient of these is the standard position vector, with initial point at the origin and terminal point at (x, y).

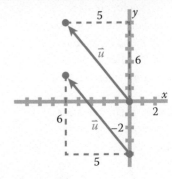

4.3.2 Finding the Magnitude and Direction of a Vector

The magnitude of a vector is equal to the length of its graphical representation (i.e., the length of the line segment from its initial point to its terminal point). Consider the graphs of $\bar{u}$ shown in Figure 4.3b. Each representation of $\bar{u}$ is the hypotenuse of a right triangle with legs 6 and 5 units (Figure 4.3c). By the Pythagorean Theorem, the length of the hypotenuse is $\sqrt{5^2 + 6^2}$, that is, $\sqrt{61}$ units. Therefore, the magnitude of $\bar{u}$ is $\sqrt{61}$.

Figure 4.3c

> **The Magnitude of a Vector**
>
> For vector $\bar{v} = \langle x, y \rangle$, the magnitude, denoted $||\bar{v}||$, is $||\bar{v}|| = \sqrt{x^2 + y^2}$.

To find the magnitude of a vector when the coordinates of the initial and terminal points are given, first find the component form of the vector, then use the x- and y-components to find the magnitude. Alternatively, use the Distance Formula.

$$|| \bar{v} || = \sqrt{(x_2 - x_1)^2 + (y_2 - y_1)^2}$$

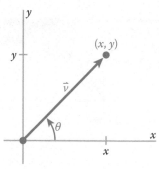

TIP

A vector's direction angle is the positive standard position angle with the vector on its terminal side.

The **direction angle** θ of $\bar{v} = \langle x, y \rangle$ is the angle formed by a counterclockwise rotation of a ray from the positive x-axis to the standard position vector (i.e., to the line segment representing the vector with endpoints at the origin and (x, y)), as shown in Figure 4.3d. It follows that (x, y) is a point on the terminal side of θ.

Figure 4.3d

In this case, we know that $\sin \theta = y/r$, $\cos \theta = x/r$, and $\tan \theta = y/x$, where x and y are the components of the vector and r is the vector's magnitude. So, a trigonometric function can be used to find θ, the vector's direction angle. This procedure is demonstrated in **Example 2**.

EXAMPLE 2   Finding the Magnitude and Direction Angle of a Vector

Find the magnitude and direction angle (to the nearest thousandth of a degree) of each vector.
A. $\bar{v} = \langle -6, 4 \rangle$ **B.** $\bar{u} = \langle -2, -2 \rangle$

SOLUTION

A. Sketch the graph of $\bar{v} = \langle -6, 4 \rangle$ in standard position.

Find the magnitude.

$$|| \bar{v} || = \sqrt{(-6)^2 + (4)^2} = \sqrt{52} = 2\sqrt{13}$$

Use $\cos \theta = x/r$ to find the direction angle.

$$\cos \theta = -6/\left(2\sqrt{13}\right) \;\Rightarrow\; \theta = \cos^{-1}\left(-3/\sqrt{13}\right) \approx 146.31°$$

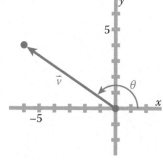

TIP

Use cosine to find the direction angle when the vector is in quadrant II. Otherwise, additional steps are necessary because the range of the inverse sine and tangent functions do not include quadrant II.

B. Sketch the graph of $\bar{u} = \langle -2, -2 \rangle$ in standard position and find the magnitude.

$$|| \bar{u} || = \sqrt{(-2)^2 + (-2)^2} = \sqrt{8} = 2\sqrt{2}$$

Use $\tan \theta = y/x$ to find the direction angle.

$$\tan \theta = -2/(-2) = 1$$

Since θ is in quadrant III, $\theta = \tan^{-1} 1 + \pi = 5\pi/4 = 225°$.

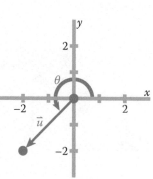

REMEMBER

The range of the inverse tangent function is $(-\pi/2, \pi/2)$.

TIP

In quadrant II,
$\theta = \cos^{-1}(x/r)$.
In quadrant III,
$\theta = 180° + \tan^{-1}(y/x)$.
In quadrant IV,
$\theta = 360° - \sin^{-1}(y/r)$.

Any trigonometric function can be used to find a vector's direction angle θ. However, because the range of the inverse trigonometric functions is not [0, 360°), the direction angle is not always equal to the value given by the inverse trigonometric function, and depends on which quadrant contains the vector and which trigonometric function is used to find the direction angle.

4.3.3   Scalar Multiplication

If $\bar{v} = \langle x, y \rangle$ is a vector and k is a **scalar** (a constant real number), then the components of the **scalar multiple** $k\bar{v}$ are found by multiplying each component of $\bar{v}$ by k.

> ### Scalar Multiplication of a Vector
>
> If $\bar{v} = \langle x, y \rangle$ and k is a scalar, then $k\bar{v} = \langle kx, ky \rangle$.

EXAMPLE 3   **Finding a Scalar Multiple of a Vector**

If $\bar{v} = \langle -3, 1 \rangle$, find each scalar multiple.

A. $2\bar{v}$ **B.** $-\bar{v}$

SOLUTION

A. Multiply each component by 2. $2\bar{v} = \langle 2(-3), 2(1) \rangle = \langle -6, 2 \rangle$

B. Multiply each component by –1. $-\bar{v} = \langle -(-3), -(1) \rangle = \langle 3, -1 \rangle$

Graphing a Scalar Multiple

If the magnitude of $\bar{v} = \langle x, y \rangle$ is $||\bar{v}||$, then the magnitude of the scalar multiple vector $k\bar{v} = \langle kx, ky \rangle$ is $|k| \cdot ||\bar{v}||$. If $k < 0$, then the direction of $k\bar{v} = \langle kx, ky \rangle$ is opposite the direction of $\bar{v} = \langle x, y \rangle$. Therefore, the vector $-2\bar{v}$ is twice the length of $\bar{v}$, and $-2\bar{v}$ points in the direction opposite $\bar{v}$, as shown in Figure 4.3e.

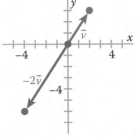

Figure 4.3e

4.3.4   Vector Arithmetic

The sum or difference of two vectors is called a **resultant vector**.

> ### Vector Addition and Subtraction
>
> If $\bar{v} = \langle v_1, v_2 \rangle$ and $\bar{u} = \langle u_1, u_2 \rangle$, then $\bar{v} + \bar{u} = \langle v_1 + u_1, v_2 + u_2 \rangle$, and $\bar{v} - \bar{u} = \langle v_1 - u_1, v_2 - u_2 \rangle$.

EXAMPLE 4 **Finding a Resultant Vector**

If $\vec{v} = \langle 5, 0 \rangle$ and $\vec{u} = \langle 2, -1 \rangle$, find each resultant vector.

A. $\vec{v} + \vec{u}$ **B.** $\vec{u} - \vec{v}$ **C.** $\vec{v} - 2\vec{u}$

SOLUTION

A. Add. $\vec{v} + \vec{u} = \langle 5, 0 \rangle + \langle 2, -1 \rangle = \langle 5 + 2, 0 + (-1) \rangle = \langle 7, -1 \rangle$

B. Subtract. $\vec{u} - \vec{v} = \langle 2, -1 \rangle - \langle 5, 0 \rangle = \langle 2 - 5, -1 - 0 \rangle = \langle -3, -1 \rangle$

C. Multiply each component of $\vec{u}$ by 2, then subtract.

$$\vec{v} - 2\vec{u} = \langle 5, 0 \rangle - 2\langle 2, -1 \rangle = \langle 5, 0 \rangle - \langle 4, -2 \rangle = \langle 1, 2 \rangle$$

Graphically, the resultant vector $\vec{v} + \vec{u}$ is the diagonal of the parallelogram formed with $\vec{v}$ and $\vec{u}$ as the adjacent sides. For example, the parallelogram formed by adjacent sides $\vec{v} = \langle 5, 0 \rangle$ and $\vec{u} = \langle 2, -1 \rangle$ is shown in Figure 4.3f.

Notice that the resultant vector $\vec{v} + \vec{u} = \langle 7, -1 \rangle$ (from **Example 4A**) is a diagonal of the parallelogram.

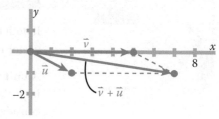

Figure 4.3f

4.3.5 Finding the Components of a Vector

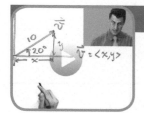

The components of a vector can be found using the vector's magnitude and direction angle (or the reference angle formed with the standard position vector), as demonstrated in **Example 5**. Recall that if the terminal point of a standard position vector is (x, y), the vector's magnitude is r, and the direction angle is θ, then $\sin \theta = y/r$, $\cos \theta = x/r$, and the vector's components are $\langle x, y \rangle$.

EXAMPLE 5 **Finding the Components of a Vector**

Find the component form of $\vec{v}$ if $||\vec{v}|| = 10$, and the vector's direction angle is 300°.

SOLUTION

Sketch $\vec{v}$ on the coordinate plane in standard position with length 10 units and direction angle 300°. Use the sine and cosine functions to find x and y (where the vector's terminal point is (x, y) and $r = 10$ is the vector's magnitude).

$$\cos 300° = x/10 \implies x = 10 \cos 300° = 10(1/2) = 5$$

$$\sin 300° = y/10 \implies y = 10 \sin 300° = 10\left(-\sqrt{3}/2\right) = -5\sqrt{3}$$

Thus, $\vec{v} = \left\langle 5, -5\sqrt{3} \right\rangle$.

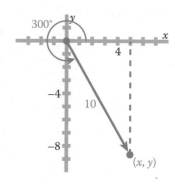

ALTERNATIVE METHOD

The reference angle of a 300° angle is 60°, so the vector is the hypotenuse of a 30°-60°-90° triangle with legs x and y.

The hypotenuse is 10, so the leg opposite the 30° angle is 5 and the leg opposite the 60° angle is $5\sqrt{3}$.

The vector is in quadrant IV, so $x > 0$ and $y < 0$. Thus, $x = 5$ and $y = -5\sqrt{3}$, and $\vec{v} = \langle 5, -5\sqrt{3} \rangle$.

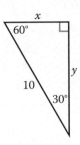

REMEMBER

The side lengths of a 30°-60°-90° triangle are a, a $\sqrt{3}$, and 2a, where the hypotenuse is 2a. In this case, a = 5.

4.3.6 Finding a Unit Vector

If both the initial and terminal points of a vector in standard position are at the origin, then that vector is called the **zero vector** $\vec{0}$. Thus, $\vec{0} = \langle 0, 0 \rangle$. The magnitude of the zero vector is 0.

A **unit vector**, denoted $\vec{u}$, is a vector with magnitude 1. When a nonzero vector's direction is important, but the magnitude is not, then the **unit vector in the same direction** can be considered. Multiply each of a nonzero vector's components by the reciprocal of its magnitude to find the components of the unit vector in the same direction.

> **Unit Vectors**
>
> If $\vec{v} = \langle x, y \rangle$ and $||\vec{v}|| \neq 0$, then the unit vector in the
>
> same direction as $\vec{v}$ is $\vec{u} = \dfrac{1}{||\vec{v}||}\vec{v} = \left\langle \dfrac{x}{||\vec{v}||}, \dfrac{y}{||\vec{v}||} \right\rangle$.

NOTICE THAT

If $\vec{u}$ is the unit vector in the same direction as $\vec{v}$, then $\vec{u}$ is a scalar multiple of $\vec{v}$.

EXAMPLE 6   Finding a Unit Vector

Find the component form of the unit vector in the same direction as $\vec{v} = \langle -3, -4 \rangle$.

SOLUTION

Find the magnitude of $\vec{v}$. $||\vec{v}|| = \sqrt{(-3)^2 + (-4)^2} = \sqrt{25} = 5$

Multiply $\vec{v}$ by the reciprocal of $||\vec{v}||$, 1/5, to find the unit vector in the same direction as $\vec{v}$.

$\vec{u} = (1/5)\langle -3, -4 \rangle = \langle -3/5, -4/5 \rangle$ *Multiply each component by the scalar 1/5.*

NOTICE THAT

The vector forms a 3:4:5 right triangle, so the vector's magnitude must be 5.

CHECK

Find the magnitude of the unit vector.

$||\vec{u}|| = \sqrt{(-3/5)^2 + (-4/5)^2} = \sqrt{25/25} = 1$ ✔

Sketch the graph of $\vec{u}$ and $\vec{v}$.
$\vec{u}$ and $\vec{v}$ have the same direction. ✔

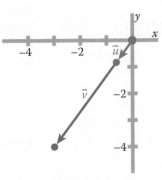

4.3.7 Applications of Vectors

A vector representing the velocity (a measure of speed and direction) of an object is called a **velocity vector**. A velocity vector's magnitude is the speed of the object and its direction is the direction the object is traveling.

EXAMPLE 7   Finding a Velocity Vector

Find the velocity vector of a boat traveling at 40 kilometers per hour at a 210° bearing.

SOLUTION

A bearing of 210° means the ray is rotated 210° clockwise from due north. So, the velocity vector is in quadrant III and its reference angle is 60°.

Use the sine and cosine functions to find x and y (where the vector's terminal point is (x, y) and $r = 40$ is the vector's magnitude).

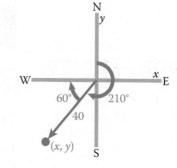

$$\cos 60° = x/40 \implies x = 40 \cos 60° = 40(1/2) = 20$$

$$\sin 60° = y/40 \implies y = 40 \sin 60° = 40\left(\sqrt{3}/2\right) = 20\sqrt{3}$$

The vector is in quadrant III, so $x < 0$ and $y < 0$. Thus, the velocity vector is $\vec{v} = \left\langle -20, -20\sqrt{3}\right\rangle$.

4.3.8 Linear Combinations and Direction Angles of Vectors

A sum of vectors is called a **linear combination** of vectors. For example, the sums $5\vec{u} + 2\vec{v}$, $-\vec{u} + 6\vec{v}$, and $\vec{u} + 3\vec{v}$ are each a linear combination of vectors $\vec{u}$ and $\vec{v}$. In general, if r and s are scalars, then $r\vec{u} + s\vec{v}$ is a linear combination of the vectors $\vec{u}$ and $\vec{v}$.

A linear combination of **standard unit vectors** is a special type of linear combination. In the coordinate plane there are two standard unit vectors, typically denoted by $\vec{i}$ and $\vec{j}$.

Standard Unit Vectors

The standard unit vectors are $\vec{i} = \langle 1, 0\rangle$ and $\vec{j} = \langle 0, 1\rangle$.

The graphs of the standard unit vectors $\vec{i}$ and $\vec{j}$ in standard position are line segments on the x- and y-axis, respectively, and are thus perpendicular. Furthermore, any scalar multiples of the two standard unit vectors in standard position are also perpendicular to each other. Therefore, the resultant vector formed from a sum of scalar multiples of the two standard unit vectors is the diagonal of a rectangle (i.e., a parallelogram with perpendicular sides).

Any vector can be written as a linear combination of the standard unit vectors $\vec{i}$ and $\vec{j}$.

$$\vec{v} = \langle x, y \rangle = x\langle 1, 0 \rangle + y\langle 0, 1 \rangle = x\vec{i} + y\vec{j}$$

NOTICE THAT

The components of $\vec{v}$, x and y, are the scalars in the linear combination.

For example, suppose $\vec{v} = \langle 2, 1 \rangle$. Then $\vec{v} = \langle 2, 1 \rangle = 2\langle 1, 0 \rangle + 1\langle 0, 1 \rangle = 2\vec{i} + \vec{j}$. So, $\vec{v} = 2\vec{i} + \vec{j}$ is the linear combination of the standard unit vectors $\vec{i}$ and $\vec{j}$ for $\vec{v} = \langle 2, 1 \rangle$.

EXAMPLE 8   Writing a Vector as a Linear Combination of Standard Unit Vectors

REMEMBER

The magnitude of each standard unit vector is 1.

Suppose $\vec{v}$ is a vector with initial point $(1, -2)$ and terminal point $(-3, 6)$. Write $\vec{v}$ as a linear combination of the standard unit vectors.

SOLUTION

Find the component form of $\vec{v}$.

$$\vec{v} = \langle x_2 - x_1, y_2 - y_1 \rangle = \langle -3 - 1, 6 - (-2) \rangle = \langle -4, 8 \rangle \qquad x_1 = 1, y_1 = -2, x_2 = -3, y_2 = 6$$

Use the horizontal and vertical components of $\vec{v}$ to write $\vec{v}$ as a linear combination of the standard unit vectors $\vec{i}$ and $\vec{j}$.

$$\vec{v} = \langle -4, 8 \rangle = -4\langle 1, 0 \rangle + 8\langle 0, 1 \rangle = -4\vec{i} + 8\vec{j}$$

The component forms of the vectors $-4\vec{i}$, $8\vec{j}$, and $\vec{v}$ from **Example 8** are $\langle -4, 0 \rangle$, $\langle 0, 8 \rangle$, and $\langle -4, 8 \rangle$, respectively. So, the terminal points of vectors $-4\vec{i}$, $8\vec{j}$, and $\vec{v}$ in standard position are $(-4, 0)$, $(0, 8)$, and $(-4, 8)$, respectively. The graph of these three vectors in standard position (Figure 4.3g) confirms that $\vec{v} = -4\vec{i} + 8\vec{j}$ is the resultant vector of $-4\vec{i}$ and $8\vec{j}$ because $\vec{v} = -4\vec{i} + 8\vec{j}$ is a diagonal of the parallelogram with adjacent sides $-4\vec{i}$ and $8\vec{j}$.

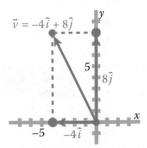

Figure 4.3g

Writing a Vector as a Linear Combination of the Standard Unit Vectors in Terms of the Vector's Direction Angle and Magnitude

A standard position vector $\vec{v} = \langle x, y \rangle$ has terminal point (x, y). So, the terminal side of the vector's direction angle θ contains the point (x, y). Therefore, by the definitions of the trigonometric functions of θ, $x = r \cos \theta$ and $y = r \sin \theta$, where r is the vector's magnitude. The components of $\vec{v}$ can thus be written in terms of the vector's magnitude r and direction angle θ.

$$\vec{v} = \langle x, y \rangle = \langle r \cos \theta, r \sin \theta \rangle = (r\cos \theta)\vec{i} + (r\sin \theta)\vec{j}$$

EXAMPLE 9 | **Finding the Direction Angle of a Vector Given as a Linear Combination of Standard Unit Vectors**

Find the direction angle of each vector. Round to the nearest tenth of a degree as needed.

A. $\vec{w} = 2(\cos 30°)\,\vec{i} + 2(\sin 30°)\,\vec{j}$ **B.** $-3\,\vec{i} - \vec{j}$

SOLUTION

A. The vector is expressed in the form $r(\cos \theta)\,\vec{i} + r(\sin \theta)\,\vec{j}$, so its direction angle is 30°.

B. Since $-3\,\vec{i} - \vec{j} = (r\cos \theta)\,\vec{i} + (r\sin \theta)\,\vec{j}$, we can conclude that $-3 = (r\cos \theta)$ and $-1 = (r\sin \theta)$, where $r = \sqrt{10}$. Solving either equation gives θ.

Use $x = r \cos \theta$.

$$-3 = \sqrt{10}\,(\cos \theta) \quad \Rightarrow \quad \cos \theta = -\frac{3}{\sqrt{10}}$$

Since θ is in quadrant III, $q = 360° - \cos^{-1}\left(-\frac{3}{\sqrt{10}}\right) \approx 360° - 161.6° = 198.4°$.

ALTERNATIVE METHOD

Use $\tan \theta = y/x$.

$$\tan \theta = -1/(-3)$$

Since θ is in quadrant III, $\theta = \tan^{-1}(1/3) + \pi \approx 198.4°$.

So, the direction angle is approximately 198.4°.

SECTION 4.3 EXERCISES

Warm Up

Find the distance between each pair of points.

1. $(2, -5), (-1, 4)$

2. $(-3, 6), (7, -2)$

3. $(-8, -3), (1, 9)$

Just the Facts

Fill in the blanks.

4. A quantity that has both magnitude and direction can be represented by a _____.

5. The magnitude of a vector is the _____ of the vector and is found using the _____ Theorem.

6. The direction angle of a vector is the _____ formed by a counterclockwise rotation of a ray from the positive x-axis to the standard position vector.

7. The magnitude of vector $\bar{v}$ is denoted by _____.

8. A vector that has magnitude 1 is a(n) _____ vector.

9. To find the unit vector $\bar{u}$ for a given vector $\bar{v} = \langle x, y \rangle$, use the formula $\bar{u} = $ _____.

10. Given the magnitude r and direction angle θ of a vector $\bar{v}$, the component form can be found using the formulas _____ for x and _____ for y.

Essential Skills

In Exercises 1–6, write the component form of each vector with an initial point at the origin and the given terminal point.

1. $(3, -5)$

2. $(-2, 4)$

3. $(-6, 7)$

4. $(-8, -8)$

5. $(-10, -15)$

6. $(4, -7)$

In Exercises 7–12, find the component form of each vector.

7.

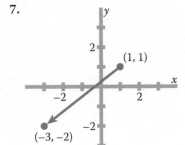

8.

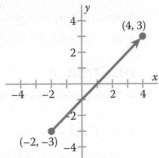

9.

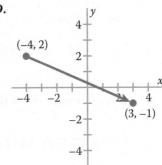

10.

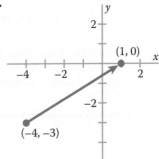

11.

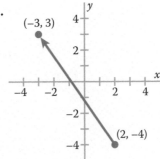

12.

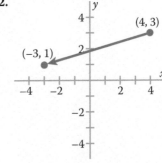

In Exercises 13–18, find the magnitude and direction angle of each vector.

13. $\langle -\sqrt{3}, 1 \rangle$

14. $\langle 3, -3 \rangle$

15. $\langle -4, -4 \rangle$

16. $\langle 3\sqrt{3}, 3 \rangle$

17. $\langle 2, -2\sqrt{3} \rangle$

18. $\langle -5, -5\sqrt{3} \rangle$

In Exercises 19–24, find the magnitude and direction angle of each vector. Round each direction angle to the nearest hundredth of a degree.

19. $\langle 3, 6 \rangle$

20. $\langle -2, 1 \rangle$

21. $\langle 7, -4 \rangle$

22. $\langle -7, -5 \rangle$

23. $\langle -5, 1 \rangle$

24. $\langle 2, 3 \rangle$

In Exercises 25–30, use $\vec{u} = \langle -2, 5 \rangle$, $\vec{v} = \langle 8.2, -1.3 \rangle$, and $\vec{w} = \langle -1, -1.5 \rangle$ to find each scalar multiple.

25. $2\vec{u}$

26. $4\vec{w}$

27. $5\vec{v}$

28. $-3\vec{u}$

29. $-2.5\vec{w}$

30. $-6\vec{v}$

In Exercises 31–36, use $\vec{u} = \langle -2, -2 \rangle$, $\vec{v} = \langle -6, 8 \rangle$, and $\vec{w} = \langle 3, 2 \rangle$ to graph each scalar multiple.

31. $3\vec{w}$

32. $-\dfrac{1}{2}\vec{v}$

33. $-1.5\vec{u}$

34. $2\vec{u}$

35. $0.5\vec{v}$

36. $-3\vec{w}$

In Exercises 37–40, use $\vec{w} = \langle 1.4, -3.6 \rangle$, $\vec{x} = \langle -3, -2 \rangle$, $\vec{y} = \langle -6, -11 \rangle$, and $\vec{z} = \langle 4, 1 \rangle$ to find each resultant vector.

37. $\vec{x} + \vec{z}$

38. $\vec{x} + \vec{y}$

39. $\vec{w} + \vec{y}$

40. $\vec{y} + \vec{z}$

In Exercises 41–44, use $\vec{u} = \langle -5, 1 \rangle$, $\vec{v} = \langle 1, 5 \rangle$, $\vec{w} = \langle 4, 3 \rangle$, and $\vec{x} = \langle -7, 6 \rangle$ to graph each resultant vector.

41. $\vec{u} + \vec{v}$

42. $\vec{v} + \vec{w}$

43. $\vec{w} + \vec{x}$

44. $\vec{v} + \vec{x}$

In Exercises 45–50, use $\vec{w} = \langle -2.8, -5.7 \rangle$, $\vec{x} = \langle -6.3, 6.3 \rangle$, $\vec{y} = \langle 8.9, 4.1 \rangle$, and $\vec{z} = \langle 3, 0 \rangle$ to find each resultant vector.

45. $\vec{x} - \vec{z}$

46. $\vec{y} - \vec{x}$

47. $\vec{w} - \vec{x}$

48. $\vec{z} - \vec{w}$

49. $\vec{y} - \vec{w}$

50. $\vec{x} - \vec{y}$

In Exercises 51–56, use $\vec{u} = \langle 5, -3 \rangle$, $\vec{v} = \langle 2, 6 \rangle$, $\vec{w} = \langle 3, 1 \rangle$, and $\vec{x} = \langle -4, -1 \rangle$ to graph each resultant vector.

51. $\vec{w} - \vec{x}$

52. $\vec{v} - \vec{w}$

53. $\vec{u} - \vec{v}$

54. $\vec{x} - \vec{u}$

55. $\vec{v} - \vec{u}$

56. $\vec{w} - \vec{v}$

In Exercises 57–66, find the component form of the vector with each given magnitude and direction angle θ.

57. $10, \theta = 30°$

58. $\sqrt{3}, \theta = 60°$

59. $9\sqrt{2}, \theta = 45°$

60. $6\sqrt{2}, \theta = 45°$

61. $6, \theta = 150°$

62. $2, \theta = 210°$

63. $3\sqrt{2}, \theta = 315°$

64. $6, \theta = 300°$

65. $10, \theta = 240°$

66. $5\sqrt{2}, \theta = 225°$

In Exercises 67–72, find the component form of each vector, to the nearest tenth, with the given magnitude and reference angle.

67.

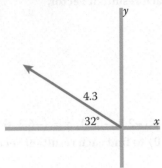

68.

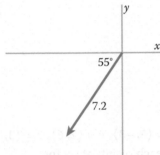

69.

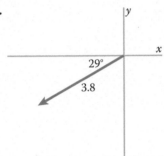

70.

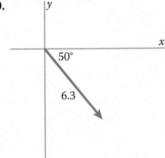

71.

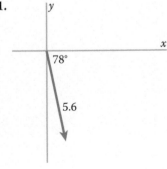

72.

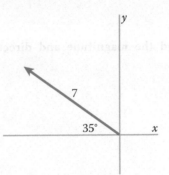

In Exercises 73–78, find a unit vector with the same direction as each given vector.

73. $\langle 3, 5 \rangle$

74. $\langle 1/2, -2/5 \rangle$

75. $\langle -1, -2 \rangle$

76. $\langle -1/4, -5/3 \rangle$

77. $\langle 1/3, -1/2 \rangle$

78. $\langle -3/2, 4/3 \rangle$

In Exercises 79–84, find the velocity vector in component form for a bus traveling at each given speed and bearing (on a compass).

79. 70 mph; 60°

80. 40 mph; 330°

81. 60 mph; 150°

82. 46 mph; 135°

83. 54 mph; 225°

84. 32 mph; 210°

In Exercises 85–88, suppose $\vec{v}$ is a vector with the given initial and terminal points. Write $\vec{v}$ as a linear combination of the standard unit vectors $\vec{i}$ and $\vec{j}$.

85. initial point (−3, −5), terminal point (1, 4)

86. initial point (1, −3), terminal point (−2, 5)

87. initial point (−2, 1), terminal point (3, −4)

88. initial point (3, 4), terminal point (−2, 0)

In Exercises 89–94, find the direction angle of each vector.

89. $\vec{w} = (3 \cos 45°)\vec{i} + (3 \sin 45°)\vec{j}$

90. $\vec{v} = (6 \cos 240°)\vec{i} + (6 \sin 240°)\vec{j}$

91. $\vec{z} = (2 \cos 330°)\vec{i} + (2 \sin 330°)\vec{j}$

92. $\vec{w} = \left(5 \cos \dfrac{\pi}{3} \right)\vec{i} + \left(5 \sin \dfrac{\pi}{3} \right)\vec{j}$

93. $\vec{y} = \left(9 \cos \dfrac{2\pi}{3} \right)\vec{i} + \left(9 \sin \dfrac{2\pi}{3} \right)\vec{j}$

94. $\vec{u} = \left(12 \cos \dfrac{5\pi}{6} \right)\vec{i} + \left(12 \sin \dfrac{5\pi}{6} \right)\vec{j}$

In Exercises 95–100, find the direction angle to the nearest tenth of a degree.

95. $\vec{z} = -2\vec{i} + \vec{j}$

96. $\vec{w} = -4\vec{i} - \vec{j}$

97. $\vec{v} = 6\vec{i} - 2\vec{j}$

98. $\vec{w} = 5\vec{i} - 3\vec{j}$

99. $\vec{x} = -7\vec{i} - 4\vec{j}$

100. $\vec{y} = -3\vec{i} + 2\vec{j}$

Extensions

In Exercises 101–104, use $\vec{w} = \langle -2.4, 1.8 \rangle$, $\vec{x} = \langle 4.5, -1.2 \rangle$, $\vec{y} = \langle -5, -2 \rangle$, and $\vec{z} = \langle 3, 4 \rangle$ to find each resultant vector.

101. $2\vec{z} - 3\vec{w}$

102. $6\vec{y} + 4\vec{x}$

103. $5\vec{x} + 2\vec{y}$

104. $3\vec{w} - 5\vec{z}$

In Exercises 105–108, write the initial velocity vector in component form for a projectile shot at the given angle and initial velocity. Round to the nearest hundredth.

105. 45°; 50 miles per hour

106. 62°; 37 miles per hour

107. 38°; 46 miles per hour

108. 29°; 56 miles per hour

109. Use $\vec{z} = \langle -5, -12 \rangle$ to find the unit vector in the same direction for $\vec{z}, 2\vec{z}$, and $3\vec{z}$.

In Exercises 110–112, use the following information.

A boat is moving due east across a river with an average velocity of 15.2 feet per second. The river current is moving due south with an average velocity of 4.8 feet per second. Round each answer to the nearest tenth.

110. What is the resultant average velocity (both magnitude and direction) of the boat?

111. If the width of the river is 60 feet, then in how many seconds will the boat travel from shore to shore?

112. How far downstream has the boat traveled when it reaches the opposite shore?

4.4 THE DOT PRODUCT

OBJECTIVES

- Find the dot product of two vectors.
- Use properties of dot products.
- Use the dot product of a vector with itself to determine its magnitude.
- Find the angle between two vectors.
- Determine whether two vectors are orthogonal, parallel, or neither.
- Find the projection of one vector onto another.
- Decompose a vector into two orthogonal vectors.

PREREQUISITE VOCABULARY TERMS

Commutative Property
magnitude
resultant vector
scalar
standard position vector
trigonometric functions
vector
zero vector

4.4.1 The Dot Product of Vectors

In Section 4.3 we discussed operations with vectors, such as scalar multiplication of a vector and vector addition. Recall that in each case the operation produced a vector (specifically, a scalar multiple of a vector and a resultant vector). In this section another vector operation is introduced, the **dot product**. In this case, the operation produces a scalar instead of a vector.

> **The Dot Product**
>
> If $\vec{u} = \langle u_1, u_2 \rangle$ and $\vec{v} = \langle v_1, v_2 \rangle$, then the dot product of $\vec{u}$ and $\vec{v}$ is $\vec{u} \cdot \vec{v} = u_1 v_1 + u_2 v_2$.

IMPORTANT

The dot product of two vectors is a scalar (a real number), not a vector.

EXAMPLE 1   Finding a Dot Product

Find the dot product $\vec{u} \cdot \vec{v}$ if $\vec{v} = \langle 10, -4 \rangle$ and $\vec{u} = \langle 3, 6 \rangle$.

SOLUTION

Find the sum of the product of the horizontal components and the product of the vertical components.

$$\vec{u} \cdot \vec{v} = 3(10) + 6(-4) = 30 + (-24) = 6$$

Since multiplication is commutative for real numbers (i.e., $ab = ba$), changing the order of the components in each product of $u_1 v_1 + u_2 v_2$ does not change the value of the sum: $u_1 v_1 + u_2 v_2 = v_1 u_1 + v_2 u_2$. Therefore, the dot product of $\vec{u}$ and $\vec{v}$ ($u_1 v_1 + u_2 v_2$) is equal to the dot product of $\vec{v}$ and $\vec{u}$ ($v_1 u_1 + v_2 u_2$), that is, $\vec{u} \cdot \vec{v} = \vec{v} \cdot \vec{u}$. This property of the dot product is listed in the following table, along with several other properties of the dot product.

Properties of the Dot Product

If $\vec{u}$, $\vec{v}$, and $\vec{w}$ are vectors and c is a scalar, then the following properties are true.

$\vec{u} \cdot \vec{v} = \vec{v} \cdot \vec{u}$	*The dot product of $\vec{u}$ and $\vec{v}$ is equal to the dot product of $\vec{v}$ and $\vec{u}$.*
$\vec{0} \cdot \vec{v} = 0$	*The dot product of the zero vector and any other vector is 0.*
$\vec{u} \cdot (\vec{v} + \vec{w}) = \vec{u} \cdot \vec{v} + \vec{u} \cdot \vec{w}$	*The dot product of a vector and a resultant vector $\vec{v} + \vec{w}$ is equal to the sum of the dot product of the vector and $\vec{v}$ and the dot product of the vector and $\vec{w}$.*
$\vec{v} \cdot \vec{v} = \|\vec{v}\|^2$	*The dot product of a vector and itself is equal to the square of the vector's magnitude.*
$c(\vec{u} \cdot \vec{v}) = c\vec{u} \cdot \vec{v} = \vec{u} \cdot c\vec{v}$	*The product of a scalar and the dot product of two vectors is equal to the dot product of one of the vectors and the scalar multiple of the other vector.*

EXAMPLE 2　Using the Properties of the Dot Product

Find $-2(\vec{u} \cdot \vec{v}) + \vec{v} \cdot \vec{v}$ if $\vec{u} = \langle 3, 1 \rangle$ and $\vec{v} = \langle -3, 4 \rangle$.

SOLUTION

Use the applicable properties of the dot product: $\vec{v} \cdot \vec{v} = \|\vec{v}\|^2$ and $c(\vec{u} \cdot \vec{v}) = c\vec{u} \cdot \vec{v} = \vec{u} \cdot c\vec{v}$.

$$-2(\vec{u} \cdot \vec{v}) + \vec{v} \cdot \vec{v} = -2\vec{u} \cdot \vec{v} + \|\vec{v}\|^2$$

$$= -2\langle 3, 1 \rangle \cdot \langle -3, 4 \rangle + \left(\sqrt{(-3)^2 + 4^2} \right)^2 \quad \textit{Apply the properties.}$$

$$= \langle -6, -2 \rangle \cdot \langle -3, 4 \rangle + 25 \qquad\qquad \textit{Find the scalar multiple and simplify.}$$

$$= -6(-3) + -2(4) + 25 \qquad\qquad \textit{Find the dot product.}$$

$$= 35 \qquad\qquad\qquad\qquad\qquad \textit{Simplify.}$$

> **ALTERNATIVE METHOD**
>
> *Instead of using a property to evaluate $\vec{v} \cdot \vec{v}$, find the dot product of the vector and itself.*
> $\vec{v} \cdot \vec{v} = \langle -3, 4 \rangle \cdot \langle -3, 4 \rangle$
> $\qquad = -3(-3) + 4(4)$
> $\qquad = 25$

EXAMPLE 3　Using the Dot Product to Find the Magnitude of a Vector

If $\vec{v} \cdot \vec{v} = 20$, what is the magnitude of $\vec{v}$?

SOLUTION

By the properties of the dot product, $\vec{v} \cdot \vec{v} = \|\vec{v}\|^2$. So, $20 = \|\vec{v}\|^2$. Taking the square root of each side gives $\|\vec{v}\| = \sqrt{20} = 2\sqrt{5}$. So, the magnitude of $\vec{v}$ is $2\sqrt{5}$.

> **REMEMBER**
>
> *The magnitude of a vector is always positive, so only the positive square root is considered.*

| EXAMPLE 7 | Finding the Projection of One Vector Onto Another |

Find the projection of $\vec{v} = -\vec{i} + 4\vec{j}$ onto $\vec{z} = 2\vec{i} + \vec{j}$. Then decompose $\vec{v}$ as the sum of two orthogonal vectors, one of which is $\text{proj}_{\vec{z}}\vec{v}$.

SOLUTION

Use $\text{proj}_{\vec{z}}\vec{v} = \left(\dfrac{\vec{v}\cdot\vec{z}}{\|\vec{z}\|^2}\right)\vec{z}$ to find the projection of $\vec{v}$ onto $\vec{z}$ where $\vec{v} = \langle -1, 4\rangle$ and $\vec{z} = \langle 2, 1\rangle$.

$\text{proj}_{\vec{z}}\vec{v} = \left(\dfrac{-1(2)+4(1)}{\sqrt{2^2+1^2}^2}\right)\langle 2, 1\rangle$ *Substitute. Find the dot product and the magnitude.*

$= \left(\dfrac{2}{5}\right)\langle 2, 1\rangle$ *Simplify the scalar.*

$= \left\langle \dfrac{4}{5}, \dfrac{2}{5}\right\rangle$ *Multiply the scalar by the components of $\vec{z}$.*

Since $\langle 4/5, 2/5\rangle$ is the projection of $\vec{v}$ onto $\vec{z}$, we know that $\vec{w}_1 = \langle 4/5, 2/5\rangle$ where $\vec{v} = \vec{w}_1 + \vec{w}_2$ and $\vec{w}_1$ and $\vec{w}_2$ are orthogonal.

Solve $\vec{v} = \vec{w}_1 + \vec{w}_2$ for $\vec{w}_2$. $\vec{w}_2 = \vec{v} - \vec{w}_1 = \langle -1, 4\rangle - \langle 4/5, 2/5\rangle = \langle -9/5, 18/5\rangle$

Therefore, $\vec{v} = \langle 4/5, 2/5\rangle + \langle -9/5, 18/5\rangle$.

CHECK

Find the sum of $\langle 4/5, 2/5\rangle$ and $\langle -9/5, 18/5\rangle$ to confirm that $\vec{v} = \langle 4/5, 2/5\rangle + \langle -9/5, 18/5\rangle$.

$\langle 4/5, 2/5\rangle + \langle -9/5, 18/5\rangle = \langle -5/5, 20/5\rangle = \langle -1, 4\rangle = \vec{v}$ ✔

Find the dot product of $\langle 4/5, 2/5\rangle$ and $\langle -9/5, 18/5\rangle$ to confirm that the vectors are orthogonal.

$\langle 4/5, 2/5\rangle \cdot \langle -9/5, 18/5\rangle = 4/5(-9/5) + 2/5(18/5) = -36/25 + 36/25 = 0$

The dot product is 0, so $\langle 4/5, 2/5\rangle$ and $\langle -9/5, 18/5\rangle$ are orthogonal. ✔

SECTION 4.4 EXERCISES

Warm Up

Identify the property demonstrated in each equation.

1. $3(x + 2y) = 3x + 6y$

2. $y \cdot 5 = 5 \cdot y$

3. $0 \cdot 2x = 0$

Just the Facts

Fill in the blanks.

4. If $\vec{v} = \langle v_1, v_2 \rangle$ and $\vec{w} = \langle w_1, w_2 \rangle$, the dot product $\vec{v} \cdot \vec{w} = $ _____.

5. If $\vec{u}$ and $\vec{v}$ are two nonzero vectors, the angle θ, $0 \le \theta \le \pi$, between $\vec{u}$ and $\vec{v}$, is determined by the formula $\cos\theta = $ _____.

6. Vectors $\vec{u}$ and $\vec{v}$ are orthogonal if $\vec{u} \cdot \vec{v} = $ _____.

7. Vectors $\vec{u}$ and $\vec{v}$ are parallel if $\theta = $ _____.

8. If $\vec{u}$ and $\vec{v}$ are two nonzero vectors, the projection of $\vec{u}$ onto $\vec{v}$ is $\text{proj}_{\vec{v}}\vec{u} = $ _____

9. The dot product of two vectors is a(n) _____, not a vector.

10. The dot product $\vec{v} \cdot \vec{v}$ is equal to the square of the vector's _____.

Essential Skills

In Exercises 1–6, find each dot product.

1. $\langle 3, -5 \rangle \cdot \langle -6.1, 0 \rangle$

2. $\langle -2.6, 3.1 \rangle \cdot \langle -1.6, -4 \rangle$

3. $\langle -1, 2 \rangle \cdot \langle -4, 5.1 \rangle$

4. $\langle 2.3, 2 \rangle \cdot \langle -1.4, -2.8 \rangle$

5. $\langle 7, 8 \rangle \cdot \langle -0.1, -6 \rangle$

6. $\langle -1.6, 0.3 \rangle \cdot \langle 3.8, -1.4 \rangle$

In Exercises 7–12, find $\vec{u} \cdot (\vec{v} + \vec{w})$, $\vec{v} \cdot \vec{v}$, and $4(\vec{u} \cdot \vec{v})$.

7. $\vec{u} = \langle 4, -5 \rangle$, $\vec{v} = \langle 8, 2 \rangle$, $\vec{w} = \langle -3, 0 \rangle$

8. $\vec{u} = \langle -2, 3 \rangle$, $\vec{v} = \langle 7, -1.4 \rangle$, $\vec{w} = \langle -3.6, 5 \rangle$

9. $\vec{u} = \langle -1.2, -1 \rangle$, $\vec{v} = \langle -3.5, 4 \rangle$, $\vec{w} = \langle -4, -2 \rangle$

10. $\vec{u} = \langle -0.3, -1.9 \rangle$, $\vec{v} = \langle -0.1, 3.3 \rangle$, $\vec{w} = \langle 3, -5 \rangle$

11. $\vec{u} = \langle 3, 0.5 \rangle$, $\vec{v} = \langle -6, -2.3 \rangle$, $\vec{w} = \langle -1, 9 \rangle$

12. $\vec{u} = \langle -4.9, 0.8 \rangle$, $\vec{v} = \langle 0.1, 3.9 \rangle$, $\vec{w} = \langle 3.4, 0.9 \rangle$

In Exercises 13–18, find the magnitude of the vector given in each equation.

13. $\vec{x} \cdot \vec{x} = 40$

14. $7\vec{v} \cdot \vec{v} = 21$

15. $6\vec{u} \cdot \vec{u} = 876$

16. $2.8\vec{z} \cdot \vec{z} = 61.6$

17. $-3\vec{v} \cdot \vec{v} = -77.43$

18. $-5\vec{u} \cdot \vec{u} = -80$

In Exercises 19–22, find the angle between each pair of vectors.

19. $\vec{y} = 3\cos\dfrac{\pi}{7}\vec{i} + 3\sin\dfrac{\pi}{7}\vec{j}$ and $\vec{w} = \cos\dfrac{2\pi}{3}\vec{i} + \sin\dfrac{2\pi}{3}\vec{j}$

20. $\vec{u} = \cos\dfrac{5\pi}{6}\vec{i} + \sin\dfrac{5\pi}{6}\vec{j}$ and $\vec{v} = \cos\dfrac{7\pi}{4}\vec{i} + \sin\dfrac{7\pi}{4}\vec{j}$

21. $\vec{v} = \cos\dfrac{5\pi}{8}\vec{i} + \sin\dfrac{5\pi}{8}\vec{j}$ and $\vec{x} = \cos\dfrac{11\pi}{6}\vec{i} + \sin\dfrac{11\pi}{6}\vec{j}$

22. $\vec{z} = \cos\dfrac{7\pi}{4}\vec{i} + \sin\dfrac{7\pi}{4}\vec{j}$ and $\vec{u} = \cos\dfrac{\pi}{2}\vec{i} + \sin\dfrac{\pi}{2}\vec{j}$

In Exercises 23–38, find the angle to the nearest tenth of a degree between each pair of vectors.

23. $\vec{x} = \cos 102°\vec{i} + \sin 102°\vec{j}$ and $\vec{w} = 5\cos 36°\vec{i} + 5\sin 36°\vec{j}$

24. $\vec{u} = 8\cos 96°\vec{i} + 8\sin 96°\vec{j}$ and $\vec{w} = \cos 21°\vec{i} + \sin 21°\vec{j}$

25. $\vec{z} = 3\cos 206°\vec{i} + 3\sin 206°\vec{j}$ and $\vec{x} = \cos 65°\vec{i} + \sin 65°\vec{j}$

26. $\vec{v} = \cos 332°\vec{i} + \sin 332°\vec{j}$ and $\vec{z} = \cos 189°\vec{i} + \sin 189°\vec{j}$

27. $\vec{x} = \langle 3, 4 \rangle$ and $\vec{z} = \langle 5, 2 \rangle$

28. $\vec{w} = \langle -2, 5 \rangle$ and $\vec{v} = \langle 1, 3 \rangle$

29. $\vec{z} = \langle -4, 2.5 \rangle$ and $\vec{y} = \langle 0, -7 \rangle$

30. $\vec{u} = \langle 4.5, -2.5 \rangle$ and $\vec{v} = \langle -2, 2.8 \rangle$

31. $\vec{y} = \langle 5.2, 1 \rangle$ and $\vec{x} = \langle -2.1, 6 \rangle$

32. $\vec{u} = \langle 3.4, 4.4 \rangle$ and $\vec{v} = \langle 0.8, -2.6 \rangle$

33. $\vec{z} = 3\vec{i} + 3\vec{j}$ and $\vec{x} = 4\vec{i} - 5\vec{j}$

34. $\vec{u} = 4\vec{i} - 2\vec{j}$ and $\vec{w} = -3\vec{i} + 2\vec{j}$

35. $\vec{u} = -2\vec{i} + 4.1\vec{j}$ and $\vec{v} = -6\vec{i} - 3\vec{j}$

36. $\vec{v} = -2.3\vec{i} - 3.8\vec{j}$ and $\vec{w} = 4.6\vec{i} - 0.6\vec{j}$

37. $\vec{y} = 2.6\vec{i} - 1.3\vec{j}$ and $\vec{z} = 0.6\vec{i} + \vec{j}$

38. $\vec{u} = 3.1\vec{i} + 2.1\vec{j}$ and $\vec{v} = -2.2\vec{i} - 1.1\vec{j}$

418 CHAPTER 4 ~ APPLICATIONS OF TRIGONOMETRY

In Exercises 39–42, using the three pairs of vectors given in each exercise, determine which pair of vectors is parallel, which pair is orthogonal, and which pair is neither.

39. $\vec{u} = -\dfrac{3}{10}\vec{i} + \dfrac{3}{4}\vec{j}$ and $\vec{w} = 3\vec{i} - \vec{j}$;

   $\vec{v} = \langle 1/3, -1/3 \rangle$ and $\vec{w} = \langle -3, -3 \rangle$;

   $\vec{u} = 3\vec{i} - 5\vec{j}$ and $\vec{v} = -9\vec{i} + 15\vec{j}$

40. $\vec{v} = \langle 1/2, -3/4 \rangle$ and $\vec{w} = \langle -2, -4 \rangle$;

   $\vec{u} = 3\vec{i} - 4\vec{j}$ and $\vec{v} = -21\vec{i} + 28\vec{j}$;

   $\vec{u} = \langle -3/5, 3/4 \rangle$ and $\vec{w} = \langle 4, -1 \rangle$

41. $\vec{v} = \langle 1/3, -1/2 \rangle$ and $\vec{w} = \langle -6, -4 \rangle$;

   $\vec{u} = 4\vec{i} - 4\vec{j}$ and $\vec{v} = -16\vec{i} + 16\vec{j}$;

   $\vec{u} = \langle -3/8, 3/4 \rangle$ and $\vec{w} = \langle 4, -1 \rangle$

42. $\vec{u} = 3\vec{i} - 4\vec{j}$ and $\vec{v} = -9\vec{i} + 12\vec{j}$;

   $\vec{u} = \langle -3/7, 3/4 \rangle$ and $\vec{w} = \langle 4, -1 \rangle$;

   $\vec{v} = \langle 1/3, -1/2 \rangle$ and $\vec{w} = \langle -9, -6 \rangle$

In Exercises 43–46, find each projection.

43. $\vec{u}$ onto $\vec{v}$ if $\vec{u} = \langle -2, 9 \rangle$ and $\vec{v} = \langle -1, 2 \rangle$

44. $\vec{v}$ onto $\vec{w}$ if $\vec{w} = \langle 2, -4 \rangle$ and $\vec{v} = \langle -1/2, 3/4 \rangle$

45. $\vec{v}$ onto $\vec{u}$ if $\vec{u} = \langle -1, 1 \rangle$ and $\vec{v} = \langle -2, 4 \rangle$

46. $\vec{v}$ onto $\vec{u}$ if $\vec{v} = \langle -1/2, 3/4 \rangle$ and $\vec{u} = \langle -1/5, -4 \rangle$

In Exercises 47–50, decompose $\vec{w}$ into the sum of two orthogonal vectors $\vec{w}_1$ and $\vec{w}_2$, where $\vec{w}_1 = \text{proj}_{\vec{v}}\vec{w}$.

47. $\vec{w} = \langle 2, 7 \rangle$ and $\vec{v} = \langle 1, -1 \rangle$

48. $\vec{w} = \langle 5, -12 \rangle$ and $\vec{v} = \langle -3, 4 \rangle$

49. $\vec{w} = \langle -6, 1 \rangle$ and $\vec{v} = \langle 2, 3 \rangle$

50. $\vec{w} = \langle 4, -12 \rangle$ and $\vec{v} = \langle -3, 2 \rangle$

Extensions

In Exercises 51–54, use vectors to find the interior angles to the nearest tenth of a degree for the triangle with the given vertices.

51. $(9, 8)$, $(3, 4)$, $(7, 7)$

52. $(1, 1)$, $(5, 2)$, $(4, 6)$

53. $(0, 3)$, $(6, 3)$, $(5, 4)$

54. $(2, 5)$, $(8, 7)$, $(5, 0)$

In Exercises 55–60, use $\vec{u} = \langle 1/2, -4 \rangle$, $\vec{v} = \langle -2, -1/3 \rangle$, and $\vec{w} = \langle -3, 2 \rangle$ to find the indicated quantity.

55. $\| \vec{u} \| - \| \vec{v} \|$

56. $(\vec{w} \cdot \vec{u}) \cdot \vec{v}$

57. $\| \vec{v} \| - 4$

58. $(\vec{w} \cdot \vec{v}) + (\vec{v} \cdot \vec{u})$

59. $(2\vec{u} + \vec{v}) \cdot \vec{w}$

60. $\| \vec{u} \|^2$

CHAPTER 4 REVIEW EXERCISES

Section 4.1 The Law of Sines

In Exercises 1–5, solve each triangle and find its area, if possible. If two triangles exist, solve and find the area of both triangles. Round to the nearest tenth, as needed.

1. $\alpha = 38°$, $a = 11$, $b = 14.5$

2. $\beta = 130°$, $a = 17$, and $b = 20$

3. $\gamma = 46°$, $a = 33$, and $c = 42$

4. $\alpha = 141°$, $a = 19.9$, and $b = 10.2$

5. $\beta = 58°$, $\gamma = 112°$, $a = 18$

Section 4.2 The Law of Cosines

In Exercises 6–10, solve each triangle and find its area and height (using the shortest side as the triangle's base). Round to the nearest tenth, as needed.

6. 41, 60, 72

7. 14, 11, 12

8. 16, 19, 91° (included angle)

9. 43, 92, 76° (included angle)

10. 24, 28, 132° (included angle)

Section 4.3 Vectors

In Exercises 11–13, find the component form of each vector. Then find the vector's magnitude, direction angle to the nearest tenth of a degree, the component form of the unit vector in the same direction, and write the vector as a linear combination of the standard unit vectors.

11. initial point $(-4, 7)$, terminal point $(2, 5)$

12. initial point $(1, -6)$, terminal point $(-8, 3)$

13. initial point $(-3.2, -5.8)$, terminal point $(4, -4)$

In Exercises 14–15, use $\vec{w} = \langle 3.5, -2 \rangle$, $\vec{x} = \langle -6.2, 4 \rangle$, $\vec{y} = \langle -7, -4 \rangle$, and $\vec{z} = \langle -2.8, 5.4 \rangle$ to find each resultant vector.

14. $-\vec{z} - 4\vec{w}$

15. $2\vec{y} + 3\vec{x}$

Section 4.4 The Dot Product

In Exercises 16–18, find $\vec{u} \cdot (\vec{v} - \vec{w})$, $\vec{u} \cdot \vec{u}$, $-3(\vec{u} \cdot \vec{v})$, and $||\vec{w}||$.

16. $\vec{u} = \langle -3, -1.8 \rangle$, $\vec{v} = \langle 8, -2 \rangle$, $\vec{w} = \langle -3, 2 \rangle$

17. $\vec{u} = \langle 2.6, 5 \rangle$, $\vec{v} = \langle -7, 3 \rangle$, $\vec{w} = \langle -5, 6 \rangle$

18. $\vec{u} = \langle -1, 4.2 \rangle$, $\vec{v} = \langle 9, -1.5 \rangle$, $\vec{w} = \langle -6.1, -3.5 \rangle$

In Exercises 19–20, determine whether $\vec{u}$ and $\vec{v}$ are parallel, orthogonal, or neither. Then find the projection of $\vec{u}$ onto $\vec{v}$ and decompose $\vec{u}$ into the sum of two orthogonal vectors $\vec{w}_1$ and $\vec{w}_2$, where $\vec{w}_1 = \text{proj}_{\vec{v}}\vec{u}$.

19. $\vec{u} = \langle -2, -4 \rangle$, $\vec{v} = \langle -5, 3 \rangle$

20. $\vec{u} = \langle -1, 8 \rangle$, $\vec{v} = \langle 1/2, -4 \rangle$

COMPLEX NUMBERS

5.1 DIVIDING POLYNOMIALS

OBJECTIVES

- Divide polynomials using long division.
- Divide polynomials using synthetic division.
- Use the Remainder Theorem to evaluate polynomials.
- Use the Factor Theorem to determine whether binomials are factors of polynomials.

PREREQUISITE VOCABULARY TERMS

binomial
degree (of a polynomial)
factor (of a polynomial)
polynomial

5.1.1 Using Long Division with Polynomials

Division with polynomials is very similar to division with numbers. One method for dividing with numbers is to write the division expression as a fraction, then remove any common factors from the numerator and denominator. For example, 12 divided by 3 can be simplified as follows.

$$\frac{12}{3} = \frac{3(4)}{3} = \frac{\cancel{3}(4)}{\cancel{3}} = 4$$ *12 is the dividend, 3 is the divisor, and 4 is the quotient.*

Similarly, a quotient of polynomials can be written as a rational expression. Recall that a rational expression can be simplified (i.e., the polynomials can be divided) by factoring the numerator and denominator and removing any common factors.

Long division can be used to divide with numbers, as well as with polynomials. In long division with numbers, the result of dividing the dividend by the divisor is the quotient plus any remainder. For example, the result of dividing 13 by 4 is 3 with a remainder of 1.

$$\boxed{13 \div 4}$$

$$
\text{divisor--}4\overline{\smash)\begin{array}{l} 3 \\ 13 \\ \underline{-12} \\ 1 \end{array}}
\begin{array}{l} \text{--quotient} \\ \text{--dividend} \\ \\ \text{--remainder} \end{array}
$$

$$\text{dividend--}\frac{13}{4} = 3 + \frac{1}{4}\text{ --remainder}$$

quotient

divisor

Also recall that long division can be checked by multiplying the quotient by the divisor and adding any remainder.

$$\text{dividend} = (\text{quotient})(\text{divisor}) + \text{remainder}$$

Division of Polynomials

If $f(x)$ and $g(x)$ are polynomials, and $g(x) \neq 0$, then $\dfrac{f(x)}{g(x)} = q(x) + \dfrac{r(x)}{g(x)}$, where $q(x)$ is the quotient and $r(x)$ is the remainder.

The degree of $r(x)$ is less than the degree of $q(x)$, and $r(x)$ can equal 0.

Multiplying $\dfrac{f(x)}{g(x)} = q(x) + \dfrac{r(x)}{g(x)}$ by $g(x)$ gives $f(x) = g(x)q(x) + r(x)$.

dividend   quotient
$$f(x) = g(x)\,q(x) + r(x)$$
divisor   remainder

quotient
$$\text{dividend--}\frac{f(x)}{g(x)} = q(x) + \frac{r(x)}{g(x)}\text{--remainder}$$
divisor

EXAMPLE 1   Long Division of Polynomials

Use long division to divide $3x^3 + x^2 + 3$ by $x + 1$.

SOLUTION

The dividend is $3x^3 + x^2 + 3$, and the divisor is $x + 1$.

$$x + 1 \overline{)3x^3 + x^2 + 0x + 3}$$

Since the dividend does not contain an x-term, use 0x as a placeholder in the dividend.

To use long division, first divide the leading term in the dividend, $3x^3$, by the leading term in the divisor, x, to get the leading term of the quotient. So, $\dfrac{3x^3}{x} = 3x^2$ is the first term of the quotient. Next, multiply $3x^2$ (the first term of the quotient) by each term in the divisor, and then subtract this product from the dividend. Repeat this process until the degree of the difference is less than the degree of the divisor.

$$
\begin{array}{r}
3x^2 \\
x + 1 \overline{)\; 3x^3 + x^2 + 0x + 3} \\
\underline{-(3x^3 + 3x^2)} \\
-2x^2 + 0x
\end{array}
$$

The quotient's leading term is $\dfrac{3x^3}{x} = 3x^2$.

Multiply: $3x^2(x + 1) = 3x^3 + 3x^2$.

Subtract $3x^3 + 3x^2$ from the dividend, and bring down 0x.

▶ *The degree of the difference, $-2x^2 + 0x$, is 2. Continue dividing since the degree of the difference is not less than the degree of the divisor.*

$$
\begin{array}{r}
3x^2 - 2x \\
x + 1 \overline{)\; 3x^3 + x^2 + 0x + 3} \\
\underline{-(3x^3 + 3x^2)} \\
-2x^2 + 0x \\
\underline{-(-2x^2 - 2x)} \\
2x + 3
\end{array}
$$

The quotient's 2nd term is $\dfrac{-2x^2}{x} = -2x$.

Multiply: $-2x(x + 1) = -2x^2 - 2x$.

Subtract $-2x^2 - 2x$, and bring down 3.

▶ *The degree of the difference, $2x + 3$, is 1. Continue dividing since the degree of the difference is not less than the degree of the divisor.*

$$
\begin{array}{r}
3x^2 - 2x + 2 \\
x + 1 \overline{)\; 3x^3 + x^2 + 0x + 3} \\
\underline{-(3x^3 + 3x^2)} \\
-2x^2 + 0x \\
\underline{-(-2x^2 - 2x)} \\
2x + 3 \\
\underline{-(2x + 2)} \\
1
\end{array}
$$

The quotient's 3rd term is $\dfrac{2x}{x} = 2$.

Multiply: $2(x + 1) = 2x + 2$.

Subtract $2x + 2$.

▶ *The degree of the difference, 1, is 0. The division is complete since the degree of the difference is less than the degree of the divisor.*

The quotient is $3x^2 - 2x + 2$ with a remainder of 1.

Therefore, $\dfrac{3x^3 + x^2 + 3}{x + 1} = 3x^2 - 2x + 2 + \dfrac{1}{x + 1}$.

The quotient and remainder in **Example 1** can be checked using $f(x) = g(x)q(x) + r(x)$ (i.e., the dividend must be equal to the product of the divisor and the quotient, plus the remainder). Specifically, $3x^3 + x^2 + 3$ (the dividend) must be equal to the product of $x + 1$ (the divisor) and $3x^2 - 2x + 2$ (the quotient) plus 1 (the remainder).

$$(x + 1)(3x^2 - 2x + 2) + 1 = (3x^3 - 2x^2 + 2x + 3x^2 - 2x + 2) + 1 = 3x^3 + x^2 + 3 \checkmark$$

5.1.2 Using Synthetic Division with Polynomials

Synthetic division is a quick way of dividing polynomials, but it can be used only when the divisor can be written in the form $x - c$, where c is a real number not equal to 0. Only the coefficients are written when using synthetic division.

EXAMPLE 2   Using Synthetic Division

Use synthetic division to divide $3x^3 + x^2 + 3$ by $x + 1$.

NOTICE THAT

Examples 1 and 2 show the same polynomials divided using the two different processes (long division and synthetic division) for comparison.

SOLUTION

The divisor is $x + 1$, or $x - (-1)$, so $c = -1$.

The dividend is $3x^3 + x^2 + 3$, or $3x^3 + x^2 + 0x + 3$. So, the coefficients are 3, 1, 0, and 3.

Write -1 outside of the box, and 3, 1, 0, and 3 inside of the box.

$$-1 \,\lvert\; 3 \quad 1 \quad 0 \quad 3$$

Bring down the first coefficient, 3. Then multiply -1 by 3. Write this product below the second coefficient (i.e., below the 1) inside the box.

$$
\begin{array}{r|rrrr}
-1 & 3 & 1 & 0 & 3 \\
& \downarrow & -3 & & \\
\hline
& 3 & & &
\end{array}
$$

The coefficient of the quotient's squared term is 3.

Add 1 and -3. Write this sum below the box.

$$
\begin{array}{r|rrrr}
-1 & 3 & 1 & 0 & 3 \\
& & -3 & & \\
\hline
& 3 & -2 & &
\end{array}
$$

The coefficient of the quotient's linear term is -2.

Multiply -1 by -2. Write this product below the third coefficient (i.e., below the 0) inside the box.

$$
\begin{array}{r|rrrr}
-1 & 3 & 1 & 0 & 3 \\
& & -3 & 2 & \\
\hline
& 3 & -2 & &
\end{array}
$$

Add 0 and 2. Write this sum below the box.

$$
\begin{array}{r|rrrr}
-1 & 3 & 1 & 0 & 3 \\
& & -3 & 2 & \\
\hline
& 3 & -2 & 2 &
\end{array}
$$

The coefficient of the quotient's constant term is 2.

Multiply -1 by 2. Write this product below the fourth coefficient (i.e., below the 3) inside the box.

$$
\begin{array}{r|rrrr}
-1 & 3 & 1 & 0 & 3 \\
& & -3 & 2 & -2 \\
\hline
& 3 & -2 & 2 &
\end{array}
$$

IMPORTANT

The last number in the row below the box is the remainder. The rest of the numbers are the coefficients of the terms in the quotient. The degree of the first term in the quotient is always 1 less than the degree of the dividend. The degree of each consecutive term in the quotient decreases by 1.

Add 3 and -2. Write this sum below the box.

$$
\begin{array}{r|rrrr}
-1 & 3 & 1 & 0 & 3 \\
& & -3 & 2 & -2 \\
\hline
& 3 & -2 & 2 & 1
\end{array}
$$

The remainder is 1.

Use the numbers in the row below the box to write the quotient and remainder.

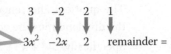

The degree of the quotient's first term is 2 because the degree of the dividend is 3.

$$
\begin{array}{cccc}
3 & -2 & 2 & 1 \\
\downarrow & \downarrow & \downarrow & \downarrow \\
3x^2 & -2x & 2 & \text{remainder} = 1
\end{array}
$$

As in **Example 1**, the quotient is $3x^2 - 2x + 2$ with a remainder of 1.

So, $\dfrac{3x^3 + x^2 + 3}{x + 1} = 3x^2 - 2x + 2 + \dfrac{1}{x + 1}$.

Steps for Using Synthetic Division

❶ Write the divisor in the form $x - c$ (c will be a positive or negative number).

❷ Draw the bottom left corner of a box. Write the c-value on the left side of the box, and write the coefficients from the dividend inside the box, as shown below.

c | *write the coefficients inside the box*

❸ Bring down the first coefficient.

❹ Multiply c by the first coefficient, and write this product below the second coefficient (inside the box).

❺ Add the product to the coefficient above, and write this sum under the box.

❻ Repeat step ❹ until a product is added to the last coefficient.

❼ Write the quotient using the sums as the coefficients, where the final sum in the list is the remainder.

5.1.3   The Remainder Theorem

The **Remainder Theorem** relates the process of division to evaluating polynomials.

Remainder Theorem

If the polynomial $f(x)$ is divided by $x - c$, then the remainder is the value $f(c)$.

For example, $f(5)$ is equal to the remainder when $f(x)$ is divided by $x - 5$. So, by the Remainder Theorem, a polynomial can be evaluated for some number c by dividing the polynomial (using long or synthetic division) by $x - c$.

EXAMPLE 3   **Using the Remainder Theorem to Evaluate a Polynomial**

Suppose $p(x)$ is a polynomial function such that $p(-2) = -14$, and the remainder is 1 when $p(x)$ is divided by $x - 3$. Use the Remainder Theorem to draw two conclusions about $p(x)$.

SOLUTION

If $p(-2) = -14$, then the remainder must be -14 when $p(x)$ is divided by $x + 2$.

If the remainder is 1 when $p(x)$ is divided by $x - 3$, then $p(3) = 1$.

5.1.4 The Factor Theorem

Recall that when f is a polynomial function and $f(c) = 0$, then c is a zero of the polynomial. Furthermore, if c is a zero of $f(x)$, then $x - c$ must be a factor of $f(x)$. For example, if 3 is a zero of $f(x)$, then $x - 3$ must be a factor of $f(x)$. The **Factor Theorem** relates a zero of a polynomial to a factor of the polynomial.

Factor Theorem

The binomial $(x - k)$ is a factor of a polynomial $f(x)$ if and only if $f(k) = 0$.

The Factor Theorem can be used to identify binomial factors of a polynomial. For example, to determine whether $(x + 7)$ is a factor of the polynomial function $f(x)$, find $f(-7)$. If $f(-7) = 0$, then $(x + 7)$ is a factor of $f(x)$. There are two methods for determining the value of $f(-7)$. One method is to evaluate $f(x)$ for $x = -7$ (i.e., substitute -7 into the function for x and simplify). The second method is to divide $f(x)$ by $(x + 7)$. By the Remainder Theorem, the remainder is equal to $f(-7)$. If the remainder is 0 when $f(x)$ is divided by $(x + 7)$, then $f(-7) = 0$, and therefore $(x + 7)$ is a factor of $f(x)$.

EXAMPLE 4   Using the Factor Theorem

Use synthetic division to show that $(x + 5)$ is a factor of $p(x) = x^3 + 5x^2 - 9x - 45$, and then factor the polynomial completely.

SOLUTION

By the Remainder Theorem, the remainder when $p(x)$ is divided by $(x + 5)$ is equal to $p(-5)$.

By the Factor Theorem, if $p(-5) = 0$, then $(x + 5)$ is a factor of $p(x)$.

So, if the remainder is 0 when $p(x)$ is divided by $(x + 5)$, then $p(-5) = 0$, and so $(x + 5)$ is a factor of $p(x)$.

Use synthetic division to find the remainder when $p(x)$ is divided by $(x + 5)$.

$$
\begin{array}{r|rrrr}
-5 & 1 & 5 & -9 & -45 \\
   &   & -5 & 0 & 45 \\
\hline
   & 1 & 0 & -9 & 0
\end{array}
$$

Since the remainder is 0, $p(-5) = 0$, and therefore $(x + 5)$ is a factor of $p(x)$.

By the synthetic division result, we know that $p(x)$ divided by $(x + 5)$ is equal to $x^2 - 9$, or $\dfrac{p(x)}{x+5} = x^2 - 9$. Therefore, $p(x) = (x^2 - 9)(x + 5)$.

Factor $x^2 - 9$ to complete the factorization of $p(x)$.

$$p(x) = x^3 + 5x^2 - 9x - 45 = (x^2 - 9)(x + 5) = (x + 3)(x - 3)(x + 5)$$

REMEMBER

The factors can be written in any order because multiplication is commutative.

SECTION 5.1 EXERCISES

Warm Up

Simplify.

1. $\dfrac{x^2 - 25}{x + 5}$

2. $\dfrac{2x^2 + 28x + 98}{x + 7}$

3. $\dfrac{2x^2 - 18}{x^2 + 6x + 9}$

Just the Facts

Fill in the blanks.

4. When dividing polynomials, use either _____ division or _____ division.

5. When using synthetic division, only the _____ are written in the box. If a term is missing, _____ is written as a placeholder.

6. To determine whether a value is a zero of a function by synthetic division, check if the remainder is _____.

7. To evaluate a polynomial $f(x)$ at a value b, synthetically divide by _____. The remainder is the same as if you evaluated _____.

8. In $\dfrac{f(x)}{g(x)} = q(x) + \dfrac{r(x)}{g(x)}$, $f(x)$ is the _____, $g(x)$ is the _____, _____ is the quotient, and _____ is the remainder.

9. Polynomial long division can be checked by multiplying the _____ by the _____.

10. To synthetically divide $f(x)$ by $x + 5$, write _____ in the left corner of the box.

Essential Skills

In Exercises 1–8, divide using long division.

1. $\dfrac{2x^3 + 3x^2 + 4x + 4}{x + 1}$

2. $\dfrac{5x^4 + 3x^3 + 2x - 5}{x - 11}$

3. $(x^3 + 4x - 7) \div (x - 2)$

4. $(2x^4 - 3x^2 - 12x - 7) \div (x - 2)$

5. $(2x^3 + 6x^2 + 5x + 3) \div (x + 2)$

6. $(4x^4 + 2x^3 + 2x - 4) \div (x - 3)$

7. $(3x^4 + 2x^3 + 9x - 4) \div (x + 2)$

8. $(-7x^5 + 5x^2 + x + 3) \div (x + 3)$

In Exercises 9–16, divide using synthetic division.

9. $\dfrac{6x^3 + 5x^2 - 7x + 12}{x - 4}$

10. $\dfrac{x^4 + 6x^3 - 19x^2 - 144x - 91}{x - 5}$

11. $(3x^4 + 2x^3 - 2x^2 + 14x + 14) \div (x + 2)$

12. $(x^3 - 7x + 6) \div (x + 6)$

13. $(4x^4 - 46x^2 - 5x - 105) \div (x - 3)$

14. $(x^4 + 7x^3 - 19x^2 - 142x - 89) \div (x - 2)$

15. $(4x^4 - 3x^2 + 7x) \div (x + 5)$

16. $(x^3 - 4x + 3) \div (x + 4)$

In Exercises 17–32, use the Remainder Theorem to draw a conclusion about each polynomial function.

17. $h(x)$ if $h(6) = -11$

18. $p(x)$ if $p(-1) = 5$

19. $f(x)$ if $f(3) = 10$

20. $s(x)$ if $s(-6) = 4$

21. $m(x)$ if $m(-2) = -7$

22. $z(x)$ if $z(2) = 8$

23. $q(x)$ if $q(-9) = 0$

24. $w(x)$ if $w(-5) = 3$

25. $g(x)$ if the remainder is 4 when $g(x)$ is divided by $x + 1$

26. $f(x)$ if the remainder is -10 when $f(x)$ is divided by $x - 4$

27. $h(x)$ if the remainder is 0 when $h(x)$ is divided by $x - 8$

28. $s(x)$ if the remainder is 7 when $s(x)$ is divided by $x - 3$

29. $k(x)$ if the remainder is 12 when $k(x)$ is divided by $x + 9$

30. $p(x)$ if the remainder is 0 when $p(x)$ is divided by $x - 2$

31. $j(x)$ if the remainder is -23 when $j(x)$ is divided by $x - 10$

32. $w(x)$ if the remainder is 1 when $w(x)$ is divided by $x + 7$

In Exercises 33–40, use the Factor Theorem to draw a conclusion about each polynomial function.

33. $g(x)$ if $g(-1) = -7$

34. $r(x)$ if $r(-9) = 0$

35. $t(x)$ if $t(6) = 0$

36. $h(x)$ if $h(8) = 12$

37. $p(x)$ if $p(-2) = 0$

38. $m(x)$ if $m(3) = 0$

39. $r(x)$ if $r(4) = -9$

40. $s(x)$ if $s(-5) = -4$

Extensions

41. Use synthetic division to determine the value of k if $f(2) = -47$ and $f(x) = -3x^4 - 2x^2 + kx - 1$.

42. Divide $p(x) = 5x^5 + 1$ by $x + 6$. Express your answer as a quotient of a polynomial with a remainder.

43. Evaluate $g(-4)$ for $g(x) = x^6 - 3x^2 + 0.5x$.

44. Use synthetic division to determine if 3 is a solution to $h(x) = -4x^4 - 27x^3 + 10x^2 + 261x + 180$.

45. Is $2x - 3$ a factor of $h(x) = 2x^7 - 9x^6 + x^5 + 12x^4$? Hint: Synthetic division can be used only when the divisor is written in the form $x - c$.

46. True or False? $\sqrt{7}$ is a zero of $g(x) = x^4 - 3x^3 - 11x^2 + 21x + 28$.

47. Simplify the rational expression using either synthetic or long division, and state the domain.

$$\frac{x^4 + 4x^3 - 18x^2 - 59x + 12}{x^2 - x - 12}$$

In Exercises 48–52, divide using synthetic division.

48. $(9x^4 + 15x^3 - 3x^2 + 12) \div (3x + 3)$

49. $(x^4 + 5x^3 + 3x^2 - x - 5) \div (x^2 + 4)$

50. $(x^4 + 5x^3 - 4x^2 - x) \div (x^2 + 3x)$

51. $(x^5 + x^3 + x) \div (x^2 + x)$

52. $\dfrac{\frac{1}{2}x^3 - \frac{1}{8}x^2 + \frac{3}{4}x + 1}{x - \frac{1}{2}}$

In Exercises 53–56, use the Factor Theorem to determine which of the given binomials are factors of the polynomial.

53. $f(x) = 4x^4 - 21x^3 - 22x^2 + 117x + 90$; $(x - 3)$, $(x - 5)$, $(x - 3/4)$, $(x - 2)$, $(x + 2)$, $(x + 5)$, $(x + 3/4)$

54. $g(x) = 3x^4 - 19x^3 - 8x^2 + 124x + 8$; $(x + 4)$, $(x - 5)$, $(x - 2/3)$, $(x - 4)$, $(x + 2)$, $(x + 5)$, $(x - 8/3)$

55. $h(x) = 2x^4 - 5x^3 - 46x^2 + 69x + 180$; $(x + 4)$, $(x - 5)$, $(x - 3/2)$, $(x - 4)$, $(x + 3/2)$, $(x + 3)$, $(x + 9/2)$

56. $k(x) = 3x^4 - 10x^3 - 41x^2 + 68x + 60$; $(x + 4/3)$, $(x - 5)$, $(x - 2/3)$, $(x - 4/3)$, $(x + 2/3)$, $(x + 5)$, $(x - 3)$

5.2 COMPLEX ZEROS AND THE FUNDAMENTAL THEOREM OF ALGEBRA

OBJECTIVES

- Simplify powers of i.
- Add, subtract, and multiply complex numbers.
- Write quotients of complex numbers in the standard form of a complex number.
- Understand the Fundamental Theorem of Algebra.
- Find all real and complex solutions of polynomial equations.
- Understand the Conjugate Pair Theorem.
- Use the Conjugate Pair Theorem to find zeros of polynomial functions.

PREREQUISITE VOCABULARY TERMS

complex number
conjugates
imaginary unit
polynomial function
Quadratic Formula
synthetic division
zero (of a function)

Review of Imaginary and Complex Numbers

REMEMBER

The imaginary unit i is not a variable. Instead, it is a letter used to represent $\sqrt{-1}$.

Recall that the imaginary unit, represented by i, is defined to be $\sqrt{-1}$. The imaginary unit is used to write the square root of a negative number. For example, $\sqrt{-25}$ is equal to $5i$, which is called an imaginary number.

A complex number is an expression that can be written in the standard form $a + bi$, where a and b are real numbers and i is the imaginary unit. Complex numbers were introduced in Chapter P, where we saw that some quadratic equations have complex solutions. For example, the solutions of the quadratic equation $(x + 2)^2 = -9$ are complex numbers.

$$(x+2)^2 = -9$$
$$x + 2 = \pm\sqrt{-9} \qquad \text{\textit{Take} $\pm$ \textit{the square root of each side.}}$$
$$x + 2 = \pm 3i \qquad \text{\textit{Simplify the square root.}}$$
$$x = -2 \pm 3i \qquad \text{\textit{Subtract 2 from each side.}}$$

REMEMBER

The standard form of a complex number is a + bi.

Operations with complex numbers will be discussed in this section, then complex solutions of polynomial equations will be found.

5.2.1 Rewriting Powers of i

A "power of i", such as i^4, is a power where the base is the imaginary unit i. Consider the powers of i with consecutive integer exponents. Notice that simplification of these powers results in a pattern with four numbers.

$$i^2 = \left(\sqrt{-1}\right)^2 = -1 \qquad\qquad i^3 = i^2 \cdot i = (-1)i = -i$$
$$i^4 = i^2 \cdot i^2 = (-1)(-1) = 1 \qquad\qquad i^5 = i^4 \cdot i = (1)i = i$$
$$i^6 = i^4 \cdot i^2 = (1)(-1) = -1 \qquad\qquad i^7 = i^4 \cdot i^3 = (1)(-i) = -i$$
$$i^8 = i^4 \cdot i^4 = (1)(1) = 1 \qquad\qquad i^9 = i^4 \cdot i^4 \cdot i = (1)(1)(i) = i$$

So, $i^2 = -1$, $i^3 = -i$, $i^4 = 1$, $i^5 = i$, $i^6 = -1$, $i^7 = -i$, $i^8 = 1$, and $i^9 = i$.

It follows that all powers of i where the exponent is a whole number are equal to either -1, 1, i, or $-i$. No matter how large the exponent is, as long as the exponent is a whole number, the power of i can be simplified to -1, 1, i, or $-i$ by using the properties of exponents.

EXAMPLE 1   Simplifying Powers of *i*

Simplify. i^{38}

SOLUTION

Use the properties of exponents to simplify the power of *i*.

$$i^{38} = i^{36} \cdot i^2 \qquad \textit{Product of Powers Property}$$
$$= (i^4)^9 \cdot i^2 \qquad \textit{Power of a Power Property}$$
$$= (1)^9(-1) \qquad \textit{Simplify: } i^4 = 1 \textit{ and } i^2 = -1.$$
$$= -1 \qquad \textit{Multiply.}$$

5.2.2   Adding and Subtracting Complex Numbers

Many of the properties of real numbers can be applied to complex numbers as well, such as the Associative Property (of Addition or Multiplication), Commutative Property (of Addition or Multiplication), and the Distributive Property. To add two complex numbers, add the real terms and add the imaginary terms separately. Similarly, to subtract two complex numbers, subtract the real terms and the imaginary terms separately. Basically, the process is the same as for adding and subtracting polynomials: combine the like terms. Once the expression is simplified, be sure to write the complex number in standard form, *a* + *bi*.

EXAMPLE 2   Adding and Subtracting Complex Numbers

Simplify. $(6 + 5i) - (2 - i) + (9 - i)$

SOLUTION

$$(6 + 5i) - (2 - i) + (9 - i)$$
$$= 6 + 5i - 2 + i + 9 - i \qquad \textit{Distributive Property}$$
$$= (6 - 2 + 9) + (5i + i - i) \qquad \textit{Group the real terms, and group the imaginary terms.}$$
$$= 13 + 5i \qquad \textit{Combine the real terms, and combine the imaginary terms.}$$

IMPORTANT

Be sure to distribute the negative to both terms within the subtracted complex number.
$-(2 - i) = -2 + i$

5.2.3   Multiplying Complex Numbers

Recall from Chapter P that two binomials can be multiplied by "FOILing," which is a way of applying the distributive steps in a particular order that makes the steps easier to remember.

$$(a + b)(c + d) = ac + ad + bc + bd$$
$$\qquad\qquad\quad \text{F} \quad \text{O} \quad \text{I} \quad \text{L}$$

The process of FOILing can also be used to multiply two complex numbers. When two complex numbers in standard form are FOILed, the final term will contain a factor of i^2. Note that this term can be simplified because $i^2 = -1$.

EXAMPLE 3   Multiplying Complex Numbers

Multiply. $(7 - 3i)(1 - 4i)$

SOLUTION

$$
\begin{aligned}
(7 - 3i)(1 - 4i) &= 7 - 28i - 3i + 12i^2 && \textit{FOIL} \\
&= 7 - 28i - 3i + 12(-1) && \textit{Simplify: } i^2 = -1. \\
&= 7 - 28i - 3i - 12 && \textit{Multiply.} \\
&= -5 - 31i && \textit{Combine the like terms.}
\end{aligned}
$$

5.2.4   Dividing Complex Numbers

Writing a Quotient of Complex Numbers in Standard Form

A quotient of complex numbers, such as $\dfrac{c + di}{g + hi}$, is simplified when it is written in the standard form of a complex number, $a + bi$. Notice that a quotient of complex numbers is a fractional expression that contains a radical in the denominator because $i = \sqrt{-1}$.

$$
\frac{c + di}{g + hi} = \frac{c + d\sqrt{-1}}{g + h\sqrt{-1}}
$$

In Chapter P, we saw that a fractional expression containing a radical in the denominator can be rationalized by multiplying the fractional expression by some number equivalent to 1 that will remove the radical from the denominator. Recall that a denominator that is a sum or difference of a real number and a radical term, such as $\dfrac{c}{a + b\sqrt{n}}$ or $\dfrac{c}{a - b\sqrt{n}}$, is rationalized by multiplying the expression by the denominator's conjugate over itself. The conjugate of $a + b\sqrt{n}$ is $a - b\sqrt{n}$.

$$
\frac{c}{a + b\sqrt{n}} \cdot \frac{a - b\sqrt{n}}{a - b\sqrt{n}} = \frac{c\left(a - b\sqrt{n}\right)}{\left(a + b\sqrt{n}\right)\left(a - b\sqrt{n}\right)} = \frac{c\left(a - b\sqrt{n}\right)}{a^2 - b^2 n} \quad \textit{The denominator is now rationalized.}
$$

It follows that multiplying a quotient of complex numbers by the denominator's **complex conjugate** over itself will remove the radical (i.e., the imaginary number) from the denominator. In this way, a quotient of two complex numbers can be written in the standard form of a complex number, and thus simplified.

DEFINITION

> Two complex numbers containing the same terms, where one is a sum of terms and the other is a difference of terms, are **complex conjugates**.
>
>
>
> Complex Conjugates
> $a + bi$ and $a - bi$
>
>

So, to simplify a quotient of complex numbers, multiply the quotient by the complex conjugate of the denominator, and write the expression in the standard form of a complex number, $a + bi$.

EXAMPLE 4   Dividing Complex Numbers

Simplify. $\dfrac{4+i}{3-2i}$

SOLUTION

The expression is a quotient of complex numbers, so multiply by the complex conjugate of the denominator over itself to simplify, and write the expression in the standard form of a complex number, $a + bi$. The complex conjugate of the denominator is $3 + 2i$.

$$\frac{4+i}{3-2i} \cdot \frac{3+2i}{3+2i}$$ *Multiply by the complex conjugate of the denominator over itself.*

$$= \frac{(4+i)(3+2i)}{(3-2i)(3+2i)}$$ *Multiply.*

$$= \frac{12+8i+3i+2i^2}{9+6i-6i-4i^2}$$ *FOIL in the numerator and in the denominator.*

$$= \frac{12+8i+3i+2(-1)}{9+6i-6i-4(-1)}$$ *Simplify: $i^2 = -1$.*

$$= \frac{12+8i+3i-2}{9+6i-6i+4}$$ *Multiply.*

$$= \frac{10+11i}{13}$$ *Combine the real terms, and combine the imaginary terms.*

$$= \frac{10}{13} + \frac{11}{13}i$$ *Write in the standard form of a complex number.*

5.2.5 The Fundamental Theorem of Algebra

So far in this course, the discussion of a polynomial function's zeros has focused on its real zeros. For the rest of this section, the discussion of a polynomial function's zeros will include complex zeros as well. We have seen polynomial functions that have one real zero, two real zeros, more than two real zeros, or even no real zeros. Polynomial functions that have no real zeros actually do have zeros, but they are complex zeros. This fact is stated in the **Fundamental Theorem of Algebra**.

> ### Fundamental Theorem of Algebra
>
> If P is a polynomial function of degree $n \geq 1$ with complex coefficients, then P has at least one complex zero.

It is important to point out that a complex number $a + bi$ may have a b-value equal to 0. In this case, the complex number is also a real number, since $a + bi = a + (0)i = a$. It follows that the real numbers are a subset of the complex numbers. In other words, any real number is also a complex number (but not all complex numbers are real numbers). So, the Fundamental Theorem of Algebra applies to polynomial functions with real coefficients as well as complex coefficients.

IMPORTANT

A complex coefficient may be a real coefficient, and a complex zero may be a real zero.

Therefore, by the Fundamental Theorem of Algebra, as long as a polynomial function has

- degree greater than or equal to 1, and
- coefficients that are all complex numbers (which includes real numbers),

then that polynomial function must have at least one complex zero (which may be a real zero).

The Relationship between a Polynomial's Degree and Number of Solutions

Every quadratic equation of the form $ax^2 + bx + c = 0$ has either one real solution (with multiplicity 2), two real solutions, or no real solution. Furthermore, when the value of $b^2 - 4ac$ (i.e., the discriminant of $ax^2 + bx + c = 0$) is negative, then $ax^2 + bx + c = 0$ has no real solution, but it does have two complex solutions. So, if complex solutions are included and a solution with multiplicity k is counted as k solutions, then we can say that every quadratic equation has exactly two complex solutions.

Recall that the degree of a quadratic equation is 2; a quadratic equation's degree is equal to its number of solutions. This is not a coincidence. When complex solutions are included, and the solutions with multiplicity k are counted as k solutions, then every polynomial equation with degree n also has n solutions.

> When complex solutions are included, and solutions with multiplicity k are counted as k solutions, then every polynomial equation with degree n has n solutions.

5.2.6 Finding All Solutions of a Polynomial Equation

Using Synthetic Division vs. Evaluating to Test Rational Zero Candidates

In all of the preceding examples, the rational zero candidates were tested by evaluating the function. Recall that synthetic division (or long division) is an alternative method for testing candidates (the candidate is a zero when the remainder is 0). When you are fairly sure that the candidate is a zero, synthetic division is a preferable method for testing.

Furthermore, to increase the chances that the candidate chosen for testing is a valid zero, graph the polynomial using a graphing calculator, and choose candidate(s) equal to the graph's x-intercept(s).

Solutions of a Polynomial Equation

A process similar to that used to find the real zeros of a polynomial function will be used to find the solutions of a polynomial equation in one variable.

IMPORTANT

The related polynomial function for a general form polynomial equation is found by replacing 0 with $f(x)$. For example, the related function for
$ax^2 + bx + c = 0$ is
$f(x) = ax^2 + bx + c$.

Steps for Factoring a General Form Polynomial Equation and Finding Its Solutions

❶ Use the Rational Zero Theorem to list candidates for possible rational zeros of the related function.

❷ Graph the related function using a graphing calculator, and identify the x-intercepts.

❸ Use synthetic division to test a zero that is equal to an x-intercept. If the remainder is 0, note the zero and use the quotient to test another zero. Repeat until the polynomial is written as a product of linear and quadratic factors.

❹ Identify the solutions from the factored form of the polynomial, using the Quadratic Formula as needed.

EXAMPLE 5 | **Finding All Solutions of a Polynomial Equation**

Factor and find all of the solutions. $2x^4 + 7x^3 - 3x^2 - 5x - 1 = 0$

SOLUTION

The polynomial's degree is 4, so there are four solutions.

❶ Possible rational zeros of the related function $f(x) = 2x^4 + 7x^3 - 3x^2 - 5x - 1$:

$$\pm 1, \pm \frac{1}{2}, \dots \quad \frac{\text{factor of 1}}{\text{factor of 2}} \quad \textit{There are only four rational zero candidates.}$$

❷ Using a graphing calculator, identify the x-intercepts of the related function.

The graph has four x-intercepts, so all four of the equation's solutions must be real solutions. However, these real solutions may or may not be rational.

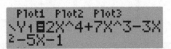

The graph appears to have an x-intercept at 1 and at $-\frac{1}{2}$.

❸ Test the zeros identified in step ❷ using synthetic division.

Here, we start with the x-intercept at 1.

```
1 | 2   7   -3   -5   -1
  |     2    9    6    1
  ------------------------
    2   9    6    1    0
```
The remainder is 0, so 1 is a solution, and $(x - 1)$ is a factor.

The polynomial factors as $(x - 1)(2x^3 + 9x^2 + 6x + 1) = 0$.

Test the other zero from step ❷ $(-1/2)$ in the quotient.

```
-1/2 | 2   9    6    1
     |    -1   -4   -1
     --------------------
       2   8    2    0
```
The remainder is 0, so $-1/2$ is a solution, and $\left(x + \frac{1}{2}\right)$ is a factor.

The polynomial factors as $(x - 1)\left(x + \frac{1}{2}\right)(2x^2 + 8x + 2) = 0$.

❹ Solve $2x^2 + 8x + 2 = 0$ to find the remaining two solutions.

$$2x^2 + 8x + 2 = 0 \implies 2(x^2 + 4x + 1) = 0 \quad \textit{Factor out 2.}$$

Use the Quadratic Formula to find the remaining two solutions.

Quadratic Formula ▶

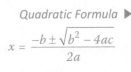

$$x = \frac{-4 \pm \sqrt{16 - 4(1)(1)}}{2(1)} = \frac{-4 \pm \sqrt{12}}{2} = \frac{-4 \pm 2\sqrt{3}}{2} = -2 \pm \sqrt{3}$$

Write the factored equation. $\quad 2(x - 1)\left(x + \frac{1}{2}\right)\left(x - \left(-2 + \sqrt{3}\right)\right)\left(x - \left(-2 - \sqrt{3}\right)\right) = 0$

The solutions are 1, $-\frac{1}{2}$, $-2 + \sqrt{3}$, and $-2 - \sqrt{3}$.

5.2.7 Finding All Solutions of a Polynomial Equation: Another Example

The polynomial equation in the previous example had four solutions: two rational solutions and two irrational solutions. Polynomial equations can also have complex solutions, as seen in the following example.

EXAMPLE 6   Finding All Solutions of a Polynomial Equation

Factor and find all of the solutions. $x^4 - 3x^3 - x^2 - 27x - 90 = 0$

SOLUTION

The polynomial's degree is 4, so there are four solutions.

❶ Possible rational zeros of the related function $f(x) = x^4 - 3x^3 - x^2 - 27x - 90$:

$$\pm 1, \pm 2, \pm 3, \pm 5, \pm 6, \ldots \qquad \textit{factor of 90/factor of 1}$$

❷ Using a graphing calculator, identify the x-intercepts of the related function.

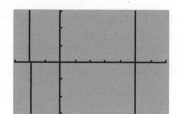

The graph has two x-intercepts, so two of the equation's four solutions must be real solutions.

```
Plot1 Plot2 Plot3
\Y1■X^4-3X^3-X²-
27X-90
```

The graph appears to have x-intercepts at -2 and at 5.

❸ Test the zeros identified in step ❷ using synthetic division. If the remainder is 0, then 1 is a solution, and the quotient is a factor of the polynomial.

Test -2.

$$\begin{array}{r|rrrrr}
-2 & 1 & -3 & -1 & -27 & -90 \\
   &   & -2 & 10 & -18 & 90 \\
\hline
   & 1 & -5 & 9 & -45 & 0
\end{array}$$

The remainder is 0, so -2 is a solution, and $(x + 2)$ is a factor.

The polynomial factors as $(x + 2)(x^3 - 5x^2 + 9x - 45) = 0$.

Test 5 in the quotient.

$$\begin{array}{r|rrrr}
5 & 1 & -5 & 9 & -45 \\
  &   & 5 & 0 & 45 \\
\hline
  & 1 & 0 & 9 & 0
\end{array}$$

The remainder is 0, so 5 is a solution, and $(x - 5)$ is a factor.

The polynomial factors as $(x + 2)(x - 5)(x^2 + 9) = 0$.

❹ Solve $x^2 + 9 = 0$ to find the remaining two solutions.

$$x^2 + 9 = 0 \;\Rightarrow\; x^2 = -9 \;\Rightarrow\; x = \pm\sqrt{-9} = \pm 3i$$

Write the fully factored equation. $(x + 2)(x - 5)(x + 3i)(x - 3i) = 0$

The solutions are -2, 5, $-3i$, and $3i$.

REMEMBER

The quadratic equation $x^2 + 9 = 0$ can be solved using the square roots method because there is no b-term. Multiply the factors to check the answer.

5.2.8   The Conjugate Pair Theorem

The solutions for the polynomial equation from the preceding example were -2, 5, $-3i$, and $3i$. Notice that the polynomial has two complex (nonreal) solutions, $-3i$ and $3i$, and that those two solutions are conjugates. You may have noticed that whenever a polynomial equation has a complex solution, that complex solution's conjugate is also a solution of the polynomial equation. In other words, complex solutions often come in pairs, as stated in the **Conjugate Pair Theorem**.

Conjugate Pair Theorem

If $a + bi$ (with $b \neq 0$) is a complex zero of a polynomial function with real coefficients, then the conjugate $a - bi$ is also a complex zero of the polynomial function.

Note that the Conjugate Pair Theorem applies to polynomials where the coefficients are real numbers.

The Conjugate Pair Theorem is used in the following example to find all zeros of a polynomial function given one complex zero.

EXAMPLE 7   **Using the Conjugate Pair Theorem to Find All Zeros of a Polynomial Function**

Factor and find all of the zeros of $f(x) = x^3 - 4x^2 + 4x - 16$ given that $-2i$ is a zero.

SOLUTION

Use the Conjugate Pair Theorem to identify another zero of $f(x)$. The conjugate of $-2i$ is $2i$, so $2i$ is also a zero.

The polynomial's degree is 3, so there are three zeros. Therefore, there is only one remaining zero to find.

At this point, you could use the Rational Zero Theorem to identify rational zero candidates, and then test candidates by evaluating or using synthetic division, as was done in the previous examples. However, an alternative method is to divide the polynomial by the product of the factors resulting from the known zeros $2i$ and $-2i$.

Find the factors related to the zeros $2i$ and $-2i$, and then multiply those factors.

$$2i \text{ is a zero of } f(x) \implies (x - 2i) \text{ is a factor of } f(x)$$
$$-2i \text{ is a zero of } f(x) \implies (x + 2i) \text{ is a factor of } f(x)$$

The product of those factors is $(x - 2i)(x + 2i) = x^2 + 4$, so $x^2 + 4$ is a factor of $f(x)$.

Divide the polynomial $x^3 - 4x^2 + 4x - 16$ by $(x^2 + 4)$ to find another factor of $f(x)$.

Synthetic division cannot be used, because the divisor $(x^2 + 4)$ is not a linear binomial.

So, use long division.

$$
\begin{array}{r}
x - 4 \\
x^2 + 0x + 4 \overline{\smash{)}\ x^3 - 4x^2 + 4x - 16} \\
\underline{-(x^3 + 0x + 4x)} \\
-4x^2 + 0x - 16 \\
\underline{-(-4x^2 + 0x - 16)} \\
0
\end{array}
$$

The quotient, $x - 4$, is linear, so the process of factoring is complete.

Write the factored polynomial.

$$f(x) = x^3 - 4x^2 + 4x - 16 = (x^2 + 4)(x - 4) = (x - 2i)(x + 2i)(x - 4)$$

The zeros are $-2i$, $2i$, and 4.

TIP

The given zero $-2i$ can be confirmed by evaluating $f(-2i)$.

$$f(-2i) = (-2i)^3 - 4(-2i)^2 + 4(-2i) - 16$$
$$= -8i^3 - 4(4i^2) + 4(-2i) - 16$$
$$= -8(-i) - 4(4)(-1) + 4(-2i) - 16$$
$$= 8i + 16 - 8i - 16$$
$$= 0$$

Since $f(-2i) = 0$, $-2i$ is a zero of $f(x)$.

REMEMBER

$$(x - 2i)(x + 2i)$$
$$= x^2 + 2ix - 2ix - 4i^2$$
$$= x^2 - 4(-1)$$
$$= x^2 + 4$$

TIP

The fact that the remainder is 0 confirms that $(x^2 + 4)$ is a factor of $x^3 - 4x^2 + 4x - 16$.

SECTION 5.2 EXERCISES

Warm Up

Simplify. Rationalize the denominator as needed.

1. $\dfrac{4}{4-\sqrt{5}}$

2. $\dfrac{7}{5+\sqrt{2}}$

3. $\left(4+\sqrt{3}\right)\left(4-\sqrt{3}\right)$

Just the Facts

Fill in the blanks.

4. The $\sqrt{-1}$ is the _____ unit, represented by _____.

5. $a + bi$ is a(n) _____ number, where a and b are _____ numbers and _____ is the imaginary unit.

6. If $a + bi$ is a complex zero of a polynomial function with real coefficients, then so is its conjugate, _____.

7. Any power of i where the exponent is a whole number is equal to _____, _____, _____, or _____.

8. It is important to remember when multiplying two complex numbers that _____ equals -1.

9. To simplify when dividing complex numbers, multiply by the denominator's complex _____ over itself.

10. The Fundamental Theorem of Algebra states that a polynomial of degree 4 with _____ coefficients will have at least _____ complex zero(s).

Essential Skills

In Exercises 1–22, simplify.

1. i^{14}

2. i^{31}

3. i^{37}

4. i^{30}

5. i^{23}

6. i^{26}

7. $(-12 - 14i) + (11 + 10i)$

8. $-2 + 3(2 - 5i) - 4(6 + i)$

9. $(4 - 2i) - 6(1 + 2i) + (7 + 8i)$

10. $-3(3 - 7i) - (5 - 9i) - 5(-7 + 2i)$

11. $5i + 4(11 - 12i) - 8(8 - 6i)$

12. $16 + 9(4 + 6i) - (3 + 10i) + (9 - 2i)$

13. $-22i + 10(4 + 6i) - 3(-6 - 4i)$

14. $4(9 + 6i) - 7(1 - 3i) - 2(-3 + 5i)$

15. $(3 + 4i)(1 + 2i)$

16. $i(9 + 8i)(3 - 2i)$

17. $i(2 - 5i)(1 - i)$

18. $(7 - 5i)(6 - 4i)$

19. $(4 - 7i)(-5 + 7i)$

20. $-3i(10 - 3i)(-1 - 6i)$

21. $-i(-9 + i)(4 - 4i)$

22. $5i(-6 - i)(7 - 5i)$

In Exercises 23–30, write each complex number in standard form.

23. $\dfrac{i}{6+i}$

24. $\dfrac{-6+3i}{-5-5i}$

25. $\dfrac{1-i}{-2-3i}$

26. $\dfrac{3-4i}{5+2i}$

27. $\dfrac{-4+6i}{-3+4i}$

28. $\dfrac{-2+7i}{8+i}$

29. $\dfrac{-9-2i}{4-7i}$

30. $\dfrac{5-8i}{-1-7i}$

In Exercises 31–46, find all the solutions of each equation.

31. $x^4 - 3x^3 - 5x^2 + 13x + 6 = 0$

32. $3x^4 - 8x^3 - 16x^2 + 24x + 32 = 0$

33. $3x^4 - 11x^3 - 11x^2 + 15x + 4 = 0$

34. $2x^4 - 9x^3 - 27x^2 + 80x + 150 = 0$

35. $2x^4 - 15x^3 + 17x^2 + 42x - 36 = 0$

36. $4x^4 - 11x^3 - 12x^2 + 26x + 20 = 0$

37. $2x^4 - 21x^3 + 37x^2 + 145x - 275 = 0$

38. $3x^4 - 28x^3 + 44x^2 + 84x - 135 = 0$

39. $x^4 - x^3 + 3x^2 - 9x - 54 = 0$

40. $x^4 + x^3 + 23x^2 + 25x - 50 = 0$

41. $x^4 - 2x^3 + x^2 - 8x - 12 = 0$

42. $x^4 - x^3 + 2x^2 - 4x - 8 = 0$

43. $x^4 - 2x^3 + 6x^2 - 18x - 27 = 0$

44. $x^4 - 2x^3 + 13x^2 - 32x - 48 = 0$

45. $x^4 - x^3 + 10x^2 - 16x - 96 = 0$

46. $x^4 + x^3 + 7x^2 + 9x - 18 = 0$

In Exercises 47–54, find all the zeros of each function with the given zero.

47. $p(x) = x^3 - x^2 + 25x - 25$, zero: $5i$

48. $f(x) = x^3 + 6x^2 - 11x + 40$, zero: $1 - 2i$

49. $g(x) = x^3 + 5x^2 + 12x + 182$, zero: $1 + 5i$

50. $f(x) = x^3 + x^2 - 14x + 272$, zero: $3 - 5i$

51. $m(x) = x^3 - 11x^2 + 44x - 60$, zero: $4 - 2i$

52. $f(x) = x^3 + 4x^2 - 19x + 104$, zero: $2 - 3i$

53. $d(x) = x^3 - x^2 - 6x + 72$, zero: $3 - 3i$

54. $f(x) = x^3 - 6x^2 + 28x - 40$, zero: $2 - 4i$

Extensions

55. Suppose $f(x)$ is a polynomial function with real coefficients and zeros $-i$, $2 + 3i$, $\sqrt{5}$, and $\dfrac{1-i}{3}$. Find three additional zeros of $f(x)$.

56. Simplify. i^{401}

In Exercises 57–63, perform the indicated operation. Write the result in standard form.

57. $\dfrac{1+i}{3-i} + \dfrac{5}{i-4}$

58. $\dfrac{-2-3i}{i} - \dfrac{6+i}{5-i}$

59. $(-5 - 8i^9)(3 + 7i^{19})$

60. $-3 + \dfrac{5i}{2-i} + \dfrac{i}{1+4i}$

61. $\dfrac{6-7i}{9+2i} \div \dfrac{-5+3i}{-9-2i}$

62. $(4 + 7i^8)(-2 - 3i^{15})$

63. $12 - \dfrac{2+i}{3+2i} + \dfrac{3i}{5-i}$

64. Find all the zeros of $p(x) = x^4 + x^3 - 29x^2 + 71x - 140$, and write the polynomial as a product of linear factors.

65. Write a polynomial function with real coefficients that has i, $2 + 3i$, $3 - 2i$, and 4 as zeros.

66. Let $p(x)$ be a cubic function with a leading coefficient of 3, where $p(5) = 0 = p(1 + i)$. Write an equation for $p(x)$.

5.3 TRIGONOMETRIC FORM AND ROOTS OF COMPLEX NUMBERS

OBJECTIVES

- Represent a complex number as a point in the complex plane.
- Find the modulus of a complex number.
- Express a complex number in trigonometric form.
- Multiply and divide complex numbers in trigonometric form.
- Use DeMoivre's Theorem to find a power of a complex number.
- Find the nth roots of a complex number.

PREREQUISITE VOCABULARY TERMS

complex number
degree of a polynomial
double-angle formulas
imaginary number
sum and difference formulas
trigonometric functions

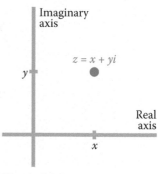

5.3.1 Graphing a Complex Number and Finding Its Modulus

Review of Complex Numbers

Complex numbers can be written in the standard form $a + bi$, where a and b are real numbers and i is the imaginary unit (i.e., $i = \sqrt{-1}$). The real numbers a and b in a complex number $a + bi$ are called the **real part** and the **imaginary part**, respectively.

Complex numbers are equal when their real parts are equal and their imaginary parts are equal. Therefore, $a + bi = c + di$ if and only if $a = c$ and $b = d$.

Complex numbers were added, subtracted, multiplied, and divided in preceding chapters.

Additionally, we saw that equations of the form $a^n = b$, where a is an algebraic expression, n is an *even* whole number, and b is a *negative* real number, have complex solutions with a nonzero imaginary part. For example, the equation $(x - 2)^2 = -9$ has two complex solutions: $2 + 3i$ and $2 - 3i$.

> **NOTICE THAT**
>
> *The bi-term in a + bi is an imaginary number.*

> **REMEMBER**
>
> *To solve $(x - 2)^2 = -9$, first take ± the square root of both sides, then add 2 to both sides. Simplifying $\pm\sqrt{-9}$ yields the imaginary term of each complex solution: 3i and −3i.*

Graphing a Complex Number

Just as real numbers can be plotted on a real number line, and ordered pairs of real numbers can be graphed on a rectangular (Cartesian) plane (where the horizontal and vertical axes are real number lines), complex numbers can be plotted on a coordinate plane called a **complex plane**.

In a complex plane, the horizontal axis (**real axis**) is a real number line and the vertical axis (**imaginary axis**) is an imaginary number line.

If z is the complex number $x + yi$, then the graph of $z = x + yi$ is the point (x, y) on a complex plane, as shown in Figure 5.3a. The procedure for graphing a complex number in a complex plane is demonstrated in **Example 1**.

Figure 5.3a

EXAMPLE 1 | **Plotting a Complex Number on the Complex Plane**

Plot $z = 3 + 2i$, $w = 2 - i$, and $p = -2i$ on the complex plane.

SOLUTION

Use each complex number's real part and imaginary part to plot the point.

In $z = 3 + 2i$, the real part is 3 (so $x = 3$) and the imaginary part is 2 (so $y = 2$). To plot $z = 3 + 2i$, move 3 units to the right from the origin (since $x = 3 > 0$), then move 2 units up (since $y = 2 > 0$). Therefore, z is in quadrant I.

To plot $w = 2 - i$, move 2 units to the right from the origin (since $2 > 0$), then move 1 unit down (since $-1 < 0$), because the real part is 2 and the imaginary part is -1. Therefore, w is in quadrant IV.

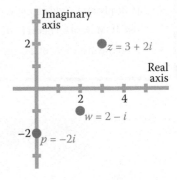

To plot $p = -2i$, move 2 units down from the origin, because the real part is 0 and the imaginary part is -2. Therefore, p is on the imaginary axis.

The Modulus of a Complex Number

The **modulus** of a complex number (or **absolute value of a complex number**) is the distance from the origin to the point corresponding to the complex number on the complex plane. This measure is sometimes referred to as the *length* of the complex number.

> **The Modulus or the Absolute Value of a Complex Number**
>
> The modulus of a complex number $z = x + yi$, denoted $|z|$, is $|z| = |x + yi| = \sqrt{x^2 + y^2}$.

EXAMPLE 2 | **Finding the Modulus of a Complex Number**

Find the modulus of $w = 2 - i$.

SOLUTION

Substitute $x = 2$ and $y = -1$ into the modulus formula and simplify.

$$|w| = |2 - i| = \sqrt{2^2 + (-1)^2} = \sqrt{5}$$

5.3.2 Expressing a Complex Number in Trigonometric or Polar Form

Let z be the complex number $x + yi$, let r be the modulus of z, and let θ be the angle between the positive real axis and the ray containing z and the origin (Figure 5.3b). Then θ is a standard position angle with the point (x, y) on its terminal side. Therefore, $\sin \theta = y/r$ and $\cos \theta = x/r$. Solving these equations for x and y, respectively, gives $y = r \sin \theta$ and $x = r \cos \theta$.

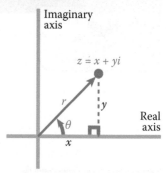

Figure 5.3b

The complex number $z = x + yi$ can be written in terms of $\sin \theta$ and $\cos \theta$ by substituting $r \cos \theta$ and $r \sin \theta$ for x and y, respectively, in $z = x + yi$, which gives $r \cos \theta + (r \sin \theta)i$. Factoring r from each term in the equation gives the complex number's **trigonometric form** (or **polar form**).

Trigonometric Form (or Polar Form) of a Complex Number

$$z = x + yi = r(\cos \theta + i \sin \theta)$$

Steps for Writing a Complex Number in Trigonometric Form

❶ Find the complex number's modulus r.

❷ Find the angle θ between the positive real axis and the ray containing the graph of the complex number and the origin.

❸ Substitute the r- and θ-values into $r(\cos \theta + i \sin \theta)$.

EXAMPLE 3   Writing a Complex Number in Trigonometric Form

Write $w = 2 - i$ in trigonometric form. Round θ to the nearest degree if an exact value of θ cannot be found.

SOLUTION

❶ From **Example 2**, the modulus of $w = 2 - i$ is $\sqrt{5}$, so $r = \sqrt{5}$.

❷ Use a trigonometric function (e.g., $\cos \theta = x/r$) to find θ.

$$\cos \theta = 2 / \sqrt{5}$$

Using a calculator, we see that $\cos^{-1}\left(2 / \sqrt{5}\right) \approx 27°$. However, since $x = 2 > 0$, and $y = -1 < 0$, θ is in quadrant IV. Therefore, $\theta \approx 360° - 27° = 333°$.

❸ Substitute $r = \sqrt{5}$ and $\theta \approx 333°$ into $r(\cos \theta + i \sin \theta)$ to write $w = 2 - i$ in trigonometric form.

$$w = 2 - i = r(\cos \theta + i \sin \theta) \approx \sqrt{5}(\cos 333° + i \sin 333°)$$

5.3.5 Roots of Complex Numbers

We have seen that all *real* solutions of the polynomial equation $x^4 = 81$ can be found by taking $\pm$ the fourth root of each side.

$$x^4 = 81 \implies x = \pm\sqrt[4]{81} = \pm 3$$

Therefore, the real solutions of $x^4 = 81$ are $x = 3$ and $x = -3$.

However, recall that (by the Fundamental Theorem of Algebra) every polynomial equation with degree n has n complex solutions. Therefore, since the degree of $x^4 = 81$ is 4, $x^4 = 81$ must have four complex solutions. All four complex solutions of $x^4 = 81$ can be found by factoring.

$x^4 - 81 = 0$	*Write the equation in general form.*
$(x + 3)(x - 3)(x^2 + 9) = 0$	*Factor.*
$x + 3 = 0$ or $x - 3 = 0$ or $x^2 + 9 = 0$	*Set each factor equal to 0.*
$x = -3 \qquad x = 3 \qquad x = \pm\sqrt{-9}$	*Solve each equation for x.*

Therefore, the four complex solutions of the fourth degree equation $x^4 = 81$ are $x = -3$, $x = 3$, $x = 3i$, and $x = -3i$. Each solution is called a "fourth root of 81" because the 4th power of each value is equal to 81.

$$3^4 = 81 \qquad (-3)^4 = 81 \qquad (3i)^4 = 3^4 \, i^4 = (81)(1) = 81 \qquad (-3i)^4 = (-3)^4 \, i^4 = (81)(1) = 81$$

In general, if z and $a + bi$ are complex numbers and n is a positive integer such that $z = (a + bi)^n$, then $a + bi$ is an **nth root of the complex number z**. From the definition of an nth root of a complex number z and DeMoivre's Theorem for powers of a complex number, the following result can be concluded.

The nth Roots of a Complex Number

If n is an integer such that $n > 0$, and z is a complex number such that
$z = x + yi = r(\cos \theta + i \sin \theta)$,
then there are exactly n distinct nth roots of z given by

$$\sqrt[n]{r}\left(\cos \frac{\theta + 2\pi k}{n} + i \sin \frac{\theta + 2\pi k}{n} \right),$$

where $k = 0, 1, 2, \ldots, n - 1$.

Steps for Finding the nth Roots of a Complex Number z

❶ Find r (the modulus of z) and θ (the angle between the positive real axis and a ray containing the graph of z and the origin).

❷ Substitute the values of n, r, and θ into $\sqrt[n]{r}\left(\cos \dfrac{\theta + 2\pi k}{n} + i \sin \dfrac{\theta + 2\pi k}{n} \right)$ and simplify.

❸ Evaluate the expression from step ❷ n times, each time using a different value of k (i.e., $k = 0$, $k = 1$, $k = 2$, $\ldots$, and $k = n - 1$).

This procedure is used in **Example 6** to find all fourth roots of 81, which we know from the preceding example are -3, 3, $3i$, and $-3i$.

REMEMBER

By the conjugate pair theorem, if $a + bi$ (where a and b are real numbers such that $b \neq 0$) is a complex solution to a polynomial equation with only real coefficients, then its conjugate $a - bi$ is also a solution.

REMEMBER

$i^4 = i^2 \, i^2 = (-1)(-1) = 1$

TIP

Each nth root of a complex number z is given by evaluating this expression. Evaluate the expression n times to find all n of the nth roots: once where $k = 0$, once where $k = 1, \ldots$, and then finally where $k = n - 1$. The value of n stays constant in each instance of the expression.

| **EXAMPLE 6** | **Finding the nth Roots of a Complex Number** |

Find all fourth roots of 81.

SOLUTION

❶ Since $81 = 81 + 0i$, 81 is the point $(81, 0)$ on a complex plane. *(81, 0) on the positive real axis.*

Substitute $x = 81$ and $y = 0$ into the modulus formula and simplify to find r.

$$r = \sqrt{81^2 + 0^2} = \sqrt{81^2} = 81$$

Use a trigonometric function (e.g., $\sin \theta = y/r$) to find θ.

$$\sin \theta = 0/81 \implies \sin \theta = 0 \quad \text{Since } \sin 0 = 0, \theta = 0.$$

❷ Substitute $n = 4$, $r = 81$, and $\theta = 0$ into $\sqrt[n]{r}\left(\cos \dfrac{\theta + 2\pi k}{n} + i \sin \dfrac{\theta + 2\pi k}{n} \right)$ and simplify.

$$\sqrt[4]{81}\left(\cos \frac{0 + 2\pi k}{4} + i \sin \frac{0 + 2\pi k}{4} \right) = 3\left(\cos \frac{\pi k}{2} + i \sin \frac{\pi k}{2} \right)$$

❸ Repeat the process of substituting a k-value into the expression and simplifying four times (once for each k-value: $k = 0$, $k = 1$, $k = 2$, and $k = 3$) to find the 4 roots.

$$k = 0: \ 3\left(\cos \frac{\pi(0)}{2} + i \sin \frac{\pi(0)}{2} \right) = 3(\cos 0 + i \sin 0) = 3(1 + i(0)) = 3$$

$$k = 1: \ 3\left(\cos \frac{\pi(1)}{2} + i \sin \frac{\pi(1)}{2} \right) = 3\left(\cos \frac{\pi}{2} + i \sin \frac{\pi}{2} \right) = 3(0 + i(1)) = 3i$$

$$k = 2: \ 3\left(\cos \frac{\pi(2)}{2} + i \sin \frac{\pi(2)}{2} \right) = 3(\cos \pi + i \sin \pi) = 3(-1 + i(0)) = -3$$

$$k = 3: \ 3\left(\cos \frac{\pi(3)}{2} + i \sin \frac{\pi(3)}{2} \right) = 3\left(\cos \frac{3\pi}{2} + i \sin \frac{3\pi}{2} \right) = 3(0 + i(-1)) = -3i$$

Therefore, the fourth roots of 81 are -3, 3, $3i$, and $-3i$.

The Solutions of an nth Degree Polynomial Equation and the nth Roots of a Complex Number

We have now seen that the complex solutions of the equation $x^4 = 81$ are the fourth roots of 81. In general, if n is a positive integer and z is a complex number, then the complex solutions of the polynomial equation $x^n = z$ are the nth roots of z. Therefore, if a polynomial equation can be written in the form $x^n = z$, then all n complex solutions of the polynomial equation can be found using the procedure for finding the nth roots of z. This procedure should be used to find the solutions of a polynomial equation when the equation cannot be solved easily by factoring.

| **EXAMPLE 7** | **Finding All Solutions of a Polynomial Equation** |

Find all solutions of $2x^4 + 32 = 0$.

SOLUTION

Subtracting 32 from each side and then dividing each side by 2 yields $x^4 = -16$. Since 4 is a positive integer and -16 is a complex number, the solutions of $2x^4 + 32 = 0$ are the fourth roots of -16. So, find the fourth roots of -16.

TIP

Since the graph of $81 + 0i$ is a point 81 units to the right of the origin on the positive real axis, we know that the distance between the origin and the point is 81. Additionally, we know that the angle between the positive real axis and itself is 0 radians. Thus, $r = 81$ and $\theta = 0$.

IMPORTANT

The complex solutions of a polynomial equation in terms of x are the nth roots of z only when the equation can be written in the form $x^n = z$, where n is positive integer and z is a complex number.

❶ On a complex plane, −16 is the point (−16, 0) on the negative real axis, so $r = 16$ and $\theta = \pi$.

❷ Substitute $n = 4$, $r = 16$, and $\theta = \pi$ into the expression for the nth roots of z and simplify.

$$\sqrt[4]{16}\left(\cos\frac{\pi+2\pi k}{4} + i\sin\frac{\pi+2\pi k}{4}\right) = 2\left(\cos\frac{\pi+2\pi k}{4} + i\sin\frac{\pi+2\pi k}{4}\right)$$

❸ Repeat the process of substituting a k-value into the expression and simplifying four times (once for each k-value: $k = 0$, $k = 1$, $k = 2$, and $k = 3$) to find the 4 roots.

$$k = 0:\ 2\left(\cos\frac{\pi}{4} + i\sin\frac{\pi}{4}\right) = 2\left(\frac{\sqrt{2}}{2} + i\frac{\sqrt{2}}{2}\right) = \sqrt{2} + i\sqrt{2} \qquad \frac{\pi+2\pi(0)}{4} = \frac{\pi}{4}$$

$$k = 1:\ 2\left(\cos\frac{3\pi}{4} + i\sin\frac{3\pi}{4}\right) = 2\left(-\frac{\sqrt{2}}{2} + i\frac{\sqrt{2}}{2}\right) = -\sqrt{2} + i\sqrt{2} \qquad \frac{\pi+2\pi(1)}{4} = \frac{3\pi}{4}$$

$$k = 2:\ 2\left(\cos\frac{5\pi}{4} + i\sin\frac{5\pi}{4}\right) = 2\left(-\frac{\sqrt{2}}{2} - i\frac{\sqrt{2}}{2}\right) = -\sqrt{2} - i\sqrt{2} \qquad \frac{\pi+2\pi(2)}{4} = \frac{5\pi}{4}$$

$$k = 3:\ 2\left(\cos\frac{7\pi}{4} + i\sin\frac{7\pi}{4}\right) = 2\left(\frac{\sqrt{2}}{2} - i\frac{\sqrt{2}}{2}\right) = \sqrt{2} - i\sqrt{2} \qquad \frac{\pi+2\pi(3)}{4} = \frac{7\pi}{4}$$

Therefore, the solutions of $2x^4 + 32 = 0$ (i.e., the fourth roots of −16) are

$$\sqrt{2} + i\sqrt{2},\ -\sqrt{2} + i\sqrt{2},\ -\sqrt{2} - i\sqrt{2},\ \text{and}\ \sqrt{2} - i\sqrt{2}.$$

5.3.6   Roots of Complex Numbers: Another Example

EXAMPLE 8   **Finding the nth Roots of a Complex Number**

Find all cube roots of −8i.

SOLUTION

❶ Since −8i is the point (0, −8) on the negative imaginary axis, $r = 8$ and $\theta = 3\pi/2$.

❷ Substitute $n = 3$, $r = 8$, and $\theta = 3\pi/2$ into the expression for the nth roots z and simplify.

$$\sqrt[3]{8}\left(\cos\frac{3\pi/2+2\pi k}{3} + i\sin\frac{3\pi/2+2\pi k}{3}\right) = 2\left(\cos\frac{3\pi/2+2\pi k}{3} + i\sin\frac{3\pi/2+2\pi k}{3}\right)$$

❸ Substitute the k-values (0, 1, and 2) to find the 3 roots.

$$k = 0:\ 2\left(\cos\frac{3\pi/2}{3} + i\sin\frac{3\pi/2}{3}\right) = 2\left(\cos\frac{\pi}{2} + i\sin\frac{\pi}{2}\right) = 2(0 + 1i) = 2i$$

$$k = 1:\ 2\left(\cos\frac{7\pi}{6} + i\sin\frac{7\pi}{6}\right) = 2\left(-\frac{\sqrt{3}}{2} + \left(-\frac{1}{2}\right)i\right) = -\sqrt{3} - i \qquad \frac{3\pi/2+2\pi(1)}{3} = \frac{7\pi}{6}$$

$$k = 2:\ 2\left(\cos\frac{11\pi}{6} + i\sin\frac{11\pi}{6}\right) = 2\left(\frac{\sqrt{3}}{2} + \left(-\frac{1}{2}\right)i\right) = \sqrt{3} - i \qquad \frac{3\pi/2+2\pi(2)}{3} = \frac{11\pi}{6}$$

Therefore, the 3 cube roots of −8i are $2i$, $\sqrt{3} - i$, and $-\sqrt{3} - i$.

SECTION 5.3 EXERCISES

Warm Up

Find the complex conjugate for each of the following.

1. $1 + 3i$

2. $-5 + 4i$

3. $-2 - 6i$

Just the Facts

Fill in the blanks.

4. In the complex plane, the x-axis is referred to as the _____ axis and the y-axis is referred to as the _____ axis.

5. Let $z = x + yi$ be a complex number. The distance from the origin to the point (x, y) is called the _____, denoted by $|z|$.

6. If $r > 0$ and $0 \le \theta \le 2\pi$, the complex number $z = x + yi$ can be written in trigonometric form as _____.

7. If $z_1 = r_1(\cos \theta_1 + i \sin \theta_1)$ and $z_2 = r_2(\cos \theta_2 + i \sin \theta_2)$, then $z_1 z_2 =$ _____.

8. If $z_1 = r_1(\cos \theta_1 + i \sin \theta_1)$, $z_2 = r_2(\cos \theta_2 + i \sin \theta_2)$, and $z_2 \ne 0$, then $z_1/z_2 =$ _____.

9. If $z = r(\cos \theta + i \sin \theta)$ is a complex number, then $z^n =$ _____.

10. Let x be a complex number, and let $n \ge 2$ denote a positive integer. Any complex number z that satisfies the equation $z^n = x$ is called a complex _____ root of x.

Essential Skills

In Exercises 1–6, plot each complex number in the complex plane.

1. $z = 1 + 5i$

2. $z = -5 - 4i$

3. $z = -3 + i$

4. $z = 2 - 3i$

5. $z = -4 - 2i$

6. $z = 2 + 6i$

In Exercises 7–12, determine the modulus of each complex number.

7. $4 + 2i$

8. $12 - 5i$

9. $-3 + 6i$

10. $-7 + 24i$

11. $1 - 4i$

12. $-9 - 12i$

In Exercises 13–18, write each complex number in trigonometric form.

13. $2 + 2\sqrt{3}i$

14. $-5 + 5i$

15. $3 - 3i$

16. $-4\sqrt{3} - 4i$

17. $-6\sqrt{3} + 6i$

18. $4\sqrt{2} + 4\sqrt{2}i$

In Exercises 19–24, write each complex number in trigonometric form. Round θ to the nearest degree.

19. $3 + 6i$

20. $2 - 3i$

21. $-1 + 2i$

22. $-5 + 4i$

23. $-4 - i$

24. $-2 - 5i$

In Exercises 25–30, find each product $z_1 z_2$.

25. $z_1 = 2(\cos 50° + i \sin 50°)$, $z_2 = 3(\cos 70° + i \sin 70°)$

26. $z_1 = 5(\cos 140° + i \sin 140°)$, $z_2 = 12(\cos 20° + i \sin 20°)$

27. $z_1 = 8(\cos 65° + i \sin 65°)$, $z_2 = 4(\cos 95° + i \sin 95°)$

28. $z_1 = 6(\cos 160° + i \sin 160°)$, $z_2 = 7(\cos 130° + i \sin 130°)$

29. $z_1 = 9(\cos 170° + i \sin 170°)$, $z_2 = 2(\cos 120° + i \sin 120°)$

30. $z_1 = 4(\cos 80° + i \sin 80°)$, $z_2 = 5(\cos 100° + i \sin 100°)$

In Exercises 31–36, find each quotient z_1/z_2.

31. $z_1 = 36(\cos 150° + i \sin 150°)$, $z_2 = 18(\cos 80° + i \sin 80°)$

32. $z_1 = 82(\cos 207° + i \sin 207°)$, $z_2 = 2(\cos 15° + i \sin 15°)$

33. $z_1 = 45(\cos 310° + i \sin 310°)$, $z_2 = 5(\cos 290° + i \sin 290°)$

34. $z_1 = 12(\cos 230° + i \sin 230°)$, $z_2 = 4(\cos 140° + i \sin 140°)$

35. $z_1 = 48(\cos 140° + i \sin 140°)$, $z_2 = 12(\cos 20° + i \sin 20°)$

36. $z_1 = 81(\cos 136° + i \sin 136°)$, $z_2 = 9(\cos 92° + i \sin 92°)$

In Exercises 37–42, write each complex number in trigonometric form.

37. $(-7i)^3$

38. $(5 - 5\sqrt{3}i)^2$

39. $(3 - 3i)^4$

40. $(-6 + 6i)^3$

41. $(-4 - 4\sqrt{3}i)^2$

42. $(2\sqrt{3} - 2i)^5$

In Exercises 43–54, simplify and write in standard form.

43. $(2 + 2i)^3$

44. $(-4 + 4i)^5$

45. $(-3\sqrt{3} + 3i)^4$

46. $(-5 - 5\sqrt{3}i)^4$

47. $(\sqrt{3} - i)^5$

48. $(4\sqrt{3} - 4i)^3$

49. $\left(2\left(\cos \dfrac{\pi}{2} + i \sin \dfrac{\pi}{2} \right) \right)^3$

50. $\left(3\left(\cos \dfrac{2\pi}{3} + i \sin \dfrac{2\pi}{3} \right) \right)^4$

51. $\left(4\left(\cos \dfrac{3\pi}{4} + i \sin \dfrac{3\pi}{4} \right) \right)^4$

52. $\left(5\left(\cos \dfrac{11\pi}{6} + i \sin \dfrac{11\pi}{6} \right) \right)^3$

53. $\left(5\left(\cos \dfrac{5\pi}{6} + i \sin \dfrac{5\pi}{6} \right) \right)^5$

54. $\left(3\left(\cos \dfrac{7\pi}{4} + i \sin \dfrac{7\pi}{4} \right) \right)^5$

In Exercises 55–62, solve.

55. $v^4 = 9$

56. $4z^4 = 100$

57. $4u^6 = 16$

58. $2v^6 = -98$

59. $u^4 - 81 = 0$

60. $z^5 + 243 = 0$

61. $v^6 - 729 = 0$

62. $t^4 + 81 = 0$

In Exercises 63–70, find the indicated roots.

63. fourth roots of 16

64. fifth roots of 243

65. cube roots of 216

66. fourth roots of 100

67. cube roots of i

68. fourth roots of $2 - 2\sqrt{3}i$

69. cube roots of $-8 - 8i$

70. cube roots of $4\sqrt{3} + 4i$

Extensions

In Exercises 71–74, write each complex number in trigonometric form. Round θ to the nearest degree.

71. $(4 - 3i)^5$

72. $(-5 - 12i)^4$

73. $(-6 + 10i)^3$

74. $(8 + 9i)^5$

In Exercises 75–78, find the indicated roots. Round each answer to the nearest hundredth, as needed.

75. fifth roots of $32(\cos 300° + i \sin 300°)$

76. fourth roots of $81(\cos 150° + i \sin 150°)$

77. cube roots of $125\left(\cos \dfrac{5\pi}{4} + i \sin \dfrac{5\pi}{4} \right)$

78. fifth roots of $1024(\cos \pi + i \sin \pi)$

CHAPTER 5 REVIEW EXERCISES

Section 5.1 Dividing Polynomials

1. Divide using long division. $\dfrac{5x^3 - 6x^2 + 8}{x - 4}$

In Exercises 2–3, divide using synthetic division.

2. $\dfrac{x^4 - 4x^3 - 5x^2 + 36x - 36}{x - 3}$

3. $\dfrac{3x^3 - 4x + 10}{x - 2}$

4. By the Remainder Theorem, what can be said about the polynomial function $f(x)$ if the remainder is 12 when $f(x)$ is divided by $x + 9$?

5. By the Factor Theorem, what can be said about the polynomial function $g(x)$ if $g(3) = 0$?

Section 5.2 Complex Zeros and the Fundamental Theorem of Algebra

In Exercises 6–7, simplify and write each complex number in standard form.

6. $i(3 - 7i)(2 + i)$

7. $\dfrac{8 - 5i}{8 + 9i}$

In Exercises 8–9, find all solutions of each equation.

8. $x^4 + x^3 - 18x^2 - 10x + 8 = 0$

9. $x^4 - 2x^3 + 13x^2 - 32x - 48 = 0$

10. Find all the zeros of $p(x) = x^4 - 4x^3 - x^2 - 16x - 20$ given that $2i$ is a zero.

Section 5.3 Trigonometric Form and Roots of Complex Numbers

11. Convert $-2 + 2\sqrt{3}i$ to trigonometric form.

12. Write both zw and z/w in the form $a + bi$, given that $w = 4(\cos 110° + i \sin 110°)$ and $z = 3(\cos 130° + i \sin 130°)$. Round to the nearest hundredth, as needed.

13. Write $(-5\sqrt{3} - 5i)^5$ in standard and trigonometric form.

14. Solve $-3v^6 = -69$.

15. Find all fourth roots of $6 - 6i$.

CONICS

6.1 PARABOLAS

OBJECTIVES

- Understand the relationship between the four types of conics (circle, ellipse, parabola, and hyperbola) and a cone.
- Find the vertex, focus, and directrix of a parabola (vertex at the origin).
- Graph a parabola (vertex at the origin).
- Write the equation of a parabola (vertex at the origin).

PREREQUISITE VOCABULARY TERMS

axis of symmetry

circle

parabola

vertex (of a parabola)

6.1.1 Introduction to Conic Sections

When a plane intersects a cone (specifically, a right double cone with a circular base) without intersecting the cone's vertex, the figure formed is known as a **conic** or **conic section**. For example, a circle, one type of conic, is formed when the intersecting plane is parallel to the base of the cone. The four basic conics are the circle, ellipse, parabola, and hyperbola, as shown in Figure 6.1a.

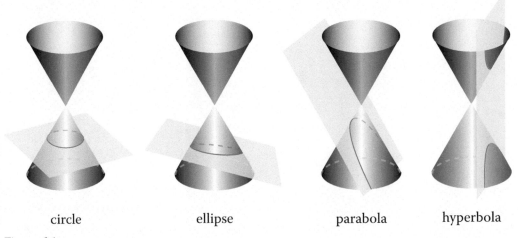

circle   ellipse   parabola   hyperbola

Figure 6.1a

An ellipse is formed by the intersection of a cone and a plane, where the plane does not intersect a base of the cone. (A special case of an ellipse is a circle, where the plane is parallel to the base.) A parabola is formed when a plane intersects only one part of the double cone through its base, and a hyperbola is formed when the plane intersects both parts of the double cone, including both bases.

When a plane intersects a double cone at the vertex of the cone, the resulting figure is called a **degenerate conic**, which can look like a single point, a single line, or a pair of lines.

The equations for two of the conics, the parabola and the circle, have been discussed previously. Recall that the standard form equation of a circle centered at the origin is $x^2 + y^2 = r^2$, where r is the radius of the circle, and the standard form equation of a parabola centered at the origin is $y = ax^2$, where the value of a describes the width and direction of the parabola. The equation of a parabola will be discussed further in this section, and the equations of the ellipse and hyperbola will be discussed in the following sections.

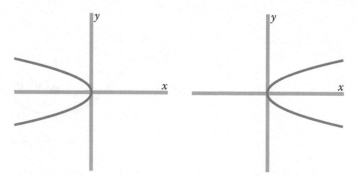

6.1.2 Graphing Parabolas

Recall that the graph of a quadratic function of the form $y = ax^2 + bx + c$ is a parabola with a vertical axis of symmetry that opens upward or downward, depending upon the value of a. The discussion of parabolas in this chapter will include parabolas that are not functions. These nonfunction parabolas, as shown in Figure 6.1b, will have a horizontal axis of symmetry and will open to the left or right.

Figure 6.1b   Parabolas with a Horizontal Axis of Symmetry

The Definition of a Parabola

Recall that, on a coordinate plane, a circle is the set of all points that are equidistant from a specific point called the circle's center. The distance from the center to any point on the circle is the circle's radius. Similarly, a **parabola**, on a coordinate plane, is the set of all points that are equidistant from a specific point and a specific line (i.e., the shortest distance from any given point on the parabola to a specified point in the plane is the same as the shortest distance from that same point on the parabola to the specified line). The point is called the parabola's **focus F**, and the line is called the parabola's **directrix**, as shown in Figure 6.1c.

DEFINITION

A **parabola** is the set of all points that are equidistant from a specific point, the **focus F**, and a specific line, the **directrix**.

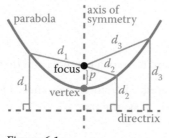

Figure 6.1c

The parabola's axis of symmetry passes through the focus and the vertex, and is perpendicular to the directrix. Since each point on the parabola is equidistant from the focus and the directrix, the parabola's vertex is the midpoint between the focus and the point at which the axis of symmetry intersects the directrix. The distance from the vertex to the focus is defined by p, where the sign of p depends on the direction of the parabola.

WHAT'S THE BIG IDEA?

Given the coordinates of a parabola's focus and the equation of the parabola's directrix, can the coordinates of the parabola's vertex be found? Explain.

Standard Form Equations of Parabolas: Vertex at the Origin		
	Vertical Axis of Symmetry	**Horizontal Axis of Symmetry**
Equation	$x^2 = 4py$	$y^2 = 4px$
Focus	$(0, p)$	$(p, 0)$
Directrix	$y = -p$	$x = -p$
$p > 0$		
$p < 0$		

EXAMPLE 1   Finding the Focus and the Directrix of a Parabola from Its Equation

Find the focus and directrix of each parabola and describe its graph.

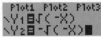
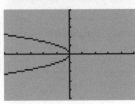
A. $y^2 + x = 0$

B. $y = \dfrac{1}{2}x^2$

SOLUTION

Write the equation in the standard form of a parabola and then identify p.

Notice that the variable y is squared. Therefore, the standard form equation is $y^2 = 4px$, and the parabola has a horizontal axis of symmetry.

$$y^2 + x = 0$$
$$y^2 = -x$$
$$y^2 = 4\left(-\frac{1}{4}\right)x \qquad\qquad \text{Therefore, } p = -\frac{1}{4}.$$

Use the value of p to find the focus $(p, 0)$ and the directrix $x = -p$.

$$\text{focus:} \quad \left(-\frac{1}{4}, 0\right) \qquad\qquad \text{directrix:} \quad x = \frac{1}{4}$$

Graph Description: Since the equation is of the form $y^2 = 4px$, the graph is a parabola with vertex at $(0, 0)$ and a horizontal axis of symmetry. Additionally, since p is less than 0, the horizontal parabola opens to the left.

B. In this equation, the variable x is squared. Therefore, the standard form equation is $x^2 = 4py$, and the parabola has a vertical axis of symmetry.

$$y = \frac{1}{2}x^2$$
$$x^2 = 2y$$
$$x^2 = 4\left(\frac{1}{2}\right)y \qquad\qquad \text{Therefore, } p = \frac{1}{2}.$$

Use the value of p to find the focus $(0, p)$ and the directrix $y = -p$.

focus: $\left(0, \frac{1}{2}\right)$ directrix: $y = -\frac{1}{2}$

Graph Description: Since the equation is of the form $x^2 = 4py$, the graph is a parabola with vertex at $(0, 0)$ and a vertical axis of symmetry. Additionally, since p is greater than 0, the vertical parabola opens upward. (The graph of the parabola is shown in Figure 6.1d.)

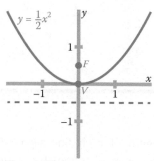

Figure 6.1d

EXAMPLE 2   Graphing a Parabola

Graph each parabola.

A. $x^2 = -2y$

B. $\dfrac{y^2}{3} - \dfrac{x}{6} = 0$

SOLUTION

A. The standard form equation is $x^2 = 4py$. Therefore, the graph is a parabola with vertex at the origin and a vertical axis of symmetry. Find the value of p to determine whether the parabola opens up or down.

$$x^2 = -2y$$
$$x^2 = 4\left(-\frac{1}{2}\right)y \qquad\qquad \text{Therefore, } p = -1/2. \text{ Since } p < 0, \text{ the parabola opens downward.}$$

Make a table to identify a few additional points on the parabola.

x	-2	-1	1	2
y	-2	$-\frac{1}{2}$	$-\frac{1}{2}$	-2

Plot the points from the table along with the vertex $(0, 0)$, and sketch the graph of the parabola.

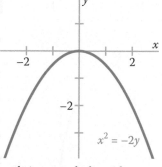

B. The standard form equation is $y^2 = 4px$. Therefore, the graph is a parabola with vertex at the origin and a horizontal axis of symmetry. Find the value of p to determine whether the parabola opens to the left or right.

$$\frac{y^2}{3} - \frac{x}{6} = 0$$
$$\frac{y^2}{3} = \frac{x}{6}$$
$$y^2 = \frac{1}{2}x$$
$$y^2 = 4\left(\frac{1}{8}\right)x \qquad\qquad \text{Therefore, } p = 1/8. \text{ Since } p > 0, \text{ the parabola opens to the right.}$$

TIP

When y is the squared variable, choose y-values for the table (instead of choosing x-values). Substitute each chosen y-value into the equation to find the corresponding x-value to complete the table.

Make a table to identify a few additional points on the parabola.

x	8	2	2	8
y	−2	−1	1	2

Plot the points from the table along with the vertex (0, 0), and sketch the graph of the parabola.

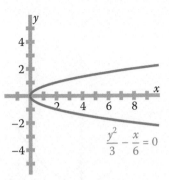

$$\frac{y^2}{3} - \frac{x}{6} = 0$$

Focal Diameter

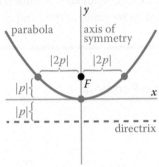

Figure 6.1e

Figure 6.1e shows that the length of each line segment perpendicular to the parabola's axis of symmetry with endpoints on the parabola and at the focus is equal to $|2p|$. The entire line segment (with endpoints on the parabola) is known as the **latus rectum**. The length of the latus rectum, $|4p|$, is the parabola's **focal diameter**. The focal diameter provides a measure of the "width" of a parabola through the focus.

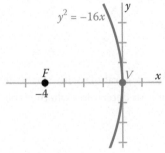

6.1.3 Writing the Equation of a Parabola

EXAMPLE 3 **Writing the Equation of a Parabola Given the Vertex and Focus**

Write the standard form equation of the parabola with focus at (−4, 0) and vertex at the origin.

SOLUTION

Since the focus is to the left of the vertex, on the x-axis, the parabola opens to the left and the axis of symmetry is horizontal. Therefore, the standard form equation is $y^2 = 4px$ where p is negative.

Since the focus, (−4, 0), is exactly 4 units to the left of the vertex, (0, 0), it follows that $p = -4$. Substitute the p-value into $y^2 = 4px$ to write the equation of the parabola.

$$y^2 = 4(-4)x$$
$$y^2 = -16x \qquad \text{(The graph of the parabola is shown in Figure 6.1f.)}$$

$y^2 = -16x$

Figure 6.1f

EXAMPLE 4	Writing the Equation of a Parabola Given the Vertex and Directrix

Write the standard form equation of the parabola with directrix $y = \dfrac{1}{4}$ and vertex at the origin.

SOLUTION

Since the directrix is a horizontal line above the vertex, the parabola opens downward and the axis of symmetry is vertical. Therefore, the standard form equation is $x^2 = 4py$, where p is negative.

For a parabola with a vertical axis, the directrix is $y = -p$. From the given equation of the directrix $y = \dfrac{1}{4}$, it follows that $-p = \dfrac{1}{4}$, and so $p = -\dfrac{1}{4}$. Substitute the p-value into $x^2 = 4py$ to write the equation of the parabola.

$$x^2 = 4\left(-\frac{1}{4}\right)y$$

$$x^2 = -y \qquad \text{(The graph of the parabola is shown in Figure 6.1g.)}$$

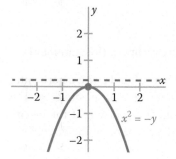

Figure 6.1g

EXAMPLE 5	Writing the Equation of a Parabola Given the Direction of the Axis of Symmetry, Vertex, and a Point on the Parabola

Write the standard form equation of the parabola that passes through $(4, -1)$, if the vertex is at the origin and the axis of symmetry is horizontal.

SOLUTION

Since the vertex is at the origin and the axis of symmetry is horizontal, the standard form equation of the parabola is $y^2 = 4px$.

Use the x- and y-coordinates of the given point to find the value of p.

$$y^2 = 4px$$

$$(-1)^2 = 4p(4)$$

$$1 = 16p$$

$$p = \frac{1}{16}$$

Then use the p-value to write the standard form equation of the parabola.

$$y^2 = 4\left(\frac{1}{16}\right)x$$

$$y^2 = \frac{1}{4}x$$

(The graph of the parabola is shown in Figure 6.1h.)

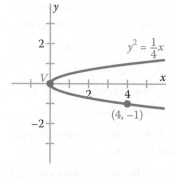

Figure 6.1h

WHAT'S THE BIG IDEA?

In each case, explain why the equation of a parabola cannot be found.

A. only the equation of the directrix and a point on the parabola are known

B. only a focus and the axis of symmetry's equation are known

C. only the vertex and a point on the parabola are known

SECTION 6.1 EXERCISES

Warm Up

Sketch the graph of each parabola and identify the vertex and axis of symmetry.

1. $f(x) = x^2$

2. $f(x) = -(x - 3)^2 + 1$

3. $f(x) = x^2 + 4x + 4$

Just the Facts

Fill in the blanks.

4. A conic is formed by the intersection of a(n) ____ and a(n) ____.

5. A parabola is the set of all points that are equidistant from a specific ____ called the focus and a specific ____ called the ____.

6. Equations of the form $x^2 = 4py$ where $p < 0$ describe ____ that open ____ with a vertical ____ on the ____, ____ at $(0, p)$, and directrix at ____.

7. Equations of the form $y^2 = 4px$ where $p > 0$ describe ____ that open ____ with a horizontal ____ on the ____, ____ at $(0, 0)$, and directrix at ____.

8. If a parabola's ____ is to the right of its ____, then the parabola opens to the left.

9. The parabolas described by $x^2 = 4py$ and $y^2 = 4px$ have the same ____, located at ____.

10. If a parabola's directrix is a vertical line, then the parabola opens ____ or ____.

Essential Skills

In Exercises 1–2, find the focus and directrix of each parabola.

1. $y = \dfrac{2}{5}x^2$

2. $x = -\dfrac{1}{8}y^2$

In Exercises 3–4, determine the direction of each parabola.

3. $-3x + 4y^2 = 0$

4. $-y = \dfrac{x^2}{5}$

In Exercises 5–6, sketch the graph of each parabola.

5. $y^2 = \dfrac{x}{2}$

6. $-y^2 + 2x = 0$

In Exercises 7–12, write the standard form equation of each parabola with vertex at the origin and the following properties.

7. focus at $\left(\dfrac{1}{8}, 0\right)$

8. focus at $(0, -6)$

9. directrix at $y = -5/6$

10. directrix at $x = -5$

11. parabola passes through $(-3, -9)$ and the axis of symmetry is vertical

12. parabola passes through $(2, -2)$ and the axis of symmetry is horizontal

Extensions

In Exercises 13–15, correct any errors in the statements.

13. The graph of $4x - 20y^2 = 0$ is a parabola with a horizontal axis of symmetry. The value of p is positive, so the parabola opens to the right. The vertex is at the origin, the focus is at $(20, 0)$, and the equation of the directrix is $y = -20$.

14. If the equation of a parabola is of the form $y^2 = 4px$ where $p < 0$, then the parabola's vertex is at $(p, 0)$, the axis of symmetry is at $x = 0$, and the parabola opens to the left.

15. The graph of $-x^2 = 6y$ is a parabola. The axis of symmetry is at $y = 0$, the vertex is at the origin, and the parabola opens to the left. Since $p = -3/2$, the focus is at $(-3/2, 0)$, and the equation of the directrix is $x = 3/2$.

16. Name the four types of conics and explain how each is formed by intersecting a plane and a cone.

17. Explain why $x^2 = 4py$ is a function and $y^2 = 4px$ is not a function.

18. If a parabola's vertex is at the origin, can the equation of the parabola's directrix be used to find the focus? Explain.

19. Can a parabola described by an equation of the form $x^2 = 4py$ have a directrix at $y = x$? Explain.

20. Can a parabola described by an equation of the form $x^2 = 4py$ have a directrix at $y = 0$? Explain.

21. Write the equations of two parabolas that pass through $(2, 4)$, where the vertex is at the origin.

22. Write the equations of two parabolas that pass through $(-1, 8)$, where the vertex is at the origin.

In Exercises 23–25, find the focal diameter of each parabola.

23. $x^2 = -\dfrac{1}{2}y$

24. $x = y^2$

25. $-x = -\dfrac{y^2}{12}$

6.2 ELLIPSES

OBJECTIVES

- Connect the geometric attributes of an ellipse (centered at the origin) to its standard form equation.
- Write the equation of an ellipse (centered at the origin).
- Graph an ellipse (centered at the origin).
- Find the vertices, co-vertices, and foci of an ellipse (centered at the origin).

PREREQUISITE VOCABULARY TERMS

circle

conic

Distance Formula

x-intercept

y-intercept

The intersection of a cone and a plane parallel to the cone's base forms a circle.

Figure 6.2a

Recall that an **ellipse** is the conic formed by the intersection of a cone and a plane that does not intersect the base of the cone. If the plane is parallel to the cone's base, then the ellipse formed is a circle, which is a special case of the ellipse, as shown in Figure 6.2a. If the plane is not parallel to the cone's base, then the ellipse formed is not circular, as shown in Figure 6.2b. The equations and graphs (on a coordinate plane) of these noncircular ellipses will be discussed in this section.

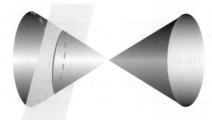

Figure 6.2b

Introduction to Ellipses

Suppose there are two fixed points F_1 and F_2 on a coordinate plane such that the distance between some point (x, y) and F_1 is d_1, and the distance between that same point (x, y) and F_2 is d_2. An ellipse is the set of all points (x, y) such that $d_1 + d_2$ is constant. Each fixed point F_1 and F_2 is called a **focus** of the ellipse.

IMPORTANT

*The definition of an ellipse does **not** imply that the distance between a point on the ellipse and each focus must be constant (i.e., equal to each other).*

$$d_1 \neq d_2$$

*Instead, it is the **sum** of those distances that is **constant**.*

$$d_1 + d_2 = d_3 + d_4$$

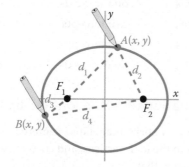

Figure 6.2c

In Figure 6.2c, A and B are points on the ellipse. For each point on the ellipse, the sum of the distances from the point to each focus is constant, n.

$$d_1 + d_2 = n = d_3 + d_4$$

In other words, the distance from a point on the ellipse to one focus plus the distance from that point to the other focus is the same for every point on the ellipse.

DEFINITION

An **ellipse** is the set of all points where the sum of the distances from two fixed points is constant. The fixed points are the **foci** of the ellipse.

Attributes of an Ellipse

Ellipses are symmetric figures with two perpendicular lines of symmetry called the **axes of symmetry**, which intersect at the **center of the ellipse**.

The **major** and **minor axes** of an ellipse are the segments on the axes of symmetry with endpoints on the ellipse. The major axis contains the foci, and its length is greater than or equal to that of the minor axis. The endpoints of the major axis are called the ellipse's **vertices,** and the endpoints of the minor axis are called the ellipse's **co-vertices** (Figure 6.2d).

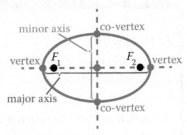

Figure 6.2d

6.2.1 Writing the Equation of an Ellipse

Horizontal and Vertical Ellipses Centered at the Origin

All of the ellipses discussed in this section will be centered at the origin. Each will be either a **horizontal ellipse** or a **vertical ellipse**.

Horizontal & Vertical Ellipse Centered at the Origin

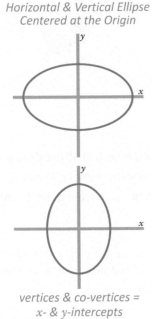

vertices & co-vertices = x- & y-intercepts

Figure 6.2e

DEFINITION

A **horizontal ellipse** is an ellipse whose major axis is a horizontal line.

A **vertical ellipse** is an ellipse whose major axis is a vertical line.

Figure 6.2e shows a horizontal and a vertical ellipse. Notice that since both are centered *at the origin* their axes of symmetry are the x- and y-axes. Specifically, the major axis of the horizontal ellipse is on the x-axis, and the major axis of the vertical ellipse is on the y-axis. Since the vertices and co-vertices are the points at which the ellipse intersects its axes of symmetry, the vertices and co-vertices are also the ellipse's x- and y-intercepts.

Horizontal and Vertical Ellipses: Centered at the Origin		
	Horizontal	**Vertical**
Major Axis	on the x-axis	on the y-axis
Minor Axis	on the y-axis	on the x-axis
Vertices	x-intercepts	y-intercepts
Co-Vertices	y-intercepts	x-intercepts
Foci	on the x-axis	on the y-axis

The Standard Form Equation of a Horizontal Ellipse Centered at the Origin

The standard form equation of a horizontal ellipse centered at the origin can be found using the distances from the origin to the foci, vertices, and co-vertices. Suppose there is a horizontal ellipse centered at the origin such that
- c is the distance between a focus and the origin,
- a is the distance between a vertex and the origin, and
- b is the distance between a co-vertex and the origin.

This ellipse's foci and vertices are on the x-axis and its co-vertices are on the y-axis (because it is horizontal and centered at the origin), so its foci occur at $(\pm c, 0)$, vertices at $(\pm a, 0)$, and co-vertices at $(0, \pm b)$.

IMPORTANT

The distance between an ellipse's vertices is greater than or equal to the distance between its co-vertices (they are equal when the ellipse is a circle), so $a \geq b > 0$.

By the definition of an ellipse, the sum of the distances from any point on the ellipse to the foci is a constant. In other words, for any point on an ellipse, the sum of the distance from the point to a focus and the distance from the point to the other focus is always the same. Use the coordinates of the vertex $(a, 0)$ and the foci $(\pm c, 0)$ to find an expression for that constant.

REMEMBER

The foci and vertices are on the x-axis, so the distance between a focus and a vertex is given by subtracting the x-coordinates.

$$\begin{matrix} \text{distance from} \\ (c, 0) \text{ to } (a, 0) \end{matrix} \quad + \quad \begin{matrix} \text{distance from} \\ (-c, 0) \text{ to } (a, 0) \end{matrix} \quad = (a - c) + (a - (-c)) = a - c + a + c = 2a$$

Thus, the sum of the distances from any point on the ellipse to the foci is $2a$.

This fact can be used to find a relationship between a, b, and c, and to write a general equation for the ellipse. Since the co-vertex $(0, b)$ is a point on the ellipse, the sum of the distances from $(0, b)$ to the foci must be $2a$. Use the Distance Formula to write an expression for this sum.

$$\begin{matrix} \text{distance from} \\ (c, 0) \text{ to } (0, b) \end{matrix} \quad + \quad \begin{matrix} \text{distance from} \\ (-c, 0) \text{ to } (0, b) \end{matrix} \quad = \sqrt{(0-c)^2 + (b-0)^2} + \sqrt{(0-(-c))^2 + (b-0)^2}$$

$$= \sqrt{c^2 + b^2} + \sqrt{c^2 + b^2}$$

$$= 2\sqrt{c^2 + b^2}$$

IMPORTANT

If a = b, the lengths of the ellipse's major and minor axes are equal and the ellipse is a circle.

Therefore, $2\sqrt{c^2 + b^2} = 2a$. Simplifying and then squaring both sides gives $c^2 + b^2 = a^2$. So, the relationship between a, b, and c is given by the equation $c^2 = a^2 - b^2$, where $a \geq b > 0$.

Now we can use the sum of the distances from a point on the ellipse (x, y) to the foci (which is equal to $2a$) to write an equation for the ellipse in terms of x and y. Again, use the Distance Formula to write an expression for this sum.

$$\begin{matrix} \text{distance from} \\ (c, 0) \text{ to } (x, y) \end{matrix} \quad + \quad \begin{matrix} \text{distance from} \\ (-c, 0) \text{ to } (x, y) \end{matrix} \quad = \sqrt{(x-c)^2 + (y-0)^2} + \sqrt{(x-(-c))^2 + (y-0)^2}$$

Thus, $\sqrt{(x-c)^2 + y^2} + \sqrt{(x+c)^2 + y^2} = 2a$. Using quite a bit of algebra gives $\dfrac{x^2}{a^2} + \dfrac{y^2}{b^2} = 1$,

which is the standard form equation of a horizontal ellipse centered at the origin.

The following table summarizes the standard form equations for a horizontal and vertical ellipses and the relationships between these equations and the attributes of ellipses.

IMPORTANT

When writing the equation of an ellipse, first determine whether the ellipse is horizontal or vertical, then choose the appropriate standard form equation.

Standard Form Equations of Ellipses: Centered at the Origin		
	Horizontal Major Axis	**Vertical Major Axis**
Equation	$\dfrac{x^2}{a^2} + \dfrac{y^2}{b^2} = 1 \quad a \geq b$	$\dfrac{y^2}{a^2} + \dfrac{x^2}{b^2} = 1 \quad a \geq b$
Vertices	$(\pm a, 0)$	$(0, \pm a)$
Foci	$(\pm c, 0)$	$(0, \pm c)$
Co-Vertices	$(0, \pm b)$	$(\pm b, 0)$

Writing the Equation of an Ellipse

The distance from the origin to a vertex a and the distance from the origin to a co-vertex b can be used to write the equation of a horizontal or vertical ellipse centered at the origin.

Steps for Writing the Equation of a Horizontal or Vertical Ellipse Centered at $(0, 0)$

❶ Determine the type of ellipse (horizontal or vertical).

❷ Find the values of a and b.

❸ Substitute the a- and b-values into the appropriate standard form equation.

EXAMPLE 1   Writing the Equation of an Ellipse Given Its Graph

Write the equation of each ellipse.

A.

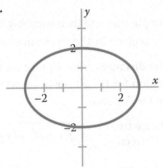

B.

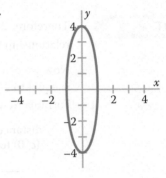

SOLUTION

A. From the graph, the x- and y-intercepts are at $(\pm 3, 0)$ and $(0, \pm 2)$, respectively, and the center is at $(0, 0)$.

❶ Since the major axis is horizontal, the ellipse is horizontal.

❷ The distance from the center to either vertex is 3, so $a = 3$.
The distance from the center to either co-vertex is 2, so $b = 2$.

❸ Substitute the values of a and b into the standard form equation of a horizontal ellipse.

$$\frac{x^2}{a^2} + \frac{y^2}{b^2} = 1 \Rightarrow \frac{x^2}{3^2} + \frac{y^2}{2^2} = 1 \Rightarrow \frac{x^2}{9} + \frac{y^2}{4} = 1$$

B. From the graph, the x- and y-intercepts are at $(\pm 1, 0)$ and $(0, \pm 4)$, respectively, and the center is at $(0, 0)$.

❶ Since the major axis is vertical, the ellipse is vertical.

❷ The distance from the center to either vertex is 4, so $a = 4$.
The distance from the center to either co-vertex is 1, so $b = 1$.

❸ Substitute the values of a and b into the standard form equation of a horizontal ellipse.

$$\frac{y^2}{a^2} + \frac{x^2}{b^2} = 1 \Rightarrow \frac{y^2}{4^2} + \frac{x^2}{1^2} = 1 \Rightarrow \frac{y^2}{16} + \frac{x^2}{1} = 1 \Rightarrow \frac{y^2}{16} + x^2 = 1$$

EXAMPLE 2	Writing the Equation of an Ellipse Given a Vertex and a Co-Vertex

Write the equation of an ellipse with center at $(0, 0)$, a vertex at $(0, -5)$, and a co-vertex at $(4, 0)$.

SOLUTION

❶ The ellipse is centered at the origin, and a vertex is at $(0, -5)$. So, the other vertex is at $(0, 5)$. The vertices are on the y-axis, so the major axis must be vertical, and so the ellipse is vertical.

❷ The distance from the center to a vertex is 5, so $a = 5$.
The distance from the center to a co-vertex is 4, so $b = 4$.

❸ Substitute $a = 5$ and $b = 4$ into the standard form equation of a vertical ellipse.

$$\frac{y^2}{a^2} + \frac{x^2}{b^2} = 1 \implies \frac{y^2}{5^2} + \frac{x^2}{4^2} = 1 \implies \frac{y^2}{25} + \frac{x^2}{16} = 1$$

EXAMPLE 3	Writing the Equation of an Ellipse Given the Length of the Major and Minor Axes

Write the equation of an ellipse centered at the origin with a vertical minor axis of length 2 units and a major axis of length 16 units.

SOLUTION

❶ The ellipse has a vertical minor axis and is centered at the origin. Therefore, the major axis must be horizontal, and so the ellipse is horizontal.

IMPORTANT

The length of the major axis of an ellipse is 2a. The length of the minor axis of an ellipse is 2b.

❷ The lengths of the major and minor axes are equal to $2a$ and $2b$, respectively. The major axis is 16 units, so $2a = 16$, giving $a = 8$. The minor axis is 2 units, so $2b = 2$, giving $b = 1$.

❸ Substitute $a = 8$ and $b = 1$ into the standard form equation of a horizontal ellipse.

$$\frac{x^2}{a^2} + \frac{y^2}{b^2} = 1 \implies \frac{x^2}{8^2} + \frac{y^2}{1^2} = 1 \implies \frac{x^2}{64} + \frac{y^2}{1} = 1 \implies \frac{x^2}{64} + y^2 = 1$$

EXAMPLE 4	Writing the Equation of an Ellipse Given Intercepts and Foci

IMPORTANT

The foci of an ellipse are always on the ellipse's major axis.

Write the equation of an ellipse with center at $(0, 0)$, y-intercepts at $(0, \pm 8)$, and foci at $(\pm 6, 0)$.

SOLUTION

❶ The ellipse has foci on the x-axis at $(\pm 6, 0)$. Since foci are always located on the major axis, the major axis must be horizontal. So, the ellipse is horizontal.

❷ Since the major axis is horizontal, the minor axis must be vertical and the y-intercepts of the ellipse are therefore the co-vertices. Since the y-intercepts are at $(0, \pm 8)$, $b = 8$.

IMPORTANT

$c^2 = a^2 - b^2$ can be used to find a when b and c are known.

Use $c^2 = a^2 - b^2$ to find a. The foci are at $(\pm 6, 0)$, so $c = 6$.

$$6^2 = a^2 - 8^2 \implies 36 = a^2 - 64 \implies a^2 = 100 \implies a = 10$$

❸ Substitute $a = 10$ and $b = 8$ into the standard form equation of a horizontal ellipse.

$$\frac{x^2}{a^2} + \frac{y^2}{b^2} = 1 \implies \frac{x^2}{10^2} + \frac{y^2}{8^2} = 1 \implies \frac{x^2}{100} + \frac{y^2}{64} = 1$$

EXAMPLE 5 **Writing the Equation of an Ellipse Given a Focus and the Length of the Major Axis**

Write the equation of an ellipse with center at (0, 0), a focus at (0, 5), and a 26 unit major axis.

SOLUTION

❶ The ellipse is centered at the origin and has a focus on the y-axis at (0, 5). Therefore, the other focus must be at (0, −5). Since the foci are on the y-axis, the ellipse's major axis must be vertical, and so the ellipse is vertical.

❷ Since the major axis is 26 units, $2a = 26$, so $a = 13$.

Use the equation $c^2 = a^2 − b^2$ to find b. The foci are at (±6, 0), so $c = 6$.

$$5^2 = 13^2 − b^2 \Rightarrow 25 = 169 − b^2 \Rightarrow b^2 = 144 \Rightarrow b = 12$$

❸ Substitute $a = 13$ and $b = 12$ into the standard form equation of a vertical ellipse.

$$\frac{y^2}{a^2} + \frac{x^2}{b^2} = 1 \Rightarrow \frac{y^2}{13^2} + \frac{x^2}{12^2} = 1 \Rightarrow \frac{y^2}{169} + \frac{x^2}{144} = 1$$

6.2.2 Graphing Ellipses

The values of a and b can be determined from the equation of an ellipse, as demonstrated in **Example 6**. The values of a and b can then be used to identify the ellipse's attributes, such as its vertices, co-vertices, and intercepts. As in Topic 6.2.1, all of the ellipses in Topic 6.2.2 will be centered at the origin.

EXAMPLE 6 **Finding the Intercepts of an Ellipse**

Find the x- and y-intercepts of each ellipse.

A. $\dfrac{x^2}{25} + \dfrac{y^2}{16} = 1$
    B. $\dfrac{y^2}{49} + \dfrac{x^2}{16} = 1$

SOLUTION

A. The equation is of the form $\dfrac{x^2}{a^2} + \dfrac{y^2}{b^2} = 1$, where $a \geq b$, so the ellipse is horizontal and centered at the origin, with intercepts at (±a, 0) and (0, ±b). Use the equation to find a and b.

$$a^2 = 25 \Rightarrow a = 5 \qquad b^2 = 16 \Rightarrow b = 4$$

The intercepts are at (±5, 0) and (0, ±4). (Figure 6.2f shows the graph of the ellipse.)

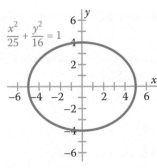

$\dfrac{x^2}{25} + \dfrac{y^2}{16} = 1$

Figure 6.2f

B. The equation is of the form $\dfrac{y^2}{a^2} + \dfrac{x^2}{b^2} = 1$, where $a \geq b$, so the ellipse is vertical and centered at the origin, with intercepts at (±b, 0) and (0, ±a). Use the equation to find a and b.

$$a^2 = 49 \Rightarrow a = 7 \qquad b^2 = 16 \Rightarrow b = 4$$

The intercepts are at (±4, 0) and (0, ±7).

EXAMPLE 7 **Finding the Length of the Major and Minor Axes of an Ellipse**

Find the lengths of the major and minor axes of each ellipse.

A. $\dfrac{x^2}{12} + y^2 = 1$ **B.** $5y^2 + 9x^2 = 45$

SOLUTION

Find a and b, then use these values to find the lengths of the major and minor axes, which are $2a$ and $2b$, respectively.

A. From the equation, $a^2 = 12$ and $b^2 = 1$, since $a \geq b$.

$$a^2 = 12 \Rightarrow a = \sqrt{12} = \sqrt{4 \cdot 3} = 2\sqrt{3} \qquad\qquad b^2 = 1 \Rightarrow b = 1$$

major axis: $2(2\sqrt{3}) = 4\sqrt{3}$ units   minor axis: $2(1) = 2$ units

> **TIP**
>
> *The denominator of the y^2-term is 1.*

B. The right side of the equation is 45, not 1, so the equation is not in the standard form. The equation must be written in the standard form before a and b can be found. Therefore, divide each side by 45 to get 1 on the right side.

$$5y^2 + 9x^2 = 45 \Rightarrow \frac{5y^2}{45} + \frac{9x^2}{45} = \frac{45}{45} \Rightarrow \frac{y^2}{9} + \frac{x^2}{5} = 1$$

From the standard form equation, $a^2 = 9$ and $b^2 = 5$, since $a \geq b$.

$$a^2 = 9 \Rightarrow a = 3 \qquad\qquad b^2 = 5 \Rightarrow b = \sqrt{5}$$

major axis: $2(3) = 6$ units   minor axis: $2(\sqrt{5}) = 2\sqrt{5}$ units

> **IMPORTANT**
>
> *Write the equation of an ellipse in standard form in order to find a and b.*

Graphing a Horizontal or Vertical Ellipse Centered at the Origin

The following table summarizes three methods for graphing a horizontal or vertical ellipse centered at the origin.

Graphing a Horizontal or Vertical Ellipse Centered at the Origin Given Its Equation

Method 1: Use the Intercepts
Find the intercepts, then sketch the ellipse through the intercepts.

Method 2: Use the Major and Minor Axes
Find the lengths of the major and minor axes (line segments, each with midpoint at the center). Next, plot the endpoints of the major and minor axes on the x- and y-axes (as appropriate), and then sketch the ellipse through the four points.

Method 3: Use a Graphing Calculator
Solve the equation for y, and then enter the two equations in a graphing calculator.

EXAMPLE 8 **Graphing an Ellipse**

Graph the equation from **Example 6B**, $\dfrac{y^2}{49} + \dfrac{x^2}{16} = 1$.

SOLUTION

Method 1: Use the Intercepts
From **Example 6B**, the intercepts are at $(\pm 4, 0)$ and $(0, \pm 7)$. First plot these four points, and then sketch the ellipse (centered at the origin, and with vertical and horizontal axes of symmetry) through the points. The graph of the ellipse is shown in Figure 6.2g.

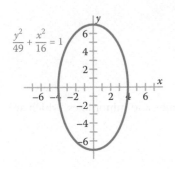

$$\frac{y^2}{49} + \frac{x^2}{16} = 1$$

Figure 6.2g

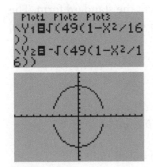

Figure 6.2h

Method 2: Use the Major and Minor Axes

The equation is of the form $\dfrac{y^2}{a^2} + \dfrac{x^2}{b^2} = 1$, where $a \geq b$, so

- the ellipse is vertical and centered at the origin,
- the major axis is vertical (on the y-axis), and
- the minor axis is horizontal (on the x-axis).

Use a and b to find the lengths of the major and minor axes. From **Example 6B**, $a = 7$ and $b = 4$.

major axis: $2a = 2(7) = 14$ units   minor axis: $2b = 2(4) = 8$ units

Each axis is a line segment with midpoint at the origin. So, the 14 unit major axis extends from -7 to 7 on the y-axis and the 8 unit minor axis extends from -4 to 4 on the x-axis. Therefore, the endpoints of the axes are at $(0, -7)$, $(0, 7)$, $(-4, 0)$, and $(4, 0)$. The ellipse passes through the endpoints of the major and minor axes, so sketch the ellipse through these points (Figure 6.2g).

Method 3: Use a Graphing Calculator

Solve the equation for y.

$$\frac{y^2}{49} + \frac{x^2}{16} = 1$$

$$\frac{y^2}{49} = 1 - \frac{x^2}{16}$$

$$y^2 = 49\left(1 - \frac{x^2}{16}\right)$$

$$y = \pm\sqrt{49\left(1 - \frac{x^2}{16}\right)}$$

The equation must be entered in two parts because it contains a $\pm$ symbol.

$$y = \sqrt{49\left(1 - \frac{x^2}{16}\right)} \text{ and } y = -\sqrt{49\left(1 - \frac{x^2}{16}\right)}$$

The calculator notation follows.

$$Y1 = \sqrt{(49(1 - X^2 / 16))}$$

$$Y2 = -\sqrt{(49(1 - X^2 / 16))}$$

The graph of the ellipse is shown in Figure 6.2h.

The Foci of an Ellipse

Recall that each focus of an ellipse is a point c units from the center on the ellipse's major axis. This distance c can be found using the relationship between the distances a and b, $c^2 = a^2 - b^2$.

EXAMPLE 9   Finding the Foci of an Ellipse

Find the foci of each ellipse.

A. $\dfrac{y^2}{9} = 1 - x^2$

B. $100x^2 + 50y^2 - 200 = 0$

SOLUTION

First, write each equation in standard form. Then, using the standard form equation, determine a^2, b^2, and whether the ellipse is horizontal with foci at $(\pm c, 0)$ or vertical with foci at $(0, \pm c)$.

A. Add x^2 to each side to write the equation in standard form. $\dfrac{y^2}{9} = 1 - x^2 \Rightarrow \dfrac{y^2}{9} + x^2 = 1$

From the equation, $a^2 = 9$ and $b^2 = 1$, because $a \geq b$. Find c.

$$c^2 = a^2 - b^2 = 9 - 1 = 8 \Rightarrow c = 2\sqrt{2}$$

Since the equation is of the form $\dfrac{y^2}{a^2} + \dfrac{x^2}{b^2} = 1$ where $a \geq b$, the ellipse is vertical with foci at $(0, \pm c)$. Thus, the foci of the ellipse are at $\left(0, \pm 2\sqrt{2}\right)$.

B. Add 200 to each side, then divide each side by 200 to write the equation in standard form.

$$100y^2 + 50x^2 - 200 = 0 \Rightarrow 100y^2 + 50x^2 = 200 \Rightarrow \frac{100y^2}{200} + \frac{50x^2}{200} = \frac{200}{200} \Rightarrow \frac{x^2}{4} + \frac{y^2}{2} = 1$$

From the equation, $a^2 = 4$ and $b^2 = 2$, because $a \geq b$. Find c.

$$c^2 = a^2 - b^2 = 4 - 2 = 2 \Rightarrow c = \sqrt{2}$$

Since the equation is of the form $\frac{x^2}{a^2} + \frac{y^2}{b^2} = 1$ where $a \geq b$, the ellipse is horizontal with foci at $(\pm c, 0)$. Thus, the foci of the ellipse are at $(\pm\sqrt{2}, 0)$.

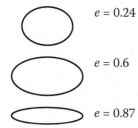

TIP

The value of a^2 in $\frac{y^2}{2} + \frac{x^2}{4} = 1$ is not 2. Since $a \geq b$ in the standard form equation of an ellipse, $a^2 = 4$.

6.2.3 The Eccentricity of an Ellipse

One ellipse can be compared with another by comparing the degree to which each is stretched (elongated vertically or horizontally). For example, the first ellipse in Figure 6.2i can be described as "less stretched" than the second ellipse in Figure 6.2i.

The first ellipse can also be described as "more circular" than the second ellipse.

less stretched   more stretched

Figure 6.2i

IMPORTANT

A circle is the special case of an ellipse where both foci are located at the center. So, for any circle, the distance between the foci and the center is 0 (i.e., $c = 0$). Therefore, the eccentricity of any circle is $0/a$, or 0.

The degree to which an ellipse is stretched is called the it's **eccentricity**. Eccentricity is measured using the ratio of c to a (i.e., the ratio of the distance between its center and a focus and the distance between its center and a vertex). Because $c \leq a$, the ratio c/a is always a number between 0 and 1.

The Eccentricity of an Ellipse

The eccentricity e of an ellipse is the ratio of c to a, $e = \frac{c}{a}$, where c is the distance from the center to a focus and a is the distance from the center to a vertex.

The eccentricity of every ellipse is a number between 0 and 1. Ellipses with eccentricity close to 0 are more circular, and ellipses with eccentricity close to 1 are more stretched.

Examples of Eccentricity

$e = 0.24$

$e = 0.6$

$e = 0.87$

Figure 6.2j

Three examples of ellipses and their eccentricity are given in Figure 6.2j. These examples illustrate that an ellipse with an eccentricity close to 0 will be more circular, and an ellipse with an eccentricity close to 1 will be more stretched.

EXAMPLE 10 Finding the Eccentricity of an Ellipse

Find the eccentricity of each ellipse.

A. $x^2 + 4y^2 = 4$　　　　　　　　**B.** $18x^2 + 9y^2 = 162$

SOLUTION

The eccentricity of an ellipse is given by c/a. Write each equation in standard form, find a, and then use $c^2 = a^2 - b^2$ to find c.

A. Divide each side by 4 to write the equation in standard form.

$$x^2 + 4y^2 = 4 \implies \frac{x^2}{4} + \frac{4y^2}{4} = \frac{4}{4} \implies \frac{x^2}{4} + y^2 = 1$$

From the equation, $a^2 = 4$ and $b^2 = 1$, since $a \geq b$. Therefore, $a = 2$. Find c.

$$c^2 = a^2 - b^2 = 4 - 1 = 3 \implies c = \sqrt{3}$$

Substitute the values of a and c into the eccentricity formula. $e = \dfrac{c}{a} = \dfrac{\sqrt{3}}{2}$

B. Divide each side by 162 to write the equation in standard form.

$$18x^2 + 9y^2 = 162 \implies \frac{18x^2}{162} + \frac{9y^2}{162} = \frac{162}{162} \implies \frac{y^2}{18} + \frac{x^2}{9} = 1$$

From the equation, $a^2 = 18$ and $b^2 = 9$, since $a \geq b$. Therefore, $a = 3\sqrt{2}$. Find c.

$$c^2 = a^2 - b^2 = 18 - 9 = 9 \implies c = 3$$

Substitute the values of a and c into the eccentricity formula.

$$e = \frac{c}{a} = \frac{3}{3\sqrt{2}} = \frac{1}{\sqrt{2}} = \frac{1}{\sqrt{2}} \cdot \frac{\sqrt{2}}{\sqrt{2}} = \frac{\sqrt{2}}{2} \qquad \textit{Rationalize the denominator.}$$

EXAMPLE 11 Using the Eccentricity of an Ellipse to Find Its Vertices

Find the vertices of an ellipse centered at the origin with eccentricity 3/4 and foci at $(0, \pm 6)$.

SOLUTION

The foci are at $(0, \pm 6)$. Therefore, $c = 6$. Use the eccentricity formula to solve for a.

$$e = \frac{c}{a} \implies \frac{3}{4} = \frac{6}{a} \implies 3a = 24 \implies a = 8$$

The foci are on the y-axis, and the ellipse is centered at the origin. Therefore, the vertices must be located at $(0, \pm a)$, that is, $(0, \pm 8)$.

EXAMPLE 12 Using the Eccentricity of an Ellipse to Write the Equation of the Ellipse

Write the equation of the ellipse centered at $(0, 0)$ with eccentricity 1/2 and vertices at $(\pm 4, 0)$.

SOLUTION

The vertices are at $(\pm 4, 0)$. So, $a = 4$ and $a^2 = 16$. Use the eccentricity formula to solve for c.

$$e = \frac{c}{a} \implies \frac{1}{2} = \frac{c}{4} \implies 2c = 4 \implies c = 2$$

Use the equation $c^2 = a^2 - b^2$ to find b^2. $\qquad 2^2 = 16 - b^2 \implies b^2 = 12$

The vertices are on the x-axis. Therefore, the ellipse is of the form $\dfrac{x^2}{a^2} + \dfrac{y^2}{b^2} = 1$.

$$\frac{x^2}{a^2} + \frac{y^2}{b^2} = 1 \implies \frac{x^2}{16} + \frac{y^2}{12} = 1$$

SECTION 6.2 EXERCISES

Warm Up

Solve each equation.

1. $c^2 = a^2 - b^2$;
   when $a = 5$ and $b = 1$

2. $c^2 = a^2 - b^2$;
   when $a^2 = 70$ and $c^2 = 20$

3. Rationalize the denominator. $\dfrac{2}{5\sqrt{3}}$

Just the Facts

Fill in the blanks.

4. An ellipse is the set of all points such that the ____ of the distances from two fixed points, called the ____, is constant.

5. A horizontal ellipse centered at the origin has its major axis on the ____-axis and its minor axis on the ____-axis.

6. A vertical ellipse centered at the origin has its major axis on the ____-axis and its minor axis on the ____-axis.

7. The ____, ____, and ____ of a vertical ellipse centered at the origin are on the y-axis.

8. The ____ and ____ of a vertical ellipse centered at the origin are on the x-axis.

9. An ellipse's co-vertices are the endpoints of its ____ .

10. An ellipse's vertices are the endpoints of its ____ .

11. The equation $\dfrac{x^2}{a^2} + \dfrac{y^2}{b^2} = 1$ where $a \geq b$ describes a ____ ellipse centered at the ____ with vertices at ____ and co-vertices at ____.

12. The equation $\dfrac{y^2}{a^2} + \dfrac{x^2}{b^2} = 1$ where $a \geq b$ describes a ____ ellipse centered at the ____ with vertices at ____ and co-vertices at ____.

Essential Skills

In Exercises 1–2, use the graph to write the equation of each ellipse.

1.   2.

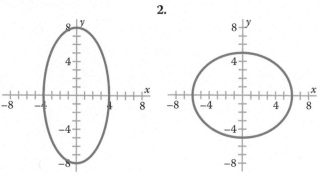

In Exercises 3–10, use the given information to write the equation of each ellipse in standard form. Assume that each ellipse is centered at the origin.

3. a vertex at $(-3, 0)$ and a co-vertex at $(0, -1)$

4. a vertex at $(0, 8)$ and a co-vertex at $(2, 0)$

5. a vertical major axis of length 8 and a horizontal minor axis of length 2

6. a vertical minor axis of length 10 and a horizontal major axis of length 14

7. x-intercepts at ± 12 and foci located at $(0, 5)$ and $(0, -5)$

8. x-intercepts at 5 and -5 and foci located at $(4, 0)$ and $(-4, 0)$

9. minor axis of length 12 and foci located at $(\pm 8, 0)$

10. major axis of length 8 and foci located at $(0, 2)$ and $(0, -2)$

In Exercises 11–12, find the intercepts of each ellipse.

11. $\dfrac{y^2}{400} + \dfrac{x^2}{121} = 1$

12. $\dfrac{x^2}{16} + \dfrac{y^2}{9} = 1$

In Exercises 13–14, find the lengths of the major and minor axes of each ellipse.

13. $2x^2 = 36 - 6y^2$

14. $8x^2 + y^2 = 8$

In Exercises 15–18, graph each ellipse.

15. $\dfrac{y^2}{4} + x^2 = 1$

16. $\dfrac{x^2}{64} + \dfrac{y^2}{25} = 1$

17. $1 - \dfrac{y^2}{16} = x^2$

18. $4x^2 + 25y^2 = 100$

In Exercises 19–20, find the foci of each ellipse.

19. $\dfrac{x^2}{12} + \dfrac{y^2}{32} = 1$

20. $\dfrac{x^2}{100} + \dfrac{y^2}{36} = 1$

In Exercises 21–24, find the eccentricity of each ellipse.

21. $\dfrac{y^2}{9} + x^2 = 1$

22. $\dfrac{x^2}{20} + \dfrac{y^2}{4} = 1$

23. $\dfrac{14y^2}{25} + 2x^2 = 28$

24. $6x^2 + 12y^2 = 24$

25. Find the foci of the ellipse centered at the origin with eccentricity 2/5 and vertices at $(0, 3)$ and $(0, -3)$.

26. Find the vertices of the ellipse centered at the origin with eccentricity 1/3 and foci at $(2, 0)$ and $(-2, 0)$.

In Exercises 27–28, use the given information to write the equation of each ellipse. Assume that each ellipse is centered at the origin.

27. $e = \dfrac{1}{10}$ and vertices at $(0, \pm 20)$

28. $e = \dfrac{2}{3}$ and foci at $\left(\pm\dfrac{3}{2}, 0\right)$

Extensions

In Exercises 29–30, find the center, foci, major axis length, minor axis length, vertices, co-vertices, and eccentricity for each ellipse. Then sketch the graph.

29. $\dfrac{y^2}{2} + 2x^2 = 18$

30. $\dfrac{3x^2}{4} + 3y^2 = 12$

In Exercises 31–32, write each equation as it would be entered into a graphing calculator (i.e., solve for y).

31. $\dfrac{y^2}{18} + \dfrac{x^2}{7} = 1$

32. $\dfrac{14x^2}{25} + 2y^2 = 28$

In Exercises 33–45, write the equation of two ellipses that satisfy the given conditions. Assume that each ellipse is centered at the origin. Check the equations using a graphing calculator.

33. a major axis of length 12

34. a minor axis of length 12

35. intercepts at ±4 and ±7

36. co-vertices at $(0, \pm 1)$

37. co-vertices at $(\pm 1, 0)$

38. vertices at $(0, \pm 4)$

39. vertices at $(\pm 4, 0)$

40. foci at ±6

41. foci at ±3

42. a major axis of length 10 and a minor axis of length 4

43. x-intercepts at ±5 and a vertical major axis

44. y-intercepts at ±6 and a horizontal major axis

45. eccentricity of 1/3

46. If an ellipse is centered at the origin, do the lengths of the horizontal and vertical axes provide enough information to write the equation of the ellipse?

47. Given that ellipse A has eccentricity 1/2, ellipse B has eccentricity 9/10, and ellipse C has eccentricity 2/9, list the ellipses in order from most circular to most stretched.

48. Write the standard form equation of a circle centered at the origin and the standard form equation of a circle centered at (h, k) and describe the difference between the two equations. How might the standard form equation of an ellipse centered at the origin change if the ellipse is centered at (h, k) instead of at the origin?

6.3 HYPERBOLAS

OBJECTIVES

- Connect the geometric attributes of a hyperbola (centered at the origin) to its standard form equation.
- Write the equation of a hyperbola (centered at the origin).
- Graph a hyperbola (centered at the origin).
- Find the vertices, co-vertices, foci, and asymptotes of a hyperbola (centered at the origin).

PREREQUISITE VOCABULARY TERMS

conic

Distance Formula

ellipse

x-intercept

y-intercept

Recall that a **hyperbola** is the conic formed by the intersection of a double cone and a plane that intersects both parts of the cone, through the cone's bases. Notice that each hyperbola in Figure 6.3a is made up of two disconnected curves, called its **branches**. The equations and graphs of hyperbolas (on a coordinate plane) will be discussed in this section.

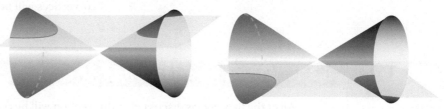

Figure 6.3a

Introduction to Hyperbolas

Like an ellipse, a hyperbola is defined on a coordinate plane using a relationship between two fixed points F_1 and F_2 called the **foci**. However, instead of the graph being all points such that the *sum* of the distances from the foci is a constant (as is the case with an ellipse), a hyperbola is the set of all points such that the *difference* of the distances from the foci is a constant.

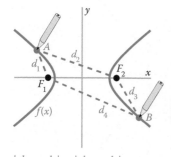

$$|d_1 - d_2| = |d_3 - d_4|$$

Figure 6.3b

DEFINITION

A **hyperbola** is the set of all points such that the difference of the distances from two fixed points is constant. The fixed points are the **foci** of the hyperbola.

The graph of $f(x)$ shown in Figure 6.3b is a hyperbola. The points F_1 and F_2 are its foci, and the points A and B are on the hyperbola. The distances from A to F_1 and F_2 are represented by d_1 and d_2 (as shown in the figure), and the distances from B to F_1 and F_2 are represented by d_3 and d_4 (as shown in the figure). Since a hyperbola is the set of all points such that the difference of the distances from the foci is a constant, the differences of the distances from the foci to any two points on the hyperbola $f(x)$ must be equal. Therefore, the difference of the distances from A to the foci, $|d_1 - d_2|$, must be equal to the difference of the distances from B to the foci, $|d_3 - d_4|$.

Attributes of a Hyperbola

TIP

A hyperbola's center is the midpoint between its vertices, which is also the midpoint of the transverse axis.

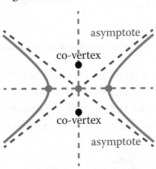

Figure 6.3c

As with an ellipse, a hyperbola is a symmetric figure with two perpendicular lines of symmetry called the axes of symmetry, intersecting at the **center of the hyperbola**. One axis of symmetry is between the branches, and the other passes through the branches and the foci, as shown in Figure 6.3c. The line segment on the axis of symmetry containing the foci, with endpoints on the hyperbola, is called the **transverse axis**. The endpoints of the transverse axis are the hyperbola's **vertices**.

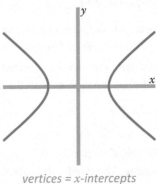

Figure 6.3d

A hyperbola has two asymptotes. Each asymptote passes through the hyperbola's center, as shown in Figure 6.3d.

As with an ellipse, a hyperbola also has co-vertices on an axis of symmetry, as shown in Figure 6.3d. However, a hyperbola's co-vertices are not points on the graph. The relationship between the coordinates of the vertices and co-vertices will be discussed later in this section.

6.3.1 Writing the Equation of a Hyperbola

All of the hyperbolas discussed in this section will be centered at the origin, and will have either a horizontal or vertical transverse axis, as shown in Figure 6.3e.

Horizontal Transverse Axis   *Vertical Transverse Axis*

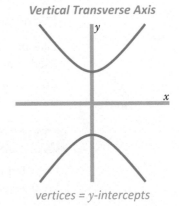

Figure 6.3e

Notice that any hyperbola *centered at the origin* with a horizontal or vertical transverse axis will be symmetric about the x- and y-axes. Therefore, a hyperbola centered at the origin with a horizontal transverse axis has vertices that are also its x-intercepts. Similarly, a hyperbola centered at the origin with a vertical transverse axis has vertices that are also its y-intercepts.

The Standard Form Equations

As with an ellipse, the standard form equations of horizontal and vertical hyperbolas centered at the origin can be derived using the Distance Formula, where a is the distance between the center and a vertex, b is the distance between the center and a co-vertex, and c is the distance between the center and a focus. For a hyperbola, the relationship between a, b, and c is defined by $c^2 = a^2 + b^2$, where $a \geq b > 0$.

REMEMBER

For an ellipse, $c^2 = a^2 - b^2$.

The following table contains the standard form equations for hyperbolas centered at the origin with a horizontal or vertical transverse axis. Additionally, the table summarizes the relationship between these equations and the attributes of the hyperbolas.

Standard Form Equations of Hyperbolas: Centered at the Origin		
	Horizontal Transverse Axis (open left/right)	**Vertical Transverse Axis (open up/down)**
Equation	$\dfrac{x^2}{a^2} - \dfrac{y^2}{b^2} = 1$	$\dfrac{y^2}{a^2} - \dfrac{x^2}{b^2} = 1$
Vertices	$(\pm a, 0)$	$(0, \pm a)$
Foci	$(\pm c, 0)$	$(0, \pm c)$
Co-vertices	$(0, \pm b)$	$(\pm b, 0)$
Asymptotes	$y = \pm \dfrac{b}{a} x$	$y = \pm \dfrac{a}{b} x$

IMPORTANT

The relationship between a, b, and c is defined by the equation $c^2 = a^2 + b^2$.

IMPORTANT

The distance from the origin to a vertex is a, so the length of the transverse axis is 2a.

The dashed-line box drawn between the hyperbola's branches is called the *central box*. Notice that the sides of the central box are horizontal and vertical lines that pass through the hyperbola's vertices and co-vertices, intersecting at the hyperbola's asymptotes.

A hyperbola's central box can be used to find its co-vertices when its vertices and asymptotes are known.

Steps for Using the Central Box to Find the Co-Vertices of a Hyperbola
Horizontal Hyperbola (centered at the origin)

❶ Through each vertex, draw a vertical line segment with endpoints on the asymptotes.

❷ Draw a horizontal line segment connecting those two endpoints that are above the hyperbola's center. Repeat for the endpoints below the center.

❸ The *y*-intercept of each horizontal line is a co-vertex.

Vertical Hyperbola (centered at the origin)

❶ Through each vertex, draw a horizontal line segment with endpoints on the asymptotes.

❷ Draw a vertical line segment connecting those two endpoints that are to the left of the hyperbola's center. Repeat for the endpoints to the right of the center.

❸ The *x*-intercept of each vertical line is a co-vertex.

Similarly, a hyperbola's vertices can be found by drawing the central box using the co-vertices and asymptotes.

Writing the Equation of a Hyperbola

The distance from the origin to a vertex (*a*) and the distance from the origin to a co-vertex (*b*) can be used to write the equation of a horizontal or vertical hyperbola centered at the origin.

Steps for Writing the Equation of a Horizontal or Vertical Hyperbola

❶ Determine the type of hyperbola (horizontal or vertical).

❷ Find the values of *a* and *b*.

❸ Substitute the values of *a* and *b* into the standard form equation of the hyperbola.

EXAMPLE 1 | **Writing the Equation of a Hyperbola Given Its Graph**

Write the equation of each hyperbola.

A.

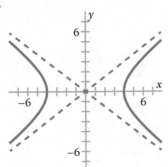

B.

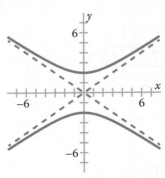

SOLUTION

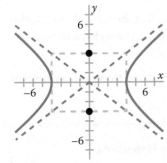

Figure 6.3f

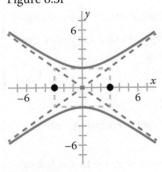

Figure 6.3g

A. From the graph, the vertices (*x*-intercepts) are at (±4, 0), and the center is at (0, 0).

❶ The hyperbola is horizontal and centered at the origin.

❷ The distance from the center to a vertex is 4, so *a* = 4.
Draw the central box to find the co-vertices (as shown in Figure 6.3f).
The distance from the center to a co-vertex is 3, so *b* = 3.

❸ Substitute *a* = 4 and *b* = 3 into the standard form equation of a horizontal hyperbola.

$$\frac{x^2}{a^2} - \frac{y^2}{b^2} = 1 \implies \frac{x^2}{4^2} - \frac{y^2}{3^2} = 1 \implies \frac{x^2}{16} - \frac{y^2}{9} = 1$$

B. From the graph, the *y*-intercepts are at (0, ±2), and the center is at (0, 0).

❶ The hyperbola is vertical and centered at the origin.

❷ The distance from the center to a vertex is 2, so *a* = 2.
Draw the central box to find the co-vertices (as shown in Figure 6.3g).
The distance from the center to a co-vertex is 3, so *b* = 3.

❸ Substitute *a* = 2 and *b* = 3 into the standard form equation of a vertical hyperbola.

$$\frac{y^2}{a^2} - \frac{x^2}{b^2} = 1 \implies \frac{y^2}{2^2} - \frac{x^2}{3^2} = 1 \implies \frac{y^2}{4} - \frac{x^2}{9} = 1$$

EXAMPLE 2	Writing the Equation of a Hyperbola Given a Vertex and a Focus

Write the equation of a hyperbola centered at the origin with a vertex at (6, 0) and a focus at (8, 0).

SOLUTION

❶ The hyperbola is centered at the origin, so the other vertex must be at (−6, 0) and the other focus at (−8, 0). Since the vertices are on the x-axis, the hyperbola must be horizontal.

❷ The distance from the center to a vertex is 6, so $a = 6$. Therefore, $a^2 = 36$.

The distance from the center to a focus is 8, so $c = 8$.

Use $c^2 = a^2 + b^2$ to find b^2.　　　$8^2 = 36 + b^2 \implies b^2 = 28$

❸ Substitute $a^2 = 36$ and $b^2 = 28$ into the standard form equation of a horizontal hyperbola.

$$\frac{x^2}{a^2} - \frac{y^2}{b^2} = 1 \implies \frac{x^2}{36} - \frac{y^2}{28} = 1$$

TIP

$c^2 = a^2 + b^2$ can be used to find b when a and c are known.

EXAMPLE 3	Writing the Equation of a Hyperbola Given the Foci and the Length of the Transverse Axis

Write the equation of a hyperbola centered at the origin with a transverse axis of length 10 units and foci at (0, ±9).

SOLUTION

❶ The hyperbola has foci at (0, ±9) and is centered at the origin. Since the foci are on the y-axis, the transverse axis must be vertical. Therefore, the hyperbola is vertical.

❷ The length of the transverse axis is equal to $2a$. Since the transverse axis is 10 units, $2a = 10$. Therefore, $a = 5$ and $a^2 = 25$.

The distance from the center to a focus is 8, so $c = 9$.

Use $c^2 = a^2 + b^2$ to find b^2.　　　$9^2 = 25 + b^2 \implies b^2 = 56$

❸ Substitute $a^2 = 25$ and $b^2 = 56$ into the standard form equation of a vertical hyperbola.

$$\frac{y^2}{a^2} - \frac{x^2}{b^2} = 1 \implies \frac{y^2}{25} - \frac{x^2}{56} = 1$$

REMEMBER

A hyperbola's transverse axis always contains the vertices.

6.3.2   Writing the Equation of a Hyperbola: Another Example

The standard form equation of a hyperbola can be found by using the equations of its asymptotes, along with additional information about the hyperbola. Recall that a horizontal hyperbola has asymptotes at $y = \pm\dfrac{b}{a}x$, and a vertical hyperbola has asymptotes at $y = \pm\dfrac{a}{b}x$.

EXAMPLE 4   Writing the Equation of a Hyperbola Given the Vertices and Asymptotes

Write the equation of a hyperbola centered at the origin with vertices at $(\pm6, 0)$ and asymptotes at $y = \pm\dfrac{4}{3}x$.

SOLUTION

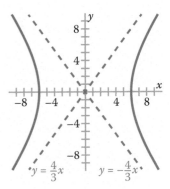

❶ Since the vertices $(\pm6, 0)$ are on the x-axis, the hyperbola is horizontal.

❷ The distance from the center to a vertex is 6, so $a = 6$. Therefore, $a^2 = 36$.

The hyperbola's asymptotes are at $y = \pm\dfrac{4}{3}x$. The asymptotes of a horizontal hyperbola centered at the origin are given by $y = \pm\dfrac{b}{a}x$. Write an equation and solve for b.

$$\pm\frac{b}{a}x = \pm\frac{4}{3}x$$

$$\frac{b}{6} = \frac{4}{3} \qquad \textit{Substitute 6 for a and simplify.}$$

$$b = 8 \qquad \textit{Solve for b.}$$

Therefore, $b^2 = 64$.

❸ Substitute the values of a^2 and b^2 into the standard form equation of a horizontal hyperbola.

$$\frac{x^2}{a^2} - \frac{y^2}{b^2} = 1 \;\Rightarrow\; \frac{x^2}{36} - \frac{y^2}{64} = 1$$

TIP

Write the equation of the asymptotes to check that $a = 6$ and $b = 8$. The hyperbola is horizontal, so the hyperbola's asymptotes are

$$y = \pm\frac{b}{a}x = \pm\frac{8}{6}x = \pm\frac{4}{3}x,$$

as given in the question.

WHAT'S THE BIG IDEA?

For a horizontal or vertical hyperbola centered at the origin, explain the relationship between the equations of the asymptotes and the coordinates of the vertices and co-vertices.

6.3.3 Graphing Hyperbolas

In this topic, the equation of a hyperbola will be used to identify the hyperbola's attributes, which will then be used to sketch the graph.

EXAMPLE 5 **Finding the Vertices, Co-Vertices, Foci, and Asymptotes of a Hyperbola Given Its Equation**

Find the vertices, co-vertices, foci, and asymptotes of each hyperbola.

A. $\dfrac{x^2}{8} - \dfrac{y^2}{18} = 1$ **B.** $y^2 - \dfrac{x^2}{4} = 1$

SOLUTION

A. The equation is of the form $\dfrac{x^2}{a^2} - \dfrac{y^2}{b^2} = 1$, so

- the hyperbola is horizontal, centered at the origin,
- the vertices are at $(\pm a, 0)$,
- the co-vertices are at $(0, \pm b)$,
- the foci are at $(\pm c, 0)$, and
- the asymptotes are at $y = \pm \dfrac{b}{a} x$.

Use the equation to find a and b.

$a^2 = 8 \Rightarrow a = \sqrt{8} = \sqrt{4 \cdot 2} = 2\sqrt{2}$ $b^2 = 18 \Rightarrow b = \sqrt{18} = \sqrt{9 \cdot 2} = 3\sqrt{2}$

vertices: $(\pm 2\sqrt{2}, 0)$ co-vertices: $(0, \pm 3\sqrt{2})$

Use $c^2 = a^2 + b^2$ to find c.

$c^2 = a^2 + b^2 = 8 + 18 = 26 \Rightarrow c = \sqrt{26}$ foci: $(\pm\sqrt{26}, 0)$

Use a and b to write the equation of the asymptotes.

$y = \pm \dfrac{b}{a} x = \pm \dfrac{3\sqrt{2}}{2\sqrt{2}} x = \pm \dfrac{3}{2} x$ asymptotes: $y = \pm \dfrac{3}{2} x$

B. The equation is of the form $\dfrac{y^2}{a^2} - \dfrac{x^2}{b^2} = 1$, so

- the hyperbola is vertical, centered at the origin,
- the vertices are at $(0, \pm a)$,
- the co-vertices are at $(\pm b, 0)$,
- the foci are at $(0, \pm c)$, and
- the asymptotes are at $y = \pm \dfrac{a}{b} x$.

Use the equation to find a and b.   Use $c^2 = a^2 + b^2$ to find c.

$a^2 = 1 \Rightarrow a = 1$ $b^2 = 4 \Rightarrow b = 2$ $c^2 = a^2 + b^2 = 1 + 4 = 5 \Rightarrow c = \sqrt{5}$

vertices: $(0, \pm 1)$ co-vertices: $(\pm 2, 0)$ foci: $(0, \pm\sqrt{5})$

Use a and b to write the equation of the asymptotes.

$y = \pm \dfrac{a}{b} x = \pm \dfrac{1}{2} x$ asymptotes: $y = \pm \dfrac{1}{2} x$

EXAMPLE 6   Graphing a Hyperbola Given Its Equation

Graph each hyperbola.

A. $\dfrac{y^2}{9} - x^2 = 1$

B. $0 = 2 + \dfrac{y^2}{8} - 2x^2$

SOLUTION

To sketch the graph of a hyperbola, first plot the vertices and sketch the asymptotes. Then, starting at a vertex, sketch a branch of the hyperbola curving toward each asymptote. Repeat for the other branch using the other vertex.

A. The equation is in the form $\dfrac{y^2}{a^2} - \dfrac{x^2}{b^2} = 1$, so

- the hyperbola is vertical, centered at the origin,
- the vertices are at $(0, \pm a)$, and
- the asymptotes are at $y = \pm \dfrac{a}{b}x$.

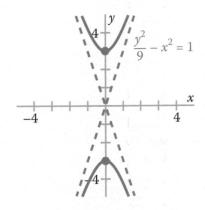

Use the given equation of the hyperbola to find a^2.

$a^2 = 9 \implies a = 3$ vertices: $(0, \pm 3)$ *Plot the vertices.*

Use the given equation of the hyperbola to find b^2.

$b^2 = 1 \implies b = 1$

Write the equation of the asymptotes.

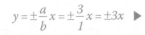

$y = \pm \dfrac{a}{b}x = \pm \dfrac{3}{1}x = \pm 3x$ ▶   asymptotes: $y = \pm 3x$ *Sketch the asymptotes.*

Starting at $(0, 3)$, sketch the top branch of the hyperbola, curving toward each asymptote. Then sketch the bottom branch starting at $(0, -3)$, curving toward each asymptote.

B. The equation is not in standard form. Write the equation in the standard form (where one side is equal to 1).

$$0 = 2 + \dfrac{y^2}{8} - 2x^2 \implies 2x^2 - \dfrac{y^2}{8} = 2 \implies x^2 - \dfrac{y^2}{16} = 1$$

Now the equation is of the form $\dfrac{x^2}{a^2} - \dfrac{y^2}{b^2} = 1$, so

- the hyperbola is horizontal, centered at the origin,
- the vertices are at $(\pm a, 0)$, and
- the asymptotes are at $y = \pm \dfrac{b}{a}x$.

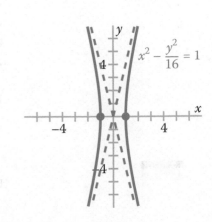

Use the given equation of the hyperbola to find a^2.

$a^2 = 1 \implies a = 1$ vertices: $(\pm 1, 0)$ *Plot the vertices.*

Use the given equation of the hyperbola to find b^2.

$b^2 = 16 \implies b = 4$

Write the equation of the asymptotes.

$y = \pm \dfrac{b}{a}x = \pm \dfrac{4}{1}x = \pm 4x$ ▶   asymptotes: $y = \pm 4x$ *Sketch the asymptotes.*

Starting at $(-1, 0)$, sketch the left branch of the hyperbola, curving toward each asymptote. Then sketch the right branch starting at $(1, 0)$, curving toward each asymptote.

6.3.4   Applying Hyperbolas: Navigation

EXAMPLE 7   Finding the Location of a Ship Following a Hyperbolic Model

The path of a ship can be described by the hyperbolic model $\frac{x^2}{2501} - \frac{y^2}{3000} = 1$, where the ship travels along one branch of the hyperbola, relative to two stations on the shore line that are located at the foci. If the ship is 100 miles east of the hyperbola's vertical axis, what is the distance to the nearest mile between the ship and the shore (i.e., the horizontal axis)?

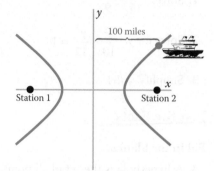

SOLUTION

The ship is following a hyperbolic model, where the hyperbola is horizontal and centered at the origin. Since the ship is located 100 miles east of the hyperbola's vertical axis, the ship is located on the hyperbola at the point $(100, y)$. Use the equation of the hyperbola to find the corresponding y-value, which is the distance between the ship and the shore.

$$\frac{x^2}{2501} - \frac{y^2}{3000} = 1$$

$$\frac{(100)^2}{2501} - \frac{y^2}{3000} = 1 \qquad \textit{Substitute 100 for x.}$$

$$y^2 = 3000\left(\frac{10000}{2501} - 1\right) \qquad \textit{Simplify and solve for } y^2.$$

$$y \approx 95 \qquad \textit{Take the square root of each side and round to the nearest mile.}$$

The distance between the ship and the shore is approximately 95 miles.

> **TIP**
>
> *Wait until the final step in the calculations to round.*

EXAMPLE 8   Finding the Equation of a Hyperbolic Model

The path of a ship can be described by a hyperbolic model centered at the origin, relative to two stations on the shore 160 miles apart that are located at the foci. If the ship is at a vertex 30 miles west of the hyperbola's center, find the equation of the hyperbola.

SOLUTION

The hyperbolic model that the ship follows is centered at the origin. Since the ship is located at a vertex, and that vertex is west of the hyperbola's center, the hyperbola is horizontal.

So, the standard form equation is $\frac{x^2}{a^2} - \frac{y^2}{b^2} = 1$, where the vertices are located at $(\pm a, 0)$.

Since the ship is at a vertex 30 miles west of the hyperbola's center, $a = 30$. So, $a^2 = 900$.

The stations are 160 miles apart from each other, so they are each 80 miles from the center. Since the stations are at the foci, $c = 80$. So, $c^2 = 6400$.

Use $c^2 = a^2 + b^2$ to find b^2. $6400^2 = 900 + b^2 \;\Rightarrow\; b^2 = 5500$

Substitute the values of a^2 and b^2 into the standard form equation of a horizontal hyperbola.

$$\frac{x^2}{a^2} - \frac{y^2}{b^2} = 1 \;\Rightarrow\; \frac{x^2}{900} - \frac{y^2}{5500} = 1$$

SECTION 6.3 EXERCISES

Warm Up

1. Solve. $\dfrac{a}{45} = \dfrac{4}{9}$

2. Solve for y. $\dfrac{x^2}{10} - \dfrac{y^2}{12} = 1$

3. Simplify. $\sqrt{54}$

Just the Facts

Fill in the blanks.

4. A hyperbola is the set of all points whose distances from two fixed points, called the ____, are a constant ____.

5. The graph of a hyperbola consists of two disconnected curves called its ____.

6. A(n) ____ hyperbola opens up and down.

7. A(n) ____ hyperbola opens left and right.

8. The ____, ____, ____, and ____ of a horizontal hyperbola centered at the origin are on the ____-axis.

9. The ____, ____, ____, and ____ of a vertical hyperbola centered at the origin are on the ____-axis.

10. The endpoints of a hyperbola's transverse axis are its ____.

11. If the distance between a hyperbola's center and a vertex is x, then the length of its transverse axis is ____.

12. True or False? A hyperbola's co-vertices are located on the hyperbola.

Essential Skills

In Exercises 1–2, find the vertices and co-vertices of each hyperbola.

1.   2.

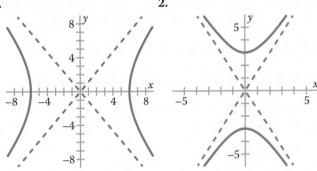

In Exercises 3–4, write the equation of each hyperbola.

3.   4.

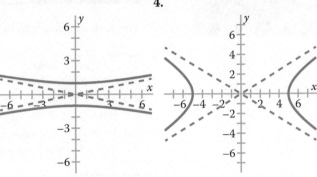

In Exercises 5–10, write the equation of each hyperbola.

5. vertices at $(0, \pm15)$ and foci at $(0, \pm20)$

6. vertices at $(\pm2, 0)$ and foci at $(\pm9, 0)$

7. centered at the origin with a focus at $(0, 11)$ and a transverse axis of length 20

8. centered at the origin with a focus at $(5, 0)$ and a transverse axis of length 8

9. vertices at $(\pm9, 0)$ and asymptotes $y = \pm5x$

10. vertices at $(0, \pm2)$ and asymptotes $y = \pm\dfrac{1}{3}x$

In Exercises 11–12, write the equation of each hyperbola using an algebraic method (i.e., without drawing the central box).

11.   12.

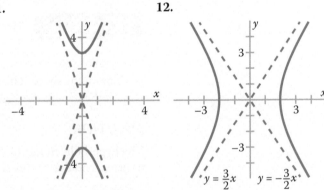

In Exercises 13–14, find the vertices, asymptotes, and foci of each hyperbola.

13. $y^2 - \dfrac{x^2}{49} = 1$

14. $\dfrac{x^2}{64} - \dfrac{y^2}{9} = 1$

In Exercises 15–18, graph each hyperbola.

15. $\dfrac{y^2}{9} - \dfrac{x^2}{4} = 1$

16. $\dfrac{x^2}{9} - \dfrac{y^2}{4} = 1$

17. $\dfrac{x^2}{2} = \dfrac{1 + y^2}{2}$

18. $16y^2 - x^2 = 16$

19. The path of a ship can be described by the hyperbolic model $\dfrac{y^2}{983} - \dfrac{x^2}{1047} = 1$, where the ship travels along one branch of the hyperbola, relative to two stations on the shore that are located at the foci. If the ship is 115 miles north of the hyperbola's horizontal axis, what is the distance to the nearest mile between the ship and the shore (i.e., the vertical axis)?

20. The path of a ship can be described by the hyperbolic model $\dfrac{x^2}{784} - \dfrac{y^2}{2025} = 1$, where the ship travels along one branch of the hyperbola, relative to two stations on the shore that are located at the foci. If the ship is 125 miles east of the hyperbola's vertical axis, what is the distance to the nearest mile between the ship and the shore (i.e., the horizontal axis)?

21. The path of a ship can be described by a hyperbolic model centered at the origin, relative to two stations on the shore 168 miles apart that are located at the foci. If the ship is 60 miles south of the center of the hyperbola at a vertex, find the equation of the hyperbola.

22. The path of a ship can be described by a hyperbolic model centered at the origin, relative to two stations on the shore 212 miles apart that are located at the foci. If the ship is 90 miles east of the center of the hyperbola at a vertex, find the equation of the hyperbola.

Extensions

In Exercises 23–29, write the equations of two hyperbolas that satisfy the given conditions. If there are not two hyperbolas that satisfy the given conditions, state the reason.

23. transverse axis of length 12

24. vertices at $(0, \pm 3)$

25. co-vertices at $(0, \pm 10)$

26. foci at $(\pm 5, 0)$

27. foci and vertices such that $|c| = |a| + 1$

28. a central box with vertices $(\pm 5, 4)$ and $(\pm 5, -4)$

29. asymptotes at $y = \pm 2$

30. Explain how the co-vertices and asymptotes of a hyperbola could be used to sketch the graph of a hyperbola.

31. When $a = b$ in the standard form equation of an ellipse, the ellipse formed is a circle. What is true about a hyperbola when $a = b$?

32. Predict how the standard form equation of a horizontal parabola will change to describe a hyperbola with a horizontal transverse axis whose center is on the y-axis, n units above the origin.

33. Correct any errors in the following statement.

The graph of $\dfrac{y^2}{m^2} - \dfrac{x^2}{n^2} = 1$ is a hyperbola centered at the origin. The hyperbola has a vertical transverse axis of length $2n$ when $n > m$, and of length $2m$ when $m > n$. The hyperbola's vertices are at $(0, \pm m)$, its co-vertices are at $(0, \pm n)$, and its foci are at $(\pm(m^2 + n^2), 0)$.

6.4 TRANSLATIONS OF CONICS

OBJECTIVES

- Connect the geometric attributes of a translated conic (parabola, ellipse, and hyperbola) to its standard form equation.
- Write the equation of a translated conic (parabola, ellipse, hyperbola).
- Graph a translated conic (parabola, ellipse, hyperbola).
- Identify a conic given its equation in the general form.

PREREQUISITE VOCABULARY TERMS

conic
discriminant
ellipse
hyperbola
parabola

All of the conics (parabolas, ellipses, and hyperbolas) discussed in the preceding sections in Chapter 6 have had a vertex or center at the origin (vertex for the parabolas, center for the ellipses and hyperbolas). In this section, the discussion focuses on conics that are horizontally or vertically translated so their vertex or center is *not* at the origin. The following examples of translated conics are translated h units horizontally and k units vertically.

Examples of Translated Conics

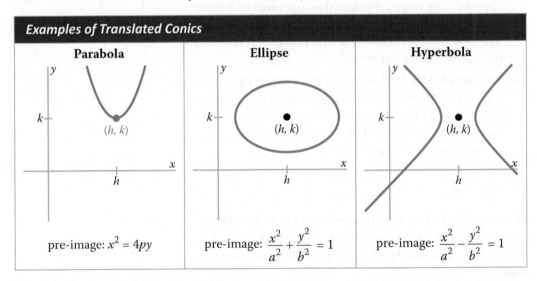

Parabola	Ellipse	Hyperbola
pre-image: $x^2 = 4py$	pre-image: $\dfrac{x^2}{a^2} + \dfrac{y^2}{b^2} = 1$	pre-image: $\dfrac{x^2}{a^2} - \dfrac{y^2}{b^2} = 1$

REMEMBER

When a tranformation is applied to the graph of an equation, the original graph is called the pre-image and the transformed graph is called the image.

The standard form equations of translated conics and conics with a center or vertex at the origin are shown in the following table.

Standard Form Equations of Conics

		Horizontal	Vertical
Parabola	vertex at (0, 0)	$y^2 = 4px$	$x^2 = 4py$
	vertex at (h, k)	$(y - k)^2 = 4p(x - h)$	$(x - h)^2 = 4p(y - k)$
Ellipse $(a \geq b)$	center at (0, 0)	$\dfrac{x^2}{a^2} + \dfrac{y^2}{b^2} = 1$	$\dfrac{y^2}{a^2} + \dfrac{x^2}{b^2} = 1$
	center at (h, k)	$\dfrac{(x - h)^2}{a^2} + \dfrac{(y - k)^2}{b^2} = 1$	$\dfrac{(y - k)^2}{a^2} + \dfrac{(x - h)^2}{b^2} = 1$
Hyperbola	center at (0, 0)	$\dfrac{x^2}{a^2} - \dfrac{y^2}{b^2} = 1$	$\dfrac{y^2}{a^2} - \dfrac{x^2}{b^2} = 1$
	center at (h, k)	$\dfrac{(x - h)^2}{a^2} - \dfrac{(y - k)^2}{b^2} = 1$	$\dfrac{(y - k)^2}{a^2} - \dfrac{(x - h)^2}{b^2} = 1$

In each standard form equation of a translated conic, the h-value gives the horizontal translation, and the k-value gives the vertical translation. A horizontal translation is either left or right, depending on the sign of h. Similarly, a vertical translation is either up or down, depending on the sign of k, as summarized in the following table.

Translations by *h*- and *k*-Units			
Horizontal Translation		**Vertical Translation**	
$h > 0$	right	$k > 0$	up
$h < 0$	left	$k < 0$	down

6.4.1 Translations of Parabolas

The Standard Form Equations

The standard form equations for translated horizontal and vertical parabolas are given in the following table. The vertex of each parabola is at (h, k). Recall that $\pm p$ is the distance between the vertex and the focus, where the sign of p depends on the direction of the parabola.

Standard Form Equations of Parabolas: Vertex *(h, k)* and Distance to Focus ±*p*			
	Equation	$p > 0$	$p < 0$
Vertical	$(x - h)^2 = 4p(y - k)$	opens upward	opens downward
Horizontal	$(y - k)^2 = 4p(x - h)$	opens to the right	opens to the left

As the vertex of a parabola is translated from $(0, 0)$ to (h, k), the parabola's focus and axis of symmetry are also translated h units horizontally and k units vertically, as summarized in the following table.

	Vertical Parabola		Horizontal Parabola	
	vertex at (0, 0)	**vertex at (*h, k*)**	**vertex at (0, 0)**	**vertex at (*h, k*)**
axis of symmetry	$x = 0$	$x = h$	$y = 0$	$y = k$
focus (*F*)	$(0, p)$	$(h, k + p)$	$(p, 0)$	$(h + p, k)$

Writing the Equation of a Translated Parabola

The process for writing the equation of a translated parabola (where the vertex is not at the origin) is very similar to the process for writing the equation of a parabola with vertex at the origin.

Steps for Writing the Equation of a Translated Parabola

❶ Determine the type of parabola (horizontal or vertical) and its direction (left or right for a horizontal parabola, or up or down for a vertical parabola).

❷ Find the coordinates of the vertex (h, k) and the p-value.

❸ Substitute the values of h, k, and p into the appropriate standard form equation, then simplify as needed.

EXAMPLE 1	Writing the Equation of a Translated Parabola Given the Vertex and Focus

Write the equation of a parabola with vertex at $(-7, 2)$ and focus at $(-7, -1)$.

SOLUTION

❶ The vertex and focus are on the vertical line $x = -7$, and the focus is below the vertex, so
  - the parabola has a vertical axis of symmetry,
  - the equation is of the form $(x - h)^2 = 4p(y - k)$, and
  - the parabola opens downward.

❷ The vertex is $(-7, 2)$, so $h = -7$ and $k = 2$.
  The distance between the vertex and the focus is 3 units. Since $p < 0$ for a parabola that opens downward, $p = -3$.

❸ Substitute $h = -7$, $k = 2$, and $p = -3$ into the standard form equation, then simplify.

$$(x - h)^2 = 4p(y - k) \Rightarrow (x - (-7))^2 = 4(-3)(y - 2) \Rightarrow (x + 7)^2 = -12(y - 2)$$

6.4.2 Translations of Ellipses

The Standard Form Equations

The standard form equations for translated horizontal and vertical ellipses centered at (h, k) are given in the following table. The table also summarizes the relationship between these equations and the attributes of a translated ellipse.

IMPORTANT

The relationship between a, b, and c is defined by the equation $c^2 = a^2 - b^2$, where $a \geq b > 0$.

Standard Form Equations of Ellipses: Centered at (h, k)		
	Horizontal Major Axis	**Vertical Major Axis**
Equation	$\dfrac{(x - h)^2}{a^2} + \dfrac{(y - k)^2}{b^2} = 1 \quad a \geq b$	$\dfrac{(y - k)^2}{a^2} + \dfrac{(x - h)^2}{b^2} = 1 \quad a \geq b$
Vertices	$(h \pm a, k)$	$(h, k \pm a)$
Foci	$(h \pm c, k)$	$(h, k \pm c)$
Co-vertices	$(h, k \pm b)$	$(h \pm b, k)$

Major and Minor Axes

The major axis of an ellipse is the line segment through the center of the ellipse, whose endpoints are the ellipse's vertices. Recall that the length of the major axis for an ellipse centered at $(0, 0)$ is $2a$. The major axis of a horizontal ellipse with center at (h, k) extends from the point $(h - a, k)$ to $(h + a, k)$, so the length of the major axis is equal to the distance between these points. Since the y-coordinate of $(h - a, k)$ and $(h + a, k)$ is k, these points form a horizontal line segment with length equal to the difference between the x-coordinates.

$$\text{length of the major axis of a horizontal ellipse centered at } (h, k):$$
$$(h + a) - (h - a) = h + a - h + a = 2a$$

Therefore, the length of the major axis for a horizontal ellipse centered at (h, k) is $2a$. A similar process can be used to show that the length of the minor axis for a horizontal ellipse centered at (h, k) is $2b$. Likewise, the lengths of the major and minor axes for a vertical ellipse centered at (h, k) are also $2a$ and $2b$, respectively.

Graphing a Translated Ellipse

To graph any ellipse, plot the vertices and co-vertices, then sketch the ellipse through these points. To find the vertices and co-vertices of a translated ellipse, identify the values of $a, b, h,$ and k from the standard form equation. Recall that the vertices and co-vertices, respectively, are given by $(h \pm a, k)$ and $(h, k \pm b)$ for a horizontal ellipse, and $(h, k \pm a)$ and $(h \pm b, k)$ for a vertical ellipse.

Note that for a horizontal ellipse, the vertices $(h \pm a, k)$ are a units to the left and right of the center (h, k), while the co-vertices $(h, k \pm b)$ are b units above and below the center (h, k). Similarly, for a vertical ellipse, the vertices $(h, k \pm a)$ are a units above and below the center (h, k), while the co-vertices $(h \pm b, k)$ are b units to the left and right of the center (h, k).

EXAMPLE 2   **Graphing a Translated Ellipse**

Find the center and graph each ellipse.

A. $\dfrac{(x - 1)^2}{9} + \dfrac{(y + 3)^2}{4} = 1$ **B.** $8(x + 5)^2 = 8 - 2y^2$

SOLUTION

A. The equation is in the standard form of a horizontal ellipse with center (h, k),

$$\frac{(x - h)^2}{a^2} + \frac{(y - k)^2}{b^2} = 1 \text{, where } a \geq b.$$

Identify the values of $a, b, h,$ and k from the standard form equation.

$$\frac{(x - 1)^2}{9} + \frac{(y + 3)^2}{4} = 1 \implies \frac{(x - 1)^2}{3^2} + \frac{(y - (-3))^2}{2^2} = 1$$

From the equation, $a = 3, b = 2, h = 1,$ and $k = -3$. So, the center, (h, k), is at $(1, -3)$.

The ellipse is horizontal and centered at $(1, -3)$. So, the major axis and the vertices are on the horizontal line $y = -3$, and the minor axis and the co-vertices are on the vertical line $x = 1$.

vertices: $(h \pm a, k) = (1 \pm 3, -3)$, that is, $(4, -3)$ and $(-2, -3)$

co-vertices: $(h, k \pm b) = (1, -3 \pm 2)$, that is, $(1, -1)$ and $(1, -5)$

Plot the vertices and co-vertices, then sketch the ellipse through these points.

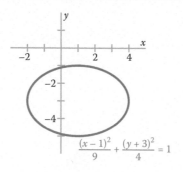

$$\frac{(x - 1)^2}{9} + \frac{(y + 3)^2}{4} = 1$$

B. The equation is not in the standard form of an ellipse. Write the equation so that the right side is equal to 1.

$$8(x+5)^2 = 8 - 2y^2$$

$$8(x+5)^2 + 2y^2 = 8$$ *Add $2y^2$ to each side to isolate the constant term on the right side.*

$$\frac{8(x+5)^2}{8} + \frac{2y^2}{8} = \frac{8}{8}$$ *Divide each side by 8 so that the right side will equal 1.*

$$(x+5)^2 + \frac{y^2}{4} = 1$$ *Simplify.*

$$\frac{y^2}{4} + (x+5)^2 = 1$$ *For an ellipse, a must be greater than or equal to b.*

Now the equation is in the standard form of a vertical ellipse with center (h, k):
$$\frac{(y-k)^2}{a^2} + \frac{(x-h)^2}{b^2} = 1 \text{, where } a \geq b.$$

Identify the values of a, b, h, and k from the standard form equation.

$$\frac{y^2}{4} + (x+5)^2 = 1 \implies \frac{(y-0)^2}{2^2} + \frac{(x-(-5))^2}{1^2} = 1$$

From the equation, $a = 2$, $b = 1$, $h = -5$, and $k = 0$. So, the center, (h, k), is at $(-5, 0)$.

The ellipse is vertical and centered at $(-5, 0)$, so the vertical line $x = -5$ contains the major axis and the vertices, while the horizontal line $y = 0$ (the x-axis) contains the minor axis and the co-vertices.

    vertices: $(h, k \pm a) = (-5, 0 \pm 2)$, that is, $(-5, 2)$ and $(-5, -2)$

    co-vertices: $(h \pm b, k) = (-5 \pm 1, 0)$, that is, $(-4, 0)$ and $(-6, 0)$

Plot the vertices and co-vertices, then sketch the ellipse through these points.

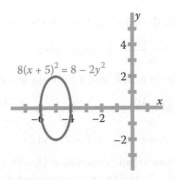

ALTERNATIVE METHOD

Vertices and Co-vertices

The center is at $(-5, 0)$, the major axis is vertical, and the a- and b-values are 2 and 1. So, the vertices are 2 units above and below the center, at $(-5, 2)$ and $(-5, -2)$, while the co-vertices are 1 unit to the left and right of the center, at $(-6, 0)$ and $(-4, 0)$.

NOTICE THAT

Length of Major Axis
$2a = 2(2) = 4$ units
Length of Minor Axis
$2b = 2(1) = 2$ units

ALTERNATIVE METHOD
Graph Using Translations
Since $h = -5$ and $k = 0$, the graph of $\frac{y^2}{4} + (x+5)^2 = 1$ is the image of $\frac{y^2}{4} + x^2 = 1$ after a translation 5 units to the left.

6.4.3 Translations of Hyperbolas

The Standard Form Equations

The standard form equations for translated horizontal and vertical hyperbolas centered at (h, k) are given in the following table. The table also summarizes the relationship between these equations and the attributes of a translated hyperbola.

Standard Form Equations of Hyperbolas: Centered at (h, k)		
	Horizontal Transverse Axis (opens left or right)	**Vertical Transverse Axis** (opens up or down)
Equation	$\dfrac{(x-h)^2}{a^2} - \dfrac{(y-k)^2}{b^2} = 1$	$\dfrac{(y-k)^2}{a^2} - \dfrac{(x-h)^2}{b^2} = 1$
Vertices	$(h \pm a, k)$	$(h, k \pm a)$
Foci	$(h \pm c, k)$	$(h, k \pm c)$
Co-vertices	$(h, k \pm b)$	$(h \pm b, k)$
Asymptotes	$y - k = \pm\dfrac{b}{a}(x-h)$	$y - k = \pm\dfrac{a}{b}(x-h)$

> **TIP**
>
> *The midpoint of a hyperbola's transverse axis is always the center of the hyperbola.*

Transverse Axis

As with the major axis of an ellipse, the length of a horizontal hyperbola's transverse axis can be found by subtracting the x-coordinates of its vertices.

> length of the transverse axis of a horizontal hyperbola centered at (h, k):
> $$(h + a) - (h - a) = h + a - h + a = 2a$$

The same is true for a vertical hyperbola centered at (h, k). Again, note that the length of the transverse axis is the same as for a hyperbola centered at the origin because a translation does not affect the size or shape of the hyperbola.

Graphing a Translated Hyperbola

To graph any hyperbola, plot the vertices and asymptotes, then sketch the two branches of the hyperbola, where each passes through a vertex and curves outward, toward the asymptotes. Use the values of a, b, h, and k (which can be identified from the standard form equation) to find the vertices and asymptotes of a translated hyperbola. Recall that the vertices and asymptotes, respectively, are given by $(h \pm a, k)$ and $y - k = \pm\dfrac{b}{a}(x-h)$ for a horizontal hyperbola, and by $(h, k \pm a)$ and $y - k = \pm\dfrac{a}{b}(x-h)$ for a vertical hyperbola.

As with an ellipse, note that for a horizontal hyperbola, the vertices $(h \pm a, k)$ are a units to the left and right of the center (h, k). Similarly, for a vertical hyperbola, the vertices $(h, k \pm a)$ are a units above and below the center (h, k).

EXAMPLE 3   **Graphing a Translated Hyperbola**

Find the center, vertices, co-vertices, and asymptotes of each hyperbola. Then sketch the graph.

A. $\dfrac{(x+1)^2}{4} - \dfrac{(y-5)^2}{9} = 1$ **B.** $\dfrac{(x+1)^2}{2} = 2y^2 - 2$

SOLUTION

A. The equation is in the standard form of a horizontal hyperbola with center (h, k).

$$\frac{(x-h)^2}{a^2} - \frac{(y-k)^2}{b^2} = 1$$

Identify the values of a, b, h, and k from the standard form equation.

$$\frac{(x+1)^2}{4} - \frac{(y-5)^2}{9} = 1 \;\Rightarrow\; \frac{(x-(-1))^2}{2^2} - \frac{(y-5)^2}{3^2} = 1$$

From the equation, $a = 2$, $b = 3$, $h = -1$, and $k = 5$.

   center: $(h, k) = (-1, 5)$

   vertices: $(h \pm a, k) = (-1 \pm 2, 5)$, that is, $(1, 5)$ and $(-3, 5)$

   co-vertices: $(h, k \pm b) = (-1, 5 \pm 3)$, that is, $(-1, 8)$ and $(-1, 2)$

   asymptotes: $y - k = \pm\dfrac{b}{a}(x - h) \;\Rightarrow\; y - 5 = \pm\dfrac{3}{2}(x + 1)$

ALTERNATIVE METHOD

Vertices and Co-vertices

The center is at (–1, 5), the transverse axis is horizontal, and the a- and b-values are 2 and 3. So, the vertices are 2 units to the left and right of the center, at (–3, 5) and (1, 5), while the co-vertices are 3 units above and below the center, at (–1, 8) and (–1, 2).

NOTICE THAT

Since h = –1 and k = 5, the graph of

$\dfrac{(x+1)^2}{4} - \dfrac{(y-5)^2}{9} = 1$ *is*

the image of $\dfrac{x^2}{4} - \dfrac{y^2}{9} = 1$

after a translation 1 unit to the left and 5 units up.

Plot the vertices and sketch the asymptotes. Then sketch the hyperbola's two branches.

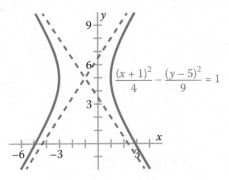

B. The equation is not in the standard form of a hyperbola. Write the equation so that the right side is equal to 1.

$$\frac{(x+1)^2}{2} = 2y^2 - 2$$

$$\frac{(x+1)^2}{2} - 2y^2 = -2 \qquad \text{\textit{Subtract } $2y^2$ \textit{ from each side to isolate the constant term on the right side.}}$$

$$\frac{(x+1)^2}{2(-2)} - \frac{2y^2}{-2} = \frac{-2}{-2} \qquad \text{\textit{Divide each side by } -2 \textit{ so that the right side will be equal to 1.}}$$

$$\frac{(x+1)^2}{-4} + y^2 = 1 \qquad \text{\textit{Simplify.}}$$

$$y^2 - \frac{(x+1)^2}{4} = 1 \qquad \text{\textit{Write the equation using subtraction.}}$$

Now the equation is in the standard form of a vertical hyperbola with center (h, k):

$$y^2 - \frac{(x+1)^2}{4} = 1 \;\Rightarrow\; \frac{(y-0)^2}{1^2} - \frac{(x-(-1))^2}{2^2} = 1$$

From the equation, $a = 1$, $b = 2$, $h = -1$, and $k = 0$.

    center: $(h, k) = (-1, 0)$

    vertices: $(h, k \pm a) = (-1, 0 \pm 1)$, that is, $(-1, 1)$ and $(-1, -1)$

    co-vertices: $(h \pm b, k) = (-1 \pm 2, 0)$, that is, $(1, 0)$ and $(-3, 0)$

    asymptotes: $y - k = \pm \dfrac{a}{b}(x - h) \;\Rightarrow\; y = \pm \dfrac{1}{2}(x+1)$

Plot the vertices and sketch the asymptotes. Then sketch the hyperbola's two branches.

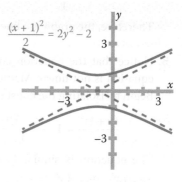

$$\frac{(x+1)^2}{2} = 2y^2 - 2$$

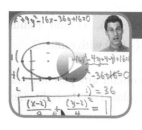

6.4.4   Identifying a Conic

When the equation of a conic is not given in standard form, the equation can be algebraically manipulated into standard form, and then the type of conic can be identified from the standard form equation.

When the equation of a conic is in the expanded form (where all parentheses have been removed by multiplying) and the right side is 0, the equation is said to be in the **general form.**

> **DEFINITION**
>
> The **general form of a conic** is $Ax^2 + Bxy + Cy^2 + Dx + Ey + F = 0$, where A, B, and C are not all equal to 0.

An equation written in general form can be algebraically manipulated into the standard form of a conic, often by completing the square.

EXAMPLE 4   **Identifying a Conic**

Identify each type of conic, if any, from its equation.

A. $y - x = \left(\dfrac{1}{2}\right)^2$ **B.** $\dfrac{(x+1)^2}{4} = 1 - \dfrac{(y-2)^2}{4}$ **C.** $2x + y^2 + 7y = x^2 + y - 4$

SECTION 6.4 EXERCISES

Warm Up

1. Complete the square to write the equation $x^2 + 10x - 8 = 1$ as a squared binomial equal to a constant.

2. Complete the square twice to write the equation $2x^2 + 4x - 3y^2 + 24y + 10 = 0$ as the difference of two squared binomials equal to a constant.

3. Find the discriminant of $7 + 5x^2 - x = 3x$.

Just the Facts

Fill in the blanks.

4. Translating an ellipse left, right, ____, or ____ does not affect the length of its ____ or ____ axes.

5. Translating a hyperbola in any direction does not affect the length of its ____ axis.

6. The vertex of the graph of $y - 2 = -4(x + 1)^2$ is at ____.

7. The graph of $(y - k)^2 = 4p(x - h)$ is a(n) ____ that opens ____ when $p < 0$.

8. If the center of an ellipse is at $(7, 9)$ and a vertex is at $(7, 12)$, then the other vertex is at ____ and the ellipse has a(n) ____ major axis on the line ____.

9. If the center of a hyperbola is at ____ and $a =$ ____, then the vertices are at $(-6, 0)$ and $(0, 0)$ and the transverse axis is ____ on the line ____.

10. In the general form of a conic, the values of A, B, and ____ cannot be ____.

Essential Skills

In Exercises 1–2, for each parabola, state the direction, determine whether the standard form equation is $(y - k)^2 = 4p(x - h)$ or $(x - h)^2 = 4p(y - k)$, and determine whether $p > 0$ or $p < 0$.

1. vertex $(-2, 0)$ and focus $(6, 0)$

2. vertex $(5, -3)$ and focus $(5, -1)$

In Exercises 3–4, write the equation of each parabola.

3. vertex at $(-2, 10)$ and focus at $(-2, 6)$

4. vertex at $(1, -4)$ and focus at $(-11, -4)$

In Exercises 5–6, find the center of each ellipse.

5. $\dfrac{(x + 4)^2}{20} + \dfrac{(y - 3)^2}{6} = 1$

6. $\dfrac{(y + 1)^2}{64} + x^2 = 1$

In Exercises 7–8, determine whether the major and minor axes of each ellipse are horizontal or vertical, and find the length of each axis.

7. $\dfrac{x^2}{40} + (y + 3)^2 = 1$

8. $\dfrac{(x - 4)^2}{9} + \dfrac{(y + 3)^2}{32} = 1$

In Exercises 9–10, sketch the graph of each ellipse.

9. $\dfrac{y^2}{4} + (x - 5)^2 = 1$

10. $\dfrac{(x + 3)^2}{16} + \dfrac{(y - 2)^2}{9} = 1$

In Exercises 11–12, find the center of each hyperbola.

11. $(x - 10)^2 - \dfrac{(y + 6)^2}{3} = 1$

12. $\dfrac{y^2}{12} - \dfrac{(x + 8)^2}{20} = 1$

In Exercises 13–14, find the vertices of each hyperbola.

13. $\dfrac{(y - 20)^2}{4} - \dfrac{(x + 2)^2}{36} = 1$

14. $\dfrac{(x + 3)^2}{25} - (y - 2)^2 = 1$

In Exercises 15–16, write the equations of each hyperbola's asymptotes in point-slope form.

15. $\dfrac{(x + 16)^2}{100} - \dfrac{(y - 9)^2}{400} = 1$

16. $\dfrac{y^2}{8} - \dfrac{(x + 5)^2}{18} = 1$

In Exercises 17–18, sketch the graph of each hyperbola.

17. $(y + 4)^2 - \dfrac{x^2}{25} = 1$

18. $\dfrac{(x - 1)^2}{36} - \dfrac{(y - 2)^2}{16} = 1$

In Exercises 19–30, determine whether each equation is a circle, ellipse (not a circle), hyperbola, parabola, or not a conic by writing the equation in the standard form of a conic.

19. $(x - 1)^2 + y + 5 = 5$

20. $x + y = 5^2$

21. $(y + 10)^3 = x$

22. $x = y^2 + 7$

23. $18(y - 2)^2 + 2x^2 = 18$

24. $(x + 1)^2 - 24 = -(y - 9)^2$

25. $\dfrac{(x - 2)^2}{2} + \dfrac{(y + 3)^2}{2} = \dfrac{1}{5}$

26. $(y - 2)^2 = 16 - \dfrac{16(x + 4)^2}{9}$

27. $2y^2 - 8x^3 + 5 = 0$

28. $-x^2 + 4y^2 - 6x - 8y - 21 = 0$

29. $x^2 + y + 133 = 22x$

30. $-4x^2 - 12y^2 + 16x - 36y + 5 = 0$

In Exercises 31–34, write each equation in the standard form of a conic.

31. $x^2 - y^2 + 224 - 30x = 0$

32. $4x^2 + 3y^2 + 8x - 6y - 29 = 0$

33. $9y^2 + x^2 + 2x - 72y + 136 = 0$

34. $4y^2 - x^2 - 24y - 4x + 16 = 0$

In Exercises 35–36, write each equation in the general form of a conic, then identify the coefficients.

35. $x(x + 2) + 2(y + 10) = -1$

36. $3x(x - 2y + 5) + y = y(1 - y) - 2$

In Exercises 37–40, use the discriminant and the coefficients to determine the type of conic represented by each equation. Explain.

37. $9x^2 - 6xy + y^2 + 2x - 10 = 0$

38. $2x^2 - 5xy + 2y^2 - 11x - 7y - 4 = 0$

39. $-x^2 - y^2 - x + y = 0$

40. $9x^2 + 4y^2 - 36x + 32y + 64 = 0$

Extensions

In Exercises 41–43, use the following information. When a figure is transformed, the original figure is called the pre-image and the transformed figure is called the image. Write the equation of each image given the translation(s) and the pre-image $x^2 = -6y$.

41. 4 units up

42. 7 units to the left

43. 3 units to the right and 1 unit down

Exercises 44–49, write the equation in the standard form of a conic of each image given the translation(s) and the pre-image.

44. pre-image: $\dfrac{x^2}{9} + \dfrac{y^2}{4} = 1$,

translations: 10 units left and 6 units up

45. pre-image: $\dfrac{y^2}{6} + x^2 = 1$,

translations: 7 units right and 2 units up

46. pre-image: $y^2 - x^2 = 1$,

translations: 1 unit right and 20 units down

47. pre-image: $\dfrac{x^2}{a^2} + \dfrac{y^2}{b^2} = 1$,

translations: m units left and n units up

48. pre-image: $4x^2 - 3y^2 = 24$,

translations: 7 units left and 6 units down

49. pre-image: $\dfrac{(x - 6)^2}{12} - \dfrac{(y + 1)^2}{8} = 1$,

translation: 4 units left

In Exercises 50–53, find all B-values such that the graph of $3x^2 + Bxy + 3y^2 + x + 2y - 1 = 0$ will be the given type of conic. Write sets of values using interval notation.

50. circle

51. ellipse (not a circle)

52. hyperbola

53. parabola

CHAPTER 6 REVIEW EXERCISES

Section 6.1 Parabolas

1. Find the focus and directrix of the graph of $x^2 + 3y = 0$.

2. Determine the direction of the graph of $-8y - 2x^2 = 0$.

3. Graph. $4x = -16y^2$

4. Write the standard form equation of the parabola with focus at (0, 2) and vertex at the origin.

5. Write the standard form equation of the parabola that passes through (−4, 8) with vertex at the origin and a vertical axis of symmetry.

Section 6.2 Ellipses

6. Use the graph to write the equation of the ellipse in standard form.

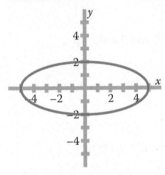

7. Write the standard form equation of an ellipse centered at the origin with a horizontal minor axis of length 4 units and a vertical major axis of length 8 units.

8. Find the intercepts and foci of $36x^2 + 100y^2 - 3600 = 0$.

9. Find the eccentricity and sketch the graph of $20x^2 + 36y^2 = 720$.

10. Write the equation of the ellipse centered at the origin with eccentricity 1/3 and foci at (±3, 0).

Section 6.3 Hyperbolas

In Exercises 11–12, write the standard form equation of each hyperbola.

11.

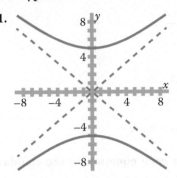

12. the hyperbola centered at the origin with a transverse axis of length 14 units and foci at $(\pm 6\sqrt{2}, 0)$

13. Find the vertices, co-vertices, foci, and asymptotes of $9x^2 - 4y^2 = 36$.

14. Graph. $\dfrac{y^2}{4} - \dfrac{x^2}{49} = 1$

15. From the LORAN system's use of hyperbolas, the equation that a ship can use to navigate its course, in nautical miles, using two stations as foci, is $\dfrac{y^2}{3025} - \dfrac{x^2}{2304} = 1$. Find the distance between the two stations.

Section 6.4 Translations of Conics

16. Write the standard form equation of the parabola with vertex (−3, −5) and focus (−7, −5).

In Exercises 17–20, find the center of each conic and graph the function.

17. $\dfrac{(x+4)^2}{9} + \dfrac{(y-2)^2}{16} = 1$

18. $\dfrac{(x-2)^2}{20} - \dfrac{(y-3)^2}{5} = 1$

19. Write $-x(x + 6) + 4y(-2 + y) = 21$ in the general form of a conic, then identify the coefficients.

20. Identify the type of conic, if any, from the equation $4x^2 - 6x + 9y^2 + 15y - 1 = 0$.

TRIGONOMETRY

ANALYTIC GEOMETRY

7.1 POLAR COORDINATES

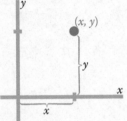

7.1.1 An Introduction to Polar Coordinates

Recall that each point on a Cartesian plane can be identified by an ordered pair (x, y) where the x-coordinate represents the horizontal distance between the point and the origin, and the y-coordinate represents the vertical distance between the point and the origin (Figure 7.1a). The x- and y-coordinates of an ordered pair on a Cartesian plane are also called rectangular coordinates.

The rectangular coordinates of a point (x, y) can be considered as directions for navigating from the origin to the point (x, y). For example, the directions for navigating to the point $(2, 2)$ are to first move 2 units right from the origin, then 2 units up. However, there are other directions from the origin that will result in the same position in the plane. An alternative way to navigate to a point in the plane, and to identify a given point, will be introduced in this chapter.

Figure 7.1a

The point with rectangular coordinates $(2, 2)$ can also be reached by moving $2\sqrt{2}$ units from the origin on the ray that is the terminal side of an angle measuring $\pi/4$ radians (Figure 7.1b).

Thus, an alternative method for navigating to a point in the plane is given by moving a distance r from the origin on the terminal side of an angle θ, rotated from the positive x-axis.

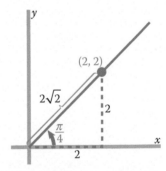

Figure 7.1b

TIP

The distance from the origin to the point (2, 2), $2\sqrt{2}$, can be found using the Pythagorean Theorem or the Distance Formula.

IMPORTANT

If $\theta > 0$, then the ray containing P is rotated counterclockwise from the polar axis. If $\theta < 0$, then the ray containing P is rotated clockwise from the polar axis.

Polar Coordinates

If P is a point in the plane, then the **polar coordinates** of P are (r, θ), where $|r|$ is the distance from the origin to P, and θ is the angle between the positive x-axis and the ray through P.

The positive x-axis is also called the **polar axis**, and the origin is also called the **pole**.

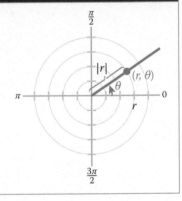

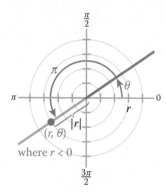

Polar Coordinates When $r < 0$

For rectangular coordinates (x, y), r represents the distance from the origin to (x, y), so r is always positive. However, for polar coordinates (r, θ), r is allowed to be negative because r represents not only the distance from the pole to (r, θ), but also the direction from the pole to (r, θ).

If P is the point (r, θ) such that $r < 0$, then P is $|r|$ units from the origin and the ray containing P is in the direction opposite to the terminal side of θ (Figure 7.1c). Specifically, the ray containing P is rotated π radians (clockwise or counterclockwise) from θ.

Figure 7.1c

> **NOTICE THAT**
>
> *Rotating a ray by π radians in the clockwise direction results in a ray that is the same position as if the original ray was rotated by π radians in the counterclockwise direction.*

EXAMPLE 1 — Plotting Polar Coordinates

Plot each point using the given polar coordinates.

A. $P(3, \pi)$ **B.** $Q(-2, 3\pi/4)$ **C.** $R(-5, -\pi/6)$

SOLUTION

A. $P(3, \pi) \Rightarrow r = 3$ and $\theta = \pi$

P is 3 units from the origin on the ray rotated π radians counterclockwise from the polar axis.

So, P is located at -3 on the negative x-axis.

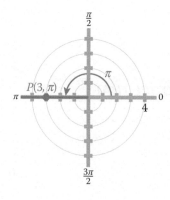

> **NOTICE THAT**
>
> *$P(3, \pi)$ is at the same location on the plane as the point $(-3, 0)$. So, the rectangular coordinates of P are $(-3, 0)$.*

B. $Q(-2, 3\pi/4) \Rightarrow r = -2$ and $\theta = 3\pi/4$

Since $r < 0$, the ray containing Q is rotated $3\pi/4$ radians counterclockwise from the polar axis (in quadrant II), and then π radians counterclockwise. Thus, the ray containing Q is in quadrant IV.

Q is 2 units from the origin on this ray.

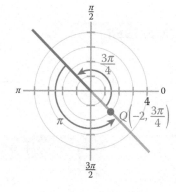

> **TIP**
>
> *Any point 2 units from the origin (on any ray) is on a circle centered at the origin with radius 2.*

C. $R(-5, -\pi/6) \Rightarrow r = -5$ and $\theta = -\pi/6$

The ray containing R is rotated $\pi/6$ radians clockwise from the polar axis (clockwise because $\theta < 0$), and then π radians clockwise (because $r < 0$). Thus, the ray containing R is in quadrant II.

R is 5 units from the origin on this ray.

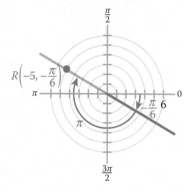

> **IMPORTANT**
>
> *When $r < 0$, the ray is rotated $\theta + \pi$ or $\theta + \pi$ radians from the polar axis (i.e., π radians clockwise or counterclockwise from θ).*

With rectangular coordinates, every point in the plane is represented by a unique ordered pair (x, y). However, this is not the case with polar coordinates. Each point can be represented by an infinite number of polar coordinates. For example, the polar coordinates (r, θ) and $(r, \theta + 2\pi n)$, where n is any integer, represent the same point in the plane because the angles θ and $\theta + 2\pi n$ have the same terminal side. Furthermore, the polar coordinates $(-r, \theta \pm \pi)$ also represent the same point in the plane as (r, θ) and $(r, \theta + 2\pi n)$.

EXAMPLE 2	**Identifying Polar Coordinates from a Graph**

Write two pairs of polar coordinates to represent each point.

A.

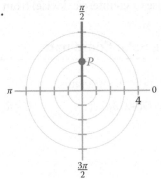

B.

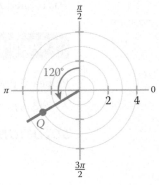

SOLUTION

A. The angle from the polar axis (i.e., the positive x-axis) to the ray containing P is $\pi/2$ radians, so $\theta = \pi/2$. P is 2 units from the origin, so $|r| = 2$. Thus, polar coordinates of P are $(2, \pi/2)$.

Alternatively, if $r = -2$, then the ray containing P can be rotated π radians from θ, so $\theta = 3\pi/2$. Thus, polar coordinates of P are also $(-2, 3\pi/2)$.

B. Since the point Q is located 120° counterclockwise from the positive y-axis, the angle from the polar axis to the ray containing Q is 210°, that is, $7\pi/6$ radians. So, $\theta = 7\pi/6$. Since Q is 3 units from the origin, $|r| = 3$. Thus, polar coordinates of Q are $(3, 7\pi/6)$.

Alternatively, if $r = -3$, then the ray containing Q can be rotated π radians from θ, so $\theta = \pi/6$. Thus, polar coordinates of Q are also $(-3, \pi/6)$.

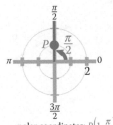

7.1.2 Converting between Polar and Rectangular Coordinates

We have seen that a point in the plane can be represented by a unique ordered pair of rectangular coordinates (x, y) or a pair of polar coordinates (r, θ). When the point is on an axis, then θ is a quadrantal angle and the polar coordinates, as well as the rectangular coordinates, are easily identified. For example, the point in Figure 7.1d has polar coordinates $(1, \pi/2)$ and rectangular coordinates $(0, 1)$. It is important to be able to convert between polar and rectangular coordinates even when the point is not on an axis.

Converting from Polar to Rectangular Coordinates

Suppose P is a point in the plane with polar coordinates (r, θ) and rectangular coordinates (x, y). Trigonometric functions can be used to determine the x- and y-values when the r- and θ-values are known.

polar coordinates: $P\left(1, \frac{\pi}{2}\right)$
rectangular coordinates: $P(0, 1)$

Figure 7.1d

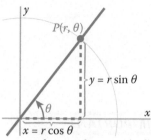

Recall that if (x, y) is a point on the terminal side of θ, then $\cos \theta = x/r$ and $\sin \theta = y/r$, where $r = \sqrt{x^2 + y^2}$. Solving the trigonometric functions for x and y respectively gives $x = r \cos \theta$ and $y = r \sin \theta$. Therefore, if the polar coordinates of a point P are (r, θ), then the rectangular coordinates of P are $(r \cos \theta, r \sin \theta)$.

polar coordinates: $P(r, \theta)$
rectangular coordinates: $P(x, y)$

Figure 7.1e

IMPORTANT

If a point in the plane has polar coordinates (r, θ) and rectangular coordinates (x, y), then $x = r \cos \theta$ and $y = r \sin \theta$.

EXAMPLE 3   **Converting from Polar Coordinates to Rectangular Coordinates**

Convert each pair of polar coordinates (r, θ) to rectangular coordinates (x, y).

A. $P(1, 5\pi/4)$　　　　　**B.** $Q(1.5, 2\pi/3)$

SOLUTION

Plot each point to visualize its location on the plane.

P is in quadrant III.

Q is in quadrant II.

Use $x = r \cos \theta$ and $y = r \sin \theta$ to find the rectangular coordinates (x, y) of P and Q.

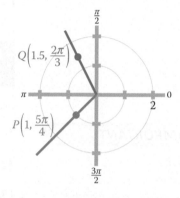

A. $P(1, 5\pi/4) \implies r = 1$ and $\theta = 5\pi/4$

$$x = r \cos \theta = (1) \cos \frac{5\pi}{4} = -\frac{\sqrt{2}}{2}$$

$$y = r \sin \theta = (1) \sin \frac{5\pi}{4} = -\frac{\sqrt{2}}{2}$$

B. $Q(1.5, 2\pi/3) \implies r = 1.5$ and $\theta = 2\pi/3$

$$x = r \cos \theta = (1.5) \cos \frac{2\pi}{3} = (1.5)\left(-\frac{1}{2}\right) = -\frac{3}{4}$$

$$y = r \sin \theta = (1.5) \sin \frac{2\pi}{3} = (1.5)\left(\frac{\sqrt{3}}{2}\right) = \frac{3\sqrt{3}}{4}$$

Therefore, the rectangular coordinates are $P\left(-\frac{\sqrt{2}}{2}, -\frac{\sqrt{2}}{2}\right)$ and $Q\left(-\frac{3}{4}, \frac{3\sqrt{3}}{4}\right)$.

CHECK

Find the location of each point on the plane using decimal approximations for the x- and y-coordinates.

Since $-\dfrac{\sqrt{2}}{2} \approx -0.7$, the approximate rectangular coordinates of P are $(-0.7, -0.7)$.

Since $\dfrac{3\sqrt{3}}{4} \approx 1.3$, the approximate rectangular coordinates of Q are $(-0.75, 1.3)$.

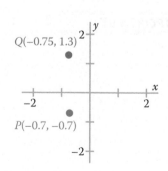

The rectangular coordinates of P and Q appear to correspond to the same positions on the plane as the polar coordinates of P and Q.

Converting from Rectangular to Polar Coordinates

A similar procedure can be used to convert from rectangular coordinates to polar coordinates. In this case, we use expressions for r and θ in terms of x and y.

Again, recall that if (x, y) is a point on the terminal side of θ, then $\sin \theta = y/r$, $\cos \theta = x/r$, and $\tan \theta = y/x$, where $r = \sqrt{x^2 + y^2}$. So, the r-value in the polar coordinates (r, θ) of a point P with rectangular coordinates (x, y) is given by $r = \sqrt{x^2 + y^2}$.

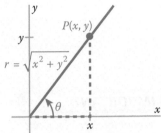

polar coordinates: $P(r, \theta)$
rectangular coordinates: $P(x, y)$

Figure 7.1f

Since $\tan \theta = y/x$, the θ-value in the polar coordinates (r, θ) of a point P with rectangular coordinates (x, y) is given by $\theta = \tan^{-1}(y/x)$, but only when θ is in the range of the inverse tangent function $(-\pi/2, \pi/2)$, that is, only when θ is in quadrant I or IV. If θ is in quadrant II or III, then $\tan^{-1}(y/x)$ can still be used to find θ, though in this case, θ will differ from $\tan^{-1}(y/x)$ by π, that is, $\theta = \tan^{-1}(y/x) \pm \pi$.

EXAMPLE 4 — Converting from Rectangular Coordinates to Polar Coordinates

Convert each pair of rectangular coordinates (x, y) to polar coordinates (r, θ).

A. $P\left(\sqrt{3}, 3\right)$ **B.** $Q(-6, 6)$ **C.** $R(5, -3)$ **D.** $S(-9, -2)$

SOLUTION

Use $r = \sqrt{x^2 + y^2}$ and $\tan^{-1} \dfrac{y}{x}$ to find the polar coordinates (r, θ) of P, Q, R, and S.

A. Since $x = \sqrt{3}$ and $y = 3$, $r = \sqrt{\sqrt{3}^2 + 3^2} = \sqrt{12} = 2\sqrt{3}$ and $\tan^{-1} \dfrac{3}{\sqrt{3}} = \tan^{-1} \sqrt{3} = \dfrac{\pi}{3}$.

P is in quadrant I, so $\theta = \pi/3$. Thus, the polar coordinates of P are $\left(2\sqrt{3}, \dfrac{\pi}{3}\right)$.

B. Since $x = -6$ and $y = 6$, $r = \sqrt{(-6)^2 + 6^2} = 6\sqrt{2}$ and $\tan^{-1} \dfrac{6}{-6} = \tan^{-1}(-1) = -\dfrac{\pi}{4}$.

Q is in quadrant II, so $\theta = -\pi/4 + \pi = 3\pi/4$. Thus, the polar coordinates of Q are $\left(6\sqrt{2}, \dfrac{3\pi}{4}\right)$.

C. Since $x = 5$ and $y = -3$, $r = \sqrt{5^2 + (-3)^2} = \sqrt{34}$ and $\tan^{-1} \dfrac{-3}{5} \approx -0.54$.

R is in quadrant IV, so $\theta \approx -0.54$.

Thus, the polar coordinates of R are approximately $\left(\sqrt{34}, -0.54\right)$.

D. Since $x = -9$ and $y = -2$, $r = \sqrt{(-9)^2 + (-2)^2} = \sqrt{85}$ and $\tan^{-1} \dfrac{-2}{-9} = \tan^{-1} \dfrac{2}{9} \approx 0.22$.

S is in quadrant III, so $\theta \approx 0.22 + \pi \approx 3.36$.

Thus, the polar coordinates of S are approximately $\left(\sqrt{85}, 3.36\right)$.

SECTION 7.1 EXERCISES

Warm Up

Determine the quadrant containing the terminal side of each angle.

1. $2\pi/3$

2. $-150°$

3. $-\pi/6$

Just the Facts

Fill in the blanks.

4. In general, if Q is a point in the plane, then the rectangular coordinates of Q are given by _____, and the polar coordinates of Q are given by _____.

5. The polar coordinates $(3, 5\pi/6)$ describe the point in the plane that is located _____ units from the origin on the ray rotated _____ radians counterclockwise from the _____, which, in rectangular coordinates, is called the positive x-axis.

6. To convert from polar coordinates to rectangular coordinates, use $r\cos\theta$ for _____ and $r\sin\theta$ for _____.

7. To convert from rectangular coordinates to polar coordinates, use $r =$ _____ and $\tan\theta =$ _____.

8. If P is a point with polar coordinates (r, θ) and $r < 0$, then the ray containing P is in the _____ direction of θ.

9. Every point in the plane can be represented by a unique pair of _____ coordinates (x, y). When using _____ coordinates, each point can be represented by multiple pairs of coordinates such as $(r, \theta), (-r, \theta \pm \pi), (-r, \theta \pm 2\pi n)$, and _____.

10. When $\theta < 0$, the ray containing the point with polar coordinates (r, θ) is rotated _____ from the polar axis.

Essential Skills

In Exercises 1–8, plot each point using the given polar coordinates.

1. $(3, 2\pi)$

2. $(4, \pi/2)$

3. $(5, 7\pi/6)$

4. $(2, \pi/4)$

5. $(-3, 4\pi/3)$

6. $(-4, \pi/9)$

7. $(-1, -\pi/4)$

8. $(-6.5, -5\pi/6)$

In Exercises 9–14, write two pairs of polar coordinates (r, θ) to represent each point, where θ is in the interval $[0, 2\pi)$.

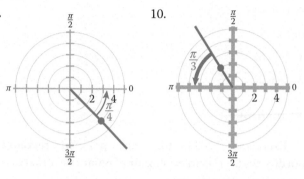

9.   10.

11. a point 2 units from the origin on a ray that forms an angle of $4\pi/3$ radians counterclockwise with the polar axis

12. a point 6 units from the origin on a ray that forms an angle of $11\pi/6$ radians counterclockwise with the polar axis

13. a point 5 units from the origin on a ray that forms a $300°$ angle counterclockwise with the polar axis

14. a point 3.8 units from the origin on a ray that forms a $225°$ angle counterclockwise with the polar axis

In Exercises 15–20, convert each pair of polar coordinates (r, θ) to rectangular coordinates (x, y).

15. $(4, -\pi/6)$

16. $(-3, 2\pi/3)$

17. $(-5, 315°)$

18. $(1, -5\pi/6)$

19. $(6.5, -150°)$

20. $(-4, 3\pi/4)$

In Exercises 21–26, convert each pair of rectangular coordinates (x, y) to polar coordinates (r, θ).

21. $\left(-\sqrt{3}, 1\right)$

22. $(4, -4)$

23. $\left(2\sqrt{2}, -2\sqrt{2}\right)$

24. $\left(-2\sqrt{3}, -2\right)$

25. $\left(\sqrt{6}, -\sqrt{2}\right)$

26. $\left(-5, 5\sqrt{3}\right)$

In Exercises 27–32, convert each pair of rectangular coordinates (x, y) to polar coordinates (r, θ). Round θ to the nearest hundredth.

27. $(2, -5)$

28. $(-1, -3)$

29. $(-4, -6)$

30. $(3, 5)$

31. $(-7, 8)$

32. $(-3, 2)$

Extensions

In Exercises 33–38, for each pair of rectangular coordinates (x, y) find every pair of polar coordinates (r, θ) that satisfy $-2\pi < \theta < 2\pi$.

33. $\left(-2\sqrt{2}, 2\sqrt{2}\right)$

34. $\left(-3\sqrt{6}, 3\sqrt{2}\right)$

35. $\left(5\sqrt{2}, -5\sqrt{6}\right)$

36. $\left(-\sqrt{3}, -1\right)$

37. $(-4, 7)$

38. $(4, -3)$

In Exercises 39–44, for each pair of rectangular coordinates (x, y) find every pair of polar coordinates (r, θ) that satisfy $0 < \theta < 4\pi$.

39. $\left(-3\sqrt{3}, 3\right)$

40. $\left(-4\sqrt{2}, -4\sqrt{2}\right)$

41. $\left(5, -5\sqrt{3}\right)$

42. $(7, 7)$

43. $(-4, -3)$

44. $(5, -12)$

45. Determine the polar coordinates of the vertices of a square that has its center at the origin, two sides parallel to the horizontal axis, and side length s. Use angles within $[0, 2\pi]$ and $r > 0$.

7.2 POLAR EQUATIONS

OBJECTIVES

- Write a polar equation in rectangular form.
- Write a rectangular equation in polar form.
- Graph a polar equation by converting to a rectangular equation.
- Graph simple polar equations.
- Graph special polar equations.

PREREQUISITE VOCABULARY TERMS

circle
inverse trigonometric functions
polar coordinates
radius
rectangular coordinates

7.2.1 Writing a Polar Equation in Rectangular Form

In the last section, we converted between rectangular coordinates and polar coordinates. Similar methods can be used to convert between rectangular equations (in terms of x and y) and **polar equations** (in terms of r and θ). To convert equations between polar form and rectangular form, make substitutions using the following equations.

$$x = r \cos \theta \qquad\qquad r^2 = x^2 + y^2$$
$$y = r \sin \theta \qquad\qquad \tan \theta = y/x$$

IMPORTANT

Squaring both sides of $r = \sqrt{x^2 + y^2}$ gives $r^2 = x^2 + y^2$.

IMPORTANT

There are often several ways in which a polar equation can be converted to a rectangular equation, but each will result in the same general form equation (if completed correctly).

EXAMPLE 1   Writing a Polar Equation in Rectangular Form

Write each polar equation as a rectangular equation in general form.

A. $r = 3 \cos \theta$ 　　　　　　　**B.** $r = -2 \tan \theta$

SOLUTION

A. Notice that the right side contains $\cos \theta$. If the right side contained $r \cos \theta$, then we could substitute x for $r \cos \theta$. So, begin by multiplying both sides of the equation by r. Then substitute using the equations for converting between polar coordinates and rectangular coordinates.

$$r = 3 \cos \theta$$
$$r^2 = r(3 \cos \theta) \qquad \textit{Multiply each side by r.}$$
$$r^2 = 3r \cos \theta \qquad \textit{Commutative Property}$$
$$x^2 + y^2 = 3x \qquad \textit{Substitute } x^2 + y^2 \textit{ for } r^2 \textit{ and x for r cos } \theta.$$
$$x^2 + y^2 - 3x = 0 \qquad \textit{Write the equation in general form.}$$

REMEMBER

An equation in general form has 0 on one side of the equation.

ALTERNATIVE METHOD

Begin by substituting x/r for $\cos \theta$.

$$r = 3 \cos \theta$$
$$r = 3x/r \qquad \textit{Substitute x/r for cos } \theta.$$
$$r^2 = 3x \qquad \textit{Multiply each side by r.}$$
$$x^2 + y^2 = 3x \qquad \textit{Substitute } x^2 + y^2 \textit{ for } r^2.$$
$$x^2 + y^2 - 3x = 0 \qquad \textit{Write the equation in general form.}$$

B. Square both sides of the equation so that the left side is r^2. Then substitute using the equations for converting between polar coordinates and rectangular coordinates.

$$r = -2 \tan \theta$$
$$r^2 = (-2 \tan \theta)^2 \qquad \textit{Square each side.}$$
$$x^2 + y^2 = (-2(y/x))^2 \qquad \textit{Substitute } x^2 + y^2 \textit{ for } r^2 \textit{ and } y/x \textit{ for } \tan \theta.$$
$$x^2 + y^2 = 4y^2/x^2 \qquad \textit{Simplify.}$$
$$x^2(x^2 + y^2) = 4y^2 \qquad \textit{Multiply each side by } x^2.$$
$$x^4 + x^2y^2 - 4y^2 = 0 \qquad \textit{Write the equation in general form.}$$

> **TIP**
>
> $$\left(\frac{-2y}{x}\right)^2 = \frac{(-2)^2(y)^2}{(x)^2}$$
> $$= \frac{4y^2}{x^2}$$

7.2.2 Writing a Polar Equation in Rectangular Form: Another Example

Any of the six definitions of the trigonometric functions of θ can be used when converting between polar and rectangular form. The same is true for any of the trigonometric identities.

EXAMPLE 2 — Writing a Polar Equation in Rectangular Form

Write each polar equation as a rectangular equation in general form.

A. $5 \sec \theta = 4r$ 　　　　**B.** $r = 4$ 　　　　**C.** $2\theta - 3\pi/2 = 0$

SOLUTION

> **IMPORTANT**
>
> Use trigonometric identities to write the equations in terms of sine, cosine, or tangent, as needed.

A. Use the reciprocal identity $\sec \theta = \dfrac{1}{\cos \theta}$ to write the equation in terms of cosine.

$$5 \sec \theta = 4r$$
$$5/(\cos \theta) = 4r \qquad \textit{Reciprocal Identity}$$
$$5 = 4r \cos \theta \qquad \textit{Multiply each side by } \cos \theta.$$
$$5 = 4x \qquad \textit{Substitute } x \textit{ for } r \cos \theta.$$
$$4x - 5 = 0 \qquad \textit{Write the equation in general form.}$$

B. Square both sides of the equation.

$$r = 4$$
$$r^2 = 16 \qquad \textit{Square each side.}$$
$$x^2 + y^2 = 16 \qquad \textit{Substitute } x^2 + y^2 \textit{ for } r^2.$$
$$x^2 + y^2 - 16 = 0 \qquad \textit{Write the equation in general form.}$$

> **NOTICE THAT**
>
> The graph of the rectangular equation is a circle centered at the origin, and with radius 4.

C. Add $3\pi/2$ to each side and then divide each side by 2 to solve the equation for θ.

$$2\theta - 3\pi/2 = 0$$
$$\theta = 3\pi/4 \qquad \textit{Solve for } \theta.$$
$$\tan \theta = \tan (3\pi/4) \qquad \textit{Take the tangent of each side.}$$
$$y/x = -1 \qquad \textit{Evaluate } \tan (3\pi/4) \textit{ and substitute } y/x \textit{ for } \tan \theta.$$
$$y = -x \qquad \textit{Multiply each side by } x.$$
$$x + y = 0 \qquad \textit{Write the equation in general form.}$$

7.2.3 Writing a Rectangular Equation in Polar Form

A polar equation is written in terms of r and θ. To write a rectangular equation (an equation in terms of x and y) in polar form, again use the formulas to convert between rectangular coordinates and polar coordinates.

EXAMPLE 3 Writing a Rectangular Equation in Polar Form

Write each rectangular equation in polar form.

A. $y = 5$ **B.** $y = 3x + 1$ **C.** $y^2 - 6x^2 = 0$

SOLUTION

Manipulate each equation as needed, then substitute using the equations for converting between polar coordinates and rectangular coordinates.

A. Use $y = r \sin\theta$ to write the rectangular equation in terms of r and θ.

$$y = 5$$
$$r \sin\theta = 5 \qquad \text{\textit{Substitute }} r \sin\theta \text{ \textit{for} } y.$$
$$r = 5/\sin\theta \qquad \text{\textit{Divide each side by} } \sin\theta \text{ \textit{to solve for} } r.$$
$$r = 5 \csc\theta \qquad \text{\textit{Reciprocal Identity}}$$

A polar form of the rectangular equation $y = 5$ is $r = 5 \csc\theta$.

B. Use $x = r \cos\theta$ and $y = r \sin\theta$ to write the rectangular equation in terms of r and θ.

$$y = 3x + 1$$
$$r \sin\theta = 3(r \cos\theta) + 1 \qquad \text{\textit{Substitute }} r \cos\theta \text{ \textit{for }} x \text{ \textit{and }} r \sin\theta \text{ \textit{for }} y.$$
$$r \sin\theta - 3r \cos\theta = 1 \qquad \text{\textit{Subtract }} 3r \cos\theta \text{ \textit{from each side.}}$$
$$r(\sin\theta - 3 \cos\theta) = 1 \qquad \text{\textit{Factor }} r \text{ \textit{from each term.}}$$
$$r = \frac{1}{\sin\theta - 3 \cos\theta} \qquad \text{\textit{Solve for }} r.$$

A polar form of the rectangular equation $y = 3x + 1$ is $r = \dfrac{1}{\sin\theta - 3 \cos\theta}$.

C. Manipulate the equation so that it contains y/x, then use $\tan\theta = y/x$ to write the rectangular equation in terms of r and θ.

$$y^2 - 6x^2 = 0$$
$$y^2 = 6x^2 \qquad \text{\textit{Add }} 6x^2 \text{ \textit{to each side.}}$$
$$y^2/x^2 = 6 \qquad \text{\textit{Divide each side by }} x^2.$$
$$(y/x)^2 = 6 \qquad \text{\textit{Power of a Quotient Property}}$$
$$(\tan\theta)^2 = 6 \qquad \text{\textit{Substitute }} \tan\theta \text{ \textit{for }} y/x.$$
$$\tan^2\theta = 6 \qquad \text{\textit{Simplify.}}$$

A polar form of the rectangular equation $y^2 - 6x^2 = 0$ is $\tan^2\theta = 6$.

IMPORTANT

Use trigonometric identities to write the equations in terms of sine, cosine, or tangent, as needed.

TIP

The equation $r \sin\theta = 5$ is in polar form because it is in terms of r and θ.

TIP

Isolate the r-terms on one side of the equation so that the equation can be solved for r.

CHECK

Write the equation in rectangular form.

$$r = 7$$
$$r^2 = 49 \qquad \textit{Square each side.}$$
$$x^2 + y^2 = 49 \qquad \textit{Substitute } x^2 + y^2 \textit{ for } r^2.$$

The resulting equation $x^2 + y^2 = 49$ describes a circle with center $(0, 0)$ and radius 7. ✔

B. The graph of $\theta = \pi/9$ is all points on the polar plane with θ-coordinate $\pi/9$. Since r is not specified in the equation, r can take on any value.

Recall that θ is the angle of rotation from the positive x-axis (or polar axis) to a ray containing a polar point. So, $\theta = \pi/9$ is the graph of all points on the ray that is rotated $\pi/9$ radians (counterclockwise) from the polar axis.

Furthermore, since r can be any positive or negative value, the ray extends out from the origin in both directions.

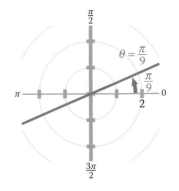

TIP

$\pi/9$ radians is 20°.

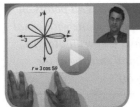

7.2.5 Graphing Special Polar Equations

Polar Equations of Circles

The equation of a circle appears simpler in polar form than it does in rectangular form. For example, the polar form of the rectangular equation $x^2 + y^2 = c^2$ (a circle centered at the origin and radius c) is simply $r = c$.

The polar equations $r = a \cos \theta$ and $r = a \sin \theta$ also define circles. However, these circles are not centered at the origin, but instead pass through the origin. The centers, in rectangular coordinates, are at $(a/2, 0)$ and $(0, a/2)$, respectively. Thus, each circle's radius is $|a|/2$. The attributes of the polar graphs of $r = a \cos \theta$ and $r = a \sin \theta$ where $a > 0$ are summarized in the following table.

TIP

When $a < 0$, the graph of $r = a \cos \theta$ is the reflection across the vertical axis of the graph of $r = |a| \cos \theta$. Similarly, when $a < 0$, the graph of $r = a \sin \theta$ is the reflection across the horizontal axis of the graph of $r = |a| \sin \theta$.

Polar Equations of Circles: $r = a \cos \theta$ and $r = a \sin \theta$, $a > 0$	
$r = a \cos \theta$	$r = a \sin \theta$
center at $(a/2, 0)$ *on the horizontal axis*	center at $(a/2, \pi/2)$ *on the vertical axis*

Also, note that the graph of $r = a \cos \theta$ is symmetric about the horizontal axis, and the graph of $r = a \sin \theta$ is symmetric about the vertical axis, as expected because cosine is an even function and sine is an odd function.

| **EXAMPLE 6** | **Graphing the Polar Equation of a Circle** |

Identify the center, radius, and symmetry of each circle, and then sketch the circle's graph.

A. $r = 9 \cos \theta$ **B.** $r = 6 \sin \theta$

SOLUTION

A. The polar graph of an equation of the form $r = a \cos \theta$, where $a = 9$, is a circle symmetric about the horizontal axis that passes through the origin. The circle is centered at $(9/2, 0)$ and its radius is $9/2$. The circle also passes through $(9, 0)$.

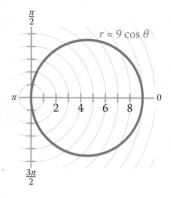

TIP

The circle is centered at (4.5, 0), which is the point 4.5 units from the origin on the polar axis. In rectangular coordinates, the center is at (4.5, 0), which is on the x-axis.

B. The polar graph of an equation of the form $r = a \sin \theta$, where $a = 6$, is a circle symmetric about the vertical axis that passes through the origin. The circle is centered at $(3, \pi/2)$ and its radius is 3. The circle also passes through $(6, \pi/2)$.

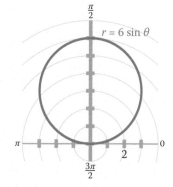

TIP

The circle is centered at (3, π/2), which is the point 3 units from the origin on the ray rotated π/2 radians from the pole (i.e., the vertical axis). In rectangular coordinates, the center is at (0, 3), which is on the y-axis.

Polar Equations of Rose Curves

If n is an integer and $n > 1$, then the graph of a polar equation of the form $r = a \sin n\theta$ or $r = a \cos n\theta$, called a **rose curve**, is composed of evenly spaced **petals**, as shown in the table below. The **radius of a petal** is the maximum r-value on the rose curve, which occurs at each point that defines the tip of a petal.

TIP

Like the equation of a circle, the equation of a rose curve appears much simpler in polar form than it does in rectangular form.

Examples of Rose Curves

$r = 5 \cos 5\theta$	$r = 2 \cos 4\theta$	$r = 4 \sin 7\theta$	$r = 4 \sin 6\theta$
5 petals, radius 5	8 petals, radius 2	7 petals, radius 4	12 petals, radius 4

The n-value and the a-value in the equation of a rose curve can be used to determine the number of petals, the radius of the petals, and the angle between the petals of a rose curve.

• A rose curve has n petals when n is odd, and $2n$ petals when n is even.
• The angle between pairs of consecutive petals is equal to 2π divided by the number of petals.
• The radius of the petals is equal to $|a|$.

Notice that if $\theta = 0$, then $r = a \cos n\theta = a \cos 0 = a(1) = a$ (which is also the petal radius). Therefore, in the graph of a rose curve defined by $r = a \cos n\theta$, the point at the tip of one of the petals is always at $(a, 0)$ on the horizontal axis.

Additionally, if $\theta = \pi/(2n)$, then $r = a \sin n\theta = a \sin (\pi/2) = a(1) = a$. Therefore, in the graph of a rose curve defined by $r = a \sin n\theta$, the point at the tip of one of the petals is always at $\left(a, \dfrac{\pi}{2n}\right)$.

The attributes of the polar graphs of $r = a \cos n\theta$ and $r = a \sin n\theta$, where $a > 0$ and $n > 1$, are summarized in the following table.

Polar Equations of Rose Curves: $r = a \cos n\theta$ and $r = a \sin n\theta$, $a > 0$ and $n > 1$				
	$r = a \cos n\theta$		$r = a \sin n\theta$	
	n is odd	n is even	n is odd	n is even
Symmetric About	the horizontal axis	the vertical and horizontal axes	the vertical axis	the vertical and horizontal axes
Number of Petals	n	$2n$	n	$2n$
Angle Between the Petals	$2\pi/n$	π/n	$2\pi/n$	π/n
Tip of One Petal	$(a, 0)$		$\left(a, \dfrac{\pi}{2n}\right)$	

If $a < 0$, then the graph of $r = a \cos n\theta$ is a reflection over the vertical axis of the graph of $r = |a| \cos n\theta$, and the graph of $r = a \sin n\theta$ is a reflection over the horizontal axis of the graph of $r = |a| \sin n\theta$.

Figure 7.2b shows the graph of $r = 2 \cos 3\theta$, which is a rose curve with 3 petals with radius 2, where the angle between each pair of consecutive petals is $2\pi/3$.

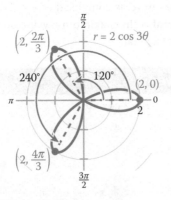

Figure 7.2b

Since the radius of each petal is also the r-coordinate at the point that defines the tip of each petal, the θ-coordinate of the tip of each petal can be found by substituting the radius in the equation of the rose curve for r, and then solving for θ.

For example, since the graph of $r = 2 \cos 3\theta$ has petals with radius 2, solving the equation $2 = 2 \cos 3\theta$ for θ gives the θ-coordinate of the tip of each petal.

$$2 = 2 \cos 3\theta \implies \cos 3\theta = 1$$

Find all solutions to $\cos 3\theta = 1$ on the interval $[0, 2\pi)$. We know that $\cos x = 1$ when $x = 0, 2\pi, 4\pi, 6\pi \ldots$. Therefore, $3\theta = 0$, $3\theta = 2\pi$, $3\theta = 4\pi \ldots$.

Solving for θ gives $\theta = 0$, $\theta = 2\pi/3$, and $\theta = 4\pi/3$. (All other solutions of $\cos 3\theta = 1$ are either less than 0 or greater than or equal to 2π.) Therefore, the polar coordinates of the point that defines the tip of the 3 petals in the graph of $r = 2 \cos 3\theta$ are $(2, 0)$, $(2, 2\pi/3)$, and $(2, 4\pi/3)$, as shown in Figure 7.2b.

TIP

Because this rose curve has 3 petals, it is necessary to find the polar coordinates for three points.

EXAMPLE 7   **Graphing the Polar Equation of a Rose Curve**

Identify the number of petals, petal radius, and symmetry (if any) of each rose curve, and then sketch its graph.

A. $r = 3 \cos 5\theta$ **B.** $r = 2 \sin 3\theta$

SOLUTION

A. The equation $r = 3 \cos 5\theta$ is of the form $r = a \cos n\theta$, where $a = 3$ and $n = 5$.

Therefore:

- The graph has 5 petals (since $n = 5$, and n is odd), each with a radius of 3 (since $r = 3$).
- The graph is symmetric about the horizontal axis (since the equation is of the form $r = a \cos n\theta$, where n is odd).
- The tip of one petal is at $(3, 0)$ because $\theta = 0$ when $r = 3$.

As with every rose curve, the petals of the graph of $r = 3 \cos 5\theta$ are evenly spaced. Since there are 5 petals, the angle between the petals is $2\pi/5$.

Plot the points for the tip of each petal: $(3, 0)$, $(3, 2\pi/5)$, $(3, 4\pi/5)$, $(3, 6\pi/5)$, and $(3, 8\pi/5)$.

Then sketch the petals from the origin to each petal tip and back.

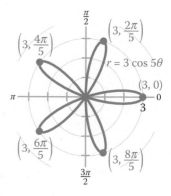

B. The equation $r = 2 \sin 3\theta$ is of the form $r = a \sin n\theta$, where $a = 2$ and $n = 3$.

Therefore:

- The graph has 3 petals (since $n = 3$, and n is odd), each with a radius of 2 (since $r = 2$).
- The graph is symmetric about the vertical axis (since the equation is of the form $r = a \sin n\theta$, where n is odd).
- The tip of one petal is at $(2, \pi/6)$ because $\theta = \pi/6$ when $r = 2$.

As with every rose curve, the petals of the graph of $r = 2 \sin 3\theta$ are evenly spaced. Since there are 3 petals, the angle between the petals is $2\pi/3$.

Plot the points for the tip of each petal: $(2, \pi/6)$, $(2, 5\pi/6)$, and $(2, 3\pi/2)$.

Then sketch the petals from the origin to each petal tip and back.

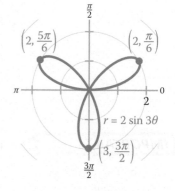

Polar Equations of Limaçons

Another type of polar equation that appears much simpler in polar form than it does in rectangular form describes a graph called a **limaçon**. The shape of a limaçon is somewhat circular, and includes either a dimple or an inner loop. Examples of limaçons are shown in the following table.

Examples of Limaçons			
$r = 5 - 4\cos\theta$	$r = 1 - 3\cos\theta$	$r = 4 - 3\sin\theta$	$r = 3 - 6\sin\theta$
dimple (right)	*inner loop (right)*	*dimple (top)*	*inner loop (top)*

A **horizontal limaçon** is symmetric about the horizontal axis. Its equation is of the form $r = a - b\cos\theta$ and its dimple or inner loop is on the left or right part of the curve (depending on the signs of a and b).

A **vertical limaçon** is symmetric about the vertical axis. Its equation is of the form $r = a - b\sin\theta$ and its dimple or inner loop is on the top or bottom part of the curve (depending on the signs of a and b).

TIP

On a polar graph, the origin is the point where $r = 0$ for any value of θ.

Limaçons have an inner loop when $|a| < |b|$. Every limaçon with an inner loop passes through the origin. Limaçons have a dimple (but no inner loop) when $|a| \geq |b|$. If $|a| \leq |b|$, then the limaçon passes through the origin.

The following table summarizes the attributes of the polar graphs of $r = a - b\cos\theta$ and $r = a - b\sin\theta$, where $a > 0$ and $b > 0$.

Polar Equations of Limaçons: $r = a - b\cos\theta$ and $r = a - b\sin\theta$, $a > 0$ and $b > 0$				
		$r = a - b\cos\theta$		$r = a - b\sin\theta$
		$a > b$	$a < b$	$a > b$	$a < b$
Graph contains		dimple (right)	inner loop (right)	dimple (top)	inner loop (top)
Symmetric about		the horizontal axis		the vertical axis	
nonzero horizontal axis intercepts		$(a + b, \pi)$ and $(a - b, 0)$		(a, π) and $(a, 0)$	
nonzero vertical axis intercepts		$(a, \pi/2)$ and $(a, 3\pi/2)$		$(a - b, \pi/2)$ and $(a + b, 3\pi/2)$	

IMPORTANT

The graph of a limaçon passes through the origin when $|a| \leq |b|$.

If $b < 0$, then the graph of $r = a - b\cos\theta$ is the reflection over the vertical axis of the graph of $r = a - |b|\cos\theta$, and the graph of $r = a - b\sin\theta$ is the reflection over the horizontal axis of the graph of $r = a - |b|\sin\theta$.

The case where $a = b$ is a special type of limaçon called a **cardioid**. The graph of a cardioid is similar to the dimpled limaçon, but it is more heart-shaped. The tip of a cardioid's dimple is always at the origin. Examples of cardioids are shown in the following table.

Examples of Cardioids			
$r = 5 - 5\cos\theta$	$r = 1 - \cos\theta$	$r = 4 - 4\sin\theta$	$r = 5 - 5\sin\theta$
dimple (right)	*dimple (right)*	*dimple (top)*	*dimple (top)*

EXAMPLE 8   Graphing the Polar Equation of a Limaçon

Graph each polar equation.

A. $r = 2 - \cos\theta$ **B.** $r = 1 - 3\sin\theta$

SOLUTION

A. The equation is of the form $r = a - b\cos\theta$, where $a = 2$ and $b = 1$. So, the graph is a horizontal limaçon symmetric about the horizontal axis with a dimple on the right. Find the polar coordinates of the horizontal and vertical axis intercepts.

$\theta = 0 \ \Rightarrow \ r = 2 - \cos 0 = 2 - 1 = 1$

$\theta = \pi \ \Rightarrow \ r = 2 - \cos \pi = 2 - (-1) = 3$

$\theta = \pi/2 \ \Rightarrow \ r = 2 - \cos(\pi/2) = 2 - 0 = 2$

$\theta = 3\pi/2 \ \Rightarrow \ r = 2 - \cos(3\pi/2) = 2 - 0 = 2$

Plot the four intercepts, $(1, 0)$, $(3, \pi)$, $(2, \pi/2)$ and $(2, 3\pi/2)$, then sketch the dimpled limaçon through the intercepts.

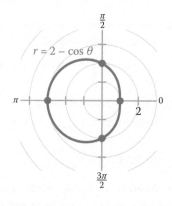

B. The equation is of the form $r = a - b\sin\theta$, where $a = 1$ and $b = 3$. Therefore, the graph is a vertical limaçon symmetric about the vertical axis with an inner loop on the top.

Find the polar coordinates of the horizontal and vertical axis intercepts. Since $|a| \le |b|$, the limaçon passes through the origin.

$\theta = 0 \ \Rightarrow \ r = 1 - 3\sin 0 = 1 - 3(0) = 1$

$\theta = \pi \ \Rightarrow \ r = 1 - 3\sin \pi = 1 - 3(0) = 1$

$\theta = \pi/2 \ \Rightarrow \ r = 1 - 3\sin(\pi/2) = 1 - 3(1) = -2$

$\theta = 3\pi/2 \ \Rightarrow \ r = 1 - 3\sin(3\pi/2) = 1 - 3(-1) = 4$

Plot the five intercepts, $(0, 0)$, $(1, 0)$, $(1, \pi)$, $(-2, \pi/2)$ and $(4, 3\pi/2)$, then sketch the limaçon through the intercepts with an inner loop at the top.

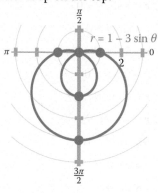

TIP

This limaçon will not pass through the origin because $|a| > |b|$.

SECTION 7.2 EXERCISES

Warm Up

Write the equation of each conic in standard form by completing the square.

1. $x^2 - 6x + y^2 = 0$

2. $x^2 - y^2 + 8y = 0$

3. $x^2 - 10x + y^2 + 2y = 0$

Just the Facts

Fill in the blanks.

4. To convert a polar equation to a rectangular equation, substitute x for _____, y for _____, y/x for _____, and $x^2 + y^2$ for _____.

5. When substituting for csc θ, sec θ, and cot θ in the conversion from a polar equation to a rectangular equation, use the _____ identities.

6. The graph of $x = c$, where c is a real number, is the graph of a(n) _____, whereas the graph of $r = c$, where c is a real number, is the graph of a(n) _____.

7. The graph of a diagonal line formed by all points along the rays θ and $\theta \pm \pi$ has the equation _____.

8. An equation in the form $r = \theta$ is the graph of a _____ starting at the origin.

9. A rose curve graph has a polar equation of the form _____ or _____.

10. The number of petals in a rose curve graph can be determined by _____ in the equation $r = a \sin n\theta$.

Essential Skills

In Exercises 1–18, write each polar equation as a rectangular equation in general form.

1. $r = 2 \cos \theta$

2. $r - 3 \sin \theta = 0$

3. $r + \sin \theta = 0$

4. $r - 5 \cos \theta = 0$

5. $r - \tan \theta = 0$

6. $r = 4 \tan \theta$

7. $r = -4 \sec \theta$

8. $-5 \cot \theta = 10r$

9. $r = 2 \csc \theta$

10. $-8 \sec \theta = 2r$

11. $6r = 2 \cot \theta$

12. $-42 \csc \theta = 7r$

13. $\theta = 5\pi/3$

14. $0 = \theta - 11\pi/6$

15. $4\theta + \pi = 0$

16. $0 = \theta - 5\pi/6$

17. $r = 2$

18. $r = -5$

In Exercises 19–28, write each rectangular equation in polar form.

19. $x = 8$

20. $y = -3$

21. $2x + 5y = 3$

22. $y = -4x + 2$

23. $-3x + 2y = 9$

24. $y = 4x - 2$

25. $x^2 + y^2 = 16$

26. $2x^2 = -2y^2 + 8$

27. $x^2 = 5y$

28. $3x^2 + 3y^2 = 27$

In Exercises 29–36, graph each polar equation.

29. $r = 5$

30. $r = 3$

31. $\theta = 5\pi/4$

32. $\theta = -\pi/6$

33. $r = 2 \cos \theta$

34. $r = -6 \sin \theta$

35. $r = 4 \sin \theta$

36. $r = -3 \cos \theta$

In Exercises 37–42, identify the center and the radius of each circle.

37. $r = 5 \sin \theta$

38. $r = 11 \cos \theta$

39. $r = 4 \cos \theta$

40. $r = -3 \sin \theta$

41. $r = -4 \sin \theta$

42. $r = 7 \cos \theta$

In Exercises 43–48, identify the number of petals and petal radius of each rose curve. Then state whether the graph has a vertical, horizontal, or no axis of symmetry.

43. $r = 6 \cos 3\theta$

44. $r = 3 \sin 4\theta$

45. $r = 5 \sin 7\theta$

46. $r = 7 \cos 6\theta$

47. $r = 4 \cos 2\theta$

48. $r = 8 \sin 5\theta$

In Exercises 49–60, graph each polar equation.

49. $r = 5 \cos 3\theta$

50. $r = 4 \sin 5\theta$

51. $r = 7 \sin 2\theta$

52. $r = 6 \cos 4\theta$

53. $r = 8 \sin 6\theta$

54. $r = 2 \cos 7\theta$

55. $r = 1 - 3 \cos \theta$

56. $r = 2 - 4 \sin \theta$

57. $r = 3 - 5 \sin \theta$

58. $r = 6 - 5 \cos \theta$

59. $r = 2 - \sin \theta$

60. $r = 4 - 5 \cos \theta$

Extensions

In Exercises 61–64, graph each pair of polar equations and determine the point(s) of intersection.

61. $r = -4 \cos \theta; r = -2 \sec \theta$

62. $r = 16 \sin \theta; r = 4 \csc \theta$

63. $r = 5 + 2 \sin \theta; r = 4$

64. $r = -\sqrt{3} + 4 \cos \theta; r = \sqrt{3}$

In Exercises 65–66, convert each polar equation to a rectangular equation.

65. $r \cos (\theta - 7\pi/4) = 5$

66. $r \sin (\theta + 4\pi/3) = 4$

In Exercises 67–68, graph each polar equation.

67. $r = 3 - 3 \sin \theta$

68. $r = 2 - 2 \cos \theta$

In Exercises 69–74, write a polar equation whose graph has the given characteristics.

69. a circle with radius 8 and center $(8, 3\pi/2)$

70. a line that passes through $(7, 4\pi/3)$

71. a rose curve with 5 petals, vertical axis of symmetry, and a petal tip at $(4, \pi/2)$

72. a rose curve with 7 petals, horizontal axis of symmetry, and petal radius 6

73. a horizontal limaçon with intercepts $(6, 0)$, $(-10, 0)$, $(8, \pi/2)$, and $(-8, \pi/2)$

74. a vertical limaçon with intercepts $(4, 0)$, $(4, \pi)$, $(1, \pi/2)$, and $(7, -\pi/2)$

7.3 ROTATION OF AXES

OBJECTIVES

- Use the rotation of axes formula to find the coordinates of a point after being rotated about the origin through an angle of ϕ.
- Identify the type of conic by its equation.
- Graph a rotated conic.

PREREQUISITE VOCABULARY TERMS

axis of symmetry

conic section

Sum of Angles Formulas

trigonometric functions

7.3.1 The Rotation of Axes Formulas

We have seen that various transformations, such as translations or reflections, can be applied to the graph of an equation.

Another type of transformation, called a **rotation**, occurs when a graph or figure is rotated about a fixed point on a plane. The fixed point is called the **center of rotation**. The **angle of rotation**, typically represented by ϕ (the Greek letter "phi"), defines the amount of rotation.

If the x- and y-axes are rotated by a given angle ϕ, then the resulting axes are referred to as the x'-axis and the y'-axis (the x-prime axis and the y-prime axis). For example, a counterclockwise rotation about the origin of the x- and y-axes by an angle of ϕ is shown in Figure 7.3a.

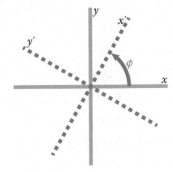

Figure 7.3a

When a point $P(x, y)$ is rotated about the origin by angle ϕ, then the image of $P(x, y)$ after the rotation is referred to as $P'(x', y')$. In this case, if P is on the terminal side of standard position angle θ, then $P'(x', y')$ is on the terminal side of a standard position angle measuring $\theta + \phi$ (Figure 7.3b). Furthermore, if the distance between the origin and P is r, where $r = \sqrt{x^2 + y^2}$, it follows that the distance from the origin to P' is also r, and the relationship between x', y', and r is given by $r = \sqrt{(x')^2 + (y')^2}$.

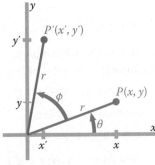

Figure 7.3b

Additionally, since $x = r \cos \theta$ and $y = r \sin \theta$ (Figure 7.3c), it follows that $x' = r \cos (\theta + \phi)$ and $y' = r \sin (\theta + \phi)$ (Figure 7.3d).

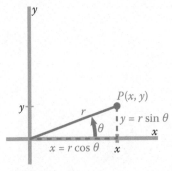

Figure 7.3c

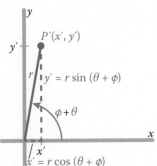

Figure 7.3d

The sum of angles formulas for sine and cosine (from Section 3.3) can be used to simplify $x' = r \cos(\theta + \phi)$ and $y' = r \sin(\theta + \phi)$.

$$\begin{aligned} x' &= r \cos(\theta + \phi) \\ &= r(\cos\theta\cos\phi - \sin\theta\sin\phi) \quad \text{\textit{Sum of Angles Formulas}} \\ &= r\cos\theta\cos\phi - r\sin\theta\sin\phi \quad \text{\textit{Distribute r.}} \\ &= x\cos\phi - y\sin\phi \quad \text{\textit{Substitute x for r cos }}\theta \\ & \qquad\qquad\qquad\qquad \text{\textit{and y for r sin }}\theta. \end{aligned}$$

$$\begin{aligned} y' &= r\sin(\theta + \phi) \\ &= r(\sin\theta\cos\phi + \cos\theta\sin\phi) \\ &= r\sin\theta\cos\phi + r\cos\theta\sin\phi \\ &= y\cos\phi + x\sin\phi \end{aligned}$$

The **rotation of axes formulas** follow from this result.

> **Rotation of Axes Formulas**
>
> If a point $P(x, y)$ on the x- and y-axes is rotated by an angle ϕ counterclockwise about the origin then the image of $P(x, y)$ is $P(x', y')$ where
>
> $$x' = x\cos\phi - y\sin\phi \quad \text{and} \quad y' = y\cos\phi + x\sin\phi.$$

EXAMPLE 1   **Using the Rotation of Axes Formulas**

Suppose a point $P(4, 1)$ is rotated by an angle of $\pi/6$ counterclockwise about the origin. Find the coordinates of P', the image of P after the rotation.

SOLUTION

Use the rotation of axes formula where $x = 4$, $y = 1$, and $\phi = \pi/6$ to find x' and y'.

$$x' = x\cos\phi - y\sin\phi = 4\cos\frac{\pi}{6} - 1\sin\frac{\pi}{6} = 4\left(\frac{\sqrt{3}}{2}\right) - 1\left(\frac{1}{2}\right) = \frac{4\sqrt{3}-1}{2}$$

$$y' = y\cos\phi + x\sin\phi = 1\cos\frac{\pi}{6} + 4\sin\frac{\pi}{6} = 1\left(\frac{\sqrt{3}}{2}\right) + 4\left(\frac{1}{2}\right) = \frac{\sqrt{3}+4}{2}$$

Therefore, P' has coordinates $\left(\dfrac{4\sqrt{3}-1}{2}, \dfrac{\sqrt{3}+4}{2}\right)$.

EXAMPLE 2   **Using the Rotation of Axes Formulas**

IMPORTANT

If the center of rotation is not stated, then the center of rotation should be assumed to be the origin.

Suppose $P'(x', y')$ is the image of $P(x, y)$ after being rotated by an angle of ϕ counterclockwise about the origin. Find y' if $\phi = 3\pi/2$, $x = 5$, and $x' = -1$.

SOLUTION

Use the rotation of axes formula for x' where $x = 5$, $x' = -1$, and $\phi = 3\pi/2$ to find y.

$$\begin{aligned} x' &= x\cos\phi - y\sin\phi \\ -1 &= 5\cos(3\pi/2) - y\sin(3\pi/2) \\ -1 &= 5(0) - y(-1) \\ -1 &= y \end{aligned}$$

Now use the rotation of axes formula for y' where $x = 5$, $y = -1$, and $\phi = 3\pi/2$ to find y'.

$$y' = y\cos\phi + x\sin\phi = (-1)\cos(3\pi/2) + 5\sin(3\pi/2) = (-1)(0) + 5(-1) = -5$$

So, $y' = -5$.

7.3.2   Rotating the Axes to Graph Conics

Recall from Chapter 6 that a conic section is a figure formed by the intersection of a cone with a plane. Parabolas, ellipses (including circles), and hyperbolas are all conic sections.

The equation of any conic can be written in the general form, $Ax^2 + Bxy + Cy^2 + Dx + Ey + F = 0$, where A, B, and C are not all equal to 0. The discriminant, $B^2 - 4AC$, and coefficients of a general form equation can be used to identify the type of conic, as summarized below.

Classifying Conics: $Ax^2 + Bxy + Cy^2 + Dx + Ey + F = 0$	
Circle	$B^2 - 4AC < 0$, $B = 0$, and $A = C$
Ellipse (non-circular)	$B^2 - 4AC < 0$, and $B \neq 0$ or $A \neq C$
Hyperbola	$B^2 - 4AC > 0$
Parabola	$B^2 - 4AC = 0$

If the equation of a conic has no B-term (i.e., $B = 0$), then the conic has an axis of symmetry that is either parallel to, or coincides with, the x- or y-axis. (This was the case for all conics in Chapter 6.)

A **rotated conic** is a conic in which the axes of symmetry have been rotated about the origin by some angle of rotation ϕ. An example of a rotated ellipse is shown in Figure 7.3e. The equation of a rotated conic will have a B-term (i.e., $B \neq 0$).

Given the equation for a conic and an angle of rotation, the rotation of axes formulas can be used to find the equation of the resulting rotated conic, as demonstrated in **Example 3**.

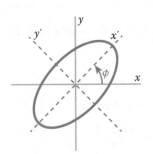

Figure 7.3e

NOTICE THAT

Writing $y = x^2$ in general form gives $y - x^2 = 0$. So, $A = 1$, $B = 0$, and $C = 0$. Therefore, since $B^2 - 4AC = 0$, the graph of $y = x^2$ is a parabola.

EXAMPLE 3   Writing the Equation of a Rotated Conic

Write the equation of the resulting conic if the graph of $y = x^2$ is rotated counterclockwise by an angle of $\pi/2$ radians about the origin. Then graph both conics.

SOLUTION

First, use the rotation of axes formulas to find expressions for x' and y' in terms of x and y. Then solve each equation for x and y, and substitute to write the equation of the rotated conic.

$$x' = x \cos \phi - y \sin \phi = x \cos (\pi/2) - y \sin (\pi/2) = x(0) - y(1) = -y$$

$$y' = y \cos \phi + x \sin \phi = y \cos (\pi/2) + x \sin (\pi/2) = y(0) + x(1) = x$$

So, $x' = -y$ and $y' = x$.

Solve for x and y.

$$y' = x \implies x = y' \quad \text{and} \quad x' = -y \implies y = -x'$$

Substitute $x = y'$ and $y = -x'$ into the original equation.

$$y = x^2 \implies -x' = y'^2 \implies y'^2 = -x'$$

The graph of $y'^2 = -x'$ is a horizontal parabola with vertex at $(0, 0)$, opening to the left.

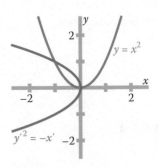

NOTICE THAT

The graph of $y'^2 = -x'$ is the image of the graph of $y = x^2$ after a counterclockwise rotation of 90° about the origin.

| **EXAMPLE 4** | **Identifying the Type of Conic** |

Identify the type of conic, if any, given by each equation.

A. $x^2 + 3xy + 2y^2 + x - 3y + 9 = 0$ **B.** $3x^2 - 2xy + y^2 + 1 = y - 7x$

SOLUTION

Identify A, B, and C from each equation (in general form), then find the discriminant.

A. Evaluate the discriminant using $A = 1$, $B = 3$, and $C = 2$. $B^2 - 4AC = 3^2 - 4(1)(2) = 1$

Since $B^2 - 4AC > 0$, the equation is a hyperbola.

REMEMBER

Write the equation in general form before identifying the values of the coefficients.

B. The general form equation is $3x^2 - 2xy + y^2 + 7x - y + 1 = 0$.

Evaluate the discriminant using $A = 3$, $B = -2$, and $C = 1$. $B^2 - 4AC = (-2)^2 - 4(3)(1) = -8$

Since $B^2 - 4AC < 0$ and $A \neq C$, the equation is an ellipse, but not a circle.

Graphing $Ax^2 + Bxy + Cy^2 + Dx + Ey + F = 0$ When $B \neq 0$

Each of the conics graphed in Chapter 6 has an equation that can be written in the general form $Ax^2 + Bxy + Cy^2 + Dx + Ey + F = 0$ where $B = 0$. When $B \neq 0$, a conic with an equation of the form $Ax^2 + Bxy + Cy^2 + Dx + Ey + F = 0$ can be graphed using the following procedure.

Rotated Conics

The graph of $Ax^2 + Bxy + Cy^2 + Dx + Ey + F = 0$ (where $B \neq 0$) is the graph of $A'(x')^2 + C'(y')^2 + D'x' + E'y' + F' = 0$ rotated counterclockwise by an angle ϕ such that $\cot 2\phi = \dfrac{A - C}{B}$ and $0 < 2\phi < \pi$.

The coefficients A', C', D', E', and F' are given by
$\quad A' = A \cos^2 \phi + B \cos \phi \sin \phi + C \sin^2 \phi,$
$\quad C' = A \sin^2 \phi - B \cos \phi \sin \phi + C \cos^2 \phi,$
$\quad D' = D \cos \phi + E \sin \phi,$
$\quad E' = -D \sin \phi + E \cos \phi,$ and
$\quad F' = F.$

NOTICE THAT

The formulas for A' and C' are very similar, and the formulas for D' and E' are very similar.

Steps for Graphing a Conic $Ax^2 + Bxy + Cy^2 + Dx + Ey + F = 0$ Where $B \neq 0$

❶ Use the discriminant to determine the type of conic given by the original equation.

❷ Calculate the angle of rotation ϕ.

❸ Calculate the coefficients A', C', D', E', and F'.

❹ Write and graph the new equation $A'(x')^2 + C'(y')^2 + D'x' + E'y' + F' = 0$.

❺ Rotate the graph counterclockwise by angle ϕ about the origin to obtain the graph of $Ax^2 + Bxy + Cy^2 + Dx + Ey + F = 0$.

IMPORTANT

The graph of the equation in terms of x' and y' is the pre-image of the rotated conic.

EXAMPLE 5 Graphing a Conic

Graph. $\sqrt{3}x^2 + 3xy + 2\sqrt{3}y^2 - 12 = 0$

SOLUTION

Identify the type of conic. $\quad B^2 - 4AC = 3^2 - 4\left(\sqrt{3}\right)\left(2\sqrt{3}\right) = 9 - 24 = -15$

Since $B^2 - 4AC < 0$ and $A \neq C$, the conic is an ellipse, but not a circle.

Calculate the angle of rotation ϕ.

$$\cot 2\phi = \frac{\sqrt{3} - 2\sqrt{3}}{3} \qquad \textit{Substitute.}$$

$$\cot 2\phi = -\frac{\sqrt{3}}{3} \qquad \textit{Simplify.}$$

> **IMPORTANT**
>
> *Since cotangent is negative in the quadrants II and IV, and $0 < 2\phi < \pi$, it follows that 2ϕ is in quadrant II.*

$$2\phi = \frac{2\pi}{3} \qquad \textit{Take the inverse cotangent of each side.}$$

$$\phi = \frac{\pi}{3} \qquad \textit{Solve for } \phi.$$

Calculate the coefficients A', C', D', E', and F'.

$$A' = \sqrt{3}\cos^2\frac{\pi}{3} + 3\cos\frac{\pi}{3}\sin\frac{\pi}{3} + 2\sqrt{3}\sin^2\frac{\pi}{3} = \sqrt{3}\left(\frac{1}{2}\right)^2 + 3\left(\frac{1}{2}\right)\left(\frac{\sqrt{3}}{2}\right) + 2\sqrt{3}\left(\frac{\sqrt{3}}{2}\right)^2 = \frac{5\sqrt{3}}{2}$$

$$C' = \sqrt{3}\sin^2\frac{\pi}{3} - 3\cos\frac{\pi}{3}\sin\frac{\pi}{3} + 2\sqrt{3}\cos^2\frac{\pi}{3} = \sqrt{3}\left(\frac{\sqrt{3}}{2}\right)^2 - 3\left(\frac{1}{2}\right)\left(\frac{\sqrt{3}}{2}\right) + 2\sqrt{3}\left(\frac{1}{2}\right)^2 = \frac{\sqrt{3}}{2}$$

> **NOTICE THAT**
>
> *Since $D = 0$ and $E = 0$, $D' = 0$ and $E' = 0$.*

$$D' = D\cos\phi + E\sin\phi = 0\cos(\pi/3) + 0\sin(\pi/3) = 0$$

$$E' = -D\sin\phi + E\cos\phi = -(0)\sin(\pi/3) + 0\cos(\pi/3) = 0$$

$$F' = F = -12$$

Write the equation of the conic in terms of x' and y' by substituting the values of the coefficients into $A'(x')^2 + C'(y')^2 + D'x' + E'y' + F' = 0$.

$$\frac{5\sqrt{3}}{2}(x')^2 + \frac{\sqrt{3}}{2}(y')^2 - 12 = 0$$

Write the equation in the standard form of an ellipse.

> **REMEMBER**
>
> *The standard form equation of a vertical ellipse is $y^2/a^2 + x^2/b^2 = 1$, where $a \geq b$.*

$$\frac{5\sqrt{3}}{2}(x')^2 + \frac{\sqrt{3}}{2}(y')^2 = 12 \;\Rightarrow\; \frac{5\sqrt{3}}{24}(x')^2 + \frac{\sqrt{3}}{24}(y')^2 = 1 \;\Rightarrow\; \frac{y'^2}{24/\sqrt{3}} + \frac{x'^2}{24/(5\sqrt{3})} = 1$$

So, $a = \sqrt{24/\sqrt{3}} \approx 3.7$ and $b = \sqrt{24/(5\sqrt{3})} \approx 1.7$.

Therefore, the ellipse's intercepts are at approximately $(0, \pm 3.7)$ and $(\pm 1.7, 0)$. Use the intercepts to graph the ellipse.

Then rotate this graph counterclockwise about the origin $\pi/3$ radians to make the graph of $\sqrt{3}x^2 + 3xy + 2\sqrt{3}y^2 - 12 = 0$.

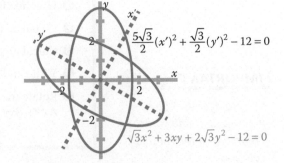

$$\frac{5\sqrt{3}}{2}(x')^2 + \frac{\sqrt{3}}{2}(y')^2 - 12 = 0$$

$$\sqrt{3}x^2 + 3xy + 2\sqrt{3}y^2 - 12 = 0$$

SECTION 7.3 EXERCISES

Warm Up

Graph each conic.

1. $y^2 - 9x^2 = 36$

2. $x^2 + 25y^2 = 225$

3. $y = -x^2 - 6x$

Just the Facts

Fill in the blanks.

4. A transformation involving a graph being turned about a fixed point on a plane is called a(n) _____.

5. When the x- and y-axes are rotated by some given angle, the resulting axes are referred to as the _____-axis and the _____-axis.

6. If a point $P(x, y)$ is rotated by an angle ϕ counterclockwise about the origin to $P(x', y')$, then $x' = $_____ and $y' = $_____.

7. To identify the type of conic given by an equation, use the _____, which is $B^2 - 4AC$.

8. The equations for ellipses, hyperbolas, and parabolas have discriminant values that are _____ 0, _____ 0, and _____ 0, respectively.

9. The angle of rotation of a conic is found using $\cot 2\phi = $_____.

10. When the general form equation of a conic, $Ax^2 + Bxy + Cy^2 + Dx + Ey + F = 0$, has no B-term, then the conic has an axis of symmetry that is _____ to the x- or y-axis.

Essential Skills

In Exercises 1–4, find the coordinates of P' if P' is the image of P after a counterclockwise rotation $\pi/4$ about the origin.

1. $P(0, 6)$

2. $P(-2, 5)$

3. $P(-4, 0)$

4. $P(-2, -8)$

In Exercises 5–8, find the coordinates of P' if P' is the image of P after a counterclockwise rotation $\pi/6$ about the origin.

5. $P(-2, 0)$

6. $P(0, -14)$

7. $P(-6, 2)$

8. $P(-3, -5)$

In Exercises 9–12, $P'(x', y')$ is the point that results when $P(x, y)$ is rotated by an angle of ϕ counterclockwise about the origin. Use the given information to find the missing coordinate.

9. $\phi = \pi/6$, $x = -4$, and $x' = -2\sqrt{3} + 10$, find y'.

10. $\phi = \pi/6$, $y = -10$, and $y' = 4 - 5\sqrt{3}$, find x'.

11. $\phi = \pi/3$, $y = 8$, and $y' = 3\sqrt{3} + 4$, find x'.

12. $\phi = \pi/3$, $x = 12$, and $x' = 6 - \sqrt{3}$, find y'.

In Exercises 13–18, identify the type of conic, if any, given by the equation.

13. $2x^2 + 3x - 4xy = y - 3y^2$

14. $y^2 - 2xy = 2y - x^2 - 6x$

15. $y + xy - y^2 - x^2 = 5x + x^2 - y^2$

16. $1 - y^2 + 3y = x - x^2 + xy$

17. $3y^2 = 5 - 2x - y$

18. $2y - 2y^2 - x^2 = 1 - 3x - xy$

In Exercises 19–24, graph each conic.

19. $xy + 2 = 0$

20. $xy = 1$

21. $x^2 + 4xy + y^2 - 3 = 0$

22. $x^2 + 2xy + y^2 + x - y = 0$

23. $5x^2 + 6xy + 5y^2 - 8 = 0$

24. $2\sqrt{3}x^2 - 6xy + \sqrt{3}x + 3y = 0$

Extensions

In Exercises 25–28, for each conic below, determine the angle of rotation from the original x- and y-axes to the axes of symmetry. Round to the nearest degree.

25. $9x^2 - 24xy + 16y^2 - 400x - 300y = 0$

26. $8x^2 + 12xy + 13y^2 - 34 = 0$

27. $4xy + 3y^2 + 4x + 6y = 0$

28. $x^2 + 2xy + y^2 + x + y - 2 = 0$

In Exercises 29–32, if P' is the image of P, find the coordinates of P' for each angle of rotation counterclockwise about the origin: $\pi/2$, π, and $3\pi/2$.

29. $P(5, 3)$

30. $P(-4, 1)$

31. $P(8, -6)$

32. $P(-7, -2)$

Polar Equations of Conics

A polar equation for a conic with its focus at the origin and its directrix parallel to either the horizontal or vertical axes (i.e., the x- or y-axis for a rectangular plane) can be derived from the geometric definition of a conic.

Suppose the directrix of a conic is a line parallel to, and p units below, the horizontal axis (Figure 7.4a). It follows that the vertical distance between any point on the directrix and the horizontal axis is p, and $PD = p + r \sin \theta$. Additionally, because the point $P(r, \theta)$ is r units from the origin (the focus of the conic), $PF = r$.

By substituting these expressions for PF and PD into the equation $PF/PD = e$, we see that the polar graph of a conic with focus at the origin and directrix parallel to, and p units below, the horizontal axis is the set of all points $P(r, \theta)$, such that $r/(p + r \sin \theta) = e$.

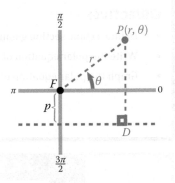

Figure 7.4a

Solving $r/(p + r \sin \theta) = e$ for r gives the standard form polar equation for this type of conic.

$$r/(p + r \sin \theta) = e$$

$$r = e(p + r \sin \theta) \qquad \text{\textit{Multiply both sides by the denominator.}}$$

$$r = ep + er \sin \theta \qquad \text{\textit{Distribute e.}}$$

$$r - er \sin \theta = ep \qquad \text{\textit{Subtract er sin θ from both sides.}}$$

$$r(1 - e \sin \theta) = ep \qquad \text{\textit{Factor r from each term.}}$$

$$r = ep/(1 - e \sin \theta) \qquad \text{\textit{Divide each side by 1 − e sin θ to solve for r.}}$$

Therefore, the polar equation for this type of conic (i.e., with focus at the origin and directrix parallel to, and p units below, the horizontal axis) is given by $r = \dfrac{ep}{1 - e \sin \theta}$, where e is the eccentricity of the conic.

The equations for the three other types of conics with focus at the origin and directrix parallel to the horizontal or vertical axes (which can be derived in a similar way) are given in the following table.

Polar Equations of Conics: $F(0, 0)$ and Directrix Parallel to the Horizontal or Vertical Axes	
$r = \dfrac{ep}{1 - e \sin \theta}$	The rectangular equation of the directrix is $y = -p$. *The directrix is parallel to, and p units below, the horizontal axis.*
$r = \dfrac{ep}{1 - e \cos \theta}$	The rectangular equation of the directrix is $x = -p$. *The directrix is parallel to, and p units to the left of, the vertical axis.*
$r = \dfrac{ep}{1 + e \sin \theta}$	The rectangular equation of the directrix is $y = p$. *The directrix is parallel to, and p units above, the horizontal axis.*
$r = \dfrac{ep}{1 + e \cos \theta}$	The rectangular equation of the directrix is $x = p$. *The directrix is parallel to, and p units to the right of, the vertical axis.*

EXAMPLE 1	Identifying a Conic by Its Polar Equation

Identify the type of conic given by each polar equation, then write the equation of its directrix.

A. $r = \dfrac{2}{4 - \cos \theta}$

B. $r = \dfrac{9}{3 + 5 \sin \theta}$

SOLUTION

A. Write the equation in the standard form of a conic with its focus at the origin.

$$r = \frac{2}{4 - \cos \theta} = \frac{2}{4\left(1 - \frac{1}{4} \cos \theta\right)} = \frac{\frac{1}{2}}{1 - \frac{1}{4} \cos \theta}$$

Thus, $e = 1/4$. Since $e < 1$, the conic is an ellipse.

Because the ellipse's equation is of the form $r = \dfrac{ep}{1 - e \cos \theta}$, its directrix is the vertical line for which the rectangular equation is $x = -p$.

From the numerator of the equation of the ellipse, $ep = 1/2$. Substituting $e = 1/4$ into this equation gives $(1/4)p = 1/2$. Therefore, $p = 2$, meaning the directrix is the vertical line $x = -2$.

B. Write the equation in the standard form of a conic with its focus at the origin.

$$r = \frac{9}{3 + 5 \sin \theta} = \frac{9}{3\left(1 + \frac{5}{3} \sin \theta\right)} = \frac{3}{1 + \frac{5}{3} \sin \theta}$$

Therefore, $e = 5/3$. Since $e > 1$, the conic is a hyperbola.

Because the hyperbola's equation is of the form $r = \dfrac{ep}{1 + e \sin \theta}$, its directrix is the horizontal line for which the rectangular equation is $y = p$.

From the numerator of the equation of the hyperbola, $ep = 3$. Substituting $e = 5/3$ into this equation gives $(5/3)p = 3$. Therefore, $p = 9/5$, meaning the directrix is the vertical line $y = 9/5$.

EXAMPLE 2	Writing the Polar Equation of a Conic

Write the polar equation of a conic with focus at the origin if its directrix is the line $x = -2$ and its eccentricity is 1.

SOLUTION

Since the directrix is the line $x = -2$, the directrix is a vertical line parallel to and 2 units to the left of the vertical axis. So, the conic is given by an equation of the form $r = \dfrac{ep}{1 - e \cos \theta}$.

Since p is the distance between the directrix and the parallel axis, $p = 2$.

Substitute $e = 1$ and $p = 2$ into the standard form equation to write the equation of the conic.

$$r = \frac{ep}{1 - e \cos \theta} = \frac{1 \cdot 2}{1 - 1 \cos \theta} = \frac{2}{1 - \cos \theta}$$

7.4.2   Graphing Polar Equations of Conics

To graph the polar equation of a conic with its directrix, first write the equation in one of the four standard polar forms of a conic with focus at the origin. Next, identify e and p from the equation. Use e to determine whether the conic is an ellipse (if $e < 1$), a parabola (if $e = 1$), or a hyperbola (if $e > 1$). Then, using the information regarding the directrix given from the standard form equation and p, graph the directrix.

We can use a conic's directrix to determine whether the conic is horizontal or vertical because the directrix of an ellipse or a hyperbola is perpendicular to its transverse axis, and because the directrix of a parabola is perpendicular to its axis of symmetry. So, if a conic's directrix is horizontal, the conic is vertical, and if a conic's directrix is vertical, the conic is horizontal.

Make a table to identify some of the points on the conic. Then, plot the points from the table and sketch the conic through those points, keeping in mind the type and direction of the conic.

EXAMPLE 3   Graphing the Polar Equation of a Conic

IMPORTANT

If a polar equation can be written in one of the four standard forms of a conic, then the conic's focus is at the origin.

Graph the conic and its directrix. $r(5 - 10 \sin \theta) = 8$

SOLUTION

Write the equation in the standard form of a conic with focus at the origin. Begin by dividing both sides by $5 - 10 \sin \theta$ in order to solve the equation for r.

$$r = \frac{8}{5 - 10 \sin \theta} = \frac{8}{5(1 - 2 \sin \theta)} = \frac{\frac{8}{5}}{1 - 2 \sin \theta}$$

Therefore, $e = 2$. Since $e > 1$, the conic is a hyperbola.

The directrix of a conic of the form $r = \dfrac{ep}{1 - e \sin \theta}$ is the horizontal line $y = -p$.

Since $e = 2$ and $ep = 8/5$, it follows that $2p = 8/5$, and $p = 4/5$. Thus, the rectangular equation of the directrix is $y = -4/5$.

REMEMBER

A hyperbola's transverse axis is perpendicular to its directrix.

Plot the focus at the origin and sketch the directrix (the line $y = -4/5$). The conic is a vertical hyperbola because the directrix is horizontal. Since the focus is at the origin and the hyperbola is vertical, the hyperbola's vertices must be on the vertical axis (i.e., the y-axis).

Make a table to identify some of the points on the hyperbola.

r	8/5	−8/5	8/5	8/15
θ	0	$\pi/2$	π	$3\pi/2$

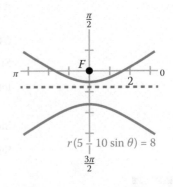

Sketch the vertical hyperbola through these points. The vertices are on the vertical axis, so the polar coordinates of the hyperbola's vertices are $(-8/5, \pi/2)$ and $(8/15, 3\pi/2)$. Note that both of these points are below the horizontal axis.

SECTION 7.4 EXERCISES

Warm Up

1. Find the focus and directrix of the graph of $2y^2 = 6x$.

2. Find the foci and eccentricity of the graph of $100x^2 + 50y^2 - 300 = 0$.

3. Find the foci and vertices of the graph of $\dfrac{y^2}{9} - x^2 = 1$.

Just the Facts

Fill in the blanks.

4. If the eccentricity of a conic _____ 1, then the conic is a parabola. If the eccentricity of a conic _____ 1, then the conic is an ellipse. If the eccentricity of a conic _____ 1, then the conic is a hyperbola.

5. The polar equation of a conic with a focus at the origin and a directrix parallel to, and p units to the left of, the vertical axis is _____.

6. The polar equation of a conic with a focus at the origin and a directrix parallel to, and p units to the right of, the vertical axis is _____.

7. The polar equation of a conic with a focus at the origin and a directrix parallel to, and p units above, the horizontal axis is _____.

8. The polar equation of a conic with focus at the origin and a directrix parallel to, and p units below, the horizontal axis is _____.

9. A horizontal directrix is either _____ to the horizontal axis or it coincides with the horizontal axis.

10. The major axis of an ellipse is _____ to its directrix.

Essential Skills

In Exercises 1–6, identify the type of conic given by each polar equation. Write the rectangular equation of its directrix and state its eccentricity.

1. $r = \dfrac{5}{10 - 15 \sin \theta}$

2. $r = \dfrac{9}{2 + 3 \cos \theta}$

3. $r = \dfrac{4}{6 - \cos \theta}$

4. $r = \dfrac{4}{1 - 3 \sin \theta}$

5. $r = \dfrac{3}{2 + 6 \sin \theta}$

6. $r = \dfrac{2}{1 - \cos \theta}$

In Exercises 7–12, write the polar equation of each conic (focus at the origin) with the given directrix and eccentricity.

7. $x = 3, e = 2/3$

8. $y = 3, e = 4$

9. $y = 2, e = 1$

10. $x = -3, e = 4/3$

11. $x = -1, e = 3/2$

12. $y = -3, e = 1$

In Exercises 13–18, graph each conic. Write the rectangular equation of its directrix and state its eccentricity.

13. $r = \dfrac{1}{1 + \sin \theta}$

14. $2r - 4r \cos \theta = 3$

15. $3r - 2r \sin \theta = 6$

16. $4r + 8r \sin \theta = 12$

17. $r(3 - 9 \sin \theta) = 6$

18. $5r + 4r \cos \theta = 10$

Extensions

In Exercises 19–22, write each polar equation as a rectangular equation in general form.

19. $r = \dfrac{12}{1 + 4 \sin \theta}$

20. $r = \dfrac{2}{1 - \cos \theta}$

21. $r = \dfrac{9}{2 + 3 \cos \theta}$

22. $r = \dfrac{5}{10 - 15 \sin \theta}$

In Exercises 23–26, find a polar equation for a parabola with focus at the pole and the given polar coordinates as its vertex.

23. $(6, \pi)$

24. $(3, 0)$

25. $(2, \pi/2)$

26. $(5, 3\pi/2)$

In Exercises 27–30, find a polar equation for each ellipse with a focus at the pole and the given polar coordinates as the endpoints of its major axis.

27. $(2, 0)$ and $(8, \pi)$

28. $(1, \pi/2)$ and $(7, 3\pi/2)$

29. $(3, \pi/2)$ and $(6, -\pi/2)$

30. $(4, 0)$ and $(2, \pi)$

In Exercises 31–34, find a polar equation for each hyperbola with a focus at the pole and the given polar coordinates as endpoints of its transverse axis.

31. $(4, \pi/2)$ and $(-8, 3\pi/2)$

32. $(1, \pi)$ and $(-5, 2\pi)$

33. $(2, 0)$ and $(-12, \pi)$

34. $(3, -\pi/2)$ and $(-6, \pi/2)$

In Exercises 35–38, graph each conic. Write the rectangular equation of its directrix and state its eccentricity.

35. $r = \dfrac{6 \sec \theta}{2 \sec \theta - 1}$

36. $r = \dfrac{12 \csc \theta}{3 \csc \theta + 2}$

37. $r = \dfrac{4 \csc \theta}{2 \csc \theta + 3}$

38. $r = \dfrac{\sec \theta}{\sec \theta - 2}$

7.5 PLANE CURVES AND PARAMETRIC EQUATIONS

OBJECTIVES

- Graph parametric equations.
- Write the rectangular form equation of a plane curve.
- Find parametric equations that describe the graph of a rectangular equation.

PREREQUISITE VOCABULARY TERMS

absolute value function

parabola

Pythagorean identities

trigonometric functions

7.5.1 Graphing Plane Curves

The equations modeling real world situations in the preceding chapters are written in terms of either one or two variables, typically x and y (or r and θ for polar equations). For example, consider a soccer ball kicked into the air. The path the ball takes can be described by an equation written in terms of x and y, where x is the ball's horizontal position relative to its starting point (i.e., the distance the ball has traveled along the ground from its starting point), and y is the ball's vertical position relative to its starting point (i.e., the distance between the ball and the ground).

However, both variables (x and y) are functions of time t because any point along the path of the ball is defined by the ball's horizontal position x at time t and its vertical position y at that same time t. So, the ball's path can be described by a pair of functions, $f(t)$ and $g(t)$, where $f(t)$ is the ball's horizontal distance from the starting point at time t and $g(t)$ is the ball's vertical height above the ground at time t. These two functions of the same variable t, $f(t)$ and $g(t)$, are called **parametric equations**.

> **IMPORTANT**
>
> *$f(t)$ and $g(t)$ are functions of the same variable, t. They can also be expressed using other letters, such as $x(t)$ and $y(t)$.*

Parametric Equations

Let $f(t)$ and $g(t)$ be continuous functions on some interval I of real numbers. A **plane curve** is the set of all ordered pairs $(f(t), g(t))$. The equations $x = f(t)$ and $y = g(t)$ are the parametric equations for the plane curve, where t (the independent variable) is called the **parameter**.

> **TIP**
>
> *If the parametric equations $x = f(t)$ and $y = g(t)$ describe a ball's horizontal and vertical position, then the plane curve represents the path of the ball.*

One method for graphing a plane curve given by a pair of parametric equations involves making a table of ordered pairs $(f(t), g(t))$. Since the parametric equations $x = f(t)$ and $y = g(t)$ are in terms of three variables, a table of ordered pairs $(f(t), g(t))$ will have three columns. The first column contains the t-values, the second column contains the $f(t)$-values, and the third column contains the $g(t)$-values.

After making the table, plot the ordered pairs $(f(t), g(t))$ as points on an xy-plane. Then draw the plane curve through the points. If the interval I is not all real numbers, then the plane curve will have endpoints.

Arrowheads drawn along the curve indicate the **orientation** of the plane curve, which is the direction of the curve as the values of the parameter increase.

EXAMPLE 1   Graphing a Plane Curve

Graph the plane curve defined by each pair of parametric equations.

A. $x(t) = t + 3$
    $y(t) = 4t - 4$
    $0 \le t \le 7$

B. $x(t) = 2t^2 - 4$
    $y(t) = 2t$
    $-2 \le t \le 3$

C. $x(t) = \sin t$
    $y(t) = \cos t$
    $-\pi/2 \le t \le \pi/2$

SOLUTION

A. The plane curve defined by $x(t) = t + 3$ and $y(t) = 4t - 4$ is all points $(x(t), y(t))$ such that $0 \le t \le 7$. Make a table of ordered pairs $(x(t), y(t))$ using t-values such that $0 \le t \le 7$.

TIP

The t-values chosen for the table do not have to be integers, but the t-values must be in the given interval. The interval's endpoints should always be chosen for the table.

Substitute a t-value into $x(t) = t + 3$ to find the $x(t)$-coordinate of a point on the plane curve. Then substitute that same t-value into $y(t) = 4t - 4$ to find the corresponding $y(t)$-coordinate of the point on the plane curve.

Repeat the process for each t-value in the table.

From the table, the plane curve passes through the points $(3, -4)$, $(4, 0)$, $(5, 4)$, $(6, 8)$, $(7, 12)$, $(8, 16)$, $(9, 20)$, and $(10, 24)$.

t	$x(t)$	$y(t)$
0	3	−4
1	4	0
2	5	4
3	6	8
4	7	12
5	8	16
6	9	20
7	10	24

IMPORTANT

Since this plane curve is all points (x(t), y(t)) such that 0 ≤ t ≤ 7, the plane curve is a continuous curve, not a set of discrete points.

Furthermore, since the endpoints of the interval are where $t = 0$ and $t = 7$, the endpoints of the plane curve are $(3, -4)$ and $(10, 24)$.

Sketch the plane curve through the points and include the endpoints $(3, -4)$ and $(10, 24)$. Draw an arrowhead pointing to the second endpoint to indicate the plane curve's orientation.

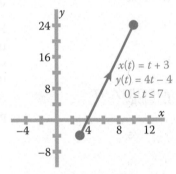

B. The plane curve defined by $x(t) = 2t^2 - 4$ and $y(t) = 2t$ is all points $(x(t), y(t))$ such that $-2 \le t \le 3$. Make a table of ordered pairs $(x(t), y(t))$ using t-values such that $-2 \le t \le 3$.

Substitute a t-value into $x(t) = 2t^2 - 4$ to find the $x(t)$-coordinate of a point on the plane curve. Then substitute that same t-value into $y(t) = 2t$ to find the corresponding $y(t)$-coordinate of the point on the plane curve.

Repeat the process for each t-value in the table. From the table, the plane curve passes through the points $(4, -4)$, $(-2, -2)$, $(-4, 0)$, $(-2, 2)$, $(4, 4)$, and $(14, 6)$.

t	$x(t)$	$y(t)$
−2	4	−4
−1	−2	−2
0	−4	0
1	−2	2
2	4	4
3	14	6

NOTICE THAT

This plane curve does not pass the Vertical Line Test. Therefore, a plane curve given by parametric equations is not always the graph of a function.

Furthermore, since the endpoints of the interval are where $t = -2$ and $t = 3$, the endpoints of the plane curve are $(4, -4)$ and $(14, 6)$.

Sketch the plane curve through the points and include the endpoints $(4, -4)$ and $(14, 6)$. Draw arrowheads pointing to the second endpoint to indicate the plane curve's orientation.

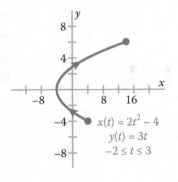

C. The plane curve defined by $x(t) = \sin t$ and $y(t) = \cos t$ is all points $(x(t), y(t))$ such that $-\pi/2 \le t \le \pi/2$. Make a table of ordered pairs $(x(t), y(t))$ using t-values such that $-\pi/2 \le t \le \pi/2$.

Substitute a t-value into $x(t) = \sin t$ to find the $x(t)$-coordinate of a point on the plane curve. Then substitute that same t-value into $y(t) = \cos t$ to find the corresponding $y(t)$-coordinate of the point on the plane curve.

Repeat the process for each t-value in the table.

t (rad)	$x(t)$	$y(t)$
$-\pi/2$	-1	0
$-\pi/4$	$-\sqrt{2}/2$	$\sqrt{2}/2$
0	0	1
$\pi/4$	$\sqrt{2}/2$	$\sqrt{2}/2$
$\pi/2$	1	0

From the table, the plane curve passes through the points $(-1, 0)$, $\left(-\sqrt{2}/2, \sqrt{2}/2\right)$, $(0, 1)$, $\left(\sqrt{2}/2, \sqrt{2}/2\right)$, and $(1, 0)$.

The endpoints of the interval are where $t = -\pi/2$ and $t = \pi/2$, so the endpoints of the plane curve are $(-1, 0)$ and $(1, 0)$.

Sketch the plane curve through the points and include the endpoints $(-1, 0)$ and $(1, 0)$. Draw arrowheads pointing to the second endpoint to indicate the plane curve's orientation.

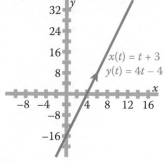

7.5.2 Eliminating the Parameter

Figure 7.5a shows the plane curve for the parametric equations $(x(t) = t + 3$ and $y(t) = 4t - 4)$, which are given in **Example 1a**, with no restrictions on the interval for t (i.e., $-\infty < t < \infty$). Notice that the unrestricted plane curve is a line with slope 4 and y-intercept -16. So, the rectangular equation of this line in terms of x and y is $y = 4x - 16$.

Generally, a plane curve can be described by parametric equations, or it can be described by a rectangular equation, which does not contain the parameter t.

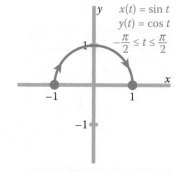

Figure 7.5a

A technique called **eliminating the parameter** is a process by which two parametric equations are written as a single rectangular equation which does not contain the parameter.

Steps for Eliminating the Parameter from Parametric Equations

❶ Solve either one of the parametric equations for the parameter t.

❷ Substitute the expression for t from step ❶ into the other parametric equation and simplify (eliminating the variable t).

TIP

The equations
$x(t) = t + 3$ and
$y(t) = 4t - 4$ can also be
written as $x = t + 3$ and
$y = 4t - 4$, respectively.

For example, to eliminate the parameter for the parametric equations $x(t) = t + 3$ and $y(t) = 4t - 4$, solve $x(t) = t + 3$ for t, then substitute the expression for t into $y(t) = 4t - 4$, as follows.

$$x(t) = t + 3 \implies t = x - 3 \qquad \text{Solve for } t.$$

$$y = 4(x - 3) - 4 = 4x - 12 - 4 = 4x - 16 \qquad \text{Substitute } x - 3 \text{ for } t \text{ and simplify.}$$

Therefore, the parametric equations can be expressed as the rectangular equation $y = 4x - 16$.

EXAMPLE 2   Eliminating the Parameter

Eliminate the parameter in each pair of parametric equations.

A. $x(t) = \sqrt{t}$ **B.** $x(t) = |t + 2|$
    $y(t) = t - 2$ $y(t) = t - 4$

SOLUTION

TIP

Start by solving either
equation for t.

A. Solve $x(t) = \sqrt{t}$ for t. $x(t) = \sqrt{t} \implies t = x^2$ when $t \geq 0$

Substitute $t = x^2$ into the second equation $y(t) = t - 2$. $y = t - 2 = x^2 - 2$

Therefore, $y = x^2 - 2$ for all $x \geq 0$.

ALTERNATIVE METHOD

First, solve $y(t)$ for t. $y(t) = t - 2 \implies t = y + 2$

IMPORTANT

The square root expression
must be greater than or
equal to 0, so $x \geq 0$.

Substitute $t = y + 2$ into the first equation. $x = \sqrt{t} = \sqrt{y + 2}$

Square both sides to solve for y. Thus, $y = x^2 - 2$ for all $x \geq 0$.

TIP

Solving $y(t) = t - 4$ for
t is easier than solving
$x(t) = |t + 2|$ for t, so
start with $y(t) = t - 4$.

B. Solve $y(t) = t - 4$ for t. $y(t) = t - 4 \implies t = y + 4$

Substitute $t = y + 4$ into the first equation $x(t) = |t + 2|$.

$$x = |t + 2| = |y + 4 + 2| = |y + 6|$$

Therefore, the rectangular equation for the plane curve described by the given parametric equations is $x = |y + 6|$.

When the parametric equations involve trigonometric functions, it is sometimes easier to use a trigonometric identity to eliminate the parameter rather than solving for the parameter in one equation and substituting that expression into the remaining equation. This process is demonstrated in **Example 3**.

| EXAMPLE 3 | Eliminating the Parameter |

Eliminate the parameter in each pair of parametric equations.

A. $x(t) = \sin t$
$\quad y(t) = \cos t$

B. $x = 5 \tan t$
$\quad y = 5 \sec t$

SOLUTION

A. Since the Pythagorean identity $\sin^2 t + \cos^2 t = 1$ gives a relationship between $\sin t$ and $\cos t$ (the two trigonometric functions in the given parametric equations), use $\sin^2 t + \cos^2 t = 1$ to write a relationship between x and y.

$$\sin^2 t + \cos^2 t = 1 \qquad \textit{Pythagorean Identity}$$

$$x^2 + y^2 = 1 \qquad \textit{Substitute x for sin t and y for cos t.}$$

> **NOTICE THAT**
>
> *The plane curve is a circle centered at the origin with radius 1.*

B. Since the Pythagorean identity $1 + \tan^2 t = \sec^2 t$ gives a relationship between $\tan t$ and $\sec t$ (the two trigonometric functions in the given parametric equations), use $1 + \tan^2 t = \sec^2 t$ to write a relationship between x and y. Note that solving $x = 5 \tan t$ for $\tan t$ gives $\tan t = x/5$, and solving $y = 5 \sec t$ for $\sec t$ gives $\sec t = y/5$.

$$1 + \tan^2 t = \sec^2 t \qquad \textit{Pythagorean Identity}$$

$$1 + (x/5)^2 = (y/5)^2 \qquad \textit{Substitute x/5 for tan t and y/5 for sec t.}$$

$$1 + x^2/25 = y^2/25 \qquad \textit{Simplify.}$$

$$1 = y^2/25 - x^2/25 \qquad \textit{Subtract } x^2/25 \textit{ from both sides.}$$

> **NOTICE THAT**
>
> *The plane curve is a vertical hyperbola centered at the origin with vertices at $(0, \pm5)$ and co-vertices at $(\pm5, 0)$.*

Eliminating the Parameter to Graph a Plane Curve

Consider again the plane curve for the parametric equations from **Example 1a**. As shown in Figure 7.5b, $x(t) = t + 3$ and $y(t) = 4t - 4$ when $0 \le t \le 7$.

Recall that the plane curve for parametric equations $x(t) = t + 3$ and $y(t) = 4t - 4$ can also be described by the rectangular equation $y = 4x - 16$, which is the result of eliminating the parameter from the original parametric equations.

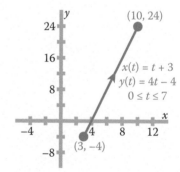

Figure 7.5b

However, the interval for x must be restricted in some way in order for $y = 4x - 16$ to represent the plane curve for $x(t) = t + 3$ and $y(t) = 4t - 4$ when $0 \le t \le 7$. If the $x(t)$-values are strictly increasing or decreasing as t increases (for all t within the interval), then the interval for x is given by writing the interval for t in terms of x. Specifically, since $x = t + 3$, the interval $0 \le t \le 7$ can be written in terms of x by adding 3 to each part of the inequality.

$$0 \le t \le 7 \implies 0 + 3 \le t + 3 \le 7 + 3 \implies 3 \le x \le 10 \qquad \textit{Simplify and substitute x for t + 3.}$$

Therefore, the plane curve for $x(t) = t + 3$ and $y(t) = 4t - 4$ when $0 \le t \le 7$ can also be represented by $y = 4x - 16$ when $3 \le x \le 10$. Notice that the graph shown in Figure 7.5b confirms the interval $3 \le x \le 10$, as the x-coordinates of the left and right endpoints are 3 and 10 respectively.

> **Steps for Graphing a Plane Curve by Eliminating the Parameter**
>
> ❶ Write the parametric equations as a single rectangular equation in terms of x and y by eliminating the parameter t from the parametric equations.
>
> ❷ Find the interval for x (or y).
>
> ❸ Graph the rectangular equation over the interval for x (or y).

TIP

The interval for x and y can sometimes be found by making a table of t-, $x(t)$-, and $y(t)$-values.

EXAMPLE 4   Graphing a Plane Curve by Eliminating the Parameter

Graph the plane curve described by the parametric equations.

A. $x(t) = \sqrt{t}$
$y(t) = t - 2$
$0 \le t \le 16$

B. $x(t) = |t + 2|$
$y(t) = t - 4$
$-4 \le t \le 8$

SOLUTION

A. From **Example 2A**, we know that the plane curve described by the given parametric equations has rectangular equation $y = x^2 - 2$. The graph of $y = x^2 - 2$ is a vertical parabola opening upward. It is the image of $y = x^2$ after a vertical translation down 2 units, so the vertex is at $(0, -2)$.

Since $x(t) = \sqrt{t}$ is strictly increasing for all t such that $0 \le t \le 16$, use the interval for t, $0 \le t \le 16$, and the equation for x, $x(t) = \sqrt{t}$, to find the interval for x.

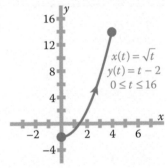

$\sqrt{0} \le \sqrt{t} \le \sqrt{16}$ *Take the square root of 0, t, and 16.*

$0 \le x \le 4$ *Substitute x for $\sqrt{t}$ and simplify.*

So, the plane curve of the given parametric equations is the parabola described by $y = x^2 - 2$ when $0 \le x \le 4$.

CHECK

Confirm several points on the plane curve (including the endpoints) by making a table for the parametric equations. Since $x(t) = \sqrt{t}$, choose perfect-square t-values from the interval $0 \le t \le 16$ for the table so that the $x(t)$-coordinates are whole numbers.

From the table, the plane curve passes through the points $(0, -2)$, $(1, -1)$, $(2, 2)$, $(3, 7)$, and $(4, 14)$, which confirms the plane curve.

t	0	1	4	9	16
$x(t)$	0	1	2	3	4
$y(t)$	-2	-1	2	7	14

B. In **Example 2B** it was shown that the plane curve described by the given parametric equations has the rectangular equation $x = |y + 6|$. The graph of $x = |y + 6|$ is an absolute value graph opening to the right. It is the image of $x = |y|$ after a vertical translation down 6 units.

Since $x(t) = |t + 2|$ decreases and then increases as t increases for all t such that $-4 \leq t \leq 8$, but $y(t) = t - 4$ only increases as t increases for all t such that $-4 \leq t \leq 8$, use the interval for t, $-4 \leq t \leq 8$, and the equation for y, $y = t - 4$, to find the interval for y.

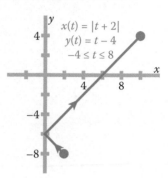

$$-4 - 4 \leq t - 4 \leq 8 - 4 \quad \text{\textit{Subtract 4 from }} -4, t, \text{\textit{ and 8.}}$$
$$-8 \leq y \leq 4 \qquad \text{\textit{Substitute y for t }} - 4 \text{\textit{ and simplify.}}$$

TIP

Since the rectangular equation is solved for x, find the interval for y instead of x.

Therefore, the plane curve of the given parametric equations is the absolute value graph described by $x = |y + 6|$ when $-8 \leq y \leq 4$.

ALTERNATIVE METHOD

Make a table for all integer t-values such that $-4 \leq t \leq 8$.

t	-4	-3	-2	-1	0	1	2	3	4	5	6	7	8
$x(t)$	2	1	0	1	2	3	4	5	6	7	8	9	10
$y(t)$	-8	-7	-6	-5	-4	-3	-2	-1	0	1	2	3	4

From the table, the least $x(t)$-value is 0 and the greatest $x(t)$-value is 10. Therefore, the interval for x is $0 \leq x \leq 10$, which is confirmed by the plane curve.

The interval for y, $-8 \leq y \leq 4$, is confirmed by the table because the least $y(t)$-value is -8 and the greatest $y(t)$-value is 4.

7.5.3   Writing Parametric Equations

Just as a plane curve for a given pair of parametric equations can also be described by a rectangular equation, the graph of any given rectangular equation $y = f(x)$ can be described by a pair of parametric equations in terms of a third variable, t.

Unlike rectangular equations which have only one simplified form, there are an infinite number of possible pairs of parametric equations that represent a given plane curve. One such pair of parametric equations can be determined by letting x be equal to the parameter t. In this case, $x(t) = t$, and so $y(t) = f(t)$.

NOTICE THAT

Substituting $t = x$ into $y = f(t)$ confirms that $y = f(x)$, as claimed.

EXAMPLE 5 Writing Parametric Equations

Find parametric equations $x(t)$ and $y(t)$ to represent the graph of each rectangular equation.

A. $y = 3x - 1$ **B.** $x^2/4 + y^2/9 = 1$

SOLUTION

A. Let $x(t) = t$. Substituting t for x in the rectangular equation $y = 3x - 1$ gives $y = 3t - 1$.

So, the parametric equations $x(t) = t$ and $y(t) = 3t - 1$ represent the graph of $y = 3x - 1$.

Additional pairs of parametric equations can be determined by choosing another expression for x in terms of t, such as $x(t) = 2t$. Substituting $2t$ for x in the rectangular equation $y = 3x - 1$ gives $y = 3(2t) - 1 = 6t - 1$.

Thus, the following pairs of parametric equations each represent the graph of $y = 3x - 1$.

$$x(t) = t \qquad\qquad\qquad x(t) = 2t$$
$$y(t) = 3t - 1 \qquad\qquad y(t) = 6t - 1$$

B. Let $x(t) = t$. Since $x^2/4 + y^2/9 = 1$ does not give y explicitly as a function of x, solve the equation for y, then find $y(t)$ by substituting t for x.

$$\frac{y^2}{9} = 1 - \frac{x^2}{4} \qquad\qquad \textit{Isolate the } y^2\textit{-term.}$$

$$y = \pm\sqrt{9\left(1 - \frac{x^2}{4}\right)} \qquad \textit{Multiply both sides by 9 and take} \pm \textit{the square root of each side.}$$

$$y = \pm 3\sqrt{1 - \frac{x^2}{4}} \qquad\qquad \textit{Simplify.}$$

IMPORTANT

Since y can take on both positive and negative values, both the positive and negative square roots must be included.

Substituting t for x in the rectangular equation gives $y = \pm 3\sqrt{1 - \frac{t^2}{4}}$.

So, $x(t) = t$ and $y(t) = \pm 3\sqrt{1 - \frac{t^2}{4}}$ represent the graph of $x^2/4 + y^2/9 = 1$.

A second pair of parametric equations can be found using the Pythagorean identity $\sin^2 t + \cos^2 t = 1$. Choose another expression for x in terms of t, such as $x(t) = 2\sin t$.

NOTICE THAT

The coefficient of sin t is chosen to be 2 so that the denominator of $x^2/4$ will cancel out after 2 sin t is squared, thus simplifying the process. However, the coefficient does not have to be 2. For example, letting $x(t) = \sin t$ gives yet another pair of parametric equations for $x^2/4 + y^2/9 = 1$.

Substitute $2\sin t$ for x in the rectangular equation $x^2/4 + y^2/9 = 1$.

$$(2\sin t)^2/4 + y^2/9 = 1 \qquad \textit{Substitute.}$$

$$(4\sin^2 t)/4 + y^2/9 = 1 \qquad \textit{Power of a Product Property}$$

$$\sin^2 t + y^2/9 = 1 \qquad\qquad \textit{Simplify.}$$

$$y^2/9 = 1 - \sin^2 t \qquad \textit{Isolate the } y^2\textit{-term.}$$

$$y^2/9 = \cos^2 t \qquad\qquad \textit{Pythagorean Identity}$$

$$y = \pm\sqrt{9\cos^2 t} \qquad \textit{Multiply each side by 9 and then take} \pm \textit{the square root.}$$

$$y = \pm 3\cos t \qquad\qquad \textit{Simplify.}$$

Thus, the following pairs of parametric equations each represent the graph of $x^2/4 + y^2/9 = 1$.

$$x(t) = t \qquad\qquad\qquad x(t) = 2\sin t$$
$$y(t) = \pm 3\sqrt{1 - \frac{t^2}{4}} \qquad\qquad y(t) = \pm 3\cos t$$

SECTION 7.5 EXERCISES

Warm Up

Evaluate each function for domain values {−2, −1, 0, 1, 2}.

1. $y = x^2 - 1$

2. $y = |3x + 4|$

3. $y = \sqrt{x + 5}$

Just the Facts

Fill in the blanks.

4. The set of all ordered pairs $(f(t), g(t))$ for all t in the interval I is called a _____.

5. If $x = f(t)$ and $y = g(t)$ are parametric equations for a plane curve, then t, the independent variable, is called the _____.

6. Eliminating the parameter is a process by which two parametric equations are written as a single _____ equation.

7. The graph of any given rectangular equation $y = f(x)$ can be described by a pair of parametric equations in terms of a _____ variable.

8. Arrowheads drawn along a plane curve indicate the _____ of the plane curve.

9. To eliminate the parameter described by the parametric equations $x(t) = \sin t$ and $y(t) = \cos t$, it is easier to use _____ identities than it is to solve for x or y.

10. Some plane curves do not pass the Vertical Line Test. Such plane curves are given by parametric equations, but they are not the graph of a(n) _____.

Essential Skills

In Exercises 1–6, use the given t-values to make a table for each pair of parametric equations.

1. $x(t) = t^2 - 4; t = -3, -2, 1, 6$
   $y(t) = \sqrt{t + 3}$

2. $x(t) = |1 - t|; t = -1, 0, 1, 2$
   $y(t) = \dfrac{1 + t^2}{2}$

3. $x(t) = \dfrac{t + 2}{t + 1}; t = -2, 0, 1, 2$
   $y(t) = t^3 + 1$

4. $x(t) = -t^3 + t^2; t = -5, 0, 3, 4$
   $y(t) = \sqrt{4 - t}$

5. $x(t) = t^2 + 3t; t = -1, 0, 1, 2$
   $y(t) = |t + 5|$

6. $x(t) = \dfrac{2}{t - 2}; t = -1, 0, 1, 3$
   $y(t) = t^2 + 3$

In Exercises 7–18, graph the plane curve defined by each pair of parametric equations.

7. $x(t) = t + 2$
   $y(t) = t^2 - 1$
   $-3 \le t \le 1$

8. $x(t) = \dfrac{t^2}{t + 2}$
   $y(t) = \sqrt{1 + t}$
   $-1 \le t \le 3$

9. $x(t) = \sqrt{t + 1}$
   $y(t) = t - 2$
   $-1 \le t \le 15$

10. $x(t) = \dfrac{t^3}{t + 5}$
    $y(t) = \sqrt{1 + t}$
    $-1 \le t \le 2$

11. $x(t) = |2t - 1|$
    $y(t) = t^2$
    $-2 \le t \le 2$

12. $x(t) = \dfrac{t^2}{t + 4}$
    $y(t) = \sqrt{t + 2}$
    $-1 \le t \le 5$

13. $x(t) = 2 \cos t$
    $y(t) = 4 \sin t$
    $0 \le t \le 3\pi/2$

14. $x(t) = 2 \cos t$
    $y(t) = -\dfrac{1}{2} \sin t$
    $-\pi/2 \le t \le \pi/2$

15. $x(t) = \sin t + 1$
    $y(t) = -3 \cos t$
    $0 \le t \le \pi$

16. $x(t) = -2 \sin t$
    $y(t) = \cos t$
    $0 \le t \le 3\pi/2$

17. $x(t) = 5 \cos t - 2$

$y(t) = 3 - \sin t$

$-\pi \le t \le \pi/2$

18. $x(t) = -\cos t$

$y(t) = -\sin t$

$-\pi \le t \le \pi/2$

In Exercises 19–30, eliminate the parameter to find the rectangular equation for the plane curve described by the parametric equations. State the domain of the rectangular equation for the plane curve.

19. $x(t) = \sqrt{t+2}$

$y(t) = t - 3$

20. $x(t) = 4 + 6t$

$y(t) = |2t|$

21. $x(t) = t - 5$

$y(t) = t^2 - 1$

22. $x(t) = |5t|$

$y(t) = 4 - 15t$

23. $x(t) = t^2 - 1$

$y(t) = 5t + 4$

24. $x(t) = 3 + 28t$

$y(t) = |4t|$

25. $x(t) = 2 \cos t$

$y(t) = \sin t$

26. $x(t) = -\cos t$

$y(t) = 3 \sin t$

27. $x(t) = -4 \csc t$

$y(t) = 2 \cot t$

28. $x(t) = 3 \tan t$

$y(t) = -\sec t$

29. $x(t) = \dfrac{\sec t}{2}$

$y(t) = \dfrac{\tan t}{3}$

30. $x(t) = -5 \cot t$

$y(t) = -2 \csc t$

In Exercises 31–36, graph the plane curve described by the parametric equations.

31. $x(t) = 4t + 1$

$y(t) = -3t + 2$

$0 \le t \le 4$

32. $x(t) = \dfrac{1}{2}t + 3$

$y(t) = t + 1$

$-2 \le t \le 2$

33. $x(t) = |-2t| + 4$

$y(t) = t + 3$

$-3 \le t \le 3$

34. $x(t) = 0.2t - 5$

$y(t) = -7t - 0.6$

$-4 \le t \le 4$

35. $x(t) = -2t + 3$

$y(t) = \sqrt{t+2}$

$-2 \le t \le 2$

36. $x(t) = -t/3 + 2$

$y(t) = 4t - 0.7$

$-2 \le t \le 2$

In Exercises 37–42, find parametric equations $x(t)$ and $y(t)$ to represent the graph of each rectangular equation.

37. $y = -x^2$

38. $y = |2 - x|$

39. $y = x^2 + 3$

40. $y = 4x^2 - 7$

41. $x^2/9 + y^2 = 1$

42. $y = |15 - 3x|$

Extensions

In Exercises 43–47, describe each plane curve for parametric equations $x(t)$ and $y(t)$. Assume that $x(t)$ and $y(t)$ are defined for all real numbers.

43. $x(t) = y(t)$

44. $x(t) = -y(t)$

45. $x(t) = 2(y(t))$

46. $-3(x(t)) = 4(y(t))$

47. $2(x(t)) = y(t)$

In Exercises 48–52, graph the plane curve described by the parametric equations.

48. $x(t) = -\cos 2t$

$y(t) = \sin t$

$-\pi/4 \leq t \leq \pi/4$

49. $x(t) = \cos t$

$y(t) = \sin 2t$

$-\pi/2 \leq t \leq \pi/4$

50. $x(t) = \sin 3t$

$y(t) = \cos 2t$

$-\pi/2 \leq t \leq \pi/6$

51. $x(t) = -\sin 4t$

$y(t) = \cos 2t$

$-\pi/8 \leq t \leq \pi/2$

52. $x(t) = -\cos 2t$

$y(t) = -2 \sin t$

$-\pi/2 \leq t \leq \pi/2$

53. True or False? The two sets of parametric equations $x(t) = 5t$, $y(t) = t^3$ and $x(t) = t$, $y(t) = t^3/125$ have the same rectangular equation.

In Exercises 54–55, eliminate the parameter to find the rectangular equation for the plane curve described by the parametric equations. State the domain of the rectangular equation for the plane curve.

54. $x(t) = \sin t + 1$

$y(t) = -3 \cos t$

55. $x(t) = 5 \cos t - 2$

$y(t) = 3 - \sin t$

CHAPTER 7 REVIEW EXERCISES

Section 7.1 Polar Coordinates

In Exercises 1–2, represent the point by writing four pairs of polar coordinates in which θ is in the interval $(-2\pi, 2\pi)$.

1. a point 4.5 units from the origin on a ray that forms an angle of $3\pi/4$ radians counterclockwise from the polar axis

2. a point 7 units from the origin on a ray that forms a 210° angle counterclockwise from the polar axis

3. Convert $(-5.5, -4\pi/3)$ to rectangular coordinates (x, y).

4. Convert $(-8\sqrt{3}, -8)$ to polar coordinates (r, θ).

5. Convert $(-3.6, -2.1)$ to polar coordinates (r, θ). Round θ to the nearest hundredth.

Section 7.2 Polar Equations

6. Write $-12 \csc \theta = 4r$ in rectangular form.

7. Write $2x + 6y^2 = 0$ in polar form.

In Exercises 8–10, graph the polar equation.

8. $\theta = 5\pi/3$

9. $r = -5 \cos \theta$

10. $r = 5 \sin 4\theta$

Section 7.3 Rotation of Axes

11. For coordinate $P(7, -3)$, find the coordinates of P' when the angle of rotation is $\pi/3$.

12. For coordinate $P(-1, -4)$, find the coordinates of P' when the angle of rotation is $11\pi/4$.

13. $P'(x', y')$ is the point that results when $P(x, y)$ is rotated by an angle of ϕ counterclockwise about the origin. Use $\phi = 5\pi/4$, $x = 6$, and $x' = -4$ to find y'.

14. Identify the type of conic, if any, given by $-2y^2 - 2x^2 = -5 - 5x - 4xy$.

15. Graph $30y + 73y^2 + 52x^2 = 75 + 40x - 72xy$.

Section 7.4 Polar Equation of Conics

In Exercises 16–17, identify the conic given by the polar equation, then determine its directrix and eccentricity.

16. $r = \dfrac{6}{3 - 2 \sin \theta}$

17. $r = \dfrac{12}{4 + 8 \cos \theta}$

In Exercises 18–19, use the given directrix and eccentricity to write the polar equation of the conic (with focus at the origin).

18. directrix $x = 6$, $e = 1/4$

19. directrix $y = -4$, $e = 2$

20. Graph the equation $3r + 3r \cos \theta = 8$ and find its directrix and eccentricity.

Section 7.5 Plane Curves and Parametric Equations

In Exercises 21–22, graph the plane curve defined by the pair of parametric equations.

21. $x(t) = t^3$
    $y(t) = |0.5t - 8|$
    $-2 \leq t \leq 2$

22. $x(t) = -2 \cos t$
    $y(t) = 3 \sin t - 1$
    $0 \leq t \leq 3\pi/2$

In Exercises 23–24, eliminate the parameter to find the rectangular equation for the plane curve described by the parametric equations. State the domain of the rectangular equation for the plane curve.

23. $x(t) = 2 - t$
    $y(t) = 3t^2 - 1$

24. $x(t) = -4 \sin t$
    $y(t) = \cos t$

25. Graph $x(t) = \sqrt{3t + 3}$.
    $y(t) = t^2 - 4$
    $-1 \leq t \leq 2$

EXPONENTIAL AND LOGARITHMIC FUNCTIONS

8.1 EXPONENTIAL FUNCTIONS

OBJECTIVES

- Evaluate exponential functions.
- Graph exponential functions.
- Model compound interest with exponential equations.
- Evaluate natural exponential functions.
- Graph natural exponential functions.
- Model population growth with natural exponential equations.

PREREQUISITE VOCABULARY TERMS

asymptote
function
interest
reflection
translation
y-intercept

8.1.1 An Introduction to Exponential Functions

In previous sections, we have seen functions that contain powers. For example, the basic quadratic function $f(x) = x^2$ contains a power where the base is a variable and the exponent is 2. An **exponential function** is another type of function that contains a power, but the base is a number (a positive real number not equal to 1) and the exponent contains the variable. Several types of exponential functions will be discussed in this section.

> **DEFINITION**
>
> A function of the form $f(x) = b^x$ where b is a real number such that $b > 0$ and $b \neq 1$ is an **exponential function**.

The following are examples of exponential functions.

$$f(x) = 2^x \qquad f(x) = 1 + 5^x \qquad f(x) = 3(0.1^{x+5}) \qquad f(x) = \left(\frac{1}{2}\right)^{-x}$$

EXAMPLE 1   Evaluating an Exponential Function

Evaluate each exponential function.

A. $f(x) = 2^x$ for $x = 3$

B. $f(x) = 5^{-x}$ for $x = 2$

C. $f(x) = 16^x$ for $x = \dfrac{3}{4}$

D. $f(x) = \left(\dfrac{3}{4}\right)^{2x}$ for $x = -1$

SOLUTION

A. $f(3) = 2^3 = 8$

$a^{-m} = \dfrac{1}{a^m}$ ▶ **B.** $f(2) = 5^{-2} = \dfrac{1}{5^2} = \dfrac{1}{25}$

$a^{\frac{m}{n}} = \left(\sqrt[n]{a}\right)^m = \sqrt[n]{a^m}$ ▶ **C.** $f\left(\dfrac{3}{4}\right) = 16^{\frac{3}{4}} = \left(\sqrt[4]{16}\right)^3 = 2^3 = 8$

$\left(\dfrac{a}{b}\right)^{-n} = \left(\dfrac{b}{a}\right)^n$ ▶ **D.** $f(-1) = \left(\dfrac{3}{4}\right)^{2(-1)} = \left(\dfrac{3}{4}\right)^{-2} = \left(\dfrac{4}{3}\right)^2 = \dfrac{4^2}{3^2} = \dfrac{16}{9}$

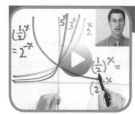

8.1.2 An Introduction to Graphing Exponential Functions

Exponential functions can be graphed by plotting points. Consider the graph of an exponential function of the form $f(x) = b^x$. Regardless of what the b-value is, the y-value will be 1 when $x = 0$, since any real number to the 0 power is 1 ($b^0 = 1$). So, the graph of $f(x) = b^x$ will always pass through $(0, 1)$. Additionally, since b must be a positive number, the value of b^x will always be positive, so the graph of $f(x) = b^x$ will have a horizontal asymptote at $y = 0$ and no x-intercepts.

> The graph of the exponential function $f(x) = b^x$ has a horizontal asymptote at $y = 0$ (i.e., the x-axis), and passes through $(0, 1)$. The domain of the function is all real numbers, and the range is $(0, \infty)$.

EXAMPLE 2　Graphing an Exponential Function $y = b^x$

Sketch the graphs of $f(x) = 2^x$ and $g(x) = \left(\frac{1}{2}\right)^x$ by plotting points.

SOLUTION

Make a table of values for each function. Then plot the points and sketch the curves.

x	$f(x)$	$g(x)$
-2	$\frac{1}{4}$	4
-1	$\frac{1}{2}$	2
0	1	1
1	2	$\frac{1}{2}$
2	4	$\frac{1}{4}$

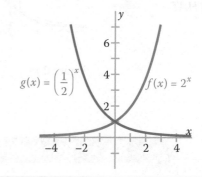

$g(x)$ can be written equivalently as $g(x) = 2^{-x}$ by applying the Negative Exponent Property and the Power of a Power Property.

$g(x) = \left(\frac{1}{2}\right)^x = \left(2^{-1}\right)^x = 2^{-x}$

Comparing the Graphs of $f(x) = b^x$ and $f(x) = b^{-x}$

Recall that the graphs of $f(x)$ and $f(-x)$ are reflections over the y-axis. It follows that the graphs of the exponential functions $f(x) = b^x$ and $f(x) = b^{-x}$ are reflections over the y-axis. Note that since $b^{-x} = \left(\frac{1}{b}\right)^x$, we can also say that the graphs of $f(x) = b^x$ and $f(x) = \left(\frac{1}{b}\right)^x$ are reflections over the y-axis. In other words, if two functions of the form $f(x) = b^x$ have reciprocal bases, then their graphs are reflections over the y-axis. For example, the functions in **Example 2** have reciprocal bases, and their graphs are reflections over the y-axis.

Exponential Functions: Reflections Over the y-Axis

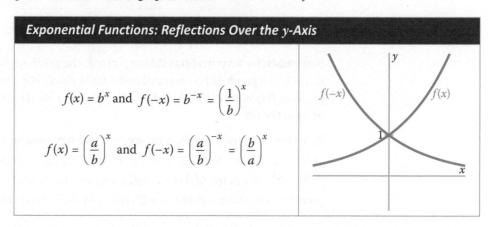

$f(x) = b^x$ and $f(-x) = b^{-x} = \left(\frac{1}{b}\right)^x$

$f(x) = \left(\frac{a}{b}\right)^x$ and $f(-x) = \left(\frac{a}{b}\right)^{-x} = \left(\frac{b}{a}\right)^x$

Examining the Graph of $f(x) = b^x$ for Different Values of b

When $b > 1$, the graph of $f(x) = b^x$ increases from left to right (i.e., as x increases, $f(x)$ increases). However, when $0 < b < 1$, the graph of $f(x) = b^x$ decreases from left to right (i.e., as x increases, $f(x)$ decreases).

Another aspect of the graph of $f(x) = b^x$ that can be deduced from the value of b is the steepness of the curve's incline (or decline). Consider the functions $f(x) = a^x$ and $f(x) = b^x$ when $b > a > 1$. For all $x > 1$, it is true that $b^x > a^x$. It follows that when $x > 1$, the y-values for $f(x) = b^x$ will increase faster than those of $f(x) = a^x$. So, the curve $f(x) = b^x$ is steeper than the curve $f(x) = a^x$ in the first quadrant. Furthermore, for all $x < 1$, $b^x < a^x$. So, the curve $f(x) = b^x$ approaches the y-axis more quickly than the curve $f(x) = a^x$ in the second quadrant. Several examples of this are shown in Figure 8.1a.

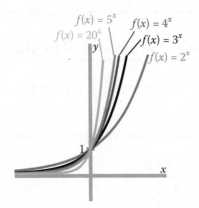

$f(x) = 5^x$ $f(x) = 4^x$
$f(x) = 20^x$ $f(x) = 3^x$
$f(x) = 2^x$

In Figure 8.1a, we see that in the first quadrant, the graph of $f(x) = 3^x$ is steeper than the graph of $f(x) = 2^x$, and the graph of $f(x) = 4^x$ is steeper than the graph of $f(x) = 3^x$. However, note that this steepness does not appear to increase at a constant rate. The difference in the steepness between the graph of $f(x) = 3^x$ and $f(x) = 2^x$ is quite obvious, but the difference in the steepness between the graph of $f(x) = 4^x$ and $f(x) = 5^x$ is much less.

NOTICE THAT

The graph of each equation passes through (0, 1).

Figure 8.1a

8.1.3 Transformations of Exponential Functions

Exponential functions can be graphed by using transformations, as we saw with other types of functions. The following table summarizes the transformations of exponential functions.

Transformations of Functions	
Vertical translation	$f(x) + k$ or $f(x) - k$
Horizontal translation	$f(x + h)$ or $f(x - h)$
Vertical stretch or compression	$cf(x)$
Reflection over the x-axis	$-f(x)$
Reflection over the y-axis	$f(-x)$

Remember, for a vertical translation $f(x) + k$, the graph of $f(x)$ is translated k units *up*, and for $f(x) - k$, the graph of $f(x)$ is translated k units *down*. For a horizontal translation $f(x - h)$, the graph of $f(x)$ is translated h units to the *right*, and for $f(x + h)$, the graph of $f(x)$ is translated h units to the *left*.

Reflections are used to graph the exponential functions in **Example 3**. Consider the function $g(x) = -2^x$. Notice that $-2^x = -(2^x)$. Therefore, $g(x) = -f(x)$ when $f(x) = 2^x$. So, the graph of $g(x) = -2^x$ is the graph of $f(x) = 2^x$ reflected over the x-axis. Specifically, this means that for every point (x, y) on the graph of $f(x) = 2^x$, the point $(x, -y)$ is on the graph of $g(x) = -2^x$.

EXAMPLE 3	Using Reflections and Stretches to Graph an Exponential Function

Sketch the graph of each function.

A. $g(x) = -3^x$ **B.** $h(x) = (0.5)2^{-x}$

IMPORTANT

The base of -3^x is 3, not -3. A base is negative only when enclosed within parentheses. For example, the base of $(-3)^x$ is -3. However, the base of an exponential function cannot be negative.

SOLUTION

A. Sketch the graph of the basic function $f(x) = 3^x$.

Then reflect that graph over the x-axis, since $g(x) = -3^x = -f(x)$.

x	$f(x)$	$g(x)$
-2	$\frac{1}{9}$	$-\frac{1}{9}$
-1	$\frac{1}{3}$	$-\frac{1}{3}$
0	1	-1
1	3	-3
2	9	-9

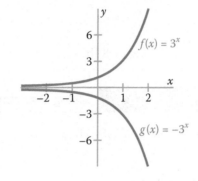

For every point (x, y) on the graph of $f(x) = 3^x$, the point $(x, -y)$ is on the graph of $g(x) = -3^x$.

B. Sketch the graph of the basic function $f(x) = 2^x$.

Then reflect that graph over the y-axis and vertically compress the curve by a factor of $1/2$ (since $g(x) = (0.5)2^{-x} = (0.5)f(-x)$ and $0.5 = 1/2$).

x	$f(x)$
-2	$\frac{1}{4}$
-1	$\frac{1}{2}$
0	1
1	2
2	4

x	$h(x)$
2	$\frac{1}{8}$
1	$\frac{1}{4}$
0	$\frac{1}{2}$
-1	1
-2	2

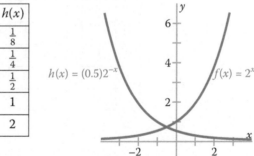

For every point (x, y) on the graph of $f(x) = 2^x$, the point $(-x, 0.5y)$ is on the graph of $g(x) = (0.5)2^{-x}$.

8.1.4 Graphing Exponential Functions: Another Example

Vertical and Horizontal Translations of $f(x) = b^x$

Translations of the exponential function $f(x) = b^x$ occur when a number is added to, or subtracted from, x or b^x. The following functions are all vertical or horizontal translations of $f(x) = b^x$.

$g(x) = b^x + 1$ *The graph of $f(x)$ is translated up 1 unit to form the graph of $g(x)$.*

$g(x) = b^x - 1$ *The graph of $f(x)$ is translated down 1 unit to form the graph of $g(x)$.*

$g(x) = b^{x+1}$ *The graph of $f(x)$ is translated to the left 1 unit to form the graph of $g(x)$.*

$g(x) = b^{x-1}$ *The graph of $f(x)$ is translated to the right 1 unit to form the graph of $g(x)$.*

For example, the graph of $g(x) = 2^x + 3$ is the graph of $f(x) = 2^x$ translated up 3 units (Figure 8.1b). Additionally, the graph of $g(x) = -3^{x-1}$ is the graph of $f(x) = 3^x$ reflected across the x-axis and translated to the right 1 unit (Figure 8.1c).

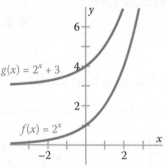

Figure 8.1b

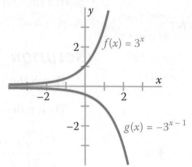

Figure 8.1c

EXAMPLE 4   Using Translations to Graph an Exponential Function

Sketch the graph of each function.

A. $g(x) = 2^{x-1}$ **B.** $h(x) = 5 + 2^x$

SOLUTION

A. Sketch the graph of the basic function $f(x) = 2^x$.

Then translate that graph 1 unit to the right since $g(x) = 2^{x-1} = f(x-1)$.

x	$f(x)$
-2	$\frac{1}{4}$
-1	$\frac{1}{2}$
0	1
1	2
2	4

x	$g(x)$
-1	$\frac{1}{4}$
0	$\frac{1}{2}$
1	1
2	2
3	4

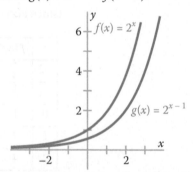

For every point (x, y) on the graph of $f(x) = 2^x$, the point $(x + 1, y)$ is on the graph of $g(x) = 2^{x-1}$.

B. Sketch the graph of the basic function $f(x) = 2^x$.

Then translate that graph 5 units up, since $h(x) = 5 + 2^x = f(x) + 5$.

x	$f(x)$
-2	$\frac{1}{4}$
-1	$\frac{1}{2}$
0	1
1	2
2	4

x	$h(x)$
-2	$5\frac{1}{4}$
-1	$5\frac{1}{2}$
0	6
1	7
2	9

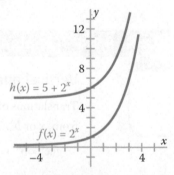

For every point (x, y) on the graph of $f(x) = 2^x$, the point $(x, y + 5)$ is on the graph of $h(x) = 5 + 2^x$.

8.1.5   Finding Present Value and Future Value

When a bank or other financial institution loans a customer sum of money, called the **principal**, the amount that is eventually repaid by the customer is greater than the principal. The difference between the principal and the total amount repaid is called **interest**. Interest can also be earned and added to a principal that is invested, instead of loaned.

There are several ways to make interest calculations. The most basic type of interest is called **simple interest**. When a principal amount P is borrowed (or invested) for t years at an **interest rate** of r, the amount of simple interest I paid (or earned) is given by the formula $I = Prt$.

When the interest on an account (or loan) is compounded (calculated and added to the principal) m times per year, the interest is called **compound interest**. Compound interest is calculated using the compound interest formula, and is an example of exponential growth.

Compound Interest Formula

$$A = P\left(1 + \frac{r}{m}\right)^{mt}$$

TIP

If the interest rate r is given as a percent, convert r to a fraction or decimal for use in the formula.

Compound interest is compounded m times per year.

   P = the principal amount (original amount) in the account

   t = the length of time that the money is invested, in years

   A = the balance in the account after t years

   r = the annual interest rate (as a decimal)

   m = the number of times per year that the interest is compounded

The compound interest formula can also be applied to debt. In that case, P is the original amount borrowed, and A is the amount owed after t years.

EXAMPLE 5   Using the Compound Interest Formula to Find a Balance

A student takes out a student loan of $18,000 at 6% interest, compounded monthly. The loan payments are deferred for 4 years, causing the loan balance to generate interest for that time before the student starts making payments. At the end of 4 years, what is the balance of the school loan?

SOLUTION

Identify the values of the quantities to be substituted into the compound interest formula from the given information.

The original amount borrowed is $18,000, so $P = 18,000$.

The interest rate is 6%, so $r = 0.06$.

The interest is compounded monthly, so $m = 12$ (because the interest is compounded 12 times per year).

Payments on the loan will begin after 4 years, so $t = 4$.

Substitute these values into the formula, and simplify to find the balance of the loan after 4 years.

IMPORTANT

Do not round until the final step in the calculations.

$$A = 18{,}000\left(1 + \frac{0.06}{12}\right)^{12(4)} = 18{,}000(1.005)^{48} \approx 22{,}868.80 \quad \textit{Round to the nearest cent.}$$

After 4 years, the balance on the original loan of $18,000 is $22,868.80.

EXAMPLE 6   Using the Compound Interest Formula to Find the Principal

How much needs to be deposited into an account offering 7% interest, compounded quarterly, in order for the account to be worth $250,000 after 30 years? Assume that no money is deposited after the initial deposit.

SOLUTION

Identify the values of the quantities to be substituted into the compound interest formula from the given information.

The original amount invested, P, is the unknown.

The interest rate is 7%, so $r = 0.07$. The interest is compounded quarterly, so $m = 4$ (because the interest is compounded 4 times per year).

The interest accumulates for 30 years, so $t = 30$.

The amount in the account after 30 years should be $250,000, so $A = 250,000$.

Substituting these values into the formula yields $250{,}000 = P\left(1 + \dfrac{0.07}{4}\right)^{4(30)}$.

Simplify, and then solve the equation for P.

Do not round until the final step in the calculations.

> **IMPORTANT**
>
> The unknown value P is multiplied by $\left(1 + \dfrac{0.07}{4}\right)^{4(30)}$. So, divide both sides by this amount to solve the equation for P.

$$250{,}000 = P\left(1 + \frac{0.07}{4}\right)^{4(30)} \qquad \text{\textit{Substitute. Use the compound interest formula.}}$$

$$250{,}000 = P(1.0175)^{120} \qquad \text{\textit{Simplify.}}$$

$$\frac{250{,}000}{(1.0175)^{120}} = P \qquad \text{\textit{Solve for P.}}$$

$$31{,}175.24 \approx P \qquad \text{\textit{Round to the nearest cent.}}$$

$31,175.24 should be deposited initially so that the value of the account will be $250,000 after 30 years.

The answer for **Example 6** can be checked by substituting the given values of r, m, and t, along with the found value of P, into the compound interest formula and simplifying to confirm that the balance after 30 years will be approximately $250,000 when $31,175.24 is deposited into a quarterly compounding account with a 7% interest rate.

$$A = 31{,}175.24\left(1 + \frac{0.07}{4}\right)^{4(30)} \approx 250{,}000 \ \checkmark$$

8.1.6   Finding an Interest Rate to Match Given Goals

In **Examples 5** and **6**, the compound interest formula was used to find A and P, respectively. The compound interest formula can also be solved for the interest rate r, as demonstrated in **Example 7**. (In Section 8.4, the compound interest formula will be solved for each exponent, m and t, using a slightly more complicated process.)

> **EXAMPLE 7** **Using the Compound Interest Formula to Find the Interest Rate**

An initial deposit of $8050 was made into an account that compounds interest semi-annually. No other deposits were made. At the end of 18 years, the balance in the account had doubled. Find the interest rate on this account to the nearest hundredth of a percent.

TIP

The rate r in the compound interest formula is a decimal value. To write the rate as a percent rounded to the nearest hundredth of a percent, round the r-value to the nearest ten thousandth and then move the decimal point two places to the right.

SOLUTION

Identify the values of the variables in the compound interest formula.

The original amount deposited is $8050, so $P = 8050$.
The interest rate is the unknown.
The interest is compounded semi-annually, so $m = 2$.
The interest accumulates for 18 years, so $t = 18$.
The amount in the account after 18 years is double the original amount deposited, so $A = 2(8050)$.

Substituting these values into the formula yields $2(8050) = 8050\left(1 + \dfrac{r}{2}\right)^{2(18)}$.

Simplify, and then solve the equation for r. Do not round until the final step in the calculations.

$$2(8050) = 8050\left(1 + \frac{r}{2}\right)^{2(18)}$$ *Substitute. Use the compound interest formula.*

$$2 = \left(1 + \frac{r}{2}\right)^{36}$$ *Divide each side by 8050 and simplify.*

$$\sqrt[36]{2} = 1 + \frac{r}{2}$$ *Take the 36th root of each side.*

$$2\left(\sqrt[36]{2} - 1\right) = r$$ *Solve for r.*

$$0.0389 \approx r$$ *Simplify and round to the nearest ten thousandth.*

The interest rate is approximately 3.89%.

8.1.7 Evaluating and Graphing a Natural Exponential Function

The Natural Base e

The base of an exponential function can be any positive number not equal to 1. A base value that is commonly seen in applications of exponential functions is the irrational **number e**. Since e is an irrational number, its decimal expansion never terminates or repeats.

$$e = 2.7182818284 \ldots$$

Any exponential function with base e is called a **natural exponential function**.

> **DEFINITION**
>
> The **natural exponential function** is the exponential function $f(x) = e^x$.

A natural exponential function can be evaluated by using a calculator or by substituting some approximation of e into the function.

EXAMPLE 8 Evaluating a Natural Exponential Function

Use a calculator to evaluate the natural exponential function $f(x) = e^x$ for $x = -2, 0, 1,$ and 5. Round the answer to the nearest hundredth, if needed.

SOLUTION

Most calculators have an exponential function key, $\boxed{e^x}$. Enter the value of the exponent after pressing the exponential function key.

$$f(-2) = e^{-2} \approx 0.14$$
$$f(0) = e^0 = 1$$
$$f(1) = e^1 = e \approx 2.72$$
$$f(5) = e^5 \approx 148.41$$

TIP

Any number to the 0 power is equal to 1, even when the base is an irrational number.

Graphing Natural Exponential Functions

The graph of the natural exponential function $f(x) = e^x$ and its corresponding table are shown in Figure 8.1d.

IMPORTANT

The natural exponential function is a type of exponential function, so all properties of exponential functions apply to natural exponential functions.

Like the graph of the exponential function $f(x) = b^x$, the graph of $f(x) = e^x$ has no x-intercepts, the y-intercept is at $(0, 1)$, and the graph of $f(x) = e^x$ approaches, but does not intersect, the x-axis as x goes to $-\infty$ (i.e., the graph has a horizontal asymptote at $y = 0$). Moreover, all properties of the exponential function $f(x) = b^x$ apply to the natural exponential function $f(x) = e^x$ since the natural exponential function is an exponential function.

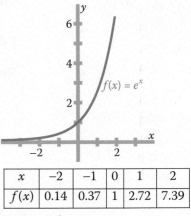

x	-2	-1	0	1	2
$f(x)$	0.14	0.37	1	2.72	7.39

Figure 8.1d

Natural exponential functions can be graphed using translations, reflections, and stretches, just like any other type of function.

EXAMPLE 9 Using Translations to Graph a Natural Exponential Function

Sketch the graph of each function.

A. $g(x) = e^{x+2}$ **B.** $h(x) = 3 + e^x$

SOLUTION

A. Sketch the graph of the basic function $f(x) = e^x$. Then translate that graph 2 units to the left, since $g(x) = e^{x+2} = f(x+2)$.

x	-2	-1	0	1	2
$f(x)$	0.14	0.37	1	2.72	7.39

x	-4	-3	-2	-1	0
$g(x)$	0.14	0.37	1	2.72	7.39

For every point (x, y) on the graph of $f(x) = e^x$, the point $(x - 2, y)$ is on the graph of $g(x) = e^{x+2}$.

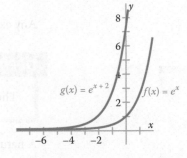

B. Sketch the graph of the basic function $f(x) = e^x$.

Then translate that graph 3 units up, since $h(x) = 3 + e^x = f(x) + 3$.

x	−2	−1	0	1	2
$f(x)$	0.14	0.37	1	2.72	7.39

x	−2	−1	0	1	2
$h(x)$	3.14	3.37	4	5.72	10.39

For every point (x, y) on the graph of $f(x) = e^x$, the point $(x, y + 3)$ is on the graph of $h(x) = 3 + e^x$.

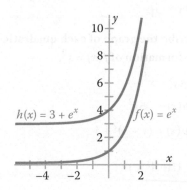

$h(x) = 3 + e^x$ $f(x) = e^x$

8.1.8   Applying Natural Exponential Functions

The natural base e is commonly used with **exponential models** involving a quantity that increases exponentially over time, such as population growth.

EXAMPLE 10   Using a Natural Exponential Model to Estimate Population

In 1990, the population of the United States was approximately 250 million people and was expected to grow according to the function $P(x) = 250{,}000{,}000e^{0.009x}$, where x is the number of years after 1990. According to the U.S. Census Bureau, the population of the United States in 2010 was approximately 310 million. Compare the actual population of the United States in 2010 to the expected population of the United States in 2010, according to this model.

SOLUTION

In the population model $P(x) = 250{,}000{,}000e^{0.009x}$, x represents the number of years after 1990. So, the population in 1990 corresponds to $x = 0$.

The expected population in 2010 corresponds to $x = 20$, because 2010 is 20 years after 1990.

Evaluate the population model for $x = 20$ to find the expected population in 2010.

$$P(20) = 250{,}000{,}000e^{0.009(20)} = 250{,}000{,}000e^{0.18} \approx 299{,}304{,}341 \approx 299{,}000{,}000$$

Thus, according to the model, the expected population in 2010 was approximately 299 million.

The model's estimate is approximately 11 million less than the actual population in 2010.

SECTION 8.1 EXERCISES

Warm Up

Describe the graph of each quadratic function as a transformation of $f(x) = x^2$.

1. $g(x) = x^2 - 4$

2. $h(x) = -5x^2$

3. $p(x) = (x + 3)^2 + 1$

Just the Facts

Fill in the blanks.

4. For a function of the general form $f(x) = b^x$ to be considered exponential, the base must be _____, _____, and not equal to _____.

5. Given the function $f(x) = b^x$, $f(x)$ will be equal to _____ for any positive real value of b if x is equal to _____.

6. If $f(x) = b^x$, then $g(x) = $ _____ is the reflection of $f(x)$ across the y-axis, and $g(x) = $ _____ is the reflection of $f(x)$ across the x-axis.

7. The graph of $f(x) = 5^x$ is _____ than the graph of $g(x) = 2^x$ for all $x > 0$.

8. A principal of $1000 was invested at 5% over 2 years. If the principal was compounded yearly using the compound interest formula, the interest gained would be _____. If the interest was calculated using the simple interest formula, the interest gained would be _____.

9. For the equation $7500 = \left(1 + \dfrac{r}{4}\right)^{40}$, the first step in isolating r is _____.

10. An exponential function with a base of e is called a(n) _____ exponential function.

Essential Skills

In Exercises 1–4, identify the exponential functions in each list.

1. $g(x) = 5^x$
$h(x) = 2^{3x}$
$p(x) = -4$
$f(x) = 1^{3x+4}$
$m(x) = 510 + x$
$q(x) = 8^x - 3$
$r(x) = x^2$
$n(x) = 5x$

2. $p(x) = x^3$
$g(x) = 7^{2x+1}$
$h(x) = (-3)^x$
$f(x) = \left(\dfrac{4}{7}\right)^x$
$q(x) = -(3)^x$
$r(x) = \pi^{2x}$
$m(x) = 1^x$
$n(x) = 0.8^{x+1}$

3. $g(x) = 2^{x+3}$
$h(x) = 16x^2 + 3$
$p(x) = \dfrac{x^4}{3}$
$r(x) = (x - 1)^5$
$m(x) = 7\pi^x$
$q(x) = -5^x - 9$
$f(x) = 8^{\frac{1}{2}x}$
$n(x) = 1^{6+2x}$

4. $d(x) = 1^{3x}$
$k(x) = (-4)^{6x}$
$q(x) = 3x^3 + 4x - 5$
$f(x) = \left(\dfrac{3}{2}\right)^{-x}$
$t(x) = -(0.9)^x$
$w(x) = 3^{5x+2}$
$n(x) = \left(-\dfrac{5}{9}\right)^{4x-3}$
$h(x) = (8x)^{1/3}$

In Exercises 5–24, evaluate each exponential function.

5. If $f(x) = 2^x$, find $f(4)$, $f(0)$, and $f(7)$.

6. If $f(x) = 8^x$, find $f(3)$, $f(-2)$, and $f\left(\dfrac{1}{2}\right)$.

7. If $g(x) = -(12)^x$, find $g(3)$, $g(-1)$, and $g\left(\dfrac{1}{2}\right)$.

8. If $c(x) = -5^x$, find $c(4)$, $c(-2)$, and $c\left(\dfrac{1}{2}\right)$.

9. If $d(x) = 3^{-x}$, find $d(5)$, $d(-3)$, and $d\left(\dfrac{3}{2}\right)$.

10. If $h(x) = 18^{-x}$, find $h(-3)$, $h(2)$, and $h\left(\dfrac{1}{2}\right)$.

11. If $r(x) = 49^x$, find $r(-2)$, $r\left(\dfrac{1}{2}\right)$, and $r\left(-\dfrac{3}{2}\right)$.

12. If $b(x) = 27^x$, find $b\left(\dfrac{1}{2}\right)$, $b\left(-\dfrac{1}{3}\right)$, and $b\left(\dfrac{2}{3}\right)$.

13. If $p(x) = \left(\dfrac{1}{27}\right)^x$, find $p(-2)$, $p\left(-\dfrac{1}{2}\right)$, and $p\left(\dfrac{2}{3}\right)$.

14. If $q(x) = \left(\dfrac{1}{32}\right)^x$, find $q(-1)$, $q(0)$, and $q\left(-\dfrac{1}{2}\right)$.

15. If $m(x) = \left(\dfrac{1}{20}\right)^x$, find $m(-3)$, $m(2)$, and $m\left(-\dfrac{3}{2}\right)$.

16. If $v(x) = \left(\dfrac{8}{5}\right)^x$, find $v(3)$, $v(-2)$, and $v\left(-\dfrac{3}{2}\right)$.

17. If $t(x) = \left(\dfrac{1}{12}\right)^{-x}$, find $t(2)$, $t(-1)$, and $t\left(\dfrac{1}{2}\right)$.

18. If $u(x) = \left(\dfrac{1}{45}\right)^{-x}$, find $u(-1)$, $u\left(-\dfrac{1}{2}\right)$, and $u\left(\dfrac{1}{2}\right)$.

19. If $n(x) = \left(\dfrac{3}{4}\right)^{-x}$, find $n(-5)$, $n(4)$, and $n\left(\dfrac{1}{2}\right)$.

20. If $w(x) = \left(\dfrac{25}{9}\right)^{-x}$, find $w(1)$, $w(-2)$, and $w\left(-\dfrac{3}{2}\right)$.

21. If $f(x) = 8^{-2x}$, find $f(2)$, $f\left(-\dfrac{3}{2}\right)$, and $f\left(\dfrac{5}{6}\right)$.

22. If $h(x) = 18^{3x}$, find $h(-1)$, $h\left(-\frac{2}{3}\right)$, and $h\left(\frac{1}{2}\right)$.

23. If $p(x) = \left(\frac{2}{3}\right)^{2x}$, find $p(0)$, $p(-1)$, and $p\left(-\frac{5}{2}\right)$.

24. If $q(x) = \left(\frac{5}{4}\right)^{2x}$, find $q(-1)$, $q(2)$, and $q\left(-\frac{3}{2}\right)$.

In Exercises 25–30, identify the equivalent exponential functions in each list.

25. $f(x) = 5^x$
$h(x) = (-5)^x$
$k(x) = -5^{-x}$
$g(x) = \left(\frac{1}{5}\right)^{-x}$
$m(x) = x^{-5}$
$b(x) = 5x^{-5}$
$g(x) = \left(\frac{1}{5}\right)^{x}$

26. $f(x) = \left(\frac{1}{3}\right)^{-x}$
$g(x) = 3^x$
$a(x) = -3^x$
$d(x) = -x^3$
$k(x) = -3^{-x}$
$m(x) = x^{-3}$
$h(x) = 3^{-x}$

27. $g(x) = -8^{-x}$
$d(x) = 8^{-x}$
$p(x) = \left(\frac{1}{8}\right)^{-x}$
$h(x) = 8^x$
$f(x) = -8^x$
$c(x) = x^{-8}$
$m(x) = \left(\frac{1}{8}\right)^{x}$

28. $p(x) = \left(\frac{4}{7}\right)^{-x}$
$q(x) = -\left(\frac{7}{4}\right)^{x}$
$m(x) = -\left(\frac{4}{7}\right)^{x}$
$f(x) = \left(\frac{7}{4}\right)^{x}$
$n(x) = -\left(\frac{7}{4}\right)^{-x}$
$c(x) = -\left(\frac{4}{7}\right)^{-x}$
$r(x) = \frac{7^{-x}}{4}$

29. $w(x) = -\left(\frac{3}{5}\right)^{-x}$
$g(x) = \left(\frac{5}{3}\right)^{x}$
$r(x) = -\left(\frac{5}{3}\right)^{x}$
$n(x) = \frac{5^{-x}}{3}$
$p(x) = -\left(\frac{5}{3}\right)^{-x}$
$f(x) = -\left(\frac{3}{5}\right)^{x}$
$h(x) = \left(\frac{3}{5}\right)^{-x}$

30. $h(x) = -\left(\frac{11}{9}\right)^{-x}$
$p(x) = \frac{11^{-x}}{9}$
$w(x) = -\left(\frac{9}{11}\right)^{x}$
$r(x) = -\left(\frac{9}{11}\right)^{-x}$
$f(x) = \left(\frac{11}{9}\right)^{-x}$
$b(x) = \left(\frac{11}{9}\right)^{x}$
$g(x) = -\left(\frac{11}{9}\right)^{-x}$

In Exercises 31–36, graph each exponential function.

31. $g(x) = 4^x$

32. $f(x) = \left(\frac{1}{5}\right)^{x}$

33. $h(x) = 3^{-x}$

34. $g(x) = \left(\frac{1}{4}\right)2^{-x}$

35. $f(x) = 4^x - 2$

36. $g(x) = 3^{x-1} + 4$

37. A \$24,000 school loan at 7% interest, compounded monthly, is deferred for 5 years. Find the balance of the loan after 5 years when the loan payments are scheduled to begin.

In Exercises 38–40, use the following information.

A credit union client deposits \$900 in an account earning 9.5% interest, compounded quarterly. Find the balance of the account at the end of the given time period.

38. 19 years

39. 25 years

40. 40 years

In Exercises 41–43, use the following information.

A painter wants to have \$100,000 at retirement in 25 years by making a one-time deposit in a bank account. How much money does the painter need to deposit, given the following account information?

41. compounds quarterly at 6% interest

42. compounds monthly at 5.5% interest

43. compounds daily at 5% interest

In Exercises 44–46, use the following information.

How much money must be deposited in an account that pays 4.75% interest, compounded semi-annually, in order to accrue a balance of \$7,000 after the given time period?

44. 5 years and 6 months

45. 8 years and 3 months

46. 12 years and 9 months

47. Suppose \$34,000 is invested in an account where interest is compounded monthly. After 18 years, the balance is \$90,481. What was the interest rate? Round the answer to the nearest hundredth of a percent.

48. Suppose \$80,000 is invested in an account where interest is compounded monthly. After 30 years, the balance is \$637,803. What was the interest rate to the nearest hundredth of a percent?

49. An initial deposit of $5525 was made into an account that compounds interest quarterly. No other deposits were made. At the end of 10 years, the balance in the account had doubled. Find the interest rate on this account. Round the answer to the nearest hundredth of a percent.

50. Suppose $600 is compounded yearly for 20 years. If no other deposits are made, what rate is needed for the balance to triple in that time? Round the answer to the nearest hundredth of a percent.

In Exercises 51–58, evaluate each exponential function for $x = -2, -1, 0, 1,$ and 2. Round each value to the nearest hundredth.

51. $g(x) = 3e^x$

52. $f(x) = 5e^{-x}$

53. $p(x) = -2e^x$

54. $q(x) = 0.25e^x$

55. $w(x) = 1.4e^{-x}$

56. $r(x) = 2.6e^{-x}$

57. $d(x) = 0.325e^x$

58. $c(x) = -0.286e^x$

In Exercises 59–60, graph the exponential function.

59. $h(x) = e^{x+3}$

60. $g(x) = 5 + e^{x-2}$

In Exercises 61–63, use the following information.

The average atmospheric pressure P in pounds per square inch is $P = 14.7e^{-0.21x}$, where x is the altitude in miles above sea level. Find the average atmospheric pressure for the given altitude. Round to the nearest tenth.

61. 5.2 miles

62. 8.6 miles

63. 3.7 miles

In Exercises 64–66, use the following information.

A certain type of bacteria grows according to the function $P(t) = 1000e^{0.1912t}$, where P is the number of bacteria present after t hours. Find the number of bacteria present after the given time period. Round to the nearest whole number.

64. 6 hours

65. 8 hours

66. 12 hours

Extensions

67. A certain type of bacteria grows according to the function $P = 1000e^{0.1912t}$, where P is the number of bacteria present after t hours. Find the number of bacteria present after 5 hours and 15 minutes, rounded to the nearest whole number.

68. Graph the exponential function $h(x) = 2e^{-x-2} + 1$.

69. The average atmospheric pressure P in pounds per square inch is $P = 14.7e^{-0.21x}$, where x is the altitude in miles above sea level. Find the average atmospheric pressure for an altitude of 12,762 feet, rounded to the nearest tenth.

In Exercises 70–74, write the equation of an exponential function $g(x)$ that has the given characteristics.

70. base of 5, translated down 3 units, left 4 units, and reflected across the x-axis

71. base of 2, translated up 6 units, and right 3 units

72. base of 4, translated down 7 units, and right 1 unit

73. base of 1/2, translated down 5 units, and reflected across the y-axis

74. base of 9/4, translated up 2 units, left 8 units, and reflected across the x-axis

In Exercises 75–77, determine whether each statement is true or false.

75. The graph of $h(x) = e^{2x+3}$ has a y-intercept of $-3/2$.

76. The graph of $p(x) = -2e^{-x}$ is a reflection of the graph of $q(x) = 2e^{-x}$ across the y-axis.

77. The graph of $d(x) = 5e^{-(4x-3)}$ is a horizontal translation of $c(x) = 5e^{-4x}$ by 3/4 units to the right.

78. A student assigned to graph $g(x) = 4 - e^{x+2}$ transformed the coordinates of $f(x) = e^x$ by subtracting 2 from the x-coordinates and subtracting 4 from the y-coordinates. State the error(s), if any, that the student made.

8.2 LOGARITHMIC FUNCTIONS

OBJECTIVES

- Convert between exponential and logarithmic forms.
- Evaluate logarithmic functions, common logs, and natural logs.
- Use properties of logarithmic functions.
- Graph logarithmic functions.
- Find the domain of natural logarithmic functions.

PREREQUISITE VOCABULARY TERMS

domain
exponential function
Horizontal Line Test
inverse function
natural exponential function

8.2.1   An Introduction to Logarithmic Functions

Recall that when the graph of a function passes the Horizontal Line Test (i.e., no horizontal line intersects the graph of the function at more than one point), then that function is one-to-one and has an inverse function. Figure 8.2a shows the graph of the general exponential function $f(x) = b^x$, where $b > 1$. This function passes the Horizontal Line Test, is one-to-one, and must therefore have an inverse function. The inverse of an exponential function $f(x) = b^x$ is called the **logarithmic function with base** b.

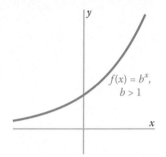

Figure 8.2a

REMEMBER

The x- and y-variables are switched for inverse functions.

TIP

The symbol $\Leftrightarrow$ is read as "if and only if." The expression $\log_b x$ is read as "log base b of x."

> **DEFINITION**
>
> The function $f(x) = \log_b x$ is called the **logarithmic function with base** b.
> If b is a positive number such that $b \neq 1$, then $y = \log_b x \iff b^y = x$.

The equation $3^2 = 9$ can be written as a logarithm (or as a "log") where the base of the power is the base of the log, and the exponent from the power is the value of the log.

$$3^2 = 9 \iff 2 = \log_3 9 \qquad \textit{The exponent is the value of the log.}$$

The equation $y = \log_b x$ states that the expression $\log_b x$ is equal to the value y. Notice that the value of y is the exponent in the equation $b^y = x$. Therefore, the value of $\log_b x$ is the exponent to which the base b must be raised to get x. So, a log is an exponent.

EXAMPLE 1   Simplifying Log Expressions

Find the value of each log.

A. $\log_5 25$ **B.** $\log_2 16$ **C.** $\log_5 125$

SOLUTION

TIP

Keep in mind that the value of a log is an exponent.

To simplify a log expression $\log_b x$, find the power of b that gives x.

A. The log's base is 5. What power of 5 is 25? $\log_5 25 = 2$ $5^2 = 25$

B. The log's base is 2. What power of 2 is 16? $\log_2 16 = 4$ $2^4 = 16$

C. The log's base is 5. What power of 5 is 125? $\log_5 125 = 3$ $5^3 = 125$

8.2.2 Converting between Exponential and Logarithmic Functions

In the previous topic, you saw that $y = \log_b x$ if and only if $b^y = x$. So, any exponential equation of the form $b^y = x$ can be written as a logarithmic equation $y = \log_b x$, and vice versa.

Exponential Form Equation	Logarithmic Form Equation
$b^y = x$	$y = \log_b x$

EXAMPLE 2   Writing an Exponential Equation in Logarithmic Form

Write each exponential equation as a log statement.

A. $5^4 = 625$　　　　**B.** $\left(\dfrac{3}{2}\right)^{-2} = \dfrac{4}{9}$　　　　**C.** $4^{\frac{3}{2}} = 8$

SOLUTION

A. The power's base is 5, and the exponent is 4, so $\log_5 625 = 4$.

B. The power's base is $\dfrac{3}{2}$, and the exponent is −2, so $\log_{\frac{3}{2}} \dfrac{4}{9} = -2$.

C. The power's base is 4, and the exponent is $\dfrac{3}{2}$, so $\log_4 8 = \dfrac{3}{2}$.

An equation in logarithmic form can be written as an equivalent equation in exponential form where the log's base is the base of the power and the log's value is the exponent.

EXAMPLE 3   Writing a Logarithmic Equation in Exponential Form

Write each logarithmic equation as an exponential statement.

A. $\log_3 2187 = 7$　　　　**B.** $\log_{81} 3 = \dfrac{1}{4}$　　　　**C.** $\log_6 \dfrac{1}{216} = -3$

SOLUTION

A. The log's base is 3, and the log's value is 7, so $3^7 = 2187$.

B. The log's base is 81, and the log's value is $\dfrac{1}{4}$, so $81^{\frac{1}{4}} = 3$.

C. The log's base is 6, and the log's value is −3, so $6^{-3} = \dfrac{1}{216}$.

REMEMBER

The 1/4th power of 81 is equivalent to the 4th root of 81.

$81^{\frac{1}{4}} = \sqrt[4]{81} = \sqrt[4]{(3)^4} = 3$

8.2.3 Evaluating Logarithms

The properties of exponents will often be used when simplifying a logarithmic expression.

> ### EXAMPLE 4   Simplifying a Logarithmic Expression

Find the value of each log.

A. $\log_3 \dfrac{1}{81}$ **B.** $\log_{25} 5$ **C.** $\log_{16} 8$

SOLUTION

A. The log's base is 3. What power of 3 is $\dfrac{1}{81}$?

$a^{-m} = \dfrac{1}{a^m}$ ▶

$$\log_3 \frac{1}{81} = -4 \qquad\qquad 3^{-4} = \frac{1}{3^4} = \frac{1}{81}$$

B. The log's base is 25. What power of 25 is 5?

$a^{\frac{1}{2}} = \sqrt{a}$ ▶

$$\log_{25} 5 = \frac{1}{2} \qquad\qquad 25^{\frac{1}{2}} = \sqrt{25} = 5$$

C. The log's base is 16. What power of 16 is 8?

$a^{\frac{m}{n}} = \left(\sqrt[n]{a}\right)^m$ ▶

$$\log_{16} 8 = \frac{3}{4} \qquad\qquad 16^{\frac{3}{4}} = \left(\sqrt[4]{16}\right)^3 = 2^3 = 8$$

8.2.4 Using Properties to Evaluate Logarithms

There are several properties of logarithms that can be used when evaluating logarithmic expressions. These log properties follow directly from the properties of exponents and the definition of a logarithmic function.

By the Zero Exponent Property, any real number to the 0 power is equal to 1 (i.e., $b^0 = 1$). Writing this exponential equation in logarithmic form yields $\log_b 1 = 0$.

Consider the power of some number b where the exponent is equal to 1 (i.e., b^1). Any number to the power of 1 is equal to that number, so $b^1 = b$. Writing this exponential equation in logarithmic form yields $\log_b b = 1$. A third property of logs follows from the fact that a power is equal to itself: $b^x = b^x$. Writing this exponential equation in logarithmic form yields $\log_b b^x = x$.

A fourth property of logs is derived by substituting the expression for y from $y = \log_b x$ into the equivalent exponential equation $b^y = x$. Since $y = \log_b x$ and $b^y = x$, it follows that $b^{\log_b x} = x$.

Properties of Logarithms with Base b		
Property	**Description**	**Exponential Form**
$\log_b 1 = 0$	*The power of b that equals 1 is 0.*	$b^0 = 1$
$\log_b b = 1$	*The power of b that equals b is 1.*	$b^1 = b$
$\log_b b^x = x$	*The power of b that equals b^x is x.*	$b^x = b^x$
$b^{\log_b x} = x$	*$\log_b x$ is the power to which b must be raised to get x.*	$y = \log_b x$ and $b^y = x$

| EXAMPLE 5 | Using Properties to Evaluate a Logarithmic Expression |

Evaluate each logarithm.

A. $\log_{12} 12$ **B.** $\log_7 7^{\sqrt{2}}$ **C.** $\sqrt{3}^{\log_{\sqrt{3}} \frac{2}{3}}$ **D.** $\log_{0.2} 1$

SOLUTION

Identify the property that applies to each log. Then use that property to evaluate the log.

A. $\log_{12} 12 = 1$ *$\log_b b = 1$*

B. $\log_7 7^{\sqrt{2}} = \sqrt{2}$ *$\log_b b^x = x$*

C. $\sqrt{3}^{\log_{\sqrt{3}} \frac{2}{3}} = \dfrac{2}{3}$ *$b^{\log_b x} = x$*

D. $\log_{0.2} 1 = 0$ *$\log_b 1 = 0$*

8.2.5   Graphing Logarithmic Functions

A logarithmic function of the form $f(x) = \log_b x$ can be graphed by making a table and plotting points. To find the ordered pairs for the table, first write the logarithmic function in exponential form: $x = b^{f(x)}$. Then choose y-values ($f(x)$-values) for the table, and find the corresponding x-values by evaluating $b^{f(x)}$.

Logarithmic Function		**Exponential Function**
$f(x) = \log_b x$	$\Leftrightarrow$	$x = b^{f(x)}$

| EXAMPLE 6 | Graphing a Logarithmic Function $y = \log_b x$ |

Sketch the graph of each logarithmic function.

A. $g(x) = \log_2 x$ **B.** $h(x) = \log_{\frac{1}{3}} x$

SOLUTION

A. In exponential form, the function is $x = 2^{g(x)}$. Make a table of values. Choose several values for $g(x)$, such as -2, -1, 0, 1, and 2, and then evaluate the power $2^{g(x)}$ to find each corresponding x-value. Plot the points from the table on a coordinate plane, and sketch a curve through the points.

x	$g(x)$		
$\dfrac{1}{4}$	-2	$2^{-2} = \dfrac{1}{2^2} = \dfrac{1}{4}$	
$\dfrac{1}{2}$	-1	$2^{-1} = \dfrac{1}{2^1} = \dfrac{1}{2}$	
1	0	$2^0 = 1$	
2	1	$2^1 = 2$	
4	2	$2^2 = 4$	

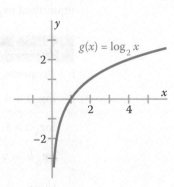

B. In exponential form, the function is $x = \left(\dfrac{1}{3}\right)^{h(x)}$. Make a table of values. Plot the points from the table, and sketch a curve through the points.

x	$h(x)$	
9	–2	$\left(\dfrac{1}{3}\right)^{-2} = 3^2 = 9$
3	–1	$\left(\dfrac{1}{3}\right)^{-1} = 3^1 = 3$
1	0	$\left(\dfrac{1}{3}\right)^{0} = 1$
$\dfrac{1}{3}$	1	$\left(\dfrac{1}{3}\right)^{1} = \dfrac{1}{3}$
$\dfrac{1}{9}$	2	$\left(\dfrac{1}{3}\right)^{2} = \dfrac{1}{9}$

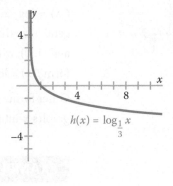

Using the Inverse to Graph a Logarithmic Function

Recall that if two functions are inverses, then their graphs are reflections over the line $y = x$ (i.e., for each point (x, y) on the graph of one function, the point (y, x) is on the graph of the other function). It follows that since $y = b^x$ and $y = \log_b x$ are inverses, their graphs are reflections over the line $y = x$, as shown in Figure 8.2b.

So, to graph a logarithmic function of the form $y = \log_b x$, graph the inverse function (the exponential function with the same base as the logarithmic function, $y = b^x$), and then reflect that graph over the line $y = x$.

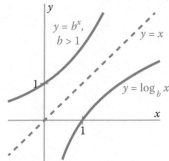

Figure 8.2b

Consider the functions graphed in **Example 6**, $g(x) = \log_2 x$ and $h(x) = \log_{\frac{1}{3}} x$.

The graphs of $g(x) = \log_2 x$ and $f(x) = 2^x$ are reflections over the line $y = x$ since f and g are inverse functions (Figure 8.2c).

The graphs of $h(x) = \log_{\frac{1}{3}} x$ and $f(x) = \left(\dfrac{1}{3}\right)^x$ are reflections over the line $y = x$ since f and h are inverse functions (Figure 8.2d).

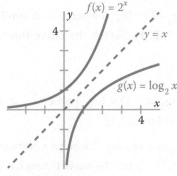

Figure 8.2c

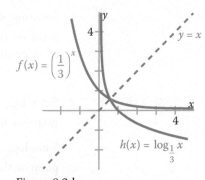

Figure 8.2d

Note that the functions $f(x) = \log_b x$ and $x = b^{f(x)}$ form the same graph. Additionally, the graph of $f(x) = \log_b x$ is the reflection of the graph of its inverse, $f(x) = b^x$, over the line $y = x$.

8.2.6 Matching Logarithmic Functions with Their Graphs

You are now familiar with the general shape of the graph of a logarithmic function of the form $f(x) = \log_b x$. By referring to two of the properties of logs, $\log_b b = 1$ and $\log_b 1 = 0$, we can generalize that all graphs of functions of the form $f(x) = \log_b x$ will pass through the points $(b, 1)$ and $(1, 0)$, which is the graph's x-intercept. You have also seen that all graphs of functions of the form $f(x) = \log_b x$ will have a vertical asymptote at $x = 0$ (i.e., at the y-axis).

Other forms of logarithmic functions can be graphed by using the property $\log_b 1 = 0$ to find the graph's x-intercept and then using $\log_b b = 1$ to find an additional point on the graph.

EXAMPLE 7   Graphing a Logarithmic Function

Sketch the graph of each logarithmic function.

A. $f(x) = \log_4 x$ **B.** $g(x) = \log_4 -2x$ **C.** $h(x) = \log_2 (x - 1)$

SOLUTION

Use the property $\log_b 1 = 0$ to find the graph's x-intercept, and use the property $\log_b b = 1$ to find another point on the graph. Then sketch the curve through those two points.

A. Since $\log_4 1 = 0$, the graph's x-intercept must be at $(1, 0)$. Since $\log_4 4 = 1$, another point on the graph is $(4, 1)$. Sketch the curve through these points.

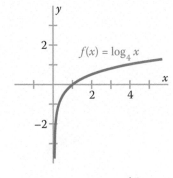

B. Because -2 is being multiplied by x in $g(x) = \log_4 -2x$, using the properties $\log_b 1 = 0$ and $\log_b b = 1$ to find two points on the graph is more complicated for $g(x) = \log_4 -2x$ than it was for $f(x) = \log_4 x$. So, find the values of x that make $-2x$ equal to 1 (to use $\log_b 1 = 0$) and equal to 4 (to use $\log_b b = 1$).

Since $\log_4 1 = 0$ and $\log_4 -2x = \log_4 1$ when $x = -\frac{1}{2}$, the graph's x-intercept must be at $\left(-\frac{1}{2}, 0\right)$.

Since $\log_4 4 = 1$ and $\log_4 -2x = \log_4 4$ when $x = -2$, another point on the graph is $(-2, 1)$. Sketch the curve through these points.

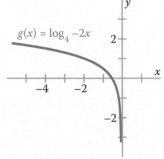

TIP

The expression $\log_4 -2x$ is equal to $\log_4 1$ when $x = -\dfrac{1}{2}$ because

$\log_4\left(-2 \cdot -\dfrac{1}{2}\right) = \log_4 1$.

So, when $x = -\dfrac{1}{2}$, $y = 0$.

ALTERNATIVE METHOD ▶

The graph of
$h(x) = \log_2 (x - 1)$
is the graph of
$f(x) = \log_2 x$ translated
1 unit to the right, since
$h(x) = f(x - 1)$.

C. Since $\log_2 1 = 0$ and $\log_2 (x - 1) = \log_2 1$ when $x = 2$, the graph's x-intercept must be at $(2, 0)$.

Since $\log_2 2 = 1$ and $\log_2 (x - 1) = \log_2 2$ when $x = 3$, another point on the graph is $(3, 1)$. Sketch the curve through these points.

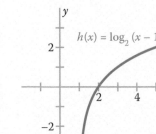

CAUTION

The expressions $\log_b (x + 1)$ and $\log_b x + 1$ are not equivalent.

$\log_b (x + 1)$ *Log base b of (x + 1)*

$\log_b x + 1$ *The sum of log base b of x and 1; equivalent to $1 + \log_b x$*

So, the graph of $y = \log_b (x + 1)$ is the graph of $y = \log_b x$ translated 1 unit to the left. The graph of $y = \log_b x + 1$ is the graph of $y = \log_b x$ translated 1 unit up.

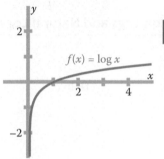

8.2.7   Common Logs and Natural Logs

Common Logs

A logarithm with base 10 is called a **common log**. The base of a common log is not written. So, when a log has no base written, the base is understood to be 10. The graph of the basic common log function $f(x) = \log x$ is shown in Figure 8.2e.

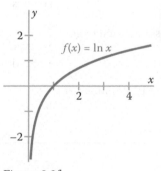

Figure 8.2e

> **DEFINITION**
>
> A **common log** is a logarithm where the base is 10.
>
> $$\log x = \log_{10} x$$
>
> The common log function $y = \log x$ is the inverse function of $y = 10^x$.

Natural Logs

Recall that the natural exponential function is the exponential function with base e, $f(x) = e^x$. There is also a **natural logarithmic function**. A natural logarithm has base e and is denoted $\ln x$. The graph of the basic natural log function $f(x) = \ln x$ is shown in Figure 8.2f.

> **DEFINITION**
>
> A **natural log** is a logarithm where the base is the number e.
>
> $$\ln x = \log_e x \quad (\text{where } x > 0)$$
>
> The natural log function $y = \ln x$ is the inverse function of $y = e^x$.

Figure 8.2f

Properties of Common Logs and Natural Logs

Recall that the exponential form of the logarithmic function $y = \log_b x$ is $b^y = x$. A common log and a natural log can also be written in exponential form. All properties of logs can also be applied to common logs and natural logs.

Logarithmic Form and Exponential Form		
	Logarithmic Form	**Exponential Form**
Logarithm with Base b	$y = \log_b x$	$b^y = x$
Common Logarithm	$y = \log x$	$10^y = x$
Natural Logarithm	$y = \ln x$	$e^y = x$

Properties of Common Logarithms and Natural Logarithms

Property	Description	Exponential Form
$\log 1 = 0$ $\ln 1 = 0$	*The power of 10 that equals 1 is 0.* *The power of e that equals 1 is 0.*	$10^0 = 1$ $e^0 = 1$
$\log 10 = 1$ $\ln e = 1$	*The power of 10 that equals 10 is 1.* *The power of e that equals e is 1.*	$10^1 = 10$ $e^1 = e$
$\log 10^x = x$ $\ln e^x = x$	*The power of 10 that equals 10^x is x.* *The power of e that equals e^x is x.*	$10^x = 10^x$ $e^x = e^x$
$10^{\log x} = x$ $e^{\ln x} = x$	*log x is the power to which 10 must be raised to get x.* *ln x is the power to which e must be raised to get x.*	$y = \log x$ and $10^y = x$ $y = \ln x$ and $e^y = x$

These properties can be used to simplify common log expressions and natural log expressions.

EXAMPLE 8 Using Properties to Evaluate Common Logs and Natural Logs

Evaluate each log without using a calculator.

A. $\log 10^7$ **B.** $(\ln e)(\ln 1)$ **C.** $10^{\log \sqrt{5}}$ **D.** $\ln e^{\log 10}$

SOLUTION

A. Since $\log 10^x = x$, $\log 10^7 = 7$.

Alternatively, find the power of 10 (the base) that equals 10^7.

Since the power of 10 that equals 10^7 is 7, $\log 10^7 = 7$.

B. By the properties, $\ln e = 1$ and $\ln 1 = 0$. So, $(\ln e)(\ln 1) = (1)(0) = 0$.

C. Since $10^{\log x} = x$, $10^{\log \sqrt{5}} = \sqrt{5}$.

Alternatively, notice that $\log \sqrt{5}$ is the power to which 10 must be raised to get $\sqrt{5}$.
So, $10^{\log \sqrt{5}} = \sqrt{5}$.

D. Since $\ln e^x = x$, $\ln e^{\log 10} = \log 10$. By the property $\log 10 = 1$, $\log 10$ simplifies to 1.

So, $\ln e^{\log 10} = 1$.

8.2.8 Evaluating Common Logs and Natural Logs Using a Calculator

Most calculators have a [LOG] key and a [LN] key. The [LOG] key is for the common log, and the [LN] key is for the natural log. For example, to simplify log 5 with a calculator, use the keystrokes [LOG] [5] [ENTER]. Similarly, use the keystrokes [LN] [5] [ENTER] to simplify ln 5 with a calculator.

EXAMPLE 9	**Using a Calculator to Evaluate Common Logs and Natural Logs**

Evaluate log 80 and ln 80 using a calculator. Round to the nearest tenth.

SOLUTION

TIP

The log's number must be entered before the log key for some scientific calculators.

The value of log 80 is the power of 10 that equals 80. Since $10^1 < 80 < 10^2$, the value of log 80 must be between 1 and 2. Furthermore, since 80 is much closer to 100 than it is to 10, the value of log 80 must be close to 2.

$$\log 80 \approx 1.9 \qquad \text{Calculator Keystrokes: } \boxed{\text{LOG}} \quad \boxed{80} \quad \boxed{\text{ENTER}}$$

The value of ln 80 is the power of e that equals 80. Since $2.7^4 < 80 < 2.7^5$ (2.7 is being used as the approximation for the value of e), the value of ln 80 must be between 4 and 5.

$$\ln 80 \approx 4.4 \qquad \text{Calculator Keystrokes: } \boxed{\text{LN}} \quad \boxed{80} \quad \boxed{\text{ENTER}}$$

8.2.9 Evaluating Logarithmic Models

Logarithms can be used to measure quantities in real-world situations.

EXAMPLE 10	**Measuring Loudness**

The loudness L (in decibels) of a sound of intensity I is given by $L = 10 \log\left(\dfrac{I}{I_0}\right)$, where I_0 is a small threshold intensity. Find the approximate loudness of an average coffee shop that has a loudness of $3{,}000{,}000 I_0$. Round to the nearest whole decibel.

SOLUTION

Substitute $3{,}000{,}000 I_0$ for I and simplify.

$$L = 10 \log\left(\frac{3{,}000{,}000 I_0}{I_0}\right) = 10 \log(3{,}000{,}000) \approx 65$$

The loudness of the coffee shop is approximately 65 decibels.

8.2.10 Domain of a Natural Log Function

The domain of any logarithmic function, $y = \log_b x$, $y = \log x$, or $y = \ln x$, is all positive real numbers.

EXAMPLE 11 **Finding the Domain of a Logarithmic Function**

Find the domain of $f(x) = \ln{(x - 4)}$.

SOLUTION

The natural logarithm $\ln{(x - 4)}$ is defined only when the expression $x - 4$ is positive. So, solve the inequality $x - 4 > 0$ to find the domain of $f(x)$.

$$x - 4 > 0 \implies x > 4$$

Therefore, the domain of $f(x) = \ln{(x - 4)}$ is $(4, \infty)$.

SECTION 8.2 EXERCISES

Warm Up

Simplify.

1. $4^0 + 5^1 - 6$

2. $27^{-\frac{2}{3}}$

3. $32^{\frac{3}{5}}$

Just the Facts

Fill in the blanks.

4. The inverse of an exponential function of base b will be a(n) _____ function with base _____.

5. $\log_b 1 =$ _____ by the _____ property.

6. One cannot take the logarithm of a(n) _____ number.

7. A logarithmic function can be graphed by converting the logarithm to _____ form and making a(n) _____ .

8. A common log is written without a(n) _____ and has a base of _____.

9. The natural log is written as _____ and has a base of _____.

10. The expression $\log_b b^x$ can be rewritten as _____.

Essential Skills

In Exercises 1–8, find each value.

1. $\log_3 9$

2. $\log_{10} 10{,}000$

3. $\log_7 343$

4. $\log_{11} 121$

5. $\log_5 625$

6. $\log_2 128$

7. $\log_3 243$

8. $\log_8 512$

In Exercises 9–22, write the exponential equation in logarithmic form.

9. $3^4 = 81$

10. $6^{-2} = \dfrac{1}{36}$

11. $\dfrac{2}{5}^{-2} = \dfrac{25}{4}$

12. $8^{\frac{2}{3}} = 4$

13. $\dfrac{1}{81} = 9^{-2}$

14. $\left(\dfrac{4}{5}\right)^4 = \dfrac{256}{625}$

15. $\left(\dfrac{4}{11}\right)^{-2} = \dfrac{121}{16}$

16. $2^{-9} = \dfrac{1}{512}$

17. $27^{\frac{5}{3}} = 243$

18. $\left(\dfrac{9}{5}\right)^3 = \dfrac{729}{125}$

19. $7^{-4} = \dfrac{1}{2401}$

20. $81^{\frac{3}{4}} = 27$

21. $\left(\dfrac{2}{7}\right)^2 = \dfrac{4}{49}$

22. $\left(\dfrac{8}{9}\right)^{-3} = \dfrac{729}{512}$

In Exercises 23–36, write the logarithmic equation in exponential form.

23. $\log_6 216 = 3$

24. $\log_{\frac{1}{2}} 8 = -3$

25. $\log_{\frac{1}{5}} 625 = -4$

26. $\log_{81} \dfrac{1}{3} = -\dfrac{1}{4}$

27. $\log_7 16{,}807 = 5$

28. $\log_{32} 8 = \dfrac{3}{5}$

29. $\log_{\frac{4}{5}} \dfrac{64}{125} = 3$

30. $\log_{14} \dfrac{1}{196} = -2$

31. $\dfrac{4}{3} = \log_{27} 81$

32. $\log_{13} 2197 = 3$

33. $\log_{\frac{4}{3}} \dfrac{16}{9} = 2$

34. $-4 = \log_6 \dfrac{1}{1296}$

35. $\log_8 128 = \dfrac{7}{3}$

36. $4 = \log_{\frac{7}{5}} \dfrac{2401}{625}$

In Exercises 37–56, simplify the expression.

37. $\log_{\frac{3}{5}} \frac{9}{25}$

38. $\log_{10} \frac{1}{1000}$

39. $\log_2 512$

40. $\log_5 \frac{1}{3125}$

41. $\log_8 4096$

42. $\log_{17} \frac{1}{289}$

43. $\log_{27} 3$

44. $\log_{25} 125$

45. $\log_{81} 27$

46. $\log_{512} 8$

47. $\log_{343} 49$

48. $\log_{216} 36$

49. $\log_{78} 78$

50. $\log_{\sqrt{7}} 1$

51. $\log_4 4^5$

52. $0.4^{\log_{0.4} 10}$

53. $\log_{2.8} 1$

54. $\log_{\sqrt{23}} \sqrt{23}$

55. $9^{\log_9 64}$

56. $\log_{\frac{2}{3}} \left(\frac{2}{3} \right)^{-5}$

In Exercises 57–60, graph the function.

57. $h(x) = \log_5 x$

58. $g(x) = \log_{\frac{1}{5}} x$

59. $m(x) = \log_5 (-x)$

60. $g(x) = \log_2 (x + 5)$

In Exercises 61–68, evaluate without using a calculator.

61. $\log 10^e$

62. $\ln e^6$

63. $\ln e^{\frac{4}{7}}$

64. $\log 10^\pi$

65. $e^{\ln 9} + \ln e$

66. $\log 1 + 10^{\log 2}$

67. $4 \cdot 10^{\log 7} + 8 \log 1$

68. $\ln e + 7e^{\ln 5}$

In Exercises 69–74, evaluate with a calculator. Round to the nearest hundredth.

69. $\ln \frac{3}{8}$

70. $(\log 5)(\ln 12)$

71. $\log 25 - \log 16$

72. $\ln 48 + \log 63$

73. $(\log 67)(\ln 8)$

74. $(\ln 93)/(\ln 7)$

In Exercises 75–77, use the following information.

The loudness L (in decibels) of a sound of intensity I is given by $L = 10 \log \left(\frac{I}{I_0} \right)$, where I_0 is a small threshold intensity.

75. Find the approximate loudness to the nearest hundredth on a calm day on Crater Lake, which has an intensity of $48{,}000 I_0$.

76. Find the approximate loudness to the nearest hundredth of a vacuum cleaner, which has an intensity of $90{,}000{,}000 I_0$.

77. Find the approximate loudness to the nearest hundredth of a normal conversation, which has an intensity of $800{,}000 I_0$.

In Exercises 78–80, use the following information.

The Richter scale magnitude R of an earthquake of intensity I is defined as $R = \log \left(\frac{I}{I_0} \right)$, where I_0 is a small threshold intensity. Find the magnitude of an earthquake to the nearest hundredth with the given intensity.

78. $52{,}000{,}000 I_0$

79. $76{,}000 I_0$

80. $8{,}500{,}000 I_0$

In Exercises 81–86, express the domain of the function in interval notation.

81. $g(x) = \ln (x - 7)$

82. $f(x) = \ln (6 - 2x)$

83. $p(x) = \log (4x + 3)$

84. $w(x) = \ln (9 - 5x)$

85. $t(x) = \log (3x - 1)$

86. $n(x) = \ln (22x + 19)$

Extensions

87. Simplify. $\log_6 6^5 + 7\ln e^3 - \log 10^{-4} + 6^0$

88. Determine the x-intercept of the graph of $m(x) = \log_4(2x)$.

89. Which are valid logarithmic equation?
$y = \log_{-5} 6, y = \log_1 4, y = \log_0 7,$
$y = \log_b 0, y = \log_6 -10, y = \log 1$

In Exercises 90–93, use the following information.

The equation $\log_b x = y$ has three variables: b, x, and y:

90. Which variable can never be negative?

91. Which variable can never be 1?

92. Which variable may at times be zero?

93. Which variable may at times be negative?

94. Express the domain of $p(x) = \log\sqrt{2x-5}$ in interval notation.

95. Which of these two functions, $g(x) = \log_4 x$ or $h(x) = \log_{\frac{9}{10}} x$, increases as x increases?

8.3 PROPERTIES OF LOGARITHMS

OBJECTIVES

- Understand the Product Property, Quotient Property, and Power Property of logarithms.
- Use the properties of logarithms to expand logarithmic expressions.
- Use the properties of logarithms to simplify logarithmic expressions.
- Use the Change of Base Formula to simplify logarithms.

PREREQUISITE VOCABULARY TERMS

common logarithm

exponential function

logarithmic function

natural logarithm

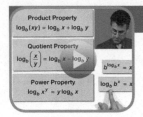

8.3.1 Properties of Logarithms

Three types of logarithms were discussed in Section 8.2: logs with base b (where b is a positive number not equal to 1), common logs (where the base is 10), and natural logs (where the base is e). Recall that each type of log can be written in logarithmic form or exponential form.

Logarithmic Form and Exponential Form		
	Logarithmic Form	**Exponential Form**
Logarithm with Base b	$y = \log_b x$	$b^y = x$
Common Logarithm	$y = \log x$	$10^y = x$
Natural Logarithm	$y = \ln x$	$e^y = x$

The following table shows the four basic properties of logarithms, which were introduced in Section 8.2.

Properties of Logarithms				
Logarithm with Base b	$\log_b 1 = 0$	$\log_b b = 1$	$\log_b b^x = x$	$b^{\log_b x} = x$
Common Logarithm	$\log 1 = 0$	$\log 10 = 1$	$\log 10^x = x$	$10^{\log x} = x$
Natural Logarithm	$\ln 1 = 0$	$\ln e = 1$	$\ln e^x = x$	$e^{\ln x} = x$

The following table lists three additional properties of logarithms. These additional properties provide alternative ways to express the log of a product, the log of a quotient, and the log of a power.

Properties of Logarithms

	Product Property	Quotient Property	Power Property
Logarithm with Base b	$\log_b (xy) = \log_b x + \log_b y$	$\log_b\left(\dfrac{x}{y}\right) = \log_b x - \log_b y$	$\log_b x^y = y \log_b x$
Common Logarithm	$\log (xy) = \log x + \log y$	$\log\left(\dfrac{x}{y}\right) = \log x - \log y$	$\log x^y = y \log x$
Natural Logarithm	$\ln (xy) = \ln x + \ln y$	$\ln\left(\dfrac{x}{y}\right) = \ln x - \ln y$	$\ln x^y = y \ln x$

> **NOTICE THAT**
>
> *The Product and Quotient Properties of logarithms are very similar to the Product and Quotient Properties of Powers.*
>
> **Product of Powers**
>
> $a^m a^n = a^{m+n}$
>
> **Quotient of Powers**
>
> $\dfrac{a^m}{a^n} = a^{m-n}$

These properties can be used to reduce a log of a product, quotient, or power into logs that can be simplified.

EXAMPLE 1 **Using Properties to Evaluate Logarithmic Expressions**

Evaluate each expression without using a calculator.

A. $\log_3 \sqrt{27}$ **B.** $\log 20 + \log 5$ **C.** $\log_2 6 - \log_2 15 + \log_2 20$

SOLUTION

A. Write the radical as a rational exponent, then apply the Power Property to the log to simplify.

> $\sqrt{a} = a^{\frac{1}{2}}$ ▶

$$\log_3 \sqrt{27} = \log_3 27^{\frac{1}{2}}$$

$$= \frac{1}{2}\log_3 27 \quad \textit{Write the radical as a rational exponent.}$$

$$= \frac{1}{2}(3) \quad \textit{Power Property}$$

$$= \frac{3}{2} \quad \textit{Simplify: } 3^3 = 27.$$

B. The expression is the sum of two common logs. Since the base is 10 for both of the logs in the sum, use the Product Property to simplify.

$$\log 20 + \log 5 = \log (20)(5) \quad \textit{Product Property}$$

$$= \log 100 \quad \textit{Multiply.}$$

$$= 2 \quad \textit{Simplify: } 10^2 = 100.$$

C. The expression is the difference and sum of three logs with base 2. Use the Product Property and the Quotient Property to simplify.

> **TIP**
>
> *Follow the order of operations. Since addition and subtraction are completed from left to right, subtract first and then add.*

$$\log_2 6 - \log_2 15 + \log_2 20 = \log_2 \frac{6}{15} + \log_2 20 \quad \textit{Quotient Property}$$

$$= \log_2 \left(\frac{6}{15}\right)(20) \quad \textit{Product Property}$$

$$= \log_2 8 \quad \textit{Multiply and divide.}$$

$$= 3 \quad \textit{Simplify: } 2^3 = 8.$$

8.3.2 Expanding Logarithmic Expressions

The properties of logs can be used to expand logarithmic expressions. For example, the log of a quotient is expanded when it is written as the difference of the log of the dividend and the log of the divisor.

EXAMPLE 2   **Using Properties to Expand Logarithmic Expressions**

Use the properties of logarithms to expand each expression.

A. $\ln \sqrt{ab}$

B. $\log \dfrac{\sqrt[3]{x^2}}{y}$

C. $\log_4 \left(\dfrac{4(p+q)}{\sqrt[3]{r}} \right)^2$

SOLUTION

A. Write the radical as a rational exponent. Then apply the Power Property, followed by the Product Property, to expand the natural log.

$$\ln \sqrt{ab} = \ln(ab)^{\frac{1}{2}} \qquad \textit{Write the radical as a rational exponent.}$$

$$= \frac{1}{2}\ln(ab) \qquad \textit{Power Property}$$

$$= \frac{1}{2}(\ln a + \ln b) \qquad \textit{Product Property}$$

$$= \frac{1}{2}\ln a + \frac{1}{2}\ln b \qquad \textit{Distribute.}$$

B. Write the radical as a rational exponent. Then apply the Quotient Property, and then the Power Property, to expand the common log.

$$\log \frac{\sqrt[3]{x^2}}{y} = \log \frac{x^{\frac{2}{3}}}{y} \qquad \textit{Write the radical as a rational exponent.}$$

$$= \log x^{\frac{2}{3}} - \log y \qquad \textit{Quotient Property}$$

$$= \frac{2}{3}\log x - \log y \qquad \textit{Power Property}$$

TIP

The Quotient Property must be applied before the Power Property, because the exponent applies to the numerator only.

C. Apply the Power Property first. Then apply the Quotient Property to expand the log. Be sure to place the difference of the logs within parentheses because the multiple 2 applies to both logs in the difference.

$$\log_4 \left(\frac{4(p+q)}{\sqrt[3]{r}} \right)^2 = 2\log_4 \frac{4(p+q)}{\sqrt[3]{r}} \qquad \textit{Power Property}$$

$$= 2\left(\log_4 4(p+q) - \log_4 \sqrt[3]{r} \right) \qquad \textit{Quotient Property}$$

$$= 2\left(\log_4 4 + \log_4 (p+q) - \log_4 r^{\frac{1}{3}} \right) \qquad \begin{array}{l}\textit{Product Property}\\ \textit{Write the radical as a rational}\\ \textit{exponent.}\end{array}$$

$$= 2\left(1 + \log_4 (p+q) - \frac{1}{3}\log_4 r \right) \qquad \begin{array}{l}\textit{Simplify: } 4^1 = 4.\\ \textit{Power Property}\end{array}$$

$$= 2 + 2\log_4 (p+q) - \frac{2}{3}\log_4 r \qquad \textit{Distribute.}$$

CAUTION

When expanding the log in **Example 2C**, you may be tempted to write the term $2\log_4 (p + q)$ as $2(\log_4 p + \log_4 q)$. However, the Product Property of logs states that $\log_b (xy) = \log_b x + \log_b y$, not that $\log_b (x + y) = \log_b x + \log_b y$.

8.3.3 Combining Logarithmic Expressions

The properties of logs can also be used to write a sum or difference of logs as a single log. This process is called combining logs, and it is the opposite of expanding logs. When combining logs, it is important to remember that the Product and Quotient Properties of logs can be applied only when the logs have the same base.

EXAMPLE 3   **Using Properties to Combine Logarithmic Expressions**

Use the properties to write each expression as a single log, if possible.

A. $5 \ln c + \ln (d + 1)$ **B.** $\log_2 x + \dfrac{1}{2}\log_2 (x + y) - 3\log_2 (x - y)$

SOLUTION

A. The expression is the sum of two natural logs: $5 \ln c$ and $\ln (d + 1)$. Since both logs are natural logs, the bases are the same. Use the Product Property to write the sum as the product of a single log, but first use the Power Property to write 5 as an exponent.

$$5 \ln c + \ln (d + 1) = \ln c^5 + \ln (d + 1) \qquad \textit{Power Property}$$
$$= \ln c^5(d + 1) \qquad \textit{Product Property}$$

B. Use the Power Property to write the coefficients as exponents first. Then, since all three log terms have base 2, the Product and Quotient Properties can be used to write the terms as a single log.

$$\log_2 x + \frac{1}{2}\log_2 (x + y) - 3\log_2 (x - y)$$

$$= \log_2 x + \log_2 (x + y)^{\frac{1}{2}} - \log_2 (x - y)^3 \quad \textit{Power Property}$$

$$= \log_2 x + \log_2 \sqrt{x + y} - \log_2 (x - y)^3 \quad \textit{Write the rational exponent as a radical.}$$

$$= \log_2 \frac{x\sqrt{x + y}}{(x - y)^3} \quad \textit{Product and Quotient Properties}$$

8.3.4   Using the Change of Base Formula

The **Change of Base Formula** provides a method for rewriting a logarithm as a quotient of logs with like bases.

Change of Base Formula

If a, b, and x are positive real numbers such that $a \neq 1$ and $b \neq 1$, then $\log_b x$ can be written as a quotient of logs with any base a by using the Change of Base Formula, $\log_b x = \dfrac{\log_a x}{\log_a b}$.

The Change of Base Formula: Evaluating a Logarithm Using a Calculator

Most calculators cannot evaluate a log unless the base is 10 (common log) or e (natural log). So, a logarithm such as $\log_2 7$ (where the base of the log is 2), for example, cannot be entered directly into a typical calculator.

> **IMPORTANT**
>
> *Since a (in the Change of Base Formula) can be any positive real number except 1, we can either let a = 10 or a = e.*

However, by using the Change of Base Formula, any logarithm can be written as a quotient of common logs or as a quotient of natural logs: $\dfrac{\log x}{\log b} = \log_b x = \dfrac{\ln x}{\ln b}$. Then, a calculator can be used to evaluate the expression.

For example, if the Change of Base Formula is used to write $\log_2 7$ as a quotient of logs with base 10 or base e, the expression can be entered into a calculator using the **LOG** key or the **LN** key, respectively, and then evaluated.

$$\log_2 7 = \frac{\log 7}{\log 2} = \frac{\ln 7}{\ln 2} = 2.807 \ldots$$

> **TIP**
>
> *The value of $\log_2 7$ is between 2 and 3, because $2^2 = 4$ and $2^3 = 8$.*

EXAMPLE 4   Using the Change of Base Formula

Use the Change of Base Formula to approximate the value of each expression to the nearest hundredth using a calculator.

A. $\log_8 20$ **B.** $\log_9 \dfrac{3}{2}$

SOLUTION

A. $\log_8 20 = \dfrac{\log 20}{\log 8} \approx 1.44$ **B.** $\log_9 \dfrac{3}{2} = \dfrac{\ln \dfrac{3}{2}}{\ln 9} \approx 0.18$

Graphing a Logarithmic Function with Base b Using a Graphing Calculator

We have now seen that the Change of Base Formula can be used to write a logarithmic expression that is not a common or natural log as a quotient of common or natural logs, thus providing a method for evaluating a log with any base using a calculator. The Change of Base Formula can also be used to write a logarithmic *function* that is not a common or natural log as a quotient of common or natural logs. Then the logarithmic function can be entered into a graphing calculator in order to graph the function.

$$f(x) = \log_b x = \frac{\log x}{\log b} = \frac{\ln x}{\ln b} \quad \text{(where b is a number such that $b > 0$ and $b \neq 1$)}$$

SECTION 8.3 EXERCISES

Warm Up

State the property used to rewrite each expression.

1. $4 \ln w + \ln (d + 3) = \ln w^4 + \ln (d + 3)$

2. $\log 23 + \log 6 = \log (23 \cdot 6)$

3. $\log_6 (5x + 2) - \log_6 (3x) = \log_6 \dfrac{5x + 2}{3x}$

Just the Facts

Fill in the blanks.

4. The Product Property of logarithms states that the log of a product xy can be rewritten as the _____ of the logarithms of _____ and _____.

5. The Quotient Property of logarithms says that the log of a quotient x/y can be rewritten as the _____ of the logarithms of _____ and _____.

6. By the Power Property of logarithms, the $\log \sqrt{20}$ can be rewritten as _____.

7. The properties of logs can be used to _____ or _____ logarithmic expressions.

8. The Product and Quotient Properties of logarithms cannot be applied to two logs if they do not share the same _____.

9. To evaluate a log that is neither common nor natural using a simple calculator, one must use the _____.

10. The Change of Base Formula allows a logarithm to be written as a quotient of logarithms with _____ bases.

Essential Skills

In Exercises 1–20, evaluate each logarithm without using a calculator.

1. $\dfrac{5}{2} \log_4 \sqrt[3]{4}$

2. $\log_5 \sqrt[4]{\dfrac{1}{125}}$

3. $\dfrac{1}{2} \log_3 \sqrt{243}$

4. $2 \log_5 \sqrt{125}$

5. $\dfrac{3}{4} \log_6 \sqrt{6}$

6. $5 \log_2 \sqrt[4]{\dfrac{1}{32}}$

7. $\log_5 3 - \log_5 75$

8. $\log_9 \dfrac{1}{27} + \log_9 3$

9. $\log_4 2 + \log_4 \dfrac{1}{32}$

10. $\log_7 8 - \log_7 56$

11. $\log_8 \dfrac{2}{3} + \log_8 48$

12. $\log_9 \dfrac{3}{5} + \log_9 45$

13. $\log_{16} \dfrac{5}{4} - \log_{16} 10$

14. $\log_4 \dfrac{3}{8} - \log_4 12$

15. $\log_4 24 - \log_4 6 + \log_4 16$

16. $\log_3 2 + \log_3 4 - \log_3 72$

17. $\log_3 4 - \log_3 648 + \log_3 2$

18. $\log_2 3 + \log_2 4 - \log_2 48$

19. $\log_6 18 + \log_6 24 - \log_6 12$

20. $\log_8 40 - \log_8 5 - \log_8 64$

In Exercises 21–34, use the properties of logarithms to expand each expression.

21. $\log_4 x^5 \sqrt[9]{y}$

22. $\log_2 \sqrt{\dfrac{8x}{x + 1}}$

23. $\log_6 \dfrac{a\sqrt{c}}{b^2}$

24. $\log_5 \dfrac{\sqrt{xy}}{z^4}$

25. $\ln x^2 y \sqrt[3]{z}$

26. $\log a^2 \sqrt[3]{bc}$

27. $\ln \dfrac{p(q + 4)^5}{r}$

28. $\log \dfrac{g}{h(k - 2)^3}$

29. $\log \dfrac{r^2}{w\sqrt{x + 1}}$

30. $\log \dfrac{\sqrt{d - 5}}{b^4 c}$

31. $\ln \sqrt[5]{\dfrac{6 + x}{y^4}}$

32. $\log_5 \sqrt[4]{\dfrac{5 + m}{625k}}$

33. $\log_2 \sqrt[3]{\dfrac{2 + t}{16s}}$

34. $\ln \sqrt[4]{\dfrac{2 - g}{h^3}}$

SOLUTION

A. $2^x = \dfrac{1}{32} \implies 2^x = 2^{-5} \implies x = -5$

B.
$$125^x = 5$$

$(5^3)^x = 5$ *Write 125 as a power with base 5.*

$5^{3x} = 5^1$ *Power of a Power Property of Exponents: $(a^m)^n = a^{mn}$*

$3x = 1$ *Set the exponents equal to each other.*

$x = \dfrac{1}{3}$ *Solve for x.*

C.
$$16^{x+2} = 64^{1-2x}$$

$(4^2)^{x+2} = (4^3)^{1-2x}$ *Write 16 and 64 as powers with base 4.*

$4^{2(x+2)} = 4^{3(1-2x)}$ *Power of a Power Property of Exponents: $(a^m)^n = a^{mn}$*

$4^{2x+4} = 4^{3-6x}$ *Simplify the exponents.*

$2x + 4 = 3 - 6x$ *Set the exponents equal to each other.*

$8x = -1$ *Set the exponents equal to each other.*

$x = -\dfrac{1}{8}$ *Solve for x.*

8.4.2 Solving Exponential Equations Using Logs

The One-to-One Property also applies to logarithmic equations with the same base.

> ### One-to-One Property (Logarithmic Equations)
>
> If $b > 0$ and $b \neq 1$, then for all x and y where $\log_b x$ and $\log_b y$ are defined,
>
> $$\log_b x = \log_b y \text{ if and only if } x = y.$$

In other words, if two values are equal, then their logs (of the same base) are also equal. Conversely, if the logs of two values are equal, then those values are equal.

When an exponential equation cannot be written in the form $b^x = b^y$ (i.e., two equivalent powers with like bases), then you can take the log of each side and algebraically manipulate the equation so that the One-to-One Property of logs can be applied.

> **Steps for Solving an Exponential Equation Using Common Logs**
>
> ❶ Write the equation in the form $a^x = b^y$ (i.e., the expressions on each side of the equation are powers).
>
> ❷ Take the common log of each side.
>
> ❸ Use the Power Property of logs to write the exponent(s) as coefficients of the logs.
>
> ❹ Use the Product or Quotient Properties of logs to expand the logs as needed.
>
> ❺ Solve for x.

TIP

Alternatively, you could take the log base b of both sides, or the natural log of both sides.

EXAMPLE 2   **Using Common Logs to Solve an Exponential Equation**

Solve each equation. Find the exact value of x and the approximate value to the nearest hundredth.

A. $2(6^x) = 22$ **B.** $8^x - 5^{x+9} = 0$

SOLUTION

A. Divide each side by 2 to write the equation in the form $a^x = b^y$. $2(6^x) = 22 \;\Rightarrow\; 6^x = 11$

Try solving the equation by taking the log of each side, because 6 and 11 cannot be written as powers with like bases. The equation is now in the form $a^x = b^y$, so begin by taking the common log of each side.

$$6^x = 11$$

$$\log 6^x = \log 11 \qquad \textit{Take the common log of each side.}$$
$$x \log 6 = \log 11 \qquad \textit{Power Property of Logs}$$
$$x = \frac{\log 11}{\log 6} \qquad \textit{Divide each side by log 6 to solve for x.}$$
$$x \approx 1.34 \qquad \textit{Simplify using a calculator.}$$

The solution is $x = \dfrac{\log 11}{\log 6} \approx 1.34$.

B. Write the equation in the form $a^x = b^y$. $8^x - 5^{x+9} = 0 \;\Rightarrow\; 8^x = 5^{x+9}$

The powers cannot be written with like bases, so take the common log of each side first.

$$8^x = 5^{x+9}$$

$$\log 8^x = \log 5^{x+9} \qquad \textit{Take the common log of each side.}$$
$$x \log 8 = (x+9)\log 5 \qquad \textit{Power Property of Logs}$$
$$x \log 8 = x \log 5 + 9 \log 5 \qquad \textit{Distribute.}$$
$$x \log 8 - x \log 5 = 9 \log 5 \qquad \textit{Group the x-terms on the left side.}$$
$$x(\log 8 - \log 5) = 9 \log 5 \qquad \textit{Factor x from each log.}$$
$$x \log \frac{8}{5} = 9 \log 5 \qquad \textit{Quotient Property of Logs}$$
$$x = \frac{9 \log 5}{\log \frac{8}{5}} \qquad \textit{Divide each side by } \log \frac{8}{5} \textit{ to solve for x.}$$
$$x \approx 30.82 \qquad \textit{Simplify using a calculator.}$$

The solution is $x = \dfrac{9 \log 5}{\log \frac{8}{5}} \approx 30.82$.

8.4.3   Solving Natural Exponential Equations

Natural exponential equations (where the base of a power is e) can also be solved by using the One-to-One Properties. When a natural exponential equation can be written in the form $e^x = e^y$, then you can set x equal to y and solve that equation.

When a natural exponential equation cannot be written in the form $e^x = e^y$, then you can take the natural log of each side and algebraically manipulate the equation so that the One-to-One Property of logs can be applied.

Steps for Solving a Natural Exponential Equation Using Natural Logs

❶ Isolate e^x on one side of the equation.

❷ Take the natural log of each side.

❸ Use the Power Property of logs to write the exponent(s) as a coefficient of the natural log.

❹ Use the fact that $\ln e = 1$ to simplify.

❺ Solve for x.

EXAMPLE 3   **Using Natural Logs to Solve a Natural Exponential Equation**

Solve $10 - 2e^{5-3x} = 4$. Find the exact value of x and the approximate value to the nearest tenth.

SOLUTION

Manipulate the equation to write it in the form $e^x = c$ (i.e., solve for the power with base e). So, subtract 10 from each side and then divide each side by -2.

$$10 - 2e^{5-3x} = 4 \implies -2e^{5-3x} = -6 \implies e^{5-3x} = 3$$

Take the natural log of each side, then solve for x.

$$e^{5-3x} = 3$$

$$\ln e^{5-3x} = \ln 3 \qquad \textit{Take the natural log of each side.}$$

$$(5-3x)\ln e = \ln 3 \qquad \textit{Power Property of Logs}$$

$$5 - 3x = \ln 3 \qquad \textit{Simplify: ln e = 1.}$$

$$-3x = -5 + \ln 3 \qquad \textit{Subtract 5 from each side.}$$

$$x = \frac{-5 + \ln 3}{-3} \qquad \textit{Divide each side by -3 to solve for x.}$$

$$x \approx 1.3 \qquad \textit{Simplify using a calculator.}$$

The solution is $x = -\dfrac{-5 + \ln 3}{3} \approx 1.3$.

8.4.4   Solving Exponential Equations of Quadratic Type

Recall that equations of quadratic type can be solved by making a special substitution that results in a quadratic equation. One of the quadratic solving techniques (such as using the Quadratic Formula or factoring) can then be used to solve the new equation. This process is illustrated in the next example with a natural exponential equation.

EXAMPLE 4   **Using Natural Logs to Solve an Equation of Quadratic Type**

Solve $e^{6x} - e^{3x} = 6$. Find the exact value of x and the approximate value to the nearest hundredth.

SOLUTION

Write the equation as a quadratic by substituting some variable, for example, z, for e^{3x}. Then solve the equation in z by using one of the techniques for solving a quadratic equation. After the equation is solved for z, substitute e^{3x} for z and solve the resulting equations for x.

$$e^{6x} - e^{3x} = 6$$

$$(e^{3x})^2 - (e^{3x}) = 6 \qquad \text{\textit{Write } } e^{6x} \text{ \textit{as a power where the exponent is 2.}}$$

$$z^2 - z = 6 \qquad \text{\textit{Substitute } } e^{3x} = z.$$

$$z^2 - z - 6 = 0 \qquad \text{\textit{Write the equation in general form.}}$$

$$(z - 3)(z + 2) = 0 \qquad \text{\textit{Factor.}}$$

$$z = 3 \quad \text{or} \quad z = -2 \qquad \text{\textit{Solve each equation for z.}}$$

$$e^{3x} = 3 \qquad e^{3x} = -2 \qquad \text{\textit{Substitute } } z = e^{3x}.$$

The equation $e^{3x} = -2$ has no solution, because $e^x > 0$ for all x.

The first equation $e^{3x} = 3$, can be solved for x.

$$\ln e^{3x} = \ln 3 \qquad \text{\textit{Take the natural log of each side.}}$$

$$3x(\ln e) = \ln 3 \qquad \text{\textit{Power Property of Logs}}$$

$$3x = \ln 3 \qquad \text{\textit{Simplify: ln e = 1.}}$$

$$x = \frac{\ln 3}{3} \qquad \text{\textit{Solve for x.}}$$

$$x \approx 0.37 \qquad \text{\textit{Simplify using a calculator.}}$$

The solution is $x = \dfrac{\ln 3}{3} \approx 0.37$.

TIP

If the quadratic expression cannot be factored easily, then use completing the square or the Quadratic Formula to solve the quadratic equation.

8.4.5   Using Exponential Form to Solve Logarithmic Equations

In a logarithmic equation, the log is of a variable. The following are examples of logarithmic equations.

$$1 + \log_2 x = 6 \qquad\qquad \log (x + 4) = 2 \qquad\qquad \ln x = e^2$$

REMEMBER

$$y = \log_b x \iff b^y = x$$

$$y = \log x \iff 10^y = x$$

$$y = \ln x \iff e^y = x$$

A logarithmic equation where the log is isolated on one side of the equation can be solved for the variable by writing the log in exponential form.

For example, to solve the logarithmic equation $\log (x + 4) = 2$, write the common log in exponential form: $10^2 = x + 4$. Then simplify and solve for x.

$$\log (x + 4) = 2$$

$$10^2 = x + 4 \qquad \text{\textit{Write the common log in exponential form.}}$$

$$100 = x + 4 \qquad \text{\textit{Simplify the power.}}$$

$$x = 96 \qquad \text{\textit{Solve for x.}}$$

Alternatively, $\log (x + 4) = 2$ can be solved by making each side a power where the base is 10 (the base of the equation's log).

$$\log (x + 4) = 2 \implies 10^{\log(x + 4)} = 10^2$$

This equation may appear to be more complicated, but the log property $b^{\log_b x} = x$ can be used to simplify the equation.

$$\log (x + 4) = 2$$

$$10^{\log(x + 4)} = 10^2 \qquad \text{\textit{Raise 10 to each side.}}$$

$$x + 4 = 10^2 \qquad \text{\textit{Use a property of logarithms to simplify: } } b^{\log_b x} = x.$$

$$x + 4 = 100 \qquad \text{\textit{Simplify the power.}}$$

$$x = 96 \qquad \text{\textit{Solve for x.}}$$

Either method can be used when solving logarithmic equations.

Steps for Solving a Logarithmic Equation

❶ Isolate the log on one side of the equation.

❷ Write the equation in exponential form (or raise the base of the log to each side of the equation).

❸ Solve the resulting equation.

EXAMPLE 5   Using Exponential Form to Solve a Logarithmic Equation

Solve each equation. Round to the nearest hundredth, if needed.

A. $\ln x^3 = 15$ **B.** $5\log_2(8x) + 1 = 16$

SOLUTION

A. Use the Power Property to write the exponent as a coefficient. Then isolate the log and write the equation in exponential form.

$\ln x^3 = 15$	
$3\ln x = 15$	*Power Property*
$\ln x = 5$	*Divide each side by 3 to isolate the natural log.*
$x = e^5$	*Write the natural log in exponential form.*

The exact solution is $x = e^5$. Using a calculator to simplify gives $x \approx 148.41$.

B. Isolate the log, and then write the equation in exponential form.

$5\log_2(8x) + 1 = 16$	
$5\log_2(8x) = 15$	*Subtract 1 from each side.*
$\log_2(8x) = 3$	*Divide each side by 5 to isolate the log.*
$8x = 2^3$	*Write the log in exponential form.*
$8x = 8$	*Simplify the power.*
$x = 1$	*Solve for x.*

CHECK

Substitute $x = 1$ into the original equation to check the solution.

$5\log_2(8 \cdot 1) + 1$

$= 5\log_2(8) + 1$

$= 5(3) + 1$

$= 16$ ✔

8.4.6   The Distance Modulus Formula

The distance modulus is a way of expressing a distance between astronomical objects. The **Distance Modulus Formula** is a logarithmic equation that relates distance modulus to distance in parsecs (1 parsec ≈ 3.3 light years).

Distance Modulus Formula

$$M = 5\log r - 5,$$

where M is the distance modulus and r is the distance in parsecs between two astronomical objects.

EXAMPLE 6   Using the Distance Modulus Formula

If a star's distance modulus from Earth is 3.6, what is the distance between the star and Earth in parsecs and in light years? Round each answer to the nearest hundredth.

SOLUTION

Substituting $M = 3.6$ into the Distance Modulus Formula yields $3.6 = 5\log r - 5$. This is a logarithmic equation. So, isolate the log and then write the log in exponential form to solve for r.

$$3.6 = 5\log r - 5$$

$$8.6 = 5\log r \qquad \textit{Add 5 to each side.}$$

$$1.72 = \log r \qquad \textit{Divide each side by 5.}$$

$$r = 10^{1.72} \qquad \textit{Write the common log in exponential form.}$$

$$r \approx 52.48 \qquad \textit{Simplify using a calculator.}$$

The distance between the star and Earth is approximately 52.48 parsecs.

Since 1 parsec ≈ 3.3 light years, the distance between the star and Earth is approximately $3.3(10^{1.72}) \approx 173.19$ light years.

8.4.7 Solving Logarithmic Equations

When a logarithmic equation contains more than one logarithmic term where the logs have the same base, use the properties of logs to combine the logs into a single log, then follow the steps for solving a logarithmic equation to solve. All possible solutions should be checked in the original equation, because it is possible to get extraneous solutions.

EXAMPLE 7   Solving Logarithmic Equations

Solve. $\log (x - 1) + \log (x + 2) = 1$

SOLUTION

The equation contains the sum of two common logs, $\log (x - 1)$ and $\log (x + 2)$. The bases are the same (both 10), so the Product Property of logs can be used to combine the logarithmic terms into a single log.

Product Property
$\log (xy) = \log x + \log y$

$$\log (x - 1) + \log (x + 2) = 1$$

$$\log (x - 1)(x + 2) = 1 \qquad \textit{Product Property of Logs}$$

$$(x - 1)(x + 2) = 10^1 \qquad \textit{Write the common log in exponential form.}$$

$$(x - 1)(x + 2) = 10 \qquad \textit{Simplify the power.}$$

The resulting equation is quadratic, so expand the binomials and subtract 10 from each side to get 0 on one side, then solve by using one of the techniques for solving a quadratic equation.

$$x^2 + x - 2 = 10 \qquad \textit{FOIL}$$

$$x^2 + x - 12 = 0 \qquad \textit{Write the equation in general form.}$$

$$(x - 3)(x + 4) = 0 \qquad \textit{Factor.}$$

$$x = 3 \ \text{ or } \ x = -4 \qquad \textit{Solve each equation for x.}$$

Substitute each solution into the original equation to check for extraneous solutions.

$$x = 3: \ \log (3 - 1) + \log (3 + 2) = \log (2) + \log (5) = \log (2)(5) = \log 10 = 1 ✔$$

The value of $\log 10$ is 1 since $10^1 = 10$. So, the solution $x = 3$ is a solution.

$$x = -4: \ \log (-4 - 1) + \log (-4 + 2) = \log (-5) + \log (-2) \neq 1$$

The log of a negative number is undefined. So, $x = -4$ is a not a solution.

8.4.8 Compound Interest

In Section 8.1, the Compound Interest Formula was used to find a total balance A, an interest rate r, and an initial amount deposited or borrowed P (the principal).

Compound Interest Formula: $A = P\left(1 + \dfrac{r}{m}\right)^{mt}$

P = the principal amount (original amount) in the account
t = the length of time (in years) that the money is invested
A = the balance in the account after t years
r = the annual interest rate (as a decimal)
m = the number of times per year that the interest is compounded

A total balance A was found by evaluating the expression $P\left(1 + \dfrac{r}{m}\right)^{mt}$ using known values for P, r, m, and t. A principal P was found by evaluating the expression $\left(1 + \dfrac{r}{m}\right)^{mt}$ using known values for r, m, and t, and then dividing the known balance A by that number. The most complicated variable solved for so far was the interest rate r, which was found by simplifying $P\left(1 + \dfrac{r}{m}\right)^{mt}$ using known values for P, m, and t, and then taking the mtth root of both sides of the equation.

If t is the unknown, then $A = P\left(1 + \dfrac{r}{m}\right)^{mt}$ is an exponential equation. The Compound Interest Formula is solved for an unknown time t in the following example.

EXAMPLE 8   Using the Compound Interest Formula

Suppose $14,900 is invested in a quarterly compounded account at 6%. In how many years will the balance reach $20,000? Round to the nearest year.

SOLUTION

Substitute the known values into the Compound Interest Formula and solve for t.

$$A = P\left(1 + \frac{r}{m}\right)^{mt}$$

$$20{,}000 = 14{,}900\left(1 + \frac{0.06}{4}\right)^{4t} \qquad \textit{Substitute the known values into the formula.}$$

$$\frac{200}{149} = (1.015)^{4t} \qquad \textit{Simplify.}$$

$$\ln\frac{200}{149} = \ln(1.015)^{4t} \qquad \textit{Take the natural log of each side.}$$
$$\textit{(Alternatively, take the common log of each side.)}$$

$$\ln\frac{200}{149} = 4t\ln 1.015 \qquad \textit{Power Property of Logs}$$

$$t = \frac{\ln\dfrac{200}{149}}{4\ln 1.015} \qquad \textit{Solve for t.}$$

$$t \approx 4.94 \qquad \textit{Simplify using a calculator.}$$

The balance will reach $20,000 after approximately 5 years.

IMPORTANT

Since
20,000/14,900 = 1.34228…,
leave the quotient as a
fraction in simplest form
so that you will not have to
round until the final step in
the calculations.

SECTION 8.4 EXERCISES

Warm Up

Rewrite each value as a power with the given base.

1. 625 with a base of 5

2. 64 with a base of 2

3. 243 with base of 3

Just the Facts

Fill in the blanks.

4. The _____ Property can be used to solve exponential equations. It states that if _____ and _____, $b^x = b^y$ if and only if $x = y$.

5. _____ are used to solve exponential equations when the powers cannot be written with like bases.

6. _____ logarithms are used to solve exponential equations of the form $e^x = c$.

7. The first step to solving a logarithmic equation is to _____ the log. Then the equation can be rewritten in _____ form.

8. If Betelgeuse has a distance modulus from Earth of 6.0, the Distance Modulus Formula can be used to calculate the distance from Earth to Betelgeuse in _____.

9. It is possible to get _____ solutions when combining multiple _____ terms in a logarithmic equation.

10. The _____ Formula can be used to solve exponential equations with two exponential terms, the exponent for one of which is twice the exponent for the other.

Essential Skills

In Exercises 1–48, solve each exponential equation. Round to the nearest hundredth, if needed.

1. $64^{7x-8} = 16$

2. $\frac{1}{125} = 25^{5x-3}$

3. $\frac{1}{81} = 27^{4m-5}$

4. $\frac{1}{256} = 32^{3m-4}$

5. $625 = 125^{3x-2}$

6. $27^{6x-2} = 81$

7. $243^{5m-5} = 729$

8. $\frac{1}{729} = 81^{6t-2}$

9. $7^{2x+3} = 49^{8-x}$

10. $9^{x+2} = \left(\frac{1}{27}\right)^{1-x}$

11. $27^{3x-4} = 81^{1-2x}$

12. $16^{4x-7} = 64^{3+x}$

13. $4^{2p+1} = 32^{3-p}$

14. $\left(\frac{1}{32,768}\right)^{3-2x} = 64^{x+3}$

15. $125^{1-2m} = 5^{3m+2}$

16. $4^{x+2} = \left(\frac{1}{32}\right)^{-2x+3}$

17. $3^x = 12$

18. $2(5^x) - 1 = 15$

19. $4(8^x) - 4 = 16$

20. $3\left(\frac{1}{2}\right)^x - 1 = 17$

21. $16 = 4\left(\frac{1}{3}\right)^m - 4$

22. $4(10^x) - 1 = 23$

23. $35 = 4\left(\frac{1}{5}\right)^m - 1$

24. $13 = 2\left(\frac{1}{10}\right)^x - 5$

25. $3^x = 4^{x+8}$

26. $\left(\frac{3}{5}\right)^x - 7^{1-x} = 0$

27. $\left(\frac{1}{8}\right)^x - 6^{5-x} = 0$

28. $5^x - 7^{6-x} = 0$

29. $\left(\frac{8}{5}\right)^x - 8^{4-x} = 0$

30. $\left(\frac{5}{4}\right)^x - 5^{3-x} = 0$

31. $0 = 10^x - 5^{4-x}$

32. $8^x - 4^{5-x} = 0$

33. $0 = -12 + 5e^{2x}$

34. $\frac{5+13e^{4-x}}{7} + 1 = 11$

35. $6e^{12x-4} - 6 = 3$

36. $3e^{6-x} + 10 = 19$

37. $47 = 11e^{4-x} + 3$

38. $\frac{24+6e^{3-x}}{6} + 1 = 10$

39. $5 + \frac{6+3e^{2-x}}{3} = 14$

40. $5 + 4e^{7x-8} = 8$

41. $e^{2x} + e^x - 12 = 0$

42. $2(5^{8x}) = 5^{4x} + 3$

43. $4(8^{6x}) - 20 = -11(8^{3x})$

44. $-13(4^{4x}) = -6 - 5(4^{8x})$

45. $3(4^{6x}) = -10 + 17(4^{3x})$

46. $4(10^{6x}) = -3(10^{3x}) + 10$

47. $-15(8^{4x}) + 18 = -2(8^{8x})$

48. $-15(3^{4x}) = -25 - 2(3^{8x})$

In Exercises 49–64, solve each logarithmic equation. Round to the nearest hundredth, if needed.

49. $8 - \ln x^5 = 0$

50. $\ln (x + 5)^3 + 12 = 21$

51. $\ln (x + 4)^5 = 20$

52. $34 = \ln (x + 3)^5 + 9$

53. $30 - \ln (x - 1)^4 = 10$

54. $\ln (x - 2)^2 - 12 = 15$

55. $18 = \ln (x - 6)^2 + 6$

56. $\ln (x + 7)^7 + 13 = 34$

57. $\log (4x + 7) = 2$

58. $-2 + \log_3 (1 - x)^5 = 8$

59. $\log_4 (3 + 2x)^4 + 3 = 27$

60. $-11 = 7 - \log_3 (3 - x)^9$

61. $-1 = 5 - \log_5 (x + 6)^3$

62. $0 = 6 - \log_7 (2 - x)^3$

63. $\log_6 (x + 6)^5 + 4 = 19$

64. $-19 + \log_2 (4 - x)^7 = 9$

In Exercises 65–68, use the Distance Modulus Formula.

65. Find the distance from Earth to a star if its distance modulus from Earth is –0.26. Round the answer to the nearest hundredth of a parsec.

66. Find the distance in light years (1 parsec ≈ 3.3 light years) from Earth to a star if its distance modulus from Earth is 0.67. Round the answer to the nearest hundredth of a light year.

67. Find the distance from Earth to a star if its distance modulus from Earth is 2.38. Round the answer to the nearest hundredth of a parsec.

68. Find the distance in light years (1 parsec ≈ 3.3 light years) from Earth to a star if its distance modulus from Earth is 0.79. Round the answer to the nearest hundredth of a light year.

In Exercises 69–76, solve.

69. $\log_2 x + \log_2 (x - 6) = 4$

70. $2\log_3 x - \log_3 (x + 4) = 2$

71. $\log_4 (x + 62) - \log_4 (x - 1) = 3$

72. $\log_2 (x + 2) + \log_2 (x + 4) = 3$

73. $\log_3 (2x + 1) - \log_3 (x - 1) = 1$

74. $\log_3 x + \log_3 (x - 6) = 3$

75. $\log_4 (x + 16) + \log_4 (x + 4) = 3$

76. $2\log_2 x - \log_2 (x + 5) = 4$

77. Suppose $2000 is invested in an annually compounding account at 12%. Find approximately how long it will take for the balance to reach $5,000.

78. Suppose $11,400 is invested in a monthly compounded account at 4.98%. Approximately how long will it take for the balance to reach $25,650? Round the answer to the nearest tenth of a year.

79. Suppose $18,700 is invested in a quarterly compounded account at 3.39%. Approximately how long will it take for the balance to reach $50,490? Round the answer to the nearest tenth of a year.

80. Suppose $23,300 is invested in a daily compounded account at 5.28%. Approximately how long will it take for the balance to reach $46,600? Round the answer to the nearest tenth of a year.

Extensions

81. Solve $\ln (10x - 5) - \ln 5 + 4 = 3$. Round to the nearest thousandth.

82. Solve $A = P\left(1 + \dfrac{r}{m}\right)^{mt}$ for t using common logs.

83. Find the extraneous solution, if any, for $\log_3 \left(x + \sqrt{19}\right) + \log_3 \left(x - \sqrt{19}\right) = 4$.

84. Solve $e^{8x} - 6e^{4x} = 7$. Find the exact value of x and the approximate value to the nearest hundredth.

85. With a distance modulus from Earth of –2.88, Sirius is the brightest star in the night sky, almost twice the brightness of the second brightest star, Canopus. How far is Sirius from Earth in parsecs and in light years (1 parsec ≈ 3.3 light years), each rounded to the nearest hundredth?

86. Solve $3^x = 8^{x-8}$. Find the exact value of x and the approximate value to the nearest hundredth.

8.5 EXPONENTIAL AND LOGARITHMIC MODELS

OBJECTIVES

- Find exponential models of growth and decay.
- Use Newton's Law of Cooling.
- Use the formula for continuously compounded interest.
- Solve logarithmic models.
- Use logistic and Gaussian models.

PREREQUISITE VOCABULARY TERMS

exponential function

interest

logarithmic function

natural exponential function

natural logarithmic function

8.5.1   Predicting Change with Logarithmic Models

The techniques used for solving a logarithmic equation can be used to solve a logarithmic model for one of its variables, or to predict some value given by the equation.

EXAMPLE 1   Using a Logarithmic Model

The power gain P for an amplifier is given by $P = 10\log\dfrac{x}{y}$, where x is the power output and y is the power input, both in watts. Solve the equation for y to find an equation for the power input in terms of P and x. If an amplifier has a power gain of 20 watts and the output is 12 watts, find the power input in watts.

SOLUTION

Solve the logarithmic equation for y, the power input.

$$P = 10\log\frac{x}{y}$$

$$\frac{P}{10} = \log\frac{x}{y} \qquad \textit{Divide each side by 10.}$$

$$10^{\frac{P}{10}} = \frac{x}{y} \qquad \textit{Write the logarithmic equation in exponential form.}$$

$$y = \frac{x}{10^{\frac{P}{10}}} \qquad \textit{Solve for y.}$$

Use the equation for y to find the power input when the power gain is 20 ($P = 20$) and the output is 12 ($x = 12$).

$$y = \frac{12}{10^{\frac{20}{10}}} = \frac{12}{10^2} = \frac{12}{100} = 0.12$$

The power input is 0.12 watts.

8.5.2   Exponential Growth and Decay

Two of the most commonly used exponential models are the **exponential growth model** and the **exponential decay model**. These models are used to make predictions concerning the time it takes for some quantity (e.g., a population) to grow (increase) or decay (decrease) to some number.

Exponential Growth and Decay Models	
Exponential Growth Model	**Exponential Decay Model**
$y = ae^{bx}$, $a > 0$ and $b > 0$	$y = ae^{-bx}$, $a > 0$ and $b > 0$

IMPORTANT

x represents the elapsed time of the growth (or decay), y represents the quantity that is growing (or decaying), and a is the quantity y at the initial time x.

EXAMPLE 2   Finding and Using an Exponential Model

The number of frogs in a wildlife preserve is increasing according to an exponential model. After the preserve has been open for 2 years, the population of frogs is 100. After 4 years, the population is 300. Use an exponential growth model to predict the preserve's frog population after 5, 6, and 10 years. According to the model, how long (to the nearest tenth of a year) will it take for the preserve's frog population to increase to 20,000 frogs?

SOLUTION

Let y be the number of frogs after x years.

Find the values of a and b, then use those values to write the exponential growth model, $y = ae^{bx}$.

Use the known values to write two equations using $y = ae^{bx}$.

TIP

The ordered pairs (2, 100) and (4, 300) are solutions to the exponential growth model $y = ae^{bx}$.

$$x = 2 \text{ and } y = 100 \implies 100 = ae^{2b} \quad \textit{After 2 years, there were 100 frogs.}$$
$$x = 4 \text{ and } y = 300 \implies 300 = ae^{4b} \quad \textit{After 4 years, there were 300 frogs.}$$

Solve one of the two equations for either a or b. Since b is in the exponent and a is a coefficient, it will be easier to solve for a. Here, $100 = ae^{2b}$ is solved for a.

TIP

If one of the equations had been solved for b (instead of for a), then the next step would be to substitute the expression for b into the other equation and solve for a.

$$100 = ae^{2b} \implies a = \frac{100}{e^{2b}} \quad \textit{Divide both sides by } e^{2b}.$$

Substitute the expression for a into $300 = ae^{4b}$, and then solve for b.

$$300 = \frac{100}{e^{2b}}\left(e^{4b}\right) \qquad \textit{Substitute } a = \frac{100}{e^{2b}} \textit{ into } 300 = ae^{4b}.$$
$$300 = 100e^{2b} \qquad \textit{Simplify.}$$
$$3 = e^{2b} \qquad \textit{Divide each side by 100.}$$
$$\ln 3 = \ln e^{2b} \qquad \textit{Take the natural log of each side.}$$
$$\ln 3 = 2b \qquad \textit{Use the Power Property of logs and simplify (ln e = 1).}$$
$$b = \frac{\ln 3}{2} \qquad \textit{Divide each side by 2 to solve for b.}$$

Substitute this b-value into $a = \dfrac{100}{e^{2b}}$ to find the a-value.

$$a = \frac{100}{e^{2\left(\frac{\ln 3}{2}\right)}} = \frac{100}{e^{\ln 3}} = \frac{100}{3}$$

Use the a- and b-values to write the exponential growth model.

$$y = ae^{bx} \implies y = \frac{100}{3}e^{\left(\frac{\ln 3}{2}\right)x}$$

Write the model in exponential form without the logarithmic exponent by simplifying.

$$y = \frac{100}{3}e^{\left(\frac{\ln 3}{2}\right)x} = \frac{100}{3}e^{\ln 3\left(\frac{x}{2}\right)} \quad \textit{Factor out ln 3 in the exponent.}$$

$$= \frac{100}{3}\left(e^{\ln 3}\right)^{\frac{x}{2}} \quad \textit{Power of a Power Property (of Exponents)}$$

$$= \frac{100}{3} \cdot 3^{\frac{x}{2}} \quad \textit{Simplify using the fact that } e^{\ln x} = x.$$

Substitute $x = 5$, 6, and 10 into the model to predict the frog population after 5, 6, and 10 years.

5 years	6 years	10 years
$y = \frac{100}{3} \cdot 3^{\frac{5}{2}} \approx 520$	$y = \frac{100}{3} \cdot 3^{\frac{6}{2}} = 900$	$y = \frac{100}{3} \cdot 3^{\frac{10}{2}} = 8100$

According to the model, the preserve's frog population will be approximately 520 after 5 years, 900 after 6 years, and 8100 after 10 years.

Substitute $y = 20{,}000$ into the model and solve for x to find the length of time it will take for the population to increase to 20,000.

$$20{,}000 = \frac{100}{3} \cdot 3^{\frac{x}{2}} \quad \textit{Substitute } y = 20{,}000 \textit{ into the model.}$$

$$600 = 3^{\frac{x}{2}} \quad \textit{Multiply each side by 3/100.}$$

$$\ln 600 = \ln 3^{\frac{x}{2}} \quad \textit{Take the natural log of each side.}$$

$$\ln 600 = \left(\frac{x}{2}\right)\ln 3 \quad \textit{Power Property of Logs}$$

$$x = \frac{2(\ln 600)}{\ln 3} \quad \textit{Multiply each side by 2 and divide each side by ln 3 to solve for x.}$$

$$x \approx 11.6 \quad \textit{Use a calculator to simplify.}$$

According to the model, it will take approximately 11.6 years for the preserve's frog population to reach 20,000.

8.5.3   Half-Life

The **half-life** of a decaying substance is the amount of time required for the substance to decrease by half. In other words, it is the period of time over which one-half of the substance decomposes. For example, consider a 6 milligram sample of some exponentially decaying substance. This substance's half-life is the amount of time it takes for the substance to decay so that there are only 3 milligrams remaining. This substance's half-life is also the amount of time it takes for the substance to decay from 3 milligrams to 1.5 milligrams, or from 1.5 milligrams to 0.75 milligrams, or from 0.75 milligrams to 0.375 milligrams, and so on.

Suppose the substance's half-life is 3 hours. Then a 10-milligram sample of the substance will decay to 5 milligrams after 3 hours. After 6 total hours, the substance will measure 2.5 milligrams, and after 9 total hours, the substance will measure 1.25 milligrams.

The amount of radioactive material and the amount of a medication in a person's body are commonly described by their half-lives.

EXAMPLE 3   Finding the Half-Life of a Substance

The amount remaining from a 90-milligram sample of a radioactive substance after t years is given by $A = 90e^{-0.052t}$. Find the substance's half-life to the nearest year.

SOLUTION

Let $A = 45$ (half of 90 milligrams) and solve for t to find the substance's half-life.

$$45 = 90e^{-0.052t} \qquad \textit{Substitute A = 45 into the model.}$$

$$\frac{1}{2} = e^{-0.052t} \qquad \textit{Divide each side by 90.}$$

$$\ln\frac{1}{2} = \ln e^{-0.052t} \qquad \textit{Take the natural log of each side.}$$

$$\ln\frac{1}{2} = -0.052t \qquad \textit{Use the Power Property of logs and simplify (ln e = 1).}$$

$$t = \frac{\ln\frac{1}{2}}{-0.052} \qquad \textit{Divide each side by −0.052 to solve for t.}$$

$$t \approx 13 \qquad \textit{Use a calculator to simplify.}$$

The half-life of the substance is approximately 13 years.

8.5.4   Newton's Law of Cooling

Newton's Law of Cooling states that the rate of change of the temperature of some object (or substance) is proportional to the difference between its own temperature and the temperature of its surrounding environment.

Newton's Law of Cooling
$$T = A + (T_0 - A)e^{-kt}$$
T = object's temperature at time t A = temperature of the object's surroundings T_0 = object's initial temperature k = constant (specific to the object) t = time

The k-value in the Newton's Law of Cooling equation depends upon the object or substance. This value may be given, or you may solve for the constant k using a given initial temperature, final temperature (i.e., temperature at time t), time, and temperature of the object's surroundings.

EXAMPLE 4   Using Newton's Law of Cooling

Suppose the temperature of a liquid decreases from 100° C to 60° C after being placed in a 5° C freezer for 10 minutes. How long (to the nearest tenth of a minute) would it take for the same liquid to cool from 90° C to 10° C in the 5° C freezer?

SOLUTION

Find the constant k.

$$60 = 5 + (100 - 5)e^{-k(10)}$$ *Substitute.*

$$55 = 95e^{-10k}$$ *Simplify.*

$$\frac{11}{19} = e^{-10k}$$ *Divide each side by 95.*

$$\ln\frac{11}{19} = \ln e^{-10k}$$ *Take the natural log of each side.*

$$\ln\frac{11}{19} = -10k$$ *Use the Power Property of logs and simplify ($\ln e = 1$).*

$$k = \frac{\ln\frac{11}{19}}{-10}$$ *Divide each side by –10.*

$$k \approx 0.055$$ *Use a calculator to simplify.*

Using this k-value, find the time needed to cool the liquid from 90° C to 10° C in the 5° C freezer.

$$10 = 5 + (90 - 5)e^{-0.055t}$$ *Substitute.*

$$5 = 85e^{-0.055t}$$ *Simplify.*

$$\frac{1}{17} = e^{-0.055t}$$ *Divide each side by 85.*

$$\ln\frac{1}{17} = \ln e^{-0.055t}$$ *Take the natural log of each side.*

$$\ln\frac{1}{17} = -0.055t$$ *Use the Power Property of logs and simplify ($\ln e = 1$).*

$$t = \frac{\ln\frac{1}{17}}{-0.055}$$ *Divide each side by –0.055.*

$$t \approx 51.5$$ *Use a calculator to simplify.*

According to this model, the liquid's temperature will decrease from 90° C to 10° C in the 5° C freezer after approximately 51.5 minutes.

8.5.5   Continuously Compounded Interest

The formulas for simple and compound interest were discussed previously. The formula for **continuously compounded interest** will be discussed in this topic, which is used when the interest is compounded continuously, instead of some set number of times per year.

Continuously Compounded Interest Formula
$$A = Pe^{rt}$$
A = balance of the account
P = the principal (initial) amount in the account
r = annual interest rate (as a decimal)
t = the length of time that the money is invested, in years

When the continuously compounded interest formula is solved for the interest rate r or the length of time the money is invested (or borrowed) t, then the equation solved is exponential.

| EXAMPLE 5 | Using the Continuously Compounded Interest Formula |

What was the interest rate (to the nearest tenth of a percent) on an account with continuously compounded interest if the initial amount deposited tripled after 14 years, assuming there were no other deposits?

SOLUTION

Since the interest is compounded continuously, the formula $A = Pe^{rt}$ can be used. The value of t is 14, and no other values are given. However, it is given that the account's balance after 14 years was triple the initial amount. Therefore, $A = 3P$. Substitute into the formula and solve for r.

$$3P = Pe^{r(14)}$$ *Substitute.*

$$3 = e^{14r}$$ *Divide each side by P.*

$$\ln 3 = \ln e^{14r}$$ *Take the natural log of each side.*

$$\ln 3 = 14r$$ *Use the Power Property of logs and simplify ($\ln e = 1$).*

$$r = \frac{\ln 3}{14}$$ *Divide each side by 14 to solve for r.*

$$r \approx 0.078$$ *Use a calculator to simplify.*

Therefore, the interest rate was approximately 7.8%.

8.5.6   Logistic Models

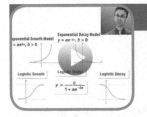

A **logistic model** is an exponential equation that describes the growth (or decay) of a population over time. A logistic model is characterized by initial rapid growth (or decay), and then a slower rate of growth (or decay) over time.

> **Logistic Model**
>
> If a population's growth (or decay) can be described by a logistic model, then the population's total y after time x is given by $y = \dfrac{c}{1 + ae^{-bx}}$, where a, b, and c are constants such that $a > 0$, $b \neq 0$, and $c > 0$.

IMPORTANT

If $b > 0$, then the logistic model describes population growth. If $b < 0$, then the logistic model describes population decay.

| EXAMPLE 6 | Using a Logistic Growth Model |

In a small town with a population of 4000 people, the total number of people y infected by a virus x days after it is introduced into the population is modeled by $y = \dfrac{4000}{1 + 2500e^{-0.9x}}$ where $x \geq 0$. To the nearest tenth of a percent, find the percent of the town's total population that will be infected after 5 days. Find the approximate number of days before 50% of the town's population will be infected.

SOLUTION

Substitute $x = 5$ into the model and simplify to find the number of people infected after 5 days.

$$y = \frac{4000}{1 + 2500e^{-0.9(5)}} \approx 139 \text{ people}$$

Since $139/4000 \approx 0.03475$, approximately 3.5% of the population will be infected after 5 days.

Substitute $y = 2000$ into the model and solve for x to find the number of days before 2000 people (i.e., 50% of the population) are infected.

$$2000 = \frac{4000}{1 + 2500e^{-0.9x}}$$ *Substitute.*

$$1 + 2500e^{-0.9x} = 2$$ *Multiply each side by $1 + 2500e^{-0.9x}$ and divide each side by 2000.*

$$2500e^{-0.9x} = 1$$ *Subtract 1 from each side.*

$$e^{-0.9x} = 0.0004$$ *Divide each side by 2500.*

$$-0.9x = \ln 0.0004$$ *Take the natural log of each side.*

$$x = \frac{\ln 0.0004}{-0.9}$$ *Divide each side by −0.9.*

$$x \approx 9$$ *Use a calculator to simplify.*

After approximately 9 days, 50% of the population will be infected.

8.5.7   Gaussian Models

A **Gaussian model** is an exponential equation of the form $y = ae^{-(x-b)^2/c}$, where a, b, and c are constants. This model describes a **normally distributed** population (represented by the independent variable, typically x), which is characterized by a graph that forms a bell-shaped curve. Moreover, the maximum y-value (i.e., the top of the bell) occurs at the mean of the x-values, and all other points on the graph are symmetric about the mean, as shown in **Example 7**.

EXAMPLE 7   Using a Gaussian Model

The weight of the dogs seen by a veterinarian during one year roughly followed the normal distribution given by $y = 0.03577e^{-(x-50)^2/325}$ where x is the weight of a dog. Use the given graph to estimate the mean weight of a dog seen by this veterinarian during that year.

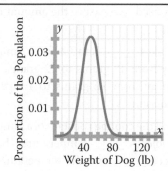

SOLUTION

From the graph, the maximum y-value corresponds to $x \approx 50$. Therefore, the mean weight of a dog seen by this veterinarian during that year was approximately 50 pounds.

SECTION 8.5 EXERCISES

Warm Up

Use a calculator to evaluate each expression to the nearest thousandth.

1. $\ln\dfrac{3}{7} - \ln 5$

2. $\log\left(\dfrac{\frac{9}{6}}{10}\right) - 4$

3. $\dfrac{\ln\left(\frac{3}{5}\right)}{-9}$

Just the Facts

Fill in the blanks.

4. $P = 10\log\dfrac{x}{y}$ is a(n) _____ equation in _____ variables.

5. The equation $y = ae^{-bx}$ is the exponential _____ model with the condition that b is _____ than 0. This model is used to predict the time it will take for some quantity to _____ .

6. If a sample contains 8 milligrams of ununtrium, which has a half-life of 20 minutes, after _____ hour(s) the sample will contain only 1 milligram of ununtrium.

7. In addition to modeling radioactive material, half-life is often used to measure the amount of _____ in a person's body.

8. If it takes _____ hour(s) for a sample of meitnerium to decay from 48 grams to 12 grams, it will take 1.5 hours to decay from 12 grams to 1.5 grams. The half-life of meitnerium is _____.

9. To find the cooling constant of a sample of some substance, the object's _____ temperature, the temperature of the object's _____, and the temperature of the substance at some time _____ are needed.

10. An investment made in an account that compounds interest continuously will earn _____ interest than an investment made in an account at the same interest rate that is compounded monthly.

Essential Skills

1. In chemistry, pH is given by the formula:

   $\text{pH} = -\log\left[H_3O^+\right]$, where H_3O^+ is the hydronium ion concentration in moles per liter. Given that the pH of the drinking water of Yukon, Oklahoma is equal to 5.3, what is the concentration of the hydronium ion in moles per liter?

2. The mathematical model for learning an assembly-line procedure needed for assembling one component of a manufactured item is $n = -5\ln\left(\dfrac{0.94}{P} - 1\right)$, where P is the proportion of correctly assembled components after n practice sessions. Solve the equation for P to find an equation for the proportion of correctly assembled components in terms of the number of practice sessions n. Use the model to predict the percent of components (to the nearest tenth of a percent) that will be correctly assembled after 5 practice sessions.

3. The population of a city has been rising according to the model $A = pe^{0.036t}$, where p is the population in 2000 and A is the population t years later. If the city's population was 468,000 in 2000, in what year is the city expected to reach 1 million people?

4. The number of bacteria in a sample is increasing according to an exponential model. After 2 hours, the sample contained 200 bacteria; and after 6 hours, the sample contained 800 bacteria. Write an exponential growth model for the number of bacteria in the sample after x hours.

5. Sodium-24 is a radioactive substance used for medical purposes. Suppose that a patient is injected with sodium-24 and the amount of sodium-24 in the patient's body in milligrams after t hours is given by $S(t) = 5e^{-0.35t}$. What is the half-life of sodium-24?

6. Find the half-life to the nearest tenth of a year of a radioactive substance that decays from 80 milligrams to 15 milligrams in 25 years according to the exponential decay model $y = ae^{-bx}$, where a is the initial amount and y is the amount remaining after x years. Hint: Find the b-value, then use this value to write the exponential decay model for this substance with initial amount 80 milligrams.

7. At time $t = 0$, a cup of coffee is placed in a room with a constant temperature of 81° F. The temperature of the coffee after t minutes in the room is described by the function $C(t) = 81 + 101e^{-0.039t}$. Based on this model, how long does it take the coffee to cool to a temperature of 92° F?

8. Suppose the temperature of a liquid decreases from 70° F to 55° F after being placed in a 33° F freezer for 60 minutes. Use Newton's Law of Cooling, $T = A + \left(T_0 - A\right)e^{-kt}$, to find the number of minutes (to the nearest minute) needed for the liquid to cool from 82° F to 60° F in a 29° F freezer.

9. Suppose a savings account offers 7.5% interest compounded continuously. How long does it take for a $3500 deposit in this account to reach $20,000? Round the number of years to the nearest tenth if needed.

10. An investor wants to analyze the earnings of a mutual fund account. Four years ago, the value of the account was $16,000 and it is now worth $24,000 (no additional deposits were made). If the account is compared to a bank account paying interest that is compounded continuously, what interest rate (rounded to the nearest hundredth of a percent) would the bank account have to pay to match the mutual fund account's earnings?

In Exercises 11–12, use the following information.

In a small town with a population of 1720, the total number of people y infected by a virus x days after it is introduced into the population is modeled by $y = \dfrac{1720}{1 + 550e^{-0.88x}}$, where $x \geq 0$.

11. Find the number of people that will be infected after 2 days.

12. Find the percent of the town's total population that will be infected after 4 days to the nearest whole number.

In Exercises 13–14, use the following information.

The amount remaining of a 45 mL sample of a liquid substance, y (in mg) after x hours is modeled by $y = \dfrac{45}{1 + 0.07e^{0.09x}}$, where $x \geq 0$.

13. To the nearest tenth of an hour, how long will it take for the substance to decay to 30 mL?

14. To the nearest tenth of an hour, how long will it take for the substance to decay from 40 mL to 30 mL?

15. The total amount spent on books by the students at a college during one year roughly followed the normal distribution given by $y = 0.00313e^{-(x-500)^2/32,500}$, where x is the total amount spent on books in dollars. Use the graph of that equation to estimate the mean amount spent on books per student during that year.

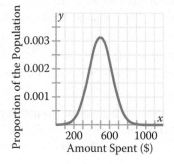
Amount Spent ($)

16. The total number of tacos eaten in a month by individuals in Austin, Texas last month roughly followed the normal distribution given by $y = 0.356825e^{-(x-7)^2/25}$, where x is the total number of tacos eaten by a given individual. Use the graph of that equation to estimate the mean number of tacos eaten per Austinite during that month.

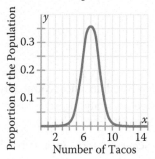
Number of Tacos

Extensions

17. The voltage across a resistor in a circuit is 12 volts at time $t = 1.2$. The formula for voltage is $V(t) = V_0\left(1 - e^{-4.5t}\right)$, where t is the time in seconds, and V_0 is the voltage at $t = 0$. Find the voltage to the nearest hundredth at $t = 0$.

18. The growth of a city is described by the population function $P(t) = P_0e^{kt}$, where P_0 is the initial population of the city, t is the time in years, and k is a constant. If the population of the city at $t = 0$ is 15,000 and the population of the city at $t = 3$ is 19,000, what is the approximation to the population of the city at $t = 6$ rounded to the nearest hundredth?

19. If 80 milligrams of a radioactive substance decays to 15 milligrams in 25 years, find its half-life. Use $A = pe^{-kt}$, where p is the initial amount, k is a constant, and A is the amount remaining after t years. Round to the nearest thousandth.

20. The loudness of sound is measured by the formula $d = 10\log\dfrac{I}{I_0}$, where d is the loudness of sound measured in decibels, I is the intensity of sound, and I_0 is the softest audible sound. Solve the formula for I_0.

21. The corpse of a famous math professor had a temperature of 80° F when it was discovered at midnight in his mansion. Two hours later, the temperature of the corpse had dropped to 75° F. The temperature of the room was kept constant at 60° F all night. Use Newton's Law of Cooling to find his time of death to the nearest minute if his body temperature was 98.6° F at the time of death.

22. Under ideal conditions, the population of a certain bacterial colony will double in 65 minutes. How long will it take for the population to increase to 16 times the initial population?

CHAPTER 8 REVIEW EXERCISES

Section 8.1 Exponential Functions

In Exercises 1–3, graph each exponential function.

1. $p(x) = 2^{x+1} - 1$

2. $h(x) = (2)3^x + 1$

3. $g(x) = -\left(\dfrac{1}{3}\right)e^x - 2$

4. How much should be deposited in an account paying 5.75% interest compounded monthly in order to have a balance of $14,000 after 5 years?

5. The number of streptococcus bacteria in a Petri dish, kept in a medical laboratory, is $A = pe^{0.047t}$, where p is the initial number (when the culture was first brought in) and A is the final number of bacteria after t hours. If a culture containing 40,000 bacteria was brought in, how many bacteria will there be after 10 hours? after a week?

Section 8.2 Logarithmic Functions

In Exercises 6–7, simplify each expression without using a calculator.

6. $\log 1000 + \log_{64} 4 - \log_{29} 1$

7. $\ln e^5 - e^{\ln 7} + \log 10^{\ln e}$

In Exercises 8–9, graph each function.

8. $f(x) = \log_2 (-x) + 1$

9. $n(x) = \log_{\frac{1}{2}} x - 2$

10. Express the domain of $k(x) = \log_4 (-x + 8) + 1$ in interval notation.

Section 8.3 Properties of Logarithms

In Exercises 11–12, simplify each expression without using a calculator.

11. $\log_6 144 - \log_6 12 + \log_6 3$

12. $\log_3 15 + \log_3 6 - \log_3 810$

13. Use the properties of logarithms to expand
$$\log_8 \left(\frac{8y(x-5)}{\sqrt[4]{x}} \right)^3.$$

14. Use the properties of logarithms to write
$$4\log_b (x+2) - \frac{1}{3}\log_b 27 + \frac{2}{3}\log_b y$$
as a single log, if possible.

15. Use the Change of Base Formula and common logs or natural logs to approximate the value of $\log_{\frac{2}{3}}\left(\dfrac{7}{9}\right)$ to the nearest hundredth, using a calculator.

Section 8.4
Exponential and Logarithmic Equations

In Exercises 16–17, solve each exponential equation. Round to the nearest hundredth, if needed.

16. $5^{3x+2} = 125^{1-2x}$

17. $3e^{4x} = 5e^{2x} + 2$

In Exercises 18–19, solve each logarithmic equation. Round to the nearest hundredth, if needed.

18. $\log_4 (x+4) + \log_4 (x+16) = 3$

19. $\log_6 (x+4) - \log_6 (x-4) = \log_6 5$

20. Suppose a total of $25,000 is invested in a semi-annually compounded account at 4.8%. Approximately how long will it take for the balance to reach $36,000? Round to the nearest tenth of a year.

Section 8.5
Exponential and Logarithmic Models

21. In an amplifier, the power gain P is given by the function
$$P = 10\log \frac{P_{OUT}}{P_{IN}}, \quad \text{where } P_{OUT} \text{ and } P_{IN} \text{ are the power}$$
output and input in watts. If an amplifier has a power gain of 24 watts and the output power was 16 watts, find the power input in watts. Round to the nearest thousandth.

22. The number of fruit flies present in a population at time t (in days) is given by the function $P(t) = \dfrac{240}{1 + 56.5e^{-0.37t}}$. How long will it take for the population to reach 200? Round to the nearest tenth.

23. If 40 milligrams of strontium-90 radioactively decays to 12 milligrams in 30 years, find its half-life. Use the formula $A = pe^{-kt}$, where p is the initial amount and A the final amount. Round to the nearest tenth.

24. When an object is removed from a furnace and placed in an environment with a constant temperature of 31° C, its core temperature is 730° C. The temperature of the object t hours after it has been removed from the furnace can be described by the function $F(t) = 31 + 699e^{-0.154t}$. How long will it take the object to cool to 510° C? Round to the nearest tenth.

25. Suppose an account offers 8.5% interest compounded continuously. How many years does it take for an investment in this account to triple? Round to the nearest tenth of a year.

ANSWERS

SECTION P.1 ANSWERS

Warm Up/Just the Facts

1. $-11/24$

$$-\frac{5}{8}-\left(-\frac{1}{6}\right)$$

$$=-\frac{5}{8}+\frac{1}{6} \qquad \textit{Write subtraction of a negative as addition.}$$

$$=-\frac{15}{24}+\frac{4}{24} \qquad \textit{Write each term as an equivalent fraction with a common denominator.}$$

$$=\frac{-15+4}{24} \qquad \textit{Combine the numerators.}$$

$$=-\frac{11}{24} \qquad \textit{Simplify the numerator.}$$

2. $-6k^2 + 8k - 4$

$$7k - 4 + k^2 + k - 7k^2 = k^2 - 7k^2 + 7k + k - 4$$
$$= -6k^2 + 8k - 4$$

3. The values of x include all numbers between -10 and 3, including 3 but not -10.

4. irrational numbers

5. whole numbers

6. Rational; integers; $\neq 0$

7. -100

8. includes b but not a; includes a but not b

9. closed; open

10. distance; 0

Essential Skills/Extensions

1. -3, 2.09, $\sqrt{10}$, $\dfrac{11}{3}$, 3.72

3. -4.11, -4.1, $1/4$, $12/5$, $\sqrt{13}$

5. whole number, integer, rational number, real number

7. rational number, real number

9. natural number, whole number, integer, rational number, real number

11. 60

13. -1

15. $11/4$

17. -100

19. $-3/4$; $4/3$

21. 8.1; $-10/81$

23. Associative Property of Addition

25. Identity Property of Multiplication

27. $(0, \infty)$

29. $(-\infty, 10]$

31. $(0, 3.2]$

33. $(7, 20]$

35. $x \leq 4$

37. $x \geq -1.5$

39. $5 \leq x \leq 10$

41. $-3.8 \leq x < 12$

43. $-4 < x < 0$; $(-4, 0)$

45. $(-\infty, 1) \cup (1, \infty)$

47. $-2 \leq x \leq 4$; $[-2, 4]$; $\{x \mid -2 \leq x \leq 4\}$

49. $\{1, 2, 3, 4, \dots\}$

51. $\{2, 4, 6, 8, \dots\}$

53. 0

55. 3

57. when $x \geq 0$, $-|x| = -x$; when $x < 0$, $-|x| = x$

59. when $x \geq 0$, $-4x + |x| = -3x$; when $x < 0$, $-4x + |x| = -5x$

61. 15 units

63. 5.75 units

65. $-10/3$, 0.15, $4/5$ (possible answers)

67. 0, -4, -9 (possible answers)

69. 0

71. The student substituted the value for n incorrectly in the denominator, which should be $5 + 1 - (-3)$.

73. $A \cup B = [-5, \infty)$, $A \cap B = [-1, 0]$

75. $A \cup B = (-\infty, -4) \cup (-3, \infty)$, $A \cap B = \varnothing$ (empty set)

77. $A \cup B = (-\infty, \infty)$, $A \cap B = [10]$

79. true

81. true

83. yes; $AB = CD = AD = BC = 11$

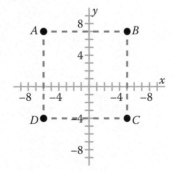

SECTION P.2 ANSWERS

Warm Up/Just the Facts

1. 125

$5^3 = 5 \cdot 5 \cdot 5 = 125$ *In 5^3, 5 is a factor 3 times.*

2. 3/7

$\left(\dfrac{3}{7}\right)^2 = \left(\dfrac{3}{7}\right)\left(\dfrac{3}{7}\right) = \dfrac{3 \cdot 3}{7 \cdot 7} = \dfrac{9}{49}$

In $\left(\dfrac{3}{7}\right)^2$, $\dfrac{3}{7}$ is a factor twice.

3. 8^4

$8 \cdot 8 \cdot 8 \cdot 8 = 8^4$ *In 8^4, 8 is a factor 4 times.*

4. nonzero; base; exponent, power

5. like bases; added

6. base; multiplied

7. Quotient of Powers; like bases; subtracted

8. Zero Exponent; zero

9. greater than or equal to; less than; power

10. negative; 1

Essential Skills/Extensions

1. 49

3. −32

5. −32

7. −1

9. x^8

11. simplified

13. m^{11}

15. $w^{13}x^6$

17. $2b^5c^3d^{14}$

19. $-16g^{12}h^5k^8$

21. d^{10}

23. h^{32}

25. $25p^{16}q^2$

27. $12g^{10}h^8k$

29. h^8

31. $1/m^7$

33. $1/j$

35. 16

37. 1/729

39. −125/8

41. 6.02×10^5

43. 3.0×10^{-5}

45. 4.69×10^9

47. 710,000

49. 0.00052

51. 0.00000018

53. 4.8×10^{10}

55. 3.0×10^{-7}

57. 9.8×10^4

59. 9.72×10^{-4}

61. $\dfrac{d^6}{2}$; Power of a Power, Product of Powers, Quotient of Powers

63. $-\dfrac{1}{27n^6}$; Zero Exponent, Negative Exponent, Power of a Product, Power of a Power, Quotient of Powers

65. $3x^0$; $\dfrac{6x^0}{2}$ (possible answers)

67. $\dfrac{4x^4}{2x^6}$; $\dfrac{6x^{10}}{3x^{12}}$ (possible answers)

69. $(2x^3y^2z)^4$; $(4x^6y^4z^2)^2$ (possible answers)

71. The error is in $2^{-3}c^{-5(-3)} = -8c^{15}$ because $2^{-3} \neq -8$.

Correction: $2^{-3}c^{-5(-3)} = \left(\dfrac{1}{2^3}\right)c^{15} = \dfrac{c^{15}}{8}$

SECTION P.3 ANSWERS

Warm Up/Just the Facts

1. 64

$2^6 = 64$ *2 is a factor 6 times.*

2. $6x + 2y - 6$

$5x - 7 - y + x + 3y + 1 = 5x + x - y + 3y - 7 + 1$
$= 6x + 2y - 6$

3. k^{11}

$k^3(k^4)^2 = k^3(k^8) = k^{11}$

4. p^n

5. square; 3

6. Even

7. -512

8. perfect squares

9. like radicals; radicand, index

10. $p - q\sqrt{n}$; conjugate

Essential Skills/Extensions

1. true

3. true

5. false

7. true

9. $5\sqrt{7}$

11. $2\sqrt[3]{2}$

13. $-24\sqrt{2}$

15. $\dfrac{8\sqrt[3]{3}}{3}$

17. $6\sqrt[3]{6}$

19. $-2\sqrt{2} + 12\sqrt{3}$

21. $3\sqrt{3}$

23. $\sqrt{2}$

25. $-\dfrac{\sqrt{3}}{3}$

27. $\dfrac{4\sqrt{14}}{7}$

29. $\dfrac{\sqrt[3]{75}}{5}$

31. $\dfrac{5\sqrt[3]{9}}{3}$

33. $-2\sqrt{7} + 6$

35. $\dfrac{5 + \sqrt{3}}{11}$

37. $\dfrac{8 - \sqrt{10}}{9}$

39. 125

41. 81

43. 32

45. $\sqrt{x}$

47. $2\sqrt[6]{32}$

49. $y\sqrt{y}$

51. 1/256

53. 1/343

55. 1/8

57. $3\sqrt{3}$

59. 2

61. 9

63. $3u^3 v\sqrt{uz}$

65. $6g^2 h^3 j\sqrt{2j}$

67. $2n^4 p^5 \sqrt[3]{2mp}$

69. $\dfrac{w\sqrt{v}}{2uv}$

71. $\dfrac{4t^3}{y^3}$

73. $mn^3 p\sqrt{7}$

75. 5 and 6; 5.6

77. 2 and 3; 2.7

79. $\dfrac{5\sqrt{2x}}{2}$

81. $\dfrac{2\sqrt{1+y}}{1+y}$

83. E only

85. $2\sqrt[4]{2}$

87. A: Writing the radical with a rational exponent gives $4^{\frac{1}{4}}$. Since $\dfrac{1}{4} = \dfrac{1}{2} \cdot \dfrac{1}{2}$, by the Power of a Power Property, the power can be written as $(4^{\frac{1}{2}})^{\frac{1}{2}}$. Simplifying the power within parentheses gives $2^{\frac{1}{2}}$, which is equal to $\sqrt{2}$ when written in radical form.

B: Writing the radical with a rational exponent and 4 as a power gives $(2^2)^{\frac{1}{4}}$. By the Power of a Power Property, $(2^2)^{\frac{1}{4}} = 2^{2 \cdot \frac{1}{4}} = 2^{\frac{1}{2}}$ which is equal to $\sqrt{2}$ when written in radical form.

SECTION P.4 ANSWERS

Warm Up/Just the Facts

1. $15x^2 - 35x + 10$

$5(3x^2 - 7x + 2) = 5(3x^2) - 5(7x) + 5(2) = 15x^2 - 35x + 10$

2. $18y + 2$

$2(4y + 1) + 10y = 2(4y) + 2(1) + 10y$
$= 8y + 2 + 10y$
$= 18y + 2$

3. $-54p^{13}qr^4$

$-54p^{13}qr^4 = -6p^5qr^2(3p^4r)^2 = -6p^5qr^2(3)^2(p^4)^2(r)^2$
$= -6p^5qr^2(9)(p^8)(r^2)$
$= -6(9)p^{5+8}qr^{2+2}$
$= -54p^{13}qr^4$

4. monomial

5. exponents

6. difference; monomials (or terms)

7. 2; 3

8. quadratic

9. degree; leading coefficient

10. multiplying; binomials

Essential Skills/Extensions

1. $k^2 - 5k + 12$; leading coefficient: 1; quadratic trinomial

3. $-5m^5 - 6m^3 + 3m^2 + 16m$; leading coefficient: -5; quintic polynomial

5. $b^4 + 4b^3 + 2b^2 - b$; leading coefficient: 1; quartic polynomial

7. $-6x^3 + x + 6$

9. $4y^3 - 3y^2 - 7y + 1$

11. $7m^3 + 5m^2 - 12m + 6$

13. $-5x^2 + 38x - 48$

15. $6a^3 - 15a^2 + 8a - 20$

17. $-7m^4 - 19m^2 + 6$

19. $3x^4 - 8x^3 + 11x^2 - 7x + 1$

21. $2x^4 + x^3 + 5x^2 - 13x + 5$

23. $36y^6 - 24y^4z - 24y^3z^2 + 4y^2z^2 + 8yz^3 + 4z^4$

25. $9x^2 + 42x + 49$

27. $125a^6 + 150a^4bc + 60a^2b^2c^2 + 8b^3c^3$

29. $4x^2 - 25$

31. $2\sqrt{2}y^3 - 42y^2z^3 + 147\sqrt{2}yz^6 - 343z^9$

33. $81n^4 - n^2$

35. $9b^4 - 19b^2 + 1$

37. $64r^6 - 48r^5 + 108r^4 - 49r^3 + 54r^2 - 12r + 8$

39. $(3x - 1)(2x - 10)$, $(3x - 1)(2x + 10)$, $(3x - 5)(2x - 2)$, $(6x - 5)(x - 2)$, $(6x - 5)(x + 2)$, $(6x + 10)(x - 1)$ (possible answers)

41. $(3x + 10)(3x - 10)$ (possible answer)

43. $(5x^2 + 1)(4x + 1)$, $(4x^2 + 1)(5x + 1)$, $(2x^2 + 1)(10x + 1)$, $(10x^2 + 1)(2x + 1)$, $(20x^2 + 1)(x + 1)$, $(x^2 + 1)(20x + 1)$ (possible answers)

45. $(3x + 1)(x + 10) - (x + 2)^2 = 2x^2 + 27x + 6$

SECTION P.5 ANSWERS

Warm Up/Just the Facts

1. $16m^4 + 2m^3 - 8m^2$

$2m^2(8m^2 + m - 4) = 2m^2(8m^2) + 2m^2(m) - 2m^2(4)$
$= 16m^4 + 2m^3 - 8m^2$

2. $b^2 + 11b + 18$

$(b + 2)(b + 9) = b^2 + 9b + 2b + 18 = b^2 + 11b + 18$

3. $4p^2 - 25$

$(2p + 5)(2p - 5) = 4p^2 - 10p + 10p - 25 = 4p^2 - 25$

4. product

5. xy

6. $6mn$

7. $5y$

8. multiplying

9. $(x - y)$

10. difference

Essential Skills/Extensions

1. $2x^3y^2(y^6 + 3x + 5x^2y^8)$

3. $(2x + 5y)(3x^2 + 7y^2)$

5. $7b(c + 4)(3b^2 + 6b - 2)$

7. $2a(b + 5)(4a^2 + a - 11)$

9. $(2x + 3y)(5x + y)$

11. $4(a + 6)(a + 2b)$

13. $5(x - 3)(x - 3y)$

15. $(k + 12)(k + 2)$

17. $(b + 15)(b - 2)$

19. $(a - 6)(a + 1)$

21. $(3h + 1)(h + 6)$

23. $(3x - 1)(2x - 3)$

25. $(b + 3)(3b - 2)$

27. $(2x + y)(7x + 4y)$

29. $(3p^2 - 2q)(p^2 + 2q)$

31. $(5w^3 - 3x)(w^3 + 3x)$

33. $4(c - 5)(2c - 3)$

35. $3(5m - 2)(4m + 5)$

37. $4(5x - 2)(4x - 5)$

39. $(n + 10)^2$

41. $(1 - 5z^2)^2$ or $(5z^2 - 1)^2$

43. $(7x - 5y)^2$

45. $(3x + 7)(3x - 7)$

47. not factorable

49. $4(6x + 5y)(6x - 5y)$

51. $(3p + 2)(9p^2 - 6p + 4)$

53. $(u^2 - 2)(u^4 + 2u^2 + 4)$

55. $(7 - 4y)(49 + 28y + 16y^2)$

57. $(q^3 + r^2)(q^6 - q^3r^2 + r^4)$

59. $((x + 2y)^2 - 2)((x + 2y)^4 + 2(x + 2y)^2 + 4)$

61. $((m + n)^3 - 3)((m + n)^6 + 3(m + n)^3 + 9)$

63. $\pi r^2 h\left(1 + \dfrac{4}{3}rh + \dfrac{1}{3}h^2\right)$

65. $-7n(3p - z^2)(4p + z)$

67. $(10y^n + 3)(2y^n + 1)$

69. $(x + a)^2 - (y - b)^2$

71. $(8(x - 5y) + 3z)(64(x - 5y)^2 - 24z(x - 5y) + 9z^2)$

73. $(m^4 + 3)(2 - a)$

75. c can be any perfect square.

SECTION P.6 ANSWERS

Warm Up/Just the Facts

1. 3/5

$$\frac{24}{40} = \frac{\cancel{8} \cdot 3}{\cancel{8} \cdot 5} = \frac{3}{5}$$

2. 3/25

$$\frac{9}{10} \div \frac{15}{2} = \frac{9}{10} \cdot \frac{2}{15} = \frac{9 \cdot 2}{10 \cdot 15} = \frac{\cancel{3} \cdot 3 \cdot \cancel{2}}{\cancel{2} \cdot 5 \cdot \cancel{3} \cdot 5} = \frac{3}{25}$$

3. 9/8

$$\frac{5}{8} + \left(\frac{2}{3} - \frac{1}{6}\right) = \frac{5}{8} + \left(\frac{4}{6} - \frac{1}{6}\right) = \frac{5}{8} + \frac{3}{6} = \frac{5}{8} + \frac{1}{2} = \frac{5}{8} + \frac{4}{8} = \frac{9}{8}$$

4. polynomials; rational expressions

5. allowable

6. all real numbers

7. 3; domain

8. common factors

9. $x + 1$

10. $x^6(x + 1)^2(x + 2)$

Essential Skills/Extensions

1. $(-\infty, \infty)$

3. $\{x \mid x \neq 0 \text{ and } x \neq -3/4\}$

5. $\{x \mid x \neq 2 \text{ and } x \neq 3\}$

7. $\dfrac{x + 3}{x - 1}$, $x \neq 4$ and $x \neq 1$

9. $\dfrac{a + 5}{a + 3}$, $a \neq 6$ and $a \neq -3$

11. $\dfrac{4}{x + 8}$, $x \neq 5$ and $x \neq -8$

13. $\dfrac{2x}{x-3}$, $x \neq 3$ and $x \neq -3$

15. $\dfrac{5a+10}{a+8}$, $a \neq 2$ and $a \neq -8$

17. $\dfrac{b-3}{6b}$, $b \neq 0$ and $b \neq -6$

19. $\dfrac{-x-1}{x-2}$, $x \neq 2$ and $x \neq 1$

21. $\dfrac{-x}{2x+5}$, $x \neq 5/2$ and $x \neq -5/2$

23. $\dfrac{-a-6}{a+5}$, $a \neq 6$ and $a \neq -5$

25. $\dfrac{15x-10}{2}$

27. $\dfrac{4}{3x}$

29. $\dfrac{8z+8}{z^2+1}$

31. $\dfrac{-x-6}{16}$

33. $\dfrac{20b^2-12b}{-2b^2-9b+5}$

35. $\dfrac{2k^2-2k}{-4k^2-17k+15}$

37. $\dfrac{3x+20}{10x^2+5x}$

39. $\dfrac{2x-1}{x^2-x-2}$

41. $\dfrac{-2x-3}{x^2+2x+1}$

43. $\dfrac{x^2+13x-16}{3x^2-3x}$

45. $\dfrac{-a^2+4a+2}{a^3}$

47. $\dfrac{7m^2-2m-4}{2m^2+3m}$

49. $3/x$

51. -4

53. $18/13$

55. $\dfrac{n}{n^2-2}$

57. $\dfrac{1}{x-3}$

59. $\dfrac{3x}{-x+4}$

61. $\dfrac{3x^2-5x+2}{15x-20}$; $\{x|\ x \neq -1$ and $x \neq 4/3\}$

63. $\dfrac{1-3y}{2y^2-y-3}$; $\{x|\ x \neq -1$ and $x \neq 3/2\}$

65. $\dfrac{5x+3}{3x+2}$

67. $\dfrac{2b\sqrt{y^2-b^2}}{y^2-b^2}$

69. $\dfrac{m^2-4m-13}{m^2-7m-9}$

71. perimeter: $\dfrac{16w+28}{15}$; area: $\dfrac{w^2+2w-8}{15}$

SECTION P.7 ANSWERS

Warm Up/Just the Facts

1. $-5x-5$

    $10 - 5(x + 3) = 10 - 5x - 15$ *Distribute.*

                $= -5x - 5$ *Combine like terms.*

2. $17m + 7$

    $8m + 11 - (4 - 2m) + 7m$

        $= 8m + 11 - 4 + 2m + 7m$ *Distribute.*

        $= 17m + 7$ *Combine like terms.*

3. $8\sqrt{5}$

    $\sqrt{125} + \sqrt{45}$

    $= \sqrt{25 \cdot 5} + \sqrt{9 \cdot 5}$

    $= 5\sqrt{5} + 3\sqrt{5}$ *Simplify the radicals.*

    $= 8\sqrt{5}$ *Combine like terms.*

4. addition; division

5. LCM

6. extraneous

7. Completing the square; Quadratic Formula

8. square roots

9. Complex numbers

10. negative

Essential Skills/Extensions

1. no solution

3. $-10/11$

5. −3

7. 4/5

9. 1/2

11. 7/4

13. −36/13

15. 25/28

17. −20

19. 31/3

21. −5

23. −7/10

25. 11

27. −9

29. 11

31. −7, 5

33. 0, 5

35. 1, 9

37. −7/2, 3

39. −5/2, 5/4

41. −5, 7/2

43. $3\sqrt{3} + 4i\sqrt{3}$

45. $-4\sqrt{7} - 3i\sqrt{5}$

47. $\sqrt{2} + 3i\sqrt{11}$

49. $-3 \pm 3\sqrt{3}$

51. $-4 \pm 3\sqrt{5}$

53. $-3 \pm 5i\sqrt{7}$

55. $-6 \pm 2\sqrt{11}$

57. $\dfrac{-42 \pm 6\sqrt{7}}{7}$

59. $-3 \pm \dfrac{3i}{2}$

61. −1, −1/11

63. $\dfrac{-3 \pm \sqrt{17}}{6}$

65. $\dfrac{3 \pm i\sqrt{23}}{8}$

67. 14 in. × 6 in.

69. 16 m × 7 m

71. $P = 16, 32$

73. $s = 2.5, 5$

75. yes

77. $413.10, $648, $52.20

79. 25%

81. $109.41

83. The first piece is 60 m, the second piece is 64 m, and the third piece is 48 m.

85. 4.4

87. 80 mi/h

89. Yes. The student should have subtracted $32x$ from both sides to make the right side of the equation equal to 0. Factoring out an x shows that there are two solutions: $x = 0$ and $x = -4$.

91. $x^2 - 4x + 1 = 0$ (possible answer)

SECTION P.8 ANSWERS

Warm Up/Just the Facts

1. −17

   $-|8 - 3(-5 + 2)| = -|8 - 3(-3)| = -|8 + 9| = -|17| = -17$

2. 37/10

   $\dfrac{3(1) + 4}{1 + 1} + \dfrac{1}{5} = \dfrac{7}{2} + \dfrac{1}{5} = \dfrac{35 + 2}{10} = \dfrac{37}{10}$

3. $(2x + 1)(3x - 4)$

4. polynomial

5. squared

6. radical

7. extraneous

8. rational; denominator of the rational exponent

9. absolute value; $A = -B$

10. multiplying the equation by a common denominator

Essential Skills/Extensions

1. −1/9, 0
3. −7, 3, 0
5. −4, −2, 0
7. −3, −1/3, 3
9. −5, 2/3, 5
11. −5, 3/4, 5
13. −6
15. 13/5
17. 1/2
19. 4
21. 12
23. 10, 46
25. 3/4
27. 1
29. −1/2
31. 4
33. 2
35. −8

37. −2
39. −1/3, 1/3
41. −2/5, 2/5
43. 1
45. 4, 11
47. −1, 254
49. no solution
51. −6, 1
53. 8/5, 4
55. −5/2, 1/2
57. −20/3, −16/3
59. −37, 27
61. 1, 2, $\frac{1}{2}\left(5-\sqrt{5}\right)$
63. 1/4, −3
65. −2/5 , 3/2
67. $y = -2 \pm \sqrt{3x-5}$
69. $p = 0, p = c/a$
71. 1 mi/h

SECTION P.9 ANSWERS

Warm Up/Just the Facts

1. $(5, \infty)$
2. $(-\infty, 0) \cup (0, \infty)$
3. $[-2, 70]$
4. inequality; multiplied, divided; negative
5. $x \geq y$
6. $x \leq y$
7. compound inequality
8. and; or
9. <, >
10. ≤, ≥

Essential Skills/Extensions

1. $(-\infty, -6]$
3. $(-1/7, \infty)$
5. $[1, \infty)$
7. $(-\infty, 2] \cup [7, \infty)$
9. $(-\infty, \infty)$
11. $(-\infty, -5) \cup [3, \infty)$
13. $[2, 5]$
15. $(6, 12]$
17. $(-7, -4]$
19. $(-\infty, -1) \cup (4, \infty)$
21. $(-6, -5)$
23. $[-5, -3]$
25. $(2, 6)$

27. $(-\infty, -8] \cup [-4, \infty)$

29. $(-\infty, 2) \cup (5, \infty)$

31. $(-\infty, 4/3] \cup [4, \infty)$

33. $(-\infty, \infty)$

35. $[-4/3, 6]$

37. $(2/3, 4)$

39. $[-8, 1/5]$

41. $(-\infty, -5/2] \cup [4/3, \infty)$

43. $(-\infty, 3/4] \cup [4, \infty)$

45. $(-\infty, -9/2] \cup [3, \infty)$

47. $(-\infty, 3/4] \cup [4, \infty)$

49. $(-\infty, -3)$

51. $(-\infty, 2]$

53. $(8, \infty)$

55. $(-\infty, -1] \cup (7/2, \infty)$

57. $[-3, 5/2)$

59. $(-\infty, -7/3) \cup (4/5, \infty)$

61. $(1, 8/3)$

63. $(-5, -2] \cup [2, \infty)$

65. $(-\infty, -2) \cup [5/7, \infty)$

67. $(-\infty, -11) \cup (1, \infty)$

69. $\left(-3, 1-\sqrt{10}\right) \cup \left(3, 1+\sqrt{10}\right)$

71. $\left(0, \dfrac{3+\sqrt{21}}{2}\right)$

73. 18 lawns

75. 1800 boxes

CHAPTER P REVIEW ANSWERS

1. -96

2. $(-10, -7]$

3. $x \geq -1$

4.

5. -2

6. $-45a^{10}b^3c$

7. $\dfrac{1}{4g}$

8. $9/128$

9. 4.7×10^{-6}

10. 2.56×10^6

11. $12\sqrt{2} - \sqrt{15}$

12. $\dfrac{5\sqrt{6} - 35}{43}$

13. $16/9$

14. $2bcd^5\sqrt{3bd}$

15. $\dfrac{5xz^3\sqrt{xy}}{y}$

16. $-5x^3 + 10x^2 - 21x - 6$; leading coefficient: -5; cubic polynomial

17. $6x^2 + x - 15$; leading coefficient: 6; quadratic trinomial

18. $x^3 - x^2 - 21x + 5$; leading coefficient: 1; cubic polynomial

19. $c^4 - 4d^2$

20. $216x^3 - 540x^2y + 450xy^2 - 125y^3$

21. $2(a-1)(3a+5)$

22. $(5n^3 - 1)(5n^3 + 1)$

23. $(3x - 2y)(x^2 + 4)$

24. $(2cd^4 + 1)(4c^2d^8 - 2cd^4 + 1)$

25. $4(z-1)^2(z+1)(z^2 + z + 1)$

26. $x + 5, x \neq 7$

27. $\dfrac{x^2 - 3x + 9}{x - 4}, x \neq -3, 4$

28. $\dfrac{2k - 2k^2}{4k^2 + 17k - 15}$

29. $-\dfrac{2}{x^2 + 2x - 3}$

30. $\dfrac{5}{-6x + 12}$

31. $2/3$

32. 4

33. 0

34. 4/7

35. 7/2, −5/4

36. $3 \pm \sqrt{11}$

37. $\dfrac{\sqrt{7} \pm i\sqrt{65}}{12}$

38. 130 mi

39. −19/23, 37/7

40. no real solution

41. 3

42. $-1, \pm\dfrac{\sqrt{2}}{2}$

43. [−21, 5)

44. $\left(-\infty, -\dfrac{23}{3}\right] \cup \left[\dfrac{25}{3}, \infty\right)$

45. $\left[-\dfrac{2}{3}, 3\right]$

46. $\left(\dfrac{1}{5}, \dfrac{4}{3}\right]$

SECTION 1.1 ANSWERS

Warm Up/Just the Facts

1. $\sqrt{113}$

2. $(-1, -3)$

3. $(x - 2)^2$

4. axes; four; origin

5. I; II; III

6. distance; (x_1, y_1), (x_2, y_2)

7. midpoint; A, B

8. collinear

9. y; x; 0; x; y

10. circle; $(0, 0)$; 10

Essential Skills/Extensions

1. quadrant I

3. on the y-axis

5. quadrant IV

7.

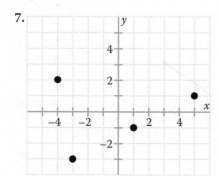

9. 9.43

11. 25.55

13. 5.83

15. $(-1, 13/2)$

17. $(1, -13/2)$

19. $(3/40, 1/16)$

21. $(-10, 1)$

23. $(-13, -7)$

25. $(-10, -11.5)$

27. not collinear

29. collinear

31. isosceles triangle

33. scalene triangle

35. equilateral triangle

37. straight line

39.

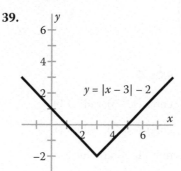

$y = |x - 3| - 2$

41.

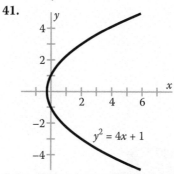

$y^2 = 4x + 1$

43.

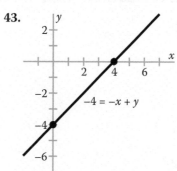

$-4 = -x + y$

45.

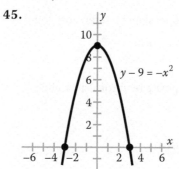

$y - 9 = -x^2$

47. $x^2 + y^2 = 49$

49. $(x + 4)^2 + (y + 3)^2 = 36$

51. $(x + 7)^2 + (y - 2)^2 = 1/4$

53. center $(0, -4)$; radius 5

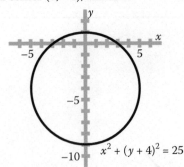

$x^2 + (y + 4)^2 = 25$

55. $(x - 1)^2 + (y + 5)^2 = 196$; center $(1, -5)$; radius 14

57. $(x + 6)^2 + (y - 7)^2 = 289$; center $(-6, 7)$; radius 17

59. $(x - 4)^2 + (y + 8)^2 = 64$; center $(4, -8)$; radius 8

61. $(x + 1)^2 + (y - 5)^2 = 17$

63. $(x - 3)^2 + (y - 2)^2 = 89$

65. $(x - 2)^2 + (y - 1)^2 = 34$

67. with respect to the y-axis

69. with respect to the y-axis

71.

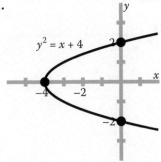

$y^2 = x + 4$

73. $(x + 3\sqrt{2})^2 + (y + 2\sqrt{2})^2 = 28$

75. true

77. $m = 0$; n can be any real number

79. false

81. $(x - 1)^2 + (y + 2)^2 = 6$

SECTION 1.2 ANSWERS

Warm Up/Just the Facts

1. $\dfrac{-4 - 6}{7 - (-1)} = \dfrac{-10}{8} = \dfrac{-5}{4}$

2. $y = -13x + 26$

3. $-3/2$

4. slope; vertical; horizontal

5. $m = \dfrac{y_2 - y_1}{x_2 - x_1}$; (x_1, y_1), (x_2, y_2)

6. slope-intercept; point-slope; slope; y-intercept; point

7. undefined; 0; horizontal; vertical

8. $Ax + By = C$

9. same; perpendicular; opposite reciprocals; parallel; $\perp$

10. q; (r, p)

Essential Skills/Extensions

1. 8/3

3. -2/3

5. -2/3

7. 0

9.

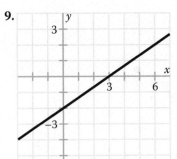

11. $y = 2x + 1$

13. $y = \dfrac{3}{5}x + 4$

15. $y = \dfrac{9}{4}x$

17.

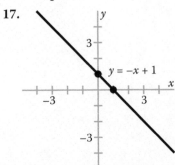

$y = -x + 1$

19. $y = x - 11$

21. $y = \dfrac{1}{2}x + 5$

23. $y = 22x + 29$

25. $y = -\dfrac{11}{4}x + \dfrac{13}{4}$

27. $y = -\dfrac{1}{3}x + \dfrac{17}{3}$

29. $y + 3 = 4(x - 5)$; $y = 4x - 23$

31. $y - 5 = \dfrac{1}{2}(x + 6)$; $y = \dfrac{1}{2}x + 8$

33. $y - 3 = 6(x - 8)$; $y = 6x - 45$

35. $y - 7 = -\dfrac{4}{5}(x - 10)$; $y = -\dfrac{4}{5}x + 15$

37. $y = -5$

39. $y = 9$

41. $x = 2$

43. slope: 3/2; y-intercept at $(0, -4)$

45. slope: $-3/4$; y-intercept at $(0, 3/4)$

47. slope: 2/3; y-intercept at $(0, -5/3)$

49. $y = -x + 13$

51. $y = -5x + 26$

53. $y = \dfrac{3}{4}x - \dfrac{29}{4}$

55. $y = -\dfrac{2}{3}x - \dfrac{5}{3}$

57. $y = -\dfrac{1}{2}x - \dfrac{1}{2}$

59. $y = \dfrac{1}{3}x - 3$

61. $y = 5x - 3$

63. $y = -\dfrac{6}{5}x + \dfrac{41}{5}$

65. $y = 73x$

67. 10 h 58 min

69. The slope is 30, so the ant travels at an average rate of 30 meters per minute.

71. yes

73. $W = 0.05S + 2250$ for $S < 10,000$, $W = 0.1S + 2250$ for $10,000 " S " 14,999$, $W = 0.12S + 2250$ for $15,000 " S " 17,999$; \$4170

75. $y = 39.25x - 74.75$

77. Approximately 279 stores; Yes, because 2009 is within the years that we are assuming linear growth.

79. $R = 23.75t$

81. 2489 h

SECTION 1.3 ANSWERS

Warm Up/Just the Facts

1. 16

2. 10/63

3. 45

4. decreases; increases

5. direct, inverse, joint, combined

6. direct; origin; k

7. $y = \dfrac{k}{x}$; x and k

8. krm^3

9. joint; jointly; m, n; k

10. combined

Essential Skills/Extensions

1. $d = \dfrac{8g}{7}$; 21.875

3. $t = 4s/7$; $t = 12$; $s = 35$

5. $p = 12q/7$; $q = 2.1$

7. $u = -10v/7$; $v = -6.44$; $u = -7$

9. $w = -28r/5$; $w = 56/3$; $r = -5/16$

11. $l = \dfrac{16w}{13}$; 78 cm

13. $l = \dfrac{34w}{25}$; 3.75 ft

15. \$38,080

17. $x = 8.4/y$; 2.1

19. $a = 22.875/b$; $b = 549/8 = 68.625$, $a = 61/40 = 1.525$

21. $y = -\dfrac{9}{x}$; $y = -33/2 = -16.5$; $x = 6$

23. $c = 2.1/d$; $d = -7/3$; $c = 28/5 = 5.6$

25. 39 days

27. 15 days

29. 8.5 ohms

31. 9.4 cd

33. 13.9 cd

35. The frequency is 1/3 the frequency of the original.

37. 20 in.

39. 155 square inches

41. 9 in.

43. $E = \dfrac{53.1}{d^2}$

45. 58 kg

47. 15 kg

49. 1129 ft

51. yes; under 5.2 lb/in^2; B. 243 lb

53. 243 lb

55. It becomes 32 times larger.

57. 11,025 lb; $F = \dfrac{3ws^2}{r}$

SECTION 1.4 ANSWERS

Warm Up/Just the Facts

1. –9

2. 26

3. 50

4. function; y-value

5. vertical line; once; function

6. y; $f(x) = 2x + 1$

7. equal

8. all real numbers

9. verbally (words), algebraically (equation), visually (graph), numerically (table); numerically

10. piecewise; domain; simplify

Essential Skills/Extensions

1. a function

3. a function

5. a function

7. a function

9. not a function

11. 28; –7

13. 2; –10

15. –1; 56

17. $|4m - 31|$

19. $-3r^2 + 32z - 85$

21. $2z^2 + 13z + 25$

23. 25; –1

25. 144; –4

27. 222; 2

29. 8/7

31. –21

33. –3/4; 5

35. –3/5; 2; 0

37. 5/6

39. –3; 7

41. all real numbers

43. –3; 0; 6

45. $p(h) = 9h$

h	0	5	15	35	60	100
$p(h)$	0	45	135	315	540	900

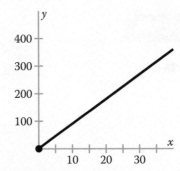

47. 18 ft

49. 71 ft

51. $f(s) = \dfrac{36 - 24s + 4s^2}{\pi}$;

$g(r) = \dfrac{36 - 12\pi r + \pi^2 r^2}{4}$

53. $\{-3, 0, 2, 4\}$

55. $(-\infty, 9]$

57. $\{x \mid x \neq -2, x \neq 12\}$

59. $\{x \mid x \neq -6, x \neq 6\}$

61. $(-\infty, -3] \cup [3, 6) \cup (6, \infty)$

63. $2x + 3 + h$

65. yes

SECTION 1.5 ANSWERS

Warm Up/Just the Facts

1. V-shaped

2. U-shaped

3. linear

4. open

5. $f(x) = [[x]]$; step

6. zeros; x-intercepts

7. >

8. maximum, minimum

9. closed; open

10. strictly increasing, strictly decreasing; V

Essential Skills/Extensions

1. domain: $[-2, 2)$; range: $[-4, 4)$

3. domain: $(-\infty, \infty)$; range: $\{y \mid y = 2\}$

5. domain: $(-\infty, \infty)$; range: $(-\infty, -4]$

7. domain: $(-\infty, \infty)$; range: $(-\infty, \infty)$

9. 8; 1

11. 2; −2

13. 0; 3

15.

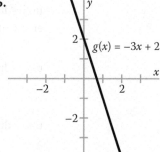

17.

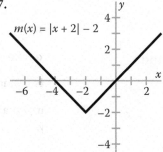

19.

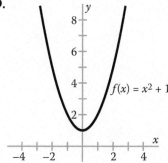

21.

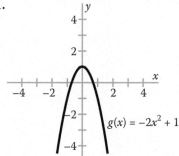

23. $p(x) = \begin{cases} x & \text{if } x < 0 \\ 3 & \text{if } 0 \le x < 2 \\ -x+4 & \text{if } x \ge 2 \end{cases}$

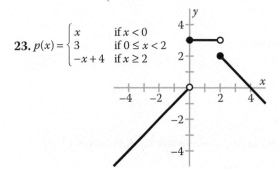

25. $g(x) = \begin{cases} x^2 - 2 & \text{if } x \le 0 \\ -|x| & \text{if } x > 0 \end{cases}$

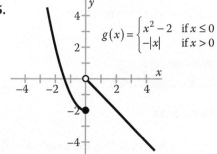

27. $f(m) = \begin{cases} 40 & \text{if } 0 \le m \le 450 \\ 60 & \text{if } 450 < m \le 900 \\ 100 & \text{if } m > 900 \end{cases}$

29. $f(m) = \begin{cases} 25 & \text{if } 0 \le m \le 200 \\ 35 & \text{if } 200 < m \le 500 \\ 60 & \text{if } m > 500 \end{cases}$

31. $f(x) = \begin{cases} 20x & \text{if } 0 < x \le 6 \\ 10x + 60 & \text{if } 6 < x \le 22 \\ 5x + 170 & \text{if } x > 22 \end{cases}$

33. 14

35. 39

37. −22

39. 4

41.

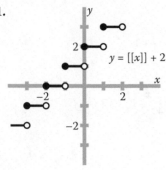

43. −6, −1

45. 0, 5

47. 5/6, −4

49. no real zeros

51. 0, 2, −2

53. 2

55. no real zeros

57. 9, −9

59. 4/5

61. −4/5, 1/3

63. strictly increasing: $(-\infty, 0)$; strictly decreasing: $(0, \infty)$

65. strictly increasing: $(-2, \infty)$

67. strictly decreasing: $(-\infty, 1)$; constant: $(1, \infty)$

69. constant: $(0, 2)$; strictly increasing: $(2, 4)$; strictly decreasing: $(4, \infty)$

71. relative minimum at $(1, -1)$; relative maximum at $(0, 0)$

73. domain: $(-\infty, \infty)$; range: $(-\infty, \infty)$; strictly increasing: $(-\infty, \infty)$

75. domain: $(-\infty, \infty)$; range: $(-2, \infty)$; strictly decreasing: $(-\infty, 3/4)$; strictly increasing: $(3/4, \infty)$

77.

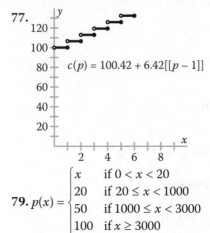

79. $p(x) = \begin{cases} x & \text{if } 0 < x < 20 \\ 20 & \text{if } 20 \leq x < 1000 \\ 50 & \text{if } 1000 \leq x < 3000 \\ 100 & \text{if } x \geq 3000 \end{cases}$

81. 5, $\pm i \dfrac{\sqrt{35}}{7}$; 1 real zero

83.

![graph for problem 83]

SECTION 1.6 ANSWERS

Warm Up/Just the Facts

1. True. $f(-x) = f(x)$, which proves that the graph of $f(x)$ is symmetric with respect to the y-axis.

2. True. The expression inside the radicand must be set greater than or equal to zero to determine the domain, but the domain might be all real numbers (e.g., when the radicand is x^2).

3. False. Zeros are x-intercepts.

4. Translations, reflections; doesn't; nonrigid

5. c units left

6. reflection; x-axis

7. wider

8. $(-2, -4)$

9. x^2; left; down

10. even

Essential Skills/Extensions

1.

![graph of f(x) = x^2 + 1]

3.

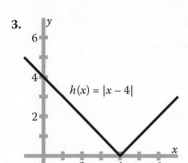

$h(x) = |x - 4|$

5.

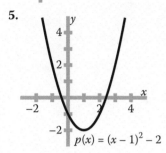

$p(x) = (x - 1)^2 - 2$

7.

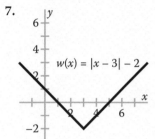

$w(x) = |x - 3| - 2$

9.

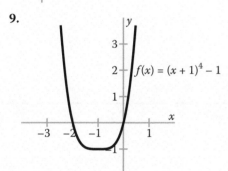

$f(x) = (x + 1)^4 - 1$

11.

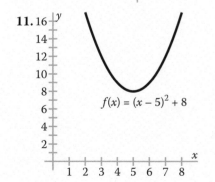

$f(x) = (x - 5)^2 + 8$

13.

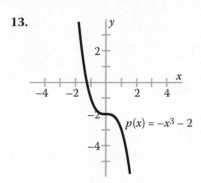

$p(x) = -x^3 - 2$

15.

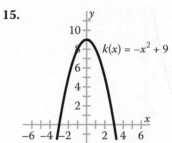

$k(x) = -x^2 + 9$

17.

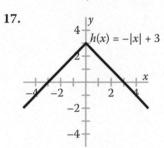

$h(x) = -|x| + 3$

19.

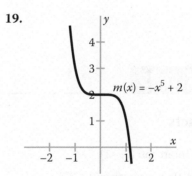

$m(x) = -x^5 + 2$

21.

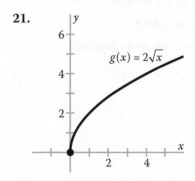

$g(x) = 2\sqrt{x}$

23.

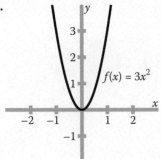

$f(x) = 3x^2$

25.

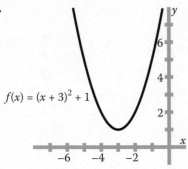

$f(x) = (x + 3)^2 + 1$

27.

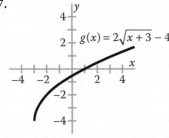

$g(x) = 2\sqrt{x + 3} - 4$

29.

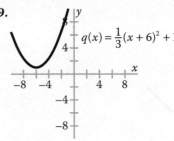

$q(x) = \frac{1}{3}(x + 6)^2 + 1$

31. even

33. even

35. neither

37. odd

39. neither

41. even

43. $h(x) = -|x + 1| + 2$

45. false

SECTION 1.7 ANSWERS

Warm Up/Just the Facts

1. x-intercept: $(1/2, 0)$; y-intercept: $(0, -1)$

2. x-intercepts: $(-3, 0)$, $(3, 0)$; y-intercept: $(0, -27)$

3. x-intercept: $(-1, 0)$; y-intercept: $(0, 1)$

4. addition, subtraction, multiplication, division

5. composition

6. g, f

7. m

8. difference quotient; h

9. Decomposing

10. $h(x)$

Essential Skills/Extensions

1. $-x + 4$

3. $2x^2 + 6$

5. $7x^2 - 11x + 15$

7. $-4x^2 - 2x + 7$

9. $\dfrac{5x - 2}{x^2 - x}$

11. $\dfrac{x^2 + 4x + 2}{x^2 - 25}$

13. $-2x^2 + 15x + 8$

15. $\dfrac{1}{x + 7}$

17. $9x^3 - 24x^2 + 24x - 64$

19. $5x - 10$

21. $\dfrac{-5x^2 - 10x}{x^2 + x - 12}$

23. $\dfrac{2x^2 - 8x + 6}{x + 4}$

25. -112

27. 7

29. -18

31. -10

33. -3

35. $-4a - 2h$

37. $12a + 6h - 4$

39. $3a^2 + 3ah + h^2 - 5$

41. 82

43. -52

45. $8/7$

47. 11

49. 13

51. $5/4$

53. $(g \circ f)(x) = 20x + 20;\ (f \circ g)(x) = 20x - 14$

55. $(g \circ f)(x) = x;\ (f \circ g)(x) = x$

57. $(g \circ f)(x) = 25x^2 - 65x + 42;\ (f \circ g)(x) = 5x^2 - 25x + 26$

59. $(g \circ f)(x) = 4x + 3;\ (f \circ g)(x) = 2\sqrt{x^2 + 3}$

61. $f(x) = -3x - 10$ (possible answer)

63. $f(x) = 2x + 6$ (possible answer)

65. $g(x) = 3x - 1$ (possible answer)

67. $g(x) = x^3$ (possible answer)

69. $p(m) = 0.80m;\ c(m) = m - 10;\ (p \circ c)(m) = 0.80m - 8;$ $(p \circ c)(m)$ represents the cost of the merchandise when the \$10-off coupon is applied first and then the 20% employee discount is applied.

71. -1

73. -6

75. $-1/2$

77. 0

79. 2

79. 31

81. 4

83. A. $t(m) = (f + p)(m)$; B. the total number of employees in July

85. $(h \circ g)(x) = \dfrac{2}{-3x + 3}$, all real numbers except 1;

$(g \circ h)(x) = \dfrac{8x - 46}{x - 5}$, all real numbers except 5

87. $(f - g)(x) = 2x^2$; graph is a vertical stretch of $y = x^2$ by a factor of 2

89. $(fg)(x) = 3x^4$; graph is a vertical stretch of $y = x^4$ by a factor of 3

91. $(g/f)(x) = 1/3$; graph is a horizontal line, $y = 1/3$, hole at $x = 0$

SECTION 1.8 ANSWERS

Warm Up/Just the Facts

1. $(-\infty, \infty)$

2. $[-3, 3]$

3. $(-\infty, -3) \cup (-3, \infty)$

4. $y = x$

5. (y, x)

6. Horizontal Line Test; inverse

7. $\{y \mid y > 9\}$

8. inverse

9. Horizontal Line Test

10. subtraction

Essential Skills/Extensions

1. 3

3. cannot be determined

5. -0.6

7. yes

9. no

11. yes

13. no

15. no

17. yes

19. yes

21. no

23.

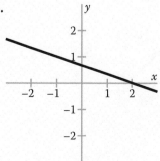

25. $g^{-1}(x) = -x + 3$

27. $p^{-1}(x) = \dfrac{x+1}{6}$

29. $t^{-1}(x) = \dfrac{2x-11}{9}$

31. $g^{-1}(x) = x^2 - 4,\ x \geq 0$

33. $h^{-1}(x) = \dfrac{x^2+1}{2};\ x \geq 0$

35. inverse does not exist

37. $k^{-1}(x) = \dfrac{1}{x} - 6$

39. $m^{-1}(x) = \dfrac{4x-7}{x-2}$

41. $s^{-1}(x) = \dfrac{x^3-7}{2}$

43. $(-\infty, 0], [0, \infty)$ (possible answers)

45. $-9/2$

47. -1

49. $(g^{-1} \circ f^{-1})(x) = \dfrac{x-4}{2}$

51. 2

53. $g^{-1}(x) = \sqrt[3]{x+27}$

CHAPTER 1 REVIEW ANSWERS

1. $AB = 6.3$; $AC = 6.3$; $BC = 12.6$; collinear

2. center $(-2, 5)$; radius 4

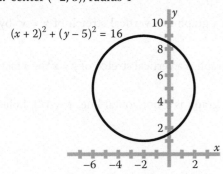

$(x+2)^2 + (y-5)^2 = 16$

3.

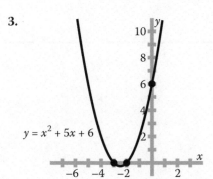

$y = x^2 + 5x + 6$

4. $(x-2)^2 + (y+3)^2 = 16$

5.

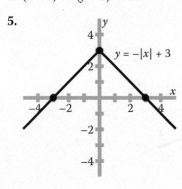

$y = -|x| + 3$

6.

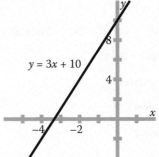

$y = 3x + 10$

7. $y = 22x + 29$

8. slope: $-5/2$; y-intercept: -2

9. $y + 2 = \dfrac{3}{4}(x-7)$

10. $y = -\dfrac{3}{4}x + 1$

11. 8 N/ft^2

12. 156

13. 32.7 h

14. $3/20$ Hz

15. 882.315 N

16. not a function

17. -5; 51; $a^2 - 9a + 15$

18. $A = \dfrac{1}{4}s^2\sqrt{3}$

19. $-3, 1$

20. $(-\infty, -1) \cup (-1, 3) \cup (3, \infty)$

21. domain: $[-2, \infty)$; range: $[0, \infty)$; 1; 2; -2

22.

$$k(x) = \begin{cases} -x-4 & \text{if } x \le -1 \\ 2x+1 & \text{if } -1 < x \le 2 \\ -4 & \text{if } x > 2 \end{cases}$$

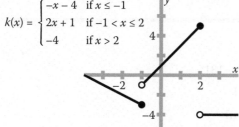

23.

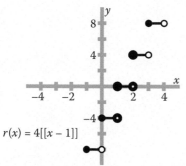

$r(x) = 4[[x-1]]$

24. −6, −2, 6

25. strictly increasing: (−1, 2); strictly decreasing: (−4, −1); constant: (2, 4)

26.

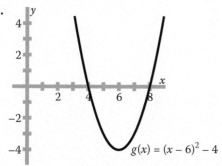

$g(x) = (x-6)^2 - 4$

27.

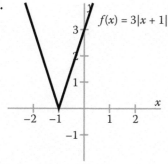

$f(x) = 3|x+1|$

28.

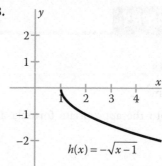

$h(x) = -\sqrt{x-1}$

29. even

30. neither

31. $3x^2 - x - 2$; 68

32. $x^2 - 7x - 8$; $\dfrac{x-8}{x+1}$

33. $-6x - 3h + 5$

34. $4x^2 - 6x - 3$; 15

35. $7x - 4$

36. −5; 6; not possible

37. yes

38. yes

39. does not exist

40. $k^{-1}(x) = \dfrac{x^2 + 45}{9}$, $x \ge 0$

SECTION 2.1 ANSWERS

Warm Up/Just the Facts

1. $C \approx 94.2$ cm, $A \approx 706.9$ cm^2

   Substitute the radius into the appropriate formula and simplify.

$C = 2\pi r$	*Circumference Formula*
$\quad = 2\pi(15)$	*Substitute.*
$\quad \approx 94.2$ cm	*Simplify.*
$A = \pi r^2$	*Area Formula*
$\quad = \pi(15)^2$	*Substitute.*
$\quad \approx 706.9$ cm^2	*Simplify.*

2. II; I; positive *x*-axis; IV; III

3. 158 in. $\cdot \dfrac{1 \text{ ft}}{12 \text{ in.}} = \dfrac{158}{12}$ ft $= 13\dfrac{1}{6}$ ft

4. *x*-axis; vertex; clockwise; positive

5. 180°; right; acute

6. coterminal

7. III; coterminal; $25\pi/18$ rad

8. linear speed

9. 45° or $\pi/4$ rad; 90° or $\pi/2$ rad

10. $\dfrac{180°}{\pi \text{ rad}}$; −600°; II

Essential Skills/Extensions

1.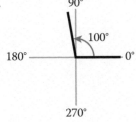

3.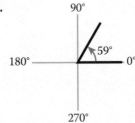

5.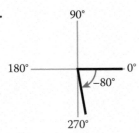

7.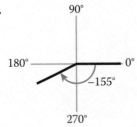

9.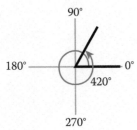

11.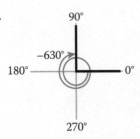

13. 195°

15. 455°, 175°, −181°

17. quadrant I

19. quadrant III

21. quadrant IV

23. quadrant II

25. B, C, E

27. A, D, E

29. B, D, E

31. 600°, −120°

33. 300°, −60°

35. 518°, −202°

37. 190°, −530°

39. 78°, −282°

41. 47°, −313°

43. 83°

45. no complement

47. 105°

49. 36°

51. $\pi/4$ rad

53. $-67\pi/60$ rad

55. $-71\pi/36$ rad

57. 30°

59. −660°

61. 269°

63. 1.75 m

65. 266.9 ft

67. 14.05 in.

69. 9 units

71. 16.6 in.

73. 123.5 m

75. 3 cm/s

77. 3.8 mm/s

79. 7 in./s

81. $\pi/5$ rad/min

83. 15.2 rad/s

85. 155,167.3 rad/h

87. 51 mm^2

89. 887 mm^2

91. 325.2 in^2

93. 11 cm

95. 9.02 in.

97. 29.5 m

99. 4°

101. 6426 mi

103. 90.9 ft/s

105. 12.1 rev/s

107. 1.2 rad. 1.2 rad is approximately 68.754935°, whereas 68° 45′ 13″ is approximately 68.753611°.

109. 3.8 m/s

111. 19.635 ft

113. 10.4 in.

115. 6.6 in./s

SECTION 2.2 ANSWERS

Warm Up/Just the Facts

1. obtuse; acute; right; straight; acute

150° 15′ 22″ is greater than 90° and less than 180°; therefore, the angle is obtuse. 32° is less than 90° and greater than 0°; therefore, the angle is acute. 90° is a right angle. 180° is a straight angle. 47.325° is less than 90° and greater than 0°; therefore, the angle is acute.

2. $10\sqrt{2}$ ft

Since an isosceles right triangle is a special right triangle (45°-45°-90°), the side lengths are a, a, and $a\sqrt{2}$, where a is the length of the leg. Therefore, the length of the hypotenuse is $10\sqrt{2}$ ft.

3. $12\sqrt{3}$ cm

The height divides the equilateral triangle into two 30°-60°-90° triangles, each with side lengths related by a, $a\sqrt{3}$, and $2a$, where $2a$ is the hypotenuse and $a\sqrt{3}$ is the leg that is also the equilateral triangle's height. Since the hypotenuse (i.e., a side of the equilateral triangle) is 24, $2a = 24$ and so $a = 12$. Thus, the height of the equilateral triangle is $12\sqrt{3}$ cm.

4. largest; hypotenuse; right or 90°; legs

5. a, $a\sqrt{3}$, $2a$; a, a, $a\sqrt{2}$

6. tangent, cotangent

7. cosine; 0

8. secant; tangent; sine

9. rationalizing

10. elevation; depression; down

Essential Skills/Extensions

1. $\sin\theta = \dfrac{\sqrt{7}}{4}$, $\cos\theta = \dfrac{3}{4}$, $\tan\theta = \dfrac{\sqrt{7}}{3}$, $\csc\theta = \dfrac{4\sqrt{7}}{7}$, $\sec\theta = \dfrac{4}{3}$, $\cot\theta = \dfrac{3\sqrt{7}}{7}$

3. $\sin\theta = \dfrac{7}{9}$, $\cos\theta = \dfrac{4\sqrt{2}}{9}$, $\tan\theta = \dfrac{7\sqrt{2}}{8}$, $\csc\theta = \dfrac{9}{7}$, $\sec\theta = \dfrac{9\sqrt{2}}{8}$, $\cot\theta = \dfrac{4\sqrt{2}}{7}$

5. $\sin\theta = \dfrac{5\sqrt{89}}{89}$, $\cos\theta = \dfrac{8\sqrt{89}}{89}$, $\tan\theta = \dfrac{5}{8}$, $\csc\theta = \dfrac{\sqrt{89}}{5}$, $\sec\theta = \dfrac{\sqrt{89}}{8}$, $\cot\theta = \dfrac{8}{5}$

7. $\sin\theta = \dfrac{\sqrt{11}}{6}$, $\cos\theta = \dfrac{5}{6}$, $\tan\theta = \dfrac{\sqrt{11}}{5}$

9. $\sin\theta = 4/5$, $\cos\theta = 3/5$, $\tan\theta = 4/3$

11. $\sin\theta = \dfrac{4\sqrt{3}}{7}$, $\cos\theta = \dfrac{1}{7}$, $\tan\theta = 4\sqrt{3}$

13. $\csc\theta = 5/3$, $\sec\theta = 5/4$, $\cot\theta = 4/3$

15. $\csc\theta = \dfrac{13}{9}$, $\sec\theta = \dfrac{13\sqrt{22}}{44}$, $\cot\theta = \dfrac{2\sqrt{22}}{9}$

17. $\csc\theta = \dfrac{\sqrt{137}}{4}$, $\sec\theta = \dfrac{\sqrt{137}}{11}$, $\cot\theta = \dfrac{11}{4}$

19. $\sin 45° = \dfrac{\sqrt{2}}{2}$, $\cos 45° = \dfrac{\sqrt{2}}{2}$, $\tan 45° = 1$, $\csc 45° = \sqrt{2}$, $\sec 45° = \sqrt{2}$, $\cot 45° = 1$

21. $\sin\theta = \dfrac{\sqrt{119}}{12}$, $\tan\theta = \dfrac{\sqrt{119}}{5}$, $\csc\theta = \dfrac{12\sqrt{119}}{119}$, $\sec\theta = \dfrac{12}{5}$, $\cot\theta = \dfrac{5\sqrt{119}}{119}$

23. $\sin\theta = \dfrac{2\sqrt{85}}{85}$, $\tan\theta = \dfrac{2}{9}$, $\csc\theta = \dfrac{\sqrt{85}}{2}$,

   $\sec\theta = \dfrac{\sqrt{85}}{9}$, $\cot\theta = \dfrac{9}{2}$

25. $\sin\theta = \dfrac{\sqrt{102}}{51}$, $\cos\theta = \dfrac{7\sqrt{51}}{51}$, $\tan\theta = \dfrac{\sqrt{2}}{7}$,

   $\csc\theta = \dfrac{\sqrt{102}}{2}$, $\cot\theta = \dfrac{7\sqrt{2}}{2}$

27. $\pi/6$ rad, 30°

29. $\pi/4$ rad, 45°

31. $\pi/3$ rad, 60°

33. $\pi/4$ rad, 45°

35. 0.239

37. −1.019

39. 1.477

41. 8.55

43. 4.66

45. 40.96

47. 8.23

49. 85.82

51. 18.7

53. 1155 ft

55. 82.2 yd

57. 344 ft

59. 57.9555 ft

61. 1.01 mi

63. 56.3 ft

65. 44.55 ft

67. 11,322.5 ft

69. 91.7 ft

71. 210 ft

73. 50/17 in²

75. 1008/53 units²

77. 1853.6 ft

79. 45°

81. 8.1 units

83. no

85. 148,513,292 km

87. 442.2 m; 542.7 m; 1199.7 m

89. 277.9 km

SECTION 2.3 ANSWERS

Warm Up/Just the Facts

1. $3\pi/4$ rad; $4\pi/3$ rad; $\pi/2$ rad; $11\pi/6$ rad

Multiply each degree measure by $\dfrac{\pi \text{ rad}}{180°}$ to convert to radians.

$135° \cdot \dfrac{\pi \text{ rad}}{180°} = \dfrac{135\pi}{180} \text{ rad} = \dfrac{3\pi}{4} \text{ rad}$;

$240° \cdot \dfrac{\pi \text{ rad}}{180°} = \dfrac{240\pi}{180} \text{ rad} = \dfrac{4\pi}{3} \text{ rad}$;

$90° \cdot \dfrac{\pi \text{ rad}}{180°} = \dfrac{90\pi}{180} \text{ rad} = \dfrac{\pi}{2} \text{ rad}$;

$330° \cdot \dfrac{\pi \text{ rad}}{180°} = \dfrac{330\pi}{180} \text{ rad} = \dfrac{11\pi}{6} \text{ rad}$

2. 120°; 225°; 36°; 270°

Multiply each radian measure by $\dfrac{180°}{\pi \text{ rad}}$ to convert to degrees.

$\dfrac{2\pi}{3} \text{ rad} \cdot \dfrac{180°}{\pi \text{ rad}} = \dfrac{360°}{3} = 120°$;

$\dfrac{5\pi}{4} \text{ rad} \cdot \dfrac{180°}{\pi \text{ rad}} = \dfrac{900°}{4} = 225°$;

$\dfrac{\pi}{5} \text{ rad} \cdot \dfrac{180°}{\pi \text{ rad}} = \dfrac{180°}{5} = 36°$;

$\dfrac{3\pi}{2} \text{ rad} \cdot \dfrac{180°}{\pi \text{ rad}} = \dfrac{540°}{2} = 270°$

3. Start at the positive *x*-axis and rotate in a counterclockwise direction.

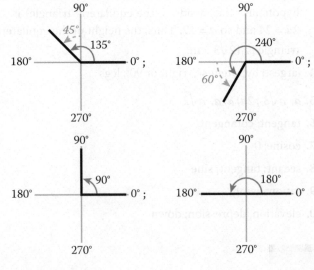

4. Pythagorean

5. cosine; tangent; cosecant; positive; tangent, cotangent

6. II

7. θ'; acute; terminal; *x*-axis

8. $\theta' = 35°$

9. positive; sine, cosecant; "students"

10. fourth

Essential Skills/Extensions

1. $\sin\theta = \dfrac{7\sqrt{65}}{65}$, $\cos\theta = \dfrac{4\sqrt{65}}{65}$, $\tan\theta = \dfrac{7}{4}$,

$\csc\theta = \dfrac{\sqrt{65}}{7}$, $\sec\theta = \dfrac{\sqrt{65}}{4}$, $\cot\theta = \dfrac{4}{7}$

3. $\sin\theta = \dfrac{2\sqrt{5}}{5}$, $\cos\theta = \dfrac{\sqrt{5}}{5}$, $\tan\theta = 2$,

$\csc\theta = \dfrac{\sqrt{5}}{2}$, $\sec\theta = \sqrt{5}$, $\cot\theta = \dfrac{1}{2}$

5. $\sin\theta = \dfrac{5\sqrt{34}}{34}$, $\cos\theta = -\dfrac{3\sqrt{34}}{34}$, $\tan\theta = -\dfrac{5}{3}$,

$\csc\theta = \dfrac{\sqrt{34}}{5}$, $\sec\theta = -\dfrac{\sqrt{34}}{3}$, $\cot\theta = -\dfrac{3}{5}$

7. $\sin\theta = \dfrac{\sqrt{5}}{5}$, $\cos\theta = -\dfrac{2\sqrt{5}}{5}$, $\tan\theta = -\dfrac{1}{2}$,

$\csc\theta = \sqrt{5}$, $\sec\theta = -\dfrac{\sqrt{5}}{2}$, $\cot\theta = -2$

9. $\sin\theta = -\dfrac{2\sqrt{5}}{5}$, $\cos\theta = -\dfrac{\sqrt{5}}{5}$, $\tan\theta = 2$,

$\csc\theta = -\dfrac{\sqrt{5}}{2}$, $\sec\theta = -\sqrt{5}$, $\cot\theta = \dfrac{1}{2}$

11. $\sin\theta = -\dfrac{3\sqrt{10}}{10}$, $\cos\theta = -\dfrac{\sqrt{10}}{10}$, $\tan\theta = 3$,

$\csc\theta = -\dfrac{\sqrt{10}}{3}$, $\sec\theta = -\sqrt{10}$, $\cot\theta = \dfrac{1}{3}$

13. $\sin\theta = -12/13$, $\cos\theta = 5/13$, $\tan\theta = -12/5$, $\csc\theta = -13/12$, $\sec\theta = 13/5$, $\cot\theta = -5/12$

15. $\sin\theta = -\dfrac{5.1\sqrt{37.57}}{37.57}$, $\cos\theta = \dfrac{3.4\sqrt{37.57}}{37.57}$, $\tan\theta = -\dfrac{3}{2}$,

$\csc\theta = -\dfrac{\sqrt{37.57}}{5.1}$, $\sec\theta = \dfrac{\sqrt{37.57}}{3.4}$, $\cot\theta = -\dfrac{2}{3}$

17. $1/2$

19. -1

21. $\sqrt{3}$

23. $-\sqrt{3}$

25. -2

27. $-\dfrac{\sqrt{3}}{2}$

29. $\sec\theta = -13/12$, $\cot\theta = 12/5$

31. $\sin\theta = 7/25$, $\cot\theta = -24/7$

33. $\cos\theta = \dfrac{2\sqrt{11}}{7}$, $\csc\theta = \dfrac{7\sqrt{5}}{5}$

35. $\sin\theta = \dfrac{\sqrt{33}}{9}$, $\tan\theta = -\dfrac{\sqrt{11}}{4}$

37. $\cos\theta = \dfrac{\sqrt{3}}{3}$, $\cot\theta = -\dfrac{\sqrt{2}}{2}$

39. $\cos\theta = \dfrac{3\sqrt{13}}{13}$, $\cot\theta = -\dfrac{3}{2}$

41. $\sec\theta = -\dfrac{\sqrt{74}}{7}$, $\csc\theta = -\dfrac{\sqrt{74}}{5}$

43. $\cos\theta = \dfrac{9\sqrt{97}}{97}$, $\sin\theta = -\dfrac{4\sqrt{97}}{97}$

45. $\tan\theta = \dfrac{\sqrt{159}}{4}$, $\csc\theta = -\dfrac{5\sqrt{1113}}{159}$

47. $\sqrt{3}$

49. $1/2$

51. 0

53. $\dfrac{\sqrt{2}}{2}$

55. $\dfrac{\sqrt{3}}{3}$

57. $\dfrac{\sqrt{3}}{2}$

59. 2

61. $\sqrt{2}$

63. 0

65. $15/4$

67. $5/2$

69. $-\dfrac{1}{\sqrt{1-a^2}}$

71. $x = 2\sqrt{3} + \sqrt{221}$ in., $x' = -2 - \dfrac{4\sqrt{663}}{221}$ in./rad

73. $x = \sqrt{2} + \sqrt{23}$ in., $x' = -\sqrt{2} - \dfrac{2\sqrt{23}}{23}$ in./rad

75. $8\sqrt{2}$ ft/s^2

77. $\pi/6$ rad

79. $\pi/3$ rad

81. A reference angle is a positive acute angle formed by the terminal side of θ and the x-axis. If θ is a quadrantal angle, then the positive angle formed by its terminal side and the x-axis is not acute.

SECTION 2.4 ANSWERS

Warm Up/Just the Facts

1. $\sqrt{3}$; $\dfrac{\sqrt{2}}{2}$; $\dfrac{\sqrt{3}}{2}$; $\dfrac{2\sqrt{3}}{3}$; 1

 From the chart in 5.3.5, $\tan 60° = \sqrt{3}$, $\cos 45° = \dfrac{\sqrt{2}}{2}$,

 $\sin 60° = \dfrac{\sqrt{3}}{2}$, $\sec 30° = \dfrac{2\sqrt{3}}{3}$, and $\cot 45° = 1$.

2. II

3. 5/7

4. $x^2 + y^2 = 1$; $(0, 0)$; 1

5. $\left(\dfrac{\sqrt{2}}{2}, -\dfrac{\sqrt{2}}{2}\right)$; $4\pi/3$; π

6. $[-1, 1]$; -1; 1

7. periodic; period

8. $f(x)$; $-f(x)$; even

9. 1; equal

10. 2π; clockwise, counterclockwise; 2π

Essential Skills/Extensions

1. $\left(-\dfrac{\sqrt{2}}{2}, \dfrac{\sqrt{2}}{2}\right)$

3. $\left(-\dfrac{1}{2}, \dfrac{\sqrt{3}}{2}\right)$

5. $\left(-\dfrac{\sqrt{3}}{2}, \dfrac{1}{2}\right)$

7. $(-1, 0)$

9. $\left(\dfrac{\sqrt{3}}{2}, \dfrac{1}{2}\right)$

11. $\left(-\dfrac{1}{2}, -\dfrac{\sqrt{3}}{2}\right)$

13. $(0, 1)$

15. $\left(\dfrac{\sqrt{2}}{2}, -\dfrac{\sqrt{2}}{2}\right)$

17. $\left(-\dfrac{\sqrt{3}}{2}, -\dfrac{1}{2}\right)$

19. $\sin \dfrac{4\pi}{3} = -\dfrac{\sqrt{3}}{2}$, $\cos \dfrac{4\pi}{3} = -\dfrac{1}{2}$, $\tan \dfrac{4\pi}{3} = \sqrt{3}$,

 $\csc \dfrac{4\pi}{3} = -\dfrac{2\sqrt{3}}{3}$, $\sec \dfrac{4\pi}{3} = -2$, $\cot \dfrac{4\pi}{3} = \dfrac{\sqrt{3}}{3}$

21. $\sin \dfrac{5\pi}{6} = \dfrac{1}{2}$, $\cos \dfrac{5\pi}{6} = -\dfrac{\sqrt{3}}{2}$, $\tan \dfrac{5\pi}{6} = -\dfrac{\sqrt{3}}{3}$,

 $\csc \dfrac{5\pi}{6} = 2$, $\sec \dfrac{5\pi}{6} = -\dfrac{2\sqrt{3}}{3}$, $\cot \dfrac{5\pi}{6} = -\sqrt{3}$

23. $\sin \dfrac{11\pi}{4} = \dfrac{\sqrt{2}}{2}$, $\cos \dfrac{11\pi}{4} = -\dfrac{\sqrt{2}}{2}$, $\tan \dfrac{11\pi}{4} = -1$,

 $\csc \dfrac{11\pi}{4} = \sqrt{2}$, $\sec \dfrac{11\pi}{4} = -\sqrt{2}$, $\cot \dfrac{11\pi}{4} = -1$

25. $\sin \pi = 0$, $\cos \pi = -1$, $\tan \pi = 0$, $\csc \pi$ is undefined, $\sec \pi = -1$, $\cot \pi$ is undefined

27. $\sin \dfrac{2\pi}{3} = \dfrac{\sqrt{3}}{2}$, $\cos \dfrac{2\pi}{3} = -\dfrac{1}{2}$, $\tan \dfrac{2\pi}{3} = -\sqrt{3}$,

 $\csc \dfrac{2\pi}{3} = \dfrac{2\sqrt{3}}{3}$, $\sec \dfrac{2\pi}{3} = -2$, $\cot \dfrac{2\pi}{3} = -\dfrac{\sqrt{3}}{3}$

29. $\sin \dfrac{\pi}{2} = 1$, $\cos \dfrac{\pi}{2} = 0$, $\tan \dfrac{\pi}{2}$ is undefined,

 $\csc \dfrac{\pi}{2} = 1$, $\sec \dfrac{\pi}{2}$ is undefined, $\cot \dfrac{\pi}{2} = 0$

31. $\sin\left(-\dfrac{\pi}{6}\right) = -\dfrac{1}{2}$, $\cos\left(-\dfrac{\pi}{6}\right) = \dfrac{\sqrt{3}}{2}$, $\tan\left(-\dfrac{\pi}{6}\right) = -\dfrac{\sqrt{3}}{3}$,

 $\csc\left(-\dfrac{\pi}{6}\right) = -2$, $\sec\left(-\dfrac{\pi}{6}\right) = \dfrac{2\sqrt{3}}{3}$, $\cot\left(-\dfrac{\pi}{6}\right) = -\sqrt{3}$

33. $\sin\left(-\dfrac{5\pi}{4}\right) = \dfrac{\sqrt{2}}{2}$, $\cos\left(-\dfrac{5\pi}{4}\right) = -\dfrac{\sqrt{2}}{2}$, $\tan\left(-\dfrac{5\pi}{4}\right) = -1$,

 $\csc\left(-\dfrac{5\pi}{4}\right) = \sqrt{2}$, $\sec\left(-\dfrac{5\pi}{4}\right) = -\sqrt{2}$, $\cot\left(-\dfrac{5\pi}{4}\right) = -1$

35. $\sin\left(-\dfrac{2\pi}{3}\right) = -\dfrac{\sqrt{3}}{2}$, $\cos\left(-\dfrac{2\pi}{3}\right) = -\dfrac{1}{2}$, $\tan\left(-\dfrac{2\pi}{3}\right) = \sqrt{3}$,

 $\csc\left(-\dfrac{2\pi}{3}\right) = -\dfrac{2\sqrt{3}}{3}$, $\sec\left(-\dfrac{2\pi}{3}\right) = -2$, $\cot\left(-\dfrac{2\pi}{3}\right) = \dfrac{\sqrt{3}}{3}$

37. $\sin\left(-\dfrac{\pi}{2}\right) = -1$, $\cos\left(-\dfrac{\pi}{2}\right) = 0$, $\tan\left(-\dfrac{\pi}{2}\right)$ is undefined,

 $\csc\left(-\dfrac{\pi}{2}\right) = -1$, $\sec\left(-\dfrac{\pi}{2}\right)$ is undefined, $\cot\left(-\dfrac{\pi}{2}\right) = 0$

39. $\sin\left(-\dfrac{3\pi}{4}\right) = -\dfrac{\sqrt{2}}{2}$, $\cos\left(-\dfrac{3\pi}{4}\right) = -\dfrac{\sqrt{2}}{2}$, $\tan\left(-\dfrac{3\pi}{4}\right) = 1$,

 $\csc\left(-\dfrac{3\pi}{4}\right) = -\sqrt{2}$, $\sec\left(-\dfrac{3\pi}{4}\right) = -\sqrt{2}$, $\cot\left(-\dfrac{3\pi}{4}\right) = 1$

41. $\sin\left(-\dfrac{5\pi}{6}\right) = -\dfrac{1}{2}$, $\cos\left(-\dfrac{5\pi}{6}\right) = -\dfrac{\sqrt{3}}{2}$, $\tan\left(-\dfrac{5\pi}{6}\right) = \dfrac{\sqrt{3}}{3}$,

 $\csc\left(-\dfrac{5\pi}{6}\right) = -2$, $\sec\left(-\dfrac{5\pi}{6}\right) = -\dfrac{2\sqrt{3}}{3}$, $\cot\left(-\dfrac{5\pi}{6}\right) = \sqrt{3}$

43. $\cot\left(-\dfrac{5\pi}{3}\right) = \dfrac{\sqrt{3}}{3}$, $\tan\left(-\dfrac{5\pi}{3}\right) = \sqrt{3}$

45. $\sin\left(-\dfrac{5\pi}{6}\right) = -\dfrac{1}{2}$, $\cos\left(-\dfrac{5\pi}{6}\right) = -\dfrac{\sqrt{3}}{2}$

47. $\csc\left(-\dfrac{3\pi}{4}\right) = -\sqrt{2}$, $\sec\left(-\dfrac{3\pi}{4}\right) = -\sqrt{2}$

49. sin (−*t*) = 4/9, csc (−*t*) = 9/4

51. tan (−*t*) = −3/5, cot (−*t*) = −5/3

53. csc (−*t*) = 5/4, sin (−*t*) = 4/5

55. π/6

57. −3.3

59. 0

61. 2/3; 0; −2/3

63. −11/3; −22/3; −11

65. 2; 0; −2

67. true

69. true

71. false

Warm Up/Just the Facts

1. $\frac{\pi}{2} + \pi n$

The values of *t* where cos *t* = 0 occur at π/2 and 3π/2. Since cosine has a period of 2π, the values occur at regular intervals of 2π. Therefore, the solutions are $\frac{\pi}{2} + 2\pi n$ and $\frac{3\pi}{2} + 2\pi n$ or simply $\frac{\pi}{2} + \pi n$.

2. $\frac{\pi}{2} + 2\pi n$

The value of *t* where sin *t* = 1 occurs at π/2. Since sine has a period of 2π, the values occur at regular intervals of 2π. Therefore, the solutions are $\frac{\pi}{2} + 2\pi n$.

3. π + 2π*n*

The value of *t* where cos *t* = −1 occurs at π. Since cosine has a period of 2π, the values occur at regular intervals of 2π. Therefore, the solutions are π + 2π*n*.

4. 2; amplitude

5. cosine; zeros; maximums

6. [−10, 10]

7. amplitude

8. π/2; *y* = *a* cos *x*

9. $\frac{2\pi}{|b|}$; 8π; 4

10. *c* > 0; *c* < 0

Essential Skills/Extensions

1. 1/2

3. 5

5.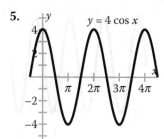

7.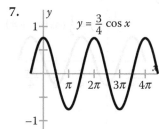

9.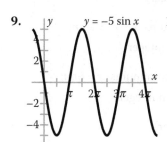
$y = -5 \sin x$

11.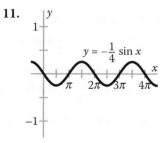
$y = -\frac{1}{4}\sin x$

13. 2

15. 8π/3

17.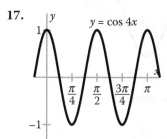
$y = \cos 4x$

19.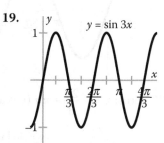
$y = \sin 3x$

21.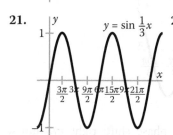
$y = \sin \frac{1}{3}x$

23.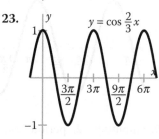
$y = \cos \frac{2}{3}x$

25. period: 2π/3; amplitude: 4

27. period: 8; amplitude: 1/2

29.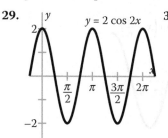
$y = 2 \cos 2x$

31.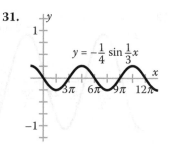
$y = -\frac{1}{4}\sin \frac{1}{3}x$

SECTION 2.6 ANSWERS

Warm Up/Just the Facts

1. $(-\infty, \infty)$; $[-1, 1]$

The domain of $y = \cos x$ is $(-\infty, \infty)$ and the range is $[-1, 1]$.

2. πn

The zeros of $y = \sin x$ occur at $0, \pi, 2\pi, 3\pi, \ldots$, which can be written as πn, where n is an integer.

3. $\frac{\pi}{2} + \pi n$

The tangent function $y = \tan x$ is undefined for $x = \frac{\pi}{2} + \pi n$ because $\tan \frac{\pi}{2} = \frac{y}{x} = \frac{1}{0}$, which is undefined. Since the period of tangent is π, the undefined values occur at intervals of π, so the answer is $\frac{\pi}{2} + \pi n$.

4. $y = \tan x$; vertical; n

5. cosecant; cosine

6. tangent; π; vertical; a; $\pi/|b|$; a

7. $\pi/2$; left, right; x-axis

8. secant; vertical; secant

9. $c > 0$; 2π

10. b-value

Essential Skills/Extensions

1. vertical asymptotes:

$x = \dfrac{\pi}{2} + \pi n$;

zeros: $x = \pi n$

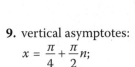

3. vertical asymptotes:

$x = \dfrac{\pi}{2} + \pi n$;

zeros: $x = \pi n$

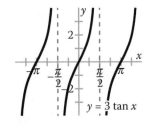

5. vertical asymptotes:

$x = \dfrac{\pi}{6} + \dfrac{\pi}{3} n$;

zeros: $x = \dfrac{\pi}{3} n$

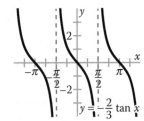

7. vertical asymptotes:

$x = 2\pi + 4\pi n$;

zeros: $x = 4\pi n$

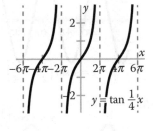

9. vertical asymptotes:

$x = \dfrac{\pi}{4} + \dfrac{\pi}{2} n$;

zeros: $x = \dfrac{\pi}{2} n$

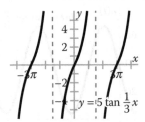

11. vertical asymptotes:

$x = \dfrac{3\pi}{2} + 3\pi n$;

zeros: $x = 3\pi n$

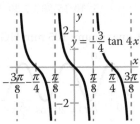

13. vertical asymptotes:

$x = \dfrac{\pi}{8} + \dfrac{\pi}{4} n$;

zeros: $x = \dfrac{\pi}{4} n$

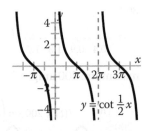

15. vertical asymptotes:

$x = 2\pi n$;

zeros: $x = \pi + 2\pi n$

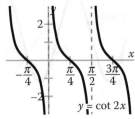

17. vertical asymptotes:

$x = \dfrac{\pi}{2} n$;

zeros: $x = \dfrac{\pi}{4} + \dfrac{\pi}{2} n$

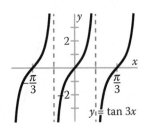

19. vertical asymptotes:

$x = \dfrac{\pi}{4} n$;

zeros: $x = \dfrac{\pi}{8} + \dfrac{\pi}{4} n$

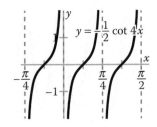

21. vertical asymptotes:

$x = \dfrac{\pi}{3}n;$

zeros: $x = \dfrac{\pi}{6} + \dfrac{\pi}{3}n$

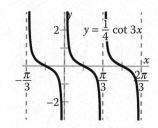

23. vertical asymptotes:
$x = 2\pi n;$
zeros: $x = \pi + 2\pi n$

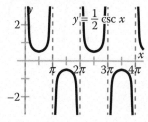

25. vertical asymptotes:
$x = 2\pi n;$
zeros: $x = \pi + 2\pi n$

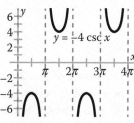

27. vertical asymptotes:
$x = \pi n;$
zeros: none

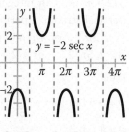

29. vertical asymptotes:
$x = \dfrac{\pi}{2} + \pi n;$
zeros: none

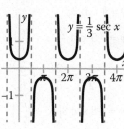

31. vertical asymptotes:
$x = \dfrac{\pi}{2} + \pi n;$
zeros: none

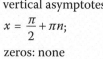

33. 4π

35. 5π

37. vertical asymptotes: $x = \dfrac{\pi}{3}n;$ zeros: none

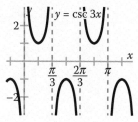

39. vertical asymptotes: $x = \dfrac{\pi}{4} + \dfrac{\pi}{2}n;$ zeros: none

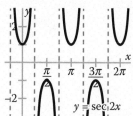

41. vertical asymptotes: $x = \dfrac{3\pi}{2} + 3\pi n;$ zeros: none

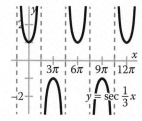

43. vertical asymptotes: $x = \dfrac{4\pi}{3}n;$ zeros: none

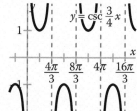

45. vertical asymptotes: $x = \dfrac{\pi}{3}n;$ zeros: none

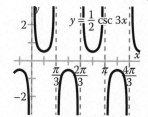

47. vertical asymptotes: $x = \dfrac{\pi}{4} + \dfrac{\pi}{2}n;$ zeros: none

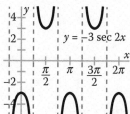

49. vertical asymptotes: $x = 2\pi n;$ zeros: none

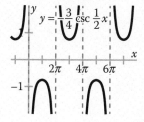

51. vertical asymptotes: $x = \dfrac{5\pi}{6} + \pi n$; zeros: $x = \dfrac{\pi}{3} + \pi n$

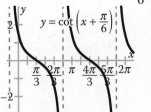

53. vertical asymptotes: $x = \dfrac{\pi}{4} + \pi n$; zeros: $x = \dfrac{3\pi}{4} + \pi n$

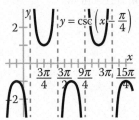

55. vertical asymptotes: $x = \dfrac{\pi}{4} + \pi n$; zeros: none

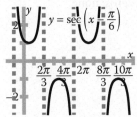

57. vertical asymptotes: $x = \dfrac{2\pi}{3} + \pi n$; zeros: none

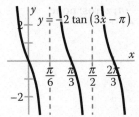

59. vertical asymptotes: $x = \dfrac{\pi}{6} + \dfrac{\pi}{3} n$; zeros: $x = \dfrac{\pi}{3} n$

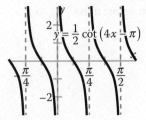

61. vertical asymptotes: $x = \dfrac{\pi}{4} n$; zeros: $x = \dfrac{\pi}{8} + \dfrac{\pi}{4} n$

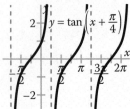

63. vertical asymptotes: $x = \dfrac{\pi}{12} + \dfrac{\pi}{2} n$; zeros: none

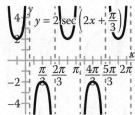

65. vertical asymptotes: $x = \dfrac{\pi}{3} n$; zeros: none

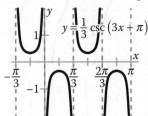

67. A

69. B

71. E

73. A

75. A

77. C

79. The graph of $y = 2 \cot \pi x$ has a vertical stretch of 2, a period of 1, vertical asymptotes at -1, 0, 1, 2, . . . or n (n is an integer), and zeros at $-1/2$, $1/2$, $3/2$, $5/2$, . . . or $1/2 + n$ (n is an integer). The graph of $y = \cot x$ has no vertical stretch, a period of π, vertical asymptotes at $-\pi$, 0, π, 2π, . . . or πn (n is an integer), and zeros at $-\pi/2$, $\pi/2$, $3\pi/2$, $5\pi/2$, . . . or $\pi/2 + \pi n$ (n is an integer).

81. true

83. $y = -5 \tan\left(4x + \dfrac{4\pi}{5}\right)$ or $y = -5 \tan 4\left(x + \dfrac{\pi}{5}\right)$

85. $y = 4 \tan 3x$

87. $y = -5 \cot \dfrac{2}{3}\left(x - \dfrac{\pi}{6}\right)$

89. $y = -\dfrac{1}{2} \csc \dfrac{2}{3}\left(x + \dfrac{\pi}{6}\right)$

91. $y = -8 \sec 8\left(x - \dfrac{2\pi}{5}\right)$

SECTION 2.7 ANSWERS

Warm Up/Just the Facts

1. $f^{-1}(x) = \dfrac{x+1}{3}$

$f(x) = 3x - 1$ is a linear equation, so the graph is a line. The line is not horizontal because the equation contains x. Any nonhorizontal line passes the Horizontal Line Test, so f is a one-to-one function and has an inverse function. To find the inverse function, interchange x and y, then solve for y.

$f(x) = 3x - 1$

$y = 3x - 1$ *Replace $f(x)$ with y.*

$x = 3y - 1$ *Interchange x and y.*

$x + 1 = 3y$ *Add 1 to both sides.*

$\dfrac{x+1}{3} = y$ *Divide both sides by 3.*

$f^{-1}(x) = \dfrac{x+1}{3}$ *Replace y with $f^{-1}(x)$.*

2. No inverse function.

$y = x^2$ is a quadratic function, so the graph is a U-shaped graph and does not pass the Horizontal Line Test. Therefore, it does not have an inverse function.

3. $h^{-1}(x) = \dfrac{x^2 - 1}{2}, x \ge 0$

$h(x) = \sqrt{2x + 1}$ is a square root function, so the graph passes the Horizontal Line Test, is a one-to-one function, and therefore has an inverse function. The domain of h is the interval $[-1/2, \infty)$, so the range of h^{-1} must also be $[-1/2, \infty)$. Furthermore, the range of h is the interval $[0, \infty)$, so the domain of h^{-1} must also be $[0, \infty)$. To find the inverse function of h, replace $h(x)$ with y, interchange x and y, then solve for y.

$h(x) = \sqrt{2x + 1}$

$y = \sqrt{2x + 1}$ *Replace $h(x)$ with y.*

$x = \sqrt{2y + 1}$ *Interchange x and y.*

$x^2 = 2y + 1$ *Square both sides.*

$\dfrac{x^2 - 1}{2} = y$ *Subtract 1 and divide by 2.*

$h^{-1}(x) = \dfrac{x^2 - 1}{2}, x \ge 0$ *Replace y with $h^{-1}(x)$.*

4. horizontal; once

5. reflections; $y = x$

6. six; Horizontal Line Test; inverses

7. $\left[-\dfrac{\pi}{2}, \dfrac{\pi}{2}\right]$; one-to-one; $\left[-\dfrac{\pi}{2}, \dfrac{\pi}{2}\right]$; domain

8. $y = \arccos x$

9. $[0, \pi]$

10. cosecant; 0; cosecant; restricted

Essential Skills/Extensions

1. $\sin^{-1}\dfrac{\sqrt{2}}{2} = \dfrac{\pi}{4}$, $\cos^{-1}\dfrac{\sqrt{2}}{2} = \dfrac{\pi}{4}$, $\tan^{-1}\dfrac{\sqrt{2}}{2}$ cannot be determined without a calculator

3. $\sin^{-1} 0 = 0$, $\cos^{-1} 0 = \pi/2$, $\tan^{-1} 0 = 0$

5. $\sin^{-1}(-1) = -\pi/2$, $\cos^{-1}(-1) = \pi$, $\tan^{-1}(-1) = -\pi/4$

7. $\sin^{-1}\dfrac{\sqrt{3}}{2} = \dfrac{\pi}{3}$, $\cos^{-1}\dfrac{\sqrt{3}}{2} = \dfrac{\pi}{6}$, $\tan^{-1}\dfrac{\sqrt{3}}{2}$ cannot be determined without a calculator

9. 1.362 rad

11. 0.177 rad

13. not possible

15. 0.846 rad

17. 0.658 rad

19. −0.068 rad

21. $-\pi/4$

23. $-\pi/3$

25. $5\pi/6$

27. $\pi/7$

29. $\pi/6$

31. $-\pi/4$

33. $\dfrac{\sqrt{21}}{2}$

35. $\dfrac{\sqrt{22}}{5}$

37. $\dfrac{\sqrt{66}}{22}$

39. $-15/17$

41. $3/5$

43. $\dfrac{5\sqrt{29}}{29}$

45. $-\dfrac{5\sqrt{26}}{26}$

47. $\csc^{-1}\dfrac{2}{\sqrt{3}} = \dfrac{\pi}{3}$, $\sec^{-1}\dfrac{2}{\sqrt{3}} = \dfrac{\pi}{6}$, $\text{arccot}\dfrac{2}{\sqrt{3}}$ cannot be determined without a calculator

49. $\csc^{-1} 2 = \pi/6$, $\sec^{-1} 2 = \pi/3$, $\cot^{-1} 2$ cannot be determined without a calculator

51. $\dfrac{5\sqrt{21}}{21}$

53. $-\dfrac{\sqrt{65}}{4}$

55. 13/5

57. $\left[-\dfrac{1}{2}, \dfrac{1}{2}\right]$

59. $\theta = \arctan \dfrac{10.32}{x}$

61. false

63. $-\dfrac{\sqrt{2}}{2}$

65. $\pi/4$

SECTION 2.8 ANSWERS

Warm Up/Just the Facts

1. N 60° W

Since 150° is in quadrant II, the north and west bearing are used. Subtract 90° from 150° to determine the acute angle θ that is rotated from the north-south line. 150° − 90° = 60°; therefore, 150° as a bearing is N 60° W.

2. N 50° E

Since 40° is in quadrant I, the north and east bearing are used. Subtract 40° from 90° to determine the acute angle θ that is rotated from the north-south line. 90° − 40° = 50°; therefore, 40° as a bearing is N 50° E.

3. S 20° E

Since 290° is in quadrant IV, the south and east bearing are used. Subtract 270° from 290° to determine the acute angle θ that is rotated from the north-south line. 290° − 270° = 20°; therefore, 290° as a bearing is S 20° E.

4. subtracting; 180°

5. subtracting; 90°

6. sine, cosine

7. acute; N, S; north, south

8. equilibrium

9. simple; 9/2; 2/9

10. coefficients; a; ke^{-ct}

Essential Skills/Extensions

1. $A = 55°$, $a \approx 9.8$, $b \approx 6.9$

3. $B = 47°$, $a \approx 6.7$, $c \approx 9.8$

5. $C = 8°$, $b \approx 172.9$, $c \approx 174.6$

7. 133.9 ft

9. 559.8 ft

11. 11.9 ft

13. 44.8 ft

15. 85.1 ft

17. bearing = N 50.12° E, distance ≈ 99.7 NM

19. bearing = S 45.03° E, distance ≈ 131.87 NM

21. bearing = N 44.18° E, distance ≈ 100.51 NM

23. 1/8 cycle per unit of time

25. 3/14 cycle per unit of time

27. 4/17 cycle per unit of time

29. $d = -12 \cos \dfrac{\pi}{8} t$

31. $d = 23 \sin \dfrac{2\pi}{11} t$

33. $d = 22 \sin \dfrac{\pi}{3} t$

35. $d = -26 \cos \dfrac{\pi}{21} t$

37. $d = 0.3 e^{-2t} \cos 523.26 \pi t$

39. $d = 0.38 e^{-2t} \cos 587.33 \pi t$

41. 82.54 ft

43. 0.00006 s

45. −12,285,622.4 mm/s^2

47. −569.3 mm/s

49. $d = 15 \cos 3\pi t, d = -15 \cos 3\pi t, d = 15 \sin 3\pi t, d = -15 \sin 3\pi t$

(possible answers)

51. $c = -\dfrac{\ln\left(\dfrac{d}{k \sin \omega t}\right)}{t}$

53. $d = 2.25 \cos \dfrac{5\pi}{6} t$

CHAPTER 2 REVIEW ANSWERS

1. I; 405°; –315°; 45°; 135°; $\pi/4$

2. II; 520°; –200°; no complement; 20°; $8\pi/9$

3. IV; 355°; –5°; no complement; no supplement; $143\pi/36$

4. IV; 320°; –40°; no complement; no supplement; $-20\pi/9$

5. 492.8 ft^2; 53.3 ft; 165°

6. $\sin\theta = \dfrac{7}{10}$, $\cos\theta = \dfrac{\sqrt{51}}{10}$, $\tan\theta = \dfrac{7\sqrt{51}}{51}$, $\csc\theta = \dfrac{10}{7}$, $\sec\theta = \dfrac{10\sqrt{51}}{51}$, $\cot\theta = \dfrac{\sqrt{51}}{7}$

7. 46.4

8. 6.1

9. 5.6

10. 330.2

11. $\sin\theta = \dfrac{5\sqrt{26}}{26}$, $\cos\theta = -\dfrac{\sqrt{26}}{26}$, $\tan\theta = -5$, $\csc\theta = \dfrac{\sqrt{26}}{5}$, $\sec\theta = -\sqrt{26}$, $\cot\theta = -\dfrac{1}{5}$

12. $\sin\theta = -\dfrac{3\sqrt{58}}{58}$, $\cos\theta = -\dfrac{7\sqrt{58}}{58}$, $\tan\theta = \dfrac{3}{7}$, $\csc\theta = -\dfrac{\sqrt{58}}{3}$, $\sec\theta = -\dfrac{\sqrt{58}}{7}$, $\cot\theta = \dfrac{7}{3}$

13. $\sin(-225°) = \dfrac{\sqrt{2}}{2}$, $\cos(-225°) = -\dfrac{\sqrt{2}}{2}$, $\tan(-225°) = -1$, $\csc(-225°) = \sqrt{2}$, $\sec(-225°) = -\sqrt{2}$, $\cot(-225°) = -1$

14. $\sin\dfrac{7\pi}{3} = \dfrac{\sqrt{3}}{2}$, $\cos\dfrac{7\pi}{3} = \dfrac{1}{2}$, $\tan\dfrac{7\pi}{3} = \sqrt{3}$, $\csc\dfrac{7\pi}{3} = \dfrac{2\sqrt{3}}{3}$, $\sec\dfrac{7\pi}{3} = 2$, $\cot\dfrac{7\pi}{3} = \dfrac{\sqrt{3}}{3}$

15. $\sin\theta = -\dfrac{2\sqrt{29}}{29}$; $\cos\theta = \dfrac{5\sqrt{29}}{29}$

16. $\sin\dfrac{7\pi}{6} = -\dfrac{1}{2}$, $\cos\dfrac{7\pi}{6} = -\dfrac{\sqrt{3}}{2}$, $\tan\dfrac{7\pi}{6} = \dfrac{\sqrt{3}}{3}$, $\csc\dfrac{7\pi}{6} = -2$, $\sec\dfrac{7\pi}{6} = -\dfrac{2\sqrt{3}}{3}$, $\cot\dfrac{7\pi}{6} = \sqrt{3}$

17. $\sin(-\pi) = 0$, $\cos(-\pi) = -1$, $\tan(-\pi) = 0$, $\csc(-\pi)$ is undefined, $\sec(-\pi) = -1$, $\cot(-\pi)$ is undefined

18. $\sin\dfrac{9\pi}{2} = 1$, $\cos\dfrac{9\pi}{2} = 0$, $\tan\dfrac{9\pi}{2}$ is undefined, $\csc\dfrac{9\pi}{2} = 1$, $\sec\dfrac{9\pi}{2}$ is undefined, $\cot\dfrac{9\pi}{2} = 0$

19. $\csc(-t) = 6/5$, $\sin(-t) = 5/6$

20. $\tan t = -7/6$ $\cot t = -6/7$

21. amplitude: 2, period: 2, phase shift: none, vertical shift: 3 units upward, maximums: $x = 2n + 1$, minimums: $x = 2n$, zeros: none (n is an integer)

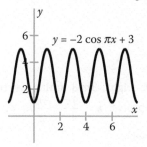

22. amplitude: 1/2, period: 2π, phase shift: left $2\pi/3$ units, vertical shift: 1 unit upward, maximums: $x = 5\pi/6 + 2\pi n$, minimums: $x = 11\pi/6 + 2\pi n$, zeros: none (n is an integer)

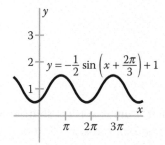

23. amplitude: 2/3, period: $2\pi/3$, phase shift: right $2\pi/3$ units, vertical shift: none, maximums: $x = \dfrac{2\pi}{3}n$, minimums: $x = \dfrac{\pi}{3} + \dfrac{2\pi}{3}n$, zeros: $x = \dfrac{\pi}{6} + \dfrac{\pi}{3}n$ (n is an integer)

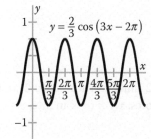

24. amplitude: 3, period: 4, phase shift: none, vertical shift: 1 unit downward, maximums: $x = 1 + 4n$, minimums: $x = 3 + 4n$ (n is an integer)

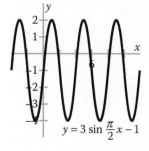

25. maximum: 80 ft

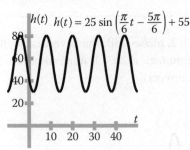

$$h(t) = 25 \sin\left(\frac{\pi}{6}t - \frac{5\pi}{6}\right) + 55$$

26. period: $3\pi/2$; phase shift: right $3\pi/8$ units; vertical shift: none; vertical asymptotes: $x = \frac{9\pi}{8} + \frac{3\pi}{2}n$; zeros: $x = \frac{3\pi}{8} + \frac{3\pi}{2}n$ (n is an integer)

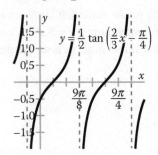

$$y = \frac{1}{2}\tan\left(\frac{2}{3}x - \frac{\pi}{4}\right)$$

27. period: 2π; phase shift: left π units; vertical shift: none; vertical asymptotes: $x = \pi + 2\pi n$; zeros: $x = 2\pi n$ (n is an integer)

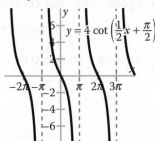

$$y = 4\cot\left(\frac{1}{2}x + \frac{\pi}{2}\right)$$

28. period: 2; phase shift: left 2 units; vertical shift: 2 units downward; vertical asymptotes: $x = n$ (n is an integer)

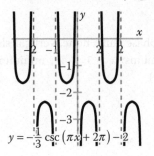

$$y = -\frac{1}{3}\csc(\pi x + 2\pi) - 2$$

29. period: π; phase shift: right $\pi/4$ units; vertical shift: 1 unit upward; vertical asymptotes: $x = \pi/2 + \pi n$ (n is an integer)

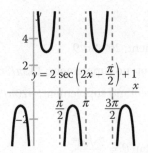

$$y = 2\sec\left(2x - \frac{\pi}{2}\right) + 1$$

30. period: $\pi/2$; phase shift: left π units; vertical shift: 1 unit downward; vertical asymptotes: $x = \frac{\pi}{2}n$ (n is an integer)

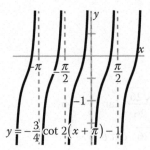

$$y = -\frac{3}{4}\cot 2(x + \pi) - 1$$

31. $\pi/6$

32. 2.65 rad

33. $2\pi/3$

34. $\frac{7\sqrt{55}}{55}$ rad

35. $-4/3$ rad

36. $A = 53.8°$, $b \approx 8.7$, $c \approx 14.7$

37. 71.1°

38. 360.73 ft

39. N 46.7° W

40. $d = 20\sin\frac{4\pi}{3}t$; 2/3

SECTION 3.1 ANSWERS

Warm Up/Just the Facts

1. True. 45° corresponds to the point $\left(\dfrac{\sqrt{2}}{2}, \dfrac{\sqrt{2}}{2}\right)$ on the unit circle, $\cot\theta = x/y$, and $\dfrac{\sqrt{2}}{2} \div \dfrac{\sqrt{2}}{2} = 1$.

2. True. 240° and 120° have the same reference angle of 60°. Since secant is negative in quadrants II and III, the values are the same for sec 240° and sec 120°.

3. False. $\sin 150° = 1/2$ and $2(1/2) \neq -1$.

4. identity

5. even-odd

6. Pythagorean

7. cofunction

8. both; equal; variables

9. $\dfrac{\sin\theta}{\cos\theta}$; $\sin\theta$

10. counterexample

Essential Skills/Extensions

1. $\cos\theta = 12/13$, $\tan\theta = -5/12$, $\csc\theta = -13/5$, $\sec\theta = 13/12$, $\cot\theta = -12/5$

3. $\sin\theta = \dfrac{4\sqrt{2}}{9}$, $\tan\theta = \dfrac{4\sqrt{2}}{7}$, $\csc\theta = \dfrac{9\sqrt{2}}{8}$, $\sec\theta = \dfrac{9}{7}$, $\cot\theta = \dfrac{7\sqrt{2}}{8}$

5. $\cos\theta = -\dfrac{\sqrt{5}}{3}$, $\tan\theta = \dfrac{2\sqrt{5}}{5}$, $\csc\theta = -\dfrac{3}{2}$, $\sec\theta = -\dfrac{3\sqrt{5}}{5}$, $\cot\theta = \dfrac{\sqrt{5}}{2}$

7. $\sin\theta = \dfrac{7\sqrt{65}}{65}$, $\cos\theta = \dfrac{4\sqrt{65}}{65}$, $\csc\theta = \dfrac{\sqrt{65}}{7}$, $\sec\theta = \dfrac{\sqrt{65}}{4}$, $\cot\theta = \dfrac{4}{7}$

9. $\sin\theta = -\dfrac{\sqrt{10}}{10}$, $\cos\theta = \dfrac{3\sqrt{10}}{10}$, $\tan\theta = -\dfrac{1}{3}$, $\csc\theta = -\sqrt{10}$, $\sec\theta = \dfrac{\sqrt{10}}{3}$

11. $\sin\theta = \dfrac{8\sqrt{65}}{65}$, $\cos\theta = -\dfrac{\sqrt{65}}{65}$, $\csc\theta = \dfrac{\sqrt{65}}{8}$, $\sec\theta = -\sqrt{65}$, $\cot\theta = -\dfrac{1}{8}$

13. $\sin\theta = -\dfrac{\sqrt{5}}{3}$, $\cos\theta = -\dfrac{2}{3}$, $\tan\theta = \dfrac{\sqrt{5}}{2}$, $\csc\theta = -\dfrac{3\sqrt{5}}{5}$, $\cot\theta = \dfrac{2\sqrt{5}}{5}$

15. $\sin\theta = -24/25$, $\cos\theta = -7/25$, $\tan\theta = 24/7$, $\sec\theta = -25/7$, $\cot\theta = 7/24$

17. $\sin\theta = -\dfrac{\sqrt{105}}{11}$, $\cos\theta = \dfrac{4}{11}$, $\tan\theta = -\dfrac{\sqrt{105}}{4}$, $\csc\theta = -\dfrac{11\sqrt{105}}{105}$, $\cot\theta = -\dfrac{4\sqrt{105}}{105}$

19. $\sec^3 x$

21. $\cos^2 x$

23. $\cos x$

25. $\sin^2 x$

27. $\cos^2 x$

29. 1

31. $\cot^3\theta$

33. $2\cot x$

35. $2\sec x$

37. 1

39. $\tan^2 x - \sin^2 x$

41. $9\cot^2 x$

43. $\csc^2 x\sec^2 x$

45. $2\sin x\cos x + 1$

47. $\cot^2\theta$

49. 1

51. $\sin^2\theta$

53. $(\tan x + 5)(\tan x + 1)$

55. $(2\cos\theta - 3)(\cos\theta + 4)$

57. $(3\sin t + 7\cos t)^2$

59. $\sin^5 t\cos^2 t$

61. $\cos^4 t$

63. $(\cos x - \sec x)^2 = \cos^2 x - \cos x\sec x - \sec x\cos x + \sec^2 x$
$= \cos^2 x - 2\cos x\sec x + \sec^2 x$
$= 1 - \sin^2 x - 2(1) + \sec^2 x$
$= -\sin^2 x - 1 + \tan^2 x + 1$
$= \tan^2 x - \sin^2 x$

(possible answer)

65. $\dfrac{1-\sin t}{\cos t}+\dfrac{\cos t}{1-\sin t}=\dfrac{1-\sin t}{\cos t}\cdot\dfrac{1-\sin t}{1-\sin t}+\dfrac{\cos t}{1-\sin t}\cdot\dfrac{\cos t}{\cos t}$

$$=\dfrac{1-\sin t-\sin t+\sin^2 t+\cos^2 t}{(\cos t)(1-\sin t)}$$

$$=\dfrac{1-2\sin t+1}{(\cos t)(1-\sin t)}$$

$$=\dfrac{2-2\sin t}{(\cos t)(1-\sin t)}$$

$$=\dfrac{2(1-\sin t)}{(\cos t)(1-\sin t)}$$

$$=\dfrac{2}{\cos t}$$

$$=2\sec t$$

(possible answer)

67. $\dfrac{1+2\cot^2 x+\cot^4 x}{1-\cot^2 x}=\dfrac{(1+\cot^2 x)(1+\cot^2 x)}{1-\cot^2 x}$

$$=\dfrac{(\csc^2 x)(\csc^2 x)}{1-\cot^2 x}$$

$$=\dfrac{\csc^4 x}{1-\cot^2 x}$$

(possible answer)

69. not an identity

71. 125

73. 12

75. $\dfrac{1+\sin x+\cos x}{1-\sin x+\cos x}=\dfrac{1+\sin x+\cos x}{1-\sin x+\cos x}\cdot\dfrac{1+\sin x-\cos x}{1+\sin x-\cos x}$

$$=\dfrac{1+2\sin x+\sin^2 x-\cos^2 x}{1+2\cos x\sin x-\sin^2 x-\cos^2 x}$$

$$=\dfrac{1+2\sin x+\sin^2 x-(1-\sin^2 x)}{1+2\cos x\sin x-(1-\cos^2 x)-\cos^2 x}$$

$$=\dfrac{1+2\sin x+\sin^2 x-1+\sin^2 x}{1+2\cos x\sin x-1+\cos^2 x-\cos^2 x}$$

$$=\dfrac{2\sin x+2\sin^2 x}{2\cos x\sin x}$$

$$=\dfrac{(2\sin x)(1+\sin x)}{2\cos x\sin x}$$

$$=\dfrac{1+\sin x}{\cos x}$$

(possible answer)

77. $\dfrac{\sec^3\theta-\cos^3\theta}{\sec\theta-\cos\theta}=\dfrac{(\sec\theta-\cos\theta)(\sec^2\theta+\sec\theta\cos\theta+\cos^2\theta)}{\sec\theta-\cos\theta}$

$$=\sec^2\theta+\cos^2\theta+1$$

(possible answer)

79. $(2\sin x+3\cos x)^2+(3\sin x-2\cos x)^2=4\sin^2 x+12\cos x\sin x+9\cos^2 x+9\sin^2 x-12\cos x\sin x+4\cos^2 x$

$$=13\sin^2 x+13\cos^2 x$$

$$=13(\sin^2 x+\cos^2 x)$$

$$=13$$

(possible answer)

81. $\tan^2 x-1$

SECTION 3.2 ANSWERS

Warm Up/Just the Facts

1. $x = 1/3$ and $x = -3/2$

$$6x^2 + 7x = 3$$

$6x^2 + 7x - 3 = 0$ *Write the equation in general form.*

$(3x - 1)(2x + 3) = 0$ *Factor.*

$3x - 1 = 0$ or $2x + 3 = 0$ *Set each factor equal to 0.*

$x = 1/3$ $x = -3/2$ *Solve each equation.*

2. $x = 0$ and $x = 5$

$$20x = 4x^2$$

$4x^2 - 20x = 0$ *Write the equation in general form.*

$4x(x - 5) = 0$ *Factor.*

$4x = 0$ or $x - 5 = 0$ *Set each factor equal to 0.*

$x = 0$ $x = 5$ *Solve each equation.*

3. $x = -2/5$ and $x = 3$

$$13x = -6 + 5x^2$$

$5x^2 - 13x - 6 = 0$ *Write the equation in general form.*

$(5x + 2)(x - 3) = 0$ *Factor.*

$5x + 2 = 0$ or $x - 3 = 0$ *Set each factor equal to 0.*

$x = -2/5$ $x = 3$ *Solve each equation.*

4. true

5. periodic

6. add; period

7. inverse

8. no solution

9. $-\tan x$

10. mode

Essential Skills/Extensions

1. $\pi/3 + 2\pi n, 2\pi/3 + 2\pi n$

3. $3\pi/4 + \pi n$

5. $5\pi/6 + \pi n$

7. $2\pi n$

9. $\pi/2 + \pi n$

11. $2\pi/3 + 2\pi n, 4\pi/3 + 2\pi n$

13. $3\pi/4 + \pi n$

15. $\pi/3 + 2\pi n, 2\pi/3 + 2\pi n$

17. $\pi/3 + \pi n, 2\pi/3 + \pi n$

19. $\pi/3 + \pi n, 2\pi/3 + \pi n$

21. $\dfrac{\pi}{4} + \dfrac{\pi}{2}n$

23. $\dfrac{\pi}{4} + \dfrac{\pi}{2}n$

25. 1.181, 5.102

27. 1.042, 2.1

29. $0, \pi$

31. $0, \pi/3, 2\pi/3, \pi, 4\pi/3, 5\pi/3$

33. $0, 3\pi/4, \pi, 7\pi/4$

35. $\pi/6, 5\pi/6, 3\pi/2$

37. no real solution

39. $\pi/3, \pi, 5\pi/3$

41. $\pi/6, 5\pi/6, \pi/2$

43. $\pi/3, \pi, 5\pi/3$

45. $0, \pi/3, 2\pi/3, \pi, 4\pi/3, 5\pi/3$

47. $x = \pi/3$

49. $x = \pi/6, 5\pi/6, 7\pi/6, 11\pi/6$

51. $3\pi/2$

53. $\pi/12, \ 5\pi/12, \ 7\pi/12, \ 11\pi/12, \ 13\pi/12, \ 17\pi/12, \ 19\pi/12,$ $23\pi/12$

55. $\pi/6, \pi/3, 2\pi/3, 5\pi/6, 7\pi/6, 4\pi/3, 5\pi/3, 11\pi/6$

57. $\pi/8, 3\pi/8, 5\pi/8, 7\pi/8, 9\pi/8, 11\pi/8, 13\pi/8, 15\pi/8$

59. $0, \pi/2, \pi, 3\pi/2$

61. $0, 2\pi/3, 4\pi/3$

63. $0, \pi/6, \pi/2, 5\pi/6, \pi, 7\pi/6, 3\pi/2, 11\pi/6$

65. $\pi/4, \pi/3, 2\pi/3, 3\pi/4, 5\pi/4, 4\pi/3, 5\pi/3, 7\pi/4$

67. $\pi/6, \pi/3, 2\pi/3, 5\pi/6, 7\pi/6, 4\pi/3, 5\pi/3, 11\pi/6$

69. 1.179, 5.104

71. 0.666, 2.475

73. 0.196, 1.375, 3.338, 4.516

75. no solution in $[0, 2\pi)$

77. 1.231, 5.052

79. $\pi/2, 3\pi/2$

81. $\pi/2$

83. $\pi/6, 5\pi/6$

85. $0, \pi$

87. no solution

89. 0.214 s

91. 0.117 s

93. 0.681 s

95. $\pi/48$ s

97. 0.004 s

99. $0, 4\pi/3, 8\pi/3, 4\pi, 16\pi/3, 20\pi/3, 8\pi, 28\pi/3$

101. 6.29°

103. $\tan 3x - \sec 3x = \tan 3 \cdot \dfrac{2\pi}{3} - \sec 3 \cdot \dfrac{2\pi}{3}$

$= \tan 2\pi - \sec 2\pi$

$= 0 - 1$

$= -1$

SECTION 3.3 ANSWERS

Warm Up/Just the Facts

1. $\pi/3 + \pi/4$

$7\pi/12 = 4\pi/12 + 3\pi/12 = \pi/3 + \pi/4$

2. $45° + 30°$

$75° = 45° + 30°$

3. $-60° + -45°$

$-105° = -60° + -45°$

4. identity

5. False

6. sum; $\dfrac{\tan\ 60° + \tan\ 45°}{1 - \tan\ 60°\ \tan\ 45°}$

7. sum; $\cos (A + B)$

8. difference; $\sin (A - B)$

9. extraneous

10. difference; $\pi/4$

Essential Skills/Extensions

1. $\sin 120° \cos 45° - \cos 120° \sin 45°$,

$\cos 120° \cos 45° + \sin 120° \sin 45°$, $\dfrac{\tan\ 120° - \tan\ 45°}{1 + \tan\ 120°\ \tan\ 45°}$

(possible answers)

3. $\sin \dfrac{7\pi}{4}\ \cos \dfrac{5\pi}{6} - \cos \dfrac{7\pi}{4}\ \sin \dfrac{5\pi}{6}$,

$\cos \dfrac{7\pi}{4}\ \cos \dfrac{5\pi}{6} + \sin \dfrac{7\pi}{4}\ \sin \dfrac{5\pi}{6}$, $\dfrac{\tan \dfrac{7\pi}{4} - \tan \dfrac{5\pi}{6}}{1 + \tan \dfrac{7\pi}{4}\ \tan \dfrac{5\pi}{6}}$

(possible answers)

5. $\dfrac{-\sqrt{2} - \sqrt{6}}{4}$

7. $\dfrac{-\sqrt{6} + \sqrt{2}}{4}$

9. $\dfrac{-\sqrt{2} - \sqrt{6}}{4}$

11. $\dfrac{\sqrt{6} + \sqrt{2}}{4}$

13. $\dfrac{1 - \sqrt{3}}{1 + \sqrt{3}}$

15. $\dfrac{1 - \sqrt{3}}{1 + \sqrt{3}}$

17. $-\dfrac{\sqrt{2}}{2}$

19. $\sqrt{3}$

21. $-\dfrac{\sqrt{2}}{2}$

23. 1/2

25. $-\sin \theta$

27. $-\tan x$

29. $-\cos x$

31. not possible

33. $\sin \left(\dfrac{\pi}{6} + x \right) = \sin \dfrac{\pi}{6} \cos x + \cos \dfrac{\pi}{6} \sin x$

$= \dfrac{1}{2} \cdot \cos x + \dfrac{\sqrt{3}}{2} \cdot \sin x$

$= \dfrac{1}{2} \left(\cos x + \sqrt{3} \sin x \right)$

(possible answer)

35. $\pi/2$

37. $5\pi/4, 7\pi/4$

39. 16/65

41. 63/65

43. 16/63

45. 4/5

47. 3/5

49. 4/3

51. $\dfrac{-\sqrt{2} - \sqrt{6}}{4}$

53. $\dfrac{1 - \sqrt{3}}{1 + \sqrt{3}}$

55. not possible

SECTION 3.4 ANSWERS

Warm Up/Just the Facts

1. $-6\sin^2 x$

   $3\cos^2 x - 3\sin^2 x - 3 = 3(1 - \sin^2 x) - 3\sin^2 x - 3$

   $= 3 - 3\sin^2 x - 3\sin^2 x - 3 = -6\sin^2 x$

2. -1

   $\tan^2 x - \sec^2 x = \tan^2 x - (1 + \tan^2 x)$

   $= \tan^2 x - 1 - \tan^2 x = -1$

3. 5

   $5\csc^2 x - 5\cot^2 x = 5(1 + \cot^2 x) - 5\cot^2 x$

   $= 5 + 5\cot^2 x - 5\cot^2 x = 5$

4. $2\sin\theta\cos\theta$

5. $\cos 2\theta$

6. $\dfrac{2\tan\theta}{1 - \tan^2\theta}$

7. $\tan^2\theta$

8. $\pm\sqrt{\dfrac{1 - \cos\theta}{2}}$

9. $\cos\theta/2$

10. $\sin^2\theta$

Essential Skills/Extensions

1. $-\sqrt{3}$

3. 0

5. $10\sin 2\theta$

7. $-10\cos 2\theta$

9. $10\tan 2\theta$

11. $\sin 2\theta = 336/625$, $\cos 2\theta = 527/625$, $\tan 2\theta = 336/527$,

    $\csc 2\theta = 625/336$, $\sec 2\theta = 625/527$, $\cot 2\theta = 527/336$

13. $\sin 2\theta = 4/5$, $\cos 2\theta = -3/5$, $\tan 2\theta = -4/3$,

    $\csc 2\theta = 5/4$, $\sec 2\theta = -5/3$, $\cot 2\theta = -3/4$

15. $\sin 2\theta = -24/25$, $\cos 2\theta = -7/25$, $\tan 2\theta = 24/7$,

    $\csc 2\theta = -25/24$, $\sec 2\theta = -25/7$, $\cot 2\theta = 7/24$

17. $\sin 2\theta = -112/113$, $\cos 2\theta = 15/113$, $\tan 2\theta = -112/15$,

    $\csc 2\theta = -113/112$, $\sec 2\theta = 113/15$, $\cot 2\theta = -15/112$

19. $\sin 2\theta = -120/169$, $\cos 2\theta = 119/169$, $\tan 2\theta = -120/119$,

    $\csc 2\theta = -169/120$, $\sec 2\theta = 169/119$, $\cot 2\theta = -119/120$

21. $\pi/4$, $\pi/2$, $3\pi/4$, $5\pi/4$, $3\pi/2$, $7\pi/4$

23. $\pi/2$, $7\pi/6$, $3\pi/2$, $11\pi/6$

25. $7\pi/6$, $11\pi/6$

27. $\pi/6$, $\pi/2$, $5\pi/6$, $7\pi/6$, $3\pi/2$, $11\pi/6$

29. $\dfrac{3 + \cos 4t + 4\cos 2t}{128}$

31. $\cos 2\theta$

33. $-2 - \sqrt{3}$

35. $\dfrac{-\sqrt{6} + \sqrt{2}}{4}$

37. $\sqrt{2} - 1$

39. $\sin\theta/2 = 3/5$, $\cos\theta/2 = 4/5$, $\tan\theta/2 = 3/4$,

    $\csc\theta/2 = 5/3$, $\sec\theta/2 = 5/4$, $\cot\theta/2 = 4/3$

41. $\sin\dfrac{\theta}{2} = \dfrac{\sqrt{5}}{5}$, $\cos\dfrac{\theta}{2} = \dfrac{2\sqrt{5}}{5}$, $\tan\dfrac{\theta}{2} = \dfrac{1}{2}$,

    $\csc\dfrac{\theta}{2} = \sqrt{5}$, $\sec\dfrac{\theta}{2} = \dfrac{\sqrt{5}}{2}$, $\cot\dfrac{\theta}{2} = 2$

43. $\dfrac{5\sqrt{26}}{26}$

45. $\dfrac{-8 + \sqrt{39}}{5}$

47. $\dfrac{1}{2}\sin 27x + \dfrac{1}{2}\sin 13x$

49. $\dfrac{1}{2}\cos 2x + \dfrac{1}{2}\cos 6x$

51. $-2\sin 8x \sin 5x$

53. $2\cos 4x \cos x$

55. $2\sin 3x \cos 2x$

57. $\pi/2$

59. $A = 2r^2\sin 2\theta$

61. $A = \dfrac{c^2\sin 2A}{4}$

63. $\tan\theta \cdot \dfrac{1 - \cos 2\theta}{1 + \cos 2\theta}$

65. $3\pi/2$

67. $\pi/8$, $3\pi/8$, $5\pi/8$, $7\pi/8$, $9\pi/8$, $11\pi/8$, $13\pi/8$, $15\pi/8$

69. $\pi/8$, $3\pi/8$, $5\pi/8$, $7\pi/8$, $9\pi/8$, $11\pi/8$, $13\pi/8$, $15\pi/8$

71. $50\pi - 100\sin 2\theta$

73. 0.84, 2.3, 3.98, 5.44

75. 0, 2, 3.14, 4.28

CHAPTER 3 REVIEW ANSWERS

1. $\sin \theta = -\dfrac{5}{12}$, $\cos \theta = -\dfrac{\sqrt{119}}{12}$, $\tan \theta = \dfrac{5\sqrt{119}}{119}$,

$\sec \theta = -\dfrac{12\sqrt{119}}{119}$, $\cot \theta = \dfrac{\sqrt{119}}{5}$

2. $-\sin x$

3. 1

4. $\dfrac{\cos^2 x + \tan^2 x - 1}{\sin^2 x} = \dfrac{1 - \sin^2 x + \tan^2 x - 1}{\sin^2 x}$

$= \dfrac{\tan^2 x - \sin^2 x}{\sin^2 x}$

$= \dfrac{\tan^2 x}{\sin^2 x} - \dfrac{\sin^2 x}{\sin^2 x}$

$= \sec^2 x - 1$

$= \tan^2 x$

(*possible answer*)

5. $\dfrac{\sec\ x + \csc\ x}{\cot x + \tan x} = \dfrac{\dfrac{1}{\cos x} + \dfrac{1}{\sin x}}{\dfrac{\cos x}{\sin x} + \dfrac{\sin x}{\cos x}}$

$= \dfrac{\dfrac{\sin\ x + \cos\ x}{\cos\ x\ \sin\ x}}{\dfrac{\cos^2 x + \sin^2 x}{\sin\ x\ \cos\ x}}$

$= \dfrac{\sin\ x + \cos\ x}{\cos\ x\ \sin\ x} \cdot \dfrac{\sin\ x\ \cos\ x}{1}$

$= \cos x + \sin\ x$

(*possible answer*)

6. $3\pi/2 + 2\pi n$

7. $\pi/6 + 2\pi n$, $5\pi/6 + 2\pi n$

8. $\pi/3 + \pi n$, $2\pi/3 + \pi n$, $3\pi/4 + \pi n$

9. 2.203, 4.081

10. 0.743, 2.927, 3.884, 6.069

11. $\dfrac{1 + \sqrt{3}}{\sqrt{3} - 1}$

12. $\dfrac{\sqrt{6} - \sqrt{2}}{4}$

13. $-\cos x$

14. $\sin\ (x + y) - \sin\ (x - y)$

$= \sin x \cos y + \cos x \sin y - (\sin x \cos y - \cos x \sin y)$

$= \sin x \cos y + \cos x \sin y - \sin x \cos y + \cos x \sin y$

$= 2 \cos x \sin y$

(*possible answer*)

15. $\dfrac{\sin\ (x + y) - \sin\ (x - y)}{\cos\ (x + y) + \cos\ (x - y)}$

$= \dfrac{\sin x \cos y + \cos x \sin y - \sin x \cos y + \cos x \sin y}{\cos x \cos y - \sin x \sin y + \cos x \cos y + \sin x \sin y}$

$= \dfrac{2 \cos x \sin y}{2 \cos x \cos y}$

$= \dfrac{\sin y}{\cos y}$

$= \tan y$

(*possible answer*)

16. $\sin 2\theta = \dfrac{12\sqrt{10}}{49}$, $\cos 2\theta = \dfrac{31}{49}$, $\tan 2\theta = \dfrac{12\sqrt{10}}{31}$,

$\csc 2\theta = \dfrac{49\sqrt{10}}{120}$, $\sec 2\theta = \dfrac{49}{31}$, $\cot 2\theta = \dfrac{31\sqrt{10}}{120}$,

$\sin \dfrac{\theta}{2} = \sqrt{\dfrac{7 - 2\sqrt{10}}{14}}$, $\cos \dfrac{\theta}{2} = \sqrt{\dfrac{7 + 2\sqrt{10}}{14}}$, $\tan \dfrac{\theta}{2} = \dfrac{7 - 2\sqrt{10}}{3}$,

$\csc \dfrac{\theta}{2} = \sqrt{\dfrac{14}{7 - 2\sqrt{10}}}$, $\sec \dfrac{\theta}{2} = \sqrt{\dfrac{14}{7 + 2\sqrt{10}}}$, $\cot \dfrac{\theta}{2} = \dfrac{3}{7 - 2\sqrt{10}}$

17. $\sin 2\theta = -36/85$, $\cos 2\theta = -77/85$, $\tan 2\theta = 36/77$,

$\csc 2\theta = -85/36$, $\sec 2\theta = -85/77$, $\cot 2\theta = 77/36$,

$\sin \dfrac{\theta}{2} = \sqrt{\dfrac{85 + 2\sqrt{85}}{170}}$, $\cos \dfrac{\theta}{2} = \sqrt{\dfrac{85 - 2\sqrt{85}}{170}}$, $\tan \dfrac{\theta}{2} = \dfrac{2 + \sqrt{85}}{9}$,

$\csc \dfrac{\theta}{2} = \sqrt{\dfrac{170}{85 + 2\sqrt{85}}}$, $\sec \dfrac{\theta}{2} = \sqrt{\dfrac{170}{85 - 2\sqrt{85}}}$, $\cot \dfrac{\theta}{2} = \dfrac{9}{2 + \sqrt{85}}$

18. $\pi/6$, $5\pi/6$, $7\pi/6$, $11\pi/6$

19. $\dfrac{30 \cos\ x + 15 \cos\ 3x + 3 \cos\ 5x}{16}$

20. $2 \sin 5x \sin x$

SECTION 4.1 ANSWERS

Warm Up/Just the Facts

1. 99.92

$\sin 15° = 25.86/c$ *Sine trigonometric function.*

$c = 25.86/\sin 15°$ *Solve for c.*

2. 8.08

$\sin 21° = b/22.55$ *Sine trigonometric function.*

$b = 22.55(\sin 21°)$ *Solve for b.*

3. 53.87°

$\sin \alpha = 73.5/91$ *Sine trigonometric function.*

$\alpha = \sin^{-1} \dfrac{73.5}{91}$ *Solve for α.*

4. oblique

5. $\dfrac{\sin \alpha}{a}, \dfrac{\sin \beta}{b}, \dfrac{\sin \gamma}{c}$

6. ambiguous

7. zero

8. one

9. two

10. $\frac{1}{2}ca \sin \beta$

Essential Skills/Extensions

1. $b \approx 2.87, c \approx 7.78, \beta = 14°$

3. $a \approx 72.92, b \approx 199.58, \beta = 142°$

5. $a \approx 23.98, b \approx 12.87, \alpha = 81°$

7. $a \approx 13.55, b \approx 15, \gamma = 60°$

9. $a \approx 10.87, c \approx 33.55, \beta = 38°$

11. $b \approx 32.78, c \approx 40.15, \alpha = 15°$

13. $a \approx 372, \alpha \approx 44.14°, \beta \approx 13.86°$

15. $c \approx 135.49, \beta \approx 30.55°, \gamma \approx 110.45°$

17. two

19. zero

21. first triangle: $\beta \approx 49.89°, \gamma \approx 95.11°, c \approx 10.42$, second triangle: $\beta \approx 130.11°, \gamma \approx 14.89°, c \approx 2.69$

23. first triangle: $\alpha \approx 57.7°, \beta \approx 97.3°, b \approx 2.35$, second triangle: $\alpha \approx 122.3°, \beta \approx 32.7°, b \approx 1.28$

25. zero triangle: $b > 17.11$, one oblique triangle: $0 \le b \le 11$, two triangles: $11 < b < 17.11$

27. zero triangle: $b > 8\sqrt{2}$, one oblique triangle: $0 \le b \le 8$, two triangles: $8 < b < 8\sqrt{2}$

29. 7377.3 in^2

31. 218.5 in^2

33. 2130.8 in^2

35. 20.2 in^2

37. 35 m

39. 148 ft

41. 14.4 mi

43. 227.45 ft

45. 374.82 ft

47. 12.98 m

49. 0.99 km

51. 22.9

53. angle 1: 109°, angle 2: 71°

SECTION 4.2 ANSWERS

Warm Up/Just the Facts

1. $\gamma = \cos^{-1}\left(-\dfrac{c^2 - a^2 - b^2}{2ab}\right)$

$c^2 = a^2 + b^2 - 2ab \cos \gamma$

$c^2 - a^2 - b^2 = -2ab \cos \gamma$ *Subtract a^2 and b^2.*

$-\dfrac{c^2 - a^2 - b^2}{2ab} = \cos \gamma$ *Divide each side by -2ab.*

$\gamma = \cos^{-1}\left(-\dfrac{c^2 - a^2 - b^2}{2ab}\right)$ *Take the inverse cosine.*

2. α: the smallest angle is opposite the shortest side.

Since side a is the shortest side, α is the smallest angle.

3. β: the largest angle is opposite the longest side.

Since side b is the longest side, β is the largest angle.

4. Cosines

5. $b^2 + c^2 - 2bc \cos \alpha$; $a^2 + c^2 - 2ac \cos \beta$; $a^2 + b^2 - 2ab \cos \gamma$

6. Sines

7. Cosines

8. Sines

9. Heron's

10. $\sqrt{s(s-a)(s-b)(s-c)}$; $\frac{1}{2}(a+b+c)$

Essential Skills/Extensions

1. 92.123°

3. 98.213°

5. 20.742°

7. 43.49°

9. 150°

11. 90.27°

13. 36.1°

15. 42 mi

17. 6.8 mi

19. 3460 m

21. 9.6 in^2

23. 764.9 ft^2

25. 2.9 in^2

27. 3.83 ft

29. 2.9 ft

31. 5.99 in

33. 6.6

35. α: 54.5, β: 44.2, and γ: 81.3

37. 42 cm^2

39. 70.2 m^2

41. 2.9 ft

SECTION 4.3 ANSWERS

Warm Up/Just the Facts

1. $3\sqrt{10}$

$d = \sqrt{(-1-2)^2 + (4-(-5))^2}$ *Substitute the coordinates into the distance formula.*

    $= 3\sqrt{10}$ *Simplify.*

2. $2\sqrt{41}$

$d = \sqrt{(7-(-3))^2 + (-2-6)^2}$ *Substitute the coordinates into the distance formula.*

    $= 2\sqrt{41}$ *Simplify.*

3. 15

$d = \sqrt{(1-(-8))^2 + (9-(-3))^2}$ *Substitute the coordinates into the distance formula.*

    $= 15$ *Simplify.*

4. vector

5. length; Pythagorean

6. angle

7. $\| \bar{v} \|$

8. unit

9. $\bar{v} / \| \bar{v} \|$

10. $r\cos\theta$; $r\sin\theta$

Essential Skills/Extensions

1. $\langle 3, -5 \rangle$

3. $\langle -6, 7 \rangle$

5. $\langle -10, -15 \rangle$

7. $\langle -4, -3 \rangle$

9. $\langle 7, -3 \rangle$

11. $\langle -5, 7 \rangle$

13. 2, 150°

15. $4\sqrt{2}$, 225°

17. 4, 300°

19. $3\sqrt{5}$, 63.43°

21. $\sqrt{65}$, 330.26°

23. $\sqrt{26}$, 168.69°

25. $\langle -4, 10 \rangle$

27. $\langle 41, -6.5 \rangle$

29. $\langle 2.5, 3.75 \rangle$

31.

33.

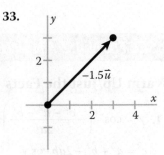

35.

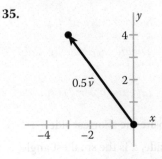

37. $\langle 1, -1 \rangle$

39. $\langle -4.6, -14.6 \rangle$

41.

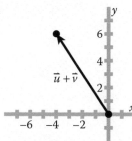

43.

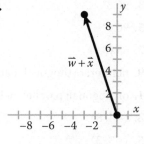

45. $\langle -9.3, 6.3 \rangle$

47. $\langle 3.5, -12 \rangle$

49. $\langle 11.7, 9.8 \rangle$

51.

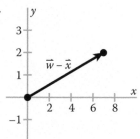

53.

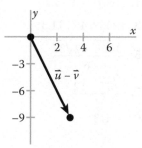

55.

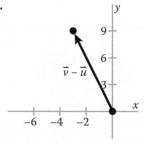

57. $\langle 5\sqrt{3}, 5 \rangle$

59. $\langle 9, 9 \rangle$

61. $\langle -3\sqrt{3}, 3 \rangle$

63. $\langle 3, -3 \rangle$

65. $\langle -5, -5\sqrt{3} \rangle$

67. $\langle -3.6, 2.3 \rangle$

69. $\langle -3.3, -1.8 \rangle$

71. $\langle 1.2, -5.5 \rangle$

73. $\left\langle \dfrac{3\sqrt{34}}{34}, \dfrac{5\sqrt{34}}{34} \right\rangle$

75. $\left\langle -\dfrac{\sqrt{5}}{5}, -\dfrac{2\sqrt{5}}{5} \right\rangle$

77. $\left\langle \dfrac{2\sqrt{13}}{13}, -\dfrac{3\sqrt{13}}{13} \right\rangle$

79. $\langle 35, 35\sqrt{3} \rangle$

81. $\langle -30\sqrt{3}, 30 \rangle$

83. $\langle -27\sqrt{2}, -27\sqrt{2} \rangle$

85. $4\vec{i} + 9\vec{j}$

87. $5\vec{i} - 5\vec{j}$

89. $45°$

91. $330°$

93. $2\pi/3$

95. $153.4°$

97. $341.6°$

99. $209.7°$

101. $\langle 13.2, 2.6 \rangle$

103. $\langle 12.5, -10 \rangle$

105. $\langle 35.36, 35.36 \rangle$

107. $\langle 36.25, 28.32 \rangle$

109. $\langle -5/13, -12/13 \rangle$; $\langle -5/13, -12/13 \rangle$; $\langle -5/13, -12/13 \rangle$

111. 3.9 s

SECTION 4.4 ANSWERS

Warm Up/Just the Facts

1. Distributive Property

2. Commutative Property of Multiplication

3. Zero Product Property

4. $v_1 w_1 + v_2 w_2$

5. $\dfrac{\vec{u} \cdot \vec{v}}{\|\vec{u}\| \cdot \|\vec{v}\|}$

6. 0

7. $180°$

8. $\left(\dfrac{\vec{u} \cdot \vec{v}}{\|\vec{v}\|^2} \right) \vec{v}$

9. scalar

10. magnitude

Essential Skills/Extensions

1. -18.3

3. 14.2

5. -48.7

7. $10; 68; 88$

9. $7; 28.25; 0.8$

11. $-17.65; 41.29; -76.6$

13. $2\sqrt{10}$

15. $\sqrt{146}$

17. $\sqrt{25.81}$

19. $11\pi/21$

21. $19\pi/24$

23. $66°$

25. $141°$

27. $31.3°$

29. $122°$

31. $98.4°$

33. $96.3°$

35. $90.6°$

37. $85.6°$

39. neither; orthogonal; parallel

41. orthogonal; parallel; neither

43. $\langle -4, 8 \rangle$

45. $\langle -3, 3 \rangle$

47. $\bar{w}_1 = \langle -5/2, 5/2 \rangle$; $\bar{w}_2 = \langle 9/2, 9/2 \rangle$

49. $\bar{w}_1 = \langle -18/13, -27/13 \rangle$; $\bar{w}_2 = \langle -60/13, 40/13 \rangle$

51. $169.7°, 7.1°, 3.2°$

53. $123.7°, 45°, 11.3°$

55. $\dfrac{3\sqrt{65} - 2\sqrt{37}}{6}$

57. $\dfrac{\sqrt{37} - 12}{3}$

59. $-41/3$

CHAPTER 4 REVIEW ANSWERS

1. $54.2°, 87.8°, 17.9, A \approx 79.7; 125.8°, 16.2°, 5, A \approx 22.3$

2. $40.6°, 9.4°, 4.3, A \approx 27.8$

3. $34.4°, 99.6°, 57.6, A \approx 683.3$

4. $18.8°, 20.2°, 10.9, A \approx 35$

5. $10°, 87.9, 96.1, A \approx 733.5$

6. $88.9°, 56.4°, 34.7°, A \approx 1229.8, h \approx 60$

7. $74.9°, 55.8°, 49.3°, A \approx 63.7, h \approx 11.6$

8. $49.3°, 39.7°, 25.1, A \approx 152, h \approx 19$

9. $76.9°, 27.1°, 91.6, A \approx 1919.2, h \approx 89.3$

10. $26°, 22°, 47.5, A \approx 249.7, h \approx 20.8$

11. $\langle 6, -2 \rangle; 2\sqrt{10}; 341.6°; \left\langle \dfrac{3\sqrt{10}}{10}, -\dfrac{\sqrt{10}}{10} \right\rangle; 6\vec{i} - 2\vec{j}$

12. $\langle -9, 9 \rangle; 9\sqrt{2}; 135°; \left\langle -\dfrac{\sqrt{2}}{2}, \dfrac{\sqrt{2}}{2} \right\rangle; -9\vec{i} + 9\vec{j}$

13. $\langle 7.2, 1.8 \rangle; 18\sqrt{0.17}; 14°; \left\langle \dfrac{40\sqrt{0.17}}{17}, \dfrac{10\sqrt{0.17}}{17} \right\rangle;$

$7.2\vec{i} + 1.8\vec{j}$

14. $\langle -11.2, 2.6 \rangle$

15. $\langle -32.6, 4 \rangle$

16. $-25.8; 12.24; 61.2; \sqrt{13}$

17. $-20.2; 31.76; 9.6; \sqrt{61}$

18. $-6.7; 18.64; 45.9; \sqrt{49.46}$

19. neither; $\langle 5/17, -3/17 \rangle$; $\bar{w}_1 = \langle 5/17, -3/17 \rangle$;

$\bar{w}_2 = \langle -39/17, -65/17 \rangle$

20. parallel; $\langle -1, 8 \rangle$; $\bar{w}_1 = \langle -1, 8 \rangle$; $\bar{w}_2 = \langle 0, 0 \rangle$

SECTION 5.1 ANSWERS

Warm Up/Just the Facts

1. $\dfrac{x^2 - 25}{x + 5} = \dfrac{\cancel{(x+5)}(x-5)}{\cancel{(x+5)}}$
$= x - 5$

2. $\dfrac{2x^2 + 28x + 98}{x + 7} = \dfrac{2(x^2 + 14x + 49)}{x + 7}$
$= \dfrac{2\cancel{(x+7)}(x+7)}{\cancel{(x+7)}}$
$= 2(x + 7)$

3. $\dfrac{2x^2 - 18}{x^2 + 6x + 9} = \dfrac{2(x^2 - 9)}{(x+3)(x+3)}$
$= \dfrac{2\cancel{(x+3)}(x-3)}{\cancel{(x+3)}(x+3)}$
$= \dfrac{2(x-3)}{x+3}$

4. long, synthetic
5. coefficients; zero
6. zero
7. $b; f(b)$
8. dividend; divisor; $q(x)$; $r(x)$
9. quotient; divisor
10. –5

Essential Skills/Extensions

1. $2x^2 + x + 3 + \dfrac{1}{x+1}$

3. $x^2 + 2x + 8 + \dfrac{9}{x-2}$

5. $2x^2 + 2x + 1 + \dfrac{1}{x+2}$

7. $3x^3 - 4x^2 + 8x - 7 + \dfrac{10}{x+2}$

9. $6x^2 + 29x + 109 + \dfrac{448}{x-4}$

11. $3x^3 - 4x^2 + 6x + 2 + \dfrac{10}{x+2}$

13. $4x^3 + 12x^2 - 10x - 35 - \dfrac{210}{x-3}$

15. $4x^3 - 20x^2 + 97x - 478 + \dfrac{2390}{x+5}$

17. The remainder must be –11 when $h(x)$ is divided by $x - 6$.

19. The remainder must be 10 when $f(x)$ is divided by $x - 3$.

21. The remainder must be –7 when $m(x)$ is divided by $x + 2$.

23. The remainder must be 0 when $q(x)$ is divided by $x + 9$.

25. $g(-1) = 4$

27. $h(8) = 0$

29. $k(-9) = 12$

31. $j(10) = -23$

33. $x + 1$ is not a factor of $g(x)$.

35. $t - 6$ is a factor of $t(x)$.

37. $p + 2$ is a factor of $p(x)$.

39. $r - 4$ is not a factor of $r(x)$.

41. 5

43. 4046

45. yes

47. $x^2 + 5x - 1$; all real numbers except –3 and 4

49. not possible

51. $x^3 - x^2 + 2x - 2 + \dfrac{3}{x+1}$

53. $(x - 3)$, $(x - 5)$, $(x + 2)$, $(x + 3/4)$

55. $(x + 4)$, $(x - 5)$, $(x + 3/2)$

SECTION 5.2 ANSWERS

Warm Up/Just the Facts

1. $\dfrac{4}{4 - \sqrt{5}} = \dfrac{4}{4 - \sqrt{5}} \cdot \dfrac{4 + \sqrt{5}}{4 + \sqrt{5}}$
$= \dfrac{16 + 4\sqrt{5}}{16 - 5}$
$= \dfrac{16 + 4\sqrt{5}}{11}$

2. $\dfrac{7}{5 + \sqrt{2}} = \dfrac{7}{5 + \sqrt{2}} \cdot \dfrac{5 - \sqrt{2}}{5 - \sqrt{2}}$
$= \dfrac{35 - 7\sqrt{2}}{25 - 2}$
$= \dfrac{35 - 7\sqrt{2}}{23}$

3. $4 + \left(4 + \sqrt{3}\right)\left(4 - \sqrt{3}\right) = 16 - 3 = 13$

4. imaginary; i

5. complex; real; i

6. $a - bi$

7. $1, -1, i, -i$

8. i^2

9. conjugate

10. complex; one

Essential Skills/Extensions

1. -1

3. i

5. $-i$

7. $-1 - 4i$

9. $5 - 6i$

11. $-20 + 5i$

13. $58 + 50i$

15. $-5 + 10i$

17. $7 - 3i$

19. $29 + 63i$

21. $40 + 32i$

23. $\dfrac{1}{37} + \dfrac{6}{37}i$

25. $\dfrac{1}{13} + \dfrac{5i}{13}$

27. $\dfrac{36}{25} - \dfrac{2i}{25}$

29. $-\dfrac{22}{65} - \dfrac{71i}{65}$

31. $3, -2, 1 - \sqrt{2}, 1 + \sqrt{2}$

33. $-4/3, 1, 2 + \sqrt{5}, 2 - \sqrt{5}$

35. $-3/2, 3, 3 + \sqrt{5}, 3 - \sqrt{5}$

37. $-5/2, 5, 4 + \sqrt{5}, 4 - \sqrt{5}$

39. $-2, 3, 3i, -3i$

41. $-1, 3, 2i, -2i$

43. $-1, 3, 3i, -3i$

45. $-2, 3, 4i, -4i$

47. $1, 5i, -5i$

49. $-7, 1 - 5i, 1 + 5i$

51. $3, 4 + 2i, 4 - 2i$

53. $-4, 3 + 3i, 3 - 3i$

55. $i, 2 - 3i, \dfrac{1 + i}{3}$

57. $-\dfrac{83}{85} + \dfrac{9}{85}i$

59. $-71 + 11i$

61. $\dfrac{3}{2} - \dfrac{i}{2}$

63. $\dfrac{293}{26} + \dfrac{17i}{26}$

65. $f(x) = x^7 - 14x^6 + 91x^5 - 344x^4 + 779x^3 - 1006x^2 + 689x - 676$,
$f(x) = 2x^7 - 28x^6 + 182x^5 - 688x^4 + 1558x^3 - 2012x^2 + 1378x - 1352$
(possible answers)

SECTION 5.3 ANSWERS

Warm Up/Just the Facts

1. $1 - 3i$. The complex conjugate of $a + bi$ is $a - bi$.

2. $-5 - 4i$. The complex conjugate of $a + bi$ is $a - bi$.

3. $-2 + 6i$. The complex conjugate of $a - bi$ is $a + bi$.

4. real; imaginary

5. modulus

6. $r(\cos \theta + i \sin \theta)$

7. $r_1 r_2 (\cos (\theta_1 + \theta_2) + i \sin (\theta_1 + \theta_2))$

8. $r_1 / r_2 (\cos (\theta_1 - \theta_2) + i \sin (\theta_1 - \theta_2))$

9. $z^n (\cos n\theta + i \sin n\theta)$

10. nth

Essential Skills/Extensions

1.

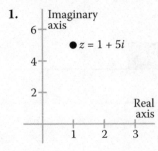

3.

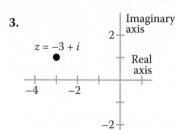

5.

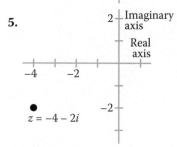

7. $2\sqrt{5}$

9. $3\sqrt{5}$

11. $\sqrt{17}$

13. $4\left(\cos\dfrac{\pi}{3} + i\sin\dfrac{\pi}{3}\right)$

15. $3\sqrt{2}\left(\cos\dfrac{7\pi}{4} + i\sin\dfrac{7\pi}{4}\right)$

17. $12\left(\cos\dfrac{5\pi}{6} + i\sin\dfrac{5\pi}{6}\right)$

19. $3\sqrt{5}\left(\cos 63° + i\sin 63°\right)$

21. $\sqrt{5}\left(\cos 117° + i\sin 117°\right)$

23. $\sqrt{17}\left(\cos 194° + i\sin 194°\right)$

25. $6(\cos 120° + i\sin 120°)$

27. $32(\cos 160° + i\sin 160°)$

29. $18(\cos 290° + i\sin 290°)$

31. $2(\cos 70° + i\sin 70°)$

33. $9(\cos 20° + i\sin 20°)$

35. $4(\cos 120° + i\sin 120°)$

37. $343\left(\cos\dfrac{\pi}{2} + i\sin\dfrac{\pi}{2}\right)$

39. $324(\cos \pi + i\sin \pi)$

41. $64\left(\cos\dfrac{2\pi}{3} + i\sin\dfrac{2\pi}{3}\right)$

43. $-16 + 16i$

45. $-648 - 648\sqrt{3}i$

47. $-16\sqrt{3} - 16i$

49. $-8i$

51. -256

53. $\dfrac{3125\sqrt{3}}{2} + \dfrac{3125}{2}i$

55. $\pm\sqrt{3}, \pm i\sqrt{3}$

57. $\pm\sqrt[3]{2}, \dfrac{\sqrt[3]{2}(-1\pm\sqrt{3}i)}{2}, \dfrac{\sqrt[3]{2}(1\pm\sqrt{3}i)}{2}$

59. $\pm 3, \pm 3i$

61. $\pm 3, \dfrac{3\pm 3\sqrt{3}i}{2}, \dfrac{-3\pm 3\sqrt{3}i}{2}$

63. $\pm 2, \pm 2i$

65. $6, -3\pm 3\sqrt{3}i$

67. $\dfrac{\sqrt{3}+i}{2}, \dfrac{-\sqrt{3}+i}{2}, -i$

69. $2\sqrt[6]{2}\left(\cos\dfrac{5\pi}{12} + i\sin\dfrac{5\pi}{12}\right), 2\sqrt[6]{2}\left(\cos\dfrac{13\pi}{12} + i\sin\dfrac{13\pi}{12}\right),$
$2\sqrt[6]{2}\left(\cos\dfrac{7\pi}{4} + i\sin\dfrac{7\pi}{4}\right)$

71. $3125(\cos 175° + i\sin 175°)$

73. $272\sqrt{34}(\cos 3° + i\sin 3°)$

75. $1 + \sqrt{3}i, -1.34 + 1.48i, -1.83 - 0.81i, 0.21 - 1.99i,$
$1.96 - 0.42i$

77. $1.29 + 4.83i, -4.83 - 1.29i, 3.53 - 3.54i$

CHAPTER 5 REVIEW ANSWERS

5. $x - 3$ is a factor of $g(x)$.

6. $11 + 13i$

1. $5x^2 + 14x + 56 + \dfrac{232}{x - 4}$

2. $x^3 - x^2 - 8x + 12$

7. $\dfrac{19}{145} - \dfrac{112}{145}i$

3. $3x^2 + 6x + 8 + \dfrac{26}{x - 2}$

8. $4, -1, -2+\sqrt{6}, -2-\sqrt{6}$

4. $f(-9) = 12$

9. $3, -1, 4i, -4i$

10. $5, -1, 2i, -2i$

11. $4(\cos 120° + i \sin 120°)$

12. $-6 - 6\sqrt{3}i\,; 0.7 + 0.26i$

13. $50{,}000\sqrt{3} - 50{,}000i\,; 100{,}000(\cos 330° + i \sin 330°)$

14. $\pm\sqrt[6]{23}, \dfrac{\sqrt[6]{23}(1 \pm \sqrt{3}i)}{2}, \dfrac{\sqrt[6]{23}(-1 \pm \sqrt{3}i)}{2}$

15. $\sqrt[8]{72}\left(\cos \dfrac{7\pi}{16} + i \sin \dfrac{7\pi}{16}\right), \sqrt[8]{72}\left(\cos \dfrac{15\pi}{16} + i \sin \dfrac{15\pi}{16}\right),$
$\sqrt[8]{72}\left(\cos \dfrac{23\pi}{16} + i \sin \dfrac{23\pi}{16}\right), \sqrt[8]{72}\left(\cos \dfrac{31\pi}{16} + i \sin \dfrac{31\pi}{16}\right)$

SECTION 6.1 ANSWERS

Warm Up/Just the Facts

1. vertex form: $f(x) = (x - 0)^2 + 0 \implies h = 0, k = 0$
vertex: $(0, 0)$; axis of symmetry: $x = 0$
Find several points on the parabola with x-values near the vertex.

x	-2	-1	1	2
$f(x)$	4	1	1	4

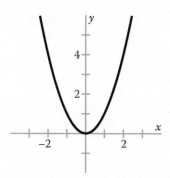

2. vertex form: $f(x) = (x - 3)^2 + 1 \implies h = 3, k = 1$
vertex: $(3, 1)$; axis of symmetry: $x = 3$
Find several points on the parabola with x-values near the vertex.

x	1	2	4	5
$f(x)$	-3	0	0	-3

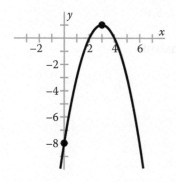

3. vertex form: $f(x) = (x + 2)^2 + 0 \implies h = -2, k = 0$
vertex: $(-2, 0)$; axis of symmetry: $x = -2$
$f(0) = (0)^2 + 4(0) + 4 = 4$: y-intercept: $(0, 4)$
Find several points on the parabola with x-values near the vertex.

x	-4	-3	-1
$f(x)$	4	1	1

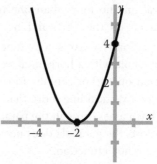

4. cone (double cone), plane
5. point; line; directrix
6. parabolas; down; axis of symmetry; y-axis; focus; $y = -p$
7. parabolas; to the right; axis of symmetry; x-axis; vertex; $x = -p$
8. vertex; focus
9. vertex; $(0, 0)$
10. right, left

Essential Skills/Extensions

1. focus: $(0, 5/8)$; directrix: $y = -5/8$
3. right
5.

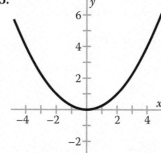

7. $y^2 = \dfrac{x}{2}$

9. $x^2 = \dfrac{10}{3}y$

11. $x^2 = -y$

13. Errors:
    a. "the focus is at (20, 0)"
      correction: the focus is at (1/20, 0)
    b. "the equation of the directrix is y = −20"
      correction: the equation of the directrix is x = −1/20

15. Errors:

  a. *"The axis of symmetry is at y = 0"*
  correction: the axis of symmetry is at x = 0

  b. *"the parabola opens to the left"*
  correction: the parabola opens downward

  c. *"the focus is at (–3/2, 0)"*
  correction: the focus is at (0, –3/2)

  d. *"the equation of the directrix is x = 3/2"*
  correction: the equation of the directrix is y = 3/2

17. The equation $x^2 = 4py$ is a function because it describes a parabola with a vertical axis of symmetry. A parabola that opens vertically (opening upward or downward) will intersect any vertical line no more than one time. Therefore, the parabola passes the Vertical Line Test and is a function. The equation $y^2 = 4px$ is not a function because it describes a parabola with a horizontal axis of symmetry. A parabola that opens horizontally (opening left or right) will intersect a vertical line more than one time (when the vertical line passes through the parabola, not at the vertex). Therefore, the parabola does not pass the Vertical Line Test and is not a function.

19. A parabola described by an equation of the form $x^2 = 4py$ cannot have a directrix at $y = x$ because the parabola's directrix must be at $y = -p$, where p is a constant. Additionally, the axis of symmetry is perpendicular to the directrix, and since the axis of symmetry is vertical, the directrix must be horizontal. The equation $y = x$ does not define a horizontal line. Therefore, $y = x$ cannot be the equation of the directrix.

21. $x^2 = y$ and $y^2 = 8x$

23. 1/2

25. 12

SECTION 6.2 ANSWERS

Warm Up/Just the Facts

1. $c^2 = a^2 - b^2$

  $c^2 = 5^2 - 1^2$ *Substitute.*

  $c^2 = 25 - 1$ *Simplify the powers.*

  $c^2 = 24$ *Subtract.*

  $c = \pm\sqrt{24}$ *Take ± the square root of each side.*

  $c = \pm 2\sqrt{6}$ *Simplify the radical.*

2. $c^2 = a^2 - b^2$

  $20 = 70 - b^2$ *Substitute.*

  $b^2 = 50$ *Solve for b^2.*

  $b = \pm\sqrt{50}$ *Take ± the square root of each side.*

  $b = \pm 5\sqrt{2}$ *Simplify the radical.*

3. $\dfrac{2}{5\sqrt{3}} = \dfrac{2}{5\sqrt{3}} \cdot \dfrac{\sqrt{3}}{\sqrt{3}} = \dfrac{2\sqrt{3}}{5\sqrt{9}} = \dfrac{2\sqrt{3}}{15}$

4. sum; foci

5. x; y

6. y; x

7. vertices (or y-intercepts), foci, major axis

8. co-vertices (or x-intercepts), minor axis

9. minor axis

10. major axis

11. horizontal; origin; $(\pm a, 0)$; $(0, \pm b)$

12. vertical; origin; $(0, \pm a)$; $(\pm b, 0)$

Essential Skills/Extensions

1. $\dfrac{y^2}{64} + \dfrac{x^2}{16} = 1$

3. $\dfrac{x^2}{9} + y^2 = 1$

5. $\dfrac{y^2}{16} + x^2 = 1$

7. $\dfrac{y^2}{169} + \dfrac{x^2}{144} = 1$

9. $\dfrac{x^2}{100} + \dfrac{y^2}{36} = 1$

11. $(\pm 11, 0)$ and $(0, \pm 20)$

13. major axis: $6\sqrt{2}$; minor axis: $2\sqrt{6}$

15.

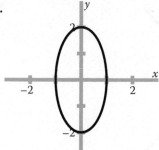

17.

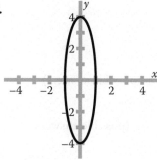

19. $(0, \pm2\sqrt{5})$

21. $\dfrac{2\sqrt{2}}{3}$

23. $\dfrac{3\sqrt{2}}{5}$

25. $\left(0, \pm\dfrac{6}{5}\right)$

27. $\dfrac{y^2}{400} + \dfrac{x^2}{396} = 1$

29. center: $(0, 0)$; foci: $(0, \pm3\sqrt{3}\,)$; vertices: $(0, \pm6)$, co-vertices: $(\pm3, 0)$, major axis: 12 units; minor axis: 6 units; eccentricity: $\dfrac{\sqrt{3}}{2}$

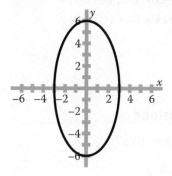

31. $y = \sqrt{(18(1 - X^2/7)}$ and $y = -\sqrt{(18(1 - X^2/7)}$

33. $\dfrac{x^2}{36} + \dfrac{y^2}{16} = 1$; $\dfrac{y^2}{36} + \dfrac{x^2}{9} = 1$ (possible answers)

35. $\dfrac{x^2}{49} + \dfrac{y^2}{16} = 1$; $\dfrac{y^2}{49} + \dfrac{x^2}{16} = 1$ (possible answers)

37. $\dfrac{y^2}{10} + x^2 = 1$; $\dfrac{y^2}{2} + x^2 = 1$ (possible answers)

39. $\dfrac{x^2}{16} + \dfrac{y^2}{9} = 1$; $\dfrac{x^2}{16} + \dfrac{y^2}{4} = 1$ (possible answers)

41. $\dfrac{y^2}{25} + \dfrac{x^2}{16} = 1$; $\dfrac{x^2}{25} + \dfrac{y^2}{16} = 1$ (possible answers)

43. $\dfrac{y^2}{49} + \dfrac{x^2}{25} = 1$; $\dfrac{y^2}{36} + \dfrac{x^2}{25} = 1$ (possible answers)

45. $\dfrac{x^2}{36} + \dfrac{y^2}{32} = 1$; $\dfrac{y^2}{36} + \dfrac{x^2}{32} = 1$ (possible answers)

47. B, A, C

SECTION 6.3 ANSWERS

Warm Up/Just the Facts

1. $\dfrac{a}{45} = \dfrac{4}{9}$

$9a = 180$ *Cross multiply.*

$a = 20$ *Divide each side by 9.*

2. $\dfrac{x^2}{10} - \dfrac{y^2}{12} = 1$

$-\dfrac{y^2}{12} = 1 - \dfrac{x^2}{10}$ *Subtract the x^2-term from each side.*

$y^2 = -12\left(1 - \dfrac{x^2}{10}\right)$ *Multiply each side by −12.*

$y = \pm\sqrt{-12\left(1 - \dfrac{x^2}{10}\right)}$ *Take ± the square root of each side.*

3. $\sqrt{54} = \sqrt{9 \cdot 6} = 3\sqrt{6}$

4. foci; difference

5. branches

6. vertical

7. horizontal

8. x-intercepts, transverse axis, foci, vertices; x

9. y-intercepts, transverse axis, foci, vertices; y

10. vertices

11. $2x$

12. false

Essential Skills/Extensions

1. vertices: $(\pm 6, 0)$; co-vertices: $(0, \pm 7)$

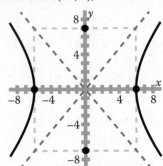

3. $y^2 - \dfrac{x^2}{25} = 1$

5. $\dfrac{y^2}{225} - \dfrac{x^2}{175} = 1$

7. $\dfrac{y^2}{100} - \dfrac{x^2}{21} = 1$

9. $\dfrac{x^2}{81} - \dfrac{y^2}{2025} = 1$

11. $\dfrac{y^2}{9} - x^2 = 1$

13. vertices: $(0, \pm 1)$; foci: $(0, \pm 5\sqrt{2})$; asymptotes: $y = \pm\dfrac{1}{7}x$

15.

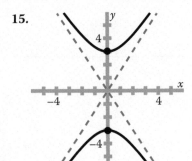

17.

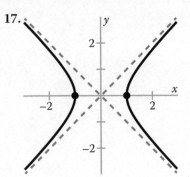

19. 114 mi

21. $\dfrac{y^2}{3600} - \dfrac{x^2}{3456} = 1$

23. $\dfrac{y^2}{36} - \dfrac{x^2}{16} = 1$; $\dfrac{x^2}{36} - \dfrac{y^2}{49} = 1$ (possible answers)

25. $\dfrac{y^2}{4} - \dfrac{x^2}{100} = 1$; $\dfrac{x^2}{121} - \dfrac{y^2}{100} = 1$ (possible answers)

27. $\dfrac{y^2}{16} - \dfrac{x^2}{9} = 1$; $\dfrac{x^2}{16} - \dfrac{y^2}{9} = 1$ (possible answers)

29. $\dfrac{y^2}{4} - x^2 = 1$; $\dfrac{x^2}{16} - \dfrac{y^2}{64} = 1$ (possible answers)

31. When $a = b$, the vertices and co-vertices are equidistant from the origin and the asymptotes are at $y = \pm x$.

33. Errors:
   a. "of length $2n$ when $n > m$, and $2m$ when $m > n$"
      correction: of length $2m$
   b. "co-vertices are at $(0, \pm n)$"
      correction: co-vertices are at $(\pm n, 0)$
   c. "foci are at $(\pm(m^2 + n^2), 0)$"
      correction: foci are at $\left(0, \left(0, \pm\sqrt{m^2 + n^2}\right)\right)$

SECTION 6.4 ANSWERS

Warm Up/Just the Facts

1. $x^2 + 10x - 8 = 1$ *Isolate the constant terms on*
     $x^2 + 10x = 9$ *the right side.*
$x^2 + 10x + 25 = 9 + 25$ *Add $(10/2)^2$ to both sides.*
     $(x + 5)^2 = 34$ *Factor.*

2. $2x^2 + 4x - 3y^2 + 24y + 10 = 0$

     $2(x^2 + 2x) - 3(y^2 - 8y) = -10$

$2(x^2 + 2x + 1) - 3(y^2 - 8y + 16) = -10 + 2 - 48$

        $2(x + 1)^2 - 3(y - 4)^2 = -56$

3. $7 + 5x^2 - x = 3x$ *Write the equation in the*
   $5x^2 - 4x + 7 = 0$ *form $ax^2 + bx + c = 0$, then*
                  identify a, b, and c from the
  $a = 5, b = -4, c = 7$ *equation.*
$b^2 - 4ac = (-4)^2 - 4(5)(7)$ *Substitute the values of a,*
       $= 16 - 140$ *b, and c into the formula for*
       $= -124$ *the discriminant, $b^2 - 4ac$.*

4. up, down; major, minor

5. transverse

6. $(-1, 2)$

7. horizontal parabola; to the left

8. $(7, 6)$; vertical; $x = 7$

9. $(-3, 0)$; 3; horizontal; $y = 0$

10. C; equal to 0

Essential Skills/Extensions

1. opens to the right; $(y - k)^2 = 4p(x - h)$; $p > 0$

3. $(x + 2)^2 = -16(y - 10)$

5. $(-4, 3)$

7. horizontal major axis: $4\sqrt{10}$ units;
vertical minor axis: 2 units

9.
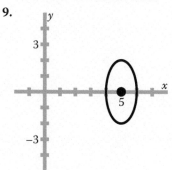

11. $(10, -6)$

13. $(-2, 18)$ and $(-2, 22)$

15. $y - 9 = \pm 2(x + 16)$

17.
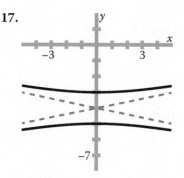

19. parabola

21. not a conic

23. ellipse (not a circle)

25. circle

27. not a conic

29. parabola

31. $(x - 15)^2 - y^2 = 1$ (hyperbola)

33. $\dfrac{(x+1)^2}{9} + (y - 4)^2 = 1$ (ellipse)

35. $x^2 + 2x + 2y + 21 = 0$;
$A = 1, B = 0, C = 0, D = 2, E = 2, F = 21$

37. parabola; $B^2 - 4AC = (-6)2 - 4(9)(1) = 0$

39. circle; $B^2 - 4AC = (0)^2 - 4(-1)(-1) = -4 < 0$,
$B = 0$, and $A = C$

41. $x^2 = -6(y - 4)$

43. $(x - 3)^2 = -6(y + 1)$

45. $\dfrac{(y-2)^2}{6} + (x - 7)^2 = 1$

47. $\dfrac{(x+m)^2}{a^2} + \dfrac{(y+n)^2}{b^2} = 1$

49. $\dfrac{(x-2)^2}{12} - \dfrac{(y+1)^2}{8} = 1$

51. $B = (-6, 0) \cup (0, 6)$

53. $B = \pm 6$

CHAPTER 6 REVIEW ANSWERS

1. focus: $(0, -3/4)$; directrix: $y = 3/4$

2. down

3.

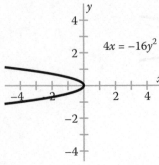

$4x = -16y^2$

4. $8y = x^2$

5. $2y = x^2$

6. $\dfrac{x^2}{25} + \dfrac{y^2}{4} = 1$

7. $\dfrac{y^2}{16} + \dfrac{x^2}{4} = 1$

8. intercepts: $(\pm 10, 0)$ and $(0, \pm 6)$; foci: $(\pm 8, 0)$

9. $e = 2/3$

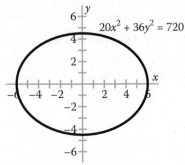

$20x^2 + 36y^2 = 720$

10. $\dfrac{x^2}{81} + \dfrac{y^2}{72} = 1$

11. $\dfrac{y^2}{25} - \dfrac{x^2}{36} = 1$

12. $\dfrac{x^2}{49} - \dfrac{y^2}{23} = 1$

13. vertices: $(\pm 2, 0)$; co-vertices: $(0, \pm 3)$; foci: $(\pm\sqrt{13}, 0)$;

asymptotes: $y = \pm\dfrac{3}{2}x$

14.

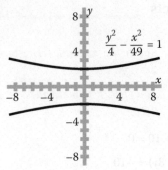

$\dfrac{y^2}{4} - \dfrac{x^2}{49} = 1$

15. 146 nautical mi

16. $(y + 5)^2 = -16(x + 3)$

17. center: $(-4, 2)$

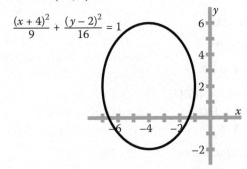

$\dfrac{(x + 4)^2}{9} + \dfrac{(y - 2)^2}{16} = 1$

18. center: $(2, 3)$

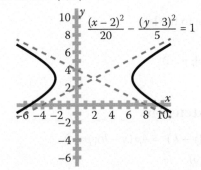

$\dfrac{(x - 2)^2}{20} - \dfrac{(y - 3)^2}{5} = 1$

19. $-x^2 + 4y^2 - 6x - 8y - 21 = 0$;

$A = -1, B = 0, C = 4, D = -6, E = -8, F = -21$

20. ellipse

SECTION 7.1 ANSWERS

Warm Up/Just the Facts

1. II

2. III

3. IV

4. (x, y); (r, θ)

5. 3; $5\pi/6$; polar axis

6. x; y

7. $\sqrt{x^2 + y^2}$; y/x

8. opposite

9. rectangular; polar; $(r, \theta + 2\pi n)$

10. clockwise

Essential Skills/Extensions

1.

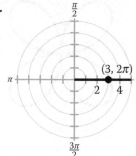

3.

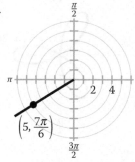

5.

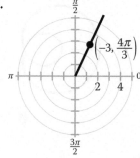

7.

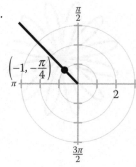

9. $(4, 7\pi/4)$, $(-4, 3\pi/4)$

11. $(2, 4\pi/3)$, $(-2, \pi/3)$

13. $(5, 5\pi/3)$, $(-5, 2\pi/3)$

15. $\left(2\sqrt{3}, -2\right)$

17. $\left(-\dfrac{5\sqrt{2}}{2}, \dfrac{5\sqrt{2}}{2}\right)$

19. $\left(-\dfrac{13\sqrt{3}}{4}, -\dfrac{13}{4}\right)$

21. $(2, 5\pi/6)$

23. $(4, -\pi/4)$

25. $\left(2\sqrt{2}, -\dfrac{\pi}{6}\right)$

27. $\left(\sqrt{29}, -1.19\right)$

29. $\left(2\sqrt{13}, 4.12\right)$

31. $\left(\sqrt{113}, 2.29\right)$

33. $(4, -5\pi/4)$, $(-4, -\pi/4)$, $(4, 3\pi/4)$, $(-4, 7\pi/4)$

35. $\left(-10\sqrt{2}, -\dfrac{4\pi}{3}\right)$, $\left(10\sqrt{2}, -\dfrac{\pi}{3}\right)$, $\left(-10\sqrt{2}, \dfrac{2\pi}{3}\right)$, $\left(10\sqrt{2}, \dfrac{5\pi}{3}\right)$

37. $\left(\sqrt{65}, -4.19\right)$, $\left(-\sqrt{65}, -1.05\right)$, $\left(\sqrt{65}, 2.09\right)$, $\left(-\sqrt{65}, 5.23\right)$

39. $(6, 5\pi/6)$, $(-6, 11\pi/6)$, $(6, 17\pi/6)$, $(-6, 23\pi/6)$

41. $(-10, 2\pi/3)$, $(10, 5\pi/3)$, $(-10, 8\pi/3)$, $(10, 11\pi/3)$

43. $(-5, 0.64)$, $(5, 3.79)$, $(-5, 6.93)$, $(5, 10.07)$

45. $\left(\dfrac{s\sqrt{2}}{2}, \dfrac{\pi}{4}\right)$, $\left(\dfrac{s\sqrt{2}}{2}, \dfrac{3\pi}{4}\right)$, $\left(\dfrac{s\sqrt{2}}{2}, \dfrac{5\pi}{4}\right)$, $\left(\dfrac{s\sqrt{2}}{2}, \dfrac{7\pi}{4}\right)$

SECTION 7.2 ANSWERS

Warm Up/Just the Facts

1. $(x - 3)^2 + y^2 = 9$

$x^2 - 6x + y^2 = 0$

$x^2 - 6x + 9 + y^2 = 9$ *Complete the square.*

$(x - 3)^2 + y^2 = 9$ *Factor.*

2. $(y - 4)^2 - x^2 = 16$

$x^2 - y^2 + 8y = 0$

$x^2 - (y^2 - 8y + 16) = -16$ *Complete the square.*

$x^2 - (y - 4)^2 = -16$ *Factor.*

$-x^2 + (y - 4)^2 = 16$ *Divide by* -1.

$(y - 4)^2 - x^2 = 16$ *Write in standard form.*

3. $(x - 5)^2 + (y + 1)^2 = 26$

$$x^2 - 10x + y^2 + 2y = 0$$

$x^2 - 10x + 25 + y^2 + 2y + 1 = 25 + 1$ *Complete the square.*

$$(x - 5)^2 + (y + 1)^2 = 26 \quad \textit{Factor.}$$

4. $r \cos \theta;\ r \sin \theta;\ \tan \theta;\ r^2$

5. reciprocal

6. vertical line; circle

7. $\theta = c$

8. spiral

9. $r = a \sin n\theta,\ r = a \cos n\theta$

10. n

Essential Skills/Extensions

1. $x^2 + y^2 - 2x = 0$

3. $x^2 + y^2 + y = 0$

5. $x^4 + x^2 y^2 - y^2 = 0$

7. $x + 4 = 0$

9. $y - 2 = 0$

11. $9y^4 + 9x^2 y^2 - x^2 = 0$

13. $\sqrt{3}x + y = 0$

15. $x + y = 0$

17. $x^2 + y^2 - 4 = 0$

19. $r = 8 \sec \theta$

21. $r = \dfrac{3}{2 \cos \theta + 5 \sin \theta}$

23. $r = \dfrac{9}{2 \sin \theta - 3 \cos \theta}$

25. $r = 4$

27. $r = 5 \tan \theta \sec \theta$

29.

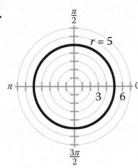

31.

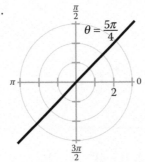

33.

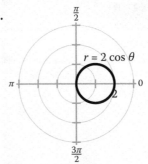

35.

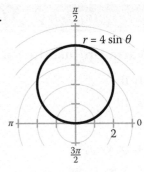

37. center $(5/2, \pi/2)$; radius 2.5

39. center $(2, 0)$; radius 2

41. center $(2, 3\pi/2)$; radius 2

43. 3 petals; petal radius 6; horizontal axis of symmetry

45. 7 petals; petal radius 5; vertical axis of symmetry

47. 4 petals; petal radius 4; horizontal axis of symmetry and vertical axis of symmetry

49.

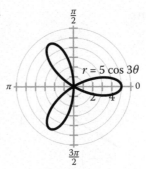

51.

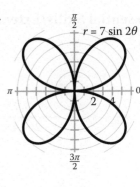

53.

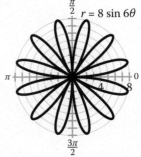

55.

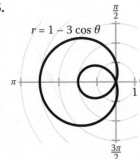

57.

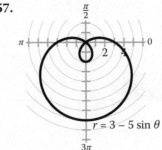

59.

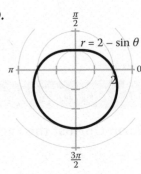

61.

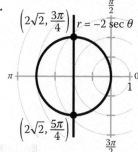

63.

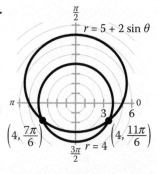

65. $\sqrt{2}x - \sqrt{2}y - 10 = 0$

67.

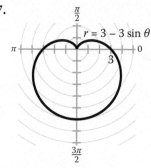

69. $r = -16 \sin \theta$

71. $r = 4 \sin 5\theta$

73. $r = 8 - 2 \cos \theta$

SECTION 7.3 ANSWERS

Warm Up/Just the Facts

1.

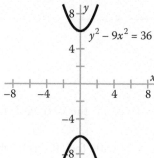

2.

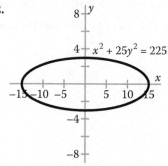

3.

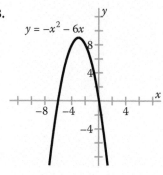

4. rotation

5. x', y'

6. $x \cos \phi - y \sin \phi$; $y \cos \phi + x \sin \phi$

7. discriminant

8. <; >; =

9. $\dfrac{A - C}{B}$

10. parallel

Essential Skills/Extensions

1. $\left(-3\sqrt{2},\ 3\sqrt{2}\right)$

3. $\left(-2\sqrt{2},\ -2\sqrt{2}\right)$

5. $\left(-\sqrt{3},\ -1\right)$

7. $\left(-3\sqrt{3} - 1,\ -3 + \sqrt{3}\right)$

9. $-10\sqrt{3} - 2$

11. $-4\sqrt{3} + 3$

13. ellipse

15. hyperbola

17. parabola

19.

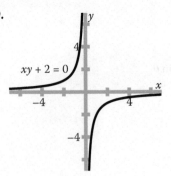

$xy + 2 = 0$

21.

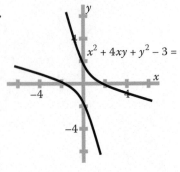

$x^2 + 4xy + y^2 - 3 = 0$

23.

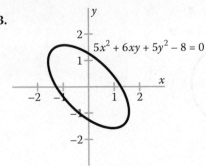

$5x^2 + 6xy + 5y^2 - 8 = 0$

25. 37°

27. 63°

29. $(-3, 5)$; $(-5, -3)$; $(3, -5)$

31. $(6, 8)$; $(-8, 6)$; $(-6, -8)$

33. $\dfrac{x'^2}{9} + \dfrac{y'^2}{4} = 1$

35. $y' = -x'^2$

37. $(3 - x')^2 - 3(2 - y')^2 = 9$

SECTION 7.4 ANSWERS

Warm Up/Just the Facts

1. focus: $(3/4, 0)$

directrix: $x = -3/4$

$2y^2 = 6x$

$y^2 = 3x$ *Write the equation in standard form $y^2 = 4px$.*

Use the value for p to find the focus $(p, 0)$ and the directrix $x = -p$. The value for p is $3/4$, therefore, the focus is at $(3/4, 0)$ and the directrix is $x = -3/4$.

2. foci: $\left(0, \pm\sqrt{3}\right)$

eccentricity: $\dfrac{\sqrt{2}}{2}$

$100x^2 + 50y^2 - 300 = 0$

$\dfrac{y^2}{6} + \dfrac{x^2}{3} = 1$ *Write the equation in standard form.*

The equation is that of an ellipse in $\dfrac{y^2}{a^2} + \dfrac{x^2}{b^2} = 1$ form. The eccentricity e is given by $e = c/a$ where $c^2 = a^2 - b^2$ and the foci are given by $(0, \pm c)$. Since the value for c is $\sqrt{3}$, the eccentricity is $\dfrac{\sqrt{2}}{2}$ and the foci are $\left(0, \pm\sqrt{3}\right)$.

3. foci: $\left(0, \pm\sqrt{10}\right)$

vertices: $(0, \pm 3)$

The equation $\dfrac{y^2}{9} - x^2 = 1$ is in the standard form of a hyperbola $\dfrac{y^2}{a^2} - \dfrac{x^2}{b^2} = 1$ with foci $(0, \pm c)$, where $c^2 = a^2 + b^2$ and the vertices are $(0, \pm a)$. Since the value for c is $\sqrt{10}$, the foci are $\left(0, \pm\sqrt{10}\right)$. The value for a is 3, therefore, the vertices are $(0, \pm 3)$.

4. =; <; >

5. $r = \dfrac{ep}{1 - e\cos\pi}$

6. $r = \dfrac{ep}{1 + e\cos\pi}$

7. $r = \dfrac{ep}{1 + e\sin\pi}$

8. $r = \dfrac{ep}{1 - e\sin\pi}$

9. parallel; coincides

10. perpendicular

Essential Skills/Extensions

1. hyperbola; directrix: $y = -1/3$; eccentricity: $3/2$

3. ellipse; directrix: $x = -4$; eccentricity: $1/6$

5. hyperbola; directrix: $y = 1/2$; eccentricity: 3

7. $r = \dfrac{6}{3 + 2\cos\pi}$

9. $r = \dfrac{2}{1 + \sin\pi}$

11. $r = \dfrac{3}{2 - 3\cos\pi}$

13. directrix: $y = 1$; $e = 1$

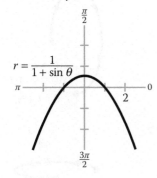

15. directrix: $y = -3$; $e = 2/3$

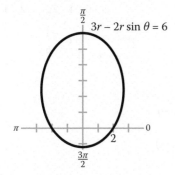

17. directrix: $y = -2/3$; $e = 3$

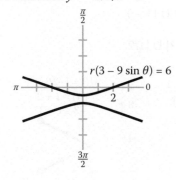

19. $x^2 - 15y^2 + 96y - 144 = 0$

21. $5x^2 - 4y^2 - 54x + 81 = 0$

23. $r = \dfrac{12}{1 - \cos\pi}$

25. $r = \dfrac{4}{1 + \sin\pi}$

27. $r = \dfrac{48}{15 + 9\cos\pi}$

29. $r = \dfrac{12}{3 + \sin\pi}$

31. $r = \dfrac{16}{1 + 3\sin\pi}$

33. $r = \dfrac{24}{5 + 7\cos\pi}$

35. directrix: $x = -6$; $e = 1/2$

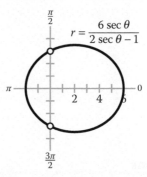

37. directrix: $y = 4/3$; $e = 3/2$

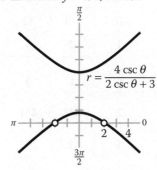

SECTION 7.5 ANSWERS

Warm Up/Just the Facts

1. $y = (-2)^2 - 1 = 3$, $y = (-1)^2 - 1 = 0$, $y = (0)^2 - 1 = -1$,
   $y = (1)^2 - 1 = 0$, $y = (2)^2 - 1 = 3$

   Substitute each x-value in $y = x^2 - 1$ to find the corresponding y-value.

2. $y = |3(-2) + 4| = 2$, $y = |3(-1) + 4| = 1$, $y = |3(0) + 4| = 4$,
   $y = |3(1) + 4| = 7$, $y = |3(2) + 4| = 10$

   Substitute each x-value in $y = |3x + 4|$ to find the corresponding y-value.

3. $y = \sqrt{-2 + 5} = \sqrt{3}$, $y = \sqrt{-1 + 5} = 2$, $y = \sqrt{0 + 5} = \sqrt{5}$,
   $y = \sqrt{1 + 5} = \sqrt{6}$, $y = \sqrt{2 + 5} = \sqrt{7}$

   Substitute each x-value in $y = \sqrt{x + 5}$ to find the corresponding y-value.

4. plane curve

5. parameter

6. rectangular

7. third

8. orientation

9. trigonometric

10. function

Essential Skills/Extensions

1.

t	-3	-2	1	6
$x(t) = t^2 - 4$	5	0	-3	32
$y(t) = \sqrt{t + 3}$	0	1	2	3

3.

t	-2	0	1	2
$x(t) = \dfrac{x + 2}{x + 1}$	0	2	3/2	4/3
$y(t) = t^3 + 1$	-7	1	2	9

5.

t	-1	0	1	2
$x(t) = t^2 + 3t$	-2	0	4	10
$y(t) = |t + 5|$	4	5	6	7

7.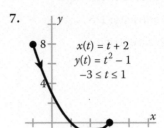
$x(t) = t + 2$
$y(t) = t^2 - 1$
$-3 \le t \le 1$

9.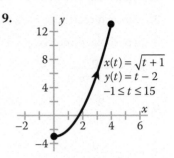
$x(t) = \sqrt{t + 1}$
$y(t) = t - 2$
$-1 \le t \le 15$

11.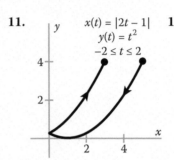
$x(t) = |2t - 1|$
$y(t) = t^2$
$-2 \le t \le 2$

13.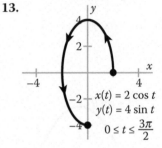
$x(t) = 2 \cos t$
$y(t) = 4 \sin t$
$0 \le t \le \dfrac{3\pi}{2}$

15.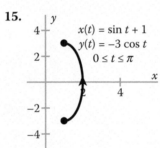
$x(t) = \sin t + 1$
$y(t) = -3 \cos t$
$0 \le t \le \pi$

17.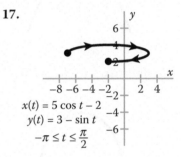
$x(t) = 5 \cos t - 2$
$y(t) = 3 - \sin t$
$-\pi \le t \le \dfrac{\pi}{2}$

19. $y = x^2 - 5$, $[0, \infty)$

21. $y = x^2 + 10x + 24$, $(-\infty, \infty)$

23. $x = \dfrac{(y - 4)^2 - 25}{25}$, $[-1, \infty)$

25. $x^2/4 + y^2 = 1$, $[-2, 2]$

27. $\dfrac{x^2}{16} - \dfrac{y^2}{4} = 1$, $(-\infty, -4] \cup [4, \infty)$

29. $4x^2 - 9y^2 = 1$, $(-\infty, -1/2] \cup [1/2, \infty)$

31.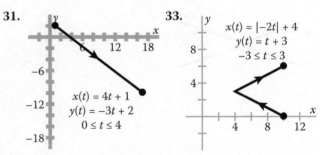
$x(t) = 4t + 1$
$y(t) = -3t + 2$
$0 \le t \le 4$

33.
$x(t) = |-2t| + 4$
$y(t) = t + 3$
$-3 \le t \le 3$

35.

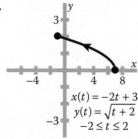

$$x(t) = -2t + 3$$
$$y(t) = \sqrt{t + 2}$$
$$-2 \leq t \leq 2$$

37. $x(t) = t, y(t) = -t^2; x(t) = -t, y(t) = t^2$ (possible answers)

39. $x(t) = t, y(t) = t^2 + 3; x(t) = t^2, y(t) = t + 3$ (possible answers)

41. $x(t) = t, \ y(t) = \pm\sqrt{1 - \dfrac{t^2}{9}} \ ; x(t) = 3\cos t, y(t) = \sin t$

(possible answers)

43. The plane curve is a line with slope 1 and y-intercept 0 (the line $y = x$).

45. The plane curve is a line with slope 2 and y-intercept 0 (the line $y = 2x$).

47. The plane curve is a line with slope 1/2 and y-intercept 0 (the line $y = x/2$).

49.

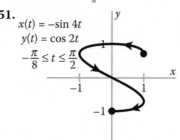

$$x(t) = \cos t$$
$$y(t) = \sin 2t$$
$$-\frac{\pi}{2} \leq t \leq \frac{\pi}{4}$$

51.

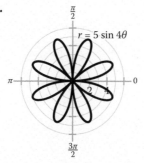

$$x(t) = -\sin 4t$$
$$y(t) = \cos 2t$$
$$-\frac{\pi}{8} \leq t \leq \frac{\pi}{2}$$

53. True. $y = x^3/125$ is the rectangular equation for both pairs of parametric equations.

55. $(x + 2)^2/25 + (3 - y)^2 = 1$

CHAPTER 7 REVIEW ANSWERS

1. $(4.5, 3\pi/4), (-4.5, 7\pi/4), (-4.5, -\pi/4), (4.5, -5\pi/4)$

2. $(-7, \pi/6), (7, 7\pi/6), (7, -5\pi/6), (-7, -11\pi/6)$

3. $(2.75, -2.75\sqrt{3})$

4. $(16, 7\pi/6)$

5. $(\sqrt{17.37}, 3.67)$

6. $y = -3$

7. $r = -\dfrac{\cot \theta \csc \theta}{3}$

8.

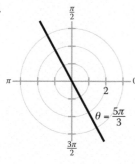

$$\theta = \frac{5\pi}{3}$$

9.

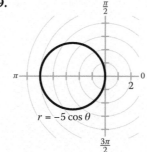

$$r = -5\cos\theta$$

10.

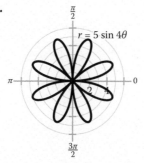

$$r = 5\sin 4\theta$$

11. $\left(\dfrac{7 + 3\sqrt{3}}{2}, \dfrac{-3 + 7\sqrt{3}}{2} \right)$

12. $\left(\dfrac{5\sqrt{2}}{2}, \dfrac{3\sqrt{2}}{2} \right)$

13. $4 - 6\sqrt{2}$

14. parabola

15.

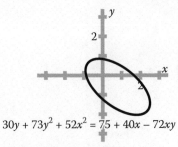

$$30y + 73y^2 + 52x^2 = 75 + 40x - 72xy$$

16. ellipse; $y = -3$; $e = 2/3$

17. hyperbola; $x = 3/2$; $e = 2$

18. $r = \dfrac{6}{4 + \cos\theta}$

19. $r = \dfrac{8}{1 - 2\sin\theta}$

20. $x = 8/3$; $e = 1$

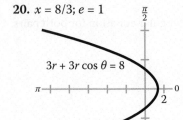

$$3r + 3r\cos\theta = 8$$

21.

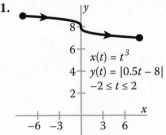

$$x(t) = t^3$$
$$y(t) = |0.5t - 8|$$
$$-2 \le t \le 2$$

22.

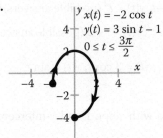

$$x(t) = -2\cos t$$
$$y(t) = 3\sin t - 1$$
$$0 \le t \le \frac{3\pi}{2}$$

23. $y = 3x^2 - 12x + 11$, $(-\infty, \infty)$

24. $x^2/16 + y^2 = 1$, $[-4, 4]$

25.

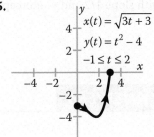

$$x(t) = \sqrt{3t + 3}$$
$$y(t) = t^2 - 4$$
$$-1 \le t \le 2$$

SECTION 8.1 ANSWERS

Warm Up/Just the Facts

1. translation 4 units down

2. reflection across the x-axis, vertical stretch by a factor of 5

3. translation left 3 units and up 1 unit

4. positive, real; 0

5. 1; 0

6. b^{-x} or $\left(\dfrac{1}{b}\right)^{x}$; $-b^{x}$

7. steeper

8. $102.50; $100

9. taking the 40th root

10. natural

Essential Skills/Extensions

1. $g(x) = 5^{x},\ h(x) = 2^{3x},\ q(x) = 8^{x} - 3$

3. $g(x) = 2^{x+3},\ m(x) = 7\pi^{x},\ q(x) = -5^{x} - 9,\ f(x) = 8^{\frac{1}{2}x}$

5. 16, 1, 128

7. $-1728, -1/12, -2\sqrt{3}$

9. $1/243, 27, \dfrac{\sqrt{3}}{9}$

11. $1/2401, 7, 1/343$

13. $729, 3\sqrt{3}, 1/9$

15. $8000, 1/400, 40\sqrt{5}$

17. $144, 1/12, 2\sqrt{3}$

19. $243/1024, 256/81, \dfrac{2\sqrt{3}}{3}$

21. $1/4096, 512, 1/32$

23. $1, 9/4, 243/32$

25. $f(x) = 5^{x}$ and $g(x) = \left(\dfrac{1}{5}\right)^{-x}$

27. $d(x) = 8^{-x}$ and $m(x) = \left(\dfrac{1}{8}\right)^{x}$;

  $p(x) = \left(\dfrac{1}{8}\right)^{-x}$ and $h(x) = 8^{x}$

29. $h(x) = \left(\dfrac{3}{5}\right)^{-x}$ and $g(x) = \left(\dfrac{5}{3}\right)^{x}$; $r(x) = -\left(\dfrac{5}{3}\right)^{x}$ and

  $w(x) = -\left(\dfrac{3}{5}\right)^{-x}$; $f(x) = -\left(\dfrac{3}{5}\right)^{x}$ and $p(x) = -\left(\dfrac{5}{3}\right)^{-x}$

31.
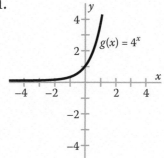

33.
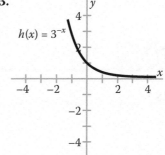

35.
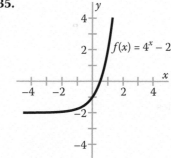

37. $34,023.01

39. $9410.96

41. $22,562.94

43. $28,652.93

45. $4752.24

47. 5.45%

49. 6.99%

51. 0.41, 1.1, 3, 8.15, 22.17

53. −0.27, −0.74, −2, −5.44, −14.78

55. 10.34, 3.81, 1.4, 0.52, 0.19

57. 0.04, 0.12, 0.325, 0.88, 2.4

59.

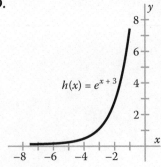

$h(x) = e^{x+3}$

61. 4.9 lb/in^2

63. 6.8 lb/in^2

65. 4616

67. 2729

69. 8.8 lb/in^2

71. $g(x) = 2^{x-3} + 6$

73. $g(x) = \left(\dfrac{1}{2}\right)^{-x} - 5$

75. False. When $x = 0$, y is approximately 20.

77. True.

SECTION 8.2 ANSWERS

Warm Up/Just the Facts

1. 0

2. 1/9

3. 8

4. logarithmic; b

5. 0; zero-exponent

6. negative

7. exponential; table of values

8. base; 10

9. $\ln x$; e

10. x

Essential Skills/Extensions

1. 2

3. 3

5. 4

7. 5

9. $\log_3 81 = 4$

11. $\log_{\frac{2}{5}} \dfrac{25}{4} = -2$

13. $\log_9 \dfrac{1}{81} = -2$

15. $\log_{\frac{4}{11}} \dfrac{121}{16} = -2$

17. $\log_{27} 243 = \dfrac{5}{3}$

19. $\log_7 \dfrac{1}{2401} = -4$

21. $\log_{\frac{2}{7}} \dfrac{4}{49} = 2$

23. $6^3 = 216$

25. $\left(\dfrac{1}{5}\right)^{-4} = 625$

27. $7^5 = 16{,}807$

29. $\left(\dfrac{4}{5}\right)^3 = \dfrac{64}{125}$

31. $27^{\frac{4}{3}} = 81$

33. $\left(\dfrac{4}{3}\right)^2 = \dfrac{16}{9}$

35. $8^{\frac{7}{3}} = 128$

37. 2

39. 9

41. 4

43. 1/3

45. 3/4

47. 2/3

49. 1

51. 5

53. 0

55. 64

57.

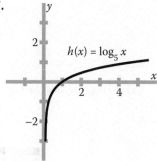

59.

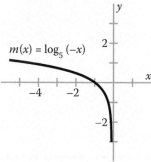

61. e

63. $4/7$

65. 10

67. 28

69. -0.98

71. 0.19

73. 3.8

75. 46.81 dB

77. 59.03 dB

79. 4.88

81. $(7, \infty)$

83. $(-3/4, \infty)$

85. $(1/3, \infty)$

87. 31

89. $y = \log 1$

91. b

93. y

95. neither

SECTION 8.3 ANSWERS

Warm Up/Just the Facts

1. Power Property

2. Product Property

3. Quotient Property

4. sum; x, y

5. difference; x; y

6. $\dfrac{1}{2}\log 20$

7. expand, combine

8. base

9. Change of Base Formula

10. equal

Essential Skills/Extensions

1. $5/6$

3. $5/4$

5. $3/8$

7. -2

9. -2

11. $5/3$

13. $-3/4$

15. 3

17. -4

19. 2

21. $5\log_4 x + \dfrac{1}{9}\log_4 y$

23. $\log_6 a + \dfrac{1}{2}\log_6 c - 2\log_6 b$

25. $2\ln x + \ln y + \dfrac{1}{3}\ln z$

27. $\ln p + 5\ln(q+4) - \ln r$

29. $2\log r - \log w - \dfrac{1}{2}\log(x+1)$

31. $\dfrac{1}{5}\ln(6+x) - \dfrac{4}{5}\ln y$

33. $\dfrac{1}{3}\log_2(2+t) - \dfrac{4}{3} - \dfrac{1}{3}\log_2 s$

35. $\log_6 \dfrac{x^4}{\sqrt[5]{y}}$

37. $\log_7 \dfrac{8m^{12}}{\sqrt[6]{2x+1}}$

39. $\log_5 \dfrac{x^3 z^4}{y^2}$

41. $\log_b \dfrac{8x^3 y^5}{z^6}$

43. $\log_8 \dfrac{16r^4 \sqrt{3w-2}}{(x+8)^2}$

45. $\log_2 \dfrac{\sqrt[4]{(6-a)^3}}{(b-4)^{12} c^3}$

47. $\log_5 \sqrt[3]{\dfrac{(5-m)^2}{16n^4 k^8}}$

49. -2.32

51. 0.47

53. 1.18

55. $\log_2(1-x) + \log_2(3+x) - \log_2(2-x)$

57. $\dfrac{3}{2}\log_a 5 + 3\log_a x + \dfrac{1}{2}\log_a(1-4x) - \dfrac{3}{2}\log_a 7 - 3\log_a(x+1)$

59. $\log_4 \dfrac{10+x}{4-x} + \log_5(3-2x)$

61. They both are correct.

63. 1.06

65. -7.13

67. -0.3

SECTION 8.4 ANSWERS

Warm Up/Just the Facts

1. $5^4 = 625$

2. $2^6 = 64$

3. $3^5 = 243$

4. One-to-One; $b > 0$, $b \neq 1$

5. Logarithms

6. Natural

7. isolate; exponential

8. parsecs

9. extraneous; logarithmic

10. Quadratic

Essential Skills/Extensions

1. $26/21$

3. $11/12$

5. $10/9$

7. $31/25$

9. $13/4$

11. $16/17$

13. $13/9$

15. $1/9$

17. 2.26

19. 0.77

21. -1.46

23. -1.37

25. -38.55

27. -31.14

29. 3.26

31. 1.65

33. 0.44

35. 0.37

37. 2.61

39. 0.05

41. $\ln 3$ or 1.1

43. 0.04

45. $-0.1, 0.39$

47. $0.05, 0.22$

49. 4.95

51. 50.6

53. 149.41

55. 409.43

57. 23.25

59. 2046.5

61. 19

63. 210

65. 8.87 parsecs

67. 29.92 parsecs

69. 8

71. 2

73. 4

75. 0

77. 8.1 yr (approximately 8 years 1 month)

79. 29.4 yr (approximately 29 years 5 months)

81. 0.684

83. −10

85. 2.65 parsecs, 8.76 light years

SECTION 8.5 ANSWERS

Warm Up/Just the Facts

1. −2.457

2. −2.824

3. 0.057

4. logarithmic; three

5. decay; greater; decrease

6. 1

7. medication

8. 1; 30 min

9. initial; surroundings; t

10. more

Essential Skills/Extensions

1. -5.011×10^{-6} mol/L

3. 2021

5. 2 h

7. 56.9 min

9. 23.2 yr

11. 18

13. 21.8 h

15. $500

17. 12.05 V

19. 10.352 yr

21. 7:26 p.m.

CHAPTER 8 REVIEW ANSWERS

1.

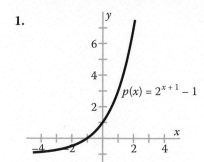

$p(x) = 2^{x+1} - 1$

2.

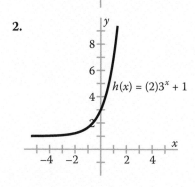

$h(x) = (2)3^x + 1$

3.

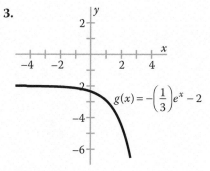

$g(x) = -\left(\frac{1}{3}\right)e^x - 2$

4. $10,509.13

5. 64,000; 107,460,590

6. 10/3

7. −1

8.

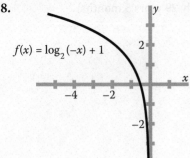

$f(x) = \log_2(-x) + 1$

9.

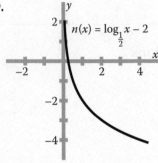

$n(x) = \log_{\frac{1}{2}} x - 2$

10. $(-\infty, 8)$

11. 2

12. -2

13. $3 + 3\log_8 y + 3\log_8(x-5) - \dfrac{3}{4}\log_8 x$

14. $\log_b \dfrac{(x+2)^4 \sqrt[3]{y^2}}{3}$

15. 0.62

16. 1/9

17. 0.35

18. 0

19. 6

20. 7.7 yr

21. 0.064 W

22. 15.3 days

23. 17.3 yr

24. 2.5 h

25. 12.9 yr

INDEX

APPENDIX A: Common Formulas and Properties

Algebra

Properties of Powers and Radicals

Product of Powers $\quad a^m a^n = a^{m+n}$

Power of a Power $\quad (a^m)^n = a^{m \cdot n}$

Power of a Product $\quad (ab)^n = a^n b^n$

Zero Exponent $\quad a^0 = 1$

Negative Exponent $\quad a^{-m} = \dfrac{1}{a^m}$

Rational Exponent $\quad a^{\frac{1}{n}} = \sqrt[n]{a} \;;\; a^{\frac{m}{n}} = \left(\sqrt[n]{a}\right)^m = \sqrt[n]{a^m}$

Quotient of Powers $\quad \dfrac{a^m}{a^n} = a^{m-n}$

Power of a Quotient $\quad \left(\dfrac{a}{b}\right)^n = \dfrac{a^n}{b^n}$

Product Property of Radicals $\quad \sqrt[n]{ab} = \sqrt[n]{a} \cdot \sqrt[n]{b}$

Quotient Property of Radicals $\quad \sqrt[n]{\dfrac{a}{b}} = \dfrac{\sqrt[n]{a}}{\sqrt[n]{b}}$

The Quadratic Formula

If $ax^2 + bx + c = 0$, then $x = \dfrac{-b \pm \sqrt{b^2 - 4ac}}{2a}$.

Special Products of Binomials

Square of a Sum $\quad (A + B)^2 = A^2 + 2AB + B^2$

Square of a Difference $\quad (A - B)^2 = A^2 - 2AB + B^2$

Cube of a Sum $\quad (A + B)^3 = A^3 + 3A^2B + 3AB^2 + B^3$

Cube of a Difference $\quad (A - B)^3 = A^3 - 3A^2B + 3AB^2 - B^3$

Special Factoring

Perfect Square $\quad A^2 + 2AB + B^2 = (A + B)^2$

Difference of Two Squares $\quad A^2 - B^2 = (A + B)(A - B)$

Sum of Two Cubes $\quad A^3 + B^3 = (A + B)(A^2 - AB + B^2)$

Difference of Two Cubes $\quad A^3 - B^3 = (A - B)(A^2 + AB + B^2)$

Binomial Theorem

$$(x + y)^n = x^n + \binom{n}{1}x^{n-1}y + \binom{n}{2}x^{n-2}y^2 + \ldots + \binom{n}{n-1}xy^{n-1} + y^n \text{ where } \binom{n}{m} = \frac{n!}{m!(n-m)!}$$

Geometric Formulas

Formulas for Perimeter P, Area A, Circumference C, Surface Area S, and Volume V

Square

$P = 4s$

$A = s^2$

Cube

$S = 6s^2$

$V = s^3$

Rectangle

$P = 2l + 2w$

$A = lw$

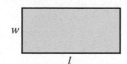

Rectangular Prism

$S = 2lw + 2lh + 2hw$

$V = lwh$

Triangle

$A = \dfrac{1}{2}bh$

Right Triangle

$A = \dfrac{1}{2}ab$

Circle

$C = 2\pi r$

$A = \pi r^2$

Sphere

$S = 4\pi r^2$

$V = \dfrac{4}{3}\pi r^3$

Cylinder

$S = 2\pi rh + 2\pi r^2$

$V = \pi r^2 h$

Cone

$S = \pi r\sqrt{r^2 + h^2} + \pi r^2$

$V = \dfrac{1}{3}\pi r^2 h$

The Pythagorean Theorem

$a^2 + b^2 = c^2$

Example: Equilateral Triangle

$h = \sqrt{s^2 - \left(\dfrac{s}{2}\right)^2} = \dfrac{s\sqrt{3}}{2}$

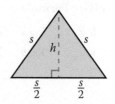

Distance and Midpoint *between points (x_1, y_1) and (x_2, y_2)*

Distance $\qquad d = \sqrt{(x_2 - x_1)^2 + (y_2 - y_1)^2}$

Midpoint $\qquad M = \left(\dfrac{x_1 + x_2}{2}, \dfrac{y_1 + y_2}{2}\right)$

Lines *through points (x_1, y_1) and (x_2, y_2) with slope m and y-intercept b*

Slope $\qquad m = \dfrac{y_2 - y_1}{x_2 - x_1}$

Slope-Intercept Form $\qquad y = mx + b$

Point-Slope Form $\qquad y - y_1 = m(x - x_1)$

Interest Formulas

Simple	$I = Prt$	*I is the amount of simple interest paid (or earned) when a principal P is borrowed (or invested) for t years at an interest rate r.*
Compound	$A = P\left(1 + \dfrac{r}{m}\right)^{mt}$	*A is the balance in an account after a principal P is borrowed (or invested) for t years at an annual interest rate r compounded m times per year.*
Continuously compounded	$A = Pe^{rt}$	*A is the balance in an account after a principal P is borrowed (or invested) for t years at an annual interest rate r compounded continuously.*

Logarithms (where a and b are positive real numbers such that $a \neq 1$ and $b \neq 1$)

	Logarithm with Base b	**Common Logarithm**	**Natural Logarithm**
Logarithmic Form	$y = \log_b x$	$y = \log x$	$y = \ln x$
Exponential Form	$b^y = x$	$10^y = x$	$e^y = x$
Properties of Logs	$\log_b 1 = 0$	$\log 1 = 0$	$\ln 1 = 0$
	$\log_b b = 1$	$\log 10 = 1$	$\ln e = 1$
	$\log_b b^x = x$	$\log 10^x = x$	$\ln e^x = x$
	$b^{\log_b x} = x$	$10^{\log x} = x$	$e^{\ln x} = x$
Product Property	$\log_b (xy) = \log_b x + \log_b y$	$\log (xy) = \log x + \log y$	$\ln (xy) = \ln x + \ln y$
Quotient Property	$\log_b\left(\dfrac{x}{y}\right) = \log_b x - \log_b y$	$\log\left(\dfrac{x}{y}\right) = \log x - \log y$	$\ln\left(\dfrac{x}{y}\right) = \ln x - \ln y$
Power Property	$\log_b x^y = y \log_b x$	$\log x^y = y \log x$	$\ln x^y = y \ln x$

Change of Base Formula

$$\log_b x = \frac{\log_a x}{\log_a b} = \frac{\log x}{\log b} = \frac{\ln x}{\ln b}$$

The Trigonometric Functions of Acute Angle θ

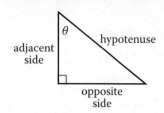

$$\text{sine } \theta = \sin \theta = \frac{\text{opp}}{\text{hyp}}$$

$$\text{cosine } \theta = \cos \theta = \frac{\text{adj}}{\text{hyp}}$$

$$\text{tangent } \theta = \tan \theta = \frac{\text{opp}}{\text{adj}}$$

$$\text{cosecant } \theta = \csc \theta = \frac{\text{hyp}}{\text{opp}}$$

$$\text{secant } \theta = \sec \theta = \frac{\text{hyp}}{\text{adj}}$$

$$\text{cotangent } \theta = \cot \theta = \frac{\text{adj}}{\text{opp}}$$

The Trigonometric Functions of Angle θ

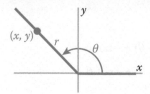

$$r = \sqrt{x^2 + y^2} \neq 0$$

$$\sin \theta = y/r$$

$$\cos \theta = x/r$$

$$\tan \theta = y/x, x \neq 0$$

$$\csc \theta = r/y, y \neq 0$$

$$\sec \theta = r/x, x \neq 0$$

$$\cot \theta = x/y, y \neq 0$$

The Trigonometric Functions of Real Number t on the Unit Circle

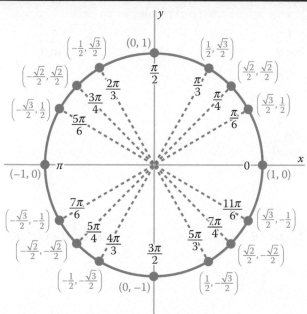

$$\sin t = y$$

$$\cos t = x$$

$$\tan t = y/x, x \neq 0$$

$$\csc t = 1/y, y \neq 0$$

$$\sec t = 1/x, x \neq 0$$

$$\cot t = x/y, y \neq 0$$

The Trigonometric Functions of Important Angles

θ (degrees)	θ (radians)	sin θ	cos θ	tan θ
0°	0	0	1	0
30°	$\pi/6$	$1/2$	$\sqrt{3}/2$	$1/\sqrt{3}$
45°	$\pi/4$	$\sqrt{2}/2$	$\sqrt{2}/2$	1
60°	$\pi/3$	$\sqrt{3}/2$	$1/2$	$\sqrt{3}$
90°	$\pi/2$	1	0	und

The Law of Sines and the Law of Cosines

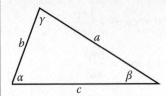

$$\frac{\sin \alpha}{a} = \frac{\sin \beta}{b} = \frac{\sin \gamma}{c}$$

$$\frac{a}{\sin \alpha} = \frac{b}{\sin \beta} = \frac{c}{\sin \gamma}$$

$$a^2 = b^2 + c^2 - 2bc \cos \alpha$$

$$b^2 = a^2 + c^2 - 2ac \cos \beta$$

$$c^2 = a^2 + b^2 - 2ab \cos \gamma$$

Trigonometric Identities

Even-Odd Identities

$\sin (-\theta) = -\sin \theta$ $\cos (-\theta) = \cos \theta$ $\tan (-\theta) = -\tan \theta$

$\csc (-\theta) = -\csc \theta$ $\sec (-\theta) = \sec \theta$ $\cot (-\theta) = -\cot \theta$

Reciprocal Identities

$$\sin \theta = \frac{1}{\csc \theta} \qquad \cos \theta = \frac{1}{\sec \theta} \qquad \tan \theta = \frac{1}{\cot \theta}$$

$$\csc \theta = \frac{1}{\sin \theta} \qquad \sec \theta = \frac{1}{\cos \theta} \qquad \cot \theta = \frac{1}{\tan \theta}$$

Quotient Identities

$$\tan \theta = \frac{\sin \theta}{\cos \theta} \qquad \cot \theta = \frac{\cos \theta}{\sin \theta}$$

Pythagorean Identities

$$\sin^2 \theta + \cos^2 \theta = 1 \qquad \tan^2 \theta + 1 = \sec^2 \theta \qquad 1 + \cot^2 \theta = \csc^2 \theta$$

Cofunction Identities

$$\sin\left(\frac{\pi}{2} - \theta\right) = \cos \theta \qquad \cos\left(\frac{\pi}{2} - \theta\right) = \sin \theta \qquad \tan\left(\frac{\pi}{2} - \theta\right) = \cot \theta$$

$$\csc\left(\frac{\pi}{2} - \theta\right) = \sec \theta \qquad \sec\left(\frac{\pi}{2} - \theta\right) = \csc \theta \qquad \cot\left(\frac{\pi}{2} - \theta\right) = \tan \theta$$

Trigonometric Formulas

Sum and Difference Formulas

$$\sin(\theta_1 + \theta_2) = \sin\theta_1\cos\theta_2 + \cos\theta_1\sin\theta_2 \qquad \sin(\theta_1 - \theta_2) = \sin\theta_1\cos\theta_2 - \cos\theta_1\sin\theta_2$$

$$\cos(\theta_1 + \theta_2) = \cos\theta_1\cos\theta_2 - \sin\theta_1\sin\theta_2 \qquad \cos(\theta_1 - \theta_2) = \cos\theta_1\cos\theta_2 + \sin\theta_1\sin\theta_2$$

$$\tan(\theta_1 + \theta_2) = \frac{\tan\theta_1 + \tan\theta_2}{1 - \tan\theta_1\tan\theta_2} \qquad \tan(\theta_1 - \theta_2) = \frac{\tan\theta_1 - \tan\theta_2}{1 + \tan\theta_1\tan\theta_2}$$

Power-Reducing Formulas

$$\sin^2\theta = \frac{1 - \cos 2\theta}{2} \qquad \cos^2\theta = \frac{1 + \cos 2\theta}{2} \qquad \tan^2\theta = \frac{1 - \cos 2\theta}{1 + \cos 2\theta}$$

Double-Angle Formulas

$$\sin 2\theta = 2\sin\theta\cos\theta \qquad \cos 2\theta = \cos^2\theta - \sin^2\theta \qquad \tan 2\theta = \frac{2\tan\theta}{1 - \tan^2\theta}$$

$$= 1 - 2\sin^2\theta$$

$$= 2\cos^2\theta - 1$$

Half-Angle Formulas

$$\sin\frac{\theta}{2} = \pm\sqrt{\frac{1 - \cos\theta}{2}} \qquad \cos\frac{\theta}{2} = \pm\sqrt{\frac{1 + \cos\theta}{2}} \qquad \tan\frac{\theta}{2} = \frac{1 - \cos\theta}{\sin\theta}$$

Product-to-Sum Formulas

$$\sin\theta_1\sin\theta_2 = \frac{1}{2}[\cos(\theta_1 - \theta_2) - \cos(\theta_1 + \theta_2)] \qquad \cos\theta_1\cos\theta_2 = \frac{1}{2}[\cos(\theta_1 - \theta_2) + \cos(\theta_1 + \theta_2)]$$

$$\sin\theta_1\cos\theta_2 = \frac{1}{2}[\sin(\theta_1 + \theta_2) + \sin(\theta_1 - \theta_2)] \qquad \cos\theta_1\sin\theta_2 = \frac{1}{2}[\sin(\theta_1 + \theta_2) - \sin(\theta_1 - \theta_2)]$$

The Graph of the Basic Sine Function: $y = \sin x$

x	0	$\pi/2$	π	$3\pi/2$	2π	$5\pi/2$	3π	$7\pi/2$	4π	$9\pi/2$
y	0	1	0	-1	0	1	0	-1	0	1

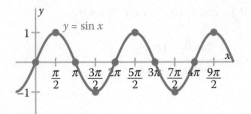

Domain: $(-\infty, \infty)$

Range: $[-1, 1]$

Period: 2π

The Graph of the Basic Cosine Function: $y = \cos x$

x	0	$\pi/2$	π	$3\pi/2$	2π	$5\pi/2$	3π	$7\pi/2$	4π	$9\pi/2$
y	1	0	-1	0	1	0	-1	0	1	0

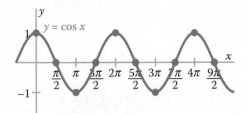

Domain: $(-\infty, \infty)$

Range: $[-1, 1]$

Period: 2π

The Graph of the Basic Tangent Function: $y = \tan x$

x	$-5\pi/4$	$-\pi$	$-3\pi/4$	$-\pi/4$	0	$\pi/4$	$3\pi/4$	π	$5\pi/4$	$7\pi/4$	2π	$9\pi/4$
y	-1	0	1	-1	0	1	-1	0	1	-1	0	1

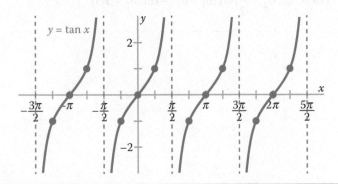

Domain: $\{x : x \neq \dfrac{\pi}{2} + \pi n\}$, where n is an integer

Range: $(-\infty, \infty)$

Vertical Asymptotes:
$x = \dfrac{\pi}{2} + \pi n$, where n is an integer

Period: π

The Graph of the Basic Cosecant Function: $y = \csc x$

x	$-3\pi/2$	$-\pi/2$	$\pi/2$	$3\pi/2$	$5\pi/2$	$7\pi/2$
y	1	-1	1	-1	1	-1

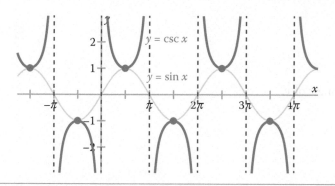

Domain: $\{x :\ x \neq \pi n\}$, where n is an integer

Range: $(-\infty, -1] \cup [1, \infty)$

Vertical Asymptotes: $x = \pi n$, where n is an integer

Period: 2π

The Graph of the Basic Secant Function: $y = \sec x$

x	$-\pi$	0	π	2π	3π	4π
y	-1	1	-1	1	-1	1

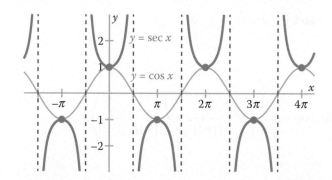

Domain: $\{x :\ x \neq \frac{\pi}{2} + \pi n\}$, where n is an integer

Range: $(-\infty, -1] \cup [1, \infty)$

Vertical Asymptotes:
$x = \frac{\pi}{2} + \pi n$, where n is an integer

Period: 2π

The Graph of the Basic Cotangent Function: $y = \cot x$

x	$-3\pi/2$	$-5\pi/4$	$-3\pi/4$	$-\pi/2$	$-\pi/4$	$\pi/4$	$\pi/2$	$3\pi/4$	$5\pi/4$	$3\pi/2$	$7\pi/4$	$9\pi/4$	$5\pi/2$
y	0	-1	1	0	-1	1	0	-1	1	0	-1	1	0

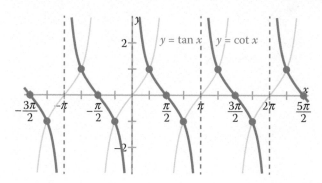

Domain: $\{x :\ x \neq \pi n\}$, where n is an integer

Range: $(-\infty, \infty)$

Vertical Asymptotes: $x = \pi n$, where n is an integer

Period: π

Vectors

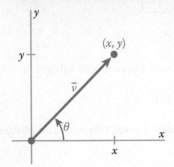

$$\vec{v} = \langle x, y \rangle$$

θ is the direction angle of $\vec{v}$.

Magnitude

If $\vec{v} = \langle x, y \rangle$, then the magnitude of $\vec{v}$ is $||\vec{v}|| = \sqrt{x^2 + y^2}$.

Vector Addition and Subtraction

If $\vec{v} = \langle v_1, v_2 \rangle$ and $\vec{u} = \langle u_1, u_2 \rangle$, then $\vec{v} + \vec{u} = \langle v_1 + u_1, v_2 + u_2 \rangle$ and $\vec{v} - \vec{u} = \langle v_1 - u_1, v_2 - u_2 \rangle$.

Unit Vector

If $\vec{v} = \langle x, y \rangle$ and $||\vec{v}|| \neq 0$, then the unit vector in the same direction as $\vec{v}$ is $\vec{u} = \dfrac{1}{||\vec{v}||}\vec{v} = \left\langle \dfrac{x}{||\vec{v}||}, \dfrac{y}{||\vec{v}||} \right\rangle$.

Dot Product

If $\vec{u} = \langle u_1, u_2 \rangle$ and $\vec{v} = \langle v_1, v_2 \rangle$, then the dot product of $\vec{u}$ and $\vec{v}$ is $\vec{u} \cdot \vec{v} = u_1 v_1 + u_2 v_2$.

APPENDIX B: ABBREVIATIONS

°C	degrees Celsius
°F	degrees Fahrenheit
A	ampere
cd	candela
cm	centimeter
ft	foot
gal	gallon
h	hour
Hz	hertz
in.	inch
K	Kelvin
kg	kilogram
km	kilometer
kPa	kilopascal
kW	kilowatt
L	liter
lb	pound
m	meter
mg	milligram
mi	mile
min	minute
mL	milliliter
N	Newton
oz	ounce
s	second
V	volt
W	watt
yd	yard
yr	year

APPENDIX C: SYMBOLS AND NOTATION

$=$	equal to		$\cup$	union
$\approx$	approximately equal to		$\cap$	disjunction
$<$	less than		$\varnothing$	empty set
$>$	greater than		$f(x)$	function notation
$\leq$	less than or equal to		$\pm$	plus or minus
$\geq$	greater than or equal to		$\%$	percent
$\neq$	not equal to		$\parallel$	parallel
$+$	addition		$\perp$	perpendicular
$-$	subtraction		$\mathbb{R}$	the set of all real numbers
$\cdot$	multiplication		$\mathbb{Q}$	the set of all rational numbers
$\div$	division		$\mathbb{Z}$	the set of all integers
$/$	division		$\mathbb{N}$	the set of all natural numbers
$\sqrt{}$	square root		i	imaginary unit
$\sqrt[n]{}$	nth root		π	pi
$\lvert\ \rvert$	absolute value		∞	infinity
$!$	factorial		$\rightarrow$	approaches
$[[\ ]]$	greatest integer		$\Leftrightarrow$	if and only if
$\circ$	composed with		$\Rightarrow$	implies
$\binom{n}{r}$	n choose r		$\begin{bmatrix}\square & \square \\ \square & \square\end{bmatrix}$	matrix
$_nC_r$	n choose r		$n \times m$	matrix dimensions
$\sum$	summation		$\begin{vmatrix}\square & \square \\ \square & \square\end{vmatrix}$	determinant